Real Analysis

A Comprehensive Course in Analysis, Part 1

Real Analysis

A Comprehensive Course in Analysis, Part 1

Barry Simon

AMERICAN MATHEMATICAL SOCIETY

Providence, Rhode Island

2010 *Mathematics Subject Classification.* Primary 26-01, 28-01, 42-01, 46-01; Secondary 33-01, 35-01, 41-01, 52-01, 54-01, 60-01.

For additional information and updates on this book, visit
www.ams.org/bookpages/simon

Library of Congress Cataloging-in-Publication Data

Simon, Barry, 1946–
    Real analysis / Barry Simon.
        pages cm. — (A comprehensive course in analysis ; part 1)
    Includes bibliographical references and indexes.
    ISBN 978-1-4704-1099-5 (alk. paper)
    1. Mathematical analysis—Textbooks.   I. Title.

QA300.S53   2015
515′.8—dc23
                                                                                    2014047381

10 9 8 7 6 5 4 3 2 1   20 19 18 17 16 15

To the memory of Cherie Galvez

extraordinary secretary, talented helper, caring person

and to the memory of my mentors,

Ed Nelson (1932-2014) and Arthur Wightman (1922-2013)

who not only taught me Mathematics
but taught me how to be a mathematician

Contents

Preface to the Series

Young men should prove theorems, old men should write books.

—*Freeman Dyson*, quoting G. H. Hardy[1]

Reed–Simon[2] starts with "Mathematics has its roots in numerology, geometry, and physics." This puts into context the division of mathematics into algebra, geometry/topology, and analysis. There are, of course, other areas of mathematics, and a division between parts of mathematics can be artificial. But almost universally, we require our graduate students to take courses in these three areas.

This five-volume series began and, to some extent, remains a set of texts for a basic graduate analysis course. In part it reflects Caltech's three-terms-per-year schedule and the actual courses I've taught in the past. Much of the contents of Parts 1 and 2 (Part 2 is in two volumes, Part 2A and Part 2B) are common to virtually all such courses: point set topology, measure spaces, Hilbert and Banach spaces, distribution theory, and the Fourier transform, complex analysis including the Riemann mapping and Hadamard product theorems. Parts 3 and 4 are made up of material that you'll find in some, but not all, courses—on the one hand, Part 3 on maximal functions and H^p-spaces; on the other hand, Part 4 on the spectral theorem for bounded self-adjoint operators on a Hilbert space and det and trace, again for Hilbert space operators. Parts 3 and 4 reflect the two halves of the third term of Caltech's course.

---

[1]Interview with D. J. Albers, The College Mathematics Journal, **25**, no. 1, January 1994.

[2]M. Reed and B. Simon, *Methods of Modern Mathematical Physics, I: Functional Analysis*, Academic Press, New York, 1972.

While there is, of course, overlap between these books and other texts, there are some places where we differ, at least from many:

(a) By having a unified approach to both real and complex analysis, we are able to use notions like contour integrals as Stietljes integrals that cross the barrier.

(b) We include some topics that are not standard, although I am surprised they are not. For example, while discussing maximal functions, I present Garcia's proof of the maximal (and so, Birkhoff) ergodic theorem.

(c) These books are written to be keepers—the idea is that, for many students, this may be the last analysis course they take, so I've tried to write in a way that these books will be useful as a reference. For this reason, I've included "bonus" chapters and sections—material that I do not expect to be included in the course. This has several advantages. First, in a slightly longer course, the instructor has an option of extra topics to include. Second, there is some flexibility—for an instructor who can't imagine a complex analysis course without a proof of the prime number theorem, it is possible to replace all or part of the (non-bonus) chapter on elliptic functions with the last four sections of the bonus chapter on analytic number theory. Third, it is certainly possible to take all the material in, say, Part 2, to turn it into a two-term course. Most importantly, the bonus material is there for the reader to peruse long after the formal course is over.

(d) I have long collected "best" proofs and over the years learned a number of ones that are not the standard textbook proofs. In this regard, modern technology has been a boon. Thanks to Google books and the Caltech library, I've been able to discover some proofs that I hadn't learned before. Examples of things that I'm especially fond of are Bernstein polynomials to get the classical Weierstrass approximation theorem, von Neumann's proof of the Lebesgue decomposition and Radon–Nikodym theorems, the Hermite expansion treatment of Fourier transform, Landau's proof of the Hadamard factorization theorem, Wielandt's theorem on the functional equation for $\Gamma(z)$, and Newman's proof of the prime number theorem. Each of these appears in at least some monographs, but they are not nearly as widespread as they deserve to be.

(e) I've tried to distinguish between central results and interesting asides and to indicate when an interesting aside is going to come up again later. In particular, all chapters, except those on preliminaries, have a listing of "Big Notions and Theorems" at their start. I wish that this attempt to differentiate between the essential and the less essential didn't make this book different, but alas, too many texts are monotone listings of theorems and proofs.

(f) I've included copious "Notes and Historical Remarks" at the end of each section. These notes illuminate and extend, and they (and the Problems) allow us to cover more material than would otherwise be possible. The history is there to enliven the discussion and to emphasize to students that mathematicians are real people and that "may you live in interesting times" is truly a curse. Any discussion of the history of real analysis is depressing because of the number of lives ended by the Nazis. Any discussion of nineteenth-century mathematics makes one appreciate medical progress, contemplating Abel, Riemann, and Stieltjes. I feel knowing that Picard was Hermite's son-in-law spices up the study of his theorem.

On the subject of history, there are three cautions. First, I am not a professional historian and almost none of the history discussed here is based on original sources. I have relied at times—horrors!—on information on the Internet. I have tried for accuracy but I'm sure there are errors, some that would make a real historian wince.

A second caution concerns looking at the history assuming the mathematics we now know. Especially when concepts are new, they may be poorly understood or viewed from a perspective quite different from the one here. Looking at the wonderful history of nineteenth-century complex analysis by Bottazzini–Grey[3] will illustrate this more clearly than these brief notes can.

The third caution concerns naming theorems. Here, the reader needs to bear in mind Arnol'd's principle:[4] *If a notion bears a personal name, then that name is not the name of the discoverer* (and the related Berry principle: *The Arnol'd principle is applicable to itself*). To see the applicability of Berry's principle, I note that in the wider world, Arnol'd's principle is called "Stigler's law of eponymy." Stigler[5] named this in 1980, pointing out it was really discovered by Merton. In 1972, Kennedy[6] named Boyer's law *Mathematical formulas and theorems are usually not named after their original discoverers* after Boyer's book.[7] Already in 1956, Newman[8] quoted the early twentieth-century philosopher and logician A. N. Whitehead as saying: "Everything of importance has been said before by somebody who

---

[3] U. Bottazzini and J. Gray, *Hidden Harmony—Geometric Fantasies. The Rise of Complex Function Theory*, Springer, New York, 2013.

[4] V. I. Arnol'd, *On teaching mathematics*, available online at http://pauli.uni-muenster.de/~munsteg/arnold.html.

[5] S. M. Stigler, *Stigler's law of eponymy*, Trans. New York Acad. Sci. **39** (1980), 147–158.

[6] H. C. Kennedy, *Classroom notes: Who discovered Boyer's law?*, Amer. Math. Monthly **79** (1972), 66–67.

[7] C. B. Boyer, *A History of Mathematics*, Wiley, New York, 1968.

[8] J. R. Newman, *The World of Mathematics*, Simon & Schuster, New York, 1956.

did not discover it." The main reason to give a name to a theorem is to have a convenient way to refer to that theorem. I usually try to follow common usage (even when I know Arnol'd's principle applies).

I have resisted the temptation of some text writers to rename things to set the record straight. For example, there is a small group who have attempted to replace "WKB approximation" by "Liouville–Green approximation", with valid historical justification (see the Notes to Section 15.5 of Part 2B). But if I gave a talk and said I was about to use the Liouville–Green approximation, I'd get blank stares from many who would instantly know what I meant by the WKB approximation. And, of course, those who try to change the name also know what WKB is! Names are mainly for shorthand, not history.

These books have a wide variety of problems, in line with a multiplicity of uses. The serious reader should at least skim them since there is often interesting supplementary material covered there.

Similarly, these books have a much larger bibliography than is standard, partly because of the historical references (many of which are available online and a pleasure to read) and partly because the Notes introduce lots of peripheral topics and places for further reading. But the reader shouldn't consider for a moment that these are intended to be comprehensive—that would be impossible in a subject as broad as that considered in these volumes.

These books differ from many modern texts by focusing a little more on special functions than is standard. In much of the nineteenth century, the theory of special functions was considered a central pillar of analysis. They are now out of favor—too much so—although one can see some signs of the pendulum swinging back. They are still mainly peripheral but appear often in Part 2 and a few times in Parts 1, 3, and 4.

These books are intended for a second course in analysis, but in most places, it is really previous exposure being helpful rather than required. Beyond the basic calculus, the one topic that the reader is expected to have seen is metric space theory and the construction of the reals as completion of the rationals (or by some other means, such as Dedekind cuts).

Initially, I picked "A Course in Analysis" as the title for this series as an homage to Goursat's *Cours d'Analyse*,[9] a classic text (also translated into English) of the early twentieth century (a literal translation would be

---

[9]E. Goursat, *A Course in Mathematical Analysis: Vol. 1: Derivatives and Differentials, Definite Integrals, Expansion in Series, Applications to Geometry. Vol. 2, Part 1: Functions of a Complex Variable. Vol. 2, Part 2: Differential Equations. Vol. 3, Part 1: Variation of Solutions. Partial Differential Equations of the Second Order. Vol. 3, Part 2: Integral Equations. Calculus of Variations*, Dover Publications, New York, 1959 and 1964; French original, 1905.

"of Analysis" but "in" sounds better). As I studied the history, I learned that this was a standard French title, especially associated with École Polytechnique. There are nineteenth-century versions by Cauchy and Jordan and twentieth-century versions by de la Vallée Poussin and Choquet. So this is a well-used title. The publisher suggested adding "Comprehensive", which seems appropriate.

It is a pleasure to thank many people who helped improve these texts. About 80% was TEXed by my superb secretary of almost 25 years, Cherie Galvez. Cherie was an extraordinary person—the secret weapon to my productivity. Not only was she technically strong and able to keep my tasks organized but also her people skills made coping with bureaucracy of all kinds easier. She managed to wind up a confidant and counselor for many of Caltech's mathematics students. Unfortunately, in May 2012, she was diagnosed with lung cancer, which she and chemotherapy valiantly fought. In July 2013, she passed away. I am dedicating these books to her memory.

During the second half of the preparation of this series of books, we also lost Arthur Wightman and Ed Nelson. Arthur was my advisor and was responsible for the topic of my first major paper—perturbation theory for the anharmonic oscillator. Ed had an enormous influence on me, both via the techniques I use and in how I approach being a mathematician. In particular, he taught me all about closed quadratic forms, motivating the methodology of my thesis. I am also dedicating these works to their memory.

After Cherie entered hospice, Sergei Gel'fand, the AMS publisher, helped me find Alice Peters to complete the TEXing of the manuscript. Her experience in mathematical publishing (she is the "A" of A K Peters Publishing) meant she did much more, for which I am grateful.

This set of books has about 150 figures which I think considerably add to their usefulness. About half were produced by Mamikon Mnatsakanian, a talented astrophysicist and wizard with Adobe Illustrator. The other half, mainly function plots, were produced by my former Ph.D. student and teacher extraordinaire Mihai Stoiciu (used with permission) using Mathematica. There are a few additional figures from Wikipedia (mainly under WikiCommons license) and a hyperbolic tiling of Douglas Dunham, used with permission. I appreciate the help I got with these figures.

Over the five-year period that I wrote this book and, in particular, during its beta-testing as a text in over a half-dozen institutions, I received feedback and corrections from many people. In particular, I should like to thank (with apologies to those who were inadvertently left off): Tom Alberts, Michael Barany, Jacob Christiansen, Percy Deift, Tal Einav, German Enciso, Alexander Eremenko, Rupert Frank, Fritz Gesztesy, Jeremy Gray,

Leonard Gross, Chris Heil, Mourad Ismail, Svetlana Jitomirskaya, Bill Johnson, Rowan Killip, John Klauder, Seung Yeop Lee, Milivoje Lukic, Andre Martinez-Finkelshtein, Chris Marx, Alex Poltoratski, Eric Rains, Lorenzo Sadun, Ed Saff, Misha Sodin, Dan Stroock, Benji Weiss, Valentin Zagrebnov, and Maxim Zinchenko.

Much of these books was written at the tables of the Hebrew University Mathematics Library. I'd like to thank Yoram Last for his invitation and Naavah Levin for the hospitality of the library and for her invaluable help.

This series has a Facebook page. I welcome feedback, questions, and comments. The page is at `www.facebook.com/simon.analysis`.

Even if these books have later editions, I will try to keep theorem and equation numbers constant in case readers use them in their papers.

Finally, analysis is a wonderful and beautiful subject. I hope the reader has as much fun using these books as I had writing them.

Preface to Part 1

> I warn you in advance that all the principles ...that I'll now tell you about, are a little false. Counterexamples can be found to each one—but as directional guides the principles still serve a useful purpose.
> —*Paul Halmos*[1]

Analysis is the infinitesimal calculus writ large. Calculus as taught to most high school students and college freshmen is the subject as it existed about 1750—I've no doubt that Euler could have gotten a perfect score on the Calculus BC advanced placement exam. Even "rigorous" calculus courses that talk about ε-δ proofs and the intermediate value theorem only bring the subject up to about 1890 after the impact of Cauchy and Weierstrass on real variable calculus was felt.

This volume can be thought of as the infinitesimal calculus of the twentieth century. From that point of view, the key chapters are Chapter 4, which covers measure theory—the consummate integral calculus—and the first part of Chapter 6 on distribution theory—the ultimate differential calculus.

But from another point of view, this volume is about the triumph of abstraction. Abstraction is such a central part of modern mathematics that one forgets that it wasn't until Fréchet's 1906 thesis that sets of points with no a priori underlying structure (not assumed points in or functions on $\mathbb{R}^n$) are considered and given a structure a posteriori (Fréchet first defined abstract metric spaces). And after its success in analysis, abstraction took over significant parts of algebra, geometry, topology, and logic.

---

[1]L. Gillman, P. R. Halmos, H. Flanders, and B. Shube, *Four Panel Talks on Publishing*, Amer. Math. Monthly **82** (1975), 13–21.

Abstract spaces are a distinct thread here, starting with topological spaces in Chapter 2, Banach spaces in Chapter 5 (and its special case, Hilbert spaces, in Chapter 3), and locally convex spaces in the later parts of Chapters 5 and 6 and in Chapter 9.

Of course, abstract spaces occur to set up the language we need for measure theory (which we do initially on compact Hausdorff spaces and where we use Banach lattices as a tool) and for distributions which are defined as duals of some locally convex spaces.

Besides the main threads of measure theory, distributions, and abstract spaces, several leitmotifs can be seen: Fourier analysis (Sections 3.5, 6.2, and 6.4–6.6 are a minicourse), probability (Bonus Chapter 7 has the basics, but it is implicit in much of the basic measure theory), convexity (a key notion in Chapter 5), and at least bits and pieces of the theory of ordinary and partial differential equations.

The role of pivotal figures in real analysis is somewhat different from complex analysis, where three figures—Cauchy, Riemann, and Weierstrass—dominated not only in introducing the key concepts, but many of the most significant theorems. Of course, Lebesgue and Schwartz invented measure theory and distributions, respectively, but after ten years, Lebesgue moved on mainly to pedagogy and Hörmander did much more to cement the theory of distributions than Schwartz. On the abstract side, F. Riesz was a key figure for the 30 years following 1906, with important results well into his fifties, but he doesn't rise to the dominance of the complex analytic three.

In understanding one part of the rather distinct tone of some of this volume, the reader needs to bear in mind "Simon's three kvetches":[2]

1. Every interesting topological space is a metric space.
2. Every interesting Banach space is separable.
3. Every interesting real-valued function is Baire/Borel measurable.

Of course, the principles are well-described by the Halmos quote at the start—they aren't completely true but capture important ideas for the reader to bear in mind. As a mathematician, I cringe at using the phrase "not completely true." I was in a seminar whose audience included Ed Nelson, one of my teachers. When the speaker said the proof he was giving was almost rigorous, Ed said: "To say something is almost rigorous makes as much sense as saying a woman is almost pregnant." On the other hand, Neils Bohr, the founding father of quantum mechanics, said: "It is the hallmark of any deep truth that its negation is also a deep truth."[3]

---

[2]http://www.merriam-webster.com/dictionary/kvetch
[3]Quoted by Max Delbruck, *Mind from Matter? An Essay on Evolutionary Epistemology*, Blackwell Scientific Publications, Palo Alto, CA, 1986; page 167.

We'll see that weak topologies on infinite-dimensional Banach spaces are never metrizable (see Theorem 5.7.2) nor is the natural topology on $C_0^\infty(\mathbb{R}^\nu)$ (see Theorem 9.1.5), so Kvetch 1 has counterexamples, but neither case is so far from metrizable: If X^* is separable, the weak topology restricted to the unit ball of X is metrizable (see Theorem 5.7.2). While $C_0^\infty(\mathbb{R}^\nu)$ is not metrizable, that is because we allow ordinary distributions of arbitrary growth. If we restrict ourselves to distributions of any growth restriction, the test function space will be metrizable (see Sections 6.1 and 6.2). But the real point of Kvetch 1 is that the reason for studying topological spaces is *not* (merely) to be able to discuss nonmetrizable spaces—it is because metrics have more structure than is needed—$(0,1)$ is not complete with its usual metric while $\mathbb{R}$ is, but they are the same as topological spaces. Topological spaces provide the proper language for parts of analysis.

$L^\infty([0,1], dx)$ and $\mathcal{L}(\mathcal{H})$, the bounded operators on a Hilbert space, $\mathcal{H}$, are two very interesting spaces which are *not* separable, so Kvetch 2 isn't strictly true. But again, there is a point to Kvetch 2. In many cases, the most important members of a class of spaces are separable and one has to do considerable gymnastics in the general case, which is never, or at most very rarely, used. Of course, the gymnastics can be fun, but they don't belong in a first course. We illustrate this by including separability as an axiom for Hilbert spaces. Von Neumann did also in his initial work, but over the years, this has been dropped in most books. We choose to avoid the complications and mainly restrict ourselves to the separable case.

Two caveats: First, the consideration of the nonseparable case can provide more elegant proofs! For example, the projection lemma of Theorem 3.2.3 was proven initially for the separable case using a variant of Gram–Schmidt. The elegant proof we use that exploits convex minimization was only discovered because of a need to handle the nonseparable case. Second, we abuse the English language. A "red book" is a "book." We include separability and complex field in our definition of Hilbert space. We'll use the terms "nonseparable Hilbert space" and "real Hilbert space," which are not Hilbert spaces!

In one sense, Kvetch 3 isn't true, but except for one caveat, it is. Every set, A, has its characteristic function associated with it. If the only interesting functions are Borel functions, the only interesting sets are Borel sets. While it is a more advanced topic that we won't consider, there are sets constructed from Borel sets, called analytic sets and Souslin sets which may not be Borel.[4] The kvetch is there to eliminate Lebesgue measurable sets and functions, that is, sets $A = B \triangle C$, where B is Borel, and $C \subset D$, a Borel set of Lebesgue measure zero. The end of Section 4.3 discusses why it is not

---

[4]See, e.g., V. Bogachev, *Measure Theory*, Springer, 2007.

a good idea to consider such sets (and functions) even though many books do and it's what the Carathéodory construction of Section 8.1 leads to.

The last issue we mention in this preface is that our approach to measure theory is different from the standard one—it follows an approach in the appendix of Lax[5] that starts with a positive functional, ℓ, on $C(X)$, completes $C(X)$ in the $\ell(|f|)$-norm, and shows that the elements of the completion are equivalence classes of Borel functions. For those who prefer more traditional approaches, Section 4.13 discusses general measure spaces and Section 8.1 discusses the Carathéodory outer measure construction.

---

[5]P. Lax, *Functional Analysis*, Wiley, 2002.

Chapter 1

Preliminaries

The White Rabbit put on his spectacles. "Where shall I begin, please your Majesty?" he asked. "Begin at the beginning," the King said very gravely, "and go on till you come to the end: then stop."
—*Lewis Carroll, Alice in Wonderland*[1] [**164**]

This chapter sets notation and reviews various subjects—most notably, metric spaces—that it is hoped the reader has seen before. We also give background on the axiom of choice, Zorn's lemma, and all that. Since it is "review," we omit most proofs.

1.1. Notation and Terminology

A foolish consistency is the hobgoblin of little minds ... Is it so bad, then, to be misunderstood? Pythagoras was misunderstood, and Socrates, and Jesus, and Luther, and Copernicus, and Galileo, and Newton, and every pure and wise spirit that ever took flesh. To be great is to be misunderstood.
—*Ralph Waldo Emerson* [**276**]

For a real number a, we will use the terms positive and strictly positive for $a \geq 0$ and $a > 0$, respectively. It is not so much that we find nonnegative bad, but the phrase "monotone nondecreasing" for $x > y \Rightarrow f(x) \geq f(y)$ is downright confusing so we use "monotone increasing" and "strictly monotone increasing" and then, for consistency, "positive" and "strictly positive." Similarly for matrices, we use "positive definite" and "strictly positive definite" where others might use "positive semi-definite" and "positive definite."

---

[1]Lewis Carroll is, of course, the pseudonym of Charles Dodgson (1832–1898), a British mathematician.

Basic Rings and Fields.

$$\mathbb{R} = real\ numbers \qquad \mathbb{Q} = rationals \qquad \mathbb{Z} = integers$$
$$\mathbb{C} = complex\ numbers = \{x + iy \mid x, y \in \mathbb{R}\}$$

with their sums and products. For $z = x + iy \in \mathbb{C}$, we use $\operatorname{Re} z = x$, $\operatorname{Im} z = y$. $|z| = (x^2 + y^2)^{1/2}$.

Products. $X^n = n$-tuples of points in X with induced vector space and/or additive structure; in particular, $\mathbb{R}^n$, $\mathbb{Q}^n$, $\mathbb{Z}^n$, $\mathbb{C}^n$.

Subsets of $\mathbb{C}$.

- $\mathbb{C}_+ =$ upper half-plane $= \{z \mid \operatorname{Im} z > 0\}$;
  $\mathbb{H}_+ =$ right half-plane $= \{z \mid \operatorname{Re} z > 0\}$
- $\mathbb{Z}_+ = \{n \in \mathbb{Z} \mid n > 0\} = \{1, 2, 3, \dots\}$;
  $\mathbb{N} = \{0\} \cup \mathbb{Z}_+ = \{0, 1, 2, \dots\}$
- $\mathbb{D} = \{z \in \mathbb{C} \mid |z| < 1\}$; $\partial\mathbb{D} = \{z \in \mathbb{C} \mid |z| = 1\}$
- $\mathbb{D}_\delta(z_0) = \{z \in \mathbb{C} \mid |z - z_0| < \delta\}$ for $z_0 \in \mathbb{C}$, $\delta > 0$

Miscellaneous Terms.

- For $x \in \mathbb{R}$, $[x] =$ greatest integer less than x, that is, $[x] \in \mathbb{Z}$, $[x] \leq x < [x] + 1$
- $\{x\} = x - [x] =$ fractional parts of x
- $\sharp(A) =$ number of elements in a set A
- $\operatorname{Ran} f =$ range of a function f
- $\log(z) =$ natural logarithm, that is, logarithm to base e; if z is complex, put the cut along $(-\infty, 0]$, i.e., $\log(z) = \log(|z|) + i \arg(z)$ with $-\pi < \arg(z) \leq \pi$
- For sets A, B subsets of X, $A \cup B =$ union, $A \cap B =$ intersection, $A^c =$ complement of A in X, $A \setminus B = A \cap B^c$, $A \triangle B = (A \setminus B) \cup (B \setminus A)$
- For matrices, M_{12} means row one, column two
- $f \restriction K = restriction$ of a function to K, a subset of the domain of f

One-Point Compactification Notation.

- $X_\infty =$ one-point compactification of a locally compact space (see Theorem 2.3.17)
- $C_\infty(X) =$ continuous functions vanishing at infinity
- $C(X_\infty) =$ continuous functions with a limit at infinity ($= C_\infty(X) + \{\alpha\mathbb{1}\}$)

Given a set, S, a *relation*, R, is a subset of $S \times S$. For $x, y \in S$, we write xRy if $(x, y) \in R$ and $\sim xRy$ if $(x, y) \notin R$. A relation is called

$$\text{reflexive} \Leftrightarrow \forall\, x \in S, \text{ we have that } xRx$$

$$\text{symmetric} \Leftrightarrow \forall\, x, y \in S, \ xRy \Rightarrow yRx$$

$$\text{transitive} \Leftrightarrow \forall\, x, y, z \in S, \ xRy \,\&\, yRz \Rightarrow xRz$$

An *equivalence relation* is a relation that is reflexive, symmetric, and transitive.

If R is an equivalence relation on S, the *equivalence class*, $[x]$, of $x \in S$ is

$$[x] = \{y \in S \mid xRy\} \tag{1.1.1}$$

By the properties of equivalence relations,

$$\forall\, x, y \in S, \quad \text{either } [x] = [y] \text{ or } [x] \cap [y] = \emptyset \tag{1.1.2}$$

The family of equivalence classes in S is denoted S/R.

We use "big oh, litttle oh" notation, e.g., $f(x) = O(|x|)$ or $f(x) = o(1)$. If the reader is not familiar with it, see Section 1.4 of Part 2A.

1.2. Metric Spaces

Definition. A *semimetric*, ρ, on space, X, is a map $\rho \colon X \times X \to [0, \infty)$ that obeys

(a) (Symmetry)
$$\forall x, y \in X, \ \rho(x, y) = \rho(y, x) \tag{1.2.1}$$

(b) (Triangle inequality)
$$\forall x, y, z \in X, \ \rho(x, z) \leq \rho(x, y) + \rho(y, z) \tag{1.2.2}$$

(c) (Weak zero property)
$$\forall x \in X, \ \rho(x, x) = 0 \tag{1.2.3}$$

A *metric* is a semimetric, ρ, that also obeys

(d) (Strong zero property)
$$\forall x, y \in X, \ \rho(x, y) = 0 \Rightarrow x = y \tag{1.2.4}$$

A *metric* (respectively, semimetric) *space* is a set, X, with a metric (respectively, semimetric).

If ρ is a semimetric on X and if we define the relation $\equiv$ on X by

$$x \equiv y \Leftrightarrow \rho(x, y) = 0 \tag{1.2.5}$$

then $\equiv$ is easily seen to be an equivalence relation $((1.2.3) \Rightarrow$ reflexivity, $(1.2.1) \Rightarrow$ symmetry, and $(1.2.2) \Rightarrow$ transitivity). We define $\tilde{\rho}$ on $\widetilde{X} \equiv X/\equiv$ by

$$\tilde{\rho}([x], [y]) = \rho(x, y) \tag{1.2.6}$$

(1.2.2) implies $\tilde{\rho}$ is well-defined. It is easy to see $\tilde{\rho}$ is a metric on $\tilde{X}$. $\tilde{X}$ is called the metric space *induced* by the semimetric space, X.

Definition. Given a metric space, (X, ρ), we define the *open ball*, $B_r(x)$, for $r > 0$, $x \in X$, by

$$B_r(x) = \{ y \mid \rho(x, y) < r \} \qquad (1.2.7)$$

The *closed ball*, $\overline{B_r(x)}$, is defined (for $r \geq 0$) with $\rho(x, y) < r$ replaced by $\rho(x, y) \leq r$.

Definition. A set $A \subset X$, a metric space, is called *open* if and only if for all $x \in X$, there exists $r > 0$ so $B_r(x) \subset A$. A is called *closed* if $X \setminus A$ is open.

The reader should check that open balls are open and that closed balls are closed. By the definition of open set, an arbitrary union of open sets is open. A finite intersection of open sets is open since $\cap_{j=1}^{n} B_{r_j}(x_0) = B_{\min(r_j)}(x_0)$, and any finite set of strictly positive numbers has a strictly positive minimum. By taking complements, any intersection and any finite union of closed sets is closed.

If A is an arbitrary set, $\bigcap \{ C \mid C \text{ closed}, A \subset C \}$ is a closed set by the above, clearly the smallest closed set containing A. It is called the *closure*, $\bar{A}$, of A. Taking complements, A contains a largest open set, A^{int}, called its *interior*. Clearly $A^{\text{int}} = \bigcup \{ U \mid U \text{ open}, U \subset A \}$. It is easy to see that $x \in \bar{A}$ if and only if for all $\varepsilon > 0$, $B_\varepsilon(x) \cap A \neq \emptyset$.

If $A \subset B$ with $B \subset \bar{A}$, we say A is *dense* in B. In particular, if $B = X$, we speak of a *dense subset* of X.

Definition. Given a sequence $\{x_n\}_{n=1}^{\infty}$ in (X, ρ) a metric space, we say x_∞ is a *limit point* of $\{x_n\}_{n=1}^{\infty}$ if and only if

$$\forall \varepsilon > 0, \ \forall N, \ \exists n > N \text{ so that } \rho(x_n, x_\infty) < \varepsilon$$

We say x_n *converges* to x_∞, written $x_n \to x_\infty$, if and only if

$$\forall \varepsilon > 0, \ \exists N, \ \forall n > N \text{ so that } \rho(x_n, x_\infty) < \varepsilon \qquad (1.2.8)$$

Put differently, x_∞ is a limit point (respectively, $x_n \to x_\infty$) if and only if for all $\varepsilon > 0$, $B_\varepsilon(x_\infty)$ contains infinitely many x_n (respectively, all but finitely many x_n). It is easy to see that x_∞ is a limit point of $\{x_n\}_{n=1}^{\infty}$ if and only if $\exists n \colon \mathbb{Z}_+ \to \mathbb{Z}_+$ with $n(j+1) > n(j)$ so $x_{n(j)} \to x_\infty$ as $j \to \infty$. We call $\{x_{n(j)}\}_{j=1}^{\infty}$ a *subsequence* of $\{x_n\}_{n=1}^{\infty}$.

Convergent sequences are related to closed sets by

Proposition 1.2.1. (a) *A is closed if and only if $\{x_n\}_{n=1}^{\infty} \subset A$ and $x_n \to x_\infty \Rightarrow x_\infty \in A$.*

(b) *For any A, $\bar{A}$ is the set of limit points of sequences in A.*

If (X, ρ) and (Y, d) are metric spaces, $f\colon X \to Y$ is said to be *continuous* at $x_0 \in X$, if

$$\forall \varepsilon > 0, \ \exists \delta > 0, \qquad \rho(x, x_0) < \delta \Rightarrow d(f(x), f(x_0)) < \varepsilon \qquad (1.2.9)$$

If f is continuous at every $x_0 \in X$, we say f is a *continuous function*. We will often use the following if Y is $\mathbb{R}$ or $\mathbb{C}$ (or, once we define them, vector spaces with norms if $\| \cdot \|$ replaces $| \cdot |$):

$$\|f\|_\infty = \sup_{x \in X} |f(x)| \qquad (1.2.10)$$

sup is defined in the next section.

Proposition 1.2.2. *Let $f\colon X \to Y$ for metric spaces (X, ρ) and (Y, d). Then the following are equivalent:*

(1) *f is continuous.*
(2) *For all open $B \subset Y$, $f^{-1}[B] \equiv \{x \mid f(x) \in B\}$ is an open subset of X.*
(3) *$x_n \to x_\infty$ in $X \Rightarrow f(x_n) \to f(x_\infty)$ in Y.*

Finally, we turn to the important notions of complete and completion.

Definition. A sequence $\{x_n\}_{n=1}^\infty$ of points in a metric space, (X, ρ), is called *Cauchy* if and only if

$$\forall \varepsilon, \ \exists N, \ n, m > N \Rightarrow \rho(x_n, x_m) < \varepsilon \qquad (1.2.11)$$

Since $\rho(x_n, x_\infty) < \varepsilon/2 \ \& \ \rho(x_m, x_\infty) < \varepsilon/2 \Rightarrow \rho(x_n, x_m) < \varepsilon$, looking at (1.2.8) and (1.2.11), we see that any convergent sequence is Cauchy. The converse may not be true: if $X = (0, 1)$ with the usual metric, $\rho(x, y) = |x - y|$, then $x_n = 1/n$ is Cauchy but does not converge to a point in X. We single out spaces where this cannot happen.

Definition. A metric space, X, is called *complete* if and only if every Cauchy sequence converges to some $x_\infty \in X$.

The real numbers, $\mathbb{R}$, are complete in their usual metric; see the next section. We want to show that any metric space can be naturally embedded as a dense subset of a complete metric space. Given a metric space (X, ρ), we form a new semimetric space $(X^\sharp, \rho^\sharp)$ as follows. The elements of $X^\sharp$ are Cauchy sequences in X. If $\{x_n\}_{n=1}^\infty$ and $\{y_n\}_{n=1}^\infty$ are two Cauchy sequences,

$$|\rho(x_n, y_n) - \rho(x_m, y_m)| \le \rho(x_n, x_m) + \rho(y_n, y_m) \qquad (1.2.12)$$

by the triangle inequality. It follows that as $n, m \to \infty$, $\rho(x_n, y_n) - \rho(x_m, y_m) \to 0$, that is, $\rho(x_n, y_n)$ is a Cauchy sequence in the reals. Thus,

$$\rho^\sharp(\{x_n\}, \{y_n\}) = \lim \rho(x_n, y_n) \qquad (1.2.13)$$

exists.

We say $\{x_n\} \equiv \{y_n\}$ if $\rho^\sharp(\{x_n\}, \{y_n\}) = 0$ and set

$$\widetilde{X} = X^\sharp / \equiv \tag{1.2.14}$$

with $\tilde{\rho}$ the associated metric. It is easy to check that $\widetilde{X}$ is a complete metric space called the *completion* of X.

Map $i^\sharp \colon X \to X^\sharp$ by $i^\sharp(x)$ is the constant sequence $i^\sharp(x)_n = x$. Clearly, $\rho^\sharp(i^\sharp(x), i^\sharp(y)) = \rho(x, y)$. Define $i \colon X \to \widetilde{X}$ by $i(x) = [i^\sharp(x)]$, the equivalence class of $i^\sharp(x)$. Then

$$\tilde{\rho}(i(x), i(y)) = \rho(x, y) \tag{1.2.15}$$

so i is an isometry and thus one-one. For any Cauchy sequence $\{x_n\}_{n=1}^\infty \in X$, $[\{x_n\}] \in \widetilde{X}$, then $i(x_n) \to [\{x_n\}]$, so $i[X]$ is dense in $\widetilde{X}$. We have thus proven the existence part of the following (uniqueness is easy):

Theorem 1.2.3. *Given any metric space (X, ρ), there is a complete metric space $(\widetilde{X}, \tilde{\rho})$ and map $i \colon X \to \widetilde{X}$ so that*

(i) *(1.2.15) holds.*

(ii) *$\mathrm{Ran}(i)$ is dense in $\widetilde{X}$.*

If $(X^\flat, \rho^\flat)$ and $i^\flat$ is another complete metric space and embedding, there is a unique bijection $g \colon \widetilde{X} \to X^\flat$ so that $g \circ i = i^\flat$ and

$$\rho^\flat(g(x), g(y)) = \tilde{\rho}(x, y) \tag{1.2.16}$$

for all $x, y \in \widetilde{X}$.

In this general construction, elements of $\widetilde{X}$ are complicated: equivalence classes of Cauchy sequences. In many concrete situations, an important step will be to find another, more transparent representation of the elements.

Notes and Historical Remarks. We will say more about the history of metric spaces in the Notes to Section 2.1. We note here that the notion of a distance function on abstract sets to obtain convergence appeared first in Fréchet's 1906 thesis [**315**]. He had a more general condition than the triangle inequality. It was F. Riesz [**777, 778**] who emphasized the triangle inequality.

The name Cauchy sequence is after Cauchy's fundamental work on the foundations of calculus in the early part of the nineteenth century.

For the basics of metric space theory, see Tao [**905**].

1.3. The Real Numbers

Logically (although not quite historically), the order of constructing the fundamental sets of numbers of analysis is

$$\mathbb{N} \to \mathbb{Z} \to \mathbb{Q} \to \mathbb{R} \to \mathbb{C} \tag{1.3.1}$$

Given $\mathbb{N}$, all these steps are algebraic except $\mathbb{Q} \to \mathbb{R}$, which is the most subtle and is essentially a metric space completion.

We start with $\mathbb{N}$ and the *Peano axioms* (see the Notes—what we use is less than Peano did):

(a) $\mathbb{N}$ contains a distinguished element 0.
(b) There is a map $S \colon \mathbb{N} \to \mathbb{N}$, called the *successor*, that obeys
    (b1) For no n is $S(n) = 0$.
    (b2) S is one-one, that is, $S(n) = S(m) \Rightarrow n = m$.
(c) (Mathematical Induction) If $A \subset \mathbb{N}$ is a subset with $0 \in A$ and $n \in A \Rightarrow S(n) \in A$, then $A = \mathbb{N}$.

It is easy to see that $\mathbb{N} = \{0, S(0), S(S(0)), S(S(S(0))), \dots\}$ an infinite set of distinct elements. We can use S to define an arithmetic on $\mathbb{N}$: addition and multiplication obey

$$a + 0 = a, \qquad a + S(b) = S(a + b) \tag{1.3.2}$$

$$a \cdot 0 = 0, \qquad a \cdot S(b) = a + (a \cdot b) \tag{1.3.3}$$

Thus, for example, if $S(0) \equiv 1$,

$$a + 1 = a + S(0) = S(a + 0) = S(a) \tag{1.3.4}$$

$$a \cdot 1 = a \cdot S(0) = a + (a \cdot 0) = a \tag{1.3.5}$$

$\mathbb{N}$ is ordered by

$$a \geq b \Leftrightarrow \exists c \in \mathbb{N} \text{ so that } a = b + c \Leftrightarrow a = S(S(\dots S(b))\dots) \tag{1.3.6}$$

With this definition, $\mathbb{N}$ is totally ordered in that for all $a, b \in \mathbb{N}$, either $a \leq b$ or $b \leq a$ with both only if $a = b$.

$\mathbb{Z}$ is obtained as follows. Put an equivalence relation on $\mathbb{N} \times \mathbb{N}$ by

$$(a, b) \equiv (c, d) \Leftrightarrow a + d = b + c \tag{1.3.7}$$

(informally, (a, b) is $a - b$). $\mathbb{Z}$ is $\mathbb{N} \times \mathbb{N} / \equiv$. Every equivalence class has either $a \geq b$ for all pairs, in which case it contains $(n, 0)$ for a unique $n \in \mathbb{N}$, or $a \leq b$ for all pairs, in which case it contains $(0, n)$ for a unique $n \in \mathbb{N}$. Set $-(a, b) = (b, a)$. Then if $\mathbb{Z}_+ = \mathbb{N} \setminus \{0\}$, we have $\mathbb{Z}$ is the disjoint union of $\mathbb{Z}_+, \mathbb{Z}_- \equiv -\mathbb{Z}_+$ and $\{0\}$. If $(a, b) + (c, d) = (a + c, b + d)$ and $(a, b) \cdot (c, d) = (ac + bd, ad + bc)$, these operations lift to $\mathbb{Z}$ and turn $\mathbb{Z}$ into a ring—indeed, an integral domain. The order extends from $\mathbb{N}$ to $\mathbb{Z}$ and is still linear.

$\mathbb{Q}$ is obtained as follows. Put an equivalence relation on $\mathbb{Z} \times (\mathbb{Z} \setminus \{0\})$,

$$(a, b) \equiv (c, d) \Leftrightarrow ad = bc \tag{1.3.8}$$

(informally, $(a, b) = a/b$). $\mathbb{Q}$ is $\mathbb{Z} \times (\mathbb{Z} \setminus \{0\}) / \equiv$. Every $q \in \mathbb{Q}$, with $q \neq 0 \equiv [(0, b)]$, has a unique element (a, b) in its equivalence class with $b > 0$ and so that a and b have no common factor (i.e., there are no k, c, d with

$a = kc$, $b = kd$). Arithmetic is the well-known rules $(a, b) \cdot (c, d) = (ac, bd)$, $(a, b) + (c, d) = (ad + bc, bd)$. This makes $\mathbb{Q}$ into a field. The order extends from $\mathbb{Z}$ to $\mathbb{Q}$ and is still total.

We'll discuss $\mathbb{R}$ from $\mathbb{Q}$ below. One gets $\mathbb{C}$ from $\mathbb{R}$ as $\mathbb{C}$ is $\mathbb{R} \times \mathbb{R}$ with $(a, b) + (c, d) = (a + c, b + d)$ and $(a, b)(c, d) = (ac - bd, ad + bc)$. $\mathbb{C}$ is discussed in Section 1.2 of Part 2A. We can now turn to the construction of $\mathbb{R}$ from $\mathbb{Q}$.

Basically, $\mathbb{R}$ *is the completion of* $\mathbb{Q}$ but some care is needed since completion is only defined for metric spaces and we defined such spaces in terms of a real-valued metric!

Define $q \mapsto |q|$ on $\mathbb{Q}$ by

$$|q| = \begin{cases} q & \text{if } q \geq 0 \\ -q & \text{if } q < 0 \end{cases} \tag{1.3.9}$$

and

$$\rho(q_1, q_2) = |q_1 - q_2| \tag{1.3.10}$$

ρ has all the properties of a metric with values in $\mathbb{Q}$ (since we don't yet have $\mathbb{R}$, that is good).

Let $\widetilde{\mathbb{R}}$ be the set of Cauchy sequences of rationals with $x \equiv y \Leftrightarrow \rho(x_n, y_n) \to 0$. $\mathbb{R}$ will be the set of equivalence classes in $\widetilde{\mathbb{R}}$. As in the last section, if $[x], [y] \in \mathbb{R}$, $\rho(x_n, y_n)$ is Cauchy, and if $\tilde{x} \equiv x$, $\tilde{y} \equiv y$, then $|\rho(x_n, y_n) - \rho(\tilde{x}_n, \tilde{y}_n)| \to 0$. We have $\rho(x_n, y_n)$ is Cauchy, but we can't say it converges to a real since we need ρ to define convergence! But that is no problem since the equivalence class of $\{\rho(x_n, y_n)\}_{n=1}^{\infty}$ *is a real number*. Thus, we define

$$\rho([x], [y]) = [\rho(x_n, y_n)] \tag{1.3.11}$$

and get a real-valued metric on $\mathbb{R}$! And it is not hard to see that $\mathbb{R}$ is then a complete metric space. If $q \in \mathbb{Q}$ is associated to $[(q, q, q, \dots)]$, that is the equivalence class of the constant (Cauchy) sequence then $\mathbb{Q}$ is a dense subset of $\mathbb{R}$.

If $x \in \mathbb{R} \setminus \mathbb{Q}$, one proves there is a unique $[x] \in \mathbb{Z}$ so that $[x] \leq x < [x] + 1$, then a unique $x_1 \in \{0, \dots, 9\}$, so $[x] + \frac{x_1}{10} \leq x < [x] + \frac{x_1 + 1}{10}, \dots$. In this way, one sees that every $x \in \mathbb{R} \setminus \mathbb{Q}$ has a unique decimal expansion $x = [x].x_1 x_2 \dots$. Further analysis shows $\mathbb{R} \setminus \mathbb{Q}$ is precisely in the decimals which are not repeating. Any $\mathbb{Q}$ has a decimal expansion also, which is unique except for the usual $.x_1 x_2 \dots x_\ell 0 \dots 0 \dots = .x_1 \dots x_{\ell_1}(x_\ell - 1)99 \dots 9 \dots$ ambiguity. Thus, elements of $\mathbb{R}$ are realized as a decimal, unique so long as $x \neq y/10^k$ for some $y \in \mathbb{Z}$, $k \in \{0, 1, 2, \dots\}$.

One can easily extend arithmetic and order to $\mathbb{R}$. A set $A \subset \mathbb{R}$ is said to be *bounded above* if there is $y \in \mathbb{R}$ so $\forall x \in A$, $x \leq y$. If $A \neq \emptyset$, we can define a sequence of upper bounds of the form $y_k \equiv z_k/10^k$, $k = 1, 2, \dots$, where $z_k \in \mathbb{Z}$ and $(z_k - 1)/10^k$ is not an upper bound. $\{y_k\}$ is Cauchy and the limit $y_\infty \equiv \sup_{x \in A} x$ is the *least upper bound* of A. In this way, one sees $\mathbb{R}$ has the critical *least upper bound property* that every set bounded above has a least upper bound. Similarly $\inf_{x \in A} x$ is the *greatest lower bound*.

Notes and Historical Remarks. The Greeks already realized that one needed to go beyond the rationals—that $\sqrt{2}$ is not rational is attributed to the school of Pythagoras (which thought of $\sqrt{2}$ as the hypotenuse of a right triangle whose two sides are both 1). But it was only as the nineteenth century developed that mathematicians realized the need for a careful definition of the reals and then even of the integers.

In 1861, Grassmann [**361**] understood that all of arithmetic could be rephrased in terms of the successor function and induction. In the 1880s, first Peirce [**711**], then Dedekind [**225**], and finally, Giuseppe Peano (1858–1932) [**706**] came up with more precise axioms. Peano actually had nine axioms, of which we only state four! The missing axioms concern the meaning of $a = b$ (that $=$ is an equivalence relation is three)—we've absorbed this into the implicit notion of $=$.

Richard Dedekind (1831–1916) also axiomatized the reals. A *Dedekind cut* is a subset A of $\mathbb{Q}$ so that A and $\mathbb{Q} \setminus A$ are both nonempty and so that if $x \in A$ and $y \in \mathbb{Q} \setminus A$, then $x < y$. An example is $\{q \in \mathbb{Q} \mid (q \leq 0) \text{ or } (q \geq 0 \text{ and } q^2 < 2)\}$. Every rational q has two cuts associated with it: $\{q' \mid q' < q\}$ and $\{q' \mid q' \leq q\}$. The other cuts are associated one-one with $\mathbb{R} \setminus \mathbb{Q}$ via A corresponding to $\sup_{x \in A} x$ (once one has the reals). Dedekind found his cuts in 1858 but only published them in 1872 in a small monograph [**224**] when he learned of the forthcoming work of Heine and Cantor, discussed shortly. He returned to the cuts in [**225**].

The approach to defining reals as equivalence classes of Cauchy sequences is due to Cantor in 1872 [**150**]. Hankel [**390**] had an early variant of this idea in 1867 and Heine [**408**] and Meray [**651**] found related but not so cogent approaches as Cantor.

An elegant and complete construction of the number systems, but using

$$\mathbb{Z}_+ \to \mathbb{Q}_+ \to \mathbb{R}_+ \to \mathbb{R} \to \mathbb{C} \tag{1.3.12}$$

in place of (1.3.1) can be found in the classic 1930 book of Landau [**543**]. (1.3.12) is closer to the historical order. For a modern treatment, fleshing out our discussion here, see Tao [**904**].

1.4. Orders

We've seen the importance of equivalence relations. To define another important class of relations, we need one more property. A relation, R, on S

is called

$$antisymmetric \Leftrightarrow \big[\forall x, y \in S, \ xRy \,\&\, yRx \Rightarrow y = x\big] \qquad (1.4.1)$$

Definition. A *partial order* is a relation that is reflexive, antisymmetric, and transitive. A set with a distinguished partial order is called a *partially ordered set* or, by some, a *poset*.

If we drop reflexivity and instead demand $\forall x, \sim xRx$, then one speaks of a *strict partial order*. We often use $\geq$ for the order. We then use $x > y$ to mean $x \geq y$ and $x \neq y$. $\mathbb{Z}$, $\mathbb{Q}$, and $\mathbb{R}$ all come with natural partial orders. If $\mathcal{F}$ is a class of functions, $f \colon X \to S$, and S has a partial order, we can induce a partial order on $\mathcal{F}$ by

$$f \geq g \Leftrightarrow \forall x \in X, \ f(x) \geq g(x) \qquad (1.4.2)$$

In particular, $C_{\mathbb{R}}(X)$, the continuous real-valued functions on X, a topological space, has a natural partial order.

We'll see later in Sections 4.8 and 5.5 that real vector spaces have a natural class of orders with $x \geq y \Rightarrow z + x \geq z + y$ and $x \geq y \,\&\, \lambda \geq 0 \Rightarrow \lambda x \geq \lambda y$. We'll also study a subclass of partially ordered sets called *lattices* (defined in Section 4.8). For now, we want to briefly single out two subclasses of partial orders which we'll need in the next section to discuss the Axiom of Choice.

Definition. A partially ordered set, S, is said to be *totally ordered* if and only if $\forall x, y \in S$, either $x \leq y$ or $y \leq x$.

For totally ordered sets, to make mutually exclusive possibilities, one sometimes writes $x < y$ or $y < x$ or $x = y$ and calls this property the *trichotomy property*. Another term that is used is comparable. In any partially ordered set, we say x is *comparable* to y if either $x \leq y$ or $y \leq x$. Thus, S is totally ordered if and only if any two elements are comparable.

In their usual order, $\mathbb{Z}$, $\mathbb{Q}$, and $\mathbb{R}$ are totally ordered, but $C_{\mathbb{R}}(X)$ is not if X is a compact Hausdorff space with at least two points. Of course, $C_{\mathbb{R}}(X)$ has totally ordered subsets, for example, the constant functions. Given $T \subset S$, a partially ordered subset, the *inherited order* of an order $R \subset S \times S$ is $R \cap (T \times T)$, i.e., $x \leq y$ in T if and only if $x \leq y$ in S. A totally ordered subset of S is called a *chain*.

Definition. A partially ordered set, S, is called *well-ordered* if it is totally ordered and any subset $T \subset S$ contains a *smallest element*, that is, $t_0 \in T$, so for all $t_1 \in T$, $t_0 \leq t_1$.

$\mathbb{N}$, in its usual order, is well-ordered, but $\mathbb{Z}$, $\mathbb{Q}$, and $\mathbb{R}$, in their usual orders, are not, since even the whole space doesn't contain a smallest element. $\mathbb{R}_+$ has the property that any $T \subset \mathbb{R}_+$ has an inf, but since the inf may not be in T, $\mathbb{R}_+$ is not well-ordered. Since $\mathbb{Q}$ can be put in one-one correspondence to $\mathbb{N}$ (see Section 1.6), one can clearly put an order on $\mathbb{Q}$ (totally unrelated to its usual order), making it into a well-ordered set. How about $\mathbb{R}$? The answer may not be clear to you—for good reason; see the next section.

Some pieces of terminology: If S is a partially ordered set and $T \subset S$, we say x is an *upper bound* (respectively, *lower bound*) for T if $x \in S$ (not necessarily in T) and $\forall y \in T$, $y \leq x$ (respectively, $x \leq y$). An element $x \in S$ is called *maximal* if $\forall y \in S$, $x \leq y \Rightarrow x = y$ (x may not be an upper bound for S since it may not be comparable to every $y \in S$).

Notes and Historical Remarks. For an extensive discussion of orders, see, for example, the book of Grätzer [**364**].

1.5. The Axiom of Choice and Zorn's Lemma

This section will discuss the following and some of its consequences:

The Axiom of Choice. Let $\{X_\alpha\}_{\alpha \in I}$ be a collection of nonempty subsets indexed by a set I. Then the *Cartesian product* $\times_{\alpha \in I} X_\alpha$ is nonempty, that is, there exists a function, $f \colon I \to \cup_\alpha X_\alpha$, so that $f(\alpha) \in X_\alpha$. Put more prosaically, given a collection of nonempty bins, one can choose one object from each bin.

To most mathematicians, this seems intuitively obvious. However (see the Notes), it is known that the "usual" axioms of set theory with this removed and replaced by its converse are as consistent as the usual axioms! This has made the use of the axiom of choice and its consequences somewhat controversial in some quarters. In these books, we will occasionally make use of the following consequence of the axiom of choice which is known, in turn, to imply the axiom of choice (if one also assumes the "usual" axioms).

Zorn's Lemma. Let X be a partially ordered set in which every chain has an upper bound. Then X has at least one maximal element.

Note. Chain, upper bound, and maximal are defined in the last section. That every chain has an upper bound is called the *chain condition*.

To see Zorn's lemma in action, the reader should consult the proof of Theorem 5.5.1. The process of setting up an ordered set, checking the chain condition, and using Zorn's lemma to get a maximal element, we'll call Zornification.

To give you an idea of the scope of the axiom of choice, we mention two other logical statements equivalent to it:

- *Well-ordering principle.* Every set X has an order in which it is well-ordered.
- *Tarski's theorem.* For every infinite set X, there is a bijection between $X \times X$ and X.

While we will not hesitate to use the axiom of choice, usually through Zorn's lemma, we do note that one can make a countable set of choices using ordinary induction. In this regard, the following trick, which we'll call the *diagonalization trick*, is often useful. Recall a subsequence of $\{a_n\}_{n=1}^\infty$ is given by a map $n(j)$ from $\{1,\dots\}$ to itself so that $n(j+1) > n(j)$. The actual subsequence is $b_j = a_{n(j)}$ which we often write as just $\{a_{n(j)}\}_{j=1}^\infty$. By composition maps, it is easy to see that a subsequence of a subsequence is a subsequence of the original sequence.

We'll illustrate the diagonalization trick in the following setting: Suppose we have functions f_n from $\mathbb{N}$ to $[0,1]$, that is, $f_n(m) \in [0,1]$. We'd like to find a subsequence $n_\infty(j)$ so for each m, $\{f_{n_\infty(j)}(m)\}_{n=1}^\infty$ converges. Because $[0,1]$ is compact, we can find a subsequence $n_1(j)$ so that $f_{n_1(j)}(1) \to a_1$. There is a subsubsequence $n_2(j)$ of $n_1(j)$ so that $f_{n_2(j)}(2) \to a_2$. Of course, because $n_2(j)$ is a subsequence of $n_1(j)$, we have $f_{n_2(j)}(1) \to a_1$.

In this way, we inductively find $n_k(j)$ so that

(a) $n_{k+1}(j)$ is a subsequence of $n_k(j)$.
(b) $f_{n_k(j)}(\ell) \to a_\ell$ for $\ell = 1, 2, \dots, k$.

How do we take $k \to \infty$? We can't take $\lim_{k\to\infty} n_k(j)$ since that may be ∞! Instead, we pick

$$n_\infty(j) = n_j(j) \tag{1.5.1}$$

It is easy to check $n_\infty(j)$ is a subsequence of $\{1, 2, \dots\}$ and that $\{f_{n_\infty(j)}\}_{j=k}^\infty$ is a subsequence of $\{f_{n_k(j)}\}_{j=1}^\infty$ so that $f_{n_\infty(j)}(k) \to a_k$ for all k!

We'll see that in many cases where an argument in some general uncountable case requires Zorn's lemma, with an underlying countability, we can use the diagonalization trick instead.

Notes and Historical Remarks.

The Axiom of Choice is obviously true, the well-ordering principle obviously false, and who can tell about Zorn's lemma?
—*Jerry Bona*, as quoted in E. Schechter [816][2]

Tarski told me the following story. He tried to publish his theorem in the Comptes Rendus Acad. Sci. Paris but Fréchet and Lebesgue refused to present it. Fréchet wrote that an implication between two well-known propositions is not a new result. Lebesgue wrote that an implication between two false propositions is of no interest.
—*J. Mycielski* in [674][3]

---

[2]Bona tells me he used this in class.
[3]Tarski proved that the axiom of choice is equivalent to the fact that for every infinite set A, there is a bijection of A and $A \times A$.

The foundations of analysis, especially the issues connected to the infinite and the axiom of choice, are subjects many mathematicians tend to be ambivalent about. On the one hand, they are aware of their importance; but, on the other, the detailed arguments are usually disconnected from the mathematics they do. Like many quantum physicists with measurement theory, they ignore the background and go on with their professional lives, using what they need without much concern.

That said, there is a small number of great mathematicians—Leopold Kronecker (1823–91), L. E. J. Brouwer (1881–1966), and Errett Bishop (1928–83) come to mind—who have been profoundly disturbed by mathematics that depends on indirect argument and who insisted that only objects that can be constructed should be allowed in mathematics. Accordingly, they have rejected proofs that depend on the law of the excluded middle (i.e., proof by contradiction) and the axiom of choice. Typically, they came to this point of view only after establishing themselves with great work that often, at least initially, used these methods. The mainstream has ignored this viewpoint as we will, using the axiom of choice without always keeping track of which arguments depend on it (e.g., we'll use Tychonoff's theorem whenever needed, usually without comment about the axiom of choice).

Still, as the quotes at the start of these Notes show, there is some unease about the subject at the rare times we bother to really think about it!

Underlying the foundations is the work that resulted from the realization near the turn of the twentieth century (going back to the work of Cantor discussed in the next section) that consideration of the infinite and of sets constructed without care can lead to paradoxes. The result is a careful set of axioms, normally called Zermelo–Fraenkel axioms, after Ernest Zermelo's fundamental 1908 paper [**1019**] and Abraham Fraenkel's 1922 contribution [**313**]. (Thoralf Skolem [**859**] independently did similar work in 1922.) When the axiom of choice is included, one gets the ZFC axioms of set theory, the "usual axioms of set theory." With regard to adding the axiom of choice, we note that Paul Cohen [**201**] proved that ZF is independent of the axiom of choice in that ZF with the negative of the axiom of choice is as consistent as ZFC.

The axiom of choice appeared first in Zermelo [**1018**] in 1904. A variant of Zorn's lemma appeared already in Kuratowski [**534**] in 1922—the full version is from Zorn [**1022**] in 1935. The name "Zorn's lemma" is from Tukey [**938**]—the name has become so standard, there was a rock group called "Zorn's lemma."

Tarski's theorem on $X \times X$ and the axiom of choice is from [**906**].

For a detailed treatment of these things from an analyst's point of view, see Halmos' classic book [**388**]. [**437**] discusses in detail the consequences of the axiom of choice. For books on the foundations of set theory, see [**198, 277, 531, 668, 841**].

The diagonalization trick goes back at least to Ascoli [**39**] in 1884 although a not unrelated idea is in P. du Bois-Reymond [**257**].

1.6. Countability

We expect that for most readers, the material in this section is something they have seen in a first analysis course. But for those who want it in the second course, we include a brief version.

Definition. A set, A, is called *countably infinite* if and only if it can be put in one-one correspondence to $\mathbb{Z}_+$, that is, there is a bijection $g \colon \mathbb{Z}_+ \to A$. If A is either finite or countably infinite, we say A is countable.

The two main results of this section are that $\mathbb{Q}$ is countably infinite (equivalently, a countable union of countable sets is countable) and that $\mathbb{R}$ is not countable (equivalently, $2^{\mathbb{Z}_+}$, the set of all subsets of $\mathbb{Z}_+$, is not countable).

Theorem 1.6.1. *A subset of a countable set is countable.*

Proof. It suffices (by using the bijection) to prove a subset, A, of $\mathbb{Z}_+$ is countable. Order the elements of A using the order on $\mathbb{Z}_+$, $x_1 < x_2 < \dots$. If A is finite, this terminates; if not, it does not. In that case, let $g(n) = x_n$. This is a bijection of $\mathbb{Z}_+$ and A.   □

Theorem 1.6.2. $\mathbb{Z}_+ \times \mathbb{Z}_+$ *is countable.*

Proof. Count $(1,1), (2,1), (1,2), (3,1), (2,2), (1,3), \dots$, that is, order $\mathbb{Z}_+ \times \mathbb{Z}_+$ by $(x_1, x_2) \leq (y_1, y_2)$ if $x_1 + x_2 \leq y_1 + y_2$ and if $x_1 + x_2 = y_1 + y_2$, then $x_1 \leq y_1$. This is a linear order with points that can be successively counted; see Figure 1.6.1.   □

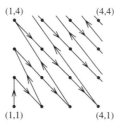

Figure 1.6.1. Counting $\mathbb{Z}_+ \times \mathbb{Z}_+$.

Corollary 1.6.3. (a) *A countable union of countable sets is countable.*
(b) $\mathbb{Z}$ *and* $\mathbb{Q}$ *are countably infinite.*

Proof. (a) Let $A_1, \ldots, A_n, \ldots$ (ending in A_N if finite). Count A_j as $\{x_{jk}\}_{k=1}^{K_j}$. Let

$$S = \{(j,k) \mid 1 \le j < N+1, 1 \le k < K_j + 1\}$$

S is a subset of $\mathbb{Z}_+ \times \mathbb{Z}_+$, so countable by the theorem. $g(j,k) = x_{jk}$ is a bijection of S and $\cup_{j=1}^N A_j$.

(b) $\mathbb{Z} = \mathbb{Z}_+ \cup -\mathbb{Z}_+ \cup \{0\}$ is a countable union of countable sets and is not finite.

By the same argument, it suffices to show $\mathbb{Q}_+ = \{q \in \mathbb{Q}, q > 0\}$ is countable. Any q can be written uniquely as p/r with $p, r \in \mathbb{Z}_+$ and relatively prime. $g(p/r) = (p,r)$ is a bijection of a subset of $\mathbb{Q}_+$ and $\mathbb{Z}_+ \times \mathbb{Z}_+$. $\quad\square$

Theorem 1.6.4 (Cantor's Diagonalization Theorem). $[0,1]$ *is not countable.*

Proof. Suppose g is a one-one map of $\mathbb{Z}_+$ to $[0,1]$. We will find $x_\infty \in [0,1]$ not in $\mathrm{Ran}(g)$, so g cannot be a bijection. Write any $b \in [0,1]$ as a decimal $.b_1 b_2 \ldots$ with $b_j \in (0, \ldots, 9)$, with the rule that only if $b = 1$ does it happen that for some N, $b_n = 9$ for all $n > N$.

Write

$$g(k) = .x_{k1}\, x_{k2}\, x_{k3}\, \cdots \tag{1.6.1}$$

Pick $x_{\infty\ell}$ to be some number in $\{0, \ldots, 9\}$ that is not 0 or 9 and not $x_{\ell\ell}$. Let

$$x_\infty = .x_{\infty 1}\, x_{\infty 2}\, x_{\infty 3}\, \cdots \tag{1.6.2}$$

Since x_∞ doesn't end in all 0's or 9's, it does not have an ambiguous expansion. Since $x_{\infty\ell} \ne x_{\ell\ell}$, $x_\infty \ne g(\ell)$ for all ℓ. Thus, $x_\infty \notin \mathrm{Ran}(g)$. $\quad\square$

It is cleaner to show $2^{\mathbb{Z}_+}$, the set of subsets of $\mathbb{Z}_+$, is not countable. Let $g(k) = A_k \subset \mathbb{Z}_+$. Define A_∞ by

$$k \in A_\infty \Leftrightarrow k \notin A_k$$

Thus, A_∞ cannot be equal to any A_k.

Notes and Historical Remarks.

> Cantor is a 'corrupter of youth'.
> —*L. Kronecker*, as quoted by Schoenflies [**822**]

> No one shall expel us from the Paradise that Cantor has created.
> —*D. Hilbert* [**428**]

The notion of different sizes of infinity and the two main results of this section are due to Georg Cantor (1845–1918) (a capsule biography appears in the Notes to Section 4.2). At the time of Cantor's work, Dedekind was also considering countable sets, and he first proved that the algebraic numbers are countable (see Problem 1).

Theorem 1.6.4 first appeared in an 1874 paper of Cantor [**151**], although the famous proof we give here is from his 1891 paper [**155**]. The 1874 proof is a lovely use of the fact that any bounded sequence on increasing reals has a limit (see Problem 2). The 1891 proof has captured the imagination because it is so elementary that it can be explained to a bright high school student.

As shown by the quotes, Cantor's work inspired considerable passion on both sides; see Dauben [**216**] for extensive discussion. In particular, Cantor's proof that $\mathbb{R}^n$ and $\mathbb{R}^m$ can be put in one-one correspondence [**152**] and his construction of even larger infinities than $\mathbb{R}$ caused considerable controversy and discomfort among mathematicians. He proved that for any infinite set, A, with cardinality $\mathfrak{c}$, 2^A, the subsets of A, has cardinality $2^{\mathfrak{c}}$, strictly larger than $\mathfrak{c}$; in this way, he constructed $\aleph_0$, the cardinality of $\mathbb{Z}_+$, $\aleph_1 \equiv 2^{\aleph_0}$, the cardinality of $\mathbb{R}$, and then $\aleph_{n+1} = 2^{\aleph_n}$.

Already in his 1874 paper [**151**], Cantor was aware of potential problems—this short five-page paper had three results: countability of the algebraic numbers, noncountability of $\mathbb{R}$, and the consequence that there had to exist many nonalgebraic (aka transcendental) numbers. Yet the title only mentions algebraic numbers, although Cantor undoubtedly knew it was the uncountability of the reals that was revolutionary. Historians speculate that he did this because of the attitude of two of his teachers: Weierstrass and Kronecker, both at Berlin where Cantor coveted a position. Weierstrass was initially skeptical of levels of infinity although he came around, but Kronecker was adamant in opposing not only Cantor but many of Weierstrass' ideas in analysis—Kronecker was known to declare that irrationals don't exist!

In the end, what is remarkable is that ideas which had great mathematicians as both passionate supporters and implacable detractors (e.g., Poincaré regarded transfinite numbers as a disease for which he hoped a cure would be found), over time, became not only accepted but part of the standard canon—taught to all students of higher mathematics.

Problems

> It is difficult and often impossible to judge the value of a problem correctly in advance; for the final award depends upon the gain which science obtains from the problem. Nevertheless we can ask whether there are general

criteria which mark a good mathematical problem. An old French mathematician said: "A mathematical theory is not to be considered complete until you have made it so clear that you can explain it to the first man whom you meet on the street." This clearness and ease of comprehension, here insisted on for a mathematical theory, I should still more demand for a mathematical problem if it is to be perfect; for what is clear and easily comprehended attracts, the complicated repels us.

—*David Hilbert* [4]

1. An *algebraic number* is a complex number, x, which solves an equation

$$\sum_{j=0}^{n} a_j x^j = 0 \tag{1.6.3}$$

with each $a_j \in \mathbb{Z}$. This problem will prove that the algebraic numbers are countable.

(a) Define the *height*, $h(x)$, of an algebraic number, x, as the minimum of $n + \sum_{j=0}^{n} |a_j|$ among all equations, (1.6.3), that x solves.

(b) For each k, prove that only finitely many x have $h(x) = k$.

(c) Prove countability of the algebraic numbers.

2. This problem will lead the reader through Cantor's first proof of the uncountability of $[0, 1]$. Let x_n be a sequence of distinct points in $[0, 1]$ which are at least dense in $[0, 1]$. Define $\{a_n, b_n\}_{n=1}^{\infty}$ inductively as follows. a_1, b_1 are the first two x_m's not equal to 0 or 1 (*not* first two successive) chosen so that $a_1 < b_1$. After picking a_n, b_n, let a_{n+1}, b_{n+1} be the next two x_m's which lie in (a_n, b_n) chosen so that $a_{n+1} < b_{n+1}$.

(a) Prove $a_1 < a_2 < \ldots$ and $b_1 > b_2 > \ldots$ and $a_n < b_n$.

(b) Prove that every x_m is either equal to an a_n or a b_n or for some n, $x_m < a_n$ or $x_m > b_n$.

(c) Show $a_\infty = \lim_{n\to\infty} a_n$, $b_\infty = \lim_{n\to\infty} b_n$ exist, and for all n, $a_n < a_\infty \leq b_\infty < b_n$.

(d) Prove a_∞ is not any of the x_n's so, in particular, $\{x_n\}$ is not all of $[0, 1]$.

3. (a) Represent $x \in \mathbb{Z}_+$ as a base 10 $x_\ell x_{\ell-1} \ldots x_1$ and then as an infinite sequence by setting $x_{\ell+1} = x_{\ell+2} = \cdots = 0$. Why doesn't Cantor's diagonalization proof show that $\mathbb{Z}_+$ is uncountable?

(b) Prove that the family of finite subsets of $\mathbb{Z}_+$ is countable. What does this have to do with (a)?

---

[4] Part of the talk given at the 1900 International Congress of Mathematicians where he presented *Hilbert's Problems*. This is from the official translation. [**425**]

1.7. Some Linear Algebra

We review some simple facts about finite-dimensional vector spaces and their linear self-maps. Here and later, we'll use $\mathbb{K}$ to indicate either $\mathbb{R}$ or $\mathbb{C}$. A *vector space* is a set, X, with two operations: addition $(x, y) \mapsto x + y$, mapping $X \times X$ to X, and scalar multiplication $(\lambda, x) \mapsto \lambda x$, mapping $\mathbb{K} \times X$ to X, with the usual properties (X is an abelian group under $+$, $\lambda(x + y) = \lambda x + \lambda y$, $\lambda \mapsto \lambda x$ is group homomorphism of $(\mathbb{K}, +)$ to $(X, +)$).

$\mathbb{K}^{\ell}$ is a vector space under the maps

$$(\mu_1, \ldots, \mu_\ell) + (\lambda_1, \ldots, \lambda_\ell) = (\mu_1 + \lambda_1, \ldots, \mu_\ell + \lambda_\ell) \tag{1.7.1}$$

$$\lambda(\mu_1, \ldots, \mu_\ell) = (\lambda\mu_1, \ldots, \lambda\mu_\ell) \tag{1.7.2}$$

We say a subset, Y, of X *spans* X if for any $x \in X$, there is $\alpha_1, \ldots, \alpha_\ell \in \mathbb{K}$ and $y_1, \ldots, y_\ell \in Y$ so that

$$x = \alpha_1 y_1 + \alpha_2 y_2 + \cdots + \alpha_\ell x_\ell \tag{1.7.3}$$

We say X is *finite-dimensional* if it has a finite spanning set.

$\{y_j\}_{j=1}^{\ell}$ are *independent* if and only if for $\{\alpha_j\}_{j=1}^{\ell} \in \mathbb{K}^{\ell}$,

$$\sum_{j=1}^{\ell} \alpha_j y_j = 0 \Rightarrow \alpha_1 = \alpha_2 = \cdots = 0 \tag{1.7.4}$$

If $\{y_j\}_{j=1}^{\ell}$ are not independent, they are called *dependent*. A *basis* for a finite-dimensional space is an independent spanning set, $\{y_j\}_{j=1}^{\ell}$. It is easy to see that a set is a basis if and only if it is a minimal spanning set and if and only if it is a maximal independent set.

Before focusing on the finite-dimensional case, we want to define some general terms and mention one fact. In a general vector space, an *algebraic basis* is a family $\{x_\alpha\}_{\alpha \in \mathcal{I}}$ of vectors in X so that any finite subset is independent (such families are called independent) and which span X, i.e., finite linear combinations are all of X. It is an easy consequence of Zorn's lemma that algebraic bases exist for, by Zorn's lemma, maximal independent families exist and if $\{x_\alpha\}_{\alpha \in \mathcal{I}}$ is such a family, the fact that we can't add x to the family and still have an independent set implies x is in the span of the $\{x_\alpha\}_{\alpha \in \mathcal{I}}$.

Once one adds a topology to X, the notion of basis is more involved and, in this series, we'll see several notions of topological basis—complete orthonormal basis, Schauder basis, Riesz basis. For now, we note that a set $\{x_\alpha\}_{\alpha \in \mathcal{I}}$ whose finite linear combination are dense in a topological vector space are called *complete* or *total*. The phrase *spanning set* is sometimes used to mean total and sometimes to mean that the span is all of X (rather than just dense).

A linear map between vector spaces X and Z is $T: X \to Z$ so that

$$T(x + y) = T(x) + T(y), \qquad T(\lambda x) = \lambda T(x) \tag{1.7.5}$$

If $\{y_j\}_{j=1}^{\ell}$ is a basis, the map

$$(\mu_1, \ldots, \mu_\ell) \mapsto \sum_{j=1}^{\ell} \mu_j y_j \tag{1.7.6}$$

sets up a linear bijection of $\mathbb{K}^\ell$ and X with linear inverse.

It is easy to see (Problem 1) by induction in ℓ that any $\ell + 1$ vectors in $\mathbb{K}^\ell$ are dependent, which implies (Problem 2) for $\ell \neq k$, $\mathbb{K}^\ell$ and $\mathbb{K}^k$ are not linearly isomorphic. This in turn implies, by (1.7.6), that the number, ℓ, of elements of a basis is independent of choice of basis. It is called the *dimension*, $\dim(X)$, of X. Thus,

Theorem 1.7.1. *Every finite-dimensional vector space, X, has a dimension, ℓ, which is the number of elements in any basis. X is linearly isomorphic to $\mathbb{K}^\ell$.*

$Y \subset X$ is called a *subspace* if it is closed under addition and scalar multiplication. If Y and Z are subspaces of X, we say they are *complementary* if and only if

$$Y \cap Z = \{0\}, \qquad Y + Z = X \tag{1.7.7}$$

We then write

$$X = Y \dotplus Z \tag{1.7.8}$$

It is easy to see (Problem 3) that any subspace has a complementary subspace even in the infinite-dimensional case (Problem 4).

Warning: In Chapter 5 and, even more, in Part 4, we will focus on closed complementary subspaces when X is a Banach space. While every subspace has an (algebraic) complement, even if Y is closed, it might not have any closed complements.

We turn next to $\mathcal{L}(X)$, the linear maps of X to itself, where X is a finite-dimensional vector space. We define the *kernel* and *range* of $T \in \mathcal{L}(X)$ by (these definitions make sense also if $T: X \to Z$)

$$\mathrm{Ker}(T) = \{x \mid Tx = 0\}, \qquad \mathrm{Ran}(T) = \{Tx \mid x \in X\} = T[X] \tag{1.7.9}$$

We begin with two special classes of operators.

Definition. A *projection* in X is a map $P \in \mathcal{L}(X)$ so that

$$P^2 = P \tag{1.7.10}$$

A *nilpotent*, N, is a map $N \in \mathcal{L}(X)$ with

$$N^k = 0 \tag{1.7.11}$$

for some k.

Proposition 1.7.2. *If P is a projection, so is $1 - P$. There is a one-one correspondence between projections, P, and complementary subspaces, Y and Z, given by*

$$Y = \mathrm{Ran}(P) = \mathrm{Ker}(1 - P), \qquad Z = \mathrm{Ran}(1 - P) = \mathrm{Ker}(P) \tag{1.7.12}$$

Remark. In Proposition 2.1.2 of Part 4, we prove an analog of this for X a Banach space, and $\mathcal{L}(X)$ the *bounded* operators. In that case, Y and Z have to be *closed* subspaces.

Proof.

$$y \in \mathrm{Ran}(P) \Leftrightarrow y = Pz \Leftrightarrow y = Py \quad (\text{since } P(Pz) = Pz = y)$$
$$\Leftrightarrow y \in \mathrm{Ker}(1 - P) \tag{1.7.13}$$

and similarly for $1 - P$. If Y and Z are defined by (1.7.12), then any $x \in X$ is $X = Px + (1 - P)x \in Y + Z$. If $W \in Y \cap Z$, then $w = Pw = (1 - P)w$, so $w = P(1 - P)w = 0$, that is, $Y \cap Z = \{0\}$.

For the converse, if Y and Z are complementary subspaces, $x = y + z$ is unique, so $x \mapsto y$ is a well-defined map, P. Since $y = y + 0$ is the decomposition if $y \in Y$, $P^2 = P$ and $Y = \mathrm{Ran}(P)$. Similarly, $Z = \mathrm{Ran}(1 - P)$. $\qquad\qquad\square$

Projections are related to invariant subspaces for linear mappings, $T: X \to X$. $Y \subset X$ is called *invariant* for T if and only if $T[Y] \subset Y$. The following is left to the reader (Problem 5):

Proposition 1.7.3. *Let P be a projection corresponding to $X = Y \dotplus Z$ (with $Y = \mathrm{Ran}(P)$, $Z = \mathrm{Ran}(1 - P)$). Then*

$$TP = PT \tag{1.7.14}$$

if and only if both Y and Z are invariant for T. Moreover,

$$PTP = T \tag{1.7.15}$$

if and only if Y and Z are invariant and $Z \subset \mathrm{Ker}(T)$.

The following structural theorem for nilpotent operators on finite-dimensional spaces is left to the reader (Problem 6):

Proposition 1.7.4. *Let N be a nilpotent operator on a finite-dimensional vector space of dimension ℓ. Then there exists a basis $\{e_{jk}\}_{j=1,\ldots,J;k=1,\ldots,m_j}$, where $J \leq \ell$ and $\sum_{j=1}^{J} m_j = \ell$, so that*

$$N e_{jk} = \begin{cases} e_{j(k-1)} & \text{if } k \geq 2 \\ 0 & \text{if } k = 1 \end{cases} \tag{1.7.16}$$

If $\{f_j\}_{j=1}^{\ell}$ is a basis for X and T is a linear map on X, the *matrix of T* in basis $\{f_j\}_{j=1}^{\ell}$ is defined by

$$T f_j = \sum_{i=1}^{\ell} t_{ij} f_i \tag{1.7.17}$$

With this definition, if, for $x \in X$, $x_i \in \mathbb{K}$ is defined by

$$x = \sum x_i f_i \tag{1.7.18}$$

Then

$$(Tx)_i = \sum_{j=1}^{\ell} t_{ij} x_j \tag{1.7.19}$$

Composition of maps in $\mathcal{L}(X)$ is, of course, mirrored in the usual matrix multiplication law

$$(TS)_{ij} = \sum_{k=1}^{\ell} t_{ik} s_{kj} \tag{1.7.20}$$

(1.7.16) can be rephrased as saying in a suitable ordering of the basis, N has all zero matrix elements except for $\ell - J$ ones directly above the diagonal. Conversely, any T which in some basis has nonzero matrix elements only strictly above the diagonal is nilpotent (Problem 7).

The last element we need for one of the two main results of this section is a generalization of complementary subspaces.

Definition. Let X be a vector space. We say subspaces $\{X_j\}_{j=1}^{m}$ are *mutually complementary* if and only if any $x \in X$ has a unique decomposition

$$x = \sum_{j=1}^{m} x_j \qquad \text{with } x_j \in X_j \tag{1.7.21}$$

We write

$$X = X_1 \dotplus X_2 \dotplus \cdots \dotplus X_m \tag{1.7.22}$$

The map $P_j \colon x \mapsto x_j$ is then a projection and the P_j's obey

$$P_j P_k = \delta_{jk} P_j \tag{1.7.23}$$

$$\sum_{j=1}^{m} P_j = \mathbb{1} \tag{1.7.24}$$

Proposition 1.7.2 extends to this situation (Problem 8):

Proposition 1.7.5. *There is a one-one correspondence between mutually complementary decompositions* (1.7.22) *and projections* $\{P_j\}_{j=1}^{m}$ *obeying* (1.7.23)/(1.7.24).

We call projections obeying (1.7.23)/(1.7.24) *mutually complementary projections.* Here is the first main result of this section:

Theorem 1.7.6 (Jordan Normal Form). *Let T be an arbitrary linear mapping of a finite-dimensional vector space, X, over $\mathbb{C}$. Then there exist distinct complex numbers $\{\lambda_j\}_{j=1}^{m}$ ($m \leq \dim(X)$), mutually complementary projections, $\{P_j\}_{j=1}^{m}$, and nilpotents $\{N_j\}_{j=1}^{m}$ so that*

(a) $P_j N_j P_j = N_j$ $\qquad\qquad\qquad\qquad\qquad\qquad\qquad\qquad$ (1.7.25)

(b) $T = \displaystyle\sum_{j=1}^{m} \lambda_j P_j + N_j$ $\qquad\qquad\qquad\qquad\qquad\qquad\quad$ (1.7.26)

Remarks. 1. (1.7.26) is called the *Jordan normal form.*

2. The canonical form, Proposition 1.7.4, for nilpotents and the fact that (1.7.25) implies $N_j P_k = 0$ for $k \neq j$ says there is a basis where the matrix of T has λ_j's along the diagonal and some 1 only directly above the diagonal (0 otherwise) with 1's only in blocks with the same λ. This is the more usually stated form of the Jordan normal form.

3. Since any nilpotent and, in particular, $N_j \upharpoonright \text{Ran}(P_j)$, has a nonzero kernel (by Proposition 1.7.4 or the simpler argument in Problem 9), every λ_j in (1.7.26) is an *eigenvalue* of T, that is, there is φ with

$$T\varphi = \lambda_j \varphi \tag{1.7.27}$$

It is easy to see (Problem 10) that these are the only eigenvalues of T.

4. The real matrix $\left(\begin{smallmatrix} 0 & 1 \\ -1 & 0 \end{smallmatrix}\right)$ on $\mathbb{R}^2$ has no eigenvalues, so this theorem does not hold on real vector spaces.

5. We provide an analytic function proof of this theorem in Section 2.3 of Part 4 (see the discussion after Corollary 2.3.6 of Part 4). Problems 11 and 12 of this Part have an algebraic proof, and Problems 9 and 10 of Section 1.3 of Part 4 have a proof using invariant subspaces.

6. If some $N_j \neq 0$, we say T has a *Jordan anomaly* (equivalently, T is not diagonalizable).

7. $\dim(P_j)$ is called the *algebraic multiplicity* of λ_j. $\dim[\mathrm{Ker}(N_j) \cap \mathrm{Ran}(P_j)] = \dim\{x \mid Tx = \lambda x\}$ is the *geometric multiplicity.*

8. The P_j are called *spectral projections* (although some reserve that for the case of self-adjoint matrices). They are also called *eigenprojections* and the N's *eigennilpotents.*

We need (in Section 7.5) a result about the form of rank one projections in $\mathbb{C}^n$ and transposes in the Jordan normal form. For any matrix A, the *transpose*, A^t, is the matrix

$$(A^t)_{ij} = A_{ji} \tag{1.7.28}$$

Proposition 1.7.7. *Let A be an $n \times n$ complex matrix and*

$$A = \sum_{k=1}^m (\lambda_k P_k + N_k) \tag{1.7.29}$$

its Jordan normal form. Then A^t has the Jordan normal form

$$A^t = \sum_{k=1}^m \lambda_k P_k^t + N_k^t \tag{1.7.30}$$

If $\dim(P_{k_0}) = 1$ for some k_0 (which implies that $N_{k_0} = 0$), then there are vectors, v, w, obeying

$$Av = \lambda_{k_0} v, \qquad A^t w = \lambda_k w \tag{1.7.31}$$

$$(P_{k_0})_{ij} = v_i w_j \tag{1.7.32}$$

$$\sum_j w_j v_j = 1 \tag{1.7.33}$$

Proof. $P_k P_\ell = \delta_{k\ell} P_k$ implies $P_\ell^t P_k^t = \delta_{k\ell} P_k^t$, $P_k N_k P_k = N_k$ implies $P_k^t N_k^t P_k^t = N_k^t$, and $N_k^{m_k} = 0$ implies $(N_k^t)^{m_k} = 0$. Thus, (1.7.30) is the Jordan normal form.

If $\dim(P_{k_0}) = 1$, (1.7.32) holds, where $v \in \mathrm{Ran}(P)$ (so $Av = \lambda_{k_0} v$), and by looking at the adjoint, $w \in \mathrm{Ran}(P^t)$ (so $A^t w = \lambda_{k_0} w$). $P^2 = P$ implies (1.7.33). $\qquad \square$

Definition. A *real inner product space* is a real vector space, X, and a map $\langle \cdot, \cdot \rangle \colon X \times X \to \mathbb{R}$ so that

(i)$_{\mathbb{R}}$ $\langle x, y \rangle = \langle y, x \rangle$ $\qquad\qquad\qquad\qquad\qquad\qquad$ (1.7.34)

(ii) $\langle x, \cdot \rangle$ is linear in $\cdot$ for all $x \in X$.

(iii) $\langle x, x \rangle \geq 0$ and $\langle x, x \rangle = 0 \Leftrightarrow x = 0$.

A (complex) *inner product space* is a complex vector space, X, and a map $\langle \cdot, \cdot \rangle \colon X \times X \to \mathbb{C}$ so that (ii), (iii) hold but (i)$_{\mathbb{R}}$ is replaced by

$$(\text{i})_{\mathbb{C}} \quad \langle x, y \rangle = \overline{\langle y, x \rangle} \tag{1.7.35}$$

Remarks. 1. Inner product spaces are discussed extensively in Chapter 3, especially the infinite-dimensional case.

2. If (1.7.34) held, then $\langle ix, ix \rangle = i^2 \langle x, x \rangle = -\langle x, x \rangle$, which is incompatible with (iii) if $\dim(X) > 0$.

3. See the Notes to Section 3.1 for a discussion of why we take linearity of $\langle x, \cdot \rangle$ in the complex case; in the mathematics literature, linearity of $\langle \cdot, x \rangle$ is more common.

Definition. Let X be a finite-dimensional (real or complex) inner product space. An operator $T \colon X \to X$ is called *self-adjoint* if and only if for all $x, y \in X$, we have

$$\langle x, Ty \rangle = \langle Tx, y \rangle \tag{1.7.36}$$

Lemma 1.7.8. (a) *Let μ be an eigenvalue of T, a self-adjoint operator, that is, there is $x \in X$ with $x \neq 0$ and*

$$Tx = \mu x \tag{1.7.37}$$

Then μ is real.

(b) *If x obeys (1.7.37) and T is self-adjoint, then*

$$[x]^{\perp} = \{ y \mid \langle y, x \rangle = 0 \} \tag{1.7.38}$$

is an invariant subspace for T.

Proof. (a) If X is a real vector space, (a) is trivial since μx doesn't make sense if $\mu \in \mathbb{C} \setminus \mathbb{R}$. If X is a complex space, (1.7.37) implies

$$\mu \|x\|^2 = \langle x, Tx \rangle = \langle Tx, x \rangle \qquad \text{(by self-adjointness)}$$
$$= \overline{\langle x, Tx \rangle} = \bar{\mu} \, \|x\|^2 \tag{1.7.39}$$

so $\mu = \bar{\mu}$.

(b) If $y \in [x]^{\perp}$, then $\langle Ty, x \rangle = \langle y, Tx \rangle = \mu \langle y, x \rangle = 0$, so $Ty \in [x]^{\perp}$. $\square$

Our second main theorem is:

Theorem 1.7.9 (Finite-Dimensional Spectral Theorem). *Let T be a self-adjoint operator on a finite-dimensional vector space, X. Then T has an orthonormal basis of eigenvectors, that is, if $n = \dim(X)$, there exist $\{x_j\}_{j=1}^n \in X^n$ and $\{\mu_j\}_{j=1}^n \in \mathbb{K}^n$ so that*

(a) $Tx_j = \mu_j x_j$ $\qquad\qquad\qquad\qquad\qquad\qquad\qquad\qquad$ (1.7.40)

(b) $\langle x_j, x_k \rangle = \delta_{jk}, \quad j, k = 1, \ldots, n$ $\qquad\qquad\qquad\qquad$ (1.7.41)

Sketch. The first key fact is that T has at least one eigenvalue. In the complex case, we'll see this below; it also follows from Theorem 1.7.6. In the real case, one can derive this from the complex case (Problem 13) or from a variational principle (Problem 14).

Once one has an eigenvalue, the proof follows by induction in $n = \dim(X)$. $n = 1$ is trivial. For general X, find an eigenvector $x_n \neq 0$ and eigenvalue μ_n. Replace x_n by $x_n/\|x_n\|$ if need be to get a unit vector. $[x_n]^\perp$ has dimension $n-1$ and is, by the lemma, invariant for T. Thus, by induction, $T \upharpoonright [x_n]^\perp$ has an orthonormal basis of eigenvectors. Since x_n is orthogonal to $[x_n]^\perp$, we have that $\{x_1, \dots, x_{n-1}\} \subset [x_n]^\perp$, so (1.7.41) holds for $i, j = 1, \dots, n$. $\qquad \square$

Remarks. 1. The extensions of this result to infinite dimensions will be a major theme of Part 4. Section 3.2 of Part 4 discusses a class of infinite-dimensional operators (compact self-adjoint) for which the extension is direct—such operators have an orthonormal basis of eigenvectors. For general operators, the extension is more subtle, and this is a major theme of Chapter 5 of Part 4 for bounded self-adjoint operators and of Chapter 7 of Part 4 for unbounded self-adjoint operators.

2. An operator on an inner product space is *unitary* if it is a linear bijection preserving the inner product. A finite matrix is *unitary* if it is a unitary operator as an operator on $\mathbb{C}^{\dim(X)}$; equivalently, if $\sum_{j=1}^{\dim(X)} \overline{u_{ij}}\, u_{kj} = \delta_{ik} = \sum_{j=1}^{\dim(X)} \overline{u_{ji}}\, u_{jk}$. One way of stating the spectral theorem is that for any self-adjoint matrix, M, there is a unitary U so that UMU^{-1} is a diagonal matrix.

As we've seen, existence of eigenvalues for $\mathbb{K} = \mathbb{C}$ is critical. Let's end by explaining an algebraic proof of this that we'll extend in Problems 11 and 12 to get the full Jordan normal form. We need the strong form of the fundamental theorem of algebra (see Theorem 3.1.11 and Problem 2 of Section 3.1 of Part 2A): If $P(X)$ is a complex polynomial of degree d,

$$P(X) = a_d X^d + a_{d-1} X^{d-1} + \cdots + a_0 \qquad (1.7.42)$$

with $\{a_j\}_{j=0}^d$ in $\mathbb{C}$, then there exist $\{z_j\}_{j=1}^d$ in $\mathbb{C}$, so that $P(X)$ factors

$$P(X) = a_d \prod_{j=1}^d (X - z_j) \qquad (1.7.43)$$

The set of $m \times m$ matrices is a vector space of dimension m^2 (a basis is the matrices with exactly one nonzero element which is 1). Thus, for any operator, T, on $\mathbb{C}^m$, by the result in Problem 1, there is a polynomial of degree at most m^2 so

$$P(T) = 0 \qquad (1.7.44)$$

Let $Q(X)$ be a polynomial of minimal degree with $Q(T) = 0$. By (1.7.43),

$$Q(T) = (T - z_1)Q_1(T) \qquad (1.7.45)$$

where $Q_1(T)$ is not identically zero since $\deg(Q_1) < \deg(Q)$ and Q has minimal degree. If $y \equiv Q_1(T)x \neq 0$, then $(T - z_1)y = 0$, that is, z_1 is an eigenvalue of T (and so are the other roots of the minimal polynomial).

Notes and Historical Remarks. Linear algebra in the guise of solving simultaneous linear equations goes back to the Babylonians and Greeks. Important advances using determinants were made in the eighteenth century. During the nineteenth century, matrices—often in the guise of quadratic forms (i.e., looking at $x \mapsto \sum_{i,j=1}^{k} x_i t_{ij} x_j$ in place of a linear transformation)—began to be studied. Gauss [**341**] introduced the term determinant, although its modern usage is due to Cauchy. Important contributions were made by Jacobi, Hermite, and especially Cayley and Sylvester. In particular, Sylvester [**898**] introduced the term matrix (from Latin—one of its meanings is womb) in 1851 and an early classic was Cayley [**176**]. In 1888, Peano [**705**], as part of a book specifying a careful approach to calculus, defined vector spaces axiomatically.

The Jordan normal form appeared in an influential 1870 book of 660 pages by C. Jordan [**454**].

The (finite-dimensional) spectral theorem entered mathematics as a statement about quadratic forms, not matrices. That quadratic forms in two variables could be written in oblique axes as those of a hyperbola or ellipse appeared already in Descartes in 1637 [**238**] in his work on analytic geometry, and the three-dimensional analog is in Euler [**284**]. In 1759, Lagrange [**539**] noted that quadratic forms in n variables could be written as sums and differences of squares. Cauchy in 1829 [**171**] wrote out the result in a way that made use of orthogonal changes of coordinates so that what we'd call eigenvalues appeared, and his work is often viewed as the place where the spectral theorem for finite-dimensional matrices was first written down. It was Sylvester [**899**] who wrote down the matrix version even having the result that the diagonal matrix elements are the roots of $\det(A - \lambda \mathbb{1}) = 0$. Hermite [**420**] singled out what we now call Hermitian quadratic forms and proved their eigenvalues were real.

Problems

1. Let $y_1, \ldots, y_{\ell+1}$ be $\ell + 1$ vectors in $\mathbb{K}^\ell$. Suppose you know that any $x_1, \ldots, x_\ell \in \mathbb{K}^{\ell-1}$ are dependent.

   (a) If $y_{j\ell} = 0$ for $j = 1, \ldots, \ell + 1$ (the ℓ-th component), prove that the y_j's are dependent.

(b) If $y_{1\ell} \neq 0$, prove for suitable $\alpha_2, \ldots, \alpha_{\ell+1}$, we have $(y_j - \alpha_j y_1)_\ell = 0$ and conclude the y_j are dependent.

2. Let $\{\delta_j\}_{j=1}^\ell$ be the standard basis for $\mathbb{K}^\ell$, that is, $(\delta_j)_n = \delta_{jn}$. Suppose $\ell > k$ and $T \colon \mathbb{K}^\ell \to \mathbb{K}^k$ is linear. Prove that $\{T\delta_j\}_{j=1}^\ell$ are dependent (see Problem 1) and conclude T cannot be one-one.

3. (a) Knowing that any maximal independent family of a finite-dimensional vector space, X, is a basis, prove that any independent $x_1, \ldots, x_n$ can be extended to a basis.

(b) Prove that any subspace of a finite-dimensional space has a complement.

4. Use Zorn's lemma to prove that any subspace of an arbitrary vector space has a complement.

5. Prove Proposition 1.7.3.

6. Let N be a nilpotent operator on a finite-dimensional vector space, X. Suppose m is such that $N^m = 0$ but $N^{m-1} \neq 0$ (although $N^{m-1}x$ may be zero for some x, just not all x). For $\ell = 1, 2, \ldots, m$, define
$$Y_j = \{x \mid N^j x = 0, \ N^{j-1}x \neq 0\} \tag{1.7.46}$$

(a) Prove that
$$X = Y_1 \dotplus Y_2 \dotplus \cdots \dotplus Y_m \tag{1.7.47}$$

(b) For $j = 2, \ldots, m$, prove that N is a bijection of Y_m and $N[Y_m] \equiv Z_{m-1,1} \subset Y_{m-1}$.

(c) Let $Y_{m-1,0}$ be a complement in Y_{m-1} of Z_{m-1}. Prove that
$$Z_{m-2,1} = T[Y_{m-1,1}] \dotplus T^2[Y_m] \tag{1.7.48}$$

(d) By iterating this construction, show there are spaces $Y_{m-j,k}$, $j = 0, \ldots, m-1$, $k = 1, \ldots, j+1$, so that
$$Y_{m-j} = Y_{m-j,1} \dotplus Y_{m-j,2} \dotplus \cdots \dotplus Y_{m-j,j+1} \tag{1.7.49}$$
$$T[Y_{m-j,k}] = Y_{m-j-1,k+1} \tag{1.7.50}$$

(e) By picking bases for each $Y_{m-j,1}$ and looking at $\{T^\ell e\}_{\ell=0}^{m-j+1}$, prove the structure result, Proposition 1.7.4.

7. Let $\{e_j\}_{j=1}^\ell$ be a basis for a finite-dimensional space, X. Say a T is m upper diagonal for $m = 1, 2, \ldots, \ell - 1$ if its matrix elements obey
$$t_{jk} = 0 \qquad \text{if } k < j + m - 1 \tag{1.7.51}$$

that is, the only nonzero matrix elements are in the upper $\ell - m$ diagonals. 1 upper diagonal is called *upper diagonal*.

(a) If T is m upper diagonal and S is n upper diagonal, prove that TS is $m + n$ upper diagonal.

(b) If T is upper diagonal, prove that $T^\ell = 0$, so T is nilpotent.

8. Prove Proposition 1.7.5.

9. Let N be nilpotent so $N^\ell x = 0$ for all x. Pick $x \neq 0$ and let $J = \min\{j \mid N^j x = 0\}$. Prove $y = N^{j-1} x \neq 0$ and $Ny = 0$, that is, $\mathrm{Ker}(N) \neq \{0\}$.

10. Suppose T has the form (1.7.26). Let $k_j = \dim(\mathrm{Ran}(P_j))$.

(a) Prove that

$$\prod_{j=1}^{n} (T - \lambda_j)^{k_j} = 0 \qquad (1.7.52)$$

(b) If $Tx = \mu x$ for some $x \in X$, $x \neq 0$, and $\mu \in \mathbb{C}$, prove that $\prod_{j=1}^{n}(\mu - \lambda_j)^{k_j} = 0$ and then that $\mu \in \{\lambda_1, \dots, \lambda_n\}$.

11. This problem will have the reader prove some results about ideals in $\mathbb{C}[X]$, the polynomials with complex coefficients, as preparation for the proof of the Jordan normal form in Problem 12. We assume the reader knows what an ideal is.

(a) If $P, Q \in \mathbb{C}[X]$, prove that there are polynomials M, R with $\deg(R) < \deg(Q)$ and

$$P = MQ + R \qquad (1.7.53)$$

(b) Let $\mathcal{I}$ be an ideal in $\mathbb{C}[X]$. Let Q be a polynomial in $\mathcal{I}$ with minimal degree (show it exists). Prove that

$$\mathcal{I} = \{MQ \mid M \in \mathbb{C}[X]\} \qquad (1.7.54)$$

that is, that $\mathbb{C}[X]$ is a principal ideal domain.

(c) Let $P_1, P_2, \dots, P_m \in \mathbb{C}[X]$ have no common factor. Prove there exist $M_1, \dots, M_m \in \mathbb{C}[X]$ so that

$$M_1 P_1 + M_2 P_2 + \cdots + M_m P_m = 1 \qquad (1.7.55)$$

(*Hint*: Prove that $\{\sum_{j=1}^{m} M_j P_j \mid M_j \text{ arbitrary in } \mathbb{C}[X]\}$ is an ideal and use (b).)

(d) If $P_1, \dots, P_m$ have a common nontrivial factor, prove that they have a common complex zero.

12. This will prove the Jordan normal form. Let $T \in \mathcal{L}(X)$, X a finite-dimensional complex vector space. Let $P(X) = X^m + \dots$ be the minimal

polynomial for T (i.e., minimal degree P with $P(T) = 0$). Let

$$P(X) = \prod_{j=1}^{n} (X - \lambda_j)^{k_j} \tag{1.7.56}$$

(a) Let

$$Q_j(X) = \prod_{p \neq j} (X - \lambda_p)^{k_p} \tag{1.7.57}$$

Prove they have no common factor and conclude that there are $\{R_j\}_{j=1}^{m}$ so that $1 = \sum_{j=1}^{m} Q_j R_j$.

(b) Prove that

$$X = \text{Ker}((T - \lambda_1)^{k_1}) + \text{Ker}(T - \lambda_2)^{k_2}) + \cdots + \text{Ker}((T - \lambda_n)^{k_n}) \tag{1.7.58}$$

(c) Prove that there exist B_{j1} and B_{j2} so that

$$1 = B_{j1}(X - \lambda_j)^{k_j} + B_{j2}Q_j(X) \tag{1.7.59}$$

(d) Suppose $x_j \in \text{Ker}((T - \lambda_j)^{k_j})$ and $x_j + \cdots + x_n = 0$. Note that $Q_j(T)x_j = -\sum_{p \neq j} Q(T)x_p = 0$ and conclude $x_j = 0$, that is, one has $\dotplus$ instead of merely $+$ in (1.7.58).

(e) Let $\{P_j\}_{j=1}^{n}$ be the complementary projections associated to the $\dotplus$ version of (1.7.58). Using

$$(T - \lambda_j)^{k_j} P_j = 0 \tag{1.7.60}$$

prove that

$$T = \sum_{j=1}^{n} (\lambda_j P_j + N_j) \tag{1.7.61}$$

where $N_j^{k_j} = 0$ and $P_j N_j P_j = N_j$, that is, conclude that you have proven the Jordan normal form theorem (Theorem 1.7.6).

13. Let A be an $n \times n$ real matrix.

    (a) View A as acting on $\mathbb{C}^n$. Suppose $Ax = \lambda x$ with $\lambda \in \mathbb{R}$. Let $[\text{Re}\, x]_j = \text{Re}\, x_j$, $[\text{Im}\, x]_j = \text{Im}\, x_j$. Prove that $A(\text{Re}\, x) = \lambda \text{Re}\, x$ and $A(\text{Im}\, x) = \lambda \text{Im}\, x$. Conclude that λ is an eigenvalue of A as an operator on $\mathbb{R}^n$.

    (b) Prove every self-adjoint operator on $\mathbb{R}^n$ has eigenvalues.

14. Let A be a self-adjoint operator on a finite-dimensional real or complex inner product space.

    (a) If $\langle x, Ax \rangle > 0$ for some x, prove that there is an x_0 with $\langle x_0, x_0 \rangle = 1$ that has

$$\sup_{x \mid \langle x, x \rangle = 1} \langle x, Ax \rangle = \langle x_0, Ax_0 \rangle \tag{1.7.62}$$

(b) Show x_0 is an eigenvector for A. (*Hint*: Use Lagrange multipliers.)

(c) Do the same if $\langle x, Ax \rangle < 0$ for some x.

(d) Conclude that A has an eigenvector.

Remark. This problem needs the fact that the continuous functions on closed, bounded subsets of $\mathbb{R}^\nu$ take their maximum value.

15. Let $T: X \to Y$ be linear with $\dim(X)$ finite. Prove that $\dim(\mathrm{Ker}(T)) + \dim(\mathrm{Ran}(T)) = \dim(X)$.

1.8. Some Calculus

Of course, we suppose the reader is familiar with basic calculus. That said, we want to point out where, later in this volume, some of the basics are explained, and we want to be explicit about what we'll mean by Taylor's theorem with remainder.

Riemann integration is discussed in Section 4.1 in order to present the Riemann–Stieltjes integral. From the definition of the Riemann integral as a limit of Riemann sums, one easily gets the first form of the Fundamental Theorem of Calculus: if f is continuous, then

$$F(x) = \int_0^x f(y)\,dy \tag{1.8.1}$$

is C^1 and $F'(x) = f(x)$.

The second form of this theorem, namely, if F is C^1 with $F(0) = 0$, then (1.8.1) holds with $f = F'$, is more subtle. It depends on a uniqueness result that if f is defined on $[0, 1]$ and f is differentiable at every point and $f'(x) = 0$ at all points, then f is constant. This is an immediate consequence of the second form of the fundamental theorem (extended slightly) but that can't be used yet. Instead, there is a subtle argument the reader provides in Problem 12 of Section 4.1.

Once one has the fundamental theorem, one can iterate it and obtain a form of Taylor's theorem with remainder involving a multiple integral. Here is a version with a single integral:

Theorem 1.8.1 (Taylor's Theorem With Remainder—First Form). *Let f be a C^n function on $(-a, a)$ for some $a > 0$. Then for all $x \in (-a, a)$, we have that*

$$f(x) = \sum_{j=0}^{n-1} \frac{x^j}{j!} f^{(j)}(x) + \int_0^x \frac{(x-y)^{n-1}}{(n-1)!} f^{(n)}(y)\,dy \tag{1.8.2}$$

Remark. Problem 1 has a proof using the iterated fundamental theorem.

Proof. Let $g(x)$ be the integral in (1.8.2). So long as $n-1 > 0$, the integrand vanishes at $y = x$, so there is no contribution from the change of upper limit, that is,

$$g'(x) = \int_0^x \frac{(x-y)^{n-2}}{(n-2)!} f^{(n)}(y)\, dy \tag{1.8.3}$$

Iterating, we get for $j = 1, 2, \ldots, n-1$,

$$g^{(j)}(x) = \int_0^x \frac{(x-y)^{n-1-j}}{(n-1-j)!} f^{(n)}(y)\, dy \tag{1.8.4}$$

Finally, at $j = n-1$, the integrand is x-independent, so

$$g^{(n)}(x) = f^{(n)}(x) \tag{1.8.5}$$

Iterating the fact that $f' = 0 \Rightarrow f = $ constant, we see that $(f - g)(x)$ is a polynomial of degree at most $n - 1$. Since (1.8.4) implies $g(0) = g'(0) = \cdots = g^{(n-1)}(0) = 0$, we see the polynomial is the sum in (1.8.3). $\square$

Theorem 1.8.2 (Taylor's Theorem With Remainder—Second Form). *Under the hypotheses of Theorem 1.8.1, for every $x \in (0, a)$, there is $y(x) \in (0, x)$ so that*

$$f(x) = \sum_{j=0}^{n-1} \frac{x^j}{j!} f^{(j)}(x) + \frac{x^n}{n!} f^{(n)}(y(x)) \tag{1.8.6}$$

Proof. $\frac{(x-y)^{n-1}}{(n-1)!}$ is a positive weight with integral $\frac{x^n}{n!}$. By the intermediate value theorem for integrals (Problem 2), the integral in (1.8.2) is $\frac{x^n}{n!}$ times the value of $f^{(n)}(y)$ at some $y \in (0, x)$. $\square$

Example 1.8.3 (Binomial Theorem). If $f(x) = (1-x)^\alpha$ for $\alpha \in \mathbb{R}$, a simple induction determines the derivatives and one finds

$$(1+x)^\alpha = \sum_{n=0}^\infty \binom{\alpha}{n} x^n \tag{1.8.7}$$

as the Taylor series. Here

$$\binom{\alpha}{n} = \frac{\alpha(\alpha-1)\cdots(\alpha-n+1)}{n!} \tag{1.8.8}$$

If α is an integer, one gets a polynomial, i.e.,

$$(x+y)^n = \sum_{j=0}^n \binom{n}{j} x^j y^{n-j}; \quad \binom{n}{j} = \frac{n!}{j!\,(n-j)!} \tag{1.8.9}$$

The complex analysis theory implies (1.8.7) converges to $(1+x)^\alpha$ for $|x| < 1$. $\square$

Two other major themes in a first rigorous calculus course are inverse/implicit function theorems and existence of solutions of ODEs. Since they appear later as examples of applications of fixed point theorems for Banach spaces, we aren't explicit here but instead point to Theorems 5.12.9 and 5.12.10 for the first subject and Theorems 5.12.5 and 5.12.24 plus Theorem 11.2.3 of Part 2A for the second.

We will occasionally need the existence of C^∞ partitions of unity:

Theorem 1.8.4 (C^∞ Partitions of Unity). *Let $K \subset \mathbb{R}^\nu$ be compact and $\{U_\alpha\}_{\alpha \in I}$ an open cover of K. Then there exist C^∞ functions, $\{j_k\}_{k=1}^n$, of compact support so that each j_k has support in some U_{α_k} and so that $\sum_{k=1}^n j_k(x) = 1$ for all $x \in K$.*

The idea of the proof is to first use products of functions of the form

$$g(x) = \begin{cases} \exp(-(x-x_0)^{-1}), & x \geq x_0 \\ 0, & x \leq x_0 \end{cases} \tag{1.8.10}$$

to get, for any $V \subset \mathbb{R}^\nu$ and $x \in V$, a function $q_{x,V}$, C^∞ of compact support so that sup $q_{x,V} \subset V, 0 \leq q_{x,V} \leq 1$, and $q_{x,V}(y) = 1$ for y in some neighborhood, $N_{x,V}$, of x.

Then, for each $\alpha \in I$ and $x \in U_\alpha$, pick such a q_{x,U_α} and N_{x,U_α}. Finitely many N_{x,U_α} cover K, so let $q_1, \ldots, q_n; N_1, \ldots, N_n$ be the corresponding functions and sets.

Finally, define $j_1, \ldots, j_n$ by

$$j_1 = q_1, \ldots, j_{k+1} = q_{k+1}(1-q_1)\ldots(1-q_k), \ldots \tag{1.8.11}$$

Then $\sum_{k=1}^n j_k = 1 - \prod_{k=1}^n (1-q_k)$ is 1 on K.

Notes and Historical Remarks. Taylor series appeared first in a 1715 work of Brook Taylor (1685–1731) [**913**], although its significance wasn't widely appreciated until work of Lagrange in 1772 (talk about a slower pace of mathematical life!). In some older books, a Taylor series about $z = 0$ is called a Maclaurin series.

The integral case of the binomial theorem was known to Pascal and Fermat. Wallis raised the issue of fractional exponents but was unable to find the expansion for $(1-x^2)^{1/2}$ which interested him. Newton found (1.8.9) in 1664 or 1665 and communicated it in a letter in 1676. It appeared in print first in 1685 in Wallis' *Treatise of Algebra* [**976**] with credit given to Newton. The idea behind the function in (1.8.10) goes back to Cauchy [**169**] who pointed out that $\exp(-\frac{1}{x^2})$ had an identically zero Taylor series at $x = 0$ but was not the zero function.

Problems

1. (a) By iterating the fundamental theorem of calculus, prove (1.8.2) holds where the integral is replaced by

$$\int_0^x dx_n \int_0^{x_n} dx_{n-1} \dots \int_0^{x_1} f^{(n)}(x_1)\, dx_1 \qquad (1.8.12)$$

(b) Prove that the volume of the $\{(x_2, \dots, x_n) \mid x_1 < x_2 < \cdots < x_n < x\}$ is for fixed x_1 and x is equal to $\frac{(x-x_1)^{n-1}}{(n-1)!}$.

(c) Prove (1.8.2).

2. (a) Let $w(x) \geq 0$ on (a, b) with $\int w(x)\, dx > 0$. For any continuous function f on (a, b), prove that

$$\min_{a \leq x \leq b} f(x) \int_a^b w(x)\, dx \leq \int_a^b f(x) w(x)\, dx \leq \max_{a \leq x \leq b} f(x) \int_a^b w(x)\, dx$$

$$(1.8.13)$$

(b) Using the fact that f takes every value in $(\min f(x), \max f(x))$ on $[a, b]$, prove that for some $c \in [a.b]$,

$$\int_a^b f(x) w(x)\, dx = f(c) \int_a^b w(x)\, dx \qquad (1.8.14)$$

This is the *intermediate value theorem for integrals*.

(c) Prove that one can choose $c \in (a, b)$.

Chapter 2

Topological Spaces

> At the basis of the distance concept lies, for example, the concept of a convergent point sequence and their defined limits, and one can, choosing these ideas as those fundamental to point set theory, eliminate the notions of distance .... Thirdly, we can associate with each point of the set certain parts of the space called neighborhoods, and these can again be made building stones of the theory with the elimination of the distance concept. Here the view of a set is in consideration of the association between elements and subsets.
> —*Felix Hausdorff* [**402**], as translated in [**628**]

Big Notions and Theorems: Topology, Open Sets, Closed Sets, Relative Topology, Relatively Open, Relatively Closed, Kuratowski Closure Axioms, Interior, Closure, Boundary, Base, Subbase, Accumulation Point, Dense Subset, Limit, Subsequence, Limit Point, Cluster Point, Continuous, Sequentially Continuous, Homeomorphism, Metric Space, Uniform Convergence, Weierstrass Uniform Convergence Theorem, Upper and Lower Semicontinuous (usc, lsc), Neighborhood, Neighborhood Base, Weak Topology, Curve, Arcwise Connected, Clopen Set, Connected, Connected Component, Locally Arcwise Connected, Totally Disconnected, Separable, First Countable, Second Countable, Lindelöf Space, T_1, Hausdorff Space (T_2), T_3, Normal (T_4), Metric Spaces are Normal, Urysohn Metrizability Theorem, Urysohn Lemma, Tietze Extension Theorem, G_δ, F_σ, Open Cover, Compact, Compact Hausdorff is Normal, Finite Intersection Property, Totally Bounded, Compactness in Metric Spaces, Locally Compact Space, One-Point Compactification, Bolzano–Weierstrass Property of $\mathbb{R}^n$, Uniform Convergence, Uniform Equicontinuity, Arzelà–Ascoli Theorem, Weierstrass Density Theorems, Bernstein Polynomials, Korovkin's Theorem, Stone–Weierstrass Theorem, Kakutani-Krein Theorem, Complex Stone–Weierstrass, Net, Frequent, Eventually, Convergent Net, Limit Point, Subnet, Cauchy Net, Bolzano–Weierstrass and Compactness, Product Topology, Tychonoff's Theorem, Quotient Space, Quotient Topology

This chapter discusses what is sometimes called point set topology, which is a fundamental language for both analysis and for the general field known as topology or as geometry. For us, the key will be a language that makes precise the notions of convergence and of continuous functions.

Of course, metric spaces—which we suppose the reader has seen (see Section 1.2)—provide a language for convergence and continuity, and so one can ask why we go beyond that. One answer is that we will very occasionally consider topologies not given by a metric. For example, a high point of the abstract theory is existence theorems based on compactness in weak-∗ topologies. We'll see in great generality that such topologies are not metric (see Theorems 3.6.8 and 5.7.2). However, we'll really be interested in this topology restricted to bounded sets—and this restricted topology is often given by a metric. Thus, with some awkwardness, we could avoid the use of nonmetric topologies in this case. There are other nonmetric topologies, for example, the topology on C^∞ functions of compact support (see Sections 9.1 and 9.2) or on uncountable products of $[0, 1]$ (see Section 2.7). So there is some validity to the reason that an occasional topology is nonmetric.

An even better reason is that we are often interested in aspects not captured by metrics. As metric spaces, $(0, 1)$ and $\mathbb{R}$ are not the same; indeed, $\mathbb{R}$ is complete and $(0, 1)$ is not. But they are the same as topological spaces, so topology provides a language that captures less than a metric but what is sometimes more essential.

In modern guise, a topology is given by the family of open subsets, $\mathcal{T}$, of a space X. $\mathcal{T}$ is a family obeying the axioms:

 (i) $\emptyset, X \in \mathcal{T}$
 (ii) Finite intersections of sets in $\mathcal{T}$ are in $\mathcal{T}$.
 (iii) Arbitrary unions of sets in $\mathcal{T}$ are in $\mathcal{T}$.

As with the axioms for a group, the richness captured by this simple set of axioms is remarkable.

The first three sections are mainly definitions. Topology is for us a language, and as with any language, a rich vocabulary is a first step. Section 2.1 is a huge number of definitions and simple relations. In Sections 2.2 and 2.3, we single out for more in-depth discussion two particularly significant sets of notions. Section 2.2 focuses on separation properties involving normality and the corresponding existence of lots of continuous functions (Urysohn's lemma). Section 2.3 discusses compactness and the notion of uniform convergence and the Arzelà–Ascoli theorem.

If this were a topology book, we'd also single out connectedness, but since this is an analysis text, we'll relegate that to the end of Section 2.1.

The next two sections focus on density theorems in the space of continuous functions on a compact Hausdorff space. Section 2.4 discusses the classical Weierstrass theorem for density of the polynomials in $C([a, b])$—we'll

prove it via Bernstein polynomials. Section 2.5 proves Stone's vast generalization (Stone–Weierstrass theorem). We'll prove the Stone–Weierstrass
theorem by first proving the Kakutani–Krein theorem, a result on density of
some sublattices. Lattices (i.e., families of functions closed under pairwise,
pointwise max and min) will be an important tool in some other places, for
example, Section 4.8.

Section 2.6 begins by showing sequences are inadequate to provide convergence criteria for some fundamental topological notions and then discusses nets, an adequate replacement for sequences. Section 2.7 then discusses the product topology and Tychonoff's theorem which says that the
product of compact spaces is compact. Finally, a brief Section 2.8 discusses
the quotient topology—useful, for example, to induce a topology on quotient
groups and on homogeneous spaces.

2.1. Lots of Definitions

> Point set topology is a disease from which the human race will soon recover.
>
> —*attributed to H. Poincaré* [1]

This section has over thirty definitions. It is not going to be scintillating
or deep but represents the dues one needs to pay to get to the good stuff.
We'll start with the basics of open and closed sets, closure, and boundary,
then turn to continuity, including semicontinuity, and end with connectivity.

Definition. A *topological space* is a set, X, and family, $\mathcal{T}$, of subsets of X
(the topology) that obeys three axioms:

(i) $\emptyset, X \in \mathcal{T}$
(ii) $A_1, \ldots, A_n \in \mathcal{T} \Rightarrow A_1 \cap \cdots \cap A_n \in \mathcal{T}$
(iii) $\{A_\alpha\}_{\alpha \in I} \subset \mathcal{T}$, any subfamily of $\mathcal{T} \Rightarrow \cup_\alpha A_\alpha \in \mathcal{T}$

The sets in $\mathcal{T}$ are called *open sets*.

Definition. A *base* of a topology, $\mathcal{T}$, is a subset, $\mathcal{B}$, of $\mathcal{T}$ so that any element
of $\mathcal{T}$ is a union of sets of $\mathcal{B}$. A *subbase* of a topology is a subset, $\mathcal{S}$, so that
the family of finite intersections of sets in $\mathcal{S}$ is a base.

If a family of sets is closed under finite intersection, it is the base of a
unique topology. Bases are used often, subbases less so.

---

[1]This quote is so widely used that you can buy a coffee mug on the internet with the quote
on the mug but it appears not to have been uttered by Poincaré! See [**365**]. If Poincaré did
express a thought like this, he meant Cantor's set theory, which he was an opponent of, not our
prosaic point set topology which was only invented after Poincaré was dead!

Example 2.1.1 (Usual Topology on $\mathbb{R}$). Let $\mathcal{B}$ be the set of open intervals $(a, b) = \{x \mid a < x < b\}$ in $\mathbb{R}$ $(a < b)$. $\mathcal{B}$ is closed under finite intersection, so it is the base of a unique topology, $\mathcal{T}$, on $\mathbb{R}$. $A \in \mathcal{T}$ if and only if $\forall x \in A$, $\exists_{a < x < b}$ so that $(a, b) \subset A$. $\qquad\square$

A set, B, in a topological space, X, is called *closed* if and only if $X \setminus B$ is open. The family of all closed sets is closed under finite union and arbitrary intersections.

If A is an arbitrary set in X, a topological space, the union over all open sets $U \subset A$ is an open set, clearly the largest open subset of A. It is called the *interior*, A^{int}, of A. Similarly, there is a smallest closed set containing A, called its *closure*, written $\bar{A}$. We have $\bar{A} = X \setminus (X \setminus A)^{\text{int}}$. Finally, one defines the *boundary* of A, ∂A, to be

$$\partial A = \bar{A} \setminus A^{\text{int}} \qquad (2.1.1)$$

Notice that

$$\partial X = \emptyset, \qquad \partial \emptyset = \emptyset \qquad (2.1.2)$$

Topologies can be described in terms of a set of axioms for the closure operator; see Problem 1.

Definition. Let X be a topological space with topology $\mathcal{T}$. Let $A \subset X$ (A need not be open or closed, but can be either or neither). Let $\mathcal{T}_A = \{B \cap A \mid B \in \mathcal{T}\}$. This defines a topology on A, called the *relative topology*. Sets in $\mathcal{T}_A$ are called *relatively open*. Their complements in A (which have the form $C \cap A$ with C closed in X) are called *relatively closed*.

Some properties of topological spaces are intrinsic in that it is meaningful to say that a subset of X has that property in the relative topology. For example, to say $A \subset X$ is compact in the relative topology is an interesting statement about A, and we'll use the term compact space and compact set. But A is always closed in the relative topology, so we won't say "closed space" and, of course, closed set has a different meaning!

Definition. Given a sequence $\{x_n\}_{n=1}^{\infty}$ in X, a topological space, we say $x_\infty \in X$ is the *limit* of $\{x_n\}_{n=1}^{\infty}$, written $x_n \to x_\infty$ ("*x_n converges to x_∞*") if and only if for any open set, A, with $x_\infty \in A$, there exists N so that $x_n \in A$ if $n \geq N$.

We'll see later in Section 2.6 that in general spaces, one needs more than sequences to properly define convergence.

Definition. A *subsequence* $\{y_n\}_{n=1}^{\infty}$ of a sequence $\{x_n\}_{n=1}^{\infty}$ in a set X is a sequence of the form

$$y_n = x_{j(n)} \qquad (2.1.3)$$

where $j\colon \{1, 2, \dots\} \to \{1, 2, \dots\}$ with $j(n+1) > j(n)$ (so, in particular, by induction, $j(n) \geq n$). Basically, we take a subset $S \subset \{1, 2, \dots\}$ and let y_n be the values along this subset with the order given by the order in $\{1, 2, \dots\}$.

Definition. Given a sequence $\{x_n\}_{n=1}^{\infty}$ in X, a topological space, we say $x_\infty \in X$ is a *limit point* or *cluster point* of $\{x_n\}_{n=1}^{\infty}$ if and only if for any open set, A, with $x_\infty \in A$, and any N, there exists $n \geq N$ so $x_n \in A$.

Note that if x_∞ is a limit point, once we have some $x_n \in A$, we can take $N = n + 1$ and find a second, and so infinitely many x_n's in A. In colorful language, we say x_∞ is a limit point if x_n is *frequently* in any open A containing x_∞, and x_∞ is the limit if x_n is *eventually* in any such A.

In many spaces, including metric spaces (see Problem 3 of Section 2.3), limit points are precisely the limits of subsequences, but this is not true in all topological spaces; see Example 2.6.2.

Definition. Let X, Y be topological spaces with topologies $\mathcal{T}_X$ and $\mathcal{T}_Y$, respectively. A function $f\colon X \to Y$ is called *open* if $f[A] \in \mathcal{T}_Y$ for any $A \in \mathcal{T}_X$, and it is called *continuous* if and only if $f^{-1}[B] \in \mathcal{T}_X$ for every $B \in \mathcal{T}_Y$.

It may be surprising that continuous maps are more basic than open maps. The reason has to do with the Boolean properties of f^{-1} on sets as contrasted with f. $f[A_1 \cup A_2] = f[A_1] \cup f[A_2]$ but $f[A_1 \cap A_2]$ may be smaller than $f[A_1] \cap f[A_2]$ (e.g., $f(x) = y_0$, a constant, and $A_1 \cap A_2 = \emptyset$, but $A_1 \neq \emptyset \neq A_2$). On the other hand, f^{-1} is a Boolean morphism, that is,

$$f^{-1}\left[\bigcap_{\alpha \in I} A_\alpha\right] = \bigcap_{\alpha \in I} f^{-1}[A_\alpha] \tag{2.1.4}$$

and

$$f^{-1}\left[\bigcup_{\alpha \in I} A_\alpha\right] = \bigcup_{\alpha \in I} f^{-1}[A_\alpha] \tag{2.1.5}$$

Moreover, if $f\colon X \to Y$,

$$f^{-1}[Y \setminus A] = X \setminus f^{-1}[A] \tag{2.1.6}$$

A bijection that is both open and continuous is called a *homeomorphism* or sometimes a *bicontinuous map*. If $f\colon X \to Y$ is open and continuous and, for any $x \in X$, there is an open set $U \subset X$ with $x \in U$ and so that $f \upharpoonright U$ is a homeomorphism of U and $f[U]$, then we say that f is a *local homeomorphism*. Note that f is locally one-one but not necessarily globally one-one. For example, $f\colon \mathbb{R} \to \mathbb{D}$ by $f(x) = e^{ix}$ is a local homeomorphism. Here is one connection between continuity and convergence:

Proposition 2.1.2. *If $f\colon X \to Y$ is continuous and $x_n \to x_\infty$ for a sequence in X, then $f(x_n) \to f(x_\infty)$ in Y.*

Proof. Let B be an open set in Y containing $f(x_\infty)$. Then $A \equiv f^{-1}[B]$ is an open set in X containing x_∞, so $\exists N$ so $x_n \in A$ if $n \geq N$. Thus, if $n \geq N$, $f(x_n) \in B$. □

A map that takes convergent sequences to convergent sequences is called *sequentially continuous*. We've just shown that continuous functions are sequentially continuous. The surprise, as we'll see in Example 2.6.1, is that the converse is false and that in general topological spaces, sequences are not sufficient to characterize continuity.

Example 2.1.3 (Two Trivial Topologies). For any X, $\mathcal{T} = \{\emptyset, X\}$ is called the *indiscrete topology*. Notice in this topology, if $A \neq \emptyset, X$, then $\partial A = X$. Moreover, if $\{x_n\}_{n=1}^\infty$ is any sequence and x_∞ is any point in X, then $x_n \to x_\infty$ (so limits are not unique). If X is any topological space and Y has the indiscrete topology, then any map $f\colon X \to Y$ is continuous.

For any X, $\mathcal{T} = 2^X$, that is, all sets are open, is called the *discrete topology*. For any set A, $\partial A = \emptyset$. A sequence $\{x_n\}_{n=1}^\infty$ in X converges to x_∞ if and only if for some N, $x_n \equiv x_\infty$ if $n \geq N$. If X has the discrete topology and Y any topology and $f\colon X \to Y$ is any function, then f is continuous. □

Example 2.1.4 (Metric Space Topologies). Metrics are discussed in Section 1.2. The topology associated to a metric ρ on X is the one where A is open $\Leftrightarrow \forall x \in A$, $\exists \varepsilon > 0$, $B_\varepsilon(x) \subset A$. The reader should check that convergent sequences and continuity given by ε, δ are equivalent to the topological notion. Notice that if

$$\rho(x, y) = \begin{cases} 0 & \text{if } x = y \\ 1 & \text{if } x \neq y \end{cases} \tag{2.1.7}$$

the induced topology is the discrete topology. As noted earlier, $(0, 1)$ and $\mathbb{R}$ in their usual metrics are homeomorphic as topological spaces under $x \mapsto \tan(\pi(x - \frac{1}{2}))$. This shows completeness is not a topological concept. Note that if X is a metric space and $A \subset X$, the relative topology on A is the metric topology generated by restricting ρ to $A \times A$. □

If X is a topological space and Y a metric space, we say a function $f\colon X \to Y$ is *bounded* if and only if for one y (and so, all y) in Y, $\sup_{x \in X} \rho(f(x), y) < \infty$. Given two bounded functions f, g from X to Y, we define

$$\widetilde{\rho}(f, g) \equiv \sup_{x \in X} \rho(f(x), g(x)) \tag{2.1.8}$$

Convergence of a sequence in $\widetilde{\rho}$ metric is called *uniform convergence*. The following generalizes a famous result of Weierstrass on uniform convergence of real-valued functions on an interval $[a, b]$—it is essentially his proof:

Theorem 2.1.5 (Weierstrass' Uniform Convergence Theorem). *Let X be a topological space and Y a metric space. Let f_n be a sequence of bounded functions of X to Y, each of which is continuous. Let f be a function from X to Y so that $\widetilde{\rho}(f_n, f) \to 0$. Then f is bounded and continuous.*

Proof. Boundedness of f is trivial. Given $x_0 \in X$ and $\varepsilon > 0$, pick n so $\widetilde{\rho}(f_n, f) < \varepsilon/3$. Pick an open set A containing x_0, so $x \in A \Rightarrow \rho(f_n(x), f_n(x_0)) < \varepsilon/3$, which is possible by continuity. For such x,

$$\rho(f(x), f(x_0)) < \rho(f(x), f_n(x)) + \rho(f_n(x), f_n(x_0)) + \rho(f_n(x_0), f(x_0))$$
$$< \frac{\varepsilon}{3} + \frac{\varepsilon}{3} + \frac{\varepsilon}{3} = \varepsilon$$

Thus, f is continuous at x_0. $\qquad\square$

Theorem 2.1.6. *Let Y be a complete metric space and $C_Y(X)$ the set of continuous bounded functions from X to Y. Let $\widetilde{\rho}$ be the metric (2.1.8) on $C_Y(X)$. Then $C_Y(X)$ is complete.*

Remark. This is used most often for $Y = \mathbb{R}$ or $\mathbb{C}$.

Proof. If $\{f_n\}_{n=1}^\infty$ is Cauchy, since Y is complete and $\{f_n(x)\}_{n=1}^\infty$ is Cauchy for each x, there is a function $f \colon X \to Y$ given by $f(x) = \lim f_n(y)$. By Theorem 2.1.5, f is continuous. It is easy to see that f is bounded and $\rho(f_n, f) \to 0$. $\qquad\square$

Example 2.1.7 (Cofinite Sets). Let X be a set and $\mathcal{F}$ the family of finite subsets of X plus X itself. $\mathcal{F}$ contains $\emptyset$ and X and is closed under finite unions and arbitrary intersections. Thus, it is the set of closed sets in a unique topology. The open sets are *cofinite*, that is, complements of finite sets (plus $\emptyset$). This topology is called the *cofinite topology*, mainly of interest as a source of examples. If $\{x_n\}_{n=1}^\infty$ is a sequence that takes a given value only finitely many times, then x_n converges to any point in X in the cofinite topology. $\qquad\square$

An amusing topology on $\mathbb{Z}$ is discussed in Problem 2. It is used to prove there are infinitely many primes.

Functions with values in $\mathbb{R}$ or $\mathbb{R} \cup \{\infty\}$ or $\mathbb{R} \cup \{-\infty\}$ play an especially important role. It will be occasionally useful to have two notions related to, but weaker than, continuity.

Definition. Let X be a topological space. Let $f \colon X \to \mathbb{R} \cup \{\infty\}$. We say that f is *lower semicontinuous (lsc)* if and only if for any $a \in \mathbb{R}$, $f^{-1}((a, \infty])$

is open. If $f \colon X \to \mathbb{R} \cup \{-\infty\}$, we say it is *upper semicontinuous* (*usc*) if and only if for any $a \in \mathbb{R}$, $f^{-1}([-\infty, a))$ is open.

Since $f^{-1}((a,b)) = f^{-1}([-\infty, b)) \cap f^{-1}((a, \infty])$, we see a function $f \colon X \to \mathbb{R}$ is continuous if and only if it is both lsc and usc. The canonical example of an lsc function is the characteristic function of an open set, $A \subset X$, that is,

$$f(x) = \begin{cases} 1, & x \in A \\ 0, & x \notin A \end{cases} \tag{2.1.9}$$

Similarly, the characteristic function of a closed set is usc.

Here is a basic fact about lsc functions:

Proposition 2.1.8. *Let X be a topological space and $x_n \to x_\infty$, a convergent sequence. Let f be an lsc function. Then*

$$f(x_\infty) \leq \liminf_{n \to \infty} f(x_n) \tag{2.1.10}$$

Remarks. 1. $\liminf a_n$ is the smallest limit point, i.e.,

$$\liminf a_n = \sup_n \left(\inf_{m \geq n} a_m \right) \tag{2.1.11}$$

Similarly $\limsup$ is the largest limit point.

2. The mnemonic is that f can be lower at the limit.

3. If X is a metric space, this is also a sufficient condition for lsc; see Problem 3. This is false in a general topological space; see Example 2.6.1.

Proof. Let $a = f(x_\infty)$. Since f is lsc, for any k, $B_k \equiv f^{-1}((a - \frac{1}{k}, \infty])$ is open. Since $x_n \to x_\infty$, for some N_k, we have $x_n \in B_k$ if $n \geq N_k$. Thus, $\liminf_{n \to \infty} f(x_n) \geq a - \frac{1}{k}$. Since k is arbitrary, $\liminf_{n \to \infty} f(x_n) \geq a$. $\qquad \square$

A main way lsc and usc functions arise is via:

Proposition 2.1.9. *Let $\mathcal{I}$ be a (nonempty) family of continuous functions $f \colon X \to \mathbb{R}$ where X is a topological space. Let*

$$f^*(x) = \sup_{f \in \mathcal{I}} f(x) \tag{2.1.12}$$

Then f^* is lsc.

Remarks. 1. The sup can be $+\infty$ (but not $-\infty$).

2. Similarly, infs are usc.

3. We'll prove a converse below (Theorem 2.3.15) when X is a compact metric space.

Proof. Fix $a \in \mathbb{R}$. Then for all $x \in X$, $f^*(x) > a \Leftrightarrow \exists f \in \mathcal{I}$ so that $f(x) > a \Leftrightarrow x \in \cup_{f \in \mathcal{I}} f^{-1}((a, \infty))$. Thus, if each $f^{-1}((a, \infty))$ is open, so is $(f^*)^{-1}(a, \infty]$). $\qquad\square$

Example 2.1.10. If $X = \mathbb{R}$, f_n, g_n defined by

$$f_n(x) = \begin{cases} 0, & |x| \geq 1 \\ 1, & |x| \leq 1 - n^{-1} \\ n(1 - |x|), & 1 - n^{-1} \leq |x| \leq 1 \end{cases}$$

$$(2.1.13)$$

$$g_n(x) = \begin{cases} 0, & |x| \geq 1 + n^{-1} \\ 1, & |x| \leq 1 \\ n(1 + n^{-1} - |x|), & 1 \leq |x| \leq 1 + n^{-1} \end{cases}$$

Then $\sup_n f_n = \chi_{(-1,1)}$ is lsc while $\inf_n g_n = \chi_{[-1,1]}$ is usc. $\qquad\square$

Definition. Let $x \in X$, a topological space. We say $N \subset X$ is a *neighborhood* of x if and only if $x \in N^{\text{int}}$, that is, if and only if there is A open so $x \in A \subset N$.

Definition. Let $x \in X$, a topological space. A *neighborhood base* of x, $\mathcal{N}$, is a family of neighborhoods of x so that if B is any neighborhood of x, then there exist $N \in \mathcal{N}$, so that $N \subset B$.

For example, in a metric space, $\mathcal{N} = \{B_{1/k}(x)\}_{k=1}^{\infty}$ is a neighborhood base for x and in any topological space, the open neighborhoods of x are a neighborhood base.

Definition. If $A \subset X$, a topological space, we say $x \in X$ is an *accumulation point* of A if and only if for any neighborhood N of x, there is $y \in A \cap N$ with $y \neq x$. A set, A, is called *perfect* if it is closed, not empty, and every point $x \in A$ is an accumulation point of A.

The canonical example of a perfect set in $[0, 1]$ is the Cantor set discussed in Section 4.2. We'll see (Problem 2 of Section 5.4) that every perfect set in $\mathbb{R}$ is uncountable. In Problem 4, the reader will prove

Proposition 2.1.11. *Let $A \subset X$, a topological space. Let B be the set of accumulation points of A. Then*

$$\bar{A} = A \cup B \qquad (2.1.14)$$

Definition. Let $A, B \subset X$, a topological space. We say A is *dense in* B if and only if $B \subset \bar{A}$. If $B = X$, we say A is *dense* (i.e., if $\bar{A} = X$).

Definition. If $\mathcal{T}_1, \mathcal{T}_2$ are two topologies on X, we say $\mathcal{T}_1$ is *weaker* than $\mathcal{T}_2$ if and only if $\mathcal{T}_1 \subset \mathcal{T}_2$. We say $\mathcal{T}_2$ is *stronger* or *finer* than $\mathcal{T}_1$.

The name weaker comes from the fact that if $x_n \to x$ in $\mathcal{T}_2$, then $x_n \to x$ in $\mathcal{T}_1$, but not necessarily vice-versa, so convergence in $\mathcal{T}_2$ is a stronger assertion than convergence in $\mathcal{T}_1$.

Notice that if $\{\mathcal{T}_\alpha\}_{\alpha \in I}$ is a family of topologies, $\cap_{\alpha \in I}\mathcal{T}_\alpha$ is a topology that is weaker than each $\mathcal{T}_\alpha$. If $\mathcal{T}_1$ is a weaker topology on X than $\mathcal{T}_2$, $f \colon X \to Y$ and Y has a fixed topology, and f is continuous in $\mathcal{T}_1$, it is continuous in $\mathcal{T}_2$. Thus, there is a weakest topology in which f is continuous, that is, $\cap_\alpha \mathcal{T}_\alpha$, where $\{\mathcal{T}_\alpha\}$ is the set of all topologies in which f is continuous. This topology is $\{f^{-1}[A] \mid A \in \mathcal{T}_Y$, the topology on $Y\}$.

More generally, if $\mathcal{F}$ is a family of functions, $f_\alpha \colon X \to Y_\alpha$ from a fixed X to an α-dependent range Y_α and each Y_α has a given topology, there is a weakest topology on X in which all f_α are continuous. For there is at least one such topology, the discrete topology on X, and this weakest topology is $\cap_\beta \mathcal{T}_\beta$ over all topologies in which all f_α are continuous. Alternatively, it is the topology with subbase $\{f_\alpha^{-1}[A_\alpha] \mid f_\alpha \in \mathcal{F}, A_\alpha$ is open in $Y_\alpha\}$. This is called the *weak topology* or $\mathcal{F}$-weak topology.

Finally, we discuss the notion of connectedness—actually, two notions: arcwise connected and (topologically) connected. Let $[0,1]$ denote $\{x \in \mathbb{R} \mid 0 \le x \le 1\}$ with the usual (metric) topology. A *curve* (also called a *path* or an *arc*) in X, a topological space, is a continuous function, $\gamma \colon [0,1] \to X$. $\gamma(0)$ and $\gamma(1)$ are called its *endpoints*. We call X *arcwise connected* if for all $x, y \in X$, there is a curve whose endpoints are x and y. In Problem 5, the reader will show in the general case that $x \sim y$ if x and y are the endpoints of a curve defines an equivalence relation on X. The equivalence classes are called *arcwise connected components* of X. They are maximal arcwise connected subsets of X (i.e., subsets that are arcwise connected in the *relative topology*).

A *clopen set*, $A \subset X$, a topological space, is a set that is both open and closed. X is called *connected* if and only if the only clopen sets in X are $\emptyset$ and X. A subset $A \subset X$ is called *connected* if and only if it is a connected space in the relative topology. Thus, a space, X, is connected if $A, B \subset X$ with $A \cap B = \emptyset$ and $A \cup B = X$ with both open (or both closed) implies either A or B is empty. It is in this way that connectedness arises most often in analysis. One proves $A = X$ by showing A is clopen in X and nonempty and X is connected.

Example 2.1.12. Let $a < b$ in $\mathbb{R}$. We claim (a,b) is connected. For suppose $A \cap B = \emptyset$, $A \cup B = (a,b)$ and both are open and closed in the relative topology. Suppose $A \ne \emptyset$ and $c \in A$. Let $B_- = \{x \in B \mid x < c\}$. If B_- is nonempty, let $x_+ = \sup\{x \in B_-\}$. Then there exist $x_n \in B$ with $x_+ - \frac{1}{n} < x_n \le x_+$. Thus, $x_n \to x_+$, so $x_+ \in B_-$ since B is closed (and $x_+ \ne c \notin B$). But since $B_- = B \cap (a,c)$ is open, B_- has points in (x_+, c), contradicting that x_+ is the sup. Thus, $B_- = \emptyset$. Similarly, $B_+ = \{x \in B \mid x > c\}$ is empty, so $B = \emptyset$. $\qquad\qquad\qquad\qquad\qquad\square$

Here are some of the most significant properties associated to connectedness:

Theorem 2.1.13. (a) *If $A \subset X$ is connected, so is $\bar{A}$.*

(b) *If $f \colon X \to Y$ is continuous and onto and X is connected, so is Y.*

(c) *Any arcwise connected space is connected.*

(d) *If $\{A_\alpha\}_{\alpha \in I}$ is a collection of connected subsets of X, a topological space, so that for all $\alpha, \beta \in I$, $A_\alpha \cap A_\beta \neq \emptyset$, then $\cup_{\alpha \in I} A_\alpha$ is connected.*

(e) *If $x \in X$, a topological space, there is a unique connected $A \subset X$ with $x \in A$ that is maximal among all connected subsets of X containing x. This A is closed.*

Remarks. 1. We'll see below (Example 2.1.15) that connected spaces need not be arcwise connected.

2. The maximal connected $A \ni x$ is called a *connected component* of X. Lying in the same connected component is an equivalence relation.

3. Connected components need not be open in X (see Example 2.1.14).

Proof. (a) Suppose $\bar{A} = B \cup C$ with $B \cap C = \emptyset$ and B, C clopen in $\bar{A}$. Then $B \cap A$ and $C \cap A$ are clopen in A so, since A is connected, one is empty, that is, we can suppose $A \subset B$. Since B is closed in $\bar{A}$, it is closed in X, and thus, $\bar{A} \subset B$ since $\bar{A}$ is the smallest closed set containing A. Thus, $\bar{A} = B$ and $C = \emptyset$.

(b) If B, C are clopen in Y, $B \cap C = \emptyset$, and $B \neq \emptyset$, then $f^{-1}[B] \cap f^{-1}[C] = \emptyset$ and both sets are clopen in X. Since X is connected, one can see $f^{-1}[C]$ must be empty. Since f is onto Y, C must be empty.

(c) Suppose X is arcwise connected, B, C are clopen in X and disjoint and nonempty and $B \cup C = X$. Pick $x \in B$, $y \in C$, and $\gamma \colon [0,1] \to X$ with $\gamma(0) = x$, $\gamma(1) = y$. $\gamma^{-1}[B]$, $\gamma^{-1}[C]$ are clopen and disjoint and cover $[0,1]$. But $0 \in \gamma^{-1}[B]$, $1 \in \gamma^{-1}[C]$, and $[0,1]$ is connected. This is a contradiction, so one of B or C is empty.

(d) Let B, C be clopen in $Y = \cup_\alpha A_\alpha$ and disjoint with $B \cup C = Y$. Then for each α, $B \cap A_\alpha$, $C \cap A_\alpha$ are clopen in A_α and disjoint, so since A_α is connected, for each A_α, either $A_\alpha \subset B$ or $A_\alpha \subset C$. Suppose that for some α, β, $A_\alpha \subset B$, $A_\beta \subset C$. Then, since $B \cap C = \emptyset$, $A_\alpha \cap A_\beta = \emptyset$, contrary to hypothesis. We conclude that either all $A_\alpha \subset B$ (so $C = \emptyset$) or vice-versa.

(e) Let $\{A_\alpha\}_{\alpha \in I}$ be a labeling of all connected subsets containing x. Clearly, $A_\alpha \cap A_\beta \neq \emptyset$ since it contains x. Thus, $A \equiv \cup A_\alpha$ is connected by (d) and is the largest connected set containing x. Since $\bar{A}$ is also connected (by (a)), $A = \bar{A}$. □

Example 2.1.14. Let $X = [0,1] \cap \mathbb{Q}$, the rationals within $[0,1]$ with the topology induced by the standard topology on $[0,1]$. If $\alpha, \beta \in A \subset X$ are distinct, and γ is an irrational number between α and β, $(-\infty, \gamma) \cap A$ and $(\gamma, \infty) \cap A$ are disjoint, clopen, cover A, and are not empty. Thus, A is not connected. That implies the only connected subsets of X are single points. Such a space is called *totally disconnected*. Notice that components are not open in X.

Section 5.4 will construct a connected subset, A, of $\mathbb{R}^2$ so that for one special point, x_∞, $A \setminus \{x_\infty\}$ is totally disconnected (see Example 5.4.23). □

Example 2.1.15. Let

$$X = \{(x,y) \in \mathbb{R}^2 \mid x \in (0,1),\ y = \sin(\tfrac{1}{x})\} \cup \{(x,y) \mid x = 0,\ |y| \le 1\} \tag{2.1.15}$$

with the topology induced by the standard one on $\mathbb{R}^2$. We'll call the right side of (2.1.15) $X_1 \cup X_2$ (see Figure 2.1.1). X_1 is connected and even arcwise connected, since if $x_1 < x_2$, $(x_1, y_1), (x_2, y_2) \in X$, then $\gamma(t) = ((1-t)x_1 + tx_2, \sin(1/((1-t)x_1 + tx_2))$ is a curve between the two points. Since X_1 is dense in X (Problem 6(a)), X is connected by Theorem 2.1.13(a). On the other hand (Problem 6(b)), X_1 and X_2 are the arcwise connected components, that is, X is connected but not arcwise connected. □

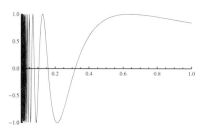

Figure 2.1.1. A connected but not arcwise connected set.

While, in general, connected sets need not be arcwise connected, there is a case in which one can prove they are.

Definition. We say a topological space, X, is *locally arcwise connected* if any $x \in X$ has an arcwise connected neighborhood.

Theorem 2.1.16. *If X, a topological space, is connected and locally arcwise connected, it is arcwise connected.*

Proof. Let $x \in X$ and $A = \{y \in X \mid \text{there is a curve } \gamma \text{ from } x \text{ to } y\}$. Obviously, A is nonempty. If we prove it is clopen, then $A = X$ and X is arcwise connected.

Let $y \in A$. By hypothesis, there is an arcwise connected neighborhood N of y. If $z \in N$, we can find a path from x to y and follow it by a path from y to z and so see that $N \subset A$, that is, A is open.

Let $y \in \bar{A} \setminus A$. Then y is an accumulation point of A. So if N is an arcwise connected neighborhood of y, we can find $z \in A \cap N$. Thus, we can follow a path from x to z by one from z to y and so see $y \in A$ after all. Thus, A is closed. $\qquad \square$

In $\mathbb{R}^n$, $\{x \mid |x - x_0| < \rho\}$ is arcwise connected, since for x, y in that ball, $\gamma(t) = (1 - t)x + ty$ is in the ball. Thus, open sets in $\mathbb{R}^n$ are locally arcwise connected, and we see

Corollary 2.1.17. *Open connected subsets of $\mathbb{R}^n$ are arcwise connected.*

Notes and Historical Remarks. Topology is a vast subject and includes areas like combinatorial topology (going back to Euler) and algebraic topology (whose father was Poincaré). Point set topology, our subject in this chapter, had its roots in the work of Cauchy and Weierstrass, discussed in the Notes to Section 3.5, and of Cantor and Baire, discussed in the Notes to Sections 4.2 and 4.3. There were two motivating aspects: First, the attempts to make sense of surfaces, especially Riemann surfaces, that led to the modern definition of manifold. Second, the work of Fredholm [**324**] on integral equations, that motivated both Hilbert's work that led to the theory of Hilbert spaces, and attempts to discuss convergence on infinite-dimensional spaces that were concerns of Fréchet and Riesz.

After several shorter papers, Maurice Réné Fréchet (1878–1973) published a comprehensive theory of convergence in his 1906 thesis [**315**] that essentially defined axiomatically what we now call metric spaces. Fréchet had a weaker condition than the triangle inequality, but mentioned the triangle inequality as a special case. It was F. Riesz (see below) who emphasized the triangle inequality. The first half of Fréchet's thesis also had an attempt at convergence without a metric. Fréchet defined Cauchy sequences and, without the name, completeness. Most importantly, he was the first to try to discuss convergence on abstract sets of points rather than $\mathbb{R}^n$ or explicit spaces of functions.

Between the work of Fréchet and Hausdorff, F. Riesz [**777, 778**] developed some ideas of point set topology and H. Weyl [**982**] wrote a path-breaking book on Riemann surfaces which emphasized the role of neighborhoods. In 1914, Felix Hausdorff gave birth to the modern theory of point set topology in his fundamental book, *Grundzüge der Mengenlehre* [**402**]. Here appeared the term "metric space" for the first time, as well an axiom scheme in terms of neighborhoods that defined what we now call topological spaces with the Hausdorff property (see Section 2.2). The modern definition in terms of open sets appeared formally in Bourbaki's 1940 book [**120**], but was championed earlier by Alexandroff [**12**]. Bourbaki is a pseudonym for a group of French mathematicians (originally in 1934, Henri Cartan, Claude Chevalley, Jean Coulomb, Jean Delsarte, Jean Dieudonné, Charles Ehresmann, René de Possel, Szolem Mandelbrojt and André Weil), who wrote a series of books with enormous influence. Two important works historically were the books of Kuratowski [**536**], who developed a lively Polish school of topologists, and of Alexandroff and Hopf [**15**]. Two modern books on the subject are Kelley [**484**] and Willard [**1004**].

While we are used to thinking of open and closed sets as fundamental objects, it took sixty years, starting about 1880, for this notion to become the accepted view in the mathematical community. The process is described in Moore [**664**]. Of course, open intervals were common early on. Borel's notion of open covers were covers by open intervals and most of the early literature on compact sets in metric spaces focused on covers by open balls.

Limits were basic from early in the nineteenth century, and about 1880, Weierstrass and Cantor began to focus on sets in $\mathbb{R}^n$ containing all their limit points, that is, closed sets. Open sets took longer, and in some of the early literature, were described as sets containing none of their boundary points. The lack of the open/closed terminology means the first modern definitions of connected (see the Notes below) were expressed in terms of sets not containing limit points of each other and explains Hausdorff's focus on neighborhoods. According to Moore, Bourbaki initially was going to use closure axioms to define topology and it took several iterations of drafts by Andre Weil critiqued by Claude Chevalley before open sets came to the fore. The books of Bourbaki and of Kelley in English finally established the closed/open basis now so common.

Felix Hausdorff (1868–1942) was a German Jewish mathematician from a wealthy Breslau family. The family moved to Leipzig in Hausdorff's youth and he stayed on to get a Ph.D. and privatdozent position at the University of Leipzig. Before age 40, he was as much interested in literature and philosophy, writing books in those areas under the pen name Paul Mongré (indeed, in a 1930s encyclopedia of German Jewish culture, Hausdorff is not listed among notable German Jewish mathematicians, but Mongré is among notable philosophers). He spent much time socializing in Leipzig cafes, so much so that he turned down an offer from Göttingen in 1902 in order to remain with his friends in Leipzig. Epple [**280**] has analyzed the possible influence of the philosopher Hausdorff on his mathematics.

A profound change occurred when Hausdorff accepted an offer to Bonn, where he became friends with Eduard Study (1862–1930), a geometer who got Hausdorff interested in what became point set topology. Hausdorff did his work on Hausdorff dimension in 1919 (see Section 8.2).

Hausdorff felt the rise of the Nazis in terrible ways. At first, as a World War I veteran, he could avoid the laws against Jews by taking an oath of allegiance to Hitler, which he did; but by the late 1930s, he was dismissed. He became concerned about being shipped to the camps, having heard stories of their horrors. On the night of January 25, 1942, having learned they were to be picked up the next day, Hausdorff and his wife took overdoses of barbiturates from which they died.

Baire introduced the notion of semicontinuous functions on $\mathbb{R}$ and Fréchet in general metric spaces.

Uniform convergence of functions is associated with the work of Weierstrass (1815–97; see the Notes to Section 9.4 of Part 2A for a capsule biography). In 1821, Cauchy published a claim that a pointwise limit of continuous functions is continuous, but examples of Abel and Fourier in the theory of Fourier series showed this theorem was false. In 1841, Weierstrass wrote a paper in which he introduced the formal notion of uniform convergence and proved Theorem 2.1.5 in case X and Y are intervals in $\mathbb{R}$. This paper was only published fifty years later in Weierstrass' complete works and the results only became known on the basis of lectures that Weierstrass gave in Berlin starting in 1856.

In the 1870s and 1880s, in trying to understand when a function is Riemann integrable (see the Notes to Sections 4.2 and 4.4), Georg Cantor (1845–1918; see the capsule biography in the Notes to Section 4.2) and Paul David Gustav du Bois-Reymond (1831–89) began to study general sets in $\mathbb{R}$ (Cantor was also pursuing his work on countability and noncountability; see Section 1.6) and first formulated notions like accumulation point.

The intuitive notion of connected is, of course, ancient. The formal definition has a complicated history, in part because the early work not only focused on subsets of $\mathbb{R}^n$ but on compact subsets. In modern parlance, a *continuum* is a nonempty, connected, compact metric space. The reader can check (Problem 8(a)) that if X is a compact metric space and $X = A \cup B$ with A, B closed and disjoint, then for some $\delta > 0$ and all $x \in A$, $y \in B$, we have $\rho(x, y) \geq \delta$. It follows (Problem 8(b)) that a compact metric space is connected if and only if it has the property that for any $x, y \in X$ and any ε, there is $x_1, \ldots, x_n \in X$, so if $x = x_1$, $y = x_{n+1}$, then $\rho(x_j, x_{j+1}) < \varepsilon$ for $j = 0, \ldots, n$. For bounded closed subsets of $\mathbb{R}$ or $\mathbb{R}^n$, this definition of "connected" or "continuous" was used by Cantor [**153**], Jordan [**456**], and Schoenflies [**819**]. This definition doesn't work for noncompact sets. For example, $\mathbb{R}^2 \setminus \{(x,0) \mid x \in \mathbb{R}\}$ has this property but is not connected.

The modern definition in the equivalent form—a space, X, connected if and only if $X = A \cup B$ with $A \cap B = \emptyset$ implies some point in A is a limit point of B or vice-versa—was made independently in 1905 by N. J. Lennes (1874–1951) [**567, 568**], who spent most of his career at the University of Montana, and by F. Riesz (see the capsule biography in the Notes to Section 4.5) [**777**]. Zitarelli [**1021**] has a discussion of the genesis of Lennes' work which was done while Lennes was a high school teacher! Hausdorff, in his 1914 book [**402**], had the same definition, apparently unaware of the earlier works, and he often gets credit for the definition! The first really deep analysis of the notion of connectedness is due to Knaster and Kuratowski [**500**], which we return to in Section 5.4 (see Example 5.4.23). For a history of the notion of connectedness, see Wilder [**1003**].

Problems

1. (a) Prove that the closure operator, $A \to \bar{A}$, obeys
   (i) $\bar{\emptyset} = \emptyset$ (Here $\emptyset$ is the empty set.)
   (ii) $A \subset \bar{A}$
   (iii) $\overline{(\bar{A})} = \bar{A}$
   (iv) $\overline{A \cup B} = \bar{A} \cup \bar{B}$

   (b) Suppose we have an operator on the subsets of a set, X, obeying (i)–(iv) above. Prove that there is a unique topology, $\mathcal{T}$, so that it is the closure operator for $\mathcal{T}$.

   Remark. (i)–(iv) are called the *Kuratowski closure axioms*.

2. Consider the integers, $\mathbb{Z}$. You'll prove that there are infinitely many primes using a clever choice of topology (so you'll use topology to prove a fact in algebra in an analysis textbook!). For any integers m, k with $m \neq 0$, let $A_{m,k} = \{mn + k \mid n \in \mathbb{Z}\}$.

   (a) Prove any intersection of two $A_{m,k}$ is either empty or another $A_{m',k'}$ so that $\{A_{m,k}\}$ is the base for a topology called the Furstenberg topology.

   (b) Prove that each $A_{m.k}$ is both open and closed in the Furstenberg topology.

   (c) Prove that every nonempty open set is infinite.

   (d) Let P be a set of primes (1 is not a prime!). Let $B = \mathbb{Z} \setminus \cup_{p \in P} A_{p,0}$. What is B?

   (e) Prove that if P is finite, then B is open.

   (f) Prove that P is infinite.

Remark. If you've seen Euclid's proof of the infinitude of primes, this proof of Furstenberg [**336**] is essentially a sneaky rewriting of it.

3. In a metric space, X, show that if a function, f, from X to $\mathbb{R} \cup \{\infty\}$ obeys (2.1.10), then f is lsc. (*Hint*: Show that $\{x \mid f(x) \leq \gamma\}$ is closed for any $\gamma \in \mathbb{R}$.)

4. (a) If $x \in X \setminus A$, where A is an arbitrary subset of a topological space, X, prove that if x is not an accumulation point of A, then $x \notin \bar{A}$.

(b) Prove Proposition 2.1.11.

5. Let X be a topological space. Prove that $x \sim y \Leftrightarrow x, y$ are the endpoints of a curve, γ, is an equivalence relation on X.

6. Let X_1, X_2 be the two sets on the right side of (2.1.15).

(a) Prove that $\overline{X}_1 = X_1 \cup X_2$.

(b) Prove that no curve joins points in X_1 and X_2. (*Hint*: If γ is a curve in $\mathbb{R}^2$, prove there cannot be $0 < t_1 < t_2 < \cdots < 1$ so that $|\gamma(t_{2j}) - \gamma(t_{2j+1})| \geq 1$.)

7. In $\mathbb{R}^2$, let $X = \{(x, y) \mid$ either x or y or both are irrational$\}$. Is X connected? You must prove your conclusion.

8. (*Note*: This problem supposes the reader knows about compact sets in metric spaces as discussed in Section 2.3.)

(a) If X is a compact metric, A, B are closed in X and disjoint, prove that $\rho(A, B) \equiv \inf_{x \in A, y \in B} \rho(x, y) > 0$.

(b) Using (a), prove that a compact metric space is connected if and only if for all $x, y \in X$ and $\varepsilon > 0$, there exist $x_1, \ldots, x_n \in X$ with $\rho(x_j, x_{j+1}) < \varepsilon$ for $y = 0, \ldots, n$ if $x_0 = x$, $x_{j+1} = y$.

(c) Let $X = \mathbb{D} \cup (\mathbb{C} \setminus \overline{\mathbb{D}})$. Prove that X has the property in (b) but is not connected. (This is an example of Riesz [**777**].)

2.2. Countability and Separation Properties

In this section, we'll consider two classes of possible properties of topological spaces: one involves countability of various objects (first and second countable, separable, Lindelöf) and the other, separation of disjoint closed sets by open sets (primarily, Hausdorff and normal spaces). The two notions are linked via:

Theorem 2.2.1 (Urysohn Metrizability Theorem). *If X is a topological space which is second countable and normal, then there is a metric on X which generates the topology of X.*

Remark. These conditions are sufficient but not necessary for X to be a metric space. The Notes discuss a necessary and sufficient set of conditions that is not so easy to check. We'll also discuss an improved version (see Problem 7).

This is one of the main theorems of this section, the other being Urysohn's lemma (Theorem 2.2.4 below).

Definition. An *open cover* of a topological space, X, with topology, $\mathcal{T}$, is a family $\mathcal{F} \subset \mathcal{T}$ so that $\bigcup_{A \in \mathcal{F}} A = X$. A *subcover* is a subset of $\mathcal{F}$, which is also a cover.

Definition. Let X be a topological space. Then

(a) X is called *first countable* if and only if every $x \in X$ has a countable neighborhood base.

(b) X is called *second countable* if and only if there is a countable base.

(c) X is called *Lindelöf* if and only if every open cover has a countable subcover.

(d) X is called *separable* if and only if X has a countable dense set.

Obviously, X second countable implies that X is first countable.

Proposition 2.2.2. (a) *Every metric space is first countable.*

(b) *Every second countable space is Lindelöf.*

(c) *Every second countable space is separable.*

(d) *In a metric space, Lindelöf $\Rightarrow$ separable $\Rightarrow$ second countable.*

(e) *Every subset of a separable metric space is a separable metric space in the relative topology.*

Remarks. 1. Thus, in a metric space, Lindelöf, separable, and second countable are equivalent.

2. Second countability is hereditary in that if $A \subset X$, a second countable topological space, then A is second countable in the relative topology, since if $\mathcal{B}$ is a base of $\mathcal{T}$, $\{B \cap A \mid B \in \mathcal{B}\}$ is a base for the relative topology, $\mathcal{T}_A$. Thus, by part (b), every second countable space has the property that all subsets are Lindelöf in the relative topology—such spaces are called *strongly Lindelöf, completely Lindelöf,* or *hereditary Lindelöf.*

Proof. (a) $\{B_{1/n}(x_0)\}_{n=1}^{\infty}$ is a countable neighborhood base for x_0.

(b) Let $\mathcal{F}$ be a cover of X, a second countable space, and let $\mathcal{B}$ be a countable base for X. Let

$$\mathcal{B}_{\mathcal{F}} = \{B \in \mathcal{B} \mid B \subset A \text{ for some } A \in \mathcal{F}\}$$

Since B is a base, every $A \in \mathcal{F}$ is a union of sets in $\mathcal{B}_{\mathcal{F}}$, so $\mathcal{B}_{\mathcal{F}}$ is a countable cover of X.

For each $B_j \in \mathcal{B}_{\mathcal{F}}$, pick some $A_j \in \mathcal{F}$ so that $B_j \subset A_j$. Since $\cup_{j=1}^{\infty} B_j = X$, we see that $\cup_{j=1}^{\infty} A_j = X$, that is, $\{A_j\}_{j=1}^{\infty}$ is a countable subcover.

(c) Suppose $\mathcal{B} = \{B_j\}_{j=1}^{\infty}$ is a countable base for X. Pick some $x_j \in B_j$ for each j. We claim $\{x_j\}_{j=1}^{\infty}$ is dense. For let $A = \overline{\{x_j\}_{j=1}^{\infty}}$. Let $C = X \setminus A$, which is open. If C is not empty, it is a nontrivial union of sets in $\mathcal{B}$, so it contains some x_j, and so a point of A. Thus, $C = \emptyset$, that is, $A = X$.

(d) If X is a Lindelöf metric space, for each n, $\{B_{1/n}(x)\}_{x \in X}$ is an open cover, so there exist $\{x_\ell^{(n)}\}_{\ell=1}^{\infty}$ so $\cup_{\ell=1}^{\infty} B_{1/n}(x_\ell^{(n)}) = X$. We claim $C = \{x_\ell^{(n)}\}_{n,\ell=1}^{\infty}$ is a dense set, proving separability. For given any x and any neighborhood N of x, there is some $B_{1/n}(x) \subset N$. Pick $x_\ell^{(j)}$ so $x \in B_{1/n}(x_\ell^{(j)})$. Then $x_\ell^{(j)} \in B_{1/n}(x) \subset N$, that is, N contains a point of C, so C is dense.

If X is a separable metric space and $\{x_\ell\}_{\ell=1}^{\infty}$ is a countable dense set, then it is easy to see that if q_m is a counting of all positive rationals, then (Problem 1) that $\{B_{q_m}(x_\ell)\}_{m,\ell=1}^{\infty}$ is a countable base.

(e) Since separability is equivalent to being second countable for metric spaces, we need only note that if $\{U_n\}_{n=1}^{\infty}$ is a countable base for open sets in X, $\{U_n \cap Y\}_{n=1}^{\infty}$ is a countable base for the open sets in the relative topology on Y. □

Countability properties often imply sequences suffice, for example, if X is first countable, $x \in \bar{A}$ if and only if there is a sequence $\{x_n\}_{n=1}^{\infty} \subset A$, so $x_n \to x$ (see Problem 2). Moreover (see Problem 3), if X is first countable and x_∞ is a limit point of a sequence $\{x_n\}_{n=1}^{\infty}$, then there is a subsequence $y_j = x_{n(j)}$ converging to x_∞. As we'll see in Section 2.6, this is not necessarily true in a general topological space (see Example 2.6.2).

We turn next to separation criteria:

Definition. Let X be a topological space. We say X is

(i) T_1 if for any distinct $x, y \in X$, there exists an open set $A \subset X$ so that $x \in A$, $y \notin A$.

(ii) T_2 or *Hausdorff* if for any distinct $x, y \in X$, there exist open sets A and B with $A \cap B = \emptyset$ and $x \in A$, $y \in B$.

(iii) T_3 if X is T_1 and for all $x \in X$ and closed $C \subset X$ with $x \notin C$, there exist open sets A and B with $A \cap B = \emptyset$ and $x \in A$, $C \subset B$.

(iv) T_4 or *normal* if X is T_1 and for all closed sets $C, D \subset X$ with $C \cap D = \emptyset$, there exist open sets A and B with $A \cap B = \emptyset$ and $C \subset A$, $D \subset B$ (see Figure 2.2.1).

Remarks. 1. These properties are called "separation axioms" or "Tychonoff separation axioms" after a mathematician who championed them.

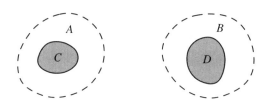

Figure 2.2.1. Normal space separation.

The "T" is not for Tychonoff, but for "Trennungsaxiom," the German for separation axiom.

2. There are also T_0, T_5, T_6, and even $T_{2\frac{1}{2}}$ and $T_{3\frac{1}{2}}$; see the Notes. $T_0 \supset$ $T_1 \supset T_2 \supset T_3 \supset T_4 \supset T_5 \supset T_6$ in that T_n implies T_{n-1}.

3. We'll care mainly about Hausdorff and normal. T_3 is called a "regular" space.

4. In some of the literature, "normal" and "regular" aren't synonyms for T_4 and T_3; the requirement that points are closed is dropped. We'll always use "normal" to mean T_1 plus the separation property on disjoint closed sets.

Proposition 2.2.3. *Let X be a topological space. Then*
(a) *X is T_1 if and only if $\{x\}$ is closed for every $x \in X$.*
(b) *If X is T_2, then limits of sequences are unique, that is, if $x_n \to y$ and $x_n \to z$, then $y = z$.*
(c) *Every metric space is normal.*

Remark. Once we have nets and a net version of (b), we will see that Hausdorff is equivalent to unique limits of nets; see Theorem 2.6.3.

Proof. (a) If every $\{x\}$ is closed, given any $y \neq x$, $X \setminus \{x\}$ is open and contains y but not x, so X is T_1. Conversely, if X is T_1, for x fixed and any y, we can find A open with $y \in A_y$ and $x \notin A_y$. Thus, $\cup_{y \neq x} A_y = X \setminus \{x\}$ is open, and so $\{x\}$ is closed.

(b) Suppose X is Hausdorff and $x_n \to y$, $x_n \to z$. If $y \neq z$, find A, B open with $z \in A$, $y \in B$, and $A \cap B = \emptyset$. Then, find N_1, N_2 so $n > N_1 \Rightarrow x_n \in A$ and $n > N_2 \Rightarrow x_n \in B$. If $n = \max(N_1, N_2) + 1$, $x_n \in A \cap B$, which is impossible.

(c) Given $C \subset X$, $C \neq \emptyset$, define the *distance from x to C* by

$$\rho(x, C) = \min_{y \in C} \rho(x, y) \tag{2.2.1}$$

We first claim that if C is closed, then

$$\rho(x, C) = 0 \Leftrightarrow x \in C \tag{2.2.2}$$

For if $x \in C$, clearly $\rho(x, C) = 0$ (take $y = x$). If $\rho(x, C) = 0$, there exists $x_n \in C$ with $\rho(x, x_n) \leq 1/n$, so $x_n \to x$, implying $x \in \overline{C} = C$.

We next claim $|\rho(x, C) - \rho(z, C)| \leq \rho(x, z)$, by the triangle inequality, so $x \to \rho(x, C)$ is continuous.

Next, given C, D closed and disjoint, define

$$f(x) = \frac{\rho(x, C) - \rho(x, D)}{\rho(x, C) + \rho(x, D)} \tag{2.2.3}$$

Since $C \cap D = \emptyset$, (2.2.2) shows $\rho(x, C) + \rho(x, D) > 0$ for all x, and thus, f is continuous. Moreover,

$$f(x) = 1 \text{ if } x \in D, \qquad f(x) = -1 \text{ if } x \in C \tag{2.2.4}$$

By the continuity, $A = f^{-1}((-\infty, 0))$ and $B = f^{-1}((0, \infty))$ are open and clearly disjoint with $C \subset A$ and $D \subset B$. $\qquad \square$

While the following is called a "lemma," it is a very useful and powerful theorem because it implies there are lots of bounded continuous functions from any normal space to $\mathbb{R}$.

Theorem 2.2.4 (Urysohn's Lemma). *Let X be a normal topological space. Let $C, D \subset X$ be closed with $C \cap D = \emptyset$. Then there exists a continuous function $f \colon X \to [0, 1]$ so that*

$$C \subset f^{-1}(\{0\}), \qquad D \subset f^{-1}(\{1\}) \tag{2.2.5}$$

Remark. In the metric space case, the proof of (c) of Proposition 2.2.3 shows we can take

$$f(x) = \frac{\rho(x, C)}{\rho(x, C) + \rho(x, D)} \tag{2.2.6}$$

Proof. A *dyadic rational* is a number in $\mathbb{R}$ of the form $\alpha = p/2^n$ for some $p \in \mathbb{Z}$, $n \in \{0, 1, 2 \dots\}$. We use $\mathcal{D}$ for the set of dyadic rationals. If $\alpha \neq 0$, there is a unique such representation with p odd. We call the corresponding n the *height*, $n(\alpha)$, of α.

We begin by rephasing normality: given $B_0 \subset V_0$ with B_0 closed and V_0 open, we claim that there are V_1 and B_1 with B_1 closed and V_1 open so that $B_0 \subset V_1 \subset B_1 \subset V_0$. For let $E_0 = X \setminus V_0$. B_0 and E_0 are closed and disjoint, so there are V_1 and V_2 open and disjoint, so $B_0 \subset V_1$ and $E_0 \subset V_2$. Let $B_1 = X \setminus V_2$ so $V_1 \subset B_1 \subset V_0$, as required.

For each dyadic $\alpha \in (0, 1)$, we'll construct A_α closed and U_α open so that if $\alpha < \beta$, then

$$C \subset U_\alpha \subset A_\alpha \subset U_\beta \subset A_\beta \subset X \setminus D \tag{2.2.7}$$

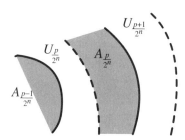

Figure 2.2.2. Urysohn's lemma construction.

We do this inductively in $n(\alpha)$, starting with $n(\alpha) = 1$. Then, only $\alpha = \frac{1}{2}$ has $n(\alpha) = 1$ for $\alpha \in (0,1)$. By the above rephasing, we can find $U_{1/2}$ open and $A_{1/2}$ closed, so

$$C \subset U_{1/2} \subset A_{1/2} \subset X \setminus D \tag{2.2.8}$$

Next, go to $n = 2$ where there are two α's in $(0,1)$ with $n(\alpha) = 2$, namely, $\frac{1}{4}$ and $\frac{3}{4}$. By the rephasing, we can find $U_{1/4}, A_{1/4}$ with

$$C \subset U_{1/4} \subset A_{1/4} \subset U_{1/2} \tag{2.2.9}$$

and $U_{3/4}, A_{3/4}$ with

$$A_{1/2} \subset U_{3/4} \subset A_{3/4} \subset X \setminus D \tag{2.2.10}$$

At order n, there are 2^{n-1} α's in $(0,1)$ with $n(\alpha) = n$, and we can inductively get (2.2.7) by picking $U_{p/2^n}$ and $A_{p/2^n}$, so

$$A_{(p-1)/2^n} \subset U_{p/2^n} \subset A_{p/2^n} \subset U_{(p+1)/2^n} \tag{2.2.11}$$

since $(p-1)/2^n$ and $(p+1)/2^n$ have height strictly less than n and have been constructed inductively (see Figure 2.2.2).

Now define $U_1 = X \setminus D$ and $f \colon X \to [0,1]$ by

$$f(x) = \begin{cases} \inf\{\beta \in \mathcal{D} \cap (0,1] \mid x \in U_\beta\}, & x \in U_1 \\ 1, & x \in D \end{cases} \tag{2.2.12}$$

We claim that f is continuous with $f \upharpoonright D = 1$, $f \upharpoonright C = 0$. Since $f \upharpoonright D = 1$ by construction and $C \subset U_\beta$ for all $\beta \in (0,1]$, $f \upharpoonright C = 0$. Thus, we need only prove continuity.

We will show that for any $\gamma \in (0,1]$,

$$f^{-1}((-\infty,\gamma)) = \bigcup_{\substack{\beta < \gamma \\ \beta \in \mathcal{D} \cap (0,1)}} U_\beta \tag{2.2.13}$$

and for any $\gamma \in [0,1)$,

$$f^{-1}((-\infty,\gamma]) = \bigcap_{\substack{\beta > \gamma \\ \beta \in \mathcal{D} \cap (0,1)}} A_\beta \tag{2.2.14}$$

Assuming these two facts, we see that if $\gamma < \beta$ and both are in $(0,1)$, then

$$f^{-1}((\gamma,\beta)) = f^{-1}((-\infty,\beta)) \cap f^{-1}((\gamma,\infty))$$
$$= f^{-1}((-\infty,\beta)) \cap [X \setminus f^{-1}((-\infty,\gamma])]$$

is open. Since $\{(\gamma,\beta)\}$ are a base for $(0,1)$, f is continuous. Thus, $(2.2.13)/(2.2.14)$ imply the result.

Note next that for any $\gamma \in \mathbb{R}$,

$$f(x) < \gamma \Leftrightarrow \exists \beta \in \mathcal{D}, \quad f(x) < \beta < \gamma$$
$$\Leftrightarrow \exists \beta \in \mathcal{D}, \quad \beta < \gamma \text{ so that } x \in U_\beta$$
$$\Leftrightarrow x \in \bigcup_{\beta < \gamma} U_\beta$$

proving $(2.2.13)$.

Moreover, by definition,

$$f(x) \leq \gamma \Leftrightarrow x \in \bigcap_{\beta > \gamma} U_\beta \tag{2.2.15}$$

Since $U_\beta \subset A_\beta$, we have that

$$\bigcap_{\beta > \gamma} A_\beta \supseteq \bigcap_{\beta > \gamma} U_\beta \tag{2.2.16}$$

For any $\beta > \gamma$, there is $\beta > \beta' > \gamma$ and then $A_{\beta'} \subset U_\beta$, so

$$\bigcap_{\beta > \gamma} A_\beta \subseteq \bigcap_{\beta' > \gamma} U_{\beta'} \tag{2.2.17}$$

Thus, by $(2.2.15)$, we have $(2.2.14)$. $\qquad\square$

In Problem 4, the reader will prove the following extension of Urysohn's lemma (using the lemma!):

Theorem 2.2.5 (Tietze Extension Theorem). *Let $E \subset X$, a normal space, be closed. Let $f \colon E \to \mathbb{R}$ be a bounded continuous function. Then there is a bounded continuous function $g \colon X \to \mathbb{R}$ so that $g \upharpoonright E = f$.*

Remark. If C, D are closed and disjoint, $E = C \cup D$ and $f \upharpoonright C \equiv 0$, $f \upharpoonright D \equiv 1$, the Tietze extension theorem yields Urysohn's lemma (if necessary, one replaces g by $\max(\min(g,1),0)$).

We emphasize that in Urysohn's lemma, we have only proven that $C \subset g^{-1}(\{0\})$, not $C = g^{-1}(\{0\})$. One can also ask when there is an g with equality. We answer this not only because it is interesting but because it is the key to the Urysohn metrizability theorem.

Definition. A G_δ (or *G-delta*) is a countable intersection of open sets. An F_σ (or *F-sigma*) is a countable union of closed sets.

Proposition 2.2.6. *In a metric space, X, every closed set is a G_δ.*

Proof. Let $A \subset X$ be closed and let ρ be the metric. Then $U_n = \{x \mid \rho(x, A) < \frac{1}{n}\} = \cup_{y \in A} B_{1/n}(y)$ is open. Clearly, $A \subset \cap_n U_n$. Conversely, if $x \in \cap_n U_n$, there is $y_n \in A$ with $\rho(y_n, x) < \frac{1}{n}$. Thus, $y_n \to x$, so $x \in A$ since A is closed. $\square$

Proposition 2.2.7. *Let X be a second countable, normal topological space. Then every closed set is a G_δ.*

Proof. Let A be closed. Then $X \setminus A$ is second countable, and so Lindelöf in the relative topology.

For each $x \in X \setminus A$, by normality, find U_x, V_x open and disjoint so that $A \subset U_x$, $x \in V_x$. Clearly, $X \setminus A = \cup_{x \in X \setminus A} V_x$ so, since $X \setminus A$ is Lindelöf, we can find $\{x_n\}_{n=1}^\infty$ so $X \setminus A = \cup_{j=1}^\infty V_{x_j}$. Since $U_{x_j} \cap V_{x_j} = \emptyset$, we see $\cap_{j=1}^\infty U_{x_j} \cap (\cup_{j=1}^\infty V_{x_j}) = \emptyset$, that is, $\cap_{j=1}^\infty U_{x_j} \subset A$. Since $A \subset U_{x_j}$, we conclude $A = \cap_{j=1}^\infty U_{x_j}$, that is, A is a G_δ. $\square$

We'll eventually see that there exist natural spaces, X, (e.g., uncountable products of $[0,1]$) in which $\{x\}$ is closed but not a G_δ; see Example 2.7.2.

Proposition 2.2.8. *Let X be a topological space and let $f \colon X \to [0,1]$ be continuous. Then $f^{-1}(\{0\})$ is a closed G_δ.*

Proof. Since $\mathbb{R}$ is a metric space, $\{0\}$ is a closed G_δ. Since f^{-1} preserves intersections, open and closed sets, $f^{-1}(\{0\})$ is a closed G_δ. $\square$

In Problem 5, the reader will prove:

Theorem 2.2.9. *Let X be a normal space and C, D closed G_δ's which are disjoint. Then there exists a continuous $f \colon X \to [0,1]$ so that $f^{-1}(\{0\}) = C$, $f^{-1}(\{1\}) = D$.*

Here we'll prove the related

Theorem 2.2.10. *Let X be a normal space and C a closed G_δ in X. Then there exists a bounded continuous function, f, with values in $[0, \infty)$ so that $f^{-1}[\{0\}] = C$.*

Proof. Since C is a closed G_δ, $X \setminus C$ is an open F_σ, that is, $X \setminus C = \cup_{n=1}^\infty A_n$ with A_n closed. By Urysohn's lemma, find continuous functions, $f_n \colon X \to [0,1]$, so that $f_n \restriction C = 0$ and $f_n \restriction A_n = 1$. Let $f = \sum_{n=1}^\infty \frac{1}{2^n} f_n$. The finite sums converge uniformly in X, so by Theorem 2.1.5, f is continuous.

Clearly, $f \restriction C = 0$ and $f \restriction A_n \geq \frac{1}{2^n}$, so $f \neq 0$ on $\cup_{n=1}^{\infty} A_n = X \setminus C$. Thus, $f^{-1}[\{0\}] = C$. $\qquad\square$

We will prove the Urysohn metrizability theorem by placing X inside a standard metric space called the Hilbert cube. When we discuss product topologies in Section 2.7, we'll see this is just the countable product of $[0, 1]$ in the product topology.

Example 2.2.11 (Hilbert Cube). Let H be the space of all sequences $\{x_n\}_{n=1}^{\infty}$ in $[0, 1]$, that is, the countable Cartesian product $\times_{n=1}^{\infty}[0, 1]$. Place a metric on H by

$$\rho(x, y) = \max_n [2^{-n}|x_n - y_n|] \qquad (2.2.18)$$

It is easy to see (Problem 6(a)) that if $x^{(\ell)}$ is a sequence of points in H, then $\rho(x^{(\ell)}, x^{(\infty)}) \to 0$ if and only if for each fixed n, $|x_n^{(\ell)} - x_n^{(\infty)}| \to 0$, and that a function $f \colon Y \to H$, given by $(f(y))_n = f_n(y)$ for $\{f_n\}_{n=1}^{\infty}$, a sequence of functions from Y to $[0, 1]$, is continuous if and only if each $f_n \colon Y \to [0, 1]$ is continuous (Problem 6(c)).

Balls, $B_r(x)$, are product sets $\times_n B_{2^n r}(x_n)$ and, in particular, once $2^n r > 1$, $B_{2^n r}(x_n) = [0, 1]$, so balls are products of a particular open set in $\times_{n=1}^{N}[0, 1]$ product with $\times_{n=N+1}^{\infty}[0, 1]$ (all of $[0, 1]$). It is not hard to see that if $\mathcal{O}$ is open in $[0, 1]^N$ in the relative topology from $\mathbb{R}^N$, then $\mathcal{O} \times \times_{n=N+1}^{\infty}[0, 1]$ is open and that these are a base of open sets (Problem 6(b)). In the next section, we'll show that the Hilbert cube is compact and, in Section 2.5, that the space of bounded real-valued functions on H is separable in $\|\cdot\|_\infty$. $\qquad\square$

Proof of Theorem 2.2.1. Let $\{U_n\}_{n=1}^{\infty}$ be a countable base for the topology on X, and $C_n = X \setminus U_n$. By Proposition 2.2.7, each C_n is a closed G_δ. Thus, by Theorem 2.2.10, there exist continuous functions $f_n \colon X \to [0, 1]$ so $f_n^{-1}[\{0\}] = C_n$ (a priori, f_n is only bounded, but replace f_n by $f_n / \max_x |f_n(x)|$).

Let $F \colon X \to H$, the Hilbert cube, by

$$F(x)_n = f_n(x) \qquad (2.2.19)$$

We claim F is continuous, one-one, and if A is open in X, then $F[A]$ is relatively open in $F[X]$. That means $\widetilde{F} \colon X \to \mathrm{Ran}(F)$ is a homeomorphism when $\mathrm{Ran}(F)$ is given the relative topology which is a metric topology, since it is obtained by restricting the metric on H to $\mathrm{Ran}(F)$. Thus, X has a metric topology. We turn to proving that F is continuous, one-one, and relatively open.

As noted, a map to H given by (2.2.19) is continuous if and only if each f_n is, so by construction, F is continuous.

Given distinct points $x, y \in X$, pick V_1, V_2 open and disjoint so that $x \in V_1$, $y \in V_2$. By the fact that $\{U_n\}_{n=1}^{\infty}$ is a base, there exists U_ℓ so $x \in U_\ell \subset V_1$. Thus, $y \notin U_\ell$, that is, $y \in C_\ell$, so $f_\ell(y) = 0$, $f_\ell(x) \neq 0$. Thus, $F(x) \neq F(y)$, that is, F is one-one.

Let $G = F^{-1} \colon \mathrm{Ran}(F) \to X$. Since F is a bijection of X and $\mathrm{Ran}(F)$, G is also a bijection and $\widetilde{F} \equiv G^{-1}$ is F interpreted as a map to $\mathrm{Ran}(F)$. To prove G is open in the relative topology, we need G continuous, that is, $G^{-1}(U)$ is open for all U in a base, that is, each $F[U_n]$ is relatively open in $F[X]$.

By construction,

$$x \in U_n \Leftrightarrow f_n(x) \in (0,1]$$
$$\Leftrightarrow F(x) \in \{u \mid u_n \in (0,1]\}$$
$$\Leftrightarrow F(x) \in \mathrm{Ran}(F) \cap \{u \mid u_n \in (0,1]\}$$

By the analysis of the topology of H, $\{u \mid u_n \in (0,1]\}$ is open, so $F[U_n]$ is relatively open in $\mathrm{Ran}(F)$. $\qquad\square$

Notes and Historical Remarks. Hausdorff [**402**] already defined first and second countability. Separability is due to Fréchet [**315**]. Ernest Leonard Lindelöf (1870–1946) was the founder of the Finnish school of complex analysis (R. Nevanlinna and L. Ahlfors, whose work is discussed in Chapter 17 of Part 2B, were his students). The term Lindelöf space comes from his 1904 paper [**593**]. The formal abstract definition and the start of the study of such spaces was by Kuratowki–Sierpinski [**537**]. Lindelöf dealt with subsets of the real line. That a general separable metric space has the Lindelöf property is a 1921 result of Fréchet [**319**].

The Hausdorff separation axiom were in the original axiom scheme of Hausdorff's 1914 book [**402**] that launched point set topology. Normal spaces were first introduced by Tietze [**919**].

As noted, Andrey Nikolayevich Tychonoff (1906–93) was an early proponent of separation axioms, emphasizing what are now called regular (i.e., T_3) spaces [**940**]. Another important paper in separation axioms is Alexandroff [**12**]. The terminology T_0, T_1, T_2, T_3, T_4 is from the book of Alexandroff and Hopf, who based "T" on "Trennungsaxiom." To present the modern listing, we say sets $A, B \subset X$, a topological set, are *separated* if and only there are open sets U, V disjoint so that $A \subset U$, $B \subset V$. We say they are *separated by a function* if there is a bounded continuous $f \colon X \to \mathbb{R}$ so $f \upharpoonright A \equiv 0$, $f \upharpoonright B \equiv 1$. We say they are *precisely separated by a function* if there is an f with $f^{-1}(\{0\}) = A$, $f^{-1}(\{1\}) = B$. Clearly, precisely separated by a function $\Rightarrow$ separated by a function $\Rightarrow$ separated. Here is a modern listing:

- T_0 (also called *Kolmogorov space))* space if $\forall x, y \in X$, with $x \neq y$, there exists an open set, A, containing exactly one of x or y.
- T_1 (also called *Fréchet property*) if $\{x\}$ is closed for each $x \in X$.
- T_2 (also called *Hausdorff*) if $\forall x, y \in X$, $x \neq y$, $\{x\}$ and $\{y\}$ are separated.
- $T_{2\frac{1}{2}}$ (also called *Urysohn*) if $\forall x, y \in X$, $x \neq y$, there exist closed disjoint sets A, B with $x \in A^{\text{int}}$, $y \in B^{\text{int}}$.
- T_3 (also called *regular*) if points are closed (i.e., X is T_1) and $x \in X$, $A \subset X$ closed, $x \notin A$ implies $\{x\}$ and A can be separated.
- $T_{3\frac{1}{2}}$ (also called *completely regular* or *Tychonoff*) if points are closed (i.e., X is T_1) and $x \in X$, $A \subset X$ closed, $x \notin A$ implies $\{x\}$ and A can be separated by a function.
- T_4 (also called *normal*) if points are closed (i.e., X is T_1) and any disjoint closed A, B can be separated (equivalently, can be separated by a function).
- T_5 (also called *completely normal*) if every subset is normal.
- T_6 (also called *perfectly normal*) if any two disjoint subsets can be precisely separated by a function; equivalently, if it is normal and every closed set is a G_δ.

Urysohn's lemma and his metrizability theorem appeared in 1925 [**943, 944**], published posthumously. Pavel Urysohn (1898–1924) was a brilliant Russian mathematician. In the summer of 1924, he and his friend Paul Alexandroff (1896–1982) went on vacation in France (after visiting Hilbert, Hausdorff, and Brouwer) and Urysohn drowned while swimming in the Atlantic off the coast of Brittany. (In 1923, Urysohn and Alexandroff formulated the modern definition of compact spaces.)

Urysohn's metrizability theorem gives sufficient but not necessary conditions for metrizability. Around 1950–51, several mathematicians independently found necessary and sufficient conditions (Bing [**91**], Nagata [**676**], Smirnov [**862**]). A collection of sets, $\mathcal{A}$, on a topological space, X, is called *locally finite* if every $x \in X$ has a neighborhood, N, so that $\{A \in \mathcal{A} \mid N \cap A \neq \emptyset\}$ is finite. A collection, $\mathcal{B}$, is called σ-*locally finite* if it is a countable union of locally finite families. One version of the Nagata–Smirnov metrizability theorem is that X is metrizable if and only if it is normal and has a σ-locally finite base of open sets. For extensive discussion of metrizability theorems, see the books of Munkres [**670**] and Willard [**1004**].

Heinrich Tietze (1880–1964) was an Austrian mathematician who proved his extension theorem for metric spaces in 1915 [**918**]. He is also known for work on group presentation methods of computing the fundamental group. Urysohn [**943**] extended Tietze's result to normal spaces using his lemma (proven much the way we present) and an argument close to the one sketched in Problem 4. For a proof along the lines Urysohn used to prove his lemma, see Mandelkern [**627**]. The traditional Hilbert cube is $\widetilde{H} \equiv \{\{a_n\}_{n=1}^\infty \mid 0 \le a_n \le \frac{1}{n}\}$, viewed as a subset of ℓ^2 (i.e., with the topology given by the metric $\rho(a,b) = (\sum_{n=1}^\infty (a_n - b_n)^2)^{1/2}$ which we'll prove is a metric in the next chapter). It is not hard to see, as with our H, the topology on this space is given by coordinate convergence, so $\varphi\colon a \to na$ (i.e., $\varphi(a)_n = na_n$) is a homeomorphism of $\widetilde{H}$ and H. While $\widetilde{H}$ is most often the model of the Hilbert cube, we are not alone in our choice of model.

Problems

1. Let S be a dense subset of a metric space, X. Let U be an open subset and $x \in U$. Find a rational $q > 0$ so $B_q(x) \subset U$ and then $y \in S$ so $y \in B_q(x)$. Conclude $x \in B_q(y)$ and then that $\{B_q(y) \mid q \in \mathbb{Q} \cap (0, \infty), y \in S\}$ is a base for X.

2. Let X be first countable. Let $x \in \bar{A}$. Prove there is a sequence x_n in A so that $x_n \to x$. (*Hint*: Let $\{N_n\}_{n=1}^\infty$ be a countable neighborhood base for x. Show, without loss of generality, that one can suppose $N_1 \supset N_2 \supset \dots$. Pick $x_n \in N_n \cap A$. Prove that $x_n \to x$.)

3. Let X be first countable. Let $x_\infty \in X$ be a limit point of a sequence $\{x_n\}_{n=1}^\infty$. Prove there is a subsequence $\{y_n\}_{n=1}^\infty$ of $\{x_n\}_{n=1}^\infty$ so that $y_n \to x_\infty$. (*Hint*: Let $\{N_n\}_{n=1}^\infty$ be a countable neighborhood base for x_∞ which, as in the hint for Problem 2, one can pick so $N_1 \supset N_2 \dots$. Pick $x_{n(j)}$ inductively so $x_{n(j)} \in N_j$ and $n(j+1) > n(j)$ and let $y_j = x_{n(j)}$.)

4. This problem will prove the Tietze extension theorem, Theorem 2.2.5. Let $E \subset X$, with X normal and E closed.

(a) Let $f\colon E \to \mathbb{R}$ be continuous with $|f(x)| \le 1$ for all $x \in E$. Prove there exists a continuous function $g_0\colon X \to \mathbb{R}$ with $\|g_0\|_\infty \le \frac{1}{3}$ and

$$|f(x) - g_0(x)| \le \tfrac{2}{3} \quad \text{for } x \in E \tag{2.2.20}$$

(*Hint*: Let $B = f^{-1}([-1, -\frac{1}{3}])$ and $C = f^{-1}([\frac{1}{3}, 1])$. Find $g_0\colon X \to [-\frac{1}{3}, \frac{1}{3}]$ so $g_0 \restriction B = -\frac{1}{3}$ and $g_0 \restriction C = \frac{1}{3}$. Verify that (2.2.20) holds.)

(b) Given $f\colon E \to \mathbb{R}$ with $|f(x)| \le 1$ for all $x \in E$, prove inductively that there exist continuous functions $g_n\colon X \to \mathbb{R}$, $n = 0, 1, 2, \dots$, so that $\|g_n\|_\infty \le \frac{1}{3}(\frac{2}{3})^n$ and

$$\left| f(x) - \sum_{n=0}^N g_n(x) \right| \le \left(\frac{2}{3} \right)^n \quad \text{for } x \in E$$

(c) Prove $g = \sum_{n=1}^{\infty} g_n$ is a bounded continuous function from X to $[-1, 1]$ with $g \restriction E = f$.

(d) Prove the Tietze extension theorem.

5. Let C and D be closed G_δ's in a normal space, X.

   (a) Find a continuous function h with $0 \leq h \leq 1$, $h \restriction C = 0$, $h \restriction D = 1$, and $h^{-1}(\{0\}) = C$. (*Hint*: By the proof of Theorem 2.2.10, find $h_1 \geq 0$, $h_1^{-1}(\{0\}) = C$, and $h_1 \geq 1$ on D, and let $h = \min(h_1, 1)$.)

   (b) Find a continuous function G with $0 \leq g \leq 1$, $g \restriction C = 0$, $g \restriction D = 1$, and $g^{-1}(\{1\}) = D$.

   (c) Let $f = (\frac{1}{2} + \frac{1}{2}g)h$. Prove that $0 \leq f \leq 1$ and $f^{-1}(\{0\}) = C$, $f^{-1}(\{1\}) = D$, and conclude Theorem 2.2.9.

6. (a) Let $\{x^{(\ell)}\}_{\ell=0}^{\infty}$ be a sequence in H, the Hilbert cube. Prove that $\rho(x^{(\ell)}, x^{(\infty)}) \to 0$ if and only if $x_n^{(\ell)} \to x_n^{(\infty)}$ for all n. (*Hint*: $\rho(x^{(\ell)}, x^{(\infty)}) < 2^{-k}$ if and only if for $n = 1, \ldots, k$, $|x_n^{(\ell)} - x_n^{(\infty)}| < 2^{-k+n}$.)

   (b) Prove that the open sets in H, the Hilbert cube, are of the form $\mathcal{O} \times \times_{n=N+1}^{\infty}[0, 1]$, where $\mathcal{O}$ is open in $[0, 1]^N$ in the usual $\mathbb{R}^n$ relative topology.

   (c) Using (b), prove that $f \colon Y \to H$, the Hilbert cube by $f(y)_n = f_n(y)$, is continuous if and only if each f_n is continuous from Y to $[0, 1]$.

7. This problem will prove Tychonoff's lemma that a T_3 space which is Lindelöf is normal. This then implies an improved version of Urysohn's metrizability theorem (sometimes called Tychonoff's metrizability theorem and sometimes still called Urysohn's metrizability theorem) that a second countable T_3 space is metrizable.

   (a) Show if $A \subset X$, a T_3 space is closed and $x \notin A$, there exists U_x open so that $x \in U_x$ and $\overline{U}_x \cap A = \emptyset$.

   (b) If A, B are closed and disjoint in X, a T_3 Lindelöf space, show there exist open sets $\{U_n\}_{n=1}^{\infty}$ and $\{V_n\}_{n=1}^{\infty}$ so that $A \subset \cup_{n=1}^{\infty} U_n$, $B \subset \cup_{n=1}^{\infty} V_n$, $\overline{U}_n \cap B = \emptyset$, $\overline{V}_n \cap A = \emptyset$ for all n.

   (c) Prove that there exist U, V open and disjoint so that $A \subset U$, $B \subset V$, that is, X is normal. (*Hint*: Let $\tilde{U}_n = U_n \setminus \cup_{k \leq n} \overline{V}_k$, $\tilde{V}_n = V_n \setminus \cup_{k \leq n} \overline{U}_k$ and let $U = \cup_{n=1}^{\infty} \tilde{U}_n$, $V = \cup_{n=1}^{\infty} \tilde{V}_n$.)

2.3. Compact Spaces

We saw Lindelöf spaces, that is, topological spaces where every open cover has a countable subcover, are useful—even more useful is a stronger condition that we study in this section.

Definition. A topological space, X, is called *compact* if and only if every open cover of X has a finite subcover.

There is a useful equivalent statement that depends on a kind of double negative:

Definition. A topological space, X, is said to have the *finite intersection property* (f.i.p.) if and only if for any family of closed sets $\{A_\alpha\}_{\alpha \in I}$ with $A_{\alpha_1} \cap \cdots \cap A_{\alpha_k} \neq \emptyset$ for any $\alpha_1, \ldots, \alpha_k \in I$, we have $\bigcap_{\alpha \in I} A_\alpha \neq \emptyset$.

Theorem 2.3.1. *A topological space, X, is compact if and only if it has the f.i.p.*

Proof. Associate to any family of open sets $\{U_\alpha\}_{\alpha \in I}$, the family of closed sets $\{A_\alpha \equiv X \setminus U_\alpha\}_{\alpha \in I}$, $A_{\alpha_1} \cap \cdots \cap A_{\alpha_k} \neq \emptyset$ if and only if $\{U_{\alpha_j}\}_{j=1}^{k}$ is not a cover of X while $\bigcap_{\alpha \in I} A_\alpha \neq \emptyset \Leftrightarrow \bigcup_{\alpha \in I} U_\alpha \neq X$. Thus, the f.i.p. says that if no finite subfamily is a cover, then $\{U_\alpha\}_{\alpha \in I}$ is not a cover, which is the contrapositive of the compactness definition. $\qquad\square$

If X is a topological space, we say $A \subset X$ is a *compact subset* if and only if A is compact in the relative topology.

Proposition 2.3.2. (a) *Any closed subset of a compact space is compact.*

  (b) *If A is a compact subset of a Hausdorff topological space, X, then A is a closed subset of X.*

  (c) *Every compact Hausdorff space is normal.*

Proof. (a) Let X be compact and $A \subset X$ closed. Let $\{V_\alpha\}_{\alpha \in I}$ be an open cover of A. Thus, there exist open sets U_α in X with $U_\alpha \cap A = V_\alpha$. Clearly, $\{U_0 \equiv X \setminus A\} \cup \{U_\alpha\}_{\alpha \in I}$ is an open cover of X, so there exist $\alpha_1, \ldots, \alpha_n \in I$, so $\{U_0\} \cup \{U_{\alpha_j}\}_{j=1}^{n}$ is an open cover of X. Then $\{V_{\alpha_j}\}_{j=1}^{n}$ is a finite subcover of A.

(b) We claim first (a claim also needed in the proof of (c)) that for any compact A and $x \notin A$ in a Hausdorff space, we can find U_x, V_x open and disjoint so $x \in U_x$, $A \subset V_x$. For given $x \notin A$, $y \in A$, pick (using the Hausdorff property) $U_{x,y}, V_{x,y}$ disjoint and open so $x \in U_{x,y}$, $y \in V_{x,y}$. Fix x. $\{V_{x,y}\}_{y \in A}$ is an open cover of A so we can find $y_1, \ldots, y_n$ so

$$A \subset V_{x,y_1} \cup \cdots \cup V_{x,y_n} \equiv V_x \qquad (2.3.1)$$

Let

$$U_x = \bigcap_{j=1}^{n} U_{x,y_j} \qquad (2.3.2)$$

Clearly, $x \in U_x$, and since it is a finite intersection, U_x is open. Moreover, $U_x \cap V_x \subset \cup_{j=1}^{n} V_{x,y_j} \cap U_{x,y_j} = \emptyset$. Thus, we've proven the claim.

To complete the proof of (b), for each $x \notin A$, pick U_x, V_x open so that $A \cap U_x = \emptyset$ and $x \in U_x$. Then $X \setminus A = \cup_{x \in X \setminus A} U_x$ is open, so A is closed.

(c) Let A, B be closed in X. By (a), both are compact. By the claim in the proof of (b), for every $x \in B$, we can find U_x, V_x open and disjoint, so $A \subset V_x$ and $x \in U_x$. Then $\{U_x\}_{x \in B}$ cover B, so by compactness of B, we can find $x_1, \dots, x_n$ so $B \subset U_{x_j} \cup \dots \cup U_{x_n} \equiv U$. If $V = \cap_{j=1}^n V_{x_j}$, then U and V are disjoint and $A \subset V$, $B \subset U$. This proves normality. $\square$

Since a compact Hausdorff space is normal, Urysohn's lemma implies $C(X)$, the set of bounded continuous functions from X to $\mathbb{C}$, and $C_{\mathbb{R}}(X)$, the set of bounded continuous functions from X to $\mathbb{R}$, are both rich spaces with lots of elements and, in particular:

Theorem 2.3.3. *If X is a compact Hausdorff space, for any $x, y \in X$ with $x \neq y$, there exists a function $f \in C(X)$ so that $f(x) = 0$, $f(y) = 1$.*

Definition. A topological space, X, is called *weakly sequentially compact* if every sequence in X has a limit point. Because in a metric space, a sequence with a limit point has a convergent subsequence, in a metric space this definition is equivalent to every sequence having a convergent subsequence (which is called *sequentially compact*).

Theorem 2.3.4. *Any compact topological space, X, is weakly sequentially compact.*

Proof. Let $\{x_n\}_{n=1}^\infty$ be a sequence in X, a compact space. Suppose that no $x \in X$ is a limit point. Then for any $x \in X$, there is an open set U_x and an integer N_x so $x_n \notin U_x$ if $n > N_x$. $\{U_x\}_{x \in X}$ is an open cover of X so we can find $U_{x_1}, \dots, U_{x_\ell}$, so $X = U_{x_1} \cup \dots \cup U_{x_\ell}$. Let $n > N \equiv \max_{j=1,\dots,\ell} N_{x_j}$. Then $x_n \notin \cup_{j=1}^\ell U_{x_j} = X$. This is a contradiction, so $\{x_n\}_{n=1}^\infty$ must have a limit point. $\square$

Next, we turn to looking at compactness for metric spaces.

Definition. A metric space, X, is called *totally bounded* if and only if for all $\varepsilon > 0$, there is a finite set $x_1, \dots, x_n$ in X so that $X \subset \cup_{j=1}^n B_\varepsilon(x_j)$.

Proposition 2.3.5. (a) *Any totally bounded metric space is separable.*

(b) *Any complete and totally bounded metric space is weakly sequentially compact.*

Proof. (a) For each n, pick $\{x_j^{(n)}\}_{j=1}^{N_n}$ so $X = \cup_{j=1}^{N_n} B_{1/n}(x_j^{(n)})$. We claim $\{x_j^{(n)}\}_{j=1,\dots,N_n; n=1,2,\dots}$ is dense (so X is separable), for if $x \in X$ and $x \in U \subset X$ with U open, then $B_{1/n}(x) \subset U$ for some n. By construction of $\{x_j^{(n)}\}_{j=1}^{N_n}$

for some $x_j^{(n)}$, $x \in B_{1/n}(x_j^{(n)})$, so $x_j^{(n)} \in B_{1/n}(x)$. Thus, some $x_j^{(n)} \in U$, that is, $\overline{\{x_j^{(n)}\}} = X$.

(b) Let $\{x_m\}_{m=1}^\infty$ be a sequence in X. Let $\{x_j^{(n)}\}_{j=1}^{N_n}$ be a sequence as in (a). Since each x_m lies in some $B_1(x_j^{(1)})$, infinitely many x_m's lie in some fixed U_1, a ball of radius 1. So there is a subsequence $x_m^{(1)}$ in U_1. By induction, there are U_ℓ, balls of radius $1/\ell$ in $U_{\ell-1}$, and subsequences $x_m^{(\ell)}$ in U_ℓ. Then the subsequence $y_\ell = x_\ell^{(\ell)}$ has the property that $\{y_j\}_{j=\ell}^\infty \subset U_\ell$, so $\rho(y_m, y_j) < 2/\ell$ if $m, j \geq \ell$, that is, y_j is Cauchy. By completeness, $y_j \to y_\infty$, so y_∞ is a limit point of $\{x_m\}_{m=1}^\infty$. $\qquad\square$

Theorem 2.3.6. *Let X be a metric space. Then the following are equivalent:*

(1) *X is compact.*
(2) *X is weakly sequentially compact.*
(3) *X is complete and totally bounded.*

Proof. $\underline{(1) \Rightarrow (2)}$. is Theorem 2.3.4.

$\underline{(2) \Rightarrow (3)}$. Suppose (2). Suppose for some $\varepsilon > 0$, $\cup_{n=1}^N B_\varepsilon(x_n) \neq X$ for any $\{x_1, \ldots, x_N\}$. Pick x_j inductively so $x_{j+1} \notin \cup_{n=1}^j B_\varepsilon(x_j)$. Then $\rho(x_j, x_\ell) \geq \varepsilon$ for all $j \neq \ell$. We claim $\{x_j\}_{j=1}^\infty$ has no limit point. For suppose x_∞ is a limit point. Then $B_{\varepsilon/2}(x_\infty)$ contains infinitely many x_j's, and so two, say x_j and x_ℓ. But then $\rho(x_j, x_\ell) < \varepsilon$, a contradiction. We conclude that for all ε, there is a finite set with $\cup_{n=1}^N B_\varepsilon(x_n) = X$, that is, X is totally bounded.

Next, suppose $\{x_n\}_{n=1}^\infty$ is a Cauchy sequence and x_∞ is a limit point. Given ε, pick N so $n, m > N$ implies $\rho(x_n, x_m) < \varepsilon/2$. Since x_∞ is a limit point, some $x_n \in B_{\varepsilon/2}(x_\infty)$ with $n > N$. It follows that for any $m > N$, $x_m \in B_\varepsilon(x_\infty)$, that is, $x_m \to x_\infty$. Thus, X is complete.

$\underline{(3) \Rightarrow (1)}$. Let X be complete and totally bounded. By Proposition 2.3.5 and Proposition 2.2.2, X is Lindelöf, so any open cover has a countable subcover and we need only prove that any countable open cover has a finite subcover. Thus, suppose $X = \cup_{n=1}^\infty U_n$, but no $U_1 \cup \cdots \cup U_n$ is X.

Let $A_n = X \setminus \bigcup_{j=1}^n U_j$ which is closed with $A_n \supset A_{n+1}$. Pick $x_n \in A_n$, which can be done since $A_n \neq \emptyset$. By (b) of Proposition 2.3.5, $\{x_n\}_{n=1}^\infty$ has a limit point, that is, $x_\infty \in \overline{\{x_n\}_{n=1}^\infty}$. Since $\{x_j\}_{j=1}^\infty \subset A_n$ and A_n is closed, $x_\infty \in \bigcap_{n=1}^\infty A_n = X \setminus \bigcup_{j=1}^\infty U_j$. But $X \setminus \bigcup_{j=1}^\infty U_j = \emptyset$. This contradiction proves $\{U_j\}_{j=1}^\infty$ has a finite subcover. $\qquad\square$

Example 2.2.11, revisited. Recall that H, the Hilbert cube, is $\times_{n=1}^\infty [0,1]$ with metric (2.2.18). We saw $x^{(\ell)} \to x^{(\infty)}$ if and only if $x_n^{(\ell)} \to x_n^{(\infty)}$ for each n. Similarly, one sees $\{x_n^{(\ell)}\}_{\ell=1}^\infty$ is Cauchy if and only if each $\{x_n^{(\ell)}\}_{\ell=1}^\infty$ is Cauchy, so completeness of $[0,1]$ implies H is complete. Because balls of radius greater than $2^{-\ell}$ are products of the form $C \times \times_{n=\ell}^\infty [0,1]$, for suitable $C \subset \times_{n=1}^{\ell-1}[0,1]$, it is easy to see H is totally bounded. Thus, it is compact.   □

For the following, we need two facts not proven until later:

(1) If X and Y are compact Hausdorff spaces and $f\colon X \to Y$ is continuous and one-one, then $\operatorname{Ran}(f)$ is closed and f is a homeomorphism of X and $\operatorname{Ran}(f)$ (we'll prove something stronger in Theorem 2.3.11).
(2) If H is the Hilbert cube, $C_\mathbb{R}(H)$, the bounded, continuous real-valued functions in $\|\cdot\|_\infty$ ($\|f\|_\infty = \sup_{x \in H}|f(x)|$), is a separable metric space (see Example 2.2.11 revisited before Theorem 2.5.4).

Theorem 2.3.7. *Let X be a compact Hausdorff space. Then the following are equivalent:*

(1) *X is metrizable.*
(2) *X is second countable.*
(3) *$C_\mathbb{R}(X)$ is separable.*

Proof. We'll show $(1) \Rightarrow (2) \Rightarrow (1)$ and $(1) \Rightarrow (3) \Rightarrow (1)$.

$\underline{(1) \Rightarrow (2)}$. By Theorem 2.3.6, X is totally bounded and then, by Proposition 2.3.5, X is separable. So by Proposition 2.2.2, X is second countable.

$\underline{(2) \Rightarrow (1)}$. This follows from Theorem 2.2.1 and Proposition 2.3.2.

$\underline{(1) \Rightarrow (3)}$. By the proof of Theorem 2.2.1 and the fact that $(1) \Rightarrow (2)$, X is homeomorphic to a subset of H, the Hilbert cube, and since X is compact, by fact (1) above, the homeomorphic image, $\widetilde{X}$, in H is closed. By fact (2), let $\{f_n\}_{n=1}^\infty$ be a dense subset of $C_\mathbb{R}(H)$ and $g_n = f_n \upharpoonright \widetilde{X} \in C_\mathbb{R}(\widetilde{X})$. If $g \in C_\mathbb{R}(\widetilde{X})$, by the Tietze extension theorem (Theorem 2.2.5), there is $f \in C_\mathbb{R}(H)$ so $f \upharpoonright \widetilde{X} = g$. Since $\{f_n\}$ is dense in $C_\mathbb{R}(H)$, find $f_{n(j)} \to f$ in $C_\mathbb{R}(H)$. Since $\|g - g_n\|_{C_\mathbb{R}(\widetilde{X})} \le \|f - f_n\|_{C_\mathbb{R}(H)}$, we see $g_{n(j)} \to g$, that is, $\{g_n\}_{n=1}^\infty$ is dense in $C_\mathbb{R}(\widetilde{X})$.

$\underline{(3) \Rightarrow (1)}$. Let $\{g_n\}_{n=1}^\infty$ be a dense subset of $C_\mathbb{R}(X)$. Let $h_n = (\|g_n\| + g_n)/2\|g_n\|$ if $g_n \not\equiv 0$ and $h_n = 0$ if $g_n = 0$. Then $h\colon X \to H$ by $h(x)_n = h_n(x)$ is a continuous map of X to H. If $h(x) = h(y)$, then $g_n(x) = g_n(y)$ for all n. Thus, by the density, $g(x) = g(y)$ for all $g \in C_\mathbb{R}(X)$. But if $x \ne y$, there is $g \in C_\mathbb{R}(X)$ with $g(x) \ne g(y)$, so $x = y$. Thus, h is one-one and so, by fact (1) above, is a homeomorphism of X to $\operatorname{Ran}(h)$. Since H is metrizable, so is $\operatorname{Ran}(h)$.   □

Here is a way to rephrase (1) ⇔ (3) in Theorem 2.3.7. If X is a topological space, $A \subset X$ is called *precompact* if and only if $\bar{A}$ is compact. Given that $A \subset \bigcup_{n=1}^{N} B_{\varepsilon_j}(x_j) \Rightarrow \bar{A} \subset \bigcup_{n=1}^{N} B_{2\varepsilon_j}(x_j)$, a rephrasing of (1) ⇔ (3) is

Theorem 2.3.8. *Let X be a complete metric space. Then $A \subset X$ is precompact if and only if it is totally bounded.*

This lets us prove the fundamental property of compactness for subsets of $\mathbb{R}^n$:

Theorem 2.3.9. *A subset, A, of $\mathbb{R}^n$ is compact (in the usual metric topology) if and only if A is closed and bounded.*

Remark. If we use the fundamental definition of compactness, this is the Heine–Borel theorem, and if we use the notion of sequential compactness, this is the Bolzano–Weierstrass theorem; see the Notes.

Proof. If A is compact, it is closed by Proposition 2.3.2(b). It is totally bounded by Theorem 2.3.6, and so $A \subset \bigcup_{n=1}^{N} B_1(x_n)$ for a finite set. Thus, $A \subset B_r(0)$ with $r = 1 + \max_{n=1,\dots,N} |x_n|$, so A is closed and bounded.

Conversely, if A is closed and bounded, it is complete because $\mathbb{R}^n$ is complete and a closed subset of a complete metric space is easily seen to be complete.

Moreover, we claim A is totally bounded. Suppose $A \subset B_r(0)$. Given ε, pick δ with $\delta\sqrt{n} < \varepsilon$. A is clearly contained in the hypercube, C, with side $2r$ centered at 0. If we take lattice points in the lattice of spacing δ, that is, $\mathcal{L}_\delta = \{ \mathbf{m}\delta \mid \mathbf{m} = (m_1, \dots, m_n) \in \mathbb{Z}^n \}$, there are at most $[\frac{2r+1}{\delta}]^n$ points of $\mathcal{L}_\delta$ in C, so C is covered by at most that many closed cubes of side δ. Each such cube is in a ball of radius ε, so A is covered by at most $(2r+1)^n$ balls of radius ε, that is, A is totally bounded. By Theorem 2.3.6, A is compact.   □

Recall that if X and Y are metric spaces, we say a function $f \colon X \to Y$ is *uniformly continuous* if and only if

$$\forall \varepsilon \, \exists \delta \, \forall x, w \in X, \quad \rho_X(x, w) < \delta \Rightarrow \rho_Y(f(x), f(w)) < \varepsilon$$

Theorem 2.3.10 (Dirichlet–Heine). *Let X be a compact metric space and Y a metric space. Any continuous function $f \colon X \to Y$ is uniformly continuous.*

Proof. Fix $\varepsilon > 0$. By continuity, for each $x \in X$, there is a $\delta(x)$, so

$$w \in B_{\delta(x)}(x) \Rightarrow \rho_Y(f(w), f(x)) < \frac{\varepsilon}{2} \qquad (2.3.3)$$

Since $\{B_{\frac{1}{2}\delta(x)}(x)\}$ cover, X, we can find $x_1, \ldots, x_n$ in X so that

$$X = \bigcup_{j=1}^{n} B_{\frac{1}{2}\delta(x_j)}(x_j) \tag{2.3.4}$$

Let

$$\delta = \min_{j=1,\ldots,n} \tfrac{1}{2}\delta(x_j) \tag{2.3.5}$$

Suppose $w, z \in X$ with $\rho_X(w, z) < \delta$. By (2.3.4), there exists x_j with $w \in B_{\frac{1}{2}\delta(x_j)}(x_j)$. Thus, both w and z lie in $B_{\delta(x_j)}(x_j)$, so by (2.3.3), we have that $\rho_Y(f(w), f(x_j)) < \varepsilon/2$ and $\rho_Y(f(z), f(x_j)) < \varepsilon/2$.

Thus,

$$\rho_X(w, z) < \delta \Rightarrow \rho_Y(f(w), f(z)) < \varepsilon \tag{2.3.6}$$

that is, we have uniform continuity. □

We now return to the general theory of compact (not necessarily metric) spaces.

Theorem 2.3.11. (a) *If X is compact and $f \colon X \to Y$ is continuous, then $f[X] = \mathrm{Ran}(f)$ is compact.*

(b) *If $f \colon X \to Y$, with X compact and Y Hausdorff, is continuous and bijective, then f is a homeomorphism. In particular, X is Hausdorff and Y is compact.*

(c) *If f is continuous from X, a compact space, to Y, a topological space, then for any closed set, A, $f[A]$ is compact.*

Proof. (a) Let $\{V_\alpha\}_{\alpha \in I}$ be a relatively open cover of $\mathrm{Ran}(f)$. Then $V_\alpha = U_\alpha \cap \mathrm{Ran}(f)$ for U_α open in Y. Thus, $\{f^{-1}[U_\alpha]\}_{\alpha \in I}$ is an open cover of X. Thus, finitely many $f^{-1}[U_{\alpha_j}]$, $j = 1, \ldots, n$, cover X, and so, $\{U_{\alpha_j}\}_{j=1}^{n}$, and therefore $\{V_{\alpha_j}\}_{j=1}^{n}$ cover $\mathrm{Ran}(f)$.

(b) It suffices to prove f takes open sets to open sets, and thus, to show that f takes closed sets to closed sets. If $A \subset X$ is closed, it is compact by Proposition 2.3.2(a). By (a), $f[A]$ is compact. Since Y is a Hausdorff space, $f[A]$ is closed by Proposition 2.3.2(b). Thus, f takes closed sets to closed sets.

(c) Immediate from (a) and Proposition 2.3.2(a). □

The following corollary is especially useful because it asserts the existence of minima which can be combined with variational principles to get the existence of certain objects (see, e.g., Section 5.9):

Theorem 2.3.12. *Let* $f\colon X \to \mathbb{R}$ *be continuous, where* X *is a compact topological space. Then* f *is bounded and there exist* $x_{\pm} \in X$, *so*

$$f(x_+) = \sup_{y \in X} f(y), \qquad f(x_-) = \inf_{y \in X} f(y) \qquad (2.3.7)$$

Proof. By (a) of the last theorem, $f[X]$ is compact in $\mathbb{R}$. Thus, $f[X]$ is bounded (by Theorem 2.3.9), so f is bounded, and since $f[X]$ is closed, it contains its inf and sup (e.g., if $\alpha = \sup f(y)$, there exist $\alpha_n \in f[X]$, so $\alpha \geq \alpha_n \geq \alpha - \frac{1}{n}$. Thus, $\alpha_n \to \alpha$ and, since $f[X]$ is closed, $\alpha \in f[X]$). $\qquad\square$

In some applications, it is important that there are one-sided results for lsc and usc functions:

Theorem 2.3.13. *Let* X *be a compact Hausdorff space. Let* $f\colon X \to \mathbb{R} \cup \{\infty\}$ *be lower semicontinuous. Then* f *is bounded from below (i.e.,* $\inf_{x \in X} f(x) > -\infty$) *and there exists* $x \in X$ *with* $f(x) = \inf_y f(y)$.

Remark. Similarly, if $f\colon X \to \mathbb{R} \cup \{-\infty\}$ is upper semicontinuous, then f is bounded above and takes its maximum value.

Proof. Let $U_n = f^{-1}((-n, \infty])$. Since f doesn't take the value, $-\infty$, $\bigcup_n U_n = X$ and, by lsc, each U_n is open. Thus, there is N with $\bigcup_{n=1}^N U_n = X$, so $\inf f(x) \geq -N$.

Let $\alpha = \inf_{y \in X} f(y)$. Let

$$A_n = f^{-1}((-\infty, \alpha + \tfrac{1}{n}]) \qquad (2.3.8)$$

which is closed by lsc. Since α is the inf, each A_n is nonempty, so $\bigcap_{n=1}^N A_n = A_N$ is nonempty. By the f.i.p. restriction on X, $\bigcap_{n=1}^{\infty} A_n \equiv f^{-1}((-\infty, \alpha])$ is nonempty. Thus, there is an x with $f(x) = \alpha$. $\qquad\square$

Compact sets in function spaces are especially important, so the Arzelà–Ascoli theorem is significant. Since we suppose the reader has previously seen it, we leave it to the Problems (see Problem 1).

Definition. Let X and Y be metric spaces. A family, $\mathcal{F}$, of functions from X to Y is called *uniformly equicontinuous* if and only if $\forall \varepsilon > 0 \, \exists \delta > 0 \, \forall x_1, x_2 \in X \, \forall f \in \mathcal{F}$,

$$\rho_X(x_1, x_2) < \delta \Rightarrow \rho_Y(f(x_1), f(x_2)) < \varepsilon \qquad (2.3.9)$$

Theorem 2.3.14 (Arzelà–Ascoli Theorem). *Let* X *be a separable metric space and* Y *a complete metric space with* $C \subset Y$ *compact. Let* $\mathcal{F}$ *be a family of uniformly equicontinuous functions from* X *to* Y *with* $\mathrm{Ran}(f) \subset C$ *for all* $f \in \mathcal{F}$. *Then any sequence in* $\mathcal{F}$ *has a subsequence converging at each* $x \in X$. *If* X *is compact, then* $\mathcal{F}$ *is precompact in the uniform topology (given by (2.1.8)).*

In typical applications, $Y = \mathbb{R}$, $\mathrm{Ran}(f) = C$ is implied by $\sup_{x \in X, f \in \mathcal{F}}(|f(x)|) < \infty$, and X is a subset of $\mathbb{R}^n$ or a manifold, and equicontinuity comes from control of derivatives or Hölder continuity conditions (see Problem 2). One gets pointwise convergence of subsequences with convergence uniform on each compact set $K \subset \mathbb{R}$ or $\mathbb{R}^n$ or the manifold.

Returning to lsc/usc functions, we note the following which supplements Proposition 2.1.9:

Theorem 2.3.15. *Let X be a compact metric space and $f \colon X \to \mathbb{R} \cup \{\infty\}$ lsc. Then there exist continuous functions $f_n \colon X \to \mathbb{R}$ so $f_{n+1} \geq f_n$ and*

$$f(x) = \lim_{n \to \infty} f_n(x) = \sup_n f_n(x) \qquad (2.3.10)$$

Remark. for f usc, we get $f_{n+1} \leq f_n$.

The following is needed as a lemma for the proof of Theorem 2.3.15 but since it is useful in other contexts, we call it a theorem:

Theorem 2.3.16 (Continuous Partition of Unity). *Let X be a compact subset of a normal topological space, Y. Let $\{U_\alpha\}_{\alpha \in I}$ be a collection of open subsets of Y whose union contains X. Then there exist n, $\alpha_1, \ldots, \alpha_n \in I$ and continuous functions $\{j_k\}_{k=1}^n$ from Y to $\mathbb{R}$ so that*

$$\text{(i)} \qquad j_k \geq 0 \qquad (2.3.11)$$

$$\text{(ii)} \qquad \sum_{k=1}^n j_k(x) = 1, \; \text{for all } x \in X$$

$$\text{(iii)} \qquad \overline{\{y \mid j_k(y) > 0\}} \subset U_{\alpha_k} \qquad (2.3.12)$$

Remarks. 1. In many applications, one has $X = Y$.

2. By using functions like

$$f_x(y) = \left(1 - \frac{2\rho(x,y)}{\rho(x,y) + \rho(y, Y \setminus U_{\alpha(x)})} \right)_+ \qquad (2.3.13)$$

one can make the j's explicit in the case that Y is a metric space.

Proof. For each x, by Urysohn's lemma, find $\alpha(x)$ so $x \in U_{\alpha(x)}$ and $f_x \colon X \to [0,1]$ so that $f_x(x) = 1$ and $\overline{\{y \mid f_x(y) > 0\}} \subset U_{\alpha(x)}$. Let $V_x = \{y \mid f_x(y) > \frac{1}{2}\}$. Then $\{V_x\}_{x \in X}$ is an open cover of X, so find $x_1, \ldots, x_n$ with $\{V_{x_j}\}_{j=1}^n$ covering X. Let $g \in C(Y)$ be 1 on X with $0 \leq g \leq 1$ and $\mathrm{supp}\, g \subset \cup_{j=1}^n V_{x_j}$. Then

$$q(y) \equiv \sum_{k=1}^n f_{x_k}(y) \geq \tfrac{1}{2} \qquad (2.3.14)$$

for all y, so we have

$$j_k(y) = \frac{f_{x_k}(y)g(y)}{q(y)} \tag{2.3.15}$$

is continuous and obeys (i)–(iii). $\square$

We will use this theorem again in Sections 4.4 and 5.12.

Proof of Theorem 2.3.15. We first claim that if $g_n(x) = \inf_{\rho(x,y)\leq 1/n} f(y)$, then

$$g_n(x) \to f(x) \tag{2.3.16}$$

For clearly, $g_n(x) \leq g_{n+1}(x) \leq f(x)$, and if $y_n \in \overline{B_{1/n}(x)}$ with $f(y_n) = g_n(x)$ (such y_n exist by Theorem 2.3.13), then $y_n \to x$ so $\lim f(y_n) \geq f(x)$. Thus, (2.3.16) holds.

Given n, find $\{y_j^{(n)}\}_{j=1}^{k_n}$ so $\{B_{1/2n}(y_j^{(n)})\}_{j=1}^{k_n}$ cover X. Let $\{j_\ell^{(n)}\}_{\ell=1}^{k_n}$ be nonnegative functions summing to 1 so $\overline{\{y \mid j_\ell^{(n)}(y) > 0\}} \subset B_{1/2n}(y_\ell^{(n)})$. Define

$$h_n(x) = \sum_{\ell=1}^{k_n} j_\ell^{(n)}(x) \inf_{\omega \in B_{1/2n}(y_\ell^{(n)})} f(\omega) \tag{2.3.17}$$

For any $x \in B_{1/2n}(y)$, $\inf_{\omega \in B_{1/2n}(y)} f(\omega) \geq \inf_{\omega \in B_{1/n}(x)} f(\omega)$, so

$$g_n(x) \leq h_n(x) \leq f(x) \tag{2.3.18}$$

so, by (2.3.16), $h_n(x) \to f(x)$. If $f_n(x) = \max_{1\leq j \leq n} h_j(x)$, we have $f_{n+1} \geq f_n$ and (2.3.10) holds. $\square$

As a final topic in this section, we turn to local compactness.

Definition. A Hausdorff topological space, X, is called *locally compact* if any $x \in X$ has a compact neighborhood.

Definition. If X is a locally compact Hausdorff topological space, its *one-point compactification* is $X_\infty \equiv X \cup \{\infty\}$, where "$\infty$" is a point not in X with the topology $\mathcal{T}_X \cup \{X_\infty \setminus C \mid C \subset X \text{ is compact in the } \mathcal{T}_X \text{ relative topology}\} \equiv \mathcal{T}_{X_\infty}$.

The reader can check (Problem 3) that the family of sets, $\mathcal{T}_{X_\infty}$, is a topology.

Theorem 2.3.17. *Let X be a locally compact Hausdorff space. Then the one-point compactification, X_∞, is a compact Hausdorff space.*

Proof. Let $\{U_\alpha\}_{\alpha \in I}$ be an open cover of X_∞. Pick α_0 so $x_\infty \in U_{\alpha_0}$. Then $U_{\alpha_0} \notin \mathcal{T}_X$, so $U_{\alpha_0} = X_\infty \setminus C$ with C compact in X. Each $U_\alpha \cap C$ is relatively open in C, for if $U_\alpha = X_\infty \setminus B$, then $U_\alpha \cap C = (X \setminus B) \cap C$ is relatively open. Thus, $\{U_\alpha\}_{\alpha \in I \setminus \{\alpha_0\}}$ is an open cover of C, so there is a finite subcover, $\{U_{\alpha_j}\}_{j=1}^n$. Clearly, $\{U_{\alpha_j}\}_{j=0}^n$ is an open cover of X_∞.

If $x, y \in X$, $x \neq y$, we can find $A, B \in \mathcal{T}_X$, and so in $\mathcal{T}_{X_\infty}$ with $A \cap B = \emptyset$, $x \in A$, $y \in B$. If $x \in X$, $y = \infty$, by the local compactness, there is A open so $x \in A \subset C$ with C compact. Let $B = X_\infty \setminus C$. Then $A \cap B = \emptyset$, $x \in A$, and $\infty \in B$ and $A, B \in \mathcal{T}_{X_\infty}$. Thus, $\mathcal{T}_{X_\infty}$ is a Hausdorff topology. $\square$

It is amusing to note that X_∞ is compact even if X is not locally compact. Local compactness is only needed to ensure that the topology on X_∞ is Hausdorff!

Notes and Historical Remarks. The historical development of compactness was in three phases: for subsets of $\mathbb{R}$ and $\mathbb{R}^n$ in the period 1817–1905, the notion for metric spaces around 1906, and the theory for general topological spaces starting in 1924.

Compactness is intimately connected with subtle properties of the real line. Indeed, once the smoke cleared, it was known for $[a, b] \subset \mathbb{R}$ that there was a logical equivalence of sequential compactness, compactness defined via open covers, and the fact that any bounded sequence has a least upper bound. As you might expect, the history is complicated with simultaneous discoveries and arguments about who really had what.

The first notion to appear is what is now called the Bolzano–Weierstrass property: that any bounded sequence of reals has a convergent subsequence. The subdivision argument needed to prove this first appeared in an 1817 paper [**108**] of Bernhard Bolzano (1781–1848), where he stated and proved (and first emphasized the importance of) the intermediate value theorem: if f is continuous on $[a, b]$ and γ lies in between $f(a)$ and $f(b)$, then for some $c \in [a, b]$, $f(c) = \gamma$.

Weierstrass included this result, even its $\mathbb{R}^n$ analogs, in his lectures, at least as early as 1861. He mentioned Bolzano by name.

As an interlude to the open cover discussion, we note that Theorem 2.3.10 appeared first (for functions on $[a, b]$) in an 1872 comprehensive paper on the foundations of analysis [**408**] by Heinrich Eduard Heine (1821–81). He had heard the argument in lectures given by Dirichlet in Berlin in 1852 (notes of these lectures were actually published in 1904). The argument used the fact that bounded increasing sequences have a limit.

That open covers of $[a, b] \subset \mathbb{R}$ have finite subcovers has come to be called the Heine–Borel theorem. It was first proven by Emile Borel (1871–1956) in 1895 [**110**]. Actually, he only proved countable covers by open intervals had finite subcovers. The extension to arbitrary covers was obtained by several mathematicians, including Lebesgue, Lindelöf, and Schoenflies. In particular, Schoenflies [**820**] said the result was an extension of Heine (referring to the work on uniform continuity) and gave the theorem the name that has stuck. Lebesgue, in particular, objected to this name, pushing instead for Borel–Schoenflies. It is sometimes called Borel–Lebesgue in the French literature. Dugac [**260**] has a report on some of the correspondence among the principals. In particular, touching all bases, he calls it the "Dirichlet–Heine–Weierstrass–Borel–Schoenflies–Lebesgue theorem"!

Félix Édouard Justin Émile Borel (1871–1956) was known as Émile. While some family members pushed him to attend École Polytechnique to prepare for jobs in industry, he wanted a scientific position and attended École Normale Supérieure where he was influenced by Appell (who became his father-in-law), Brillouin, Goursat, Jordan, Painlevé, Picard, and his advisor, Darboux. After several years in Lille, Borel returned to Paris where he spent the rest of his career.

During the First World War, he volunteered and served for a time as commander of an artillery battery, but Painlevé, then Minister of War, brought him back to serve in the War Office. From 1924 onwards, while remaining mathematically active, he served in the government, including Minister of the Navy from 1925–40. During the Second World War, even though he was over seventy, he was active in the Resistance, receiving the Grande Croix Légion d'Honneur.

Besides his work on compactness, Borel is most known for his work on the basis of measure theory (which is how he came to consider covers by intervals), a method for summing infinite series, and important work in complex variables (such as the Borel–Carathéodory theorem; see Section 3.2 of Part 2A) and probability (the Borel–Cantelli lemma; see Section 7.2). His students included Lebesgue, Montel, and Valiron.

The finite intersection property way of looking at compactness is due to Riesz [**778**], although earlier, Cantor had made use of the fact that a decreasing family of compact subsets of $\mathbb{R}$ had a nonempty intersection. The definition of compact in metric spaces is in Fréchet's thesis [**315**], the original place metric spaces were defined. The definition for general topological spaces is due to Alexandroff and Urysohn [**16**]. To distinguish the notion from the metric space case, they called sets in the general topological context "bicompact," a name still used occasionally. But Bourbaki [**120**] insisted on "compact" and the name has remained. For a time, there was a competition among bicompact, sequentially compact, and several other inequivalent notions that are equivalent on metric spaces. In the end, it was Tychonoff's theorem (discussed in Section 2.7) that settled the open cover definition as the "right" one.

The first person to consider $C([a,b])$ as a space of functions seems to be Hadamard [**378**] in 1903. In this paper, Hadamard considered what we would now call linear functionals on $C([a,b])$. (Hadamard's student, Fréchet, introduced the name functional, referring to this paper, although the Italians had used "functional operator" prior to Hadamard.) Hadamard showed that every such functional was a limit of functionals of the form $f \mapsto \int_a^b f(x)g(x)\,dx$; this theme will be explored in Section 4.5.

The notion of locally compact space and one-point compactification was invented independently in 1923–24 by Tietze [**919**] and Alexandroff [**11**].

The extension of Theorem 2.3.7 to the locally compact case involves the notion of σ-compact: X is σ-*compact* if there exists $K_1 \subset K_2^{\text{int}} \subset K_2 \subset \dots$ with K_j compact and $\bigcup K_j = X$. It also involves $C_{\infty,\mathbb{R}}(X)$, the real-valued functions on X, with $\lim_{x \to \infty} f(x) = 0$, that is, $\forall \varepsilon$, $\exists K$ compact so that $x \in X \setminus K \Rightarrow |f(x)| < \varepsilon$. Then one has (see Problem 5):

Theorem 2.3.18. *Let X be a locally compact Hausdorff space. Then the following are equivalent:*

(1) *X_∞ is metrizable.*
(2) *X is second countable and σ-compact.*
(3) *$C_{\infty,\mathbb{R}}(X)$ is separable.*

Sequential compactness is used more often than what we call "weak sequential compactness" (close to, but different from, what is sometimes called limit compactness). For our purposes, it is convenient to talk about the limit point definition.

The Arzelà–Ascoli theorem is named after works of the Italian mathematicians Cesare Arzelà (1847–1912) [**38**] and Giulio Ascoli (1843–96) [**39**] done in 1885–86. Ascoli invented equicontinuity and Arzelà proved the theorem which has their names on it.

Another notion related to open covers is paracompactness. An open cover $\{V_\beta\}_{\beta \in J}$ is called a *refinement* of an open cover $\{U_\alpha\}_{\alpha \in I}$ if $\forall \beta \in J$ $\exists \alpha \in I\ V_\beta \subset U_\alpha$. An open cover, $\{U_\alpha\}_{\alpha \in I}$, of a topological space, X, is called *locally finite* if every $x \in X$ has a neighborhood, N_x, so $\{\beta \mid N_x \cap U_\beta \neq \emptyset\}$ is finite. X is called *paracompact* if every open cover has a locally finite refinement. Every metric space is paracompact. Paracompactness is useful in discussing partitions of unity.

Problems

1. (a) Prove that a subset of a metric space is precompact if and only if every sequence has a convergent subsequence.

(b) Let X be a separable metric space with dense set $\{x_n\}_{n=1}^{\infty}$. Let $\{f_m\}_{m=1}^{\infty}$ be a sequence of uniformly equicontinuous functions from X to a complete metric space Y. Suppose for each n, $f_m(x_n)$ has a limit y_n. Prove that f_m converges uniformly to a continuous function $f \colon X \to Y$.

(c) Given a sequence of continuous functions $f_n \colon X \to Y$, where X, Y obey the hypotheses of (b), suppose $\{f_n(x_1)\}_{n=1}^{\infty}$ lies in a compact subset of Y. Show there is a subsequence so $\{f_{n(j)}(x_1)\}$ has a limit.

(d) Conclude the proof of the pointwise convergence part of the Arzelà–Ascoli theorem. (*Hint*: Use a diagonalization trick of Section 1.5 to get convergence at each x_m.)

(e) If X is compact, prove the sequence converges uniformly and finish the proof of the Arzelà–Ascoli theorem. (*Hint*: X is covered by finitely many δ-balls.)

2. Let (X, ρ) be a metric space. A function $f \in C(X)$ is called *Hölder continuous* of exponent α $(\alpha > 0)$ if the quantity

$$N_\alpha(f) = \sup_{x \neq y} \frac{|f(x) - f(y)|}{\rho(x, y)^\alpha}$$

is finite. Prove that if X is compact and α is fixed in $(0, 1]$, $\{f \in C(X) \mid \|f\|_\infty \leq 1 \text{ and } N_\alpha(f) \leq 1\}$ is compact in $C(X)$.

3. Let X be a compact Hausdorff space.

(a) If $C \subset X$ is compact and A is open, prove that $A \cap (X \setminus C)$ is open.

(b) Check that the set $\mathcal{T}_{X_\infty}$, presented in the definition of one-point compactification, is a topology.

4. (a) Let X be a compact metric space. Let $h \colon X \to X$ be an isometry (i.e., if ρ is the metric, then $\rho(h(x), h(y)) = \rho(x, y)$). Prove that h is a bijection. (*Hint*: If $x_1 \notin \operatorname{Ran}(h)$, show that $\rho(x_1, \operatorname{Ran}(h)) > 0$, then define x_j by $x_{j+1} = h(x_j)$ and consider convergent subsequences.)

(b) Let X be a compact metric space and Y another metric space. Suppose f is an isometry of X into a subset of Y and g an isometry of Y to a subset of X. Prove that f is a bijection of X to Y.

5. Prove Theorem 2.3.18. (*Hint*: Translate (2) and (3) into statements about X_∞.)

2.4. The Weierstrass Approximation Theorem and Bernstein Polynomials

In this section, we'll prove the first of two remarkable theorems of Weierstrass. Recall that $C(X)$ is the bounded continuous functions from a topological space, X, to $\mathbb{C}$.

Theorem 2.4.1 (Weierstrass' First Theorem). *The polynomials in x are $\|\cdot\|_\infty$-dense in $C([a,b])$ for any bounded interval, $[a,b]$, in $\mathbb{R}$, that is, for any $f \in C([a,b])$ and any $\varepsilon > 0$, there is a polynomial, P, with*

$$\|f - P\|_\infty < \varepsilon \qquad (2.4.1)$$

Remark. While we state this result for $[a,b]$, it holds for any compact $K \subset \mathbb{R}$. Indeed, if $a = \inf K$, $b = \sup K$, given $f \in C(K)$, we can find $g \in C([a,b])$ so $g \restriction K = f$. For example, one can linearly interpolate f on each maximal connected interval in $[a,b] \setminus K$. Finding P with $\|g - P\|_{[a,b],\infty} \le \varepsilon$, we have $\|f - P\|_{K,\infty} \le \varepsilon$.

Theorem 2.4.2 (Weierstrass' Second Theorem). *The polynomials in $e^{\pm i\theta}$ are $\|\cdot\|_\infty$-dense in $C(\partial\mathbb{D})$, the continuous functions on $\partial\mathbb{D} = \{z \in \mathbb{C} \mid |z| = 1\}$.*

Remark. This is often stated in terms of periodic functions on $\mathbb{R}$ with period 2π and in terms of series in $\{\cos(n\theta)\}_{n=0}^\infty$ and $\{\sin(n\theta)\}_{n=1}^\infty$.

Both theorems are special cases of a very general theorem that we'll prove in the next section (see Theorem 2.5.2). We prove Theorem 2.4.1 here and Theorem 2.4.2 in Section 3.5 (see Theorem 3.5.3), for two reasons. First, the general theorem requires as input the following special case:

Proposition 2.4.3. *For any ε, there is a polynomial P so that $\sup_{|x| \le 1} |P(x) - |x|| < \varepsilon$.*

Second, the proofs we give will be explicit and elegant—we'll provide simple formulae for the polynomials and, in particular, be able to relate the degree of P to ε when f has extra properties (see Problems 1 and 2).

We note there is a simple direct proof of Proposition 2.4.3 using the binomial expansion for $\sqrt{1-y}$ (see Problem 13) and that it is easy to get either Weierstrass' theorem from the other (Problems 11 and 12). Finally, we want to note the following that show the limitation of polynomial approximation:

Proposition 2.4.4. *Let $f \in C(\partial\mathbb{D})$ be a uniform limit of polynomials in z. Then*

$$\int_0^{2\pi} f(e^{i\theta}) e^{in\theta} \frac{d\theta}{2\pi} = 0 \quad \text{for } n = 1, 2, \dots \qquad (2.4.2)$$

Remarks. 1. For example, $f(e^{i\theta}) = e^{-i\theta}$ is not a limit of polynomials in $e^{i\theta}$.

2. It can be seen (Problem 27 of Section 3.5) that if (2.4.2) holds, then f is a uniform limit of polynomials in z.

3. One way of understanding this result is that if P_n is $\|\cdot\|_\infty$-Cauchy in $C(\partial\mathbb{D})$, then by the maximum principle for analytic functions (see Theorem 3.6.2 of Section 3.6 of Part 2A), P_n is $\|\cdot\|_\infty$-Cauchy in $C(\overline{\mathbb{D}})$, which

implies they converge to a function analytic in $\mathbb{D}$ (by Theorem 3.1.5 of Section 3.1 of Part 2A).

Proof. If $P(z) = \sum_{k=0}^{N} a_k z^k$, then $\int_0^{2\pi} P(e^{i\theta}) e^{in\theta} \frac{d\theta}{2\pi} = \sum_{k=0}^{N} a_k \int_0^{2\pi} e^{i(k+n)\theta} \frac{d\theta}{2\pi} = 0$ since $k + n \geq 1$. Thus, if (2.4.1) holds,

$$\left| \int_0^{2\pi} f(e^{i\theta}) e^{in\theta} \frac{d\theta}{2\pi} \right| = \left| \int_0^{2\pi} [f(e^{i\theta}) - P(e^{i\theta})] e^{in\theta} \frac{d\theta}{2\pi} \right|$$

$$\leq \int_0^{2\pi} |f(e^{i\theta}) - P(e^{i\theta})| \frac{d\theta}{2\pi} < \varepsilon \qquad (2.4.3)$$

Since ε is arbitrary, (2.4.2) holds. $\qquad\qquad\qquad\qquad\qquad\qquad\qquad$ □

We now turn to a proof of Theorem 2.4.1. We begin by noting that to approximate $f(x)$ on $[a, b]$, it is enough to approximate $g(x) = f((1 - x)a + xb)$ on $[0, 1]$, so we need only consider the case $[a, b] = [0, 1]$.

Definition. Given a continuous f on $[0, 1]$, we define the *Bernstein polynomials*, $B_n(f)$, by

$$B_n(f)(x) = \sum_{j=0}^{n} f\left(\frac{j}{n}\right) \left[\binom{n}{j} x^j (1 - x)^{n-j} \right] \qquad (2.4.4)$$

Here $\binom{n}{j} = n!/j!(n - j)!$ is a binomial coefficient.

We will prove the following which implies Theorem 2.4.1 by first taking $n \to \infty$ and then ε to 0.

Theorem 2.4.5 (Bernstein's Approximation Theorem). *For any $\varepsilon > 0$,*

$$\|f - B_n(f)\|_\infty \leq \frac{\|f\|_\infty}{2n\varepsilon^2} + \sup_{|x-y| \leq \varepsilon} |f(x) - f(y)| \qquad (2.4.5)$$

In particular, for any continuous function, f, on $[0, 1]$, as $n \to \infty$, we have that

$$\|f - B_n(f)\|_\infty \to 0 \qquad (2.4.6)$$

and Theorem 2.4.1 holds.

We'll prove the estimate (2.4.5) shortly. Here we note that it implies (2.4.6), since it implies that for any $\varepsilon > 0$,

$$\limsup_{n \to \infty} \|f - B_n(f)\|_\infty \leq \sup_{|x-y| \leq \varepsilon} |f(x) - f(y)| \qquad (2.4.7)$$

and uniform continuity of f (see Theorem 2.3.10) implies the right side of (2.4.7) goes to zero as $\varepsilon \downarrow 0$.

The intuition behind (2.4.5) comes from the fact that

$$w_{x,n,j} = \binom{n}{j} x^j (1-x)^{n-j} \qquad (2.4.8)$$

is, for each fixed x and n, a probabilistic weight, that is,

$$w_{x,n,j} > 0, \qquad \sum_{j=0}^{n} w_{x,n,j} = 1 \qquad (2.4.9)$$

which is the *Bernoulli distribution*, discussed further in Sections 7.1–7.3. This is the distribution of the number of 1's obtained for n independent trials of a $0 - 1$ process with probability x of a 1. Thus, we use expectation probability notation and define

$$\mathbb{E}_{x,n}(f) = \sum_{j=0}^{n} f_{x,n,j} w_{x,n,j} \qquad (2.4.10)$$

for a function f of j depending parametrically on x and n and

$$\mathbb{P}_{x,n}(A) = \mathbb{E}_{x,n}(\chi_A) \qquad (2.4.11)$$

for a set A, where χ_A is its characteristic function. The combination of the law of large numbers (see Section 7.2) and central limit theorem (see Section 7.3) says that for n large, the weight is concentrated near those j with $j/n \approx x$ with a width $\sim 1/\sqrt{n}$. This is seen in Figure 2.4.1 and made precise in Lemma 2.4.6.

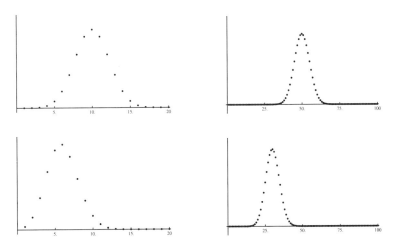

Figure 2.4.1. The Bernoulli weights $w_{x,n,j}$ for variable j. The top row is $x = 0.5$ and the bottom is $x = 0.3$. The left column is $n = 20$ and the right is $n = 100$.

Lemma 2.4.6.

(a) $\mathbb{E}_{x,n}(j) = xn$ (2.4.12)

(b) $\mathbb{E}_{x,n}(j(j-1)) = x^2 n(n-1)$ (2.4.13)

(c) $\mathbb{E}_{x,n}(j^2) = x^2 n(n-1) + xn$ (2.4.14)

(d) $\mathbb{E}_{x,n}\left(\left(x - \dfrac{j}{n}\right)^2\right) = \dfrac{x(1-x)}{n} \leq \dfrac{1}{4n}$ *for all* x (2.4.15)

(e) $\mathbb{P}_{x,n}\left(\left\{j \,\Big|\, \left|x - \dfrac{j}{n}\right| \geq \varepsilon\right\}\right) \leq \dfrac{1}{4n\varepsilon^2}$ (2.4.16)

(f) $\mathbb{E}_{x,n}\left(\left|f\left(\dfrac{j}{n}\right) - f(x)\right|\right) \leq \dfrac{\|f\|_\infty}{2n\varepsilon^2} + \sup_{|x-y|\leq\varepsilon} |f(x) - f(y)|$ (2.4.17)

Proof. (a), (b)   By the binomial theorem,

$$\sum_{j=0}^{n} \binom{n}{j}(x+a)^j(1-x)^{n-j} = (1+a)^n \tag{2.4.18}$$

so taking $x\frac{d}{da}$ and $x^2\frac{d^2}{da^2}$ at $a = 0$, we get (2.4.12) and (2.4.13).

(c) $\mathbb{E}_{x,n}(j^2) = \mathbb{E}_{x,n}(j(j-1)) + \mathbb{E}_{x,n}(j)$, so (2.4.14) follows from (2.4.12) and (2.4.13).

(d) $(x - \frac{j}{n})^2 = x^2 - 2x\frac{j}{n} + \frac{j^2}{n^2}$, so by (a) and (c),

$$\mathbb{E}_{x,n}\left(\left(x - \frac{j}{n}\right)^2\right) = x^2 - 2x^2 + x^2\left(\frac{n-1}{n}\right) + \frac{x}{n}$$

$$= -\frac{x^2}{n} + \frac{x}{n} = \frac{x(1-x)}{n}$$

The final inequality in (2.4.15) comes from $\max_{x\in[0,1]} x(1-x) = \frac{1}{4}$, with the max occurring at $x = \frac{1}{2}$.

   (e)   (2.4.16) comes from (2.4.15) and

$$\mathbb{E}_{x,n}\left(\left(x - \frac{j}{n}\right)^2\right) \geq \mathbb{E}_{x,n}\left(\left(x - \frac{j}{n}\right)^2 \chi_{\{j\,||x-\frac{j}{n}|\geq\varepsilon\}}\right)$$

$$\geq \varepsilon^2 \mathbb{P}\left(\left\{j \,\Big|\, \left|x - \frac{j}{n}\right| \geq \varepsilon\right\}\right) \tag{2.4.19}$$

(f)   We sum over two sets: $A = \{j \mid |x - \frac{j}{n}| \geq \varepsilon\}$ and $B = \{j \mid |x - \frac{j}{n}| < \varepsilon\}$. On A, $|f(\frac{j}{n}) - f(x)| \leq 2\|f\|_\infty$, and on B, $|f(\frac{j}{n}) - f(x)| \leq \sup_{|x-y|\leq\varepsilon}|f(x) - $

$f(y)|$. Thus,

$$\mathbb{E}_{x,n}\left(\left|f\left(\frac{j}{n}\right) - f(x)\right|\right) \leq 2\|f\|_\infty \mathbb{P}(A) + \sup_{|x-y|\leq\varepsilon} |f(x) - f(y)|\,\mathbb{P}(B) \quad (2.4.20)$$

We get (2.4.17) from (2.4.16) and $\mathbb{P}(B) \leq 1$. $\qquad\square$

Remark. (2.4.19) is a special case of

$$\mathbb{P}(|f| \geq \varepsilon) \leq \varepsilon^{-2}\mathbb{E}(|f|^2) \quad (2.4.21)$$

a result known as *Markov's inequality*, which is discussed further in Theorem 4.4.6 and the Notes to Sections 4.4 and 7.2.

Proof of Theorem 2.4.5. Since (2.4.9) holds,

$$|f(x) - B_n(f)| = \left|\sum_{j=0}^n w_{x,n,j}\left(f(x) - f\left(\frac{j}{n}\right)\right)\right|$$

$$\leq \mathbb{E}\left(\left|f(x) - f\left(\frac{j}{n}\right)\right|\right) \quad (2.4.22)$$

so (2.4.17) implies (2.4.5). $\qquad\square$

Notes and Historical Remarks.

> A time came when there was no longer any distinction in inventing a proof of Weierstrass's theorem, unless the new method could be shown to possess some specific excellence, in the way of simplicity, for example, or rapidity of convergence.
>
> —*D. Jackson* [**446**]

For a comprehensive look at the history and many proofs of the Weierstrass theorem, see Pinkus [**728**].

Weierstrass found his theorems and published them as a Note of the Berlin Academy in the Proceedings in 1885 [**979**]. At the time, he was seventy. His proofs showed his motivation in connection with his work on analytic functions. In proving his first theorem, he started with functions, f, bounded and continuous on all of $\mathbb{R}$ and formed for each real $y > 0$,

$$f_y(z) = \frac{1}{y\sqrt{\pi}}\int_{-\infty}^\infty f(x)\exp\left[\frac{-(z-x)^2}{y^2}\right]dx \quad (2.4.23)$$

and, as we do in Section 3.5, showed

$$\lim_{y\downarrow 0} f_y(x) = f(x) \quad (2.4.24)$$

uniformly on compact subsets of $\mathbb{R}$. He noted the striking fact that the approximations, f_y, were entire analytic functions of z and, as he well knew, the Taylor series of those entire functions converged uniformly on compacts, so he concluded that f could be approximated uniformly on compacts of

$\mathbb{R}$ by polynomials. He completed the proof of the first theorem by taking $f\colon [a,b] \to \mathbb{R}$ and extending it by setting $f(x) = f(a)$ if $x < a$ and $f(x) = f(b)$ if $x > b$.

For the second theorem, he noted that if f were periodic of period 2π, the f_y's were entire periodic functions of period 2π, and he knew (see Theorem 3.10.1 of Part 2A) that any such f_y could be written

$$f_y(z) = g_y(e^{2\pi i z}) \tag{2.4.25}$$

where g_y was analytic in $\mathbb{C} \setminus \{0\}$. Laurent series for g_y then gave him the second theorem.

Bernstein presented his proof in a 1912/1913 paper [**82**] that emphasized, as we do, the connection to probability. Sergei Natanovich Bernstein (1880–1968) was a Jewish Ukrainian mathematician born in Odessa, where his father was a medical doctor and university professor. In 1898, after graduation from high school, he went to Paris to study, and after a year spent three terms in Göttingen studying with Hilbert. He returned to Paris and, in 1904, submitted his Ph.D. thesis to a committee including Hadamard and Poincaré and headed by Picard. In the thesis, Bernstein solved Hilbert's 19th problem on analytic solutions of elliptic differential equations. Despite this record, when he returned to Russia in 1905, he had to reenter graduate school because foreign degrees were not recognized in Russia. He only got a regular professorship in Kharkov in 1920. He moved to Leningrad in 1932. While he successfully fled during the German siege in 1941, his son was killed in the conflict. After the war, he moved to Moscow where he finished his career. Besides his polynomials and work on Hilbert's 19th problem, he is known for his characterization of totally monotone functions on $[0, \infty)$ (functions which are C^∞ with $(-1)^n f^{(n)}(x) \geq 0$) and a famous inequality on polynomials on $\mathbb{C}$ that $\max_{|z| \leq 1} |P'(z)| \leq n \max_{|z| \leq 1} |P(z)|$, where n is the degree of P (see Problem 28 of Section 3.5).

Besides the Bernstein polynomial proof of the first theorem that we give in this section and Fejér's proof of the second theorem that we give in Section 3.5, there are alternate proofs of the Weierstrass theorems. Among them are proofs of Picard for the second theorem [**723**] in Problem 12 of Section 3.5, of Landau [**542**] for the first theorem in Problem 15 of Section 3.5, and of Lerch [**573**]. Volterra [**955**] proved the second theorem, by noting that piecewise linear continuous functions are $\| \ \|_\infty$-dense in $C(\partial \mathbb{D})$ (see Problem 12) and that Dirichlet had proven uniform convergence of Fourier series for such functions (see Theorem 3.5.5). We also mention proofs of Lebesgue [**555**], who first handled $|x|$ (see Problem 13) and then piecewise affine and continuous functions (see Problem 12), and one of the second theorem by de la Vallée Poussin [**229**], sketched in Problem 13 of Section 3.5. There is a proof of Fejér for the first theorem [**299, 300**], who proved if $f \in C[-1, 1]$

and if $x_j^{(n)} = \cos(2j-1)\pi/2n$ $(j = 1, \ldots, n)$, then the unique polynomial $H_n(x)$ (called the Hermite–Fejér interpolation) of degree at most $2n-1$ that obeys $H_n'(x)(x_j) = 0$, $H_n(x_j) = f(x_j)$, $j = 1, \ldots, n$, has $\|H_n - f\|_\infty \to 0$ (for the details of this proof, see Pinkus [**728**]).

Interestingly enough, the Weierstrass theorem using all polynomials is overkill—for example, it is easy to see (Problem 14) in $C[0,1]$ that any f can be approximated by polynomials in x^2. More generally, it is a theorem that if $t_0 \equiv 0 < t_1 < t_2 < \ldots$ is a sequence of real numbers and $\sum_{j=1}^\infty t_j^{-1} = \infty$, then finite linear combinations of $\{1, x^{t_1}, x^{t_2}, \ldots\}$ are dense in $C[0,1]$ in $\|\cdot\|_\infty$-norm. This is the Müntz–Satz theorem, which we'll prove as Theorem 9.9.5 of Section 9.9 of Part 2A ; see the Notes to that section for the historical references.

An important property of the maps of $C[0,1]$ to itself given by $B_n : f \to B_n(f)$ is that it is *positivity-preserving*, i.e., $f \geq 0 \Rightarrow B_n(f) \geq 0$ which is immediate given that $x^j(1-x)^{n-j} \geq 0$ for all $x \in [0,1]$. In this regard, there is a remarkable convergence result which the reader will prove in Problem 5.

Definition. Let X be a compact Hausdorff space. A *Korovkin set* is a finite set $\{f_1, \ldots, f_m\}$ of elements of $C(X)$ for which there exist $a_1, \ldots, a_m \in C(X)$ so that

$$P(x,t) = \sum_{j=1}^m a_j(t)\, f_j(x) \qquad (2.4.26)$$

obeys

$$P(x,t) \geq 0 \text{ for all } x,t; \quad P(x,t) = 0 \Leftrightarrow x = t \qquad (2.4.27)$$

The canonical example is $\{1, x, x^2\} \subset C([0,1])$ where $P(x,t) = (x-t)^2$ works.

Theorem 2.4.7 (Korovkin's Theorem). *Let $\{T_n\}_{n=1}^\infty$ be a family of positivity-preserving operators on $C(X)$ and $\{f_j\}_{j=1}^m$ a Korovkin set. If $\|T_n f_j - f_j\|_\infty \to 0$ as $n \to \infty$ for each f_j, $j = 1, \ldots, m$, then $\|T_n f - f\|_\infty \to 0$ for all $f \in C(X)$.*

The special case of $X = [0,1]$, $\{f_j\} = \{1, x, x^2\}$ is due to Korovkin [**514**] in 1953. Since Bohman [**106**] had a related idea somewhat earlier, some call it the Bohman–Korovkin theorem. The version above is due to Lorentz [**605**]. For books and review articles on the subject, see [**515, 25, 653, 24, 729**].

Problems 1–3 explore slightly the question of how small $\|f - P_n\|_\infty$ is over polynomials of degree n depending on the regularity of f (i.e., rate of convergence over best approximation) and there we only look at $P_n = B_n(f)$. There is a huge literature on the general question for $f \in C([0,1])$; see the books of DeVore–Lorentz [**239**], Ditzian–Totik [**250**], and Mhaskar–Pai [**653**].

Problems

1. Let f be a function on $[0, 1]$ which obeys

$$|f(x) - f(y)| \leq C|x - y|^\theta \tag{2.4.28}$$

   for some C and $\theta \in [0, 1]$. Prove that there is a constant D so that

$$\|f - B_n(f)\|_\infty \leq Dn^{-\theta/(2+\theta)} \tag{2.4.29}$$

   (*Hint*: Optimize ε in (2.4.5).)

2. Suppose that f is C^1.
   (a) Prove that $\mathbb{E}_{x,n}(f'(x)(x - \frac{j}{n})) = 0$.
   (b) Prove that

$$|f(x) - B_n(f)(x)| \leq \mathbb{E}_{x,n}(|f(x) - f(\tfrac{j}{n}) - f'(x)(x - \tfrac{j}{n})|) \tag{2.4.30}$$

   (c) Prove that

$$\|f - B_n(f)\|_\infty \leq \frac{\|f_\infty\| + \|f'\|_\infty}{2n\varepsilon^2} \\ + \sup_{|x-y|\leq\varepsilon} |f(x) - f(y) - f'(x)(x - y)| \tag{2.4.31}$$

   (d) If f is C^2, prove that

$$\|f - B_n(f)\|_\infty \leq Dn^{-1/2} \tag{2.4.32}$$

3. (a) Let $f(x) = e^x$. Prove that $B_n(f)(x) = [1 + (e^{1/n} - 1)x]^n$.
   (b) For this case, prove that $n\|B_n(f) - f\|_\infty$ approaches a nonzero constant.

4. This problem will show the surprising fact discovered by Pál [**697**] in 1914 that any continuous function f on $[\theta, 1 - \theta]$ ($0 < \theta < \frac{1}{2}$) can be uniformly approximated by polynomials with integer coefficients!
   (a) Let $f \in C([0, 1])$ and define

$$(\delta B_n)(f)(x) = \sum_{j=0}^{n} \left\{ \binom{n}{j} f\left(\frac{j}{n}\right) \right\} x^j (1 - x)^{n-j} \tag{2.4.33}$$

$$\equiv \sum_{j=0}^{n} \delta b(f)_{n,j}\, x^j (1 - x)^{n-j} \tag{2.4.34}$$

   where $\{y\} \in [0, 1)$ is the fractional part of y.

(b) Prove that $(n \geq 2)$

$$\delta b(f)_{n,j} \leq \frac{1}{n} \binom{n}{j}, \quad j = 0, n-1$$

$$\delta b(f)_{n,j} \leq \frac{4}{n^2} \binom{n}{j}, \quad 2 \leq j \leq n-2$$

(2.4.35)

(c) Prove that if $f(0), f(1) \in \mathbb{Z}$,

$$\|\delta B_n(f)\|_\infty \leq \frac{6}{n}$$

(2.4.36)

(d) Conclude that f can be approximated by polynomials with integral coefficients if and only if $f(0), f(1) \in \mathbb{Z}$.

(e) Prove that for any $f \in C([\theta, 1-\theta]), \quad 0 < \theta < \frac{1}{2}$, can be uniformly approximated by polynomials with integer coefficients.

(f) Prove Pál's original result that for $0 < a < 1$, $f \in C([-a, a])$ can be uniformly approximated by polynomials with integral coefficients if and only if $f(0)$ is an integer.

5. This problem will take the reader through a proof of Korovkin's theorem (Theorem 2.4.7).

(a) If T is a positivity-preserving operator on $C(X)$ prove that

(a1) $|Tf| \leq T|f|$.

(a2) Prove that $f \geq g \geq 0 \Rightarrow Tf \geq Tg$.

(a3) If $f \in C(X)$ and $f(x) \geq 1$ for all x, prove that

$$\|Tg\|_\infty \leq \|Tf\|_\infty \|g\|_\infty$$

(2.4.37)

(b) Let $\{f_j\}_{j=1}^m$ be a Korovkin set. Let $t_1 \neq t_2$ be two points in X and let

$$\rho(x) = C[P(x, t_1) + P(x, t_2)]$$

(2.4.38)

where C is chosen so that

$$1 = \inf_x \rho(x) \leq \sup \rho(x) = \|\rho\|_\infty$$

(2.4.39)

Prove that if $T_n f_j \to f_j$ for each j

$$\sup_n \|T_n\| < \infty$$

(2.4.40)

(*Hint*: Use (2.4.37) with $f = \rho$.)

(c) For any $\varepsilon > 0$ and $f \in C(X)$, show there is a constant D_ε so that for all $x, t \in X$

$$|f(x)\rho(t) - f(t)\rho(x)| \leq \varepsilon + D_\varepsilon \sum_{j=1}^{m} \rho(t)a_j(t)f_j(x) \tag{2.4.41}$$

$$\leq \varepsilon + D_\varepsilon \sum_{j=1}^{n} a_j(t)\left[\rho(t)f_j(x) - \rho(x)f_j(t)\right] \tag{2.4.42}$$

(d) Prove that

$$\|\rho(T_n f) - f(T_n \rho)\|_\infty \leq \varepsilon \|T_n\| + $$
$$D_\varepsilon \sum_{j=1}^{m} \|a_j\|_\infty \|\rho(T_n f_j) - f_j(T_n \rho)\| \tag{2.4.43}$$

(e) Conclude that if $T_n f_j \to f_j$ for $j = 1, \ldots, m$, then $\|T_n f - f\|_\infty \to 0$ for all f.

(f) Compute $B_n g$ for $g = 1, x, x^2$ and conclude that $B_n f \to f$ uniformly for all $f \in C([0,1])$.

6. This problem will prove multivariate Bernstein polynomial approximation and use it to prove Weierstrass' approximation theorem for compact subsets of $\mathbb{R}^\nu$. In the next problem, this will be used to prove Weierstrass' second theorem. Given $f \in C([0,1]^\nu)$ and $n = 1, 2, \ldots$, define

$$(B_{n,\nu}f)(x) = \sum_{j_1,\ldots,j_\nu=0}^{n} f\left(\frac{j_1}{n},\ldots,\frac{j_\nu}{n}\right)\prod_{k=1}^{\nu}\binom{n}{j_k}x_k^{j_k}(1-x_k)^{n-j_k} \tag{2.4.44}$$

(a) Prove that $\{1, x_1, \ldots, x_\nu, \sum_{j=1}^{\nu} x_j^2\}$ is a Korovkin set and use that to prove that for any f

$$\|B_{n,\nu}f - f\|_\infty \to 0 \text{ as } n \to \infty \tag{2.4.45}$$

(b) Prove (2.4.45) by mimicking the proof in the text when $\nu = 1$.

(c) If $K \subset \mathbb{R}^\nu$ is compact, prove that the polynomials in $x_1, \ldots, x_\nu$ are dense in $C(K)$ in $\|\cdot\|_\infty$. (*Hint*: Tietze extension theorem.)

7. (a) Let $K \subset \mathbb{C}$ be compact. Prove that the polynomials in z and $\bar{z}$ are dense in $C(K)$.

(b) Prove that the functions $\sum_{n=-N}^{N} a_n e^{in\theta}$ are dense in $C(\partial\mathbb{D})$.

Remark. This problem requires Problem 6.

8. Define

$$(\Delta_h f)(x) = f(x+h) - f(x); \quad \Delta_h^n = \Delta_h(\Delta_h^{n-1}), n \geq 2 \tag{2.4.46}$$

(a) Prove that $B_n f$ is C^1 and

$$(B_n f)'(x) = n \sum_{j=0}^{n-1} (\Delta_{1/n} f)\left(\frac{j}{n}\right) x^j (1-x)^{n-1-j} \qquad (2.4.47)$$

(b) Prove that $B_n f$ is C^ℓ for each ℓ with

$$(B_n f)^{(\ell)}(x) = n(n-1)\cdots(n-\ell+1) \sum_{j=0}^{n-\ell} (\Delta^\ell_{1/n} f)\left(\frac{j}{n}\right) x^j (1-x)^{n-\ell-j}$$

$$(2.4.48)$$

(c) If f is C^ℓ, prove that uniformly in x, $n^\ell (\Delta^\ell_{1/n} f)(x) \to f^{(\ell)}(x)$.

(d) Prove that if f is C^ℓ, $(B_n f)^{(\ell)} \to f^{(\ell)}$ uniformly.

(e) If f is convex, prove that each $B_n f$ is convex.

9. (a) With Δ^n_h given by (2.4.46), prove that

$$(B_n f)(x) = \sum_{r=0}^{n} (\Delta^r_{1/n} f)(0) \binom{n}{r} x^r \qquad (2.4.49)$$

(b) If f is a polynomial of degree N, prove that for $n > N$, $B_n f$ is a polynomial of degree N.

(c) If $(B_n f) = f$ for some n, prove that f is a constant.

10. (a) Let $f \in C([0,1])$. Show for some α, $g(x) = f(x) - \alpha x$ is the restriction to $[0,1]$ for a continuous periodic function, h, on $\mathbb{R}$ with $h(x+1) = h(x)$.

(b) Prove that $e^{2\pi i n x}$ is a uniform limit of polynomials on x in $C([0,1])$.

(c) Show that the second Weierstrass theorem implies the first.

11. (a) Let $f \in C(\partial\mathbb{D})$. Show that f is a uniform limit of functions of the form $g(e^{i\theta}) + \sin(\theta) h(e^{i\theta})$, where g, h obey

$$g(e^{-i\theta}) = g(e^{i\theta}) \qquad (2.4.50)$$

Thus, to prove the second Weierstrass theorem, it suffices to prove it for g's obeying (2.4.50).

(b) Assuming the first Weierstrass theorem, show that any $g \in C(\partial\mathbb{D})$ obeying (2.4.50) is a uniform limit of polynomials in $\cos(\theta)$.

(c) Show that the first Weierstrass theorem implies the second.

12. Let $P([0,1])$ be the continuous functions on $[0,1]$ which are piecewise affine.

(a) Show that any $f \in C([0,1])$ is a uniform limit of elements of $P([0,1])$.

(b) Let $x_+ = x$ if $x \geq 0$ and 0 if $x \leq 0$. Prove that any g in $P([0,1])$ can be written as a finite linear combination of $f(x) \equiv 1$ and $\{h_y(x)\}_{y \in [0,1]}$, where $h_y(x) = (x - y)_+$.

(c) Assuming $|x|$ can be approximated by polynomials on $[-1, 1]$, prove that x_+ can be so approximated on any $[a, b]$.

(d) Assuming $|x|$ can be approximated by polynomials in x on $[-1, 1]$, prove the first Weierstrass theorem (and see Problem 13 for $|x|$).

13. (a) Prove that the binomial expansion of $\sqrt{1-x}$ has the form $\sqrt{1-x} = 1 - \sum_{n=1}^{\infty} c_n x^n$ with $c_n \geq 0$.

(b) Prove that $\sum_{n=1}^{\infty} c_n = 1$. (*Hint:* $\lim_{x \uparrow 1} 1 - \sqrt{1-x} = 1$.)

(c) Prove that for $y \in [0, 1]$, $\sqrt{1-y}$ is a uniform limit of polynomials in y.

(d) Prove that, on $[-1, 1]$, $|x|$ is a uniform limit of polynomials in x^2. (*Hint:* $|x| = \sqrt{1 - (1 - x^2)}$.)

Remark. This expansion will play an important role in our proof of the existence of square roots of positive operators on a Hilbert space in Section 2.4 of Part 4.

14. Fix $\alpha \in (0, \infty)$. Prove that any $f \in C([0,1])$ is a uniform limit of polynomials in x^α. (*Remark.* Consider $\alpha = 2, 3, \ldots$.)

2.5. The Stone–Weierstrass Theorem

Recall that $C_{\mathbb{R}}(X)$ is the bounded continuous real-valued functions on X, a topological space.

Definition. We say a set $S \subset C_{\mathbb{R}}(X)$, with X a topological space, *separates points* if for all $x, y \in X$, with $x \neq y$, there is $f \in S$ so $f(x) \neq f(y)$. We say S *strongly separates points* if for each $x, y \in X$ with $x \neq y$, $\{(f(x), f(y))\}_{f \in S}$ is all of $\mathbb{R}^2$.

The following is easy (Problem 1):

Proposition 2.5.1. *If $S \subset C_{\mathbb{R}}(X)$ is a vector space (i.e., $f, g \in S$ and $\lambda \in \mathbb{R} \Rightarrow f + g$ and λf lie in S), separates points, and $\mathbb{1} \in S$, then S strongly separates points.*

In this section, we'll prove the following spectacular generalization of Weierstrass' theorems:

Theorem 2.5.2 (Stone–Weierstrass Theorem). *Let X be a compact Hausdorff space. Let $S \subset C_{\mathbb{R}}(X)$ obey*

(i) S is a subalgebra of $C_{\mathbb{R}}(X)$, that is, $f, g \in S$ and $\lambda \in \mathbb{R} \Rightarrow f + g,$
    $fg, \lambda f \in S$.
(ii) S separates points.
(iii) $\mathbb{1} \in S$.
Then the $\|\cdot\|_\infty$-closure of S is all of $C_{\mathbb{R}}(X)$.

Remark. One can replace (ii) and (iii) by the weaker condition that S strongly separates points; see Problem 2.

After noting that this implies the Weierstrass theorems, we show it is implied by another density theorem that requires some definitions:

Definition. If f, g lie in $C_{\mathbb{R}}(X)$, define the *sup* and *inf* of f and g by

$$(f \vee g)(x) = \max(f(x), g(x)) \qquad (2.5.1)$$
$$(f \wedge g)(x) = \min(f(x), g(x)) \qquad (2.5.2)$$

Note that $f \vee g$ and $f \wedge g$ both lie in $C_{\mathbb{R}}(X)$ and that $h = f \vee g$ has the property that $h - f$, $h - g \geq 0$ and $k \geq f$, $k \geq g \Rightarrow k \geq h$, that is, h is the smallest upper bound.

Definition. A *sublattice* of $C_{\mathbb{R}}(X)$ is a subset, L, with $f, g \in L \Rightarrow f \vee g$, $f \wedge g \in L$. A *vector lattice* is a sublattice that also obeys $f, g \in L, \lambda \in \mathbb{R} \Rightarrow f + g, \lambda f \in L$.

Notice since

$$f \vee g + f \wedge g = f + g \qquad (2.5.3)$$

if L is a subspace of $C_{\mathbb{R}}(X)$, it is enough to suppose $f, g \in L \Rightarrow f \vee g \in L$.

Section 4.8 has a detailed study of certain vector lattices.

Theorem 2.5.3 (Kakutani–Krein Theorem). *Let X be a compact Hausdorff space and $L \subset C_{\mathbb{R}}(X)$ obey*

(i) *L is a vector lattice.*
(ii) *L strongly separates points.*
Then the $\|\cdot\|_\infty$-closure of L is all of $C_{\mathbb{R}}(X)$.

Notice that the polynomials with real coefficients on $[a, b]$ obey all the hypotheses of the Stone–Weierstrass theorem, so it implies the first Weierstrass theorem (since density of the real polynomials in $C_{\mathbb{R}}([a, b])$ easily yields density of the complex polynomials in $C([a, b])$). A similar argument using realizations of sin and cos shows the Stone–Weierstrass theorem also implies the second Weierstrass theorem (Problem 3).

We'll first show Theorem 2.5.3 implies Theorem 2.5.2, and then prove Theorem 2.5.3. Finally, we explore various extensions of Theorem 2.5.2.

Proof of Theorem 2.5.2 using Theorem 2.5.3. Let $f \in S$. By Proposition 2.4.3 and scaling, for any ε, there is a polynomial P_ε so

$$\sup_{\substack{|y| \leq \|f\|_\infty \\ y \in \mathbb{R}}} ||y| - P_\varepsilon(y)| \leq \varepsilon \tag{2.5.4}$$

Thus, $|f| = \|\cdot\|_\infty\text{-}\lim_{\varepsilon \downarrow 0} P_\varepsilon(f)$.

Since S is an algebra, polynomials in f lie in S, so we conclude that $|f| \in \bar{S}$. We have

$$f \vee g = \tfrac{1}{2}\left[f + g + |f - g|\right] \tag{2.5.5}$$

$$f \wedge g = \tfrac{1}{2}\left[f + g - |f - g|\right] \tag{2.5.6}$$

It follows that $\bar{S}$ is a vector lattice.

By Proposition 2.5.1, $\bar{S}$ strongly separates points. Thus, by the Kakutani–Krein theorem, $\overline{\bar{S}} = \bar{S} = C_\mathbb{R}(X)$. $\qquad\square$

Proof of Theorem 2.5.3. Given $f \in C_\mathbb{R}(x)$ and $\varepsilon > 0$, we need to find $g \in L$ so for all x,

$$f(x) - \varepsilon \leq g(x) \leq f(x) + \varepsilon \tag{2.5.7}$$

By the strong separation property, for any $x, y \in X$, we can find $h_{x,y} \in L$ so

$$h_{x,y}(x) = f(x), \qquad h_{x,y}(y) = f(y) \tag{2.5.8}$$

Fix x. By continuity, for each y there is an open set U_y with $y \in U_y$, so

$$h_{x,y}(z) < f(z) + \varepsilon \quad \text{if } z \in U_y \tag{2.5.9}$$

Clearly, $\bigcup_y U_y = X$, so we can find $y_1, \ldots, y_n$ so

$$\bigcup_{j=1}^{n} U_{y_j} = X \tag{2.5.10}$$

Let

$$g_x(z) = \min_{j=1,\ldots,n} h_{x,y_j}(z) \tag{2.5.11}$$

which lies in L since L is a lattice. Notice since (2.5.9) and (2.5.10) hold and since $h_{x,y}(x) = f(x)$, we have

$$g_x(x) = f(x), \qquad g_x(z) < f(z) + \varepsilon \quad \text{for all } z \in X \tag{2.5.12}$$

Now we repeat the argument "upside down." By continuity, for each x, there exists V_x so $x \in V_x$ and

$$g_x(z) > f(z) - \varepsilon \quad \text{if } z \in V_x \tag{2.5.13}$$

$\bigcup_x V_x = X$, so we can find $x_1, \ldots, x_m \in X$, so

$$\bigcup_{j=1}^{m} V_{x_j} = X \qquad (2.5.14)$$

Let

$$g(z) = \max_{j=1,\ldots,m} g_{x_j}(z) \qquad (2.5.15)$$

Since L is a lattice, $g \in L$.

By (2.5.12), for all z, we have $g(z) < f(z) + \varepsilon$. By (2.5.13) and (2.5.14), for all z, $g(z) > f(z) - \varepsilon$. It follows that we constructed the required g obeying (2.5.7). $\qquad \square$

Example 2.2.11, revisited. If H is the Hilbert cube and x_j the j-th coordinate functions, polynomials in $\{x_j\}_{j=1}^{\infty}$ with rational coefficients are $\|\cdot\|_\infty$ dense in the polynomials in $\{x_j\}_{j=1}^{\infty}$ which are an algebra separating points, so $C_\mathbb{R}(H)$ is separable. $\qquad \square$

Having proven the main theorems, we now turn to some variants.

Theorem 2.5.4. *Let $a \in X$, a compact Hausdorff space. Let $C_a(X) = \{f \in C_\mathbb{R}(X) \mid f(a) = 0\}$. Suppose $S \subset C_a(X)$ obeys*

(i) *S is a subalgebra of $C_a(X)$.*
(ii) *S separates points.*

Then the $\|\cdot\|_\infty$-closure of S is all of $C_a(X)$.

Proof. Let $\widetilde{S} = \{\lambda \mathbb{1} + g \mid \lambda \in \mathbb{R}, g \in S\}$. Then it is easy to see that $\widetilde{S}$ obeys all the hypotheses of Theorem 2.5.2, so $\widetilde{S}$ is dense in $C_\mathbb{R}(X)$. Thus, for any $f \in C_a(X)$, there exist $\lambda_n \in \mathbb{R}$ and $g_n \in S$ so $\|\lambda_n \mathbb{1} + g_n - f\|_\infty \to 0$ as $n \to \infty$. Since $f(a) = g_n(a) = 0$, we have that $\lambda_n \to 0$, so $\|g_n - f\|_\infty \to 0$, that is, $f \in \bar{S}$. Since $C_a(X)$ is closed, $\bar{S} \subset C_a(X)$, so $\bar{S} = C_a(X)$. $\qquad \square$

Theorem 2.5.5. *Let X be a locally compact Hausdorff space. Let $C_\infty(X) = \{f \in C_\mathbb{R}(X) \mid f \to 0 \text{ at } \infty \text{ in the sense that for all } \varepsilon > 0, \text{ there is a compact } K \subset X, \text{ so that } \sup_{x \notin K}|f(x)| < \varepsilon\}$. Let $S \subset C_\infty(X)$ obey*

(i) *S is a subalgebra.*
(ii) *S separates points of X.*
(iii) *For any $x \in X$, there is $f \in S$ so $f(x) \neq 0$.*

Then the $\|\cdot\|_\infty$-closure of S is $C_\infty(X)$.

Proof. Let $X_\infty = X \cup \{\infty\}$ be the one-point compactification of X. Extend $f \in C_\infty(X)$ to X_∞ by setting $f(\infty) = 0$. Then it is easy to see f is continuous at ∞, so $f \in C(X_\infty)$. Thus, $C_\infty(X) = C_\infty(X_\infty)$, where the latter means the object in Theorem 2.5.4 with $a = \infty$.

Theorem 2.5.4 implies this theorem. $\qquad \square$

We now turn to complex-valued functions.

Example 2.5.6. Let $S \subset C(\partial\mathbb{D})$ be the polynomials in z. As we've seen (Proposition 2.4.4), $\bar{S}$ is much smaller than all of $C(\partial\mathbb{D})$ (e.g., it is the functions analytic in $\mathbb{D}$ and continuous in $\mathbb{S}$). But it obeys all the hypotheses of Theorem 2.5.2 except $S \subset C(\partial\mathbb{D})$, not $C_\mathbb{R}(\partial\mathbb{D})$. This shows that one needs an additional assumption to get a $C(X)$ theorem. That explains the complex conjugate condition below. $\square$

Theorem 2.5.7 (Complex Stone–Weierstrass Theorem). *Let X be a compact Hausdorff space. Let $S \subset C(X)$ obey*

(i) *S is a subalgebra of $C(X)$, that is, $f, g \in S$ and $\lambda \in \mathbb{C} \Rightarrow f + g, fg, \lambda f \in S$.*
(ii) *S is complex conjugate invariant, that is, $f \in S \Rightarrow \bar{f} \in S$.*
(iii) *S separates points.*
(iv) *$\mathbb{1} \in S$.*

Then the $\|\cdot\|_\infty$-closure of S is all of $C(X)$.

Proof. Let $S_\mathbb{R} = C_\mathbb{R}(X) \cap S$. $S_\mathbb{R}$ is clearly a real subalgebra with $\mathbb{1} \in S_\mathbb{R}$. It separates points; for given distinct $x, y \in X$, find $f \in S$ with $f(x) \neq f(y)$. By multiplying, by i if necessary, we can suppose $\operatorname{Re} f(x) \neq \operatorname{Re} f(y)$. Since $f, \bar{f} \in S$, $\frac{1}{2}(f + \bar{f}) \in S_\mathbb{R}$ and it separates x and y. Thus, by Theorem 2.5.2, $S_\mathbb{R}$ is dense in $C_\mathbb{R}(X)$.

Given $f \in C(X)$, find $g_n, h_n \in S_\mathbb{R}$, so $g_n \to \operatorname{Re} f$, $h_n \to \operatorname{Im} f$ in $\|\cdot\|_\infty$. Then $f_n \equiv g_n + ih_n \in S$ and $f_n \to f$. $\square$

Remark. It is interesting to see what fails if S is the polynomials in z on $\partial\mathbb{D}$. In that case, $S_\mathbb{R}$ consists of only multiples of $\mathbb{1}$ and it does not separate points. $f \in S$ does not imply $\operatorname{Re} f \in S$, so our proof under the assumption of S closed under complex conjugation doesn't apply.

Notes and Historical Remarks. The Stone–Weierstrass theorem appeared in 1937 in M. Stone [**885**]. His original proof was quite involved, and the now standard proof only appeared in his 1948 paper [**886**]. He says the simplification comes from suggestions of Kakutani and Chevalley. In essence, it depends on a reformulation of a 1941 theorem we call the Kakutani–Krein theorem, after work of Kakutani [**469**] and of Mark and Selim Krein [**526**], two brothers (Mark has a capsule biography in the Notes to Section 7.5 of Part 4). Because of roughly simultaneous work of Stone [**886**] and Yoshida [**1007**], it is sometimes called the Kakutani–Krein–Stone–Yoshida theorem, or after Kadison [**463**], the Kakutani–Krein–Kadison theorem.

These authors didn't look at lattices in $C_\mathbb{R}(X)$; rather, following up on developments initiated by F. Riesz (and discussed in Section 4.8), they studied a class of Banach lattices and showed they were a $C_{\mathbb{R}}(X)$ for a certain X. Implicitly, they proved our Theorem 2.5.3.

Marshall Harvey Stone (1903–89) was the son of Harlan Stone, who served on the U.S. Supreme Court for twenty-one years, five of them as Chief Justice. Despite his background as a republican, Harlan Stone was supportive of the New Deal, so much so that he, Brandeis, and Cardozo were known as the three musketeers. There is a famous story of a chance meeting at tea of Stone and Francis Hopkins, Roosevelt's Secretary of Health and Welfare where Stone dropped hints about how to formulate the Social Security Act so it would meet constitutional muster. Marshall was an undergraduate and graduate student at Harvard where he studied under George David Birkhoff (1884–1944). He served on the Harvard and Yale faculties, moving in 1946 to be chair at Chicago, where he spent the rest of his career. He made fundamental contributions to functional analysis, most notably his work on the spectral theorem and its applications. Stone's students include Calkin, Eberlein, Hewitt, Kadison, and Mackey.

Problems

1. Prove Proposition 2.5.1. (*Hint*: What is the dimension of $\mathbb{R}^2$?)

2. (a) Suppose $f \in C([a,b])$ with $0 \in [a,b]$ has $f(0) = 0$. Prove that there are polynomials $P_n(x)$ with $P_n(0) = 0$ so $\|P_n - f\|_\infty \to 0$.

   (b) Knowing that there are polynomials $P_n(x)$ converging uniformly to $|x|$ on $[-1,1]$, prove there are such polynomials $P_n(x)$ with $P_n(0) = 0$.

   (c) If $S \subset C_{\mathbb{R}}(X)$ is a subalgebra, without knowing that $\mathbb{1} \in S$, prove that S is a lattice.

   (d) Prove Theorem 2.5.2 with (b) and (c) replaced by the condition that S strongly separates points.

3. (a) Prove that $\cos(nx)$, $n = 0, 1, 2, \ldots$, is a polynomial in $\cos(x)$ and $\sin(nx)/\sin(x)$, $n = 1, 2, \ldots$, is a polynomial in $\cos(x)$.

   (b) Show that to prove the second Weierstrass theorem, it suffices to show that polynomials in $\cos(x)$ and $\sin(x)$ are dense in $C_{\mathbb{R}}(\partial\mathbb{D})$.

   (c) Show that the span of 1, $\cos(\theta)$, $\sin(\theta)$ strongly separates $\partial\mathbb{D}$.

   (d) Prove the second Weierstrass theorem from the Stone–Weierstrass theorem.

2.6. Nets

A huge number of topological notions in a metric space can be described in terms of convergent sequences. For example, if X has two metrics, ρ_1 and

ρ_2, with exactly the same convergent sequences, then the induced topologies are identical (see (2) below).

There are two themes in this section. The first, summarized by the words "sequences are inadequate in general topological spaces," shows that rather than the equivalences in the metric space case, one often gets at best one direction. The second, summarized by "but nets are adequate," shows that there is a replacement, called nets, that restores the equivalences if one replaces sequences by nets.

To emphasize the themes, in the list below of sequential equivalences for metric space, we'll provide for each an example number where it is shown the sequence equivalence fails in general topological spaces and a theorem number where the net version is proven. Here is a list of metric space results.

(1) In a metric space, X, if $A \subset X$, then $x \in \bar{A}$ if and only if there is a sequence x_n converging to x (Example 2.6.1, Theorem 2.6.3).

(2) In a metric space, two metrics with exactly the same convergent sequences have identical open sets. This follows from (1) since they have the same closed sets (Example 2.6.1, Theorem 2.6.3).

(3) In a metric space, X, $f \colon X \to Y$, another metric space is continuous if and only if $x_n \to x$ in $X \Rightarrow f(x_n) \to f(x)$ in Y (Example 2.6.1, Theorem 2.6.3).

(4) In a semimetric space ($\rho(x,y) = 0 \Rightarrow x = y$ is dropped), the topology is Hausdorff if and only if limits of sequences are unique (Example 2.6.1, Theorem 2.6.3).

(5) In a metric space, if x is a limit point of a sequence $\{x_n\}_{n=1}^{\infty}$, there is a subsequence converging to x (Example 2.6.2, Theorem 2.6.4).

(6) A metric space is compact if and only if every sequence has a convergent subsequence (Example 2.6.2, Theorem 2.6.4).

(7) A function from a metric space, X, to $\mathbb{R} \cup \{\infty\}$ is lsc if and only if $x_n \to x \Rightarrow f(x) \leq \liminf f(x_n)$ (Example 2.6.1, Theorem 2.6.3).

Here are two examples of topological spaces that show the limitations of sequences:

Example 2.6.1 (Cocountable Sets). Let X be $[0,1]$ (all that matters is that X is uncountable—the order on $[0,1]$ plays no role in this example). The closed sets will be X and all countable sets, a family closed under arbitrary intersections and finite (even countable) unions. Thus, the topology, $\mathcal{T}$, that is, the open sets are $\emptyset$ and the complements of countable sets.

Suppose $x_n \to x$ in this topology. Let $A = \{y = x_n \mid \text{some } n,\ x_n \neq x\}$. A is countable, so $X \setminus A$ is open and $x \notin A$, so $X \setminus A$ is a neighborhood of x. Thus, for some N, $x_n \notin A$ if $n \geq N$, that is, $x_n = x$ if $n \geq N$. Of course, if

$x_n = x$ for all large n, $x_n \to x$. Therefore, in this topology, $x_n \to x$ if and only if $x_n = x$ for n large.

Thus, this topology and the discrete topology have the *same* convergent sequences, so the convergent sequences do not determine the topology. Let $X = [0, 1]$ with this topology and $\widetilde{X} = [0, 1]$ with the discrete topology. Let $f : X \to \widetilde{X}$ by $f(x) = x$. Then f takes convergent sequences to convergent sequences, but f is not continuous since $\{x_0\}$ is open in $\widetilde{X}$ for each x_0, but $f^{-1}[\{x_0\}]$ is not.

Since $X \setminus \{x_0\}$ is not closed, $\overline{X \setminus \{x_0\}} = X$, but no sequence $\{x_n\}_{n=1}^\infty$ with $x_n \in X \setminus \{x_0\}$ converges to $x_0 \in \overline{X \setminus \{x_0\}}$. Even though limits of sequences are unique, this topology is not Hausdorff but only T_1 ($\{x_0\}$ is closed, but since all neighborhoods have countable complements, $x \neq y$ cannot have disjoint neighborhoods).

Since every convergent sequence is eventually constant, every real-valued function obeys $f(x) \leq \liminf f(x_n)$ for all convergent sequences, but, for example, in this topology the characteristic function of $[0, \frac{1}{2}]$ is not lsc (or usc) since $\{x \mid f(x) > \frac{1}{2}\} = \{x \mid f(x) \geq \frac{1}{2}\}$ is neither open or closed.

This example shows (1), (2), (3), (4), and (7) fail in general topological spaces. □

Example 2.6.2 (Unit Ball in $(\ell^\infty)^*$ in Weak-$*$ Topology). This example gives a compact topological space with a sequence $\{x_n\}_{n=1}^\infty$ with no convergent subsequence. It thus directly violates a putative extension of (6) to general topological spaces. By Theorem 2.3.4, $\{x_n\}_{n=1}^\infty$ has a limit point, x_∞, so this is an example of a sequence with a limit point but no subsequence converging to it, showing that (5) does not hold in general topological spaces.

This example depends on various aspects of the theory of Banach spaces, which we refer to, even though the results we need are only in Chapter 5. Let ℓ^∞ be the space of bounded sequences, $\{a_n\}_{n=1}^\infty$, in $\|a\| = \sup_n |a_n|$. Let X be the unit ball of the dual space, $(\ell^\infty)^*$. By the Banach–Alaoglu theorem (Theorem 5.8.1), X is compact if the weak-$*$ topology is put on X, that is, the weakest topology in which $\ell \mapsto \ell(a)$ is continuous for each $a \in \ell^\infty$.

Let $\delta_n \in (\ell^\infty)^*$ be defined by $\delta_n(a) = a_n$. $\delta_n \in X$. If $y_j = \delta_{n(j)}$ is a subsequence, let $a \in \ell^\infty$ be defined by

$$
a_n = \begin{cases} 1 & n = n(2j), & j = 1, 2, \ldots \\ -1 & n = n(2n+1), & j = 0, 1, 2, \ldots \\ 0 & n \neq \dot{n}(j), & \text{for any } j \end{cases}
$$

Then $y_j(a) = \{-1, 1, -1, \ldots\}$ does not converge. Thus, $\{\delta_n\}_{n=1}^\infty$ has no convergent subsequence, as required. □

Having diagnosed the disease, let us turn to the cure.

Definition. A *directed set* is a partially ordered set Z with the property that for all $\alpha, \beta \in Z$, there exists γ with $\gamma > \alpha$, $\gamma > \beta$. If $S(\alpha)$ is an α-dependent statement, we say $S(\alpha)$ is *eventually* true if and only if for some $\alpha_0 \in Z$, $S(\alpha)$ is true if $\alpha > \alpha_0$. We say $S(\alpha)$ is *frequently* true if for all $\alpha_0 \in Z$, there exists $\beta > \alpha_0$ so that $S(\beta)$ is true.

Notice that $S(\alpha)$ is frequently false if and only if it is not eventually true.

Definition. A *net*, $\{x_\alpha\}_{\alpha \in Z}$, in a topological space, X, is a function from a directed set Z to X. If $x \in X$, we say x_α *converges* to x, writing $x_\alpha \to x$, if and only if for any neighborhood, N, of x, eventually $x_\alpha \in N$. We say x is a *limit point* (also called a *cluster point*) of x_α if and only if for any neighborhood, N, of x, frequently $x_\alpha \in N$.

Notice that if $\mathbb{Z}_+$ has its natural order, a sequence is just a net indexed by $\mathbb{Z}_+$, and convergence and limit point have their usual meaning.

Theorem 2.6.3. *Let X be a topological space with topology, $\mathcal{T}$.*

(a) *If $A \subset X$, $x \in \bar{A}$ if and only if there exists a net $\{x_\alpha\}_{\alpha \in Z}$ with $x_\alpha \in A$ for all α and $x_\alpha \to x$.*

(b) *If $\widetilde{X}$ is X with a potentially distinct topology $\widetilde{\mathcal{T}}$ so that X and $\widetilde{X}$ have exactly the same convergent nets, then $\mathcal{T} = \widetilde{\mathcal{T}}$.*

(c) *If Y is a second topological space, then $f \colon X \to Y$ is continuous if and only if $x_\alpha \to x$ in X implies $f(x_\alpha) \to f(x)$ in Y.*

(d) *$f \colon X \to \mathbb{R} \cup \{\infty\}$ is lsc if and only if for any net $\{x_\alpha\}_{\alpha \in Z}$ in X which converges to some $x \in X$, we have*

$$f(x) \le \liminf f(x_\alpha) \tag{2.6.1}$$

(e) *X is a Hausdorff space if and only if no net has two distinct points to which it converges.*

Remark. If $\{x_\alpha\}_{\alpha \in Z}$ is a net in $\mathbb{R}$, we say $a \in \mathbb{R}$ is its liminf if and only if for all $\varepsilon > 0$, eventually $x_\alpha > a - \varepsilon$ and frequently $x_\alpha < a + \varepsilon$. (See Problem 1 for a proof of the existence of liminf if x_α is bounded below.)

Proof. (a) Let $x \in \bar{A}$. In constructing a net for which $x_\alpha \to x$, we'll see the power of the definition of nets. The key observation is that if $\{N\}_{N \in Z}$ are the neighborhoods of x with $N_1 > N_2$ if and only if $N_1 \subset N_2$, then we have a directed set. For if N_1, N_2 are neighborhoods, then $N_1 \cap N_2$ is a neighborhood and $N_1 \cap N_2 > N_1$, $N_1 \cap N_2 > N_2$. Since $x \in \bar{A}$, $N \cap A \ne \emptyset$ (if not, $\bar{A} \subset X \setminus N^{\text{int}}$, so $x \notin \bar{A}$), so pick $x_N \in N \cap A$. We claim $\{x_N\}_{N \in Z}$, which has $x_N \in A$ for all N, converges to x. For if N_0 is a neighborhood of x and $N > N_0$, $x_N \in N \subset N_0$, so x_N is eventually in N_0.

Conversely, if $x_\alpha \in A$, $x_\alpha \to x$, and $x \notin \bar{A}$, $N \equiv X \setminus \bar{A}$ is a neighborhood of x and x_α is never in N, so clearly, it cannot eventually lie in N. Thus, $x \in \bar{A}$.

(b) By (a), if $\mathcal{T}$ and $\tilde{\mathcal{T}}$ have the same convergent nets, they have the same closure operations, and so the same closed sets. Conversely, if $\mathcal{T} = \tilde{\mathcal{T}}$, then neighborhoods are the same and, thus, also convergence.

(c) Suppose first that f is continuous and $x_\alpha \to x$ in X. If U is a neighborhood of $f(x)$, then $f^{-1}[U]$ is a neighborhood of x, so eventually $x_\alpha \in f^{-1}[U]$. Thus, eventually $f(x_\alpha) \in U$, so $f(x_\alpha) \to f(x)$.

Conversely, suppose f takes convergent nets to convergent nets. Let $A \subset Y$ be closed and choose any $x \in \overline{f^{-1}[A]}$. Then, by (a), there exists $x_\alpha \in f^{-1}[A]$, so $x_\alpha \to x$. By hypothesis, $f(x_\alpha) \to f(x)$, so since A is closed, $f(x) \in A$, that is, $\overline{f^{-1}[A]} \subset f^{-1}[A]$, so $f^{-1}[A]$ is closed. Thus, f is continuous.

(d) This is a one-sided version of the arguments of (c) and is left to the reader (Problem 2).

(e) If X is Hausdorff and $x \neq y$ in X, then there are disjoint neighborhoods, U and V, of x and y. If $\{x_\alpha\}_{\alpha \in Z}$ is a net eventually in U and V, there are α_U and α_V so that $\alpha > \alpha_U \Rightarrow x_\alpha \in U$ and $\alpha > \alpha_V \Rightarrow x_\alpha \in V$. Since X is directed, there is $\beta > \alpha_U$, $\beta > \alpha_V$, so $x_\beta \in U \cap V = \emptyset$. This contradiction shows it cannot be that x_α converges to both x and y.

Conversely, suppose that limits are unique. Let $x \neq y$ in X. Let Z be the set of pairs, U, V, of open neighborhoods U of x and V of y ordered by $(U_1, V_1) > (U_2, V_2)$ if and only if $U_1 \subset U_2$, $V_1 \subset V_2$. Suppose for every such pair, $U \cap V \neq \emptyset$. Pick $x_{(U,V)} \in U \cap V$. This is a net which it is easy to see converges to both x and to y. Thus, uniqueness of limits shows that for some U, V, we have $U \cap V = \emptyset$, that is, X is Hausdorff. $\square$

Definition. Let $\{x_\alpha\}_{\alpha \in Z}$ be a net in a space X. A *subnet* is a net of the form $\{y_\beta\}_{\beta \in Y}$ so that there is a function $F \colon Y \to Z$ so that

$$y_\beta = x_{F(\beta)} \tag{2.6.2}$$

and so that for any $\alpha_0 \in Z$, there is a $\beta_0 \in Y$ so $F(\beta) > \alpha_0$ if $\beta > \beta_0$.

Theorem 2.6.4. (a) *Let* $\{x_\alpha\}_{\alpha \in Z}$ *be a net. Then* x *is a limit point of* $\{x_\alpha\}_{\alpha \in Z}$ *if and only if there is a subnet* $\{y_\beta\}_{\beta \in Y}$ *converging to* x.

(b) *A topological space is compact if and only if every net has a convergent subnet (equivalently, if and only if every net has a limit point).*

Proof. (a) Suppose first that $y_\beta \to x$ for some subnet $\{y_\beta\}_{\beta \in Y}$. For any neighborhood, U, of x, there is $\beta_0 \in Y$ so $\beta > \beta_0$ implies $y_\beta \in U$. Given α, find β_1 so $F(\beta) > \alpha$ if $\beta > \beta_1$. Pick β_2 so that $\beta_2 > \beta_0$ and $\beta_2 > \beta_1$. Then if $\alpha_1 = F(\beta_2)$, we have $\alpha_1 > \alpha_0$ and $x_{\alpha_1} = y_{\beta_2} \in U$. Thus, x_α is frequently in U, that is, x is a limit point of $\{x_\alpha\}_{\alpha \in Z}$.

Conversely, suppose x is a limit point of $\{x_\alpha\}_{\alpha \in Z}$. Let $Y = \{(\alpha, U) \mid \alpha \in Z, U$ an open neighborhood of $x\}$, which is a directed set under the order $(\alpha_2, U_2) > (\alpha_1, U_1)$ if and only if $\alpha_2 > \alpha_1$ and $U_2 \subset U_1$.

For each (α_0, U), let $F(\alpha_0, U) \in Z$ be chosen so that $F(\alpha_0, U) > \alpha_0$ and $x_{F(\alpha_0, U)} \in U$. Since x_α is frequently in U, this is possible. Let $y_{(\alpha, U)} = x_{F(\alpha, U)}$. Since $F(\alpha_0, U) > \alpha_0$, $\{y_{(\alpha, U)}\}_{(\alpha, U) \in Y}$ is a subnet of x_α. Fix $\alpha_0 \in Z$. If $(\alpha, \tilde{U}) > (\alpha_0, U)$, then $y_{(\alpha, \tilde{U})} \in \tilde{U} \subset U$, so eventually $y_{(\alpha, U)}$ lies in U, that is, $y_{(\alpha, U)} \to x$.

(b) By (a), every net has a convergent subnet if and only if every net has a limit point. Suppose X is compact and $\{x_\alpha\}_{\alpha \in Z}$ is a net with no limit point. Then for any $x \in X$, there is a U_x an open neighborhood of x and α_x, so $x_\alpha \notin U_x$ if $\alpha > \alpha_x$. Since $\{U_x\}_{x \in X}$ covers X and X is assumed compact, we can find $U_{x_1}, \dots, U_{x_\ell}$ covering X. If $\alpha > \alpha_{x_j}$ for $j = 1, \dots, \ell$, then $x_\alpha \notin U_{x_j}$, and so $x_\alpha \notin X$. This contradiction shows that if X is compact, then every net has a limit point.

Conversely, suppose that every net in X has a limit point and let $\{U_\alpha\}_{\alpha \in Z}$ be an open cover of X with no finite subcover. Let Y consist of all finite subsets, B, of Z, ordered by $B > C$ if $C \subset B$. For each $B = \{\alpha_1, \dots, \alpha_\ell\}$, let $x_B \in X \setminus \cup_{j=1}^\ell U_{\alpha_j}$, which is possible since we are supposing there is no finite subcover. Let x be a limit point of $\{x_B\}_{B \in Y}$ which exists by hypothesis. By the fact that $\{U_\alpha\}_{\alpha \in Z}$ is a cover of X, there is α_0, so $x \in U_{\alpha_0}$. If $B > \{\alpha_0\}$, then $x_B \notin U_{\alpha_0}$, so x_B is not frequently in U_{α_0}. Thus, x is not a limit point. This contradiction proves there is a finite subcover and X is compact. $\qquad\square$

Notes and Historical Remarks. The idea behind nets goes back to a 1922 paper of Moore and Smith [**663**] called by them "generalized convergence." The modern version of this, as well as the "net" and "subnet" terminology is due to Kelley [**481**].

It was Kelley's intention to use the name "way" rather than "net," so he could then refer to "subways," a rather horrendous pun. But he was persuaded by Norman Steenrod (1910–71) to drop this idea. Steenrod, an outstanding geometer, was quite proper and very much a straight arrow. The story is told that after the Second World War, he killed the quota on admission of Jewish graduate students in mathematics at Princeton, put in place by Lefschetz (a Jewish refugee from Europe, by then long-time chair at Princeton) by obstinately insisting "but shouldn't we accept the most qualified students, period."

Outside France, nets are the standard way to describe convergence in topological spaces, but because of the influence of Bourbaki [**120**], who use an alternate called filters, nets are not universal in France.

Problems

1. Let $\{x_\alpha\}_{\alpha \in Z}$ be a net with values in $\mathbb{R}$ so that for some C, $|x_\alpha| \leq C$ for all C.

   (a) Prove that there is a unique $a \in \mathbb{R}$ so that for all $\varepsilon > 0$, eventually $x_\alpha > a - \varepsilon$ and frequently $x_\alpha < a + \varepsilon$. Call $a = \liminf x_\alpha$.

   (b) Prove that $a = \inf\{b \mid b \text{ is a limit point of } \{x_\alpha\}_{\alpha \in Z}\}$.

   (c) Extend $\liminf$ to the case $x_\alpha \geq -C$ for some C and all α.

2. Prove (d) of Theorem 2.6.3.

3. Let X be a complete metric space. A net $\{x_\alpha\}_{\alpha \in Z}$ is called a *Cauchy net* if $\forall \varepsilon > 0$, $\exists \alpha_0 \in Z$ so that $\beta, \gamma > \alpha_0 \Rightarrow \rho(x_\beta, x_\gamma) < \varepsilon$. Prove that every Cauchy net converges. (*Hint:* Pick α_n inductively so $\alpha_{n+1} > \alpha_n$ and α_n is bigger than the α_0 for $\varepsilon = 1/n$. Prove $y_n \equiv x_{\alpha_n}$ is a Cauchy sequence, and then that x_α converges to the limit of y_n.)

2.7. Product Topologies and Tychonoff's Theorem

Suppose for each $\alpha \in I$, an index set, we are given a topological space, X_α. We let X (or X_I) denote the Cartesian product $\times_\alpha X_\alpha$, the set of objects, $\{x_\alpha\}_{\alpha \in I}$, indexed by $\alpha \in I$ with $x_\alpha \in X_\alpha$. Let $\pi_\alpha \colon X \to X_\alpha$ by $x \mapsto x_\alpha$. More generally, if $J \subset I$ and $X_J = \times_{\alpha \in J} X_\alpha$, then $\pi_J = X \to X_J$ by $\pi_J(x)_\alpha = x_\alpha$ if $\alpha \in J$. More generally still, if $J \subset K \subset I$, we define $\pi_{KJ} \colon X_K \to X_J$ by $\pi_{KJ}(x)_\alpha = x_\alpha$ if $\alpha \in J \subset K$.

There are, a priori, two natural topologies to put on X. First, the *product topology*, the weakest topology on X in which each $\pi_\alpha \colon X \to X_\alpha$ is continuous. This has a subbase, $\{\pi_\alpha^{-1}(U_\alpha) \mid U_\alpha \in \mathcal{T}_\alpha\}$, where α runs through all $\alpha \in I$ and U_α arbitrary open sets in X_α.

The other topology, called the *box topology*, has as a base $\mathcal{O}_{\{U_\alpha\}_{\alpha \in I}} \equiv \{x \mid x_\alpha \in U_\alpha, \text{ all } \alpha \in I\}$ products of open sets in X_α. The product topology is weaker since its base only has box sets for which $U_\alpha = X_\alpha$ for all but finitely many α's.

It turns out that the box topology is too strong. For example, if $I = \mathbb{Z}_+$ and each $X_\alpha = \{0, 1\}$, the two point set, then the box topology is the discrete topology (Problem 1(a)) so X is not compact (Problem 1(b)) in the box topology but, as we'll see, it is compact in the product topology. Once this was understood, the box topology became a curiosity, and it is only the product topology we'll discuss. The product topology has the following properties (Problems 2 and 3):

(1) As we've seen, $\{\pi_{\alpha_1}^{-1}(U_{\alpha_1})\cap\cdots\cap\pi_{\alpha_n}^{-1}(U_{\alpha_n})\}$ is a base, as $\alpha_1,\ldots,\alpha_n$ runs through all finite subsets of I and each U_{α_j} is open in X_{α_j}.

(2) $\{x^\beta\}_{\beta\in Z}\to x$ if and only if for each $\alpha\in I$, $(x^\beta)_\alpha\to x_\alpha$. More generally, x is a limit point of $\{x^\beta\}_{\beta\in Z}$ if and only if for each finite $\alpha_1,\ldots,\alpha_k$ in I, $\pi_{\{\alpha_1,\ldots\alpha_k\}}(x)$ is a limit point of $\pi_{\{\alpha_1,\ldots,\alpha_k\}}(x^\beta)$.

(3) $f\colon Y\to X$ is continuous if and only if each $\pi_\alpha\circ f$ is continuous from Y to X_α.

(4) If $I=\mathbb{Z}_+$ and each X_n is a metric space with metric, ρ_n, then X is a metric space with metric

$$\rho(x,y)=\sum_{n=1}^{\infty}\min(2^{-n},\rho(x_n,y_n)) \tag{2.7.1}$$

or several equivalent metrics.

In particular, the Hilbert cube of Section 2.2 is just $\times_{n=1}^{\infty}[0,1]$ in the product topology.

The most significant result about product spaces is:

Theorem 2.7.1 (Tychonoff's Theorem). *Suppose each X_α, $\alpha\in I$, is a compact Hausdorff space. Then $X=\times_\alpha X_\alpha$ is a compact Hausdorff space in the product topology.*

We want to first note how simple this is if $I=\mathbb{Z}_+$ and each X_n is a compact metric space, and then turn to the general case. In this countable metric case, let $\{x^{(m)}\}_{m=1}^{\infty}$ be a sequence in X. Since $x_1^{(m)}$ is a sequence in X_1, we can find a subsequence $x_1^{m_1(j)}$ and $y_1\in X$ so $x_1^{m_1(j)}\to y_1$ as $j\to\infty$. Then $y_2\in X_2$ and a subsubsequence, so $x_2^{m_2(j)}\to y_2$, and inductively, $x^{m_{n+1}(j)}$ a subsequence of $x^{m_n(j)}$ and $y_{n+1}\in X_{n+1}$, so $x_{n+1}^{m_{n+1}(j)}\to y_{n+1}$. Now the diagonalization trick completes the proof that $x^{(m)}$ has a convergent subsequence since $x_\ell^{m_j(j)}\to y_\ell$ for all ℓ. Thus, X is compact.

In general, we can't use the diagonalization trick if I is uncountable and we are using nets. But by using limit points and Zorn's lemma, we can handle the general case.

Proof of Theorem 2.7.1. It is easy to see that the product of Hausdorff spaces is Hausdorff (Problem 2(f)).

Let $\{x^\beta\}_{\beta\in Z}$ be a net in X. Define a partial limit point of $\{x^\beta\}_{\beta\in Z}$ to be a subset $J\subset I$ and a point $u\in X_J$ so that u is a limit point of $\pi_J(x^\beta)$. Notice that a partial limit point with $J=I$ is a limit point.

Let $\mathcal{P}$ be the family of all partial limit points. $\mathcal{P}$ is not empty since X_α is compact and we can pick $J = \{\alpha\}$. The idea will be to put a natural order on $\mathcal{P}$, use Zorn's lemma to get a maximal point, and show, if the corresponding $J \neq I$, that we can add one additional α to J, violating maximality.

Let $(J, u), (K, v) \in \mathcal{P}$. We say $(K, v) \rhd (J, u)$ if and only if $J \subset K$ and $\pi_{KJ}(v) = u$. Let $\{(J_\gamma, u_\gamma)\}_{\gamma \in Q}$ be a chain in $\mathcal{P}$ (see Section 1.4). We claim, if $\tilde{J} = \bigcup_\gamma J_\gamma$, that there is a unique $\tilde{u} \in X_{\tilde{J}}$ with $\pi_{\tilde{J}J_\gamma}(u) = u_\gamma$ and that $(\tilde{J}, \tilde{u})$ is an upper bound for the chain. For define $\tilde{u}_\alpha$ for α in $\tilde{J}$ to be $(u_\gamma)_\alpha$ for any γ with $\alpha \in J_\gamma$ (they are all the same by the order and the fact that we have a chain). Thus, $\mathcal{P}$ with order $\rhd$ obeys the chain condition. So, by Zorn's lemma, there exists a maximal element (J, u) in $\mathcal{P}$.

Suppose $J \neq I$. Pick $\alpha_0 \in I \setminus J$. By Theorem 2.6.4, let $\{y^\delta\}_{\delta \in \tilde{Z}}$ be a subnet of $\{x^\beta\}_{\beta \in Z}$ so $\pi_J(y^\delta) \to u$. Since X_{α_0} is compact, we can find a subnet of $\{y^\delta\}_{\delta \in \tilde{Z}}$, $\{w^\varepsilon\}_{\varepsilon \in Z^\sharp}$, so $(w^\varepsilon)_{\alpha_0} \to v$ for some $v \in X_{\alpha_0}$. Let $\tilde{J} = J \cup \{\alpha_0\}$ and $\tilde{u} \in X_{\tilde{J}}$, by

$$(\tilde{u})_\alpha = \begin{cases} u_\alpha & \text{if } \alpha \in J \\ v & \text{if } \alpha = \alpha_0 \end{cases} \tag{2.7.2}$$

Then $(\tilde{J}, \tilde{u}) \in \mathcal{P}$ since $\pi_{\tilde{J}}(w^\varepsilon) \to \tilde{u}$, and clearly, $(\tilde{J}, \tilde{u}) \rhd (J, u)$ with $(\tilde{J}, \tilde{u}) \neq (J, u)$, violating maximality of (J, u). This contradiction shows $J = I$, and so u is a limit point of $\{x^\beta\}_{\beta \in Z}$ in X. It follows that every net in X has a limit point, so X is compact by Theorem 2.6.4. $\qquad\square$

Example 2.7.2 (Uncountable Product of $[0, 1]$). For each $\alpha \in [0, 1]$, take a copy of $[0, 1]$ and let $X = \times_\alpha [0, 1]$, that is, $x \in X$ is a function from $[0, 1]$ to $[0, 1]$. By Tychonoff's theorem, X is a compact Hausdorff space.

We claim that no $\{x_0\}$ is a G_δ. For suppose that $\{x_0\} = \bigcap_{n=1}^\infty U_n$ for a countable family of open sets, $\{U_n\}_{n=1}^\infty$. Given the standard base of X, we can find $\{x_0\} \in V_n \subset U_n$, where $V_n = A_n \times [0, 1]^{B_n}$, where $A_n \subset [0, 1]^{C_n}$ open in a finite product, C_n, and $B_n = [0, 1] \setminus C_n$. Thus, $\{x_0\} = \bigcap_{n=1}^\infty V_n$ also.

Let $C = \bigcup C_n$, a countable set, and $B = [0, 1] \setminus C$. Then we can write $V_n = \tilde{A}_n \times [0, 1]^B$ with $\tilde{A}_n$ open in $[0, 1]^C$. Thus, $\bigcap_{n=1}^\infty V_n = \bigcap_{n=1}^\infty \tilde{A}_n \times [0, 1]^B$ cannot be $\{x_0\}$, that is, $\{x_0\}$ is closed but not a G_δ. $\qquad\square$

Notes and Historical Remarks. In 1929, Tychonoff [**940**] proved that an arbitrary product of closed intervals in $\mathbb{R}$ is compact in the product topology. Čech [**177**] then proved the general theorem.

For many years, the standard simple proof used filters—specifically, a class of filters called ultrafilters; it first appeared in Cartan [**165, 166**] and was popularized by Bourbaki [**120**]. Net versions of this proof are due to Chevalley–Frink [**186**] and Kelley [**481**]. A variant appears in Problems 4–6.

The elegant proof of Tychonoff's theorem that we present is due to Chernoff [**185**].

It is no coincidence that all proofs use the axiom of choice since Kelley [**482**] proved that Tychonoff's theorem implies the axiom of choice.

Problems

1. (a) Prove that the box topology on $\times_{\alpha \in I}\{0,1\}$ is the discrete topology.

   (b) Prove that a discrete space is compact if and only if it is finite so that $\times_{n=1}^{\infty}\{0,1\}$ is not compact in the box topology.

2. (a) Prove that a net $\{x^{\beta}\}_{\beta \in Z} \to x$ in the product topology if and only if $(x^{\beta})_{\alpha} \to x_{\alpha}$ for each α. (*Hint*: Look at a base.)

   (b) Let $X = \times_{n=1}^{\infty}\{0,1\}$ in the box topology Let

   $$(x^{(m)})_n = \begin{cases} 0, & n \le m \\ 1, & n > m \end{cases}$$

   Prove that $x_n^{(m)} \to 0$ for all n, but that $x^{(m)} \nrightarrow x$ in the box topology.

   (c) Prove that x is a limit point of $\{x^{\beta}\}_{\beta \in Z}$ (in the product topology) if and only if for each $\alpha_1, \ldots, \alpha_\ell \in I$, $\pi_{\{\alpha_1,\ldots,\alpha_\ell\}}(x)$ is a limit point of $\{\pi_{\{\alpha_1,\ldots,\alpha_\ell\}}(x^{\beta})\}_{\beta \in Z}$.

   (d) Find an example of a sequence $\{x^{(n)}\}_{n=1}^{\infty}$ in $[0,1] \times [0,1]$ so that $(0,1)$ is not a limit point of $x^{(n)}$ even though 0 is a limit point of $x_1^{(n)}$ and 1 is a limit point of $x_2^{(n)}$.

   (e) Prove that $f\colon Y \to X$ is continuous if and only if each $\pi_\alpha \circ f$ is continuous from Y to X_α.

   (f) Prove that an arbitrary product of Hausdorff spaces is Hausdorff. (*Hint*: Use unique limits.)

3. (a) Show that (2.7.1) is a metric on $X = \times_{n=1}^{\infty} X_n$ that defines the product topology.

   (b) Show the topology on X is the same if in (2.7.1), 2^{-n} is replaced by any sequence $a_n > 0$ with $\sum_{n=1}^{\infty} a_n < \infty$.

   (c) Let

   $$\tilde{\rho}(x,y) = \max_n(\min(2^{-n}, \rho(x_n, y_n))) \tag{2.7.3}$$

   Show $\tilde{\rho}$ defines the same topology on X.

4. A net $\{x^{\beta}\}_{\beta \in Z}$ in a topological space, X, is called *universal* if and only if for any $A \subset X$, either eventually $x^{\beta} \in A$ or eventually $x^{\beta} \in X \setminus A$.

This problem will lead the reader through a proof that every net has a universal subnet.

(a) Consider families of nonempty subsets $\{A\}_{A \in \mathcal{C}}$ of X with the property that $\mathcal{C}$ is closed under finite intersections, and for each $A \in \mathcal{C}$, the net $\{x^\beta\}_{\beta \in Z}$ is frequently in A. Prove that there are maximal families of such sets. (*Hint:* Zorn.)

(b) Prove that if $\mathcal{C}$ is such a maximal family and $A \subset X$, either $A \in \mathcal{C}$ or $X \setminus A \in \mathcal{C}$.

(c) Order $\mathcal{C} \times Z$ by $(A, \alpha) > (B, \beta)$ if and only if $A \subseteq B$ and $\alpha > \beta$. For each $(A, \beta) \in \mathcal{C} \times Z$, define $\alpha(A, \beta)$ to be a point in Z so $\alpha > \beta$ and $x^\alpha \in A$. Show that $y^{(A,\beta)} = x^{\alpha(A,\beta)}$ is a subnet of $\{x^\beta\}_{\beta \in Z}$.

(d) Prove that the subnet constructed in (c) is universal.

5. (a) Prove that a limit point of a universal net (as defined in Problem 4) is actually a point to which the net converges.

(b) Prove that a topological space, X, is compact if and only if every universal net converges. (*Hint:* You need Problem 4.)

6. This problem will prove Tychonoff's theorem using universal nets as in Problems 4 and 5.

(a) Let $X = \times_\alpha X_\alpha$ be a product space of compact sets. Let $\{x^\beta\}_{\beta \in Z}$ be a universal net in X. Prove that $\{\pi_\alpha(x^\beta)\}_{\beta \in Z}$ is a universal net in X_α.

(b) Prove that each $\pi_\alpha(x^\beta)$ has a limit y_α.

(c) Prove x^β has as a limit the point y with $(y)_\alpha = y_\alpha$.

(d) Conclude Tychonoff's theorem.

2.8. Quotient Topologies

Let X be a set with an equivalence relation, $\sim$. As we've seen (Section 1.1), X is a disjoint union of the equivalence classes under $\sim$. We denote the set of equivalence classes by $X/\!\sim$, called the *quotient space*. Thus, an element of $X/\!\sim$ is a subset of X of the form

$$\sim (x_0) = \{y \in X \mid y \sim x_0\} \tag{2.8.1}$$

We define $q_\sim \colon X \to X/\!\sim$ by $q_\sim(x_0) = \sim (x_0)$.

Our goal in this section is to show that a topology, $\mathcal{T}$, on X induces a natural topology, $\mathcal{T}_\sim$, on $X/\!\sim$ called the *quotient topology*. This construction occurs in this series rarely, while the product topology is used in several critical places. A set $U \in \mathcal{T}_\sim$ if and only if $q_\sim^{-1}[U]$ is open, that is, we consider those open sets $V \in \mathcal{T}$ which are unions of equivalent classes, that is, $x \in V$ and $x \sim y \Rightarrow y \in V$. By construction, $q_\sim$ is continuous, and a moment's thought shows it is the strongest topology in which $q_\sim$ is continuous. That is, if $\widetilde{\mathcal{T}}$ is a topology on $X/\sim$ in which $q_\sim$ is continuous, then $\widetilde{\mathcal{T}} \subset \mathcal{T}_\sim$. The construction shows that closed sets in $X/\sim$ correspond to closed sets in X which are unions of equivalence classes.

Notice that product topologies are weakest topologies in which certain maps from a space are continuous, and thus, quotient topology is a kind of dual. It is easy to see that $A \subset X/\sim$ is closed if and only if $q_\sim^{-1}[A]$ is closed in X. Our first example shows that sometimes quotient topologies are not very useful.

Example 2.8.1. In $[0,1]$ (with its usual topology), say $x \sim y \Leftrightarrow x - y \in \mathbb{Q}$, the rational numbers. Then all equivalence classes are dense, and so the only closed set which is a union of equivalence classes is all of $[0,1]$ (and $\emptyset$). It follows that $\mathcal{T}_\sim$ in this case is the indiscrete topology. In particular, even though $[0,1]$ has a Hausdorff topology, $\mathcal{T}_\sim$ is not Hausdorff. $\qquad\square$

Here are distinct but related conditions, one necessary and one sufficient, for $\mathcal{T}_\sim$ to be Hausdorff—the reader will prove this in Problem 1.

Theorem 2.8.2. *Let $\sim$ be an equivalence relation on a topological space, X, and let $X/\sim$ be the quotient space with the quotient topology. Define*

$$\Delta_\sim = \{(x,y) \in X \times X \mid x \sim y\} \tag{2.8.2}$$

in the product topology. Then

(a) *If the topology on $X/\sim$ is Hausdorff, then $\Delta_\sim$ is closed.*
(b) *If $\Delta_\sim$ is closed and $q_\sim$ is an open map, then $X/\sim$ is Hausdorff.*

Here is one way quotient topologies arise.

Theorem 2.8.3. *Let X, Y be topological spaces and $f \colon X \to Y$ continuous and onto Y. Define a relation, $\sim$, on X by*

$$x \sim z \Leftrightarrow f(x) = f(z) \tag{2.8.3}$$

for all $x, z \in X$. Then

(a) *$\sim$ is an equivalence relation and there is a unique map $g \colon X/\sim \Rightarrow Y$ so that*

$$g \circ q_\sim = f \tag{2.8.4}$$

Moreover, g is a bijection.
(b) *g is continuous.*
(c) *If f is open, then g is a homeomorphism of Y and $X/\sim$ so that Y is "essentially" the quotient space with quotient topology, and f is "essentially" $q_\sim$.*

Proof. (a) It is immediate that $\sim$ is an equivalence relation. Define g on $\sim (x)$, the equivalence class of x, by $g(\sim (x)) = f(x)$. This is well defined, (2.8.4) holds, and it is easy to see g is a bijection.

(b) Let U be open in Y. Then $f^{-1}[U]$ is open and a union of equivalence classes, so $g^{-1}[U]$ is open in $X/\sim$ by definition of the topology on $X/\sim$.

(c) Let V be open in $X/\sim$. Let $W = q_\sim^{-1}(V)$. By definition of the topology on $X/\sim$, W is open in X. By hypothesis, $f[W] = g[V]$ is open, so g is open, continuous, and a bijection, so a homeomorphism. $\qquad\square$

Example 2.8.4 (*n*-dimensional Torus). In $\mathbb{R}^n$, say $x \sim y$ if and only if $x - y \in \mathbb{Z}^n$, the set of elements in $\mathbb{R}^n$ with integral coordinates. It is easy to see $\mathbb{R}^n/\sim$ is just $\mathbb{R}^n/\mathbb{Z}^n$, the torus of dimension n with its usual topology. In this case, $q_\sim$ is a local homeomorphism. $\qquad\square$

Example 2.8.5. It is tempting to think that the key to $q_\sim$ being a local homeomorphism in Example 2.8.4 is that each equivalence class is a discrete subset of $\mathbb{R}^n$. This is, however, not sufficient. For example, in $(0,1)$, let $x \sim y$ if and only if either $x = y$ or $x + y = 1$. Then $(0,1)/\sim$ is naturally $[\frac{1}{2}, 1)$ with the usual topology (associating $x \in [\frac{1}{2}, 1)$ to the class $\{x, 1-x\}$). $q_\sim$ is a local homeomorphism on $(0, \frac{1}{2}) \cup (\frac{1}{2}, 1)$, but not at $\frac{1}{2}$. $\qquad\square$

Example 2.8.6 (Homogeneous Space). A *topological group*, G, is a group with a Hausdorff topology so that maps $(x, y) \mapsto xy$ from $G \times G \to G$ and $x \mapsto x^{-1}$ from G to G are continuous (when $G \times G$ has the product topology). A *homogeneous space* for G is a topological space, X, with a group action, that is, $\varphi \colon G \times X \to X$ is continuous with

$$\varphi(g, \varphi(h, x)) = \varphi(gh, x), \quad \varphi(e, x) = x \qquad (2.8.5)$$

often written $\varphi_g(x) \equiv \varphi(g, x)$ and $\varphi_g \circ \varphi_h = \varphi_{gh}$. We require that the action is *transitive*, that is, $\forall x, y \in X$, $\exists g \in G$ so $\varphi(g, x) = y$.

Fix $x_0 \in X$. Then

$$I_{x_0} = \{g \in G \mid \varphi(g, x_0) = x_0\} \qquad (2.8.6)$$

is always a subgroup of G and which is closed in G by the continuity of φ. The equivalence classes, defined by

$$f_{x_0}(g) = \varphi(g, x_0) \qquad (2.8.7)$$

via (2.8.3) are exactly the left cosets of I_{x_0}. If f_{x_0} is open as well as continuous, by Theorem 2.8.3, X has the quotient topology. Thus, homogeneous spaces for topological groups are often quotient spaces. This generalizes Example 2.8.4 with $G = \mathbb{R}^n$, $X = \partial\mathbb{D}^n$, and $I_{x_0} = \mathbb{Z}^n$. $\qquad\square$

Example 2.8.7. Having started with an example where quotient topologies are inadequate, we end with one! This involves a group action, but one that is not transitive. Pick $\alpha \in \mathbb{R}$ irrational. Map $\partial \mathbb{D} \times \mathbb{Z} \xrightarrow{\varphi} \partial \mathbb{D}$ by

$$\varphi(e^{i\theta}, n) = e^{i(\theta + 2\pi n \alpha)} \tag{2.8.8}$$

As in Example 2.8.1, equivalence classes (defined by (2.8.6)) are dense and the quotient topology is indiscrete. □

Notes and Historical Remarks. The quotient topology appeared first in Moore [**665**] and Alexandroff [**13**]. The importance of open mappings in this context is in Aronszajn [**33**]. Further developments occurred in the monographs of Seifert–Threlfall [**837**], Alexandroff–Hopf [**15**], and Bourbaki [**120**]. For modern presentations, see Kelley [**484**] and Willard [**1004**].

Problems

1. (a) Let $X/\sim$ be a Hausdorff space. Prove that the set, $\Delta_\sim$, of (2.8.2) is closed. (*Hint*: If $(x, y) \notin \Delta_\sim$, pick disjoint U, V containing $q_\sim(x)$ and $q_\sim(y)$ respectively, and look at $q_\sim^{-1}[U] \times q_\sim^{-1}[V]$ in $X \times X$.)

   (b) If $\Delta_\sim$ is closed and $q_\sim$ is open, prove that $X/\sim$ is Hausdorff. (*Hint*: If $(x, y) \notin \Delta_\sim$, find U, V open in X so $x \in U$, $y \in V$ so $U \times V \cap \Delta_\sim = \emptyset$. What do $q_\sim[U]$ and $q_\sim[V]$ do for you?)

Chapter 3

A First Look
at Hilbert Spaces
and Fourier Series

> Fejér discovered his theorem at the age of 19, Weierstrass published this theorem at the age of 70. With time, the reader may come to appreciate why so many mathematicians regard the second circumstance as even more romantic and heart warming than the first."
>
> —*T. W. Körner* [**512**] [1]

Big Notions and Theorems: Antilinear Maps, Sesquilinear Form, Inner Product Space, Associated Norm, Parallelogram Law, Pythagorean Theorem, Bessel's Inequality, Cauchy–Schwarz Inequality, Triangle Inequality, Hilbert Space, Convex Set, Variational Principle for Convex Sets, Orthogonal Decomposition, Orthogonal Projection, Orthogonal Complement, Dual Space, Riesz Representation Theorem, Orthonormal Set, Orthonormal Basis, Abstract Fourier Series, Abstract Fourier Coefficients, Abstract Parseval Relation, Gram–Schmidt Procedure, Classical Fourier Series, Dirichlet Kernel, Dini's Test, Dini Condition, Fejér Kernel, Approximate Identity, Fejér's Theorem, Weierstrass Density Theorem for Fourier Series, Weierstrass Function, Nowhere Differentiable Continuous Function, Gibbs Phenomenon, Jordan's Theorem, Jackson Kernel, Fast Fourier Transform, Weak Topology, Strong Operator Topology, Weak Operator Topology, Isometry, Unitary Operator, Partial Isometry, Self-adjoint Operators, Positive Operators, Normal Operators, Tensor Product of Hilbert Spaces, Antisymmetric Tensors, Symmetric Tensors

---

[1] referring to Fejér's theorem discussed in Section 3.5 and Weierstrass's theorem discussed in Section 2.4

Traditionally, real analysis is the study of functions on $\mathbb{R}$ or $\mathbb{R}^n$ or (a, b) or $\Omega \subset \mathbb{R}^n$, an open connected subset, and the integral and differential calculus of such functions. The remarkable realization at the start of the twentieth century was the power of abstract vector spaces with a topology, usually one generated by a norm or metric, to study the traditional problems of analysis. Part of it was the geometric view that such spaces allowed. In this chapter, we discuss the simplest of such topological vector spaces, the Hilbert space, and we'll see that geometry is central.

A Hilbert space, $\mathcal{H}$, will have an inner product (defined in Section 3.1), $\varphi, \psi \in \mathcal{H} \mapsto \langle \varphi, \psi \rangle \in \mathbb{C}$. It will turn out that $\rho(\varphi, \psi) = \sqrt{\langle \varphi - \psi, \varphi - \psi \rangle}$ defines a metric. $\mathcal{H}$ will be required to be complete in that metric and $\mathcal{H}$ will be separable. The two highlights of the general theory in this chapter will be the Riesz representation theorem, which identifies the set of all continuous linear maps of $\mathcal{H}$ to $\mathbb{C}$, and the existence of an orthonormal basis, $\{\varphi_n\}_{n=1}^N$ (where N is finite or infinite), with the associated abstract Fourier expansion

$$\varphi = \sum_{n=1}^N \langle \varphi_n, \varphi \rangle \varphi_n \tag{3.0.1}$$

For both of these high points, the key is a geometric notion of orthogonal vectors; that is, the vectors φ, ψ with $\langle \varphi, \psi \rangle = 0$. Since bases are maximal sets with $\langle \varphi_n, \varphi_m \rangle = 0$ for $n \neq m$, this is evident in (3.0.1). In identifying continuous linear functionals, ℓ, on $\mathcal{H}$, we'll use vectors orthogonal to all vectors in $\mathrm{Ker}(\ell)$.

The basic geometry of $\mathcal{H}$ is needed in various equalities and inequalities, which are the subject of Section 3.1. In particular, we'll show that if $\|\varphi\| = \sqrt{\langle \varphi, \varphi \rangle}$, then $\varphi, \psi \mapsto \|\varphi - \psi\|$ defines a metric, and this will allow us to define a Hilbert space.

Section 3.2 introduces the notion of convex set, which will also play a critical role in later chapters (see Section 5.3 and other sections in Chapter 5) and, in particular, prove that if K is a closed convex set and $\varphi \in \mathcal{H}$, there is a unique ψ in K so that

$$\|\varphi - \psi\| = \inf_{\eta \in K} \|\varphi - \eta\| \tag{3.0.2}$$

If K is a closed subspace of $\mathcal{H}$, (3.0.2) will prove $\varphi - \psi$ is orthogonal to K, and so show that if $K \neq \mathcal{H}$, there are nonzero ξ in

$$K^\perp = \{\xi \mid \langle \xi, \eta \rangle = 0 \text{ for all } \eta \in K\} \tag{3.0.3}$$

This will be the key in the proof of the Riesz representation theorem in Section 3.3.

Section 3.4 turns to the issue of orthogonal basis and abstract Fourier series. The concrete version of this is $L^2(\partial \mathbb{D}, \frac{d\theta}{2\pi})$ with the basis $\{\varphi_n\}_{n=1}^\infty$, where

$$\varphi_n(\theta) = e^{in\theta} \qquad (3.0.4)$$

In Section 3.5, this basis is studied, including several key pointwise convergence results due to Dirichlet/Dini and Fejér. Also in connection with pointwise convergence, we'll see Fourier approximation near jump discontinuities causes overshoot (see Figure 3.5.4), something called the *Gibbs phenomenon*. We'll also use Fourier series to construct a continuous but nowhere differentiable function, a function so rough that its graph has dimension larger than one! Our analysis of Fourier series balances out the abstract considerations that dominate this chapter. The reader shouldn't lose sight of the fact that while abstraction is powerful, its purpose is to shed light on concrete, practical issues like Fourier series. The other side of Fourier analysis, the Fourier transform, is a major theme in Chapter 6.

Sections 3.6 and 3.7 return to the general theory with brief discussions of weak topology and the definitions of classes of operators that will concern us in Part 4. We will freely use the language of linear algebra discussed in Section 1.7 including the terms subspaces, range, and kernel.

Notes and Historical Remarks. We have placed this chapter before the one on measure theory because we will use the Riesz representation to prove some advanced results in measure theory. We pay a price. A basic Hilbert space is $L^2(\mathbb{R}, dx)$ and, in particular, $L^2(\partial\mathbb{D}, \frac{d\theta}{2\pi})$ is the natural arena for Fourier series. In this chapter, L^2 will be defined via an abstract completion, so its elements are equivalence classes of Cauchy sequences. The more natural view is as equivalence classes of measurable functions equal almost everywhere. That will be available, but only in the next chapter after Section 4.4. Since, in this chapter, we'll concentrate mainly on Fourier series for continuous functions, there is no great loss other than a little awkwardness of language.

3.1. Basic Inequalities

There are a number of equalities and inequalities central to the theory of Hilbert spaces. After defining an inner product space, we'll prove two fundamental geometric equalities: the parallelogram law and the Pythagorean theorem, which is the mother of all inequalities of this section since we'll get inequalities by dropping manifestly positive terms. That will lead to the Schwarz inequality and triangle inequality which will let us define a Hilbert space.

Definition. An *antilinear map* is a map $\ell\colon V \to \mathbb{C}$ where V is a complex vector space that obeys

$$\ell(x + y) = \ell(x) + \ell(y) \qquad (3.1.1)$$

for all $x, y \in V$ and

$$\ell(\lambda x) = \bar{\lambda}\ell(x) \qquad (3.1.2)$$

for all $x \in V$ and all $\lambda \in \mathbb{C}$ where $\bar{\lambda}$ is the complex conjugate.

Definition. A *sesquilinear form*, $\langle \cdot, \cdot \rangle$, on a complex vector space V is a map from $V \times V \to \mathbb{C}$ so that for all $x \in V$, $y \mapsto \langle x, y \rangle$ is linear and $y \mapsto \langle y, x \rangle$ is antilinear.

See the Notes for a discussion of the convention that often takes linearity in the first factor and antilinearity in the second.

Definition. An *inner product space* is a complex vector space, V, with a distinguished sesquilinear form $\langle \cdot, \cdot \rangle$ that obeys

(a) (*Strict positivity*) For all $x \in V$ with $x \neq 0$, $\langle x, x \rangle \in \mathbb{R}$ and

$$\langle x, x \rangle > 0 \qquad (3.1.3)$$

(b) (*Symmetry*) For all $x, y \in V$,

$$\langle x, y \rangle = \overline{\langle y, x \rangle} \qquad (3.1.4)$$

Remarks. 1. It follows from (anti)linearity that $\langle x, x \rangle = 0$ for $x = 0$.

2. By polarization (see below), reality of $\langle x, x \rangle$ implies antisymmetry. Thus, (a) implies (b), that is, (b) is not needed as a separate condition.

A *real inner product space* is a real vector space with a real bilinear form $x, y \mapsto \langle x, y \rangle$ that is strictly positive and symmetric in the sense that for all $x, y \in V$,

$$\langle x, y \rangle = \langle y, x \rangle \qquad (3.1.5)$$

One defines

$$\|x\| = (\langle x, x \rangle)^{1/2} \qquad (3.1.6)$$

the positive square root, so (3.1.3) implies

$$x \neq 0 \Rightarrow \|x\| > 0 \qquad (3.1.7)$$

For complex inner product spaces, one can recover $\{\langle x, y \rangle\}_{x,y \in V}$ from $\{\langle x, x \rangle\}_{x \in V}$ by the *polarization* identity

$$\langle x, y \rangle = \tfrac{1}{4}\|x + y\|^2 - \tfrac{1}{4}\|x - y\|^2 + \tfrac{1}{4i}\|x + iy\|^2 - \tfrac{1}{4i}\|x - iy\|^2 \qquad (3.1.8)$$

which is straightforward algebra, given linearity and antilinearity.

Theorem 3.1.1 (Parallelogram Identity). *For any $x, y \in V$, we have*

$$\|x + y\|^2 + \|x - y\|^2 = 2\|x\|^2 + 2\|y\|^2 \qquad (3.1.9)$$

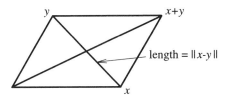

Figure 3.1.1. The parallelogram identity.

Remark. The name comes from the fact that this expresses the result from Euclidean geometry that in any parallelogram, the sums of the squares of the lengths of the diagonals equals the sum of the squares of the four sides (see Figure 3.1.1 and Problem 1).

Proof. Straightforward algebra since

$$\|x \pm y\|^2 = \|x\|^2 + \|y\|^2 \pm 2\operatorname{Re}\langle x, y \rangle \tag{3.1.10}$$

$\square$

We'll use this below (see Theorem 3.1.6) and in the next section. The master relation of this section, also crucial in Section 3.4, depends on the notion of orthonormal vectors:

Definition. A collection of vectors, $\{x_\alpha\}_{\alpha \in I}$, in an inner product space, V, is called *orthonormal* if and only if

$$\langle x_\alpha, x_\beta \rangle = \delta_{\alpha, \beta} \tag{3.1.11}$$

that is, $\langle x_\alpha, x_\beta \rangle = 0$ if $\alpha \neq \beta$ and $\|x_\alpha\| = 1$ for all $\alpha \in I$.

Theorem 3.1.2 (Pythagorean Theorem—First Version). *Let V be an inner product space and $\{x_j\}_{j=1}^n$ a finite orthonormal set. Then for any $y \in V$,*

$$\sum_{j=1}^n |\langle x_j, y \rangle|^2 + \left\| y - \sum_{j=1}^n \langle x_j, y \rangle x_j \right\|^2 = \|y\|^2 \tag{3.1.12}$$

Proof. We have, with $\tilde{y} = \sum_{j=1}^n \langle x_j, y \rangle x_j$, that

$$\langle y, \tilde{y} \rangle = \sum_{j=1}^n |\langle x_j, y \rangle|^2 \tag{3.1.13}$$

$$\langle \tilde{y}, \tilde{y} \rangle = \sum_{j=1}^n |\langle x_j, y \rangle|^2 \tag{3.1.14}$$

so

$$\|y - \tilde{y}\|^2 = \|y\|^2 + \|\tilde{y}\|^2 - 2\operatorname{Re}\langle y, \tilde{y}\rangle = \|y\|^2 - \sum_{j=1}^{n} |\langle x_j, y\rangle|^2 \qquad (3.1.15)$$

proving (3.1.12).   □

Corollary 3.1.3 (Bessel's Inequality—First Version).

$$\sum_{j=1}^{n} |\langle x_j, y\rangle|^2 \le \|y\|^2 \qquad (3.1.16)$$

Proof. One drops a manifestly nonnegative term on the left of (3.1.12).   □

Corollary 3.1.4 (Cauchy–Schwarz Inequality). *Let V be an inner product space. For any $x, y \in V$, we have*

$$|\langle x, y\rangle| \le \|x\| \, \|y\| \qquad (3.1.17)$$

Proof. If $x = 0$, both sides of (3.1.17) are 0, so the inequality holds. If $x \ne 0$, let $x_1 = x/\|x\|$, so $\{x_1\}$ is a one-element orthonormal set, and Bessel's inequality says

$$|\langle x_1, y\rangle| \le \|y\| \qquad (3.1.18)$$

which is (3.1.17).   □

Remarks. 1. By the full Pythagorean theorem, to get equality in (3.1.18), and so in (3.1.17), requires $y = \langle x_1, y\rangle x_1$. That is, if $x \ne 0$, equality holds in (3.1.17) $\Leftrightarrow y = \lambda x$ for some $\lambda \in \mathbb{C}$.

2. This basic inequality has many other proofs; see Problems 2 and 3.

Corollary 3.1.5 (Triangle Inequality). *For all $x, y \in V$, an inner product space, we have*

$$\|x + y\| \le \|x\| + \|y\| \qquad (3.1.19)$$

Proof. We compute

$$\begin{aligned}
\|x + y\|^2 &= \|x\|^2 + \|y\|^2 + 2\operatorname{Re}\langle x, y\rangle \\
&\le \|x\|^2 + \|y\|^2 + 2|\langle x, y\rangle| \qquad (3.1.20) \\
&\le (\|x\| + \|y\|)^2
\end{aligned}$$

by (3.1.17). This proves (3.1.19).   □

Definition. A *norm* on a vector space, X, over $\mathbb{C}$ or $\mathbb{R}$ is a function $\|\cdot\|$ from X to $[0, \infty)$ with

(i) $\|x\| = 0 \Leftrightarrow x = 0$ (3.1.21)

(ii) $\|\lambda x\| = |\lambda| \, \|x\|$ (3.1.22)

for all λ in $\mathbb{C}$ or $\mathbb{R}$ (if X is a vector space over $\mathbb{C}$ or $\mathbb{R}$) and all x in X.

(iii) $\|x + y\| \leq \|x\| + \|y\|$ (3.1.23)

for all $x, y \in X$. If condition (i) is dropped, $\|\cdot\|$ is called a *seminorm*. A vector space with a distinguished norm is called a *normed linear space* (NLS).

Remark. We often have an expression like

$$\left(\int |f(x)|^2 \, dx \right)^{1/2} \equiv \|f\|_2$$

which is defined for any continuous function on $\mathbb{R}$ if we interpret $\|f\|_2$ as ∞ if the integral diverges. That is, we have a vector space, V, with $\|\cdot\| \to [0, \infty]$ with ∞ allowed. If it obeys (3.1.22) (with $0 \cdot \infty = 0$, $\alpha \cdot \infty = \infty$ if $\alpha > 0$) and (3.1.23) (with $\infty + \alpha = \infty$ for any $\alpha \geq 0$), we often still call it a norm. $V_0 = \{v \mid \|v\| < \infty\}$ is then a vector space and $\|\cdot\| \upharpoonright V_0$ a norm in the above sense. This is a standard abuse of notation.

(3.1.21) says the "norm" $\sqrt{\langle x, x \rangle}$ on an inner product space is a norm. In any NLS,

$$\rho(x, y) = \|x - y\|$$ (3.1.24)

defines a metric, and so all the features of a metric space.

One can ask when a norm comes from an inner product. Here is the simple elegant answer:

Theorem 3.1.6 (Jordan–von Neumann Theorem). *Let X be a complex NLS. Then $\|\cdot\|$ comes from an inner product if and only if $\|\cdot\|$ obeys the parallelogram law* (3.1.9).

The reader will prove this in Problem 4.

Definition. A *Banach space* (aka B space) is an NLS which is complete in the induced metric.

Definition. A *Hilbert space*, $\mathcal{H}$, is an inner product space which is complete and separable in the induced metric.

We'll say more about the separability requirement in the Notes. For now, we abuse the English language by using adjectives to extend rather than limit a noun. A *nonseparable Hilbert space* is an $\mathcal{H}$ with the separability requirement dropped. A *real Hilbert space* is a real inner product space which is a complete separable metric space in the induced metric. Of course, a Hilbert space is a special kind of a Banach space.

Example 3.1.7 ($\mathbb{C}^n$). On $\mathbb{C}^n$, define

$$\langle (\alpha_1, \dots, \alpha_n), (\beta_1, \dots, \beta_n) \rangle = \sum_{j=1}^{n} \bar{\alpha}_j \beta_j \qquad (3.1.25)$$

It is easy to see this is an inner product, called the *Euclidean inner product*, and it makes $\mathbb{C}^n$ into a Hilbert space. Notice that it is easier to check the inner product conditions (3.1.1)–(3.1.4) than to directly check the norm inequality, (3.1.23). $\qquad\square$

Example 3.1.8 (ℓ^2). One defines $\ell^2(\mathbb{Z}_+)$ (or ℓ^2 for short) to be sequences $\{x_n\}_{n=1}^{\infty}$ obeying

$$\|x\|^2 \equiv \sum_{n=1}^{\infty} |x_n|^2 < \infty \qquad (3.1.26)$$

If $x, y \in \ell^2$, then by the Schwarz inequality on $\mathbb{C}^N$,

$$\sum_{n=1}^{N} |\bar{x}_n y_n| \le \left(\sum_{n=1}^{N} |x_n|^2 \right)^{1/2} \left(\sum_{n=1}^{N} |y_n|^2 \right)^{1/2} \qquad (3.1.27)$$

$$\le \|x\| \, \|y\| \qquad (3.1.28)$$

Thus, $\sum_{n=1}^{\infty} |\bar{x}_n y_n| < \infty$ and we can define

$$\langle x, y \rangle = \sum_{n=1}^{\infty} \bar{x}_n y_n \qquad (3.1.29)$$

It is easy to show (Problem 5) that this defines an inner product on ℓ^2, that $\|\cdot\|$ is the norm in this inner product, and that ℓ^2 is complete and so a Hilbert space. $\ell^2(\mathbb{Z})$ is sequences labeled by $n \in \mathbb{Z}$ obeying an analog of (3.1.26). Similarly, one can define $\ell^2(\mathbb{Z}^\nu)$ or ℓ^2 of any countable set. $\qquad\square$

Example 3.1.9 ($L^2([0,1], dx)$). Consider $C([0,1])$, the continuous function on $[0,1]$, and for $f, g \in C([0,1])$, let

$$\langle f, g \rangle = \int_0^1 \overline{f(x)} \, g(x) \, dx \qquad (3.1.30)$$

where the integral is a Riemann integral. It is easy to see this is an inner product and easy to see it is not complete; for example, if

$$f_n(x) = \begin{cases} 1, & x \le \frac{1}{2} - \frac{1}{n} \\ 0, & x \ge \frac{1}{2} + \frac{1}{n} \\ \text{affine in} & [\frac{1}{2} - \frac{1}{n}, \frac{1}{2} + \frac{1}{n}] \end{cases} \qquad (3.1.31)$$

where affine means of the form $ax + b$ for x in that interval (i.e., making the graph have a line segment with f_n continuous).

Then (Problem 6) f_n is Cauchy in $\|\cdot\|$ but does not have a limit in $C([0,1])$.

$C([0,1])$ is a metric space in $\|\cdot\|$ so it has an abstract completion, $L^2([0,1], dx)$, whose elements are equivalence classes of Cauchy sequences in $C([0,1])$. It is easy to see $\langle\,\cdot\,,\,\cdot\,\rangle$ extends continuously to the completion and makes L^2 into a Hilbert space. For now, this is what we mean by L^2. In the next chapter (Sections 4.4 and 4.6), we'll see L^2 can be realized as equivalence classes of certain functions. $\square$

Example 3.1.10 ($\mathfrak{A}_2(\Omega)$)**.** If $\Omega \subset \mathbb{C}$ is an open connected set, the set of functions, $f \colon \Omega \to \mathbb{C}$ which are analytic in Ω and obey

$$\|f\|^2 = \int |f(z)|^2 \, d^2 z < \infty \tag{3.1.32}$$

is a Hilbert space under $\langle f, g\rangle = \int \bar{f}(z) g(z) \, d^2 z$. Completeness uses a fact from the theory of analytic functions. It is sometimes called the *Bergman space* for Ω and will be the subject of Sections 12.5 and 12.6 of Part 2B. An important feature is that it has a reproducing kernel. Reproducing kernel Hilbert spaces are the subject of Problems 4–11 of Section 3.3, Problem 8 of Section 3.4, Problem 20 of Section 6.6, and Section 4.4 of Part 3. $\square$

We end this section by using completeness to extend the Pythagorean theorem and Bessel's inequality to more general orthonormal sets than finite ones. The key is:

Theorem 3.1.11. *Let $\mathcal{H}$ be a Hilbert space. Suppose $\{x_\alpha\}_{\alpha \in I}$ is an orthornomal set and $\{\beta_\alpha\}_{\alpha \in I}$ a set of complex numbers with*

$$\sum_{\alpha \in I} |\beta_\alpha|^2 < \infty \tag{3.1.33}$$

For any finite set $F \subset I$, let

$$x_F = \sum_{\alpha \in F} \beta_\alpha x_\alpha \tag{3.1.34}$$

Order finite subsets F in I by $F \lhd F'$ if $F \subset F'$. Then the net $\{x_F\}_{F \subset I}$ has a limit, x, in $\mathcal{H}$.

Remarks. 1. If $\langle x_\alpha, x_\beta\rangle = \delta_{\alpha,\beta}$, then for $\alpha \neq \beta$, $\|x_\alpha - x_\beta\| = \sqrt{2}$, so separability implies that any orthonormal set is countable. In fact, the proof below also works in any nonseparable Hilbert space.

2. By (3.1.33), we mean

$$\sup_{F \subset I} \left(\sum_{\alpha \in F} |\beta_\alpha|^2 \right) < \infty \tag{3.1.35}$$

It is easy to see that this implies $\{\alpha \mid \beta_\alpha \neq 0\}$ is countable, since if the sup in (3.1.35) is C, $\{\alpha \mid |\beta_\alpha| \geq \varepsilon > 0\}$ is finite for any ε; indeed, $\#\{\alpha \mid |\beta_\alpha| \geq \varepsilon\} \leq C\varepsilon^{-2}$.

3. We write x as $\sum_{\alpha \in I} \beta_\alpha x_\alpha$.

Proof. It is easy to see (Problem 7) that (3.1.35) implies that if

$$\varepsilon_F = \sup_{\substack{G \subset I \setminus F \\ G \text{ finite}}} \sum_{\alpha \in G} |\beta_\alpha|^2 \tag{3.1.36}$$

then

$$\lim_F \varepsilon_F = 0 \tag{3.1.37}$$

If $F \subset I$ and $F' \rhd F$, $F'' \rhd F$, then (recall that $A \triangle B = (A \setminus B) \cup (B \setminus A)$)

$$\|x_{F'} - x_{F''}\|^2 = \sum_{\alpha \in F' \triangle F''} |\beta_\alpha|^2 \leq \varepsilon_F$$

so (3.1.37) implies x_F is a Cauchy net (see Problem 3 of Section 2.6). By completeness and that problem, $\lim_F x_F$ exists. $\qquad \square$

Theorem 3.1.12. *Let $\{x_\alpha\}_{\alpha \in I}$ be an orthonormal set in a Hilbert space $\mathcal{H}$. Let $y \in \mathcal{H}$. Then*

(a) *(General form of Bessel's inequality)*

$$\sum_{\alpha \in I} |\langle x_\alpha, y \rangle|^2 \leq \|x\|^2 \tag{3.1.38}$$

(b) *(General form of the Pythagorean theorem)* *If*

$$\tilde{y} = \sum_{\alpha \in I} \langle x_\alpha, y \rangle x_\alpha \tag{3.1.39}$$

then

$$\sum_{\alpha \in I} |\langle x_\alpha, y \rangle|^2 + \|y - \tilde{y}\|^2 = \|y\|^2 \tag{3.1.40}$$

Proof. The ordinary Bessel inequality proves (3.1.38) for arbitrary finite $F \subset I$, and so for the arbitrary sum. By Theorem 3.1.11, the sum in (3.1.39) is convergent in $\mathcal{H}$ norm, so taking limits in the calculation (3.1.13)/(3.1.14),

$$\langle \tilde{y}, \tilde{y} \rangle = \langle y, \tilde{y} \rangle = \sum_{\alpha \in I} |\langle x_\alpha, y \rangle|^2 \tag{3.1.41}$$

and (3.1.40) follows. $\qquad \square$

Notes and Historical Remarks. This section uses two conventions which are contrary to the majority of mathematics texts. First, we include separability as an axiom in our definition of Hilbert space, using the term "nonseparable Hilbert space" for the usual notion. We do this for two reasons: First, as part of our general attitude about separability—while, occasionally, a nonseparable metric space occurs in applications, nonseparable Hilbert spaces never do. Second, in some places where the general case requires Zorn's lemma, we can instead use simple induction. We note that von

Neumann's original axioms for abstract Hilbert spaces [**960, 962**] included separability, but this was removed several years later by Löwig [**607**].

Our second minority convention concerns the linearity (antilinearity) of sesquilinear forms. We require they are antilinear in the first vector and linear in the second, while the more common convention is the opposite. Theoretical physicists are virtually uniform in using the convention we do, probably because they all go back to Dirac's influential book on quantum mechanics. Mathematicians are split, but a substantial majority prefer the convention oppposite to ours. I would prefer saying we do what we do as an attempt at multicultural outreach to physicists. In fact, the real reason concerns my background in mathematical physics and the result that I've used this convention throughout my career.

The use of the closed unit ball in ℓ_2 goes back to Hilbert in his 1906 work on quadratic forms [**426**] (an early version of the spectral theorem). In 1908, Schoenflies [**821**] used the term "Hilbert space" for this ball. Riesz [**782**] began the use of the name for all of ℓ_2. von Neumann [**960, 962**] then used the name as we currently do for the abstract object. Stone's book [**884**], begun in 1928 when Stone was 25 years old, was influential in establishing Hilbert space theory as fundamental. See Section 2.1 of Part 4, Section 4.5 below, Section 2.5 above, and Section 7.1 of Part 4, for capsule biographies of Hilbert, Riesz, Stone, and von Neumann, respectively.

The Pythagorean theorem and parallelogram laws are, of course, generalizations of results in Euclidean geometry that go back to the Greeks. Bessel's inequality is named after an 1828 result of Bessel [**88**] who proved the result for classical Fourier series. It was given that name in a general context by Schmidt [**818**]. Friedrich Wilhelm Bessel (1784–1846) spent his career as a German astronomer, moving from a job in an import-export firm to astronomy because of his calculation of the orbit of Halley's comet. Among mathematicians, he is most known for Bessel functions. He was good friends with Gauss, who also first came to prominence because of an astronomical calculation. More biographical information on Bessel is given in the Notes to Section 14.5 of Part 2B where Bessel functions are discussed.

The Schwarz inequality for $\mathbb{R}^3$ is due to Lagrange and Cauchy [**168**]. The version for integrals of continuous functions on $[0,1]$ is due first to Buniakowski [**118**] in 1859 and then to Schwarz [**829**] only in 1885. The Russians call it the Buniakowski or Cauchy–Schwarz–Buniakowski inequality, but in the West, in a use of Arnold's principle, it is called the Cauchy–Schwarz or Schwarz inequality. Schmidt [**818**] noted it for ℓ_2 and von Neumann [**960, 962**] for general Hilbert space.

The Jordan–von Neumann theorem is from their 1935 paper [**457**]. This Jordan is not the mathematician known for the Jordan curve theorem and

Jordan normal form (see the Notes to Section 4.8 of Part 2A for him), but Pascual Jordan (1902–80), a German theoretical physicist (of Spanish descent). He was a student of Max Born. Some of the basic papers of the Göttingen development of quantum mechanics were in a joint paper of Born, Heisenberg, and Jordan (known as the "dreimännerarbeit"—three-man paper). He also developed Jordan algebras in this context. Jordan joined the Nazi party and the SA early (1933 and 1934), but his ideas for weapons were dismissed because of his earlier association with Courant, Born, and Pauli—all regarded as Jewish. Some have conjectured that were it not for his Nazi association, Jordan might have shared Born's 1954 Nobel prize. Due to Pauli's help, he was allowed to return to his professorship in 1953.

The Jordan–von Neumann theorem implies that if X is a complex Banach space so that every two-dimensional subspace is isometric to $\mathbb{C}^2$ with its Euclidean metric, then X is isometric to a Hilbert space. Earlier, Fréchet [**323**] proved a similar result where two-dimensional is replaced by three-dimensional. While Fréchet's work motivated Jordan–von Neumann, his result is weaker and doesn't discuss the parallelogram law. Despite this, many French authors call Theorem 3.1.6 the "Fréchet–Jordan–von Neumann theorem." The book of Kannappan [**477**] has a whole chapter on norm relations that imply a Banach space is a Hilbert space.

Problems

1. Let a parallelogram have sides of length ℓ_1 and ℓ_2 and diagonals $d_\pm$. Let h be the (perpendicular) distance between the two sides of length ℓ_1 (see Figure 3.1.2). Using the classical plane geometry Pythagorean theorem, prove that
$$d_\pm^2 = h^2 + \left(\ell_1 \pm \sqrt{\ell_2^2 - h^2} \right)^2$$
and conclude the classical parallelogram law that $d_+^2 + d_-^2 = 2\ell_1^2 + 2\ell_2^2$.

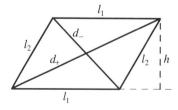

Figure 3.1.2. Some classical plane geometry.

2. For x, y in V, an inner product space, and for $\lambda = re^{i\theta} \in \mathbb{C}$, use $\|x + \lambda y\|^2 \geq 0$ for θ fixed to get a quadratic equation in r whose roots must be

either equal or nonreal. Show that this implies $|\mathrm{Re}[\langle e^{i\theta}y, x\rangle]| \leq \|x\|^2\|y\|^2$, and so conclude the Schwarz inequality.

3. Let $\{a_k\}_{k=1}^n$ and $\{b_k\}_{k=1}^n$ be real numbers. Prove Lagrange's identity that

$$\left(\sum_{k=1}^n a_k^2\right)\left(\sum_{k=1}^n b_k^2\right) - \left(\sum_{k=1}^n a_k b_k\right)^2 = \frac{1}{2}\sum_{k,\ell=1}^n (a_k b_\ell - a_\ell b_k)^2$$

and so conclude that the Schwarz inequality holds on $\mathbb{R}^n$.

4. This problem will prove the Jordan–von Neumann theorem (Theorem 3.1.6). Suppose $\|\cdot\|$ is a norm on a complex NLS, X. Define $\langle\cdot,\cdot\rangle$ via the polarization identity. Show that if $\|\cdot\|$ obeys the parallelogram law, then $\langle\cdot,\cdot\rangle$ is sesquilinear. (*Hint*: Prove it first for sums of vectors, then rational multiples and for $\pm i$, and then, by proving continuity, for all complex numbers.)

5. Verify that (3.1.29) defines an inner product and that ℓ^2 is complete.

6. Verify that (3.1.31) is Cauchy in the norm induced by (3.1.30) but has no limit in $C([0,1])$.

7. Provide the missing details in the proof of Theorem 3.1.11.

8. (a) Find a closed bounded subset of a Hilbert space which is not compact in the $\|\cdot\|$-topology.

   (b) Let $\{u_n\}_{n=0}^\infty$ be an orthonormal basis of a separable Hilbert space. Let d_n be a sequence in $[0,\infty)$ and let

$$C = \left\{\sum x_n u_n \;\middle|\; \{x_n\} \in \ell^2 \text{ and } |x_n| \leq d_n\right\}$$

   For which d_n is C compact?

3.2. Convex Sets, Minima, and Orthogonal Complements

The main goal of this section is to construct orthogonal complements via a variational principle. Since the variational principle works for arbitrary closed convex sets, we get to also introduce convexity, a major theme throughout this volume (see, e.g., Chapter 5).

Definition. A subset, S, of a (real or complex) vector space, X, is called *convex* if and only if for all $x, y \in S$, $\theta \in [0,1]$, one has

$$\theta x + (1-\theta)y \in S \tag{3.2.1}$$

The vector in (3.2.1) is called a *convex combination* of x and y.

It is remarkable how rich are this notion and the related one of convex function defined in Section 5.3.

Theorem 3.2.1. *Let S be a closed convex set in $\mathcal{H}$, a Hilbert space. Let $x \in \mathcal{H}$. Then there is a unique $y \in S$ with*

$$\|x - y\| = \inf\{\|x - z\| \mid z \in S\} \tag{3.2.2}$$

Proof. This is an elegant use of the parallelogram law. The parallelogram law for $a = x - w_1$, $b = x - w_2$ says

$$\|x - \tfrac{1}{2}(w_1 + w_2)\|^2 + \tfrac{1}{4}\|w_1 - w_2\|^2 = \tfrac{1}{2}(\|x - w_1\|^2 + \|x - w_2\|^2) \tag{3.2.3}$$

Let

$$c = \inf\{\|x - z\| \mid z \in S\} \tag{3.2.4}$$

If $w_1, w_2 \in S$ with $\|x - w_1\| = \|x - w_2\| = c$, then since $\tfrac{1}{2}(w_1 + w_2) \in S$, we have $\|x - \tfrac{1}{2}(w_1 + w_2)\|^2 \geq c^2$, so (3.2.3) implies $\|w_1 - w_2\| = 0$, that is, $w_1 = w_2$. We have thus proven there is at most one minimizer.

By definition of c, there exist y_n so that

$$c^2 \leq \|x - y_n\|^2 \leq c^2 + \frac{1}{n} \tag{3.2.5}$$

Thus, by (3.2.3) and $\|x - \tfrac{1}{2}(y_n + y_m)\| \geq c$,

$$\|y_n - y_m\|^2 \leq 2\left(c^2 + \frac{1}{n} + c^2 + \frac{1}{m} - 2c^2\right) = 2\left(\frac{1}{n} + \frac{1}{m}\right)$$

so y_n is Cauchy and $y_n \to y_\infty \in S$ since S is closed. By (3.2.5) and continuity of the norm, $\|x - y_\infty\| = c$, proving existence of a minimizer. $\square$

Definition. For any subspace, S, in $\mathcal{H}$, define its *orthogonal complement* by

$$S^\perp = \{y \in \mathcal{H} \mid \langle y, x \rangle = 0 \text{ for all } x \in S\} \tag{3.2.6}$$

Proposition 3.2.2. *Let S be a closed subspace in $\mathcal{H}$. Let $x \in \mathcal{H}$ and let $y \in S$ obey (3.2.2). Then $x - y \in S^\perp$.*

Proof. Let $\lambda \in \mathbb{C}$ and $z \in S$. Then, by (3.2.2),

$$\|x - y\|^2 \leq \|x - y - \lambda z\|^2 \tag{3.2.7}$$

so for all such λ and z,

$$-2\operatorname{Re}\langle x - y, \lambda z \rangle + |\lambda|^2 \|z\|^2 \geq 0 \tag{3.2.8}$$

Write $\lambda = |\lambda|e^{i\theta}$, fix θ, divide by $|\lambda|$, and take $|\lambda| \to 0$ to see that

$$-2\operatorname{Re}\langle x - y, e^{i\theta} z \rangle \geq 0 \tag{3.2.9}$$

For this to be true for all θ, we must have $\langle x - y, z \rangle = 0$, that is, $x - y \in S^\perp$. $\square$

Theorem 3.2.3 (The Projection Lemma). *Let S be a closed subspace of $\mathcal{H}$. Then any $x \in \mathcal{H}$ can be written*

$$x = y + z \qquad y \in S, z \in S^\perp \tag{3.2.10}$$

and in a unique way.

Proof. Given x, let $y \in S$ obey (3.2.2) and let $z = x - y$. By the proposition, $z \in S^\perp$, so (3.2.10) holds.

For uniqueness, suppose that

$$x = y_1 + z_1 = y_2 + z_2 \tag{3.2.11}$$

with $y_1, y_2 \in S$, $z_1, z_2 \in S^\perp$. Then

$$y_1 - y_2 = z_2 - z_1 \in S \cap S^\perp = \{0\} \tag{3.2.12}$$

so $y_1 = y_2$, $z_1 = z_2$. $\qquad\square$

The name of this theorem comes from the following

Definition. A *projection* on a vector space, V, is a linear transformation $P: V \to V$ so

$$P^2 = P \tag{3.2.13}$$

Corollary 3.2.4. *For any closed subspace, S, of $\mathcal{H}$, there is a unique projection P obeying*

(i) $\operatorname{Ran}(P) = S, \quad \operatorname{Ran}(1 - P) = S^\perp$

(ii) $\|Px\| \le \|x\| \quad$ *for all x* $\tag{3.2.14}$

Conversely, any projection with

$$\operatorname{Ran}(1 - P) \subset (\operatorname{Ran}(P))^\perp \tag{3.2.15}$$

has $\operatorname{Ran}(P)$ closed and associated to a (3.2.10) decomposition.

Proof. Let $Px = y$ where y is from (3.2.10). Clearly, $\operatorname{Ran}(P) \subset S$, and if $x \in S$, then $Px = x$, so $P^2 = P$ and $S \subset \operatorname{Ran}(P)$. By (3.2.10), $(1 - P)x = z \in S^\perp$, so as above, $\operatorname{Ran}(1 - P) = S^\perp$.

Since $y \perp z$ in (3.2.10), we have

$$\|x\|^2 = \|y\|^2 + \|z\|^2 \tag{3.2.16}$$

proving (3.2.14).

If (3.2.15) holds and $y = Px$, $z = x - y$, then (3.2.16) holds, so (3.2.14) holds. If $y_n = Px_n$ and $y_n \to y_\infty$, then $Py_\infty = \lim Py_n = \lim y_n = y_\infty$, that is, $\operatorname{Ran}(P)$ is closed. $\qquad\square$

Corollary 3.2.5. *If S is a proper closed subspace, then $S^\perp \ne \{0\}$.*

Remark. *Proper* means not all of $\mathcal{H}$.

Proof. Let $x \notin S$. Then in (3.2.10), $z \neq 0$. Since $z \in S^\perp$, $S^\perp \neq \{0\}$. $\quad\square$

More generally, one has the following, whose proof is left to Problem 1:

Corollary 3.2.6. *For any subspace (not necessarily closed) T of a Hilbert space, $\mathcal{H}$, one has*

$$(T^\perp)^\perp = \overline{T} \tag{3.2.17}$$

Notes and Historical Remarks. Orthogonal complements of subspaces go back to Schmidt's work on integral equations, for example, his 1908 book [**818**]. They were constructed using bases and the Gram–Schmidt procedure. The need to extend to the nonseparable case produced the elegant construction via a minimization that we use in this section. It is due to F. Riesz [**787**] and F. Rellich [**767**] in 1934.

Problems

1. (a) Using the projection lemma, prove that if S is a closed subspace of a Hilbert space, $\mathcal{H}$, then $S^{\perp\perp} = S$.

   (b) For any arbitrary subspace, T, of $\mathcal{H}$, prove that $\overline{T} \subset (T^\perp)^\perp$.

   (c) If T, Q are subspaces and $T \subset Q$, prove that $(T^\perp)^\perp \subset (Q^\perp)^\perp$.

   (d) Prove Corollary 3.2.6.

3.3. Dual Spaces and the Riesz Representation Theorem

Some of the most significant results in the abstract tools of real analysis are the identification of the dual spaces of important spaces. Many interesting theorems in analysis, for example, the Radon-Nikodym theorem (see Section 4.7), Herglotz theorem (see Section 5.9 of Part 3), and spectral theorem (see Section 5.1 of Part 4), rely on the use of suitable representation theorems for linear functionals. In this section, our goal will be to identify the dual space of a general Hilbert space. But first we'll need to define the dual space and prove a few general facts about continuous linear functionals.

Definition. A *topological vector space* is a real or complex vector space, V, with a Hausdorff topology in which $(x, y) \mapsto x + y$ from $V \times V \to V$ is continuous and $(\lambda, x) \mapsto \lambda x$ from $\mathbb{K} \times V \to V$ ($\mathbb{K}$ is $\mathbb{R}$ or $\mathbb{C}$) is continuous.

We'll use $\mathbb{K}$ generally for $\mathbb{R}$ or $\mathbb{C}$, the underlying field for V.

Definition. The *dual space* of a topological vector space, V, is the vector space, V^*, of continuous linear maps of V to $\mathbb{K}$ (called *continuous linear functionals*).

Of course, an NLS is a topological vector space when given the induced metric. Eventually, we'll see that there are topological vector spaces (not given by a norm) with no nonzero continuous linear functional (see Proposition 5.7.4), but that, in contrast, any normed linear space has enough linear functionals to separate points (see Theorem 5.5.9). For now, we focus on continuous linear transformations between NLS, one of which can, but need not, be $\mathbb{K}$.

Theorem 3.3.1. *Let $(X, \|\cdot\|_X)$ and $(Y, \|\cdot\|_Y)$ be two normed linear spaces over the same field and let $T \colon X \to Y$ be linear. Then T is continuous if and only if there exists C with*

$$\|Tx\|_Y \leq C\|x\|_X \tag{3.3.1}$$

for all $x \in X$.

Proof. If (3.3.1) holds and $x_n \to x$ in X, then $\|x_n - x\|_X \to 0$, so $\|Tx_n - Tx\|_Y \to 0$, so $Tx_n \to Tx$, that is, T is continuous.

Conversely, suppose T is continuous. Since $\{y \mid \|y\| < 1\}$ is open, $T^{-1}[\{y \mid \|y\| < 1\}]$ is open. Since the second set contains 0, for some $r > 0$, $\{x \mid \|x\| < r\} \subset T^{-1}(\{y \mid \|y\| < 1\}$, that is,

$$\|x\| < r \Rightarrow \|Tx\| < 1 \tag{3.3.2}$$

Thus, for any $0 < \alpha < 1$ and any $x \neq 0$, we have $T(\frac{\alpha r x}{\|x\|}) < 1$, that is, by linearity, $\|Tx\| < \frac{1}{\alpha r}\|x\|$. It follows that (3.3.1) holds with $C = 1/r$ (since α is arbitrary in $(0, 1)$). $\qquad\square$

A linear map obeying (3.3.1) is called a *bounded linear transformation* (BLT) and Theorem 3.3.1 is called the BLT theorem. If $Y = \mathbb{K}$, the one-dimensional space, we speak of *bounded linear functional* (BLF). The terms "continuous" and "bounded" can thus be used interchangeably.

We define $\|T\|$ to be the smallest constant, C, that works in (3.3.1), that is,

$$\|T\| = \sup_{x \neq 0} \frac{\|Tx\|_Y}{\|x\|_X} \tag{3.3.3}$$

It is easy to see $\|\cdot\|$ turns $\mathrm{BLT}(X, Y)$, the set of all BLTs into a normed linear space, and it is not hard to show (Problem 1) that if Y is a Banach space, so is $\mathrm{BLT}(X, Y)$.

In particular, $\|\cdot\|$ turns the dual space, X^*, of an NLS into a Banach space.

Theorem 3.3.2. *Let X be a topological vector space and $L \colon X \to \mathbb{K}$ a nonzero linear functional. Then*

(a) L *is continuous if and only if* $\mathrm{Ker}(L)$ *is closed.*

(b) L *is not continuous if and only if* $\mathrm{Ker}(L)$ *is dense in* X.

Proof. If suffices to prove the "only if" parts of (a) and (b) since, for $L \not\equiv 0$, the contrapositive of the "only if" parts of (b) and (a) imply the "if" parts of (a) and (b).

That L continuous implies $\mathrm{Ker}(L)$ is closed is immediate since $\mathrm{Ker}(L) = L^{-1}(\{0\})$.

Suppose L is not continuous. Pick a net $x_\alpha \to x_\infty$ so $L(x_\alpha) \not\to L(x_\infty)$. Since $L \not\equiv 0$, we can add a common vector to all x_α and x_∞ so that

$$L(x_\infty) = 1 \tag{3.3.4}$$

By a compactness argument, we can pass to a subnet and suppose either

$$\lim_\alpha |L(x_\alpha)| = \infty \qquad \text{or} \qquad \lim_\alpha L(x_\alpha) = a \neq 1 \tag{3.3.5}$$

If the first statement in (3.3.5) holds, let $w_\alpha = x_\alpha / L(x_\alpha)$, so $w_\alpha \to 0$ and $L(w_\alpha) = 1$. For any $y \in X$, let $y_\alpha = y - L(y)w_\alpha$, so $y_\alpha \in \mathrm{Ker}(L)$ and $y_\alpha \to y$, proving $\mathrm{Ker}(L)$ is dense.

If the second statement in (3.3.5) holds, let

$$w_\alpha = L(x_\infty)x_\alpha - L(x_\alpha)x_\infty \tag{3.3.6}$$

so $L(w_\alpha) = 0$. Given $y \in X$, let

$$y_\alpha = y + \frac{L(y)}{1-a}\left(w_\alpha - x_\infty(1-a)\right)$$

Then $L(y_\alpha) = 0$ by (3.3.4). By (3.3.5), $w_\alpha \to (1-a)x_\infty$, so $y_\alpha \to y$. Thus, $\mathrm{Ker}(L)$ is dense. $\qquad\qquad\qquad\qquad\qquad\qquad\qquad\qquad\qquad\qquad\square$

That completes what we want to say for now about general dual spaces. We turn to the dual space of a Hilbert space and the main theorem of this section:

Theorem 3.3.3 (Riesz Representation Theorem). *Let* $\mathcal{H}$ *be a Hilbert space. For each* $\varphi \in \mathcal{H}$, *define* $\ell_\varphi \colon \mathcal{H} \to \mathbb{C}$ *by*

$$\ell_\varphi(\psi) = \langle \varphi, \psi \rangle \tag{3.3.7}$$

Then $\ell_\varphi = \ell_\eta \Leftrightarrow \varphi = \eta$, *each* ℓ_φ *defines a BLF and every BLF is an* ℓ_φ *for some* $\varphi \in \mathcal{H}$.

Remark. The subtle part of this, namely, the final assertion that every BLF is an ℓ_φ, is sometimes called the Riesz representation theorem.

Proof. $\ell_\varphi(\varphi - \eta) - \ell_\eta(\varphi - \eta) = \|\varphi - \eta\|^2$, so $\ell_\varphi = \ell_\eta \Rightarrow \varphi = \eta$. By the Schwarz inequality,

$$|\ell_\varphi(\psi)| \le \|\varphi\|\,\|\psi\| \qquad (3.3.8)$$

proving each ℓ_φ is a BLF.

For the converse, let $L \in \mathcal{H}^*$. If $L = 0$, $L = \ell_{\varphi=0}$, so we can suppose $L \not\equiv 0$. Thus, $\mathrm{Ker}(L)$ is a proper closed subspace of $\mathcal{H}$. Therefore, by Corollary 3.2.5, we can pick $\eta \in (\mathrm{Ker}(L))^\perp$, $\eta \ne 0$. Since $\eta \notin \mathrm{Ker}(L)$, we have $L(\eta) \ne 0$.

Let

$$\varphi = \frac{\overline{L(\eta)}\,\eta}{\|\eta\|^2} \qquad (3.3.9)$$

Then

$$\ell_\varphi(\eta) = \langle \varphi, \eta \rangle = L(\eta) \qquad (3.3.10)$$

and

$$\ell_\varphi(\psi) = L(\psi) \quad \text{if } \psi \in \mathrm{Ker}(L) \qquad (3.3.11)$$

Given any $\xi \in \mathcal{H}$, let

$$\psi = \xi - \frac{L(\xi)\eta}{L(\eta)} \qquad (3.3.12)$$

so $L(\psi) = 0$. Thus, by (3.3.10) and (3.3.11), $L(\xi) = \ell_\varphi(\xi)$, that is, $L = \ell_\varphi$. $\qquad\qquad\square$

Notice that since $\ell_\varphi(\varphi) = \|\varphi\|^2$, (3.3.8) implies

$$\|\ell_\varphi\| = \|\varphi\| \qquad (3.3.13)$$

Since $\varphi \mapsto \ell_\varphi$ preserves sums and differences, (3.3.13) implies $\|\ell\|$ obeys the parallogram law. Thus, by Theorem 3.1.6, $\mathcal{H}^*$ has an inner product and thus is a Hilbert space.

Definition. An *anti-unitary* map, T, of one Hilbert space, $\mathcal{H}$, into another, $\widetilde{\mathcal{H}}$, is an antilinear map $T\colon \mathcal{H} \to \widetilde{\mathcal{H}}$, which is a bijection, and $\|Tx\|_{\widetilde{\mathcal{H}}} = \|x\|_{\mathcal{H}}$ (see Problem 3).

We thus have the following restatement of Theorem 3.3.3:

Theorem 3.3.4 (Riesz Representation Theorem: Reformulation). *The map* $\varphi \mapsto \ell_\varphi$ *is an anti-unitary map of* $\mathcal{H}$ *onto* $\mathcal{H}^*$.

Notes and Historical Remarks. The term dual space was proposed by Bourbaki [**119**].

In 1906, Hilbert [**426**] considered linear forms on ℓ^2 and proved they were given by $x \to (y, x)$ for some $y \in \ell^2$. Fréchet [**316**] and Riesz [**776**] extended this in 1907 to what we would now call L^2. The abstract result was made explicit by Riesz [**787**] for general (nonseparable) Hilbert spaces.

There are other results (e.g., the Riesz–Markov theorem of Section 4.5) that
are sometimes called the Riesz representation theorem.

Reproducing kernel Hilbert spaces (the subject of Problems 4 through
11) go back to a 1907 paper of Zaremba [**1017**] who found them in connection with spaces of harmonic functions (not unrelated to the example in
Problem 9). The theory was developed in the early 1920s by Bergman [**73**],
Bochner [**100**], and Szegő [**901**]. The abstract theory is due to Aronszajn
[**34, 35**], Krein [**524**], and Schwartz [**833**]. It has been developed in classical analysis (Saitoh [**809**]), probability theory (Kolmogorov [**509**], Parzen
[**702, 703**] and the book of Berlinet–Thomas-Agnan [**77**]), interpolation theory (Ando [**27**]), boundary value problems (Bergman–Schiffer [**74, 75, 76**]),
and systems theory via J-contractive matrix functions (Alpay [**23**] and Dym
[**267**]).

Problems

1. (a) If X and Y are NLS, prove that $\|\cdot\|$ of (3.3.3) turns $\mathrm{BLT}(X, Y) \equiv$
   $\{T \in \mathrm{Hom}(X, Y) \mid \|T\| < \infty\}$ into an NLS.

   (b) If Y is a Banach space, prove that so is $\mathrm{BLT}(X, Y)$.

2. Let $X_1 \subset X$ be a subspace of X, an NLS, and $\bar{X}_1$ the closure of X_1 in X.
   Let $T \colon X_1 \to Y$ obey (3.3.1) for some C and all $x \in X_1$. Prove that T
   has unique continuous extension to $\bar{X}_1$ and that this extension is linear
   and obeys (3.3.1).

3. If T is an anti-unitary map, prove that for all $\varphi, \psi \in \mathcal{H}$, $\langle T\varphi, T\psi \rangle =$
   $\langle \psi, \varphi \rangle$. (*Hint*: Polarization.)

   The next few problems present some of the basics of reproducing kernel Hilbert spaces and make explicit some facts we won't prove until later
   (we'll note where). The subject is intimately connected to the subject of
   coherent states, which will appear again in Sections 4.4–4.6 of Part 3.

4. A *reproducing kernel Hilbert space* is a Hilbert space, $\mathcal{H}$, of functions, f
   on a set, E, so that
   (i) For any f, there is $x \in E$ with $f(x) \neq 0$
   (ii) For any $x \in E$, there is $f \in \mathcal{H}$ so $f(x) \neq 0$
   (iii) For any $x, y \in E$, there is f in $\mathcal{H}$ so $f(x) \neq f(y)$
   (iv) For any $x \in E$, there is C_x so that

   $$|f(x)| \leq C_x \|f\|_{\mathcal{H}} \tag{3.3.14}$$

   (a) Prove that for any $x \in E$, there is $k_x \in \mathcal{H}$ so that for any $f \in \mathcal{H}$,

   $$f(x) = \langle k_x, f \rangle \tag{3.3.15}$$

   (b) Prove that each $k_x \neq 0$ and $x \neq y \Rightarrow k_x \neq k_y$.

(c) Prove that finite linear combinations of $\{k_x\}_{x \in E}$ are dense in $\mathcal{H}$. (*Hint*: If S is the closure of the span of the $\{k_x\}_{x \in E}$ and $f \in S^\perp$, what can you say about $f(x)$?)

(d) The *reproducing kernel* of $\mathcal{H}$ is the function K on $E \times E$ given by

$$K(x, y) = \langle k_y, k_x \rangle = k_x(y) \tag{3.3.16}$$

Prove that

$$K(y, x) = \overline{K(x, y)} \tag{3.3.17}$$

(e) Prove that for any $x_1, \dots, x_n \in E$ and $\zeta \in \mathbb{C}^n$, we have

$$\sum_{i,j=1}^{n} \bar{\zeta}_i \zeta_j K(x_i, x_j) \geq 0 \tag{3.3.18}$$

Such a function K on $E \times E$ is called a *positive definite kernel*.

Remarks. 1. We'll see examples in Problems 8–11.

2. We'll return to reproducing Hilbert spaces in Problem 8 of Section 3.4, Problem 20 of Section 6.6, Section 12.5 of Part 2B, and the study of coherent states in Section 4.4 of Part 3.

3. Positive definite kernels and functions will also appear many times. If f is a function on $\mathbb{R}^\nu$ and $K(x, y) = f(x - y)$ is a positive definite kernel, we call f a *positive definite* function. We'll discuss them in Section 6.6 and when $\mathbb{R}^\nu$ is replaced by more general groups in Sections 6.3, 6.7, 6.8, and 6.9 of Part 4. Section 3.11 of Part 4 provides a representation theorem for positive definite continuous kernels on compact spaces.

4. Notice that we have put no topology on X. In further developments, one often wants to make X a topological space and demand that $x \mapsto k_x$ be continuous.

5. Let K be a function on $E \times E$ which is positive definite in the sense of (3.3.18). Let $c_0(E)$ be the functions on E of the form

$$\sum_{i=1}^{m} \zeta_i K(x_i, \cdot) \equiv f(\zeta) \tag{3.3.19}$$

for finitely many points $x_1, \dots, x_m$. For $f(\eta), f(\zeta) \in c_0(E)$, define

$$\langle f(\eta), f(\zeta) \rangle = \sum_{i,j=1}^{n} \bar{\eta}_i \zeta_j K(x_i, x_j) \tag{3.3.20}$$

(a) Prove $\langle \cdot, \cdot \rangle$ is an inner product except perhaps for the strict positivity.

(b) Let $k_x = K(x, \cdot) \in c_0(E)$. Prove that

$$\langle k_x, f(\zeta) \rangle = f(\zeta)(x) \qquad (3.3.21)$$

(c) Let $I = \{f(\eta) \in c_o(E) \mid \langle f(\eta), f(\zeta) \rangle = 0\}$ and $\mathcal{H}$ be the completion of $c_0(E)/I$. Prove that $\mathcal{H}$ is a Hilbert space (except perhaps for the separability axiom).

(d) Prove that $\mathcal{H}$ is a reproducing kernel Hilbert space with reproducing kernel $K(x, y)$.

6. Let X be a locally compact, σ-compact metric space (these are discussed in Section 4.10) and $\ell \colon C_0(X) \to \mathbb{R}$, where $C_0(X)$ is the set of functions, $f \colon X \to \mathbb{R}$ with $\mathrm{supp}(f) = \overline{\{x \mid f(x) \neq 0\}}$ compact. Suppose that $f \geq 0$, $f \not\equiv 0$ implies $\ell(f) > 0$. With the measure theory of Section 4.10 in mind, we write $\ell(f) = \int f(x)\, d\mu(x)$. Put an inner product on $C_0(X)$ by $\langle f, g \rangle_{L^2} = \ell(\bar{f}g)$. $L^2(X, d\mu)$ will denote the completion of $C_0(X)$. If $g_n \in C_0(X)$ with $0 \leq g_n \leq 1$, $g_n \equiv 1$ on K_n, $\mathrm{supp}(g_n) \in K_{n+1}$, we say $f \in C(X)$ is in L^2 if and only if fg_n is Cauchy in $C_0(X)$, in which case we view f as an element of L^2.

   An L^2 *reproducing kernel Hilbert space* is $Y \subset C(X)$ so that $Y \subset L^2(X, d\mu)$, and $\{f \in X \mid \|f\|_{L^2} < 1\}$ is locally uniformly bounded and locally uniformly equicontinuous, that is, for every compact $Q \subset X$, there is C_Q so that for all $f \in Y$,

$$\sup_{x \in Q} |f(x)| \leq C_Q \|f\|_{L^2} \qquad (3.3.22)$$

and for every Q and $\varepsilon > 0$, there is δ so that for all $f \in Y$,

$$x, y \in Q,\ \rho(x, y) < \delta \Rightarrow |f(x) - f(y)| \leq \varepsilon \|f\|_{L^2} \qquad (3.3.23)$$

(a) Prove that Y is closed in L^2-norm, so Y is a Hilbert space in $\langle \cdot, \cdot \rangle_{L^2}$.

(b) For every $x \in X$, prove that there is $k_x \in Y$ so that for all $f \in Y$,

$$f(x) = \langle k_x, f \rangle \qquad (3.3.24)$$

(c) Prove that $\sup_{x \in Q} \|k_x\| \leq C_Q$.

(d) Prove that $x \to \|k_x\|$ is continuous in L^2-norm. (*Hint*: If $x_n \to x$, prove that $\langle k_{x_n} - k_x, k_{x_n} \rangle \to 0$.)

(e) If $x_n \to x$, prove that $\|k_{x_n} - k_x\| \to 0$, that is, $x \to k_x$ is continuous.

(f) Define

$$K(x, y) = \langle k_y, k_x \rangle \qquad (3.3.25)$$

Prove that K is jointly continuous in x and y and obeys

$$K(x, y) = \overline{K(y, x)} \qquad (3.3.26)$$

and

$$k_y(x) = K(x, y) \tag{3.3.27}$$

(g) Prove that for all $x, z \in X$, we have

$$\int K(x, y) K(y, z) \, d\mu(y) = K(x, z) \tag{3.3.28}$$

Note. (3.3.24), (3.3.26), and (3.3.27) say that if $f \in Y$,

$$f(x) = \int K(x, y) f(y) \, d\mu(y) \tag{3.3.29}$$

so K is called the *reproducing kernel* for Y.

Once we can use functional notation for elements of L^2, $(Pf)(x) = \int K(x, y) f(y) \, d\mu(y)$.

7. Let X be a compact metric space. Let K be a jointly continuous positive definite kernel on $X \times X$ (i.e., obey (3.3.18)) and also obey (3.3.28) for a Baire measure, μ. Define P from $C(X)$ to itself by

$$(Pf)(x) = \int K(x, y) f(y) \, d\mu(y) \tag{3.3.30}$$

Let $Y = \operatorname{Ran}(P)$. Prove that Y is a closed subspace of $L^2(X, d\mu)$ and an L^2 reproducing kernel Hilbert space with kernel K.

8. Let X be a countable set thought of as a discrete topological space. Let $\ell^2(X)$ be sequences with $\sum_{x \in X} |a_x|^2 < \infty$ with the usual inner product. Prove that $Y = \ell^2(X)$ is an L^2 reproducing kernel Hilbert space. What is K?

9. The space in this problem is the Hardy space, $H^2(\mathbb{D})$, which we study in Section 5.2 of Part 3. This problem assumes some small amount of familiarity with analytic functions, the subject of Part 2.

(a) Recall that $\ell^2(\mathbb{Z}_+)$ is sequences $\{a_n\}_{n=1}^\infty$ with $\sum_{n=1}^\infty |a_n|^2 < \infty$ (Example 3.1.8). For each $a \in \ell^2$ and $z \in \mathbb{D}$ (i.e., $z \in \mathbb{C}$ with $|z| < 1$), define

$$f(a; z) = \sum_{n=0}^\infty a_{n+1} z^n \tag{3.3.31}$$

Prove that $f(a; \cdot)$ is an analytic function on $\mathbb{D}$. This set of analytic functions is called $H^2(\mathbb{D})$. Prove that $H^2(\mathbb{D})$ as a set of functions with $\|f(a; \cdot)\| = \|a\|_2$ is a reproducing kernel Hilbert space on $\mathbb{D}$.

(b) Prove that

$$K(z, w) = \frac{1}{1 - z\bar{w}} \tag{3.3.32}$$

This is called the *Szegő kernel*.

(c) Prove that there is no measure on $\mathbb{D}$ for which

$$\|f\|^2 = \int |f(z)|^2 \, d\mu(z) \tag{3.3.33}$$

for all $f \in H^2$, so that H^2 is not an L^2 reproducing kernel Hilbert space. (*Hint*: Consider first the possibility of a measure, ν, on $\overline{\mathbb{D}}$ so (3.3.33) holds if $f(z) = z^n$ for all n. Prove first that ν is supported on $\partial \mathbb{D}$ and then that $\nu = \frac{d\theta}{2\pi}$. Thus, μ is not a measure on $\mathbb{D}$.)

10. Let X be the C^1 functions on $[0,1]$ with $f(0) = 0$ and let

$$\langle f, g \rangle = \int_0^1 \overline{f'(x)} \, g'(x) \, dx \tag{3.3.34}$$

(a) Prove that $\mathcal{H}$, the completion of X, is a reproducing kernel Hilbert space. (*Hint*: If $f \in X$, $f(x) = \int_0^x f'(y) \, dy$.)

(b) Prove that

$$K(x,y) = \min(x,y) \tag{3.3.35}$$

(c) Prove that there is no measure on $[0,1]$ so that for $f \in X$,

$$\|f\|_{\mathcal{H}}^2 = \int_0^1 |f(x)|^2 \, d\mu(x) \tag{3.3.36}$$

(*Hint*: What is $\|x^n\|$?) Thus, $\mathcal{H}$ is not an L^2 reproducing kernel Hilbert space.

11. For this problem, you'll need two facts about the function (on $\mathbb{R}$)

$$f_0(x) = e^{-\frac{1}{2}x^2} \tag{3.3.37}$$

First, $f_0(x-y)$ is a positive definite kernel (see Proposition 6.6.8); and second, that finite linear combinations of translates of f_0 are dense in $\mathcal{S}(\mathbb{R})$, the Schwartz space (see Problem 23 of Section 6.6).

(a) Prove there is a reproducing kernel Hilbert space, $\mathcal{H}$, of functions on $\mathbb{R}$ with

$$K(x,y) = f_0(x-y) \tag{3.3.38}$$

(b) Prove there is no measure on $\mathbb{R}$ with

$$\|f\|_{\mathcal{H}}^2 = \int |f(x)|^2 \, d\mu(x) \tag{3.3.39}$$

(*Hint*: Prove first that $d\mu$ must be $c \, dx$ for ($c \in (0,\infty)$) and then that if $K_x(y) = K(x-y)$ that $c\langle k_x, k_w \rangle_{L^2(\mathbb{R},dx)} \neq K(x,w)$.) Thus, $\mathcal{H}$ is not an L^2 reproducing kernel Hilbert space.

3.4. Orthonormal Bases, Abstract Fourier Expansions, and Gram–Schmidt

In this section, we'll consider maximal orthonormal sets $\{x_\alpha\}_{\alpha\in I}$ in a Hilbert space, $\mathcal{H}$, and prove that any $x \in \mathcal{H}$ has an expansion, called an abstract Fourier expansion, in terms of $\{x_\alpha\}$ in that

$$x = \sum_{\alpha\in I} \langle x_\alpha, x\rangle x_\alpha \tag{3.4.1}$$

We'll prove the existence of a countable maximal orthonormal set in a Hilbert space using separability and an inductive procedure known as the Gram–Schmidt process.

Recall that we proved in Theorems 3.1.11 and 3.1.12 that for any orthonormal set $\{x_\alpha\}_{\alpha\in I}$ and $x \in \mathcal{H}$, the sum on the right side of (3.4.1) exists in that the sum over finite subsets converges as the finite sets approach I.

Definition. An *orthonormal basis* in a Hilbert space, $\mathcal{H}$, is a maximal orthonormal family.

Theorem 3.4.1. *Let $\{x_\alpha\}_{\alpha\in I}$ be an orthonormal basis and $x \in \mathcal{H}$. Then (abstract Fourier expansion)*

$$x = \sum_{\alpha\in I} \langle x_\alpha, x\rangle x_\alpha \tag{3.4.2}$$

and (abstract Plancherel theorem, aka abstract Parseval relation)

$$\|x\|^2 = \sum_{\alpha\in I} |\langle x_\alpha, x\rangle|^2 \tag{3.4.3}$$

Proof. Let

$$y = x - \sum_{\alpha\in I} \langle x_\alpha, x\rangle x_\alpha \tag{3.4.4}$$

and suppose $y \neq 0$. Let $\tilde{y} = y/\|y\|$. Then $\langle \tilde{y}, x_\alpha\rangle = 0$, so $\{x_\alpha\}_{\alpha\in I} \cup \{\tilde{y}\}$ is an orthonormal set, violating maximality. Thus, $y = 0$, that is, (3.4.2) holds. (3.1.40) then implies (3.4.3). $\qquad\square$

In general, not necessarily separable Hilbert spaces, the existence of maximal orthonormal sets is a simple Zornification (see Problem 1). In the separable case, we can be more constructive. We begin by noting

Proposition 3.4.2. *In any separable Hilbert space, there exist countable, independent spanning sets, that is, $\{y_j\}_{j=1}^N$ with N finite or countably infinite, that obey*

(i) $\sum_{j=1}^n \alpha_j y_j = 0 \Rightarrow \alpha_1 = \alpha_2 = \cdots = \alpha_n = 0$
(ii) $\{\sum_{j=1}^n \alpha_j y_j \mid (\alpha_1, \ldots, \alpha_n) \in \mathbb{C}^n, \, n \in \{j\}_{j=1}^N\}$ *is dense in $\mathcal{H}$.*

Proof. Pick $z_1, \ldots, z_n, \ldots$, a countable dense set with all $z_j \neq 0$. Let $y_1 = z_1$. If z_k is linearly dependent on $z_1, \ldots, z_{k-1}$, that is, $z_k = \sum_{j=1}^{k-1} \gamma_j z_j$ for some $(\gamma_1, \ldots, \gamma_{k-1}) \in \mathbb{C}^{k-1}$, drop z_k. Otherwise, let it be the next y. It is easy to see we have (i) and (ii). $\qquad\square$

Theorem 3.4.3 (Gram–Schmidt Procedure). *Let $\{y_j\}_{j=1}^N$ be a countable, independent spanning set of a Hilbert space, $\mathcal{H}$. Define x_j inductively by*

$$x_j = \frac{y_j - \sum_{\ell=1}^{j-1} \langle x_\ell, y_j \rangle x_\ell}{\|y_j - \sum_{\ell=1}^{j-1} \langle x_\ell, y_j \rangle x_\ell\|} \tag{3.4.5}$$

Then $\{x_j\}_{j=1}^N$ is an orthonormal basis.

Proof. By condition (i) for spanning sets, the vector in the numerator in (3.4.5) is nonzero, so we can divide it by its norm and get an orthonormal family.

Since

$$y_j = \left\| y_j - \sum_{\ell=1}^{j-1} \langle x_\ell, y_j \rangle x_\ell \right\| x_j + \sum_{\ell=1}^{j-1} \langle x_\ell, y_j \rangle x_\ell \tag{3.4.6}$$

we see that, for each n,

$$\left\{ \sum_{j=1}^n \alpha_j y_j \;\middle|\; (\alpha_1, \ldots, \alpha_n) \in \mathbb{C}^n \right\} = \left\{ \sum_{j=1}^n \beta_j x_j \;\middle|\; (\beta_1, \ldots, \beta_n) \in \mathbb{C}^n \right\} \tag{3.4.7}$$

so the union over n of right-side sets is dense in $\mathcal{H}$. If $w \in [\{x_j\}_{j=1}^\infty]^\perp$, then w is orthogonal to that union, and so to all $\mathcal{H}$. Thus, $\|w\|^2 = \langle w, w \rangle = 0$. It follows that $\{x_j\}_{j=1}^\infty$ is a maximal orthonormal set. $\qquad\square$

It is sometimes useful to consider

$$w_j = y_j - \sum_{\ell=1}^{j-1} \langle x_\ell, y_j \rangle x_\ell \tag{3.4.8}$$

called *unnormalized Gram–Schmidt*. The w_j are orthogonal and have

$$w_j = \sum_{k=1}^j A_{jk} y_k, \qquad y_j = \sum_{k=1}^j B_{jk} w_k \tag{3.4.9}$$

for matrices with $A_{jj} = B_{jj} = 1$.

We also note that (3.4.5)/(3.4.6) can be written

$$x_j = \sum_{k=1}^j C_{jk} y_k, \qquad y_j = \sum_{k=1}^j D_{jk} w_k \tag{3.4.10}$$

$$
\begin{array}{ccccc}
\times & \times & \times & \times & \times \\
0 & \times & \times & \times & \times \\
0 & 0 & \times & \times & \times \\
0 & 0 & 0 & \times & \times \\
0 & 0 & 0 & 0 & \times
\end{array}
$$

Figure 3.4.1. An upper-triangular matrix.

and that $C_{jj} > 0$, $D_{jj} > 0$. It is natural to extend A, B, C, D to matrices, that is, define them for all j, k with

$$M_{jk} = 0 \quad \text{if} \quad j > k \tag{3.4.11}$$

Such matrices are called *upper triangular* for obvious geometric reasons; see Figure 3.4.1. If $M_{jk} = 0$ for $j < k$, M is called *lower triangular*. Sometimes *superdiagonal* and *subdiagonal* are used as synonyms for upper and lower triangular.

Problems 3 and 4 explore these upper-triangular matrix representations, including uniqueness of the x_j and w_j's if one demands suitable matrix representations and Cholesky factorization, that is, the fact that any $n \times n$ strictly positive definite matrix, Q, can be factored uniquely as

$$Q = M^*M \tag{3.4.12}$$

where $(M^*)_{jk} = \overline{M}_{kj}$ and M is upper triangular and positive along the diagonal. As we explain in the Notes, Gram–Schmidt is an effective way of inverting positive matrices.

Example 3.4.4 (Orthogonal Polynomials). In $L^2([0,1], dx)$, consider $1, x, x^2, \dots$. If we apply unnormalized Gram–Schmidt, we get a family P_0, P_1, P_2 of monic (i.e., leading coefficient 1) polynomials with $\deg(P_j) = j$, so $\int_0^1 P_j(x)P_k(x)\, dx = 0$ for $j \neq k$. These are the unnormalized *Legendre polynomials*. More generally, if $d\mu$ is a probability measure on $\mathbb{R}$ with finite moments, we can obtain in this way monic polynomials, $P_n(x, d\mu)$, which are orthogonal and called (monic) *orthogonal polynomials*. They'll be studied in some detail in Chapter 4 of Part 4. For $d\mu = \pi^{-\frac{1}{2}} e^{-\frac{1}{2}x^2}\, dx$, these are the Hermite polynomials, which will play a major role in Section 6.4. We'll discuss more on this subject in the Notes. $\qquad\square$

Returning to orthonormal bases, we note the following which we leave to the Problems:

(a) A (separable) Hilbert space only has countable orthonormal sets (Problem 5).

(b) If $\{x_j\}_{j=1}^N$ and $\{z_j\}_{j=1}^M$ are two orthonormal bases, then $N = M$, that is, either both are (countably) infinite or both are finite and the size is equal (Problem 6). N is called the *dimension* of $\mathcal{H}$.

One consequence of the existence of O.N. bases is

Definition. A *unitary operator* between two Hilbert spaces, $\mathcal{H}$ and $\widetilde{\mathcal{H}}$, is a linear bijection, $U \colon \mathcal{H} \to \widetilde{\mathcal{H}}$, that obeys

$$\langle Ux, Uy \rangle_{\widetilde{\mathcal{H}}} = \langle x, y \rangle_{\mathcal{H}} \tag{3.4.13}$$

If such a map exists, we say $\mathcal{H}$ and $\widetilde{\mathcal{H}}$ are unitarily equivalent.

Theorem 3.4.5. *Every Hilbert space, $\mathcal{H}$, is unitarily equivalent to one of $\{\mathbb{C}^n\}_{n=1}^\infty$ or to $\ell^2(\mathbb{Z}_+)$, where $\mathbb{C}^n$ has the usual Euclidean inner product.*

Proof. Pick an O.N. basis $\{x_j\}_{j=1}^N$ for $\mathcal{H}$. Define $U \colon \mathcal{H}$ to sequence $\{\alpha_j\}_{j=1}^N$ by

$$(Ux)_j = \langle x_j, x \rangle \tag{3.4.14}$$

By (3.4.3), if $N = \infty$, $Ux \in \ell^2$, so U maps into $\mathbb{C}^N$ if N is finite or ℓ^2 if N is infinite.

For any orthonormal basis, by polarization of (3.4.3), we have

$$\langle x, y \rangle = \sum_{j=1}^N \langle x, x_j \rangle \langle x_j, y \rangle \tag{3.4.15}$$

so U obeys (3.4.13).

Finally,

$$U^{-1}(\{\alpha_j\}_{j=1}^N) = \sum_{j=1}^N \alpha_j x_j \tag{3.4.16}$$

is a two-sided inverse to U, proving U is a bijection. $\qquad\qquad\square$

Notes and Historical Remarks. During the period 1905–10, Hilbert and Schmidt, who was Hilbert's student, developed eigenfunction expansions in ℓ^2 (this is discussed in Section 3.2 of Part 4). The abstraction to general Hilbert spaces was part of the development of the abstract theory by von Neumann, Stone, and Riesz discussed in the Notes to Section 3.1. And, of course, the background is the concrete Fourier series, whose history we'll discuss in the next section. In particular, the names Plancherel and Parseval are after their work mentioned there.

The Gram–Schmidt process is named after Gram [**359**] in 1883 and Schmidt [**818**] in 1908, although the idea was used much earlier by Laplace. Gram was looking at least square fits and Schmidt in the modern general inner product space context. Jørgen Pedersen Gram (1850–1916) was a

Danish actuary who, despite a nonacademic career, did not only this work but contributed to prime counting and to non-Gaussian statistics. He died after being hit by a bicycle while walking. Section 3.2 of Part 4 has a capsule biography of Schmidt.

Through the Cholesky decomposition (see Problem 3), the Gram–Schmidt decomposition plays a role in numerical analysis, especially the inversion of positive matrices.

The theory of orthogonal polynomials is, roughly speaking, broken into two parts, sometimes called the algebraic theory, which deals with specific examples, and the analytic theory, which focuses on connections of the measures and their recursion coefficients and on the norms of the monic polynomials. We'll say a little bit more about the algebraic theory in Section 14.4 of Part 2B and about the analytic theory in Chapter 4 of Part 4. The classic reference for both is Szegő's book [**902**]. More recent references are Ismail [**444**] for the algebraic theory and Simon [**852, 853, 855**] for the analytic theory.

Problems

1. Let $\mathcal{S}$ be the set of all orthonormal sets in a not necessarily separable Hilbert space. Let $A, B \in \mathcal{S}$, say $A \geq B$ if $B \subseteq A$. If $\{A_\alpha\}_{\alpha \in I}$ is a chain, prove that $\bigcup A_\alpha \in \mathcal{S}$ is an upper bound. Use Zorn's lemma to prove $\mathcal{S}$ contains maximal elements.

2. (a) Let $\{y_j\}_{j=1}^N$ be a finite subset of a Hilbert space, $\mathcal{H}$. Prove that they are independent if and only if their *Gram determinant* $G_N(y) \equiv \det(\langle y_j, y_k\rangle)_{1 \leq j,k \leq N}$ is nonzero.

   (b) In that case, prove that the orthonormal result of Gram–Schmidt, $\{x_j\}_{j=1}^N$, can be written as $x_j = \|y_j - z_j\|^{-1}(y_j - z_j)$ with

$$z_j = -G_j(y)^{-1} \det \begin{pmatrix} \langle y_1, y_1\rangle & \langle y_2, y_2\rangle & \cdots & \langle y_1, y_j\rangle \\ \vdots & & & \vdots \\ \langle y_{j-1}, y_1\rangle & \cdots & \cdots & \langle y_{j-1}, y_j\rangle \\ y_1 & \cdots & y_{j-1} & 0 \end{pmatrix}$$

3. Let Q be a strictly positive matrix on $\mathbb{C}^n$. Define an inner product (which we'll call the Q inner product) on $\mathbb{C}$ by $\langle x, y\rangle = \sum_{i,j=1}^n \bar{x}_i Q_{ij} y_j$. Let $\delta_1, \ldots, \delta_n$ be the bases of vectors in $\mathbb{C}^n$ with $(\delta_j)_k = \delta_{jk}$.

   (a) Find an upper triangular matrix, M, and orthogonal basis in Q inner product, $\eta_1, \ldots, \eta_n$, so that $\delta_j = \sum_{k=1}^j M_{jk} \eta_k$.

   (b) Prove that $Q = M^*M$, proving that every strictly positive matrix has such a factorization.

(c) Prove that the factorization is unique if one also demands that $M_{jj} > 0$ for all j.

Remark. This is known as *Cholesky factorization*.

4. Let M be upper triangular with strictly positive diagonal elements. Find M^{-1} without taking determinants. (*Hint*: Solve $Mx = y$, given y, by finding $x_n, x_{n-1}, \ldots$ inductively.)

5. If $\{x_\alpha\}_{\alpha \in I}$ is an orthonormal set in $\mathcal{H}$, prove that $\|x_\alpha - x_\beta\| = \sqrt{2}$ and conclude that if $\mathcal{H}$ is separable, then I is countable.

6. (a) Let $\{\varphi_\alpha\}_{\alpha=1}^N$ and $\{\psi_\beta\}_{\beta=1}^M$ be two orthonormal bases in a Hilbert space, $\mathcal{H}$. Define an $N \times M$ matrix, $T_{\alpha\beta}$, by $T_{\alpha\beta} = \langle \varphi_\alpha, \psi_\beta \rangle$. Prove that T is the matrix of a bounded invertible operator from $\mathbb{C}^M$ to $\mathbb{C}^N$ (where $\mathbb{C}^\alpha$ means ℓ^2).

(b) Prove $N = M$. (*Hint*: You'll need some linear algebra.)

7. (a) Prove that $\{\chi_{(a,x)} \mid x \in [a,b]\}$ is total in $L^2([a,b], dx)$ where $\chi_{(c,d)}$ is the characteristic function of (c, d).

(b) Prove Vitali's theorem: $\{\varphi_n(x)\}_{n=1}^\infty$, an orthonormal set, is a basis of $L^2([a,b], dx)$ if and only if for all $x \in [a,b]$,

$$\sum_{n=1}^\infty \left| \int_a^x \varphi_n(t)\, dt \right|^2 = x - a \qquad (3.4.17)$$

(c) Prove Dalzell's theorem: $\{\varphi_n(x)\}_{n=1}^\infty$, an orthonormal set, is a basis of $L^2([a,b], dx)$ if and only if

$$\sum_{n=1}^\infty \int_a^b \left| \int_a^x \varphi_n(t) dt \right|^2 dx = \frac{1}{2}(b-a)^2 \qquad (3.4.18)$$

(*Hint*: for (a) and (b): Bessel's inequality.)

Remark. (b) is from Vitali [**950**] and (c) from Dalzell [**213**].

8. Within the L^2 reproducing kernel Hilbert space framework and notation of Problem 6 of Section 3.3, prove that if $\{\varphi_n\}_{n=1}^\infty$ is any orthonormal basis for Y, then for any compact set $Q \subset X$,

(a) $\displaystyle \sup_{x \in Q} \sum_{n=1}^\infty |\varphi_n(x)|^2 \le C_Q^2$ \qquad (3.4.19)

(b) $\displaystyle K(x, y) = \sum_{n=1}^\infty \varphi_n(x) \overline{\varphi_n(y)}$ \qquad (3.4.20)

3.5. Classical Fourier Series

> I turn away with fear and horror from this lamentable plague of continuous functions that do not have a derivative.
>
> *—Charles Hermite (1822-1901)*
> in a letter to Thomas Stieltjes, 1893

Fourier series involve expanding functions periodic with period L in terms of $\{\sin(\frac{2\pi kx}{L})\}_{k=1}^{\infty}$ and $\{\cos(\frac{2\pi kx}{L})\}_{k=0}^{\infty}$. Without loss, we can take $L = 2\pi$ and so consider functions on $\partial\mathbb{D} = \{e^{i\theta} \mid \theta \in \mathbb{R}\}$. The modern approach uses $e^{\pm 2\pi ikx/L}$ rather than sin and cos. The essence of analysis in classical Fourier series is thus $(L^2(\partial\mathbb{D}, \frac{d\theta}{2\pi})$ is for now defined as in Example 3.1.9 by completion)

Theorem 3.5.1. $\{e^{ik\theta}\}_{k=-\infty}^{\infty}$ *is an orthonormal basis for* $L^2(\partial\mathbb{D}, \frac{d\theta}{2\pi})$.

Accepting this for a moment, we have, by Theorem 3.4.1, that

Theorem 3.5.2. *For f a continuous function on $\partial\mathbb{D}$, define*

$$f_k^{\sharp} = \int_0^{2\pi} e^{-ik\theta} f(e^{i\theta}) \frac{d\theta}{2\pi} \tag{3.5.1}$$

Then

$$f(e^{i\theta}) = \sum_{k=-\infty}^{\infty} f_k^{\sharp} e^{ik\theta} \tag{3.5.2}$$

in the sense that

$$\lim_{K\to\infty} \int_0^{2\pi} \left| f(e^{i\theta}) - \sum_{k=-K}^{K} f_k^{\sharp} e^{ik\theta} \right|^2 \frac{d\theta}{2\pi} = 0 \tag{3.5.3}$$

and

$$\sum_{k=-\infty}^{\infty} |f_k^{\sharp}|^2 = \int_0^{2\pi} |f(e^{i\theta})|^2 \frac{d\theta}{2\pi} \tag{3.5.4}$$

Remark. Since $\partial\mathbb{D}$ is compact, f is bounded so all the integrals converge.

This result is sometimes called the Riesz–Fischer theorem. It is not hard to extend this to piecewise continuous functions (Problem 1) and then for a proper choice of f to prove a celebrated formula of Euler (see the Notes) that

$$\sum_{n=1}^{\infty} \frac{1}{n^2} = \frac{\pi^2}{6} \tag{3.5.5}$$

(Problem 21).

We will prove Theorem 3.5.1 as a corollary of

Theorem 3.5.3 (Weierstrass Trigonometric Density Theorem). $\{\sum_{k=-K}^{K} a_k e^{ik\theta} \mid \{a_k\}_{k=-K}^{K} \in \mathbb{C}^{2K+1}, K \in \mathbb{N}\}$ *is* $\|\cdot\|_\infty$*-dense in* $C(\partial\mathbb{D})$.

Proof that Theorem 3.5.3 $\Rightarrow$ Theorem 3.5.1. It is easy to see that if $\varphi_k(e^{i\theta}) = e^{ik\theta}$, then $\langle \varphi_k, \varphi_\ell \rangle = \delta_{k\ell}$. If $\varphi \in L^2$ obeys $\langle \varphi_k, \varphi \rangle = 0$ for all k and $f \in C(X)$ is given, find $\sum_{k=-K}^{K} a_k^{(K)} e^{ik\theta}$ converging in $\|\cdot\|_\infty$ to f. A posteriori, it converges in L^2, so $\langle f, \varphi \rangle = 0$. By construction of L^2, $C(\partial\mathbb{D})$ is dense, so $\langle \varphi, \varphi \rangle = 0$, that is, $\{\varphi_k\}_{k=-\infty}^{\infty}$ is a maximal orthonormal set. $\square$

Theorem 3.5.3 is a restatement of the second density theorem of Weierstrass (Theorem 2.4.2). We'll first prove it using the Stone–Weierstrass theorem. Then we'll find more concrete proofs involving convergence of the Fourier series. We'll give two proofs in the text. In the Problems (see Problems 10, 12, and 3; see also Theorem 3.5.18), we'll provide other results on convergence of Fourier series.

Proof of Theorem 3.5.3 using Stone–Weierstrass. Let $\mathcal{A}$ be the set of finite series of the form $\sum_{k=-K}^{K} a_k e^{ik\theta}$. Since $e^{ik\theta} e^{i\ell\theta} = e^{i(k+\ell)\theta}$, $\mathcal{A}$ is an algebra. Since $\overline{e^{ik\theta}} = e^{-ik\theta}$, $\mathcal{A}$ is closed under conjugation. Since $e^{i\theta}$ separates points on $\partial\mathbb{D}$ and $e^{ik\theta}\big|_{k=0} = 1$, $\mathcal{A}$ obeys all the hypotheses of the complex Stone–Weierstrass theorem (see Theorem 2.5.7), so $\mathcal{A}$ is $\|\cdot\|_\infty$-dense in $C(\partial\mathbb{D})$. $\square$

In the remainder of this section, we'll study three aspects of Fourier series: pointwise or uniform convergence, and so alternate proofs of Theorem 3.5.1; the use of Fourier series to construct nowhere differentiable function; and convergence near discontinuities (an overshoot known as the Gibbs phenomenon).

Given a continuous function, f, on $\partial\mathbb{D}$, define $f_k^{\sharp}$ by (3.5.1) and the *partial sums* and *Cesàro averages* by

$$S_N(f)(e^{i\theta}) = \sum_{k=-N}^{N} f_k^{\sharp} e^{ik\theta} \tag{3.5.6}$$

$$C_N(f)(e^{i\theta}) = \frac{1}{N} \sum_{n=0}^{N-1} S_n(f)(e^{i\theta}) \tag{3.5.7}$$

We will prove the following three results about convergence of Fourier series.

Theorem 3.5.4 (Dini's Test). *Let f be a continuous function on $\partial\mathbb{D}$ and let θ_0 be such that*

$$\int_0^{2\pi} \frac{|f(e^{i\theta}) - f(e^{i\theta_0})|}{|\theta - \theta_0|} \frac{d\theta}{2\pi} < \infty \tag{3.5.8}$$

Then

$$\lim_{N \to \infty} S_N(f)(e^{i\theta_0}) = f(e^{i\theta_0}) \tag{3.5.9}$$

Remark. See Problem 5 for versions that allow jump discontinuities and don't require f to be continuous away from $e^{i\theta_0}$.

Definition. Let (X, ρ) be a metric space. $f \colon X \to V$, a normed linear space, is called *Hölder continous* of order $\alpha \in (0, 1]$ if and only if for some $C > 0$ and all $x, y \in X$ with $\rho(x, y) < 1$, we have that

$$\|f(x) - f(y)\| \le C\rho(x, y)^\alpha \tag{3.5.10}$$

If $\alpha = 1$, f is called *Lipschitz continuous*.

For example, if X is a compact manifold and f is real-valued and differentiable, f is Lipschitz continuous. If (3.5.10) holds for a fixed y and all x with $\rho(x, y) < 1$, we say that f is Hölder (or Lipschitz) continuous at y.

Theorem 3.5.5. *Suppose f on $\partial\mathbb{D}$ is complex-valued and Hölder continuous of some order $\alpha > 0$. Then $S_N(f) \to f$ uniformly in $C(\partial\mathbb{D})$.*

Remark. The proof shows that it suffices that the *modulus of continuity*, $\Delta_f(\theta)$, defined by

$$\Delta_f(\theta) = \sup_{\substack{e^{i\eta}, e^{i\psi} \in \partial\mathbb{D} \\ |\eta - \psi| \le \theta}} |f(e^{i\eta}) - f(e^{i\psi})| \tag{3.5.11}$$

obeys a *Dini-type condition*,

$$\int_0^1 \frac{\Delta_f(\theta)\, d\theta}{\theta} < \infty \tag{3.5.12}$$

Hölder continuity says $|\Delta_f(\theta)| \le C|\theta|^\alpha$ obeys (3.5.12), but so does the weaker condition $|\Delta_f(\theta)| \le (\log(\theta^{-1}))^{-\beta}$ for any $\beta > 1$.

Since $C^\infty(\partial\mathbb{D})$ is $\|\cdot\|_\infty$-dense in $C(\partial\mathbb{D})$ (see Problem 6) and any C^1 function is Hölder continuous, this proves Theorem 3.5.3, and so Theorem 3.5.1. The following also proves Theorems 3.5.3, and so Theorem 3.5.1. It is not true that $S_N(f)$ converges uniformly to f for all $f \in C(\partial\mathbb{D})$. Indeed, there exist $f \in C(\partial\mathbb{D})$ with $\sup_N \|S_N f\|_\infty = \infty$ (see Problem 10 of Section 5.4). But for C_N, the situation is different.

Theorem 3.5.6 (Fejér's Theorem). *For any $f \in C(\partial\mathbb{D})$, $C_N(f) \to f$ uniformly.*

We now turn to the proofs of these three theorems. For the first two, we need an "explicit" formula for $S_N(f)$.

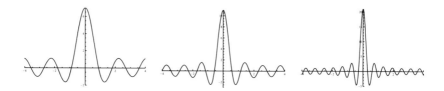

Figure 3.5.1. The Dirichlet kernel for N = 3, 5, 10.

Theorem 3.5.7 (Dirichlet Kernel). *For any continuous function, f, we have*

$$S_N(f)(e^{i\theta}) = \int_0^{2\pi} D_N(\theta - \psi) f(e^{i\psi}) \frac{d\psi}{2\pi} \tag{3.5.13}$$

where

$$D_N(\eta) = \frac{\sin\left[(2N+1)(\frac{\eta}{2})\right]}{\sin(\frac{\eta}{2})} \tag{3.5.14}$$

Remarks. 1.   Once we have defined L^2 and L^1, (3.5.13) holds for any $f \in L^1$.

2. D_N is called the *Dirichlet kernel.*

3. $D_N(\eta)$ must be invariant under $\eta \to \eta + 2\pi$. While the numerator and denominator of (3.5.14) change sign under this change, the ratio is invariant!

4. See Figure 3.5.1 for plots of D_N for $N = 3, 5, 10$ with scaled y-axis.

Proof. By interchanging the finite sum and integral defining $f_k^\sharp$, we get (3.5.13) where

$$D_N(\eta) = \sum_{k=-N}^{N} e^{ik\eta} \tag{3.5.15}$$

$$= \frac{e^{i(N+1)\eta} - e^{-iN\eta}}{e^{i\eta} - 1} \tag{3.5.16}$$

$$= \frac{e^{i(N+\frac{1}{2})\eta} - e^{-i(N+\frac{1}{2})\eta}}{e^{i\eta/2} - e^{-i\eta/2}} \tag{3.5.17}$$

$$= \frac{\sin\left[(2N+1)(\frac{\eta}{2})\right]}{\sin(\frac{\eta}{2})} \tag{3.5.18}$$

To get (3.5.16), we summed a geometric series, and to get (3.5.17), we multiplied the numerator and denominator by $e^{-i\eta/2}$.   □

Proof of Theorem 3.5.4. By rotation covariance, we can suppose, for notational simplicity, that $\theta_0 = 0$, that is, $e^{i\theta_0} = 1$. So using

$$\int_{-\pi}^{\pi} D_N(\theta) \frac{d\theta}{2\pi} = \sum_{k=-N}^{N} \int_{-\pi}^{\pi} e^{ik\theta} \frac{d\theta}{2\pi} = 1 \qquad (3.5.19)$$

we have (using $D_N(0-\theta) = D_N(\theta)$) for all small δ that

$$S_N(f)(1) - f(1) = \int_{-\pi}^{\pi} D_N(\theta)[f(e^{i\theta}) - f(1)] \frac{d\theta}{2\pi} \qquad (3.5.20)$$

$$= a_N^{\delta} + b_N^{\delta} \qquad (3.5.21)$$

where a_N^{δ} is the integral from $-\delta$ to δ and b_N^{δ} the integral from $-\pi$ to $-\delta$ and δ to π. Since we are focusing on $\theta_0 = 0$, it is convenient to take integrals from $-\pi$ to π rather than 0 to 2π.

Let $g^{\delta}(e^{i\theta})$ be given by

$$g^{\delta}(e^{i\theta}) = \begin{cases} 0, & |\theta| < \delta \\ \frac{f(e^{i\theta}) - f(1)}{\sin(\frac{\theta}{2})}, & \delta \le |\theta| \le \pi \end{cases} \qquad (3.5.22)$$

Let $g_{\pm}^{\delta}(e^{i\theta}) = e^{\pm i\theta/2} g^{\delta}(e^{i\theta})$, so

$$b_N^{\delta} = \frac{(g_+^{\delta})_{-N}^{\sharp} - (g_-^{\delta})_N^{\sharp}}{2i} \qquad (3.5.23)$$

Since, for δ fixed, $g_{\pm}^{\delta}$ are bounded, they are in L^2, so $\sum_N |(g_{\pm}^{\delta})_N^{\sharp}|^2 < \infty$ by (3.5.4). Thus, $\lim_{N \to \infty} (g_{\pm}^{\delta})_{\mp N}^{\sharp} = 0$. So, for each fixed δ, $b_N^{\delta} \to 0$ and

$$\limsup_{N \to \infty} |S_N(f)(1) - f(1)| \le \sup_N |a_N^{\delta}| \qquad (3.5.24)$$

$$\le \int_{-\delta}^{\delta} \frac{|f(e^{i\theta}) - f(1)|}{|\sin(\frac{\theta}{2})|} \frac{d\theta}{2\pi} \qquad (3.5.25)$$

since $|D_N(\theta)| \le |\sin(\frac{\theta}{2})|^{-1}$.

By hypothesis, the integral over all θ is finite, so $\lim_{\delta \downarrow 0}(\text{RHS of } (3.5.25)) = 0$. Since the left side is δ-independent, we conclude that $\lim_{N \to \infty} |S_N(f)(1) - f(1)| = 0$. $\square$

Proof of Theorem 3.5.5. We sketch the proof, leaving the details to the reader (Problem 8). One looks at the proof above of Theorem 3.5.4 and restores the θ_0-dependence. Since we have a bound on $\sup_{|\theta - \psi| \le \delta} |f(e^{i\theta}) - f(e^{i\psi})| \equiv \Delta_f(\delta)$ that obeys (3.5.12), the $a_N^{\delta}(\theta_0), b_N^{\delta}(\theta_0)$ terms obey $\sup_{\theta_0, N} |a_N^{\delta}(\theta_0)| \to 0$ as $\delta \downarrow 0$, so one only needs, for each fixed $\delta > 0$, that

$$\lim_{N \to \infty} \left(\sup_{\theta_0} |b_N^{\delta}(\theta_0)| \right) = 0 \qquad (3.5.26)$$

One first shows that if $\{h_\alpha(e^{i\theta})\}$ is a compact set of h_α's in L^2, then $(h_\alpha^\sharp)_n \to 0$ uniformly in α, and then that $g^\delta_{\pm,\theta_0}$ is continuous in $e^{i\theta_0} \in \mathbb{D}$ to get compactness (see Problem 7). □

The argument that $b^\delta_N \to 0$ in the proof of Theorem 3.5.4 implies a nice localization result going back to Riemann:

Theorem 3.5.8 (Riemann Localization Principle). *Assume that f is in $L^2(\partial\mathbb{D}, \frac{d\theta}{2\pi})$ and for some θ_0 and some $\varepsilon > 0$, $f(e^{i\theta}) = 0$ for $|\theta - \theta_0| < \varepsilon$. Then $(S_N f)(e^{i\theta_0}) \to 0$ as $N \to \infty$. In particular, if f and g are in L^2 and equal near $e^{i\theta_0}$ and $(S_N f)(e^{i\theta_0})$ has a limit, then $(S_N g)(e^{i\theta})$ has the same limit.*

Remark. Once we have L^1 and the more general Riemann–Lebesgue lemma (Theorem 6.5.3), this extends to L^1.

Finally, to prove Fejér's theorem, we need an analog of (3.5.9) for the Cesàro averages, $C_N(f)$:

Theorem 3.5.9 (Fejér Kernel). *For any continuous function, f, we have*

$$C_N(f)(e^{i\theta}) = \int_0^{2\pi} F_N(\theta - \psi) f(e^{i\psi}) \frac{d\psi}{2\pi} \tag{3.5.27}$$

where

$$F_N(\eta) = \frac{1}{N}\left[\frac{\sin(\frac{N\eta}{2})}{\sin(\frac{\eta}{2})}\right]^2 \tag{3.5.28}$$

Remark. See Figure 3.5.2 for plots of C_N for $N = 3, 5, 10$.

Proof. By Theorem 3.5.7, we have (3.5.27) where

$$F_N(\eta) = \frac{1}{N}\sum_{j=0}^{N-1} D_j(\eta) \tag{3.5.29}$$

$$= \frac{1}{N\sin(\frac{\eta}{2})} \mathrm{Im}\left(\sum_{j=0}^{N-1} e^{i(j+\frac{1}{2})\eta}\right) \tag{3.5.30}$$

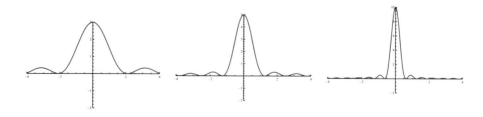

Figure 3.5.2. The Fejér kernel for N = 3, 5, 10.

$$= \frac{1}{N\sin(\frac{\eta}{2})} \, \text{Im}\left[\frac{e^{i(N+\frac{1}{2})\eta} - e^{i\eta/2}}{e^{i\eta} - 1}\right] \tag{3.5.31}$$

$$= \frac{1}{N\sin(\frac{\eta}{2})} \, \text{Im}\left[\frac{e^{iN\eta} - 1}{e^{i\eta/2} - e^{-i\eta/2}}\right] \tag{3.5.32}$$

$$= \frac{(-1)}{N\sin^2(\frac{\eta}{2})} \frac{1}{2} \, \text{Re}[e^{iN\eta} - 1] \tag{3.5.33}$$

$$= \frac{(-1)}{N\sin^2(\frac{\eta}{2})} \frac{1}{2} \, \text{Re}\left[2i\sin\left(\frac{N\eta}{2}\right) e^{iN\eta/2}\right] \tag{3.5.34}$$

$$= \frac{1}{N\sin^2(\frac{\eta}{2})} \sin^2\left(\frac{N\eta}{2}\right) \tag{3.5.35}$$

$$= \text{RHS of } (3.5.28) \tag{3.5.36}$$

We get (3.5.31) by summing a geometric series, (3.5.32) by multiplying numerator and denominator by $e^{-i\eta/2}$, (3.5.33) from $e^{i\eta/2} - e^{-i\eta/2} = 2i\sin(\frac{\eta}{2})$, (3.5.34) by $(x^2 - 1) = (x - x^{-1})x$, and (3.5.35) by $\text{Re}[ie^{ia}] = -\sin(a)$. $\qquad\square$

Proposition 3.5.10. $g_N(\eta) \equiv F_N(\eta)$ *obeys*

(i)

$$g_N(\eta) \geq 0 \tag{3.5.37}$$

(ii)

$$\int_0^{2\pi} g_N(\eta) \frac{d\eta}{2\pi} = 1 \tag{3.5.38}$$

(iii) *For any* $\varepsilon > 0$,

$$\lim_{N\to\infty} \int_{\varepsilon < \eta < 2\pi - \varepsilon} g_N(\eta) \frac{d\eta}{2\pi} = 0 \tag{3.5.39}$$

Proof. (i) is trivial and (ii) is immediate from (3.5.19) and (3.5.29). Since $|\sin(\frac{\eta N}{2})| \leq 1$ and $\sin^2(\frac{\eta}{2})$ is monotone increasing on $[0, \pi]$ and decreasing on $[\pi, 2\pi]$, we have

$$F_N(\eta) \leq \frac{1}{N\sin^2(\frac{\varepsilon}{2})} \qquad \text{if } \varepsilon < \eta < 2\pi - \varepsilon \tag{3.5.40}$$

from which (iii) is immediate. $\qquad\square$

Definition. A sequence of continuous functions $\{g_N\}_{N=1}^\infty$ on $\partial\mathbb{D}$ obeying (i)–(iii) of Proposition 3.5.10 is called an *approximate identity*.

Theorem 3.5.11. *If* $\{g_N\}_{N=1}^\infty$ *is an approximate identity and* $f \in C(\partial\mathbb{D})$, *then*

$$g_N * f \to f \tag{3.5.41}$$

uniformly on $\partial\mathbb{D}$, where

$$(h * f)(e^{i\theta}) = \int_0^{2\pi} h(\theta - \psi) f(e^{i\psi}) \frac{d\psi}{2\pi} \tag{3.5.42}$$

Remarks. 1. One application of this is to prove that $C^\infty(\partial\mathbb{D})$ is $\|\cdot\|_\infty$-dense in $C(\partial\mathbb{D})$; see Problem 6.

2. This result is only stated for continuous $\{g_N\}_{N=1}^\infty$ because, at this point, we only know how to integrate continuous functions. Once one has L^1, one can define L^1 approximate identities by the above definition with "continuous" replaced by L^1. This theorem extends with no change in the proof.

Proof. By periodicity and (3.5.38),

$$(g_N * f)(e^{i\theta}) - f(e^{i\theta}) = \int_0^{2\pi} g_N(\psi)[f(e^{i(\theta - \psi)}) - f(e^{i\theta})] \frac{d\psi}{2\pi} \tag{3.5.43}$$

so breaking the integral into $0 < \psi < \varepsilon$ or $2\pi - \varepsilon < \psi < 2\pi$ and its complement, we get

$$\|g_N * f - f\|_\infty \leq \sup_{|\psi| < \varepsilon} |f(e^{i(\theta - \psi)}) - f(e^{i\theta})| + 2\|f\|_\infty \int_\varepsilon^{2\pi - \varepsilon} g_N(\psi) \frac{d\psi}{2\pi} \tag{3.5.44}$$

using (i) and (ii) of the definition of approximate identity.

By property (iii),

$$\limsup_{N \to \infty} \|g_N * f - f\|_\infty \leq \sup_{|\psi| < \varepsilon} |f(e^{i(\theta - \psi)}) - f(e^{i\theta})| \tag{3.5.45}$$

Since f is continuous, it is uniformly continuous (by Theorem 2.3.10), so the sup goes to zero as $\varepsilon \downarrow 0$. $\square$

Proof of Theorem 3.5.6. Immediate from Theorems 3.5.9 and 3.5.11 and Proposition 3.5.10, $\square$

There is nothing special about $\partial\mathbb{D}$.

Definition. A sequence of functions, $\{g_N(x)\}_{N=1}^\infty$ on $\mathbb{R}^\nu$ is called an *approximate identity* if and only if

(i) $g_N(x) \geq 0$ $\hspace{8cm}$ (3.5.46)

(ii) $\displaystyle\int g_N(x) \, d^\nu x = 1$ $\hspace{6.5cm}$ (3.5.47)

(iii) For any $\varepsilon > 0$,

$$\lim_{N \to \infty} \int_{|x| \geq \varepsilon} g_N(x) \, d^\nu x = 0 \tag{3.5.48}$$

If h and g are functions on $\mathbb{R}^\nu$, one defines their convolution by

$$(h * g)(x) = \int h(y)g(x - y)\, d^\nu y \qquad (3.5.49)$$

$$= \int h(x - y)g(y)\, d^\nu y \qquad (3.5.50)$$

Note that if $\int g(x)\, d^\nu x < \infty$ and $\|h\|_\infty < \infty$, then the integrals converge uniformly and absolutely.

The same argument that led to Theorem 3.5.11 implies

Theorem 3.5.12. *Let $\{g_N\}_{N=1}^\infty$ be an approximate identity. If f is bounded and uniformly continuous on $\mathbb{R}^\nu$, then as $N \to \infty$,*

$$g_N * f \xrightarrow{\|\cdot\|_\infty} f \qquad (3.5.51)$$

If there is a compact set $K \subset \mathbb{R}^\nu$ so $\operatorname{supp}(g_N) \subset K$ for all N and f is continuous (but not necessarily bounded or uniformly continuous on all of $\mathbb{R}^\nu$), then

$$\lim_{N \to \infty} (g_N * f)(x) = f(x) \qquad (3.5.52)$$

uniformly for x in each compact subset of $\mathbb{R}^\nu$.

With the Fejér kernel in hand, we can construct examples of nowhere differentiable continuous functions of the form first studied by Weierstrass. We'll consider

$$f(x) = \sum_{n=1}^\infty a^n n^\gamma \cos(b^n x) \qquad (3.5.53)$$

where b is an integer with $b \geq 2$, $\gamma \in \mathbb{R}$, and $0 < a < 1$ or $a = 1$, $\gamma < -1$. Since $|a| < 1$ (or $a = 1$, $\gamma < -1$), the finite sum converges uniformly, and so f is a continuous periodic function. We'll prove below that if $ab > 1$, f is nowhere differentiable. The key is that the Fourier coefficients have large gaps, so we not only have that $\frac{1}{2}a^n n^\gamma = \int e^{-ib^n x} f(x)\, dx$, but we can insert $F_N(x)$ if $N < b^n - b^{n-1}$ in front of f without changing the integral. The key will then be:

Lemma 3.5.13. *There exists constant c_α, $0 < \alpha \leq 1$, so that for all $N \geq 2$,*

$$(2\pi)^{-1} \int_{-\pi}^\pi |x|^\alpha F_N(x)\, dx \leq \begin{cases} c_\alpha N^{-\alpha} & 0 < \alpha < 1 \\ c_1 \dfrac{\log(N)}{N} & \alpha = 1 \end{cases} \qquad (3.5.54)$$

Proof. Clearly, by (3.5.15), $|D_N(x)| \leq D_N(0)$, so

$$|F_N(x)| \leq F_N(0) = N \qquad (3.5.55)$$

Since $\lim_{\eta \to 0} |\eta|/|\sin \eta| = 1$ and, by computing derivatives, increasing on $(0, \pi/2)$, $|\sin \eta| \geq (2/\pi)|\eta|$ for $|\eta| \leq \pi/2$. It follows that

$$|F_N(x)| \leq \frac{\pi^2}{Nx^2} \tag{3.5.56}$$

(3.5.54) follows by using (3.5.55) on $\{x \mid |x| \leq 1/N\}$ and (3.5.56) on $\{x \mid 1/N \leq |x| \leq \pi\}$. □

Proposition 3.5.14. *Let $f(x)$ be an L^2 function on $(-\pi, \pi)$ with Fourier coefficients $f_j^\sharp$. Suppose that f is extended periodically to $\mathbb{R}$, and for some x_0, $C > 0$ and $\alpha \in (0, 1]$, we have that for all x,*

$$|f(x) - f(x_0)| \leq C|x - x_0|^\alpha \tag{3.5.57}$$

Suppose also that for some $k \neq 0$ and N with $1 < N < |k|$, we have that

$$f_j^\sharp = 0 \qquad for\ 0 < |j - k| \leq N - 1 \tag{3.5.58}$$

Then, with c_α given by (3.5.54),

$$|f_k^\sharp| \leq \begin{cases} Cc_\alpha N^{-\alpha}, & 0 < \alpha < 1 \\ Cc_1 \frac{\log(N)}{N}, & \alpha = 1 \end{cases} \tag{3.5.59}$$

Proof. Since shifting x by $-x_0$ multiplies $f_j^\sharp$ by a phase factor, we can suppose $x_0 = 0$. Since replacing f by $f - f(0)$ doesn't change $f_j^\sharp$ for $j \neq 0$ or (3.5.57), we can suppose $x_0 = 0$ and $f(x_0) = 0$.

Let $\varphi_j(x) = e^{ijx}$. Then since $F_N(x)$ is a linear combination of $\{\varphi_\ell\}_{\ell=-(N-1)}^{N-1}$ with constant term 1,

$$\varphi_k F_N = \varphi_k + \text{linear combination of } \{\varphi_\ell\}_{1 \leq |\ell - k| \leq N-1}$$

so

$$f_k^\sharp = \langle \varphi_k, f \rangle = \langle \varphi_k F_N, f \rangle \tag{3.5.60}$$

so that

$$|f_k^\sharp| \leq (2\pi)^{-1} \int |F_N(x)| \, |f(x)| \, dx \tag{3.5.61}$$

$$\leq C(2\pi)^{-1} \int |F_N(x)| \, |x|^\alpha \, dx \tag{3.5.62}$$

so (3.5.54) implies (3.5.59). □

Write the function in (3.5.53) as $f_{a,b,\gamma}$. Then

Theorem 3.5.15. (a) *For $0 < a \leq 1$, $f_{a,b,\gamma}$ is Hölder continuous of order α if $ab^\alpha < 1$ or $ab^\alpha = 1$, $\gamma < -1$. If $\alpha = 1$ and these conditions hold, $f_{a,b,\gamma}$ is C^1.*

(b) *For $0 < \alpha < 1$, if $ab^\alpha > 1$ or $ab^\alpha = 1$ and $\gamma > 0$, then $f_{a,b,\gamma}$ is nowhere Hölder continuous of order α. If $ab > 1$ or $ab = 1$ and $\gamma > 1$, then f is nowhere Lipschitz and, in particular, nowhere differentiable.*

Proof. (a) Since $|\cos x - \cos y| \le 2$ and

$$|\cos x - \cos y| \le \left| \int_x^y \sin u\, du \right| \le |x - y|$$

we have for any $\alpha \in [0, 1]$ that $|\cos x - \cos y| \le 2^{1-\alpha}|x - y|^\alpha$, so

$$|f_{a,b,\gamma}(x) - f_{a,b,\gamma}(y)| \le 2^{1-\alpha}|x - y|^\alpha \sum_{n=1}^\infty a^n b^{n\alpha} n^\gamma \qquad (3.5.63)$$

If either $ab^\alpha < 1$ or $ab^\alpha = 1$ and $\gamma < -1$, the sum in (3.5.63) converges and we get global Hölder continuity.

(b) We consider the case $\alpha = 1$. $\alpha < 1$ is similar (Problem 16). If $f_{a,b,\gamma}$ is Lipschitz continuous at some x_0, by Proposition 3.5.14 and (3.5.59) with $k = b^n$ and $N = b^n - b^{n-1} = b^n(1 - b^{-1})$, we get that for some constant K,

$$a^n n^\gamma \le Knb^{-n} \qquad (3.5.64)$$

or

$$(ab)^n n^{\gamma-1} \le K \qquad (3.5.65)$$

If $ab > 1$ or $ab = 1$ and $\gamma > 1$, this is false for n large, so $f_{a,b,\gamma}$ cannot be Lipschitz at any point. $\qquad\square$

Example 3.5.16. For $a = \frac{1}{2}$, $b = 2$, and $\gamma = 2$, $f_{a,b,\gamma}$ is nowhere Lipschitz continuous (and so nowhere differentiable) but Hölder continuous for all $\alpha < 1$. This result is true also for $\gamma = 0$; see the Notes and Problem 17.

Fix α_0 with $0 < \alpha_0 < 1$. For $a = (\frac{1}{2})^{\alpha_0}$, $b = 2$, $\gamma = 2$, $f_{a,b,\gamma}$ is Hölder continuous for $\alpha < \alpha_0$ and nowhere Hölder continuous for $\alpha \ge \alpha_0$. If instead, $\gamma = -2$, one gets Hölder continuity for $\alpha \le \alpha_0$ and nowhere Hölder continuous for $\alpha > \alpha_0$.

If $b = 2$, $a = 1$, $\gamma = -2$, $f_{a,b,\gamma}$ is continuous, but nowhere Hölder continuous for any $\alpha > 0$. $\qquad\square$

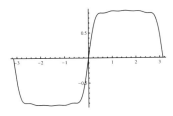

Figure 3.5.3. C_{11} for a step function.

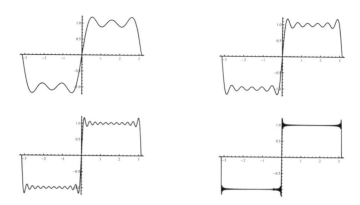

Figure 3.5.4. S_n, $n = 5, 12, 21, 101$ for a step function.

Finally, we turn to an aspect of convergence of Fourier series known as the *Gibbs phenomenon*. Consider the function on $\partial\mathbb{D}$,

$$f(e^{i\theta}) = \begin{cases} 1, & 0 < \theta < \pi \\ -1, & \pi < \theta < 2\pi \\ 0, & \theta = 0 \text{ or } \pi \end{cases} \qquad (3.5.66)$$

By Dini's test extended to nonglobally continuous functions (Problem 9), $S_n(f)(e^{i\theta}) \to f(e^{i\theta})$ uniformly on each set $\{e^{i\theta} \mid \varepsilon < \theta < \pi - \varepsilon, \pi + \varepsilon < \theta < 2\pi - \varepsilon\}$ for $\varepsilon > 0$. Since $f(e^{-i\theta}) = -f(e^{i\theta})$, $f_{-k}^\sharp = -\overline{f_k^\sharp}$, so $S_n(f)(1) = S_n(f)(-1) = 0$. Thus, one might think that $S_n(f)$ for n large looks like the graph in Figure 3.5.3, hugging f closely except for a linear piece extending from -1 to 1 or 1 to -1 at $\theta = 0, \pi$. Indeed, this is what happens for $C_n(f)$— in fact, Figure 3.5.3 is $C_{11}(f)$ and the reader will prove $\|C_n(f)\|_\infty \le \|f\|_\infty$ in Problem 20. However, Figure 3.5.4 plots $S_n(f)$ for $n = 5, 12, 21, 101$. The Gibbs phenomenon is the systematic overshoots shown in this figure.

Theorem 3.5.17 (Gibbs Phenomenon). *For the step function, f, given by* (3.5.66),

$$\lim_{n\to\infty} \|S_n f\|_\infty = \frac{2}{\pi} \int_0^\pi \frac{\sin s}{s}\, ds = 1.178979744\ldots \qquad (3.5.67)$$

Moreover, the points where $|S_n f|$ is maximal are given by $\pm(\pi/n + O(1/n^2))$.

Sketch. We'll leave the justifications to the Problems (Problem 21). By a simple calculation, we have

$$f_{2n}^\sharp = 0, \qquad f_{2n+1}^\sharp = \frac{2}{i(2n+1)\pi} \qquad (3.5.68)$$

so using the fact that

$$\frac{1}{i(2j+1)} e^{(2j+1)ix} = \int_0^x e^{(2j+1)it}\, dt + \frac{1}{i(2j+1)} \tag{3.5.69}$$

and the cancellation of the constants, one finds that, after summing a geometric series,

$$(S_{2n}f)(x) = (S_{2n-1}f)(x) = \frac{2}{\pi} \int_0^x \frac{\sin(2nt)}{\sin t}\, dt \tag{3.5.70}$$

$$= G(2nx) + O(x^2) \tag{3.5.71}$$

where $O(x^2)$ means an error bounded by Cx^2 uniformly in n, and where

$$G(y) = \frac{2}{\pi} \int_0^y \frac{\sin s}{s}\, ds$$

This comes from $1/\sin t - 1/t = O(t)$.

Since $S_n(f) \to f$ uniformly away from $0, \pi$, we see that if $\pm y_\infty$ are the points where $|G(y)|$ is maximum, then $\lim_{n\to\infty} \|S_n f\|_\infty$ is $\sup|G(y)|$ and the maximum point is $\pm y_\infty/2n + O(1/n^2)$.

Since $G'(y) = (2\sin y)/\pi y$, the relative maxima of $|G|$ occur at multiples of π, and using the oscillations and decay of y^{-1}, one sees that the maximum occurs at $y_\infty = \pi$ with $\sup|G(y)| = G(\pi)$. $\qquad\square$

Notes and Historical Remarks.

> Apart from his prefectorial duties Fourier helped organise the "Description of Egypt" ... Fourier's main contribution was the general introduction—a survey of Egyptian history up to modern times. (An Egyptologist with whom I discussed this described the introduction as a masterpiece and a turning point in the subject. He was surprised to hear that Fourier also had a reputation as a mathematician.)
> —*T. W. Körner* [**512**]

We are hampered in this section by the fact that we only discuss measurable and L^p functions in the next chapter. So we've made use of the vague term "function" without descriptive adjectives. For now, we interpret this as continuous functions. But we emphasize, as the reader should check after L^1 is defined, that Theorems 3.5.11 and 3.5.12 are valid if the g_N's are only L^1 functions (with all the formal properties of an approximate identity).

Fourier series are such a fundamental part of analysis that there are many books devoted solely or at least substantially to them. Among these are [**263, 309, 356, 357, 479, 512, 871, 875, 935, 974, 1024**]. In particular, Zgymund [**1024**] remains a readable classic.

The history of Fourier analysis is intimately wrapped up with an understanding of what a function is, and later, which functions have integrals. In the early history, a key role was played by Euler and the Bernoullis. Part 2A has capsule biographies for them (Section 9.2 for Euler and Section 9.7 for the Bernoulli family).

The early history revolved around the wave equation in one dimension, $\frac{\partial^2}{\partial t^2}u(x,t) = \frac{\partial^2}{\partial x^2}u(x,t)$. (We use units in which the wave speed is 1; the eighteenth-century work had a speed of propagation.) In about 1750, d'Alembert [212] and Euler [285] independently found general solutions of the form $f(x-t) + g(x+t)$, where f and g are "arbitrary functions." The eighteenth-century notion of function meant given by an explicit analytic expression involving sums, powers, trigonometric functions, and the like. A sharp controversy partially in letters and partially in papers developed. Euler argued that you needed to allow an initial condition like $u(x,0) = \frac{1}{2} - |\frac{1}{2} - \frac{x}{\pi}|$ on $[0,\pi]$, thinking of a plucked string which was viewed as two analytic expressions, ($\frac{x}{\pi}$ on $(0, \frac{\pi}{2})$ and $1 - \frac{x}{\pi}$ on $(\frac{\pi}{2}, \pi)$), and d'Alembert didn't like that.

Shortly after that, Daniel Bernoulli [78], following a 1715 observation of Brook Taylor [913], pointed out that $\cos(kt)\sin(kx)$ is also a solution (shifting variables for our $(0,\pi)$ case), and if one wanted $u(\pm\pi, z) = 0$ boundary conditions, one could take $k = 1, 2, \ldots$. He claimed that the d'Alembert–Euler solutions could be represented as sums of solutions of this $\cos(nt)\sin(nx)$ form. There followed lively exchanges among the three, joined also by Lagrange and then Laplace, that involved what kind of functions could be represented by infinite sums of sines and cosines. Euler argued that only functions with a single expression could be so represented—which was ironic given that he had elsewhere considered the sums that converge to the jump, as we do in Theorem 3.5.17. Only Bernoulli was in the "any function can" camp. This issue of what kinds of functions Fourier sums could represent stayed open until the work of Dirichlet (and, even more broadly, of Riesz–Fischer) discussed below. Because of its importance to the understanding of functions, and to the history of Fourier analysis and of waves in physics, this controversy has seen considerable historical analysis: see Ravetz [760], Grattan-Guinness [362], and Wheeler–Crummett [986].

In his work on planetary motion, Euler [286] also used sine and cosine sums. Using orthogonality and formal interchange of sum and integral, he essentially found the formula (3.5.1) for the coefficients (he used $\sin(k\theta)$ and $\cos(k\theta)$, not $e^{\pm ik\theta}$).

In 1799, Parseval [700] also considered such sums and wrote what was essentially (3.5.4) without any explicit proof or calculations. So, on the basis of this work, one of only five published works, Marc-Antoine Parseval des Chênes (1755–1836) is known to posterity. For example, we used his name for the abstract Hilbert space result, (3.4.3). We also used the name of Michel Plancherel (1885–1967), a Swiss mathematician, who in 1910 [730] provided one of the first proofs of the analog for Fourier transforms and thereby got his name on all sorts of L^2 relations of transforms, such as (3.4.3).

Next in the picture was Jean Baptiste Joseph Fourier (1768–1830). Fourier was more a physicist than a mathematician and his engineering expertise led to high political appointments. He started life as the ninth child of a tailor and became a baron of the First French Empire. He was active in revolutionary politics and was imprisoned during the reign of terror. It is likely that it was only the fall of Robespierre that prevented him from losing his head long before his scientific discoveries! He was involved with Napoleon's 1798–99 campaign in Egypt, starting as scientific adviser and ending as governor of Lower Egypt. In 1801, Napoleon appointed him as prefect (administrative head) of a province that included Grenoble, where he lived, supervising the construction of a highway from Grenoble to Turin, among other tasks. He initially supported the new king at the time of Napoleon's escape from Elba and had to flee Grenoble to avoid Napoleon's army. He then shifted back to Napoleon and was distrusted by the king after Waterloo, enough so that for a time, the king prevented his election to the French Academy. After Waterloo, he returned to Paris, and in 1822 he became the secretary of the Academy. For more on his life, see Körner [**512**, Sects. 92–93] and Herival [**419**].

Undoubtedly, Fourier is most known for his book on heat [**311**] written in 1804–07, while he was prefect in Grenoble. He submitted it to the French Academy in 1807. He used what we now call Fourier series and the Fourier transform (see Sections 6.3 and 6.5) in solving the heat equation (see Section 6.9). His claims about expanding arbitrary functions were only one of the controversial elements of his book, leading the committee of Lagrange, Laplace, Monge, and Lacroix to hold up publication. Along the way, the work got a prize from a committee of Lagrange, Laplace, Malus, Haüy, and Legendre. It was finally published in 1822.

This book established the usefulness of the method and many basic formulae. One of Fourier's results was the sin/cos version of (3.5.1), which he found not knowing of Euler's earlier derivation. Unlike Euler, who used orthogonality, Fourier's proof was very complicated and involved expanding sine in a Taylor series, collecting terms, and manipulating the power series for f—a procedure especially questionable for the discontinuous functions Fourier claimed one could expand in Fourier series!

The validity of Fourier expansions was established by the seminal paper [**249**] of Johann Peter Gustav Lejeune Dirichlet (1805–59). A capsule biography of Dirichlet appears in the Notes to Section 13.4 of Part 2B. We note here that this paper was published in 1829 when Dirichlet was only twenty-four years old, that he studied under Fourier in Paris, and that Fourier was instrumental in Dirichlet getting a position in Germany around that time.

Dirichlet used his kernel to show that many noncontinuous functions, f, had convergent Fourier series, with the requirement that the limit at the point of discontinuity is $\frac{1}{2}(f(x+0) + f(x-0))$ (see Problem 5). He supposed his functions were continuous except at finitely many points, smooth in between (exactly how smooth wasn't made explicit), had left and right limits at the points of discontinuity, and had only finitely many maxima and minima. We now know these conditions are overkill—smoothness by itself is enough, as is the maximum-minimum condition alone if interpreted as functions of bounded variation (see below). Nevertheless, Dirichlet's result was radical for its time. Shortly before, in one his texts on Analysis, Cauchy had claimed that a pointwise limit of continuous functions is continuous. It took the clarifying notion of uniform convergence (pushed by Weierstrass) to settle these questions.

We note that in 1873, Paul du Bois-Reymond (1831–1889) [**256**] constructed a continuous function on $\partial\mathbb{D}$ whose Fourier series was divergent at a given point. Fejér [**297**] found a different example of this sort and in Problem 4 we expose his idea. (In Problem 10 of Section 5.4, the reader will show there exists $f \in C(\partial\mathbb{D})$ so $\|S_N f\|_\infty \to \infty$, a closely related fact. In Problem 12 of that section, the reader will prove that, in the language of that section, a Baire generic function has $|(S_N f)(1)| \to \infty$ and in Problem 13 that for a Baire generic function, $|(S_N f)(e^{i\theta})| \to \infty$ for a Baire generic set of θ.)

Dirichlet's work set the baseline for all later work on Fourier series convergence, of which we want to mention five: that of Dini, Jordan, Fejér, Riesz–Fischer, and Carleson.

Ulisse Dini (1845–1918) wrote a book on Fourier series [**247**] that includes Theorem 3.5.4. (3.5.8) is called the *Dini test* or *Dini condition*. Occasionally, a function that obeys (3.5.12) is called *Dini continuous*.

Another basic convergence theorem is due to Camille Jordan (1838–1922) [**455**]:

Theorem 3.5.18 (Jordan's Theorem). *If f is a function of bounded variation on $\partial\mathbb{D}$, then $S_n(f(e^{i\theta})) \to \frac{1}{2}[f(e^{i(\theta+0)}) + f(e^{i(\theta-0)})]$ for any $x \in (0,1)$.*

Functions of bounded variation (which were first defined in this paper of Jordan) are defined and discussed in Sections 4.1 and 4.15. In particular, Theorem 4.15.2 shows any such function is a difference of monotone functions, so it is sufficient to prove Jordan's theorem for monotone functions, which the reader does in Problem 3.

Lipót Fejér (1880–1959) proved Theorem 3.5.6 along the lines we do in his 1900 paper [**298**], written when he was only nineteen. For a discussion of the impact of his discovery on the revival of interest in Fourier analysis, see Kahane [**465**]. Fejér was born Lipót Weiss (German for "white") and was a student of Hermann Schwarz (German for "black"). He changed his name to Fejér (archaic Hungarian for "white") around 1900 and one of his students was Fekete (Hungarian for "black"). Among Fejér's other students were Paul Erdős, George Pólya, Tibor Radó, Marcel Riesz, Gabor Szegő, Paul Turán, and John von Neumann. Fejér spent most of his career at the University of Budapest, although he initially had trouble with his appointment because he was Jewish. He suffered during the Nazi occupation of Hungary in 1944, treatment that it is believed led to a loss of his mental capacity after the Second World War.

The last of the classical convergence results is the fact we regard as the definition of Fourier expansion, namely, for any $f \in L^2(\partial\mathbb{D}, \frac{d\theta}{2\pi})$, $\int |(S_n f)(e^{i\theta}) - f(e^{i\theta})|^2 \frac{d\theta}{2\pi} \to 0$, a result sometimes called the Riesz–Fischer theorem after [**775, 305**]. These papers completed the story of which functions can be represented as Fourier series. To do this, the authors needed to prove completeness of L^2 (defined as classes of measurable functions), and it is this that we (along with many others) will call the Riesz–Fischer theorem. We discuss it further in Section 4.4 and its Notes.

In 1928, M. Riesz proved that for $1 < p < \infty$, for $f \in L^p(\partial\mathbb{D}, \frac{d\theta}{2\pi})$, we have $\|f - S_n f\|_p \to 0$ [**790**]. We'll prove this in Section 5.8 of Part 3. For $p = 1$ or ∞, it is known that there are f's in L^p with $\|S_N f\|_p \to \infty$; see Problem 10 of Section 5.4.

No discussion of pointwise convergence would be complete without mention of Lennart Carleson's (1928–   ) famous 1966 result [**162**] that for any f in $L^2(\partial\mathbb{D}, \frac{d\theta}{2\pi})$, $(S_N f)(e^{i\theta})$ converges to f for Lebesgue a.e. θ. This result is a famous conjecture of Lusin and was extended to all L^p, $p > 1$, by Hunt [**438**]. As mentioned, for a generic continuous function $(S_N f)(e^{i\theta})$ diverges on a (dense) generic set, but, by Carleson's theorem, one of Lebesgue measure zero.

For $p = 1$, Kolmogorov [**501**] gave an $L^1(\partial\mathbb{D}, \frac{d\theta}{2\pi})$ function whose Fourier series diverges at every point in $\partial\mathbb{D}$. Three years earlier, when he was twenty-one, Kolmogorov found a similar function with almost everywhere divergence. Katznelson [**479**, Sect. II.3.5] has a proof of this result using the de la Vallée Poussin kernel of Problem 14. While the proof of Carleson's theorem is beyond the scope of these volumes, we'll prove a related result in Section 2.11 of Part 3: namely, if f has $f^\sharp \in \ell^p$, $1 \leq p < 2$, then for a.e. θ, $(S_N f)(e^{i\theta}) \to f(e^{i\theta})$ ($p = 2$ is Carleson's theorem).

In Problem 12, an alternate result to Fejér's theorem is presented, proving abelian limits of Fourier series to a continuous function. It is due to Picard and Fatou (see the remark to the problem). Littlewood [**596**] has proven that if $\sum_{n=0}^{N} a_n$ has an abelian limit α and $|a_n| \leq C(n+1)^{-1}$, then the sum itself converges to α (see Section 6.11 of Part 4, especially Problem 5). Thus, any continuous function, f, on $\partial\mathbb{D}$ with $f_n^\sharp = O(n^{-1})$ has a convergent Fourier series. By an integration by parts in a Stieltjes integral, it is easy see if f has bounded variation $f_n^\sharp = O(n^{-1})$, so this provides another proof of Jordan's theorem.

Underlying Fourier series is a group structure. $\partial\mathbb{D}$ is a group under multiplication $e^{i\theta_1}, e^{i\theta_2} \mapsto e^{i(\theta_1+\theta_2)}$ and $d\omega/2\pi$ is the unique measure invariant under this multiplication. The functions $\varphi_n(e^{i\theta}) = e^{in\theta}$ are exactly the only continuous functions, χ, on $\partial\mathbb{D}$ obeying

$$\chi(e^{iy}e^{ix}) = \chi(e^{iy})\chi(e^{ix}) \tag{3.5.72}$$

Extensions of Fourier series where the group is $\mathbb{R}^\nu$ will occur in Chapter 6 while general locally compact abelian groups will appear in Section 6.9 of Part 4.

Relevant to this section is the group, $\mathbb{Z}_N$, a cyclic group of order N thought of as $\mathbb{Z}/N\mathbb{Z}$, for integers mod N. Given f on $\mathbb{Z}$ of period N, we define

$$(\mathcal{F}_N f)(m) = \frac{1}{N} \sum_{j=0}^{N-1} f(j)\bar{\omega}_N^{mj} \tag{3.5.73}$$

where ω_N is a primitive Nth root of unity, i.e.,

$$\omega_N = \exp(2\pi i/N) \tag{3.5.74}$$

Since $\varphi_j(m) = \omega^{mj}$ are an orthonormal basis for functions on $\{1, \ldots, N\}$ (with $\langle c, d \rangle = \frac{1}{N}\sum_{i=1}^{N} \bar{c}_i d_i$ inner product), the inverse is

$$(\mathcal{F}_N^{-1} h)(m) = \sum_{j=0}^{N-1} h(j)\omega_N^{mj} \tag{3.5.75}$$

$\mathcal{F}_N$ is called the *discrete Fourier transform*.

Clearly, if f is continuous on $\partial\mathbb{D}$ and $f_N(j) = f(\omega_N^j)$, then $\mathcal{F}_N f_N \to f^\sharp$ pointwise, so $\mathcal{F}_N$ is of interest not only for its own sake but as a method of numerical approximation of the map $f \mapsto f^\sharp$. In this regard, there is an important algorithm for $\mathcal{F}_N$ called the *Fast Fourier Transform* (FFT).

The purpose of the FFT is to dramatically reduce the number of computations to get $\mathcal{F}_N$ from $O(N^2)$ to $O(N \log N)$ at least when $N = 2^m$ (so for $m = 20$, i.e., $N \approx 1,000,000$) from about a trillion calculations to more like twenty million! Since multiplication is much slower than addition, we'll only count multiplications and we'll ignore the N multiplications needed to get the powers $\{\omega_N^j\}_{j=0}^{N-1}$ given ω_N.

If one uses (3.5.73) naively, one needs N^2 multiplications (of $\bar{\omega}_N^{mj}$ and $f(j)$). If one writes

$$(\mathcal{F}_{2N}f)(m) = \frac{1}{2N} \sum_{j=0}^{N-1} f(2j)\bar{\omega}_{2N}^{2mj} + \frac{\bar{\omega}_{2N}^m}{2N} \sum_{j=0}^{N-1} f(2j\pi)\bar{\omega}_{2N}^{2mj} \qquad (3.5.76)$$

and defines f_e and f_0 (for sum and add) on $\{0, 1, \ldots, N-1\}$ by

$$f_e(j) = f(2j), \quad f_0(j) = f(2j+1) \qquad (3.5.77)$$

then

$$(\mathcal{F}_{2N}f)(m) = \frac{1}{2}\left(\mathcal{F}_N f_e\right)(m) + \frac{\bar{\omega}_{2N}^m}{2}\left(\mathcal{F}_N f_0\right)(m) \qquad (3.5.78)$$

if $0 \leq m < N$ and, if $N \leq m \leq 2N - 1$.

If we have an algorithm to compute $\mathcal{F}_N$ in a_N multiplication steps, we can compute $\mathcal{F}_{2N}$ in

$$a_{2N} = 2a_N + N \qquad (3.5.79)$$

multiplication steps (the N comes from the N multiplications by ω_{2N}^m). When $N = 2^{\ell-1}$, we can iterate ℓ times and use $a_1 = 1$ to get

$$a_{2^\ell} = (l+1)2^\ell \qquad (3.5.80)$$

yielding to $O(N \log N)$ algorithm.

This algorithm was popularized by and is sometimes named after a 1965 paper of Cooley–Tukey [**204**]. They rediscovered an idea that Gauss knew about—it appeared in Gauss' complete works as an unpublished note. The Cooley–Tukey algorithm came at exactly the right time—just as digital computers became powerful enough to compute Fourier transforms of data important in the real world, and there was an explosion of applications. In fact, Tukey came up with the basic algorithm as a member of President Kennedy's Presidential Scientific Advisory Committee to try to figure out a way to analyze seismic data in order to get information on Russian nuclear tests! Garwin from IBM, also at the meeting, put Tukey in touch with Cooley who actually coded the algorithm!

One reason that Weierstrass' example had such impact is that earlier in the century, Ampère [**26**] seemed to claim that every continuous function was differentiable. Medvedev [**647**, Ch. 5], in a summary of these developments, argues that the problem was one of terminology. When Ampère wrote, neither "function" nor "continuous" had clearly accepted definitions and, Medvedev says, Ampère had in mind functions given locally by convergent power series! Shortly afterwards, Cauchy gave more careful notions (and Weierstrass, later, even more so). Be that as it may, many mid-century analysis texts stated and proved (!) what they called Ampère's theorem: that every continuous function was differentiable. In his lectures as early as the 1860s, Weierstrass claimed that all these proofs were wrong.

The first results on the existence of nondifferentiable continuous functions are due to Bernhard Bolzano (1781–1848), a Czech priest (his father was from Italy). He found them around 1830 but never published them—they were finally published about a hundred years later; see Pinkus [**728**] for details. Around 1880, Charles Cellérier (1818–89) proved that for a large positive integer, a, the function $f(x) = \sum_{n=1}^{\infty} a^{-n} \sin(a^n x)$ is continuous but nowhere differentiable. He never published the result but it was discovered among his papers and published posthumously [**178**].

Weierstrass [**978**] claimed that in lectures given in 1861, Riemann asserted that $\sum_{n=1}^{\infty} n^{-2} \sin(n^2 x)$, a function that enters in elliptic function theory, was continuous but nondifferentiable on a dense set. It is now known to be nondifferentiable, except for an explicit countable set. Weierstrass couldn't verify Riemann's claim. Instead, in 1872, he considered the function in (3.5.53) for $\gamma = 0$ and proved that if $a < 1$, b is an odd integer, and if $ab > 1 + \frac{3}{2}\pi$, then f is nowhere differentiable. This example of Weierstrass had a profound effect on his contemporaries.

There were intermediate improvements by Bromwich, Darboux, Dini, Faber, Hobson, Landsberg, and Lerch, until Hardy [**393**] got the definitive result $ab \geq 1$ (and it is differentiable if $ab < 1$). In the text, we only handled $ab > 1$; $ab = 1$ (and $\gamma = 0$) can be handled using the Jackson kernel related to the square of the Fejér kernel (see Problem 17). I don't know who found this Fejér- and Jackson-kernel approach, but I've found it in several books from the 1960s.

There are close connections between nowhere differentiable functions and natural boundaries, especially lacunary series; see Problem 16 of Section 2.3 of Part 2A and Kahane [**464**].

A sign of the roughness of the functions $f_{a,b,\gamma}$ is that their graphs (i.e., $\{(x,y) \mid y = f(x)\}$) have dimension greater than one. Indeed, it is known that with a suitable definition of dimension ("box dimension," believed also for Hausdorff dimension; see Section 8.2), then for $ab > 1$ and b sufficiently large,

$$\dim(\mathrm{graph}(f_{a,b,\gamma=0})) = 2 - \frac{\log(a^{-1})}{\log(b)}$$

This is discussed in Falconer [**293**]; see Figure 3.5.5. For extensive additional literature on nowhere differentiable functions, see the bibliography at http://mathworld.wolfram.com/WeierstrassFunction.html.

The Gibbs phenomenon is named after J. Willard Gibbs (1839–1903), the famous American physicist known for his work on statistical mechanics

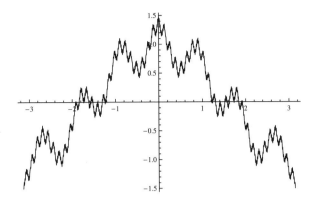

Figure 3.5.5. $F_{a,b,\gamma}$ for $a = \frac{1}{3}$, $b = 7$. This graph has dimension approximately 1.44.

after his paper [**348**]. It was so named by Maxime Bôcher (1867–1918), who found the first comprehensive mathematical treatment [**98, 99**], much like the one we sketch. The name is a good example of Arnold's principle, since fifty years before Gibbs, Henry Wilbraham (1825–83) discovered the phenomenon [**1001**]; see Hewitt–Hewitt [**423**] for the history. The Gibbs phenomenon has been rediscovered many times, for example, by engineers working on radar during the Second World War.

(3.5.5) was proven in several ways first by Euler in 1734–35 thereby solving a famous problem; see the discussion in the Notes to Sections 5.7 and 9.2 of Part 2A. Even though Euler proved (3.5.4) (much later), he doesn't seem to have noticed the connection.

Problems

1. Let f be piecewise continuous on $\partial\mathbb{D}$ in that there are $0 \le \theta_1 < \cdots < \theta_k < 2\pi$, so $f(e^{i\theta})$ is continuous at any $e^{i\theta_0} \in \partial\mathbb{D} \setminus \{e^{i\theta_j}\}_{j=1}^k$, and for any k, $\lim_{\varepsilon\downarrow 0} f(e^{i(\theta_k+\varepsilon)}) \equiv f(e^{i(\theta_k+0)})$ and $\lim_{\varepsilon\uparrow 0} f(e^{i(\theta_k-\varepsilon)}) \equiv f(e^{i(\theta_k-0)})$ exist.

   (a) Prove there are continuous f_n on $\partial\mathbb{D}$ so $\int_0^{2\pi} |f(e^{i\theta}) - f_n(e^{i\theta})|^2 \frac{d\theta}{2\pi} \to 0$ as $n \to \infty$.

   (b) Prove that if $f_k^\sharp$ is defined by (3.5.1), then (3.5.4) holds.

2. In this problem, the reader will prove that for all N and $0 < a < b < 2\pi$

$$\left| \int_a^b D_N(x)\, dx \right| \le 4\pi \qquad (3.5.81)$$

   a result that will be useful in the next two problems.

   (a) Prove it suffices to prove this for $0 < a < b < \pi$ with 4π replaced by 2π. (*Hint*: $D_N(2\pi - x) = D_N(x)$.)

(b) For $0 < x < \pi - \frac{2\pi}{(N+\frac{1}{2})}$, show that $D_N(x)$ and $D_N(x + \frac{2\pi}{(N+\frac{1}{2})})$ have opposite signs with $|D_N(x)| > |D_N(x + \frac{2\pi}{(N+\frac{1}{2})})|$ and use this to prove for $0 < a < b < \pi$, the integral has maximum absolute value for $a = 0$, $b = \pi/(N + \frac{1}{2})$ (Look at the right halves of the graph in Figure 3.5.1).

(c) Prove that $\left| \int_0^{\pi/(N+\frac{1}{2})} D_N(x)\, dx \right| \le D_N(0) \frac{\pi}{(N-\frac{1}{2})} = 2\pi.$

Remark. We'll see later (Problem 10 in Section 5.4) that $\sup_N \int_0^{2\pi} |D_N(\theta)| \frac{d\theta}{2\pi} = \infty$.

3. This problem will prove Theorem 3.5.18. You'll need to know about functions of bounded variation (see Sections 4.1 and 4.15) and the second mean value theorem (see Problem 5 of Section 4.15). Since any function of bounded variation is a difference of monotone increasing functions (see Theorem 4.15.2), you can suppose that $f(e^{i\theta})$ is monotone in θ on $[-\pi, \pi]$.

(a) For each $x_0 \in [-\pi, \pi]$, show that it suffices to find a small δ so that, as $N \to \infty$,

$$\int_{x_0}^{x_0+\delta} f(e^{ix}) D_N(x_0 - x)\, dx \to \tfrac{1}{2} f(e^{i(x_0+0)})$$

$$\int_{x_0-\delta}^{x_0} f(e^{ix}) D_N(x_0 - x)\, dx \to \tfrac{1}{2} f(e^{i(x_0-0)})$$

(b) Prove that it suffices to show for g monotone on $[0, \delta]$ and $g(0) = g(0+) = 0$ then, as $N \to \infty$,

$$\int_0^\delta g(x) D_N(x)\, dx \to g(0) = 0 \tag{3.5.82}$$

(c) For some $c \in (0, \delta)$, prove that

$$\int_0^\delta g(x) D_N(x)\, dx = g(\delta-) \int_c^\delta D_N(x)\, dx$$

(d) Prove $\limsup |\int_0^\delta g(x) D_N(x)\, dx| \le 4\pi g(\delta-)$. (*Hint:* Use Problem 2.)

(e) For any $0 < \delta' < \delta$, prove that $\lim_{N\to\infty} |\int_{\delta'}^\delta g(x) D_N(x)\, dx| = 0$. (*Hint:* Look at the proof of Theorem 3.5.8.)

(f) Prove (3.5.82), and so, Jordan's theorem.

4. This problem will construct (following ideas of Fejér [**297**]) a continuous function f on $\partial \mathbb{D}$ so that $\overline{\lim}\, S_N(f)(0) = \infty$.

(a) As a preliminary, prove that for all n and $x \in [-\pi, \pi]$

$$\left| \sum_{k=1}^{n} \frac{\sin(kx)}{k} \right| \leq \frac{3\pi}{2} \qquad (3.5.83)$$

(*Hint*: Show that the sum is $\frac{1}{2} \int_0^x (D_n(t) - 1) \, dt$ and use Problem 2.)

(b) Define

$$G_n(\theta) = \sum_{j=0}^{n-1} \frac{1}{n-j} \left[e^{ij\theta} - e^{i(2n-j)\theta} \right] \qquad (3.5.84)$$

Prove that uniformly in n for $\theta \in [-\pi, \pi]$

$$|G_n(\theta)| \leq 3\pi$$

(c) Now pick $0 < n_1 < n_2 < \ldots$ and $m_1, m_2, \ldots$ so that $m_k > m_{k-1} + 2n_{k-1}$ and a sequence of positive numbers $\{a_k\}_{k=1}^{\infty}$ with $\sum_{k=1}^{\infty} a_k < \infty$ and let

$$f(e^{i\theta}) = \sum_{k=1}^{\infty} a_k \, e^{im_k\theta} \, G_{n_k}(\theta) \qquad (3.5.85)$$

Show the sum is absolutely and uniformly convergent so that f is a continuous function.

(d) Prove that $\sum_{j=1}^{n} j^{-1} > \log(n+1)$.

(e) Prove that if $N_k = m_k + n_k$, then

$$(S_{N_k} f)(\theta = 0) \geq a_k \log(n_k + 1) - \sum_{j=1}^{\infty} a_j \qquad (3.5.86)$$

(f) Pick $n_k = 2^{k^3} = m_k$ and $a_k = k^{-2}$ and show that $(S_{N_k} f)(\theta = 0) \to \infty$.

5. This problem supposes you know about elements of L^2 as Borel functions, as discussed in Sections 4.4 and 4.6.

(a) Suppose that $f \in L^2(\partial\mathbb{D})$ and for some θ_0 and δ, we have

$$\int_{|\theta - \theta_0| \leq \delta} \frac{|f(e^{i\theta}) - f(e^{i\theta_0})|}{|\theta - \theta_0|} \frac{d\theta}{2\pi} < \infty \qquad (3.5.87)$$

Prove that (3.5.9) holds. (*Hint*: See Theorem 3.5.8.)

(b) Suppose that instead of (3.5.87) you have $f_\pm = \lim_{\varepsilon \downarrow 0} f(e^{i(\theta_0 \pm \varepsilon)})$ exists and

$$\int_{\theta_0}^{\theta_0 + \delta} \frac{|f(e^{i\theta}) - f_+|}{|\theta - \theta_0|} \frac{d\theta}{2\pi} + \int_{\theta_0 - \delta}^{\theta_0} \frac{|f(e^{i\theta}) - f_-|}{|\theta - \theta_0|} \frac{d\theta}{2\pi} < \infty \qquad (3.5.88)$$

Prove that

$$(S_N f)(e^{i\theta_0}) \to \tfrac{1}{2} (f_+ + f_-) \qquad (3.5.89)$$

(*Hint*: Find g with $g(\theta) = -g(-\theta)$, so $(S_N f)(1) \equiv 0$ and so that $h(e^{i\theta}) \equiv f(e^{i\theta}) - g(\theta - \theta_0)$ is continuous at θ_0 and obeys (3.5.87).)

6. (a) Let h be C^∞ on $\partial \mathbb{D}$ and f continuous. Prove that $h * f$ is C^∞.

   (b) By constructing C^∞ approximate identities, prove $C^\infty(\partial \mathbb{D})$ is $\|\cdot\|_\infty$ dense in $C(\partial \mathbb{D})$.

7. Let K be a compact subset of $L^2(\partial \mathbb{D})$. Prove that for any ε, there is an N so that for all $f \in K$ and $n \geq N$, $|f_n^\sharp| \leq \varepsilon$. (*Hint*: First find $f^{(1)}, \ldots, f^{(n)}$ so that $K \subset \cup_{j=1}^{\ell} \{g \mid \|g - f^{(j)}\|_2 \leq \frac{\varepsilon}{2}\}$.)

8. Fill in the details of the proof of Theorem 3.5.5.

9. Suppose for some open interval $I \subset \partial \mathbb{D}$ and $f \in L^2(\partial \mathbb{D}, \frac{d\theta}{2\pi})$, we have

$$\sup_{\theta \in I} \int \frac{|f(e^{i\psi}) - f(e^{i\theta})|}{|\psi - \theta|} \frac{d\psi}{2\pi} < \infty$$

   Prove that for every compact $K \subset I$, we have $\sup_{\theta \in K} |S_N f(e^{i\theta}) - f(e^{i\theta})| \to 0$.

10. (a) Suppose $\sum_{n \in \mathbb{Z}} |a_n| < \infty$. Prove that $\sum_{|n| \leq N} a_n e^{in\theta} \equiv g_N(\theta)$ converges uniformly to a continuous function $g(\theta)$ on $\partial \mathbb{D}$.

   (b) If f is C^1 on $\partial \mathbb{D}$, prove that $(f')_n^\sharp = in f_n^\sharp$.

   (c) If f is C^1 on $\partial \mathbb{D}$, prove that $\sum_{n \in \mathbb{Z}} (1 + |n|^2)|f_n^\sharp|^2 < \infty$.

   (d) If f is C^1 on $\partial \mathbb{D}$, prove that $\sum_{n \in \mathbb{Z}} |f_n^\sharp| < \infty$.

   (e) If f is C^1 on $\partial \mathbb{D}$, prove that $S_N(f)$ converges uniformly to f. (*Hint*: If g is the uniform limit of $S_N(f)$, prove that $g^\sharp = f^\sharp$, and then that $f = g$.)

   Remark. There exist f's in $C(\partial \mathbb{D})$ for which $\sum_{n \in \mathbb{Z}} |f_n^\sharp| = \infty$; see Problem 10(e) and the Notes to Section 6.7.

11. (a) Prove that $\{1, \cos \theta, \sin \theta\}$ is a Korovkin set in the sense discussed in Theorem 2.4.7. (*Hint*: $|e^{i\theta} - e^{i\theta_0}|^2$.)

   (b) Use Korovkin's theorem to prove Fejér's theorem.

12. This shows that abelian summation, rather than Cesàro summation, provides uniform convergence of Fourier series, and so provides yet another proof of Theorem 3.5.3. Given f a continuous function on $\partial \mathbb{D}$, define the Abel sum of the Fourier series for each $a > 0$ by

$$(A_a f)(e^{i\theta}) = \sum_{n=-\infty}^{\infty} e^{-a|n|} f_n^\sharp e^{in\theta} \tag{3.5.90}$$

(a) Prove that

$$(A_a f)(e^{i\theta}) = \int_0^{2\pi} P_a(\theta - \psi) f(e^{i\psi}) \frac{d\psi}{2\pi} \tag{3.5.91}$$

where

$$P_a(\theta) = \frac{1 - e^{-2a}}{1 + e^{-2a} - 2e^{-a}\cos\theta} \tag{3.5.92}$$

known as the *Poisson kernel*.

(b) Prove that $\{P_a(\theta)\}$ is an approximate identity as $a \downarrow 0$ (with an obvious extension of the notion to continuous a rather than discrete n).

(c) Conclude that for any $f \in C(\partial\mathbb{D})$, $A_a f \to f$ uniformly as $a \downarrow 0$.

Remark. This proof of the second Weierstrass theorem is due to Picard [723]. In one of the first papers applying Lebesgue's theory, this approach was extended by Fatou [295] in his 1906 thesis. It had earlier been used by Lebesgue himself in proving uniqueness of Fourier coefficients. We will have a lot more to say about the Poisson kernel in Section 5.3 of Part 2A and Sections 2.4 and 3.1, and Chapter 5 of Part 3. Part 3 will discuss an analog of this problem for spherical harmonic expansions.

13. This provides another proof of Theorem 3.5.3. The approximate identity is simpler than Fejér's, although without the direct Fourier series interpretation.

(a) Let

$$\gamma_n = \int_{-\pi}^{\pi} (1 + \cos\theta)^n \frac{d\theta}{2\pi}$$

Prove that $W_n(\theta) = \gamma_n^{-1}(1 + \cos\theta)^n$ is an approximate identity.

(b) For any continuous f, prove that $f * W_n$ is of the form $\sum_{j=-n}^{n} a_j^{(n)} e^{ij\theta}$. Conclude that Theorem 3.5.3 holds.

Remarks. 1. This proof of the second Weierstrass theorem is due to de la Vallée Poussin [229].

2. This is sometimes written as $W_n(\theta) = \tilde{\gamma}_n^{-1} \cos^{2n}(\frac{\theta}{2})$.

14. This will prove that given any $f \in L^1(\partial\mathbb{D}, \frac{d\theta}{2\pi})$, there is a sequence of trigonometric polynomials (i.e, finite sums of $e^{ij\theta}$, $j \in \mathbb{Z}$), $P_n(e^{i\theta})$, so that (i) $\|P_n\|_1 \leq 3\|f\|_1$; (ii) $P_n^\sharp(k) = f^\sharp(k)$ if $|k| \leq n$; (iii) $f^\sharp(k) = 0$ if $|k| \geq 2n$.

(a) Define the de la Vallée Poussin kernel, $V_n(\eta)$, by

$$V_n(\eta) = 2F_{2n-1}(\eta) - F_{n-1}(\eta) \tag{3.5.93}$$

where F_n is the Fejér kernel. Prove that

$$F_n^\sharp(j) = \begin{cases} 1 - \frac{|j|}{n+1} & \text{if } |j| \leq n \\ 0 & \text{if } |j| \geq n+1 \end{cases} \tag{3.5.94}$$

and

$$V_n^\sharp(j) = \begin{cases} 1 & \text{if } |j| \leq n \\ 2 - \frac{|j|}{n} & \text{if } n+1 \leq |j| \leq 2n-1 \\ 0 & \text{if } |j| \geq 2n \end{cases} \tag{3.5.95}$$

(b) Prove $\|V_n\|_{L^1} \leq 3$ for all n.

(c) If $P_n = V_n * f$, prove that P_n has the properties (i)–(iii).

Remark. The de la Vallée Poussin kernel first appeared in his 1918 paper [**230**].

15. This will lead the reader through a proof of the classical Weierstrass approximation theorem (see Section 2.4) due to Landau [**542**]. The *Landau kernel* is defined by

$$L_n(x) = \begin{cases} \gamma_n^{-1}(1-x^2)^n, & |x| \leq 1 \\ 0, & |x| \geq 1 \end{cases} \tag{3.5.96}$$

where

$$\gamma_n = \int_{-1}^1 (1-x^2)^n \, dx \tag{3.5.97}$$

(a) Prove that $2 \geq \gamma_n \geq Cn^{-1}$ for some C. (*Hint:* $1 - x^2 \geq (1 - |x|)$ and use $y = x/n$; *Remark:* In fact (see Theorem 15.2.2 of Part 2B), $\gamma_n \sim Cn^{-1/2}$.)

(b) Prove that L_n is an approximate identity for $\mathbb{R}$, so that if f is a continuous function on $\mathbb{R}$ with compact support, then $f * L_n \to f$ uniformly.

(c) Let

$$\tilde{L}_n(x) = \gamma_n^{-1}(1-x^2)^n \qquad \text{for all } x \tag{3.5.98}$$

For f continuous with $\operatorname{supp}(f) \subset [-\frac{1}{2}, \frac{1}{2}]$, prove that

$$\int f(y)[L_n(x-y) - \tilde{L}_n(x-y)] \, dy = 0 \tag{3.5.99}$$

for $x \in [-\frac{1}{2}, \frac{1}{2}]$.

(d) Conclude for such f that $\tilde{L}_n * f \to f$ uniformly on $[-\frac{1}{2}, \frac{1}{2}]$. Prove that $\tilde{L}_n * f$ is a polynomial in x.

(e) If f is a continuous function on $[-\frac{1}{2}, \frac{1}{2}]$, prove that there are α, β so $f(x) - \alpha x - \beta$ vanishes at $\pm\frac{1}{2}$, and conclude that f is a uniform limit on $[-\frac{1}{2}, \frac{1}{2}]$ of polynomials in x.

(f) Prove the Weierstrass theorem for any interval.

16. Prove Theorem 3.5.15(b) when $0 < \alpha < 1$.

17. The *Jackson kernel* is defined by

$$J_N(\theta) = \gamma_N^{-1} F_N(\theta)^2 \qquad (3.5.100)$$

where

$$\gamma_N = \int F_N(\theta)^2 \frac{d\theta}{2\pi} \qquad (3.5.101)$$

(a) Prove that $(J_N)_k^{\sharp} = 1$ if $k = 0$ and $= 0$ if $k > 2(N-1)$.

(b) Prove that if f obeys

$$f_j^{\sharp} = 0 \quad \text{for } 0 < |j - k| < 2(N-1) \qquad (3.5.102)$$

then

$$|f_k^{\sharp}| \leq (2\pi)^{-1} \int J_N(x) |f(x)| \, dx \qquad (3.5.103)$$

(c) Prove that $\gamma_N > N/2$. (*Hint*: Look at the Fourier coefficients of F_N.)

(d) For some constant, c_1, prove that

$$|J_N(x)| \leq \frac{c_1}{N^3 x^4} \qquad (3.5.104)$$

(e) For some constant, c_2, prove that

$$\int_{-\pi}^{\pi} J_N(x)|f(x)| \frac{d\theta}{2\pi} \leq c_2 \left(N^{-2} \int |f(x)| \, dx + N^{-1} \sup_{|x| \leq N^{-1/4}} |f(x)| \right) \qquad (3.5.105)$$

(*Hint*: For $|x| \leq N^{-1}$, use $\int_{-\pi}^{\pi} J_N(x) \frac{dx}{2\pi} = 1$; for $N^{-1} \leq |x| \leq N^{-1/4}$, use (3.5.104) and $\int_{N^{-1}}^{N^{-1/4}} t^{-3} \, dt \leq N^2$; for $N^{-1/4} \leq |x| \leq \pi$, use (3.5.104) to see $\sup_{|x| \geq N^{-1/4}} |J_N(x)| \leq c_2 N^{-2}$.)

(f) If f is continuous and Lipschitz at some point and obeys (3.5.102), prove for some constant, c_3, that

$$|f_k^{\sharp}| \leq c_3 (N^{-2} + o(N^{-1})) \qquad (3.5.106)$$

(g) Prove that if $ab = 1$, $a < 1$, then $f_{a,b,\theta=0}$ is nowhere differentiable.

Remark. The Jackson kernel is named after Dunham Jackson (1888–1946), an American mathematician who spent most of his career at the University of Minnesota. He introduced his kernel in his 1912 dissertation done under Edmund Landau. The index on it is sometimes one-half the one used in this problem, so that in (3.5.102), twice the index is replaced by the index.

Figure 3.5.6. A tent function.

18. This problem will construct what is probably the simplest nowhere differentiable function (or perhaps the variant in the next problem). For $x \in \mathbb{R}$, let $Q(x) = 2 \operatorname{dist}(x, \mathbb{Z})$, a period 1 "tent function" (see Figure 3.5.6). Let

$$f(x) = \sum_{n=0}^{\infty} \frac{1}{2^n} Q(2^n x) \qquad (3.5.107)$$

(a) Suppose g is any function differentiable at some point x and $y_n \le x \le z_n$, where $y_n \ne z_n$ and $\lim_{n \to \infty}(z_n - y_n) = 0$. Prove that

$$\lim_{n \to \infty} \frac{g(z_n) - g(y_n)}{z_n - y_n} \to g'(x)$$

(b) Prove that f, given by the sum in (3.5.107), defines a continuous function on $\mathbb{R}$.

(c) Let $\mathbb{D}_\ell = \{j/2^\ell \mid j \in \mathbb{Z}\}$ be the dyadic rationals of order ℓ, and define for any $x \in \mathbb{R}$, $y_\ell(x), z_\ell(x) \in \mathbb{D}_\ell$ by $y_\ell(x) = 2^{-\ell}[2^\ell x]$ and $z_\ell(x) = y_\ell(x) + 1/2^\ell$. Prove that $y_\ell(x) \le x \le z_\ell(x)$.

(d) For any x, prove that if $m \ge \ell$, then $Q(2^m y_\ell(x)) = Q(2^m z_\ell(x)) = 0$.

(e) Let $\widetilde{R}(x) = 2\chi_{[0,\frac{1}{2})}(x) - 2\chi_{[\frac{1}{2},1)}(x)$ and $R(x) = \sum_{n \in \mathbb{Z}} \widetilde{R}(x - n)$. For any $m < \ell$ and any $x \in \mathbb{R}$, prove that $2^{-m}[Q(2^m z_\ell(x)) - Q(2^m y_\ell(x))] = 2^{-\ell} R(2^m x)$. (*Hint:* If $Q_m(x) = 2^{-n} Q(2^m x)$, prove $Q_m(y) - Q_m(z) = \int_y^z Q_m'(w)\, dw$, where Q_m' exists for all but a discrete set of points, and then that on $[y_\ell(x), z_\ell(x)]$, we have (except for a discrete set) that $Q_m'(x) = R(2^m x)$. Note that you'll need to give careful consideration to the case where $x \in \mathbb{D}_\ell$.)

(f) Let $q_n(x) = [f(z_n(x)) - f(y_n(x))]/[z_n(x) - y_n(x)]$. Prove that $q_n(x) = \sum_{j=0}^{n-1} R(2^n x)$ and conclude that $|q_{n+1}(x) - q_n(x)| = 2$ for all x and n. Show that f is nowhere differentiable.

Remark. This function is due to Takagi [**903**] in 1903, although the example is sometimes named after van der Waerden who rediscovered it (with 2^n replaced by 10^n) twenty-five years later. The function is sometimes called the *blancmange function* since its graph looks like the French dessert of that name (see Figure 3.5.7). This approach is from de Rham [**237**]. It is known that $\{x \mid f(x) = \sup_y f(y)\}$ is an uncountable set of Hausdorff dimension $\frac{1}{2}$; see Baba [**43**].

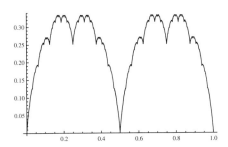

Figure 3.5.7. The Takagi function.

19. This has a variant of the Takagi function of Problem 18 due to Mc-Carthy [**645**]. Let $g_n(x) = 2Q(\frac{1}{4}2^{2^n}x)$, where Q is the tent function of Problem 18. Let

$$f(x) = \sum_{n=1}^{\infty} 2^{-n} g_n(x) \qquad (3.5.108)$$

(a) Prove that f is continuous.

(b) Prove that g_k has constant slope $\pm 2^{2^k}$ on intervals of size $2\,2^{-2^k}$ and has period $4\,2^{-2^k}$.

(c) Given k and x, pick $\Delta_k x = \pm 2^{-2^k}$ so x and $x + \Delta_k x$ lie in a single interval where g_k has constant slope. Prove this can be done and that, if $(\Delta_k h) = h(x + \Delta_k x) - h(x)$, then $|\Delta_k g_k| = 1$.

(d) For $n > k$, prove that $\Delta_k g_n = 0$. (*Hint*: The period of g_n divides $\Delta_k x$.)

(e) For $n < k$, prove that $|\Delta_k g_n| \le 2^{-2^{(k-1)}}$. (*Hint*: Look at g_n'.)

(f) Prove that

$$\frac{\sum_{n \ne k} 2^{-n} |\Delta_k g_n|}{|2^{-k} \Delta_k g_k|} \le 2^{k+1} 2^{-2^{(k-1)}}$$

(g) Prove that $\Delta f / 2^{-k} \Delta_k g_k \to 1$ as $k \to \infty$.

(h) Prove that $|\Delta f|/|\Delta_k x| \to \infty$ as $k \to \infty$ and conclude that f is nowhere differentiable.

Remark. McCarthy seems to have been unaware of the work of Takagi and van der Waerden and, in turn, de Rham seems to have been unaware of McCarthy.

20. Prove that $\|C_N f\|_\infty \le \|f\|_\infty$.

21. This problem will fill in the details of the proof of Theorem 3.5.17 and also prove (3.5.5).

(a) If f is given by (3.5.66), verify (3.5.68) for $n = 0, \pm 1, \pm 2, \ldots$.

(b) Prove (3.5.70).

(c) Prove (3.5.71).

(d) Complete the proof of Theorem 3.5.17.

(e) Prove that $\sum_{n=0}^{\infty} \frac{1}{(2n+1)^2} = \frac{\pi^2}{8}$. (*Hint*: Use (3.5.68) and (3.5.4).)

(f) If $S = \sum_{n=1}^{\infty} \frac{1}{n^2}$ and $E = \sum_{n=0}^{\infty} \frac{1}{(2n+1)^2}$, prove that $S = E + \frac{1}{4}S$.

(g) Prove (3.5.5).

22. (a) Compute $g_n^\sharp$ if $g(\theta) = |\theta - \frac{\pi}{2}|$ on $[0, 2\pi]$.

   (b) Verify that $\sum_{n=1}^{\infty} \frac{1}{n^4} = \frac{\pi^4}{90}$.

23. (a) Let h be given on $[0, 2\pi]$ by

$$h(\theta) = \begin{cases} \theta(\pi - \theta), & 0 \le \theta \le \pi \\ (\pi - \theta)(2\pi - \theta), & \pi \le \theta \le 2\pi \end{cases}$$

Compute $h_n^\sharp$.

   (b) Verify that $\sum_{n=1}^{\infty} \frac{1}{n^6} = \frac{\pi^6}{945}$.

Remark. Problem 4 of Section 9.2 of Part 2A will find $\sum_{n=1}^{\infty} \frac{1}{n^{2k}}$ for all k (in terms of rationals known as the Bernoulli numbers).

24. Suppose that for some C, $\alpha > 0$, and $\varepsilon > 0$, we have $0 < x < y < \varepsilon$ or $0 > x > y > -\varepsilon \Rightarrow |f(x) - f(y)| \le C|x - y|^\alpha$, and that $\lim_{\delta \downarrow 0} f(\pm \delta) \equiv f(\pm 0)$ exist. Let $\Delta = |f(+0) - f(-0)|$. Prove that

$$\lim_{\delta \downarrow 0} \limsup_{n \to \infty} \left[\sup_{|x| \le \delta} (S_n f)(x) - \inf_{|x| \le \delta} S_n(f) \right] = \left(\frac{2}{\pi} \int_0^\pi \frac{\sin s}{s} \, ds \right) \Delta$$

showing that the Gibbs phenomenon is generally true at jumps.

25. This problem will prove *Wirtinger's inequality*: if $f(e^{i\theta})$ is a C^1 real-valued function on $\partial \mathbb{D}$ with

$$f(1) = f(-1) = 0 \tag{3.5.109}$$

then

$$\int_0^{2\pi} |f(e^{i\theta})|^2 \, \frac{d\theta}{2\pi} \le \int_0^{2\pi} |f'(e^{i\theta})|^2 \, \frac{d\theta}{2\pi} \tag{3.5.110}$$

You'll also prove (3.5.110) if

$$\int_0^{2\pi} f(e^{i\theta}) \, \frac{d\theta}{2\pi} = 0 \tag{3.5.111}$$

(a) Compute $(f')_n^\sharp$ in terms of $f_n^\sharp$ and deduce (3.5.110) if (3.5.111) holds.

(b) Suppose next that

$$f(e^{i\theta}) = -f(e^{-i\theta}) \tag{3.5.112}$$

Prove that (3.5.110) holds.

(c) Given any f obeying (3.5.109), find C^1 g, h obeying (3.5.112) so $f \upharpoonright \{e^{i\theta} \mid 0 \le \theta \le \pi\} = g \upharpoonright \{e^{i\theta} \mid 0 \le \theta \le \pi\}$, $f \upharpoonright \{e^{i\theta} \mid -\pi \le \theta \le 0\} = h \upharpoonright \{e^{i\theta} \mid -\pi \le \theta \le 0\}$. Using (3.5.110) for g and h, prove it for f.

(d) Prove that when (3.5.109) holds, equality holds in (3.5.110) only if $f(e^{i\theta}) = \sin\theta$.

Remark. (3.5.110) was noted by Wirtinger if either (3.5.109) or (3.5.111) holds, but he never published it. He mentioned it to Blaschke who included it in his famous book on geometric inequalities [**95**].

26. This problem will prove a version of the *isoperimetric inequality*: namely, if $\gamma(s)$ is a smooth simple closed curve in $\mathbb{R}^2$ of length 2π, then the area is at most π with equality only for the circle. Without loss, we can suppose γ is arclength parametrized, that is, $\gamma(s) = (x(s), y(s))$, for $0 \le s \le 2\pi$, with

$$|x'(s)|^2 + |y'(s)|^2 = 1 \tag{3.5.113}$$

Thus,

$$\int_0^{2\pi} |x'(s)|^2 + |y'(s)|^2 \, ds = 2\pi \tag{3.5.114}$$

(a) Use Green's formula (see Section 1.4 of Part 3) to prove that

$$\text{Area within } \gamma = \int_0^{2\pi} \tfrac{1}{2} \left(x(s)y'(s) - x'(s)y(s) \right) ds \tag{3.5.115}$$

(b) Expanding x, y in Fourier series and using $|\alpha\beta| \le \tfrac{1}{2}|\alpha|^2 + |\beta|^2$, prove that

$$\text{Area within } \gamma \le \tfrac{1}{2} \int_0^{2\pi} \left(|x'(s)|^2 + |y'(s)|^2 \right) ds = \pi$$

with equality only if γ is a circle.

Remark. This simple proof of the isoperimetric inequality in dimension 2 is due to Hurwitz [**440**, **441**] in work done in 1901–02. See Groemer–Schneider [**370**] and Groemer [**369**] for results in dimension higher than 2 using spherical harmonic expansions (see Section 3.5 of Part 3). In particular, Groemer [**369**] has many other results on applying Fourier series to geometric inequalities.

27. Prove that a function $f \in C(\partial\mathbb{D})$ is a uniform limit of polynomials in z if and only if $\int_0^{2\pi} e^{in\theta} f(e^{i\theta}) \frac{d\theta}{2\pi} = 0$ for $n = 1, 2, \ldots$. (*Hint:* One direction is already in Proposition 2.4.4; for the other, use Fejér's theorem.)

28. (a) Let P_n be a polynomial of degree n in a complex variable z. Prove that

$$-iP_n^\star(e^{i\theta}) = \int_0^{2\pi} F_n(\theta - \varphi)\, e^{in(\theta-\varphi)} P_n(e^{i\varphi})\, \frac{d\varphi}{2\pi}$$

where

$$F_n(\theta) = \sum_{j=-n+1}^{n-1} (n - |j|)\, e^{ij\theta}$$

and $P_n^\star(e^{i\theta})$ means $\frac{d}{d\theta} f(\theta)$ with $f(\theta) = P_n(e^{i\theta})$ so $|P_n^\star(e^{i\theta})| = |P_n'(e^{i\theta})|$.

(b) Find an explicit formula for F_n (not as a sum) and prove $F_n(\theta) \geq 0$ and $\int F_n(\theta)\, \frac{d\theta}{2\pi} = n$.

(c) Conclude that

$$\sup_{\theta \in [0,2\pi]} |P_n'(e^{i\theta})| \leq n \sup_{\theta \in [0,2\pi]} |P_n(e^{i\theta})|$$

(This is known as *Bernstein's inequality*.)

3.6. The Weak Topology

The central parts of this chapter are concluded. The final three brief sections hint at further directions. In this section, we introduce the weak topology and explain the basic compactness result that is responsible for its interest. This material will be largely subsumed in the discussion of the general Banach space case in Sections 5.5 and 5.7. In the next section, we introduce some special classes of operators, whose discussion will be a central part of Part 4 and in the final section, we discuss tensor products.

So far, the only topology we've put on a Hilbert space, $\mathcal{H}$, is the norm (aka strong) topology, where a net, φ_α converges to φ if and only if $\lim_\alpha \|\varphi_\alpha - \varphi\| = 0$.

Definition. The weak topology on $\mathcal{H}$ is the weakest topology on $\mathcal{H}$ in which, for all $\psi \in \mathcal{H}$, $\varphi \mapsto \langle \psi, \varphi \rangle$ is continuous.

Thus, a neighborhood base for $\eta \in \mathcal{H}$ is given by

$$\{\varphi \mid |\langle \psi_1, \varphi - \eta \rangle| < \varepsilon_1, \ldots, |\langle \psi_n, \varphi - \eta \rangle| < \varepsilon_n\} \equiv N_{\psi_1,\varepsilon_1;\psi_2,\eta_2;\ldots;\psi_n,\varepsilon_n}(\eta) \tag{3.6.1}$$

as $\psi_1, \ldots, \psi_n$ runs through all n-tuples in $\mathcal{H}$, $\varepsilon_j > 0$, but otherwise arbitrary, and $n = 1, 2, \ldots$. Equivalently, a net $\varphi_\alpha \to \varphi$ is in the weak topology if and only if $\langle \psi, \varphi - \varphi_\alpha \rangle \to 0$ for all $\psi \in \mathcal{H}$.

If $\psi = \sum_{j=1}^n a_j \psi_j$ for $(a_1, \ldots, a_n) \in \mathbb{C}^n$, then

$$|\langle \psi, \varphi \rangle| \leq \sum_{j=1}^n |a_j|\, |\langle \psi_j, \varphi \rangle| \tag{3.6.2}$$

so if $|\langle \psi_j, \varphi \rangle| \leq \varepsilon / \sum_{j=1}^{n} |a_j|$, then $|\langle \psi, \varphi \rangle| \leq \varepsilon$, and thus, any $N_{\psi,\varepsilon;\psi_1,\varepsilon_1;\ldots;\psi_n,\varepsilon_n}(\eta)$ contains an $N_{\psi_1,\tilde{\varepsilon}_1,\ldots,\psi_n,\tilde{\varepsilon}_n}(\eta)$. By induction, this makes it easy to see that we get a neighborhood base by considering only independent $\psi_1, \ldots, \psi_n$.

Example 3.6.1. Let $\mathcal{H}$ be an infinite-dimensional Hilbert space and $\{\varphi_n\}_{n=1}^{\infty}$ an orthonormal basis. Then, for any ψ, $\sum_{n=1}^{\infty} |\langle \psi, \varphi_n \rangle|^2 < \infty$, so $\langle \psi, \varphi_n \rangle \to 0$. Thus, $\varphi_n \to 0$ weakly. Since $\|\varphi_n\| = 1$, it does not converge in norm. This shows the weak and norm topologies are different. $\square$

While weak convergence does not, in general, imply norm convergence, in one case it does:

Theorem 3.6.2. *If $\{\varphi_\alpha\}_{\alpha \in I}$ is a net, $\varphi_\alpha \to \varphi$ weakly, and $\|\varphi_\alpha\| \to \|\varphi\|$, then $\|\varphi - \varphi_\alpha\| \to 0$, that is, $\varphi_\alpha \to \varphi$ in $\|\cdot\|$.*

Proof.
$$\|\varphi - \varphi_\alpha\|^2 = \|\varphi\|^2 + \|\varphi_\alpha\|^2 - 2\operatorname{Re}\langle \varphi, \varphi_\alpha \rangle \qquad (3.6.3)$$
By hypothesis, $\|\varphi_\alpha\|^2 \to \|\varphi\|^2$ and $\langle \varphi, \varphi_\alpha \rangle \to \|\varphi\|^2$, so the right side of (3.6.3) goes to zero. $\square$

Remark. In Problem 5 of Section 5.7, this fact is extended to any "uniformly convex Banach space," in particular, for L^p space, $1 < p < \infty$. In Problems 6 and 7 of Section 5.7, you'll show the analog fails for $L^1([0,1]; dx)$ and for $C([0,1])$.

The critical facts we'll establish in this section are

(1) The weak topology restricted to any ball, $\{\varphi \mid \|\varphi\| \leq R\}$ is metrizable.
(2) The weak topology on all of $\mathcal{H}$ is not metrizable.
(3) While $\{\varphi \mid \|\varphi\| \leq 1\}$ is not compact in the norm topology, it is in the weak topology.

Given an O.N. basis, $\{\varphi_j\}_{j=1}^{\infty}$, we define a metric on $\mathcal{H}$ by

$$\rho(\psi, \eta) = \sum_{j=1}^{\infty} \min(2^{-j}, |\langle \varphi_j, \psi - \eta \rangle|) \qquad (3.6.4)$$

Because of the 2^{-j} cutoff, the sum is always convergent. Since

$$\rho(\psi, \eta) < 2^{-j} \Rightarrow |\langle \varphi_j, \psi - \eta \rangle| \leq \rho(\psi, \eta) \qquad (3.6.5)$$

we see that as $k \to \infty$

$$\rho(\psi_k, \eta) \to 0 \Leftrightarrow \forall j \ |\langle \varphi_j, \psi_k - \eta \rangle| \to 0 \qquad (3.6.6)$$

Theorem 3.6.3. *Fix $R > 0$ and let $B_R = \{\psi \in \mathcal{H} \mid \|\psi\| \leq R\}$. Let $\{\varphi_j\}_{j=1}^{\infty}$ be an O.N. basis. Then the following are equivalent for a net $\{\eta_\alpha\}_{\alpha \in I}$ and ψ, all in B_R:*

(1) $\eta_\alpha \to \psi$ in the weak topology
(2) $\langle \varphi_j, \eta_\alpha \rangle \to \langle \varphi_j, \psi \rangle$ for each j
(3) $\rho(\eta_\alpha, \psi) \to 0$

Proof. (2) $\Leftrightarrow$ (3) is (3.6.6) and (1) $\Rightarrow$ (2) by the definition of the weak topology. Thus, we need to show that (2) $\Rightarrow$ (1).

Suppose (2) holds and let $\varphi \in \mathcal{H}$. Write

$$\varphi = \sum_{j=1}^\infty a_j \varphi_j \tag{3.6.7}$$

where $\sum_{j=1}^\infty |a_j|^2 < \infty$. Given ε_0, pick N so

$$\left(\sum_{j=N+1}^\infty |a_j|^2 \right)^{1/2} \le \varepsilon_0 \tag{3.6.8}$$

and write $\varphi = \varphi_<^{(N)} + \varphi_>^{(N)}$, where

$$\varphi_<^{(N)} = \sum_{j=1}^N a_j \varphi_j \qquad \varphi_>^{(N)} = \sum_{j=N+1}^\infty a_j \varphi_j \tag{3.6.9}$$

By (2), $\langle \varphi_<^{(N)}, \eta_\alpha - \psi \rangle \to 0$ and by (3.6.8) and the Schwarz inequality,

$$|\langle \varphi_>^{(N)}, \eta_\alpha - \psi \rangle| \le \varepsilon_0 \|\eta_\alpha - \psi\| \le 2R\varepsilon_0 \tag{3.6.10}$$

Since ε_0 can be made arbitrarily small, we see $\langle \varphi, \eta_\alpha - \psi \rangle \to 0$, that is, we have proven weak convergence. $\square$

Thus, we have proven that the weak topology on each B_R is metrizable. That it is not metrizable on $\mathcal{H}$ is more subtle. The idea will be to show that if it were, then $\mathcal{H}$ would have countable algebraic dimension (i.e., there would be a countable subset so every vector is a finite linear combination of those vectors) and to separately show it has uncountable algebraic dimension. We begin with the latter:

Lemma 3.6.4. *Let $\{\psi_n\}_{n=1}^\infty$ be a countable subset of an infinite-dimensional Hilbert space, $\mathcal{H}$. Then there exists $\eta \in \mathcal{H}$ which is not a finite linear combination of the ψ's.*

Proof. First, inductively, thin out the ψ's by dropping the dependent ones. That is, drop ψ_k if it is a finite linear combination of $\{\psi_j\}_{j=1}^{k-1}$. Then use Gram–Schmidt on the remaining ψ's to get an orthonormal set $\{\varphi_j\}_{j=1}^N$ (N finite or infinite) so the finite linear span of the ψ's and φ's are the same.

If $N < \infty$, their span is $\mathbb{C}^N$, so since $\dim(\mathcal{H})$ is infinite, there is $\eta \in (\{\varphi_j\}_{j=1}^N)^\perp$ which is not a linear combination.

If $N = \infty$, let

$$\eta = \sum_{n=1}^{\infty} \frac{1}{n} \varphi_n \qquad (3.6.11)$$

which lies in $\mathcal{H}$ since $\sum_{n=1}^{\infty} \frac{1}{n^2} < \infty$. If η were a finite linear combination, then pick φ_ℓ not in the finite set. Then $\langle \eta, \varphi_\ell \rangle = 0$. But, by (3.6.11), $\langle \eta, \varphi_\ell \rangle = 1/\ell \neq 0$. Thus, η is not in the finite linear span of the $\{\varphi_j\}_{j=1}^{\infty}$. $\quad\square$

Lemma 3.6.5. *Let X be an arbitrary vector space over $\mathbb{K} = \mathbb{R}$ or $\mathbb{C}$. Let $\ell_1, \dots, \ell_n$ be linearly independent maps of X to $\mathbb{K}$. Then for all $\langle a_1, \dots, a_n \rangle \in \mathbb{K}^n$, there exists $x \in X$ so that $\ell_j(x) = a_j$.*

Remark. Since X does not have a topology, the ℓ's are not assumed continuous.

Proof. Let $Q = \{(\ell_1(x), \ell_2(x), \dots, \ell_n(x)) \mid x \in X\} \subset \mathbb{K}^n$. If $Q \neq \mathbb{K}^n$, then find $(b_1, \dots, b_n) \in Q^\perp$, $b \neq 0$, that is,

$$\left(\sum_{j=1}^{n} b_j \ell_j \right)(x) = 0 \qquad (3.6.12)$$

for all x, that is, $\sum_{j=1}^{n} b_j \ell_j = 0$, so there is linear dependence. As a result, $Q = \mathbb{K}^n$, which was to be proven. $\quad\square$

Proposition 3.6.6. *Let X be an arbitrary vector space over $\mathbb{K} = \mathbb{R}$ or $\mathbb{C}$ and let $\ell_1, \dots, \ell_n$ be linearly independent maps from X to $\mathbb{K}$. Let $\ell \colon X \to \mathbb{C}$ be linear so that for some $\varepsilon > 0$,*

$$\{x \mid |\ell(x)| < 1\} \supset \{x \mid |\ell_1(x)| < \varepsilon, \dots, |\ell_n(x)| < \varepsilon\} \qquad (3.6.13)$$

Then ℓ is a linear combination of $\{\ell_j\}_{j=1}^n$.

Proof. If ℓ is not a linear combination of the $\{\ell_j\}_{j=1}^n$, then $(\ell, \ell_1, \dots, \ell_n)$ are linearly independent. So by Lemma 3.6.5, there exists x_0 so that $\ell(x_0) = 1$ but $\ell_j(x_0) = 0$, a contradiction. $\quad\square$

Corollary 3.6.7. *Let ℓ be a linear functional on a Hilbert space, $\mathcal{H}$, so that ℓ is continuous as a map from $\mathcal{H}$ to $\mathbb{C}$ when $\mathcal{H}$ is given the weak topology. Then $\ell \in \mathcal{H}^*$.*

Proof. By the continuity assumption, $\{x \mid |\ell(x)| < 1\}$ is a weak neighborhood of 0 and so obeys (3.6.13) where $\ell_1, \dots, \ell_n \in \mathcal{H}^*$. By the proposition, $\ell \in \mathcal{H}^*$. $\quad\square$

Theorem 3.6.8. *Let $\mathcal{H}$ be an infinite-dimensional Hilbert space. Then the weak topology does not have a countable neighborhood base at $\psi = 0$. In particular, the weak topology is not given by a metric.*

Proof. Suppose $\{U_\ell\}_{\ell=1}^{\infty}$ is a countable neighborhood base for the weak topology. Since $\{N_{\psi_1,\varepsilon_1;\psi_2,\varepsilon_2;\dots;\psi_n,\varepsilon_n}(0)\}$ as ψ_j runs through $\mathcal{H}$ and $(\varepsilon_1,\dots,\varepsilon_n)$ through $(0,\infty)^n$ and $n=1,2,\dots$ is a neighborhood base for 0, there exist $n_1, n_2, \dots$ and, for each ℓ, $\{\psi_j^{(\ell)}\}_{j=1}^{n_\ell}$ and $(\varepsilon_1^{(\ell)},\dots,\varepsilon_{n_\ell}^{(\ell)}) \in (0,\infty)^{n_\ell}$ so that

$$N_{\psi_j^{(\ell)},\varepsilon_j^{(\ell)}}(0) \subset U_\ell \tag{3.6.14}$$

$\{\psi_j^{(\ell)}\}_{j=1,\,\ell=1}^{n_\ell,\infty}$ is a countable set, so by Lemma 3.6.4, there is $\eta \in \mathcal{H}$ not a linear finite linear combination of $\{\psi_j^{(\ell)}\}$.

Since $\{\varphi \mid |\langle \eta, \varphi \rangle| < 1\}$ is weakly open and contains 0, there exists U_ℓ so $U_\ell \subset \{\varphi \mid |\langle \eta, \varphi \rangle| < 1\}$, and so by (3.6.14), $N_{\psi_j^{(\ell)},\varepsilon_j^{(\ell)}}(0) \subset \{\varphi \mid |\langle \eta, \varphi \rangle| < 1\}$. Thus, (3.6.13) holds if $\varepsilon = \min_{j=1,\dots,n_\ell}(\varepsilon_j^{(\ell)})$, so η is a finite linear combination of the $\{\psi_j^{(\ell)}\}_{j=1}^{n_\ell}$. This is a contradiction. $\qquad\square$

Example 3.6.9. Let $\mathcal{H}$ be an infinite-dimensional Hilbert space. We'll construct a net $\{\varphi_\alpha\}_{\alpha \in I}$ converging weakly to zero with $\lim_\alpha \|\varphi_\alpha\| = \infty$. This is particularly interesting because we'll prove later (Theorem 5.4.19) that for a sequence $\{\varphi_n\}_{n=1}^{\infty}$ converging weakly, we have $\sup_n \|\varphi_n\| < \infty$.

Let I consist of all finite sets $s = \{\psi_1,\dots,\psi_n\}$ of distinct vectors in $\mathcal{H}$. We say $s \triangleright t$ if and only if $s \supset t$. I is directed since $s \cup t \triangleright s$ and $s \cup t \triangleright t$. For any $s \in I$, pick $\varphi_s \in \mathcal{H}$ as follows: Let $m = \#s$ and $s = \{\psi_1,\dots,\psi_m\}$. Pick $\varphi_s \in \{\psi_1,\dots,\psi_m\}^{\perp}$ with $\|\varphi_s\| = m$.

For any $\psi_1,\dots,\psi_m$ and $\varepsilon_1,\dots,\varepsilon_m > 0$, $\varphi_s \in N_{\psi_1,\varepsilon_1;\psi_2,\varepsilon_2;\dots\varepsilon_m}(0)$ so long as $s \triangleright \{\psi_1,\dots,\psi_m\}$. Thus, $\varphi_s \to 0$ weakly. Since $\|\varphi_s\| = \#s$, we have $\|\varphi_s\| \to \infty$. $\qquad\square$

Example 3.6.10. Let $\mathcal{H}_1 = \{\varphi \in \mathcal{H} \mid \|\varphi\| \leq 1\}$, where $\mathcal{H}$ is an infinite-dimensional Hilbert space. Then $\mathcal{H}_1$ is not compact in the norm topology. For let $\{\varphi_n\}_{n=1}^{\infty}$ be an orthonormal basis. Then $\|\varphi_n - \varphi_m\| = \sqrt{2}$ for $n \neq m$, so no subsequence is Cauchy and so not convergent. Thus, $\{\varphi_n\}_{n=1}^{\infty}$ has no convergent subsequence, implying a lack of compactness. $\qquad\square$

The above counterexample has $\varphi_n \to 0$ weakly (see Example 3.6.1), so it might be that $\mathcal{H}_1$ is weakly compact. Indeed,

Theorem 3.6.11. *$\mathcal{H}_1$, the closed unit ball in $\mathcal{H}$, an infinite-dimensional Hilbert space, is compact in the weak topology.*

Remark. In the argument below, we essentially reprove Tychonoff's theorem in the countably infinite case. One can instead appeal to it, as we will do in Section 5.8.

Proof. Let $\{\varphi_n\}_{n=1}^{\infty}$ be an orthonormal basis and $\{\eta_m\}_{m=1}^{\infty}$ a sequence of vectors in $\mathcal{H}_1$. Let

$$\eta_j^{(m)} = \langle \varphi_j, \eta_m \rangle \in \overline{\mathbb{D}} = \{z \in \mathbb{C} \mid |z| \leq 1\} \qquad (3.6.15)$$

Since $\overline{\mathbb{D}}$ is compact, by the diagonalization trick (see the discussion in Section 1.5), we can find a subsequence $\{m_\ell\}_{\ell=1}^{\infty}$ so that for each $j = 1, \ldots$, as $\ell \to \infty$,

$$\eta_j^{(m_\ell)} \to \eta_j^{(\infty)} \qquad (3.6.16)$$

For any k, by Bessel's inequality

$$\sum_{j=1}^{k} |\eta_j^{(\infty)}|^2 = \lim_{\ell \to \infty} \sum_{j=1}^{k} |\langle \varphi_j, \eta_{m_\ell} \rangle|^2 \leq 1$$

and therefore $\sum_{j=1}^{\infty} |\eta_j^{(\infty)}|^2 \leq 1$ and

$$\eta_\infty = \sum_{j=1}^{\infty} \eta_j^{(\infty)} \varphi_j \qquad (3.6.17)$$

lies in $\mathcal{H}_1$.

By Theorem 3.6.3 and (3.6.16), $\eta_{m_\ell} \to \eta_\infty$ in the weak topology. Since that same theorem says this topology is metrizable, $\mathcal{H}_1$ is compact in this topology. $\qquad \square$

This compactness result is one reason why weak topologies are so useful in analysis. Compactness is a useful tool in existence theorems. For an illustration in a more general context than Hilbert space, see Section 5.9.

Just as $\mathcal{H}$ has two natural topologies, $\mathcal{L}(\mathcal{H})$, the family of bounded operators in a Hilbert space, has three natural topologies. Besides the *norm topology* ($A_k \to A \Leftrightarrow \|A_k - A\| \to 0$), we have

Definition. The *strong operator topology* on $\mathcal{L}(\mathcal{H})$ is the weakest topology in which, for each fixed $\varphi \in \mathcal{H}$, $A \to A\varphi$ is continuous as a map of $\mathcal{L}(\mathcal{H})$ to $\mathcal{H}$ with its norm topology. The *weak operator topology* is the weakest topology in which all these maps are continuous when the weak vector topology is put on $\mathcal{H}$. Equivalently, it is the weakest topology in which, for each fixed $\varphi, \psi \in \mathcal{H}$, $A \mapsto \langle \varphi, A\psi \rangle \in \mathbb{C}$ is continuous.

We'll explore these topologies further in Sections 2.1, 5.4, 7.2, and 7.5 of Part 4.

Notes and Historical Remarks. The weak vector and operator topologies on a Hilbert space were introduced by von Neumann in 1929 [**964**], with further developments of the operator topologies in his 1936 paper [**967**]. We'll say a lot more about them, including the history of the compactness result when we discuss the Banach space situation in Sections 5.7 and 5.8.

Problems

1. Prove that the unit ball of $\mathcal{L}(\mathcal{H})$ in the weak and strong operator topologies is metrizable and all of $\mathcal{L}(\mathcal{H})$ is not metrizable in either.

3.7. A First Look at Operators

Part 4 is devoted to the theory of operators, mainly those on a Hilbert space. In this section, we'll introduce the cast of characters for that volume and advertise a very few of the results.

If $A \in \mathcal{L}(\mathcal{H})$ and ℓ_φ is given by (3.3.7), then $\psi \mapsto \ell_\varphi(A\psi)$ is also a bounded linear functional. So, by the Riesz representation theorem (Theorem 3.3.3), there is a unique vector, $A^*\varphi$, so

$$\ell_\varphi(A\psi) = \ell_{A^*\varphi}(\psi) \tag{3.7.1}$$

or equivalently,

$$\langle \varphi, A\psi \rangle = \langle A^*\psi, \varphi \rangle \tag{3.7.2}$$

It is easy to see that $\psi \mapsto A^*\psi$ is a linear transformation and not hard to see (Problem 1) that A^* is bounded and

$$\|A\| = \|A^*\| \tag{3.7.3}$$

$$\|A^*A\| = \|A\|^2 \tag{3.7.4}$$

A^* is called the *adjoint* of A.

It is a simple exercise (Problem 2) that

$$U \text{ is unitary } \Leftrightarrow U^*U = UU^* = \mathbb{1} \tag{3.7.5}$$

Since (3.7.2) implies $\langle A\psi, \varphi \rangle = \langle \varphi, A^*\psi \rangle$, we see

$$(A^*)^* = A \tag{3.7.6}$$

We've already defined unitary (and anti-unitary) operators and orthogonal projections earlier in this chapter. An extension is:

Definition. A *partial isometry* is an element of $\mathcal{L}(\mathcal{H})$ so that there is a closed subspace, $\mathcal{H}_I \subset \mathcal{H}$, in $\mathcal{H}$ with

$$\|U\varphi\| = \|\varphi\| \qquad \text{if } \varphi \in \mathcal{H}_I \tag{3.7.7}$$

$$U\varphi = 0 \qquad \text{if } \varphi \in \mathcal{H}_I^\perp \tag{3.7.8}$$

$\mathcal{H}_I$ is called the *initial subspace* and $\mathrm{Ran}(U)$, which is closed (by Problem 3), is called $\mathcal{H}_F$, the *final subspace*.

If P_I (respectively, P_F) are the orthogonal projections onto $\mathcal{H}_I$ and $\mathcal{H}_F$, respectively, then (Problem 3)

$$U^*U = P_I, \qquad UU^* = P_F \qquad (3.7.9)$$

Moreover, any U, where U^*U and UU^* are orthogonal projections, is a partial isometry. In particular, U^* is a partial isometry if U is. Basically, U is a unitary map from $\mathcal{H}_I$ onto $\mathcal{H}_F$ and U^* is its inverse.

Definition. An operator is called *self-adjoint* if $A^* = A$ and *normal* if $AA^* = A^*A$.

Unitary and self-adjoint operators are normal.

Definition. An operator is called *positive* if $\langle \varphi, A\varphi \rangle \geq 0$ for all $\varphi \in \mathcal{H}$.

$(\varphi, \psi) \mapsto \langle \varphi, A\psi \rangle$ is a (semi)-definite sesquilinear form, so by polarization, A is self-adjoint if A is positive.

The *polar decomposition* (see Section 2.4 of Part 4) asserts that the operator A can be written

$$A = U|A| \qquad (3.7.10)$$

where $|A|$ is a positive operator, U is a partial isometry, and the initial space for U is $\mathrm{Ker}(A)^\perp$. The decomposition with these properties is unique.

An operator is called *compact* if and only if $A[\{\varphi \mid \|\varphi\| \leq 1\}]$ has compact closure in the norm topology. It is not hard to see (see Section 3.1 in Part 4) that A is compact if and only if $\varphi_n \xrightarrow{w} \varphi \Rightarrow A\varphi_n \xrightarrow{\|\ \|} A\varphi$ for any sequence (sequence, not general net). The *Hilbert–Schmidt theorem* (see Section 3.2 of Part 4) says any compact self-adjoint operator has an orthonormal basis of eigenvectors.

On $L^2([0,1], dx)$, one can define an interesting A by

$$(Af)(x) = xf(x) \qquad (3.7.11)$$

in that this holds for $f \in C([0,1])$ and is the unique bounded operator with that property. Thus, A is self-adjoint but has no eigenvectors (Problem 4)! The *spectral theorem*, the subject of Chapter 5 of Part 4, involves the proper generalizations of the notion of eigenvectors in this case.

Notes and Historical Remarks. We'll say a lot more about the history of operator theory in Part 4. For now, we note that unitary operators were introduced by Antonne [29] and first extensively studied by Schur [826], and normal operators by Toeplitz [924]. The name Hermitean is often used instead of self-adjoint after their introduction in Hermite [421].

Problems

1. (a) Prove that an operator A is bounded if and only if

$$\sup_{\|\varphi\|=\|\psi\|=1} |\langle \varphi, A\psi \rangle| < \infty$$

and that, indeed, this sup is $\|A\|$.

(b) Prove that if A is bounded, so is A^* and $\|A\| = \|A^*\|$.

(c) Prove $\|A\|^2 \leq \|A^*A\|$, and so, $\|A\|^2 = \|A^*A\|$. (*Hint*: $\|A\varphi\|^2 = \langle \varphi, A^*A\varphi \rangle$.)

2. (a) Let U map $\mathcal{H} \to \mathcal{K}$ for two Hilbert spaces. Prove that $\|U\varphi\| = \|\varphi\|$ for all φ if and only if $U^*U = \mathbb{1}$.

(b) If U is invertible and $U^*U = \mathbb{1}$, prove that $UU^* = \mathbb{1}$. (*Hint*: Multiply by U and U^{-1}.)

3. (a) If U is a partial isometry, prove that $U^*U\varphi$ is φ (respectively, 0) if $\varphi \in \mathcal{H}_I$ (respectively, $\mathcal{H}_I^\perp$).

(b) If U is a partial isometry, prove that U is a bijection of $\mathcal{H}_I$ and $\mathcal{H}_F \equiv \mathrm{Ran}(U)$ and that the inverse of this map is $U^* \restriction \mathrm{Ran}(U)$.

(c) Prove that $\mathcal{H}_F \equiv \mathrm{Ran}(U)$ is closed. (*Hint*: If ψ_n is Cauchy in $\mathcal{H}_F$, consider $\varphi_n = U^*\psi_n$.)

(d) Prove that U^* is a partial isometry with initial space $\mathcal{H}_F$ and final space $\mathcal{H}_I$, and conclude that (3.7.9) holds.

4. If $(x - \lambda)f(x)$ is zero for Lebesgue a.e. x and a fixed λ, prove that f is a.e. zero. Conclude that the operator (3.7.10) has no eigenvectors. *Note*: This problem supposes you know L^2 is a set of functions equal a.e., as will be shown in Sections 4.4 and 4.6.

3.8. Direct Sums and Tensor Products of Hilbert Spaces

In this section, we start with two Hilbert spaces, $\mathcal{H}_1$ and $\mathcal{H}_2$, and generate two new Hilbert spaces, $\mathcal{H}_1 \oplus \mathcal{H}_2$ and $\mathcal{H}_1 \otimes \mathcal{H}_2$ (their direct sum and tensor product). The constructions easily extend to finitely many spaces: $\mathcal{H}_1, \ldots, \mathcal{H}_k$. We leave the details to the reader, including issues like that $\mathcal{H}_1 \oplus (\mathcal{H}_2 \oplus \mathcal{H}_3)$, $(\mathcal{H}_1 \oplus \mathcal{H}_2) \oplus \mathcal{H}_3$, and $\mathcal{H}_1 \oplus \mathcal{H}_2 \oplus \mathcal{H}_3$ (defined directly on $\mathcal{H}_1 \times \mathcal{H}_2 \times \mathcal{H}_3$) are all naturally isomorphic. In this section, we'll only discuss the formalism. Applications appear in Section 4.11 (see Corollary 4.11.9) and in Section 3.10 of Part 4.

We say "new" Hilbert spaces, although if $\mathcal{H}_1$ and $\mathcal{H}_2$ are infinite-dimensional, so are $\mathcal{H}_1 \oplus \mathcal{H}_2$ and $\mathcal{H}_1 \otimes \mathcal{H}_2$. All infinite-dimensional Hilbert spaces are isomorphic, so in one sense, these spaces aren't new, but the isomorphism isn't "natural," that is, it depends on choices and changing that choice can change the isomorphism. We also note that it follows from the results below (Problem 1) that if $n_1, n_2 < \infty$, we have

$$\mathbb{C}^{n_1} \oplus \mathbb{C}^{n_2} \cong \mathbb{C}^{n_1 + n_2}, \qquad \mathbb{C}^{n_1} \otimes \mathbb{C}^{n_2} \cong \mathbb{C}^{n_1 n_2} \qquad (3.8.1)$$

We'll eventually prove that $L^2([0,1], dx) \otimes L^2([0,1], dx) \cong L^2([0,1] \times [0,1], d^2x)$. Again, $L^2([0,1], dx)$ and this two-dimensional object are, as abstract spaces, unitarily equivalent, but there is an underlying structure very different if we go beyond the abstract inner product.

Definition. Let $\mathcal{H}_1, \mathcal{H}_2$ be two Hilbert spaces. Define $\mathcal{H}_1 \oplus \mathcal{H}_2$, their *direct sum*, as the Cartesian product $\mathcal{H}_1 \times \mathcal{H}_2$ with component-wise vector-space structure (i.e., $(\varphi_1, \varphi_2) \oplus (\psi_1, \psi_2) = (\varphi_1 + \psi_1, \varphi_2 + \psi_2)$ and inner product

$$\langle (\varphi_1, \varphi_2), (\psi_1, \psi_2) \rangle = \langle \varphi_1, \psi_1 \rangle + \langle \varphi_2, \psi_2 \rangle \qquad (3.8.2)$$

It is easy to see (Problem 2) that $(\varphi_1^{(n)}, \psi_2^{(n)})$ is Cauchy in $\mathcal{H}_1 \oplus \mathcal{H}_2$ if and only if $\varphi_1^{(n)}$ is Cauchy in $\mathcal{H}_1$ and $\psi_2^{(n)}$ is Cauchy in $\mathcal{H}_2$, so $\mathcal{H}_1 \oplus \mathcal{H}_2$ is complete. If we write $\varphi \oplus \psi$ for (φ, ψ), then it is also easy (Problem 3) that if $\{\varphi_1^{(j)}\}_{j=1}^{J_1}$ is an O.N. basis in $\mathcal{H}_1$ and $\{\psi_2^{(j)}\}_{j=2}^{J_2}$ is an O.N. basis of $\mathcal{H}_2$, then $\{\varphi_1^{(j)} \oplus 0\}_{j=1}^{J_1} \cup \{0 \oplus \psi_2^{(j)}\}_{j=1}^{J_2}$ is a basis for $\mathcal{H}_1 \oplus \mathcal{H}_2$. We summarize in

Theorem 3.8.1. *Let $\mathcal{H}_1, \mathcal{H}_2$ be two Hilbert spaces and $\mathcal{H}_1 \oplus \mathcal{H}_2$ their direct sum. Then*

(a) $\mathcal{H}_1 \oplus \mathcal{H}_2$ *is a Hilbert space (i.e., is compete and separable).*

(b) *If $\{\varphi_k^{(j)}\}_{j=1}^{J_k}$ is an orthonormal basis for $\mathcal{H}_k$ ($k = 1, 2$), then $\{\varphi_1^{(j)} \oplus 0\}_{j=1}^{J_1} \cup \{0 \oplus \varphi_2^{(j)}\}_{j=1}^{J_2}$ is an orthonormal basis for $\mathcal{H}_1 \oplus \mathcal{H}_2$.*

If $A \in \mathcal{L}(\mathcal{H}_1)$ and $B \in \mathcal{L}(\mathcal{H}_2)$, we define $A \oplus B$ by

$$(A \oplus B)(\psi_1 \oplus \psi_2) = A\psi_1 \oplus B\psi_2 \qquad (3.8.3)$$

It is easy to see (Problem 4) that $A \oplus B \in \mathcal{L}(\mathcal{H}_1 \oplus \mathcal{H}_2)$ and

$$\|A \oplus B\| = \max(\|A\|, \|B\|) \qquad (3.8.4)$$

We turn now to the more subtle tensor product. Given two Hilbert spaces, $\mathcal{H}_1$ and $\mathcal{H}_2$, let $\widetilde{\mathcal{B}}(\mathcal{H}_1, \mathcal{H}_2)$ be the antibilinear forms on $\mathcal{H}_1 \times \mathcal{H}_2$, that is, maps $B : \mathcal{H}_1 \times \mathcal{H}_2 \to \mathbb{C}$ so that for each $\varphi \in \mathcal{H}_1$, $\varphi_2 \mapsto B(\varphi_1, \varphi_2)$ is antilinear in φ_2, and for each $\varphi_2 \in \mathcal{H}_2$, $\varphi_1 \to B(\varphi_1, \varphi_2)$ is antilinear in φ_1. If $\psi_j \in \mathcal{H}_j$ for $j = 1, 2$, we define $\psi_1 \otimes \psi_2 \in \widetilde{\mathcal{B}}(\mathcal{H}_1, \mathcal{H}_2)$ by

$$\psi_1 \otimes \psi_2(\varphi_1, \varphi_2) = \langle \varphi_1, \psi_1 \rangle \langle \varphi_2, \psi_2 \rangle \qquad (3.8.5)$$

Note that $\psi_1 \mapsto \psi_1 \otimes \psi_2$ is linear in ψ_1 for ψ_2 fixed and vice-versa.

We call the algebraic subspace of $\widetilde{\mathcal{B}}(\mathcal{H}_1, \mathcal{H}_2)$ generated by $\{\psi_1 \otimes \psi_2 \mid \psi_j \in \mathcal{H}_j\}$ (i.e., finite linear combinations of $\psi_1 \otimes \psi_2$) $\mathcal{H}_1 \widehat{\otimes} \mathcal{H}_2$. We are going to define an inner product of this space and then define $\mathcal{H}_1 \otimes \mathcal{H}_2$ as the completion (and we'll prove it is also a subspace of $\widetilde{\mathcal{B}}(\mathcal{H}_1, \mathcal{H}_2)$). Since $c(\psi_1 \otimes \psi_2) = (c\psi_1) \otimes \psi_2$, we can deal with sums.

Proposition 3.8.2. *There is a unique inner product on $\mathcal{H}_1 \widehat{\otimes} \mathcal{H}_2$ so that*

$$\langle \psi_1 \otimes \psi_2, \varphi_1 \otimes \varphi_2 \rangle = \langle \psi_1, \varphi_1 \rangle \langle \psi_2, \varphi_2 \rangle \tag{3.8.6}$$

Proof. We need to prove that $\langle \, , \, \rangle$ on $\{\varphi \otimes \psi\}$ has a well-defined sesquilinear extension and that this extension is strictly positive.

If

$$\eta = \sum_{j=1}^{J} \psi_1^{(j)} \otimes \varphi_1^{(j)}, \qquad \kappa = \sum_{k=1}^{K} \psi_2^{(k)} \otimes \varphi_2^{(k)} \tag{3.8.7}$$

we can try to define

$$\langle \eta, \kappa \rangle = \sum_{j,k=1}^{J,K} \langle \psi_1^{(j)}, \psi_2^{(k)} \rangle \langle \varphi_1^{(j)}, \varphi_2^{(k)} \rangle \tag{3.8.8}$$

The issue is to show this is well-defined, that is, if η, κ have two different expressions, those expressions yield the same $\langle \eta, \kappa \rangle$ in (3.8.7). Since the right side of (3.8.7) is additive in κ for η fixed, it suffices to show that if κ is the 0 functional and has the form (3.8.7), then the right side of (3.8.8) is 0. This is immediate if we note that

$$\langle \eta, \kappa \rangle = \sum_{j=1}^{J} \kappa(\psi_1^{(j)}, \varphi_1^{(j)}) \tag{3.8.9}$$

We need to show $\eta \neq 0 \Rightarrow \langle \eta, \eta \rangle > 0$. If η has the form (3.8.7), we note $\{\psi_1^{(j)}\}_{j=1}^{J}$ and $\{\varphi_1^{(j)}\}_{j=1}^{J}$ generate finite-dimensional spaces in $\mathcal{H}_1$ and $\mathcal{H}_2$. We can pick an orthonormal basis for those spaces and so, using the bilinearity of $\psi \otimes \varphi$, write

$$\eta = \sum_{k,\ell=1}^{K,L} c_{k\ell} \psi_3^{(k)} \otimes \varphi_3^{(\ell)}$$

where

$$\langle \psi_3^{(k)}, \psi_3^{(k')} \rangle_{\mathcal{H}_1} = \delta_{kk'}, \qquad \langle \varphi_3^{(j)}, \varphi_3^{(j')} \rangle_{\mathcal{H}_2} = \delta_{jj'} \tag{3.8.10}$$

Thus, $\{\psi_3^{(k)} \otimes \varphi_3^{(\ell)}\}$ are orthonormal in $\mathcal{H}_1 \widehat{\otimes} \mathcal{H}_2$ and thus,

$$\langle \eta, \eta \rangle = \sum_{k,\ell=1}^{K,L} |c_{k\ell}|^2 \tag{3.8.11}$$

is strictly positive unless $c_{k\ell} \equiv 0 \Rightarrow \eta = 0$. $\qquad\square$

$\mathcal{H}_1 \otimes \mathcal{H}_2$ is the completion of $\mathcal{H}_1 \widehat{\otimes} \mathcal{H}_2$ in the inner product on $\mathcal{H}_1 \widehat{\otimes} \mathcal{H}_2$ and is called the *tensor product* of $\mathcal{H}_1$ and $\mathcal{H}_2$.

Theorem 3.8.3. (a) $\mathcal{H}_1 \otimes \mathcal{H}_2$ *has a natural realization as a subset of* $\widetilde{\mathcal{B}}(\mathcal{H}_1, \mathcal{H}_2)$ *so that* $\mathcal{H}_1 \widehat{\otimes} \mathcal{H}_2$ *is realized in its usual way.*

(b) *If* $\{\varphi_1^{(j)}\}_{j=1}^J$ *and* $\{\varphi_2^{(k)}\}_{k=1}^K$ *are O.N. bases of* $\mathcal{H}_1$ *and* $\mathcal{H}_2$, *then* $\{\varphi_1^{(j)} \otimes \varphi_2^{(k)}\}_{j=1 \ k=1}^{J \quad K}$ *is an O.N. basis of* $\mathcal{H}_1 \otimes \mathcal{H}_2$.

Proof. (a) If $\ell \in \mathcal{H}_1 \otimes \mathcal{H}_2$, define

$$B_\ell(\psi_1, \psi_2) = \langle \psi_1 \otimes \psi_2, \ell \rangle \tag{3.8.12}$$

Then $B_\ell \in \widetilde{\mathcal{B}}(\mathcal{H}_1, \mathcal{H}_2)$ and $B_{\varphi_1 \otimes \varphi_2}$ is $\varphi_1 \otimes \varphi_2$. Moreover, if $B_\ell = 0$, ℓ is orthogonal to each $\psi_1 \otimes \psi_2$ and so to $\mathcal{H}_1 \widehat{\otimes} \mathcal{H}_2$, and thus, $\ell = 0$, so $\ell \mapsto B_\ell$ is one-one.

(b) Clearly, $\{\varphi_1^{(j)} \otimes \varphi_2^{(k)}\}$ is orthonormal. If ℓ is orthogonal to each $\varphi_1^{(j)} \otimes \varphi_2^{(k)}$, we have

$$B_\ell(\varphi_1^{(j)}, \varphi_2^{(k)}) = 0 \tag{3.8.13}$$

and thus, if $\widetilde{\mathcal{H}}_1$ (respectively, $\widetilde{\mathcal{H}}_2$) is the set of finite linear combinations of $\{\varphi_1^{(j)}\}$ (respectively, $\varphi_2^{(k)}$), we have

$$\psi_1 \in \widetilde{\mathcal{H}}_1, \ \psi_2 \in \widetilde{\mathcal{H}}_2 \Rightarrow B_\ell(\psi_1, \psi_2) = 0 \tag{3.8.14}$$

by antibilinearity.

By the Schwarz inequality,

$$|B_\ell(\psi_1, \psi_2)| = |\langle \ell, \psi_1 \otimes \psi_2 \rangle| \le \|\ell\| \|\psi_1\| \|\psi_2\| \tag{3.8.15}$$

so by antibilinearity, $B_\ell(\psi_1, \psi_2) = 0$ for all ψ_1, ψ_2. Thus, $B_\ell = 0 \Rightarrow \ell = 0$. Therefore, the set is complete. $\qquad\square$

Thus if $\ell^2(S)$ is the set of functions, $\alpha \mapsto u_\alpha$, from a set S to $\mathbb{C}$ with $\sum_{\alpha \in S} |a_\alpha|^2 < \infty$, it is a Hilbert space if S is countable and $\ell^2(S_1) \otimes \ell^2(S_2)$ is naturally isomorphic to $\ell^2(S_1 \times S_2)$.

If $A \in \mathcal{L}(\mathcal{H}_1)$, $B \in \mathcal{L}(\mathcal{H}_2)$, we define $A \otimes B \in \mathcal{L}(\mathcal{H}_1 \otimes \mathcal{H}_2)$ by

$$(A \otimes B)B_\ell(\psi_1, \psi_2) = B_\ell(A^* \psi_1, B^* \psi_2) \tag{3.8.16}$$

Then it is easy to see (Problem 5) that $A \otimes B$ is bounded with

$$\|A \otimes B\| = \|A\| \|B\| \tag{3.8.17}$$

(More carefully, since we don't know which $B \in \widetilde{\mathcal{B}}(\mathcal{H}_1, \mathcal{H}_2)$ are B_ℓ's, we define $A \otimes B$ by (3.8.16) for $\mathcal{H}_1 \widehat{\otimes} \mathcal{H}_2$ and use (3.8.17) to get the definition in general.) Notice that

$$(A \otimes B)(\varphi_1 \otimes \varphi_2) = A\varphi_1 \otimes B\varphi_2 \tag{3.8.18}$$

This condition together with linearity determines $A \otimes B$.

From (3.8.18), we have

$$(A \otimes B)(C \otimes D) = AC \otimes BD \tag{3.8.19}$$

$$(A_1 + A_2) \otimes B = A_1 \otimes B + A_2 \otimes B \tag{3.8.20}$$

Finally, we want to talk about symmetric and antisymmetric tensor products. If $\mathcal{H}_1 = \mathcal{H}_2 = \cdots = \mathcal{H}_n = \mathcal{H}$, we use $\otimes^n \mathcal{H}$ for $\mathcal{H} \otimes \cdots \otimes \mathcal{H}$ (n times). As above, $\otimes^n$ is a set in $\mathcal{B}_n(\mathcal{H})$, the set of antibilinear functionals on $\mathcal{H}$.

Definition. Let Σ_n be the group of permutations ($\equiv$ bijections) of $\{1, \ldots, n\}$. If $\pi \in \Sigma_n$ and $B \in \mathcal{B}_n(\mathcal{H})$, define

$$\sigma_\pi(B)(\varphi_1, \ldots, \varphi_n) = B(\varphi_{\pi^{-1}(1)}, \ldots, \varphi_{\pi^{-1}(n)}) \tag{3.8.21}$$

We use π^{-1} so that (Problem 6)

$$\sigma_{\pi_1 \pi_2} = \sigma_{\pi_1} \sigma_{\pi_2} \tag{3.8.22}$$

It is also easy to see (Problem 7) that σ_π leaves $\{B_\ell \mid \ell \in \otimes^n \mathcal{H}\}$ invariant. Indeed,

$$\sigma_\pi(\psi_1 \otimes \cdots \otimes \psi_n) = \psi_{\pi(1)} \otimes \cdots \otimes \psi_{\pi(n)} \tag{3.8.23}$$

so σ_π takes $\mathcal{H} \widehat{\otimes} \mathcal{H} \widehat{\otimes} \cdots \widehat{\otimes} \mathcal{H} \equiv \widehat{\otimes}^n \mathcal{H}$ to itself. Moreover, on $\widehat{\otimes}^n \mathcal{H}$, σ_π is unitary, so it has a unitary extension to $\otimes^n \mathcal{H}$.

Recall that every $\pi \in \Sigma_n$ has a *sign*, $(-1)^\pi$, determined by

$$\prod_{1 \leq i < j \leq n} (x_{\pi(i)} - x_{\pi(j)}) = (-1)^\pi \prod_{1 \leq i < j \leq n} (x_i - x_j) \tag{3.8.24}$$

Definition.

$$\wedge^n(\mathcal{H}) = \{\ell \in \mathcal{H} \otimes^n \mathcal{H} \mid \forall \pi \in \Sigma_n, \, \sigma_\pi(\ell) = (-1)^\pi \ell\} \tag{3.8.25}$$

$$\mathcal{S}^n(\mathcal{H}) = \{\ell \in \mathcal{H} \otimes^n \mathcal{H} \mid \forall \pi \in \Sigma_n, \, \sigma_\pi(\ell) = \ell\} \tag{3.8.26}$$

called the *antisymmetric tensors* and *symmetric tensors*. Define

$$A_n = \frac{1}{n!} \sum_{\pi \in \Sigma_n} (-1)^\pi \sigma_\pi \tag{3.8.27}$$

$$S_n = \frac{1}{n!} \sum_{\pi \in \Sigma_n} \sigma_\pi \tag{3.8.28}$$

Thus if $\mathcal{H} = \ell^2(S)$ for S a countable set, $\otimes^n \mathcal{H} = \ell^2(S^n)$, functions of $(\alpha_1, \ldots, \alpha_n) \in S^n$, and $S^n(\mathcal{H})$ (respectively, $\wedge^n(\mathcal{H})$) are those functions which are symmetrical (respectively, antisymmetrical) under any pairwise interchange.

Proposition 3.8.4. (a) S_n *(respectively, A_n) is the orthogonal projection onto $\mathcal{S}_n(\mathcal{H})$ (respectively, $\wedge^n(\mathcal{H})$).*

(b) *For any $A \in \mathcal{L}(\mathcal{H})$, $\otimes^n(A)$ ($= A \otimes \cdots \otimes A$ n times) leaves $\mathcal{S}_n(\mathcal{H})$ and $\wedge^n(\mathcal{H})$ invariant.*

Remark. We use $\wedge^n(A)$, respectively, $\mathcal{S}^n(A)$ for the restrictions of $\otimes^n A$ to $\wedge^n(\mathcal{H})$ and $\mathcal{S}^n(\mathcal{H})$, respectively.

Proof. (a) Since $\sigma_{\pi_1\pi_2} = \sigma_{\pi_1}\sigma_{\pi_2}$ and $(-1)^{\pi_1\pi_2} = (-1)^{\pi_1}(-1)^{\pi_2}$, one sees $S_n^2 = S_n$, $A_n^2 = A_n$. Since $\sigma_\pi^* = \sigma_\pi$, we see $S_n^* = S_n$, $A_n^* = A_n$, so both are orthogonal projections. It is immediate from the fact that for any fixed π_1, $\pi \mapsto \pi_1\pi$ is a bijection of Σ_n to itself, that

$$\sigma_\pi S_n = S_n, \qquad \sigma_\pi A_n = (-1)^\pi A_n \tag{3.8.29}$$

so $\mathrm{Ran}(S_n) \subset \mathcal{S}^n(\mathcal{H})$ (respectively, $\mathrm{Ran}(A_n) \subset \wedge^n(\mathcal{H})$). Conversely, if $\sigma_\pi(\ell) = \ell$ (respectively, $\sigma_\pi(\ell) = (-1)^\pi \ell$), then clearly, $S_n(\ell) = \ell$ (respectively, $A_n(\ell) = \ell$). Thus, $\mathrm{Ran}(S_n) = \mathcal{S}^n(\mathcal{H})$ (respectively, $\mathrm{Ran}(A_n) = \wedge^n(\mathcal{H})$).

(b) (3.8.23) and (3.8.18) imply

$$(\otimes^n A)\sigma_\pi = \sigma_\pi(\otimes^n A) \tag{3.8.30}$$

which implies

$$S_n(\otimes^n A) = (\otimes^n A)S_n, \qquad A_n(\otimes^n A) = (\otimes^n A)A_n \tag{3.8.31}$$

By (a), this implies $\otimes^n A$ leaves $\mathcal{S}^n(\mathcal{H})$ and $\wedge^n(\mathcal{H})$ invariant. $\qquad\square$

By (3.8.19), we have

$$\wedge^n(AB) = \wedge^n(A) \wedge^n(B), \qquad S^n(AB) = S^n(A)S^n(B) \tag{3.8.32}$$

Given $\varphi_1, \ldots, \varphi_n \in \mathcal{H}$, we'll define

$$\varphi_1 \wedge \cdots \wedge \varphi_n = \sqrt{n!}\, A_n(\varphi_1 \otimes \cdots \otimes \varphi_n) \tag{3.8.33}$$

We put in $\sqrt{n!}$, so we have

Proposition 3.8.5. (a) *If $\varphi_1, \ldots, \varphi_n$ are an orthonormal family, then $\|\varphi_1 \wedge \cdots \wedge \varphi_n\| = 1$.*

(b) *More generally,*

$$\langle \varphi_1 \wedge \cdots \wedge \varphi_n, \psi_1 \wedge \cdots \wedge \psi_n \rangle = \det(\langle \varphi_i, \psi_j \rangle) \tag{3.8.34}$$

Proof. Since orthonormal families have $\langle \varphi_i, \varphi_j \rangle$ as the unit matrix, (b) implies (a). By the $\sqrt{n!}$,

$$\langle \varphi_1 \wedge \cdots \wedge \varphi_n, \psi_1 \wedge \cdots \wedge \psi_n \rangle$$
$$= \frac{1}{n!} \sum_{\pi_1,\pi_2 \in \Sigma_n} (-1)^{\pi_1}(-1)^{\pi_2} \langle \sigma_{\pi_1}(\varphi_1 \otimes \cdots \otimes \varphi_n), \sigma_{\pi_2}(\psi_1 \otimes \cdots \otimes \psi_n) \rangle$$

$$\tag{3.8.35}$$

$$= \sum_{\pi}(-1)^{\pi}\langle \varphi_1 \otimes \cdots \otimes \varphi_n, \sigma_{\pi}(\psi_1 \otimes \cdots \otimes \psi_n)\rangle \qquad (3.8.36)$$

$$= \sum_{\pi}(-1)^{\pi}\langle \varphi_1, \psi_{\pi(1)}\rangle \cdots \langle \varphi_n, \psi_{\pi(n)}\rangle \qquad (3.8.37)$$

$$= \det(\langle \varphi_i, \psi_j\rangle)$$

(3.8.36) uses $\sigma_{\pi_1}^* \sigma_{\pi_2} = \sigma_{\pi_1^{-1}\pi_2}$, $(-1)^{\pi_1}(-1)^{\pi_2} = (-1)^{\pi_1^{-1}\pi_2}$, and that as π_1, π_2 run through Σ_n, $\pi = \pi_1^{-1}\pi_2$ in $n!$ ways. $\qquad \square$

Theorem 3.8.6. *Let $\{\varphi_j\}_{j=1}^J$ be an orthonormal basis for $\mathcal{H}$. If $J \geq n$, $\{\varphi_{j_1} \wedge \cdots \wedge \varphi_{j_n} \mid 1 \leq j_1 < j_2 < \cdots < j_n \leq J\}$ is an orthonormal basis for $\wedge^n(\mathcal{H})$.*

Proof. By (3.8.34), the set we claim is a basis is orthornormal. Since $\{\varphi_{j_1} \otimes \cdots \otimes \varphi_{j_n}\}_{j_1,j_2,\dots,j_n}$ is a basis for $\otimes^n \mathcal{H}$, $\{A_n(\varphi_{j_1} \otimes \cdots \varphi_{j_n}\}_{j,\dots,j_n}$ span $\wedge^n(\mathcal{H})$. If $j_1 = j_2$ and $\pi = (12)$, the permutation that interchanges 1 and 2,

$$\sigma_{\pi} A_n(\varphi_{j_1} \otimes \varphi_{j_2} \otimes \dots) = A_n(\varphi_{j_1} \otimes \cdots \otimes \varphi_{j_n}) = -A_n(\varphi_{j_1} \otimes \cdots \otimes \varphi_{j_n})$$

so $A_n(\varphi_{j_1} \otimes \cdots \otimes \varphi_{j_n}) = 0$. It follows that $A_n(\varphi_{j_1} \otimes \cdots \otimes \varphi_{j_n}) = 0$ if any two j's are equal. If $j_1, \dots, j_n$ are distinct, there is a unique π with $j_{\pi(1)} < j_{\pi(2)} < \cdots < j_{\pi(n)}$ and $A_n(\varphi_{j_1} \otimes \cdots \otimes \varphi_{j_n}) = (-1)^{\pi}\eta$, where η is our claimed O.N. set. Thus, the O.N. set spans $\wedge^n(\mathcal{H})$. $\qquad \square$

In Problem 9, the reader will consider the analogs for $\mathcal{S}^n(\mathcal{H})$.

In case $J = \dim(\mathcal{H}) < \infty$, we see $\wedge^J(\mathcal{H})$ is one-dimensional (and $\wedge^\ell(\mathcal{H}) = 0$ if $\ell > J$ and has dimension $\binom{J}{\ell}$ if $\ell \leq J$). Thus, $\wedge^J(A)$ is a number called $\det(A)$ which is given by

$$\langle \varphi_1 \wedge \cdots \wedge \varphi_J, \wedge^J(A)(\varphi_1 \wedge \cdots \wedge \varphi_J)\rangle = \sum_{\pi \in \Sigma_J}(-1)^{\pi} a_{1\pi(1)}\dots a_{J\pi(J)} \quad (3.8.38)$$

where $a_{ij} = \langle \varphi_i, A\varphi_j\rangle$. By (3.8.32),

$$\det(AB) = \det(A)\det(B) \qquad (3.8.39)$$

This is the simplest and most elegant way to prove the determinant defined by (3.8.38) obeys (3.8.39).

Notes and Historical Remarks. Tensor products of Hilbert spaces appeared first in a 1936 paper of Murray and von Neumann [**672**]. They used the name "direct product." "Tensor products" in an algebraic context was introduced by Whitney [**989**] and the name was later used in the infinite-dimensional case.

Tensor products of Banach spaces have several natural norms. The classic papers on the subject are Schatten [**813**] and Grothendieck [**373**]. See Trèves [**932**] for a monograph discussion of the subject.

Problems

1. Prove (3.8.1).

2. Let $\{\varphi_1^{(n)}\}_{n=1}^\infty$ and $\{\psi_2^{(n)}\}_{n=1}^\infty$ be sequences in Hilbert spaces $\mathcal{H}_1$ and $\mathcal{H}_2$. Prove that $(\varphi_1^{(n)}, \psi_2^{(n)})$ is Cauchy in $\mathcal{H}_1 \otimes \mathcal{H}_2$ if and only if $\varphi_1^{(n)}$ is Cauchy in $\mathcal{H}_1$ and $\psi_2^{(n)}$ is Cauchy in $\mathcal{H}_2$.

3. If $\{\varphi_1^{(j)}\}_{j=1}^{J_1}$ is an O.N. basis for $\mathcal{H}_1$ and $\{\psi_2^{(j)}\}_{j=1}^{J_2}$ is an O.N. basis for $\mathcal{H}_2$, prove that $\{\varphi_1^{(j)} \oplus 0\}_{j=1}^{J_1} \cup \{0 \oplus \psi_2^{(j)}\}_{j=1}^{J_2}$ is an O.N. basis for $\mathcal{H}_1 \oplus \mathcal{H}_2$.

4. Prove (3.8.4).

5. (a) If $\|A\varphi\| \geq \|A\| - \varepsilon$ and $\|B\psi\| \geq \|B\| - \varepsilon$, prove that $\|A \otimes B\|(\varphi \otimes \psi) \geq (\|A\| - \varepsilon)(\|B\| - \varepsilon)$.

   (b) Prove (3.8.17).

6. Prove (3.8.22).

7. Prove σ_π is a unitary map of $\mathcal{H}\widehat{\otimes}\cdots\widehat{\otimes}\mathcal{H}$ and so extends to a unitary map of $\otimes^n \mathcal{H}$ to itself.

8. Let n, ℓ be given. Let $k_1, k_2, \ldots, k_n$ obey

$$k_j \in \{0, \ldots, \ell\}, \qquad k_1 + k_2 + \cdots + k_n = \ell \tag{3.8.40}$$

   (a) If $(\otimes^{k_1}\varphi_1) \otimes (\otimes^{k_2}\varphi_2) \otimes \cdots \otimes (\otimes^{k_n}\varphi_n) \equiv e$ means the ℓ-fold tensor product of φ_j, k_j and $\{\varphi_j\}_{j=1}^n$ is orthonormal, compute $\|S_\ell(e)\|$.

   (b) Let $N(n, \ell)$ be the number of distinct solutions of (3.8.40). Prove $\dim(\mathcal{S}^\ell(\mathbb{C}^n)) = N(n, \ell)$.

   (c) Prove that $N(n, \ell) = \binom{\ell+n-1}{n-1}$. (*Hint*: Put down the numbers from 1 to $\ell + n - 1$ and pick $\ell - 1$ as dividers. What's left are ℓ sets of size between 0 and n so that the total size of these ℓ sets is n.)

9. This will prove for n arbitrary vectors that

$$\|\varphi_1 \wedge \cdots \wedge \varphi_n\| \leq \|\varphi_1\|\|\varphi_2\| \ldots \|\varphi_n\| \tag{3.8.41}$$

   (a) Let $\psi_1, \ldots, \psi_n$ be the result of unnormalized Gram–Schmidt, that is, if P_j is the projection onto the orthogonal complement of $\{\varphi_1, \ldots, \varphi_j\}$, then $\psi_j = P_{j-1}\varphi_j$. Prove that $\varphi_1 \wedge \cdots \wedge \varphi_n = \psi_1 \wedge \cdots \wedge \psi_n$.

   (b) Show that $\|\psi_1 \wedge \cdots \wedge \psi_n\| = \|\psi_1\| \ldots \|\psi_n\|$.

   (c) Prove (3.8.41).

Chapter 4

Measure Theory

There is a conundrum in mathematical analysis similar to the chicken-or-egg question: Which comes first, the Lebesgue integral or the Lebesgue measure? My answer is: Neither; first comes the space L^1.

—*Peter Lax* [**553**]

Big Notions and Theorems: Riemann Integral, Riemann–Stieltjes Integral, Functions of Bounded Variation, Finitely Additive Set Functions and Induced Integrals on $C(X)$, The Cantor Set, A Cantor Set, Cantor Function, Alexandroff–Hausdorff Theorem, Vitali Set, Banach–Steinhaus Paradox, σ-Algebra, Measurable Functions, Borel Sets, Baire Sets, L^1, Riesz–Fischer Theorem, Monotone Convergence Theorem, Negligible Sets, Baire Measures, Riesz–Markov Theorem, Regularity of Baire Measures, Regular Borel Measures, Fatou's Lemma, Dominated Convergence Theorem, Brézis–Lieb Theorem, Scheffé's Lemma, L^p Spaces, Minkowski Inequality, Hölder's Inequality, Littlewood's Three Principles, Egorov's Theorem, Lusin's Theorem, Absolutely Continuous Measure, Mutually Singular Measures, Lebesgue Decomposition Theorem, Radon–Nikodym Theorem, Riesz Spaces, Banach Lattices, Duality Theory for Banach Lattices, Signed Measures, Complex Measures, Jordan Decomposition Theorem, Hahn Decomposition Theorem, Duality for L^p, Dunford–Pettis Theorem, Measures on Locally Compact Spaces, Product Measures, Fubini's Theorem, Infinite Product Spaces, Kakutani Dichotomy, Cantor Measure, Weak Law of Large Numbers, Bounded Variation as Difference of Monotone, Derivatives of Monotone Functions, Banach Indicatrix Theorem, Hausdorff Moment Problem, Stieltjes Moment Problem, Hamburger Moment Problem, Brownian Motion, General Measure Sapce, Polish Space, Portmanteau Theorem, Tight Measures, Regularity of Probability Measures on Polish Spaces, Prokhorov's Theorem, Pettis Integral, Bochner Mesurable, Pettis' Theorem, Bochner's Integrability Theorem, Haar Measure, Modular Function, Existence and Uniqueness of Haar Measure

Perhaps the most intractable problem in nineteenth-century analysis was determining the proper theory of integration for discontinuous functions (an issue we discuss further in the Notes to Sections 4.2 and 4.4). The Riemann integral which, by using Riemann sums, divided up the domain of f had too many problems. Lebesgue's great discovery at the start of the twentieth century relied instead on dividing up the range. The usual presentations of measure theory at least implicitly follow Lebesgue's path. Instead, in this chapter, fleshing out ideas of Peter Lax [**553**], we'll present an almost magical approach that, to a functional analyst, is exceedingly natural and beautiful although, as we explained in the Preface, likely to be controversial.

This approach appears in Sections 4.4 and 4.5, the central sections of the chapter. In the case of Lebesgue measure (we'll be much more general), one looks at $C([0,1])$ with the metric

$$\rho(f,g) = \int_0^1 |f(x) - g(x)|\, dx \qquad (4.0.1)$$

and completes this metric space—the completion is $L^1([0,1], dx)$. One shows elements of this space can be viewed as functions or, more precisely, as equivalence classes of functions equal "almost everywhere." If $f \geq 0$, $\rho(f,0)$ will be used to *define* $\int_0^1 f(x)\, dx$, so defining the Lebesgue integral. Recognizing that the characteristic functions of many sets lie in L^1, we define Lebesgue measure. Section 4.5 will show that this construction sets up a one-one correspondence between positive linear functionals on $C([0,1])$ (or, more generally, $C(X)$ for any compact Hausdorff space) and all positive Baire measures on X—this is the Riesz–Markov Theorem. This approach makes this theorem the centerpiece of measure theory, rather than an afterthought.

We'll require some preliminaries. We need to define the $\int_0^1$ appearing for continuous functions in (4.0.1). This and the more general Riemann–Stieltjes integral appear in Section 4.1. Section 4.2 discusses an important example of a Riemann—Stieltjes integral: the integral associated to the Cantor function. In the Notes to Section 4.2, we'll see that a variant of the Cantor set construction, due to Volterra, provides a continuous function, f, on $[0,1]$ so that f has a derivative (albeit, not continuous) everywhere, f', so that f' is not Riemann integrable. Therefore we can't form the integral to get $f(x) = f(0) + \int_0^x f'(y)\, dy$ (!). But we'll see in Problem 8 of Section 4.4 that f' is Lebesgue integrable, and thereby restore the fundamental theorem of calculus. Section 4.3 shows that not all sets are going to have a Lebesgue measure and shows the way to overcome this difficulty.

With the fundamentals in place in Sections 4.1–4.5, we turn to detailed properties of measures and integration in the next four sections: convergence and approximation theorems in Section 4.6, the Lebesgue decomposition and Radon–Nikodym theorems in Section 4.7, the Jordan and Hahn decomposition theorems in Section 4.8, and duality theory for L^p in Section 4.9. In particular, Section 4.8 studies the set of measures as a lattice by developing the theory of dual spaces of Banach lattices.

Sections 4.10–4.19 discuss extensions of measure theory to locally compact spaces and to product spaces and the integration of Banach space-valued functions. Section 4.15 returns to the study of functions of bounded variation begun in Section 4.1—we use the tools of measure theory to analyze such functions. Four bonus sections end the chapter.

While the central measure theory we present (starting in Section 4.4) is Baire measures on compact spaces, many alternative measure theories appear later: measures on σ-compact spaces in Section 4.10 and on Polish spaces in Section 4.14. Abstract measures and the associated construction of integrals is in Section 4.13 while Section 8.1 discusses the Carathéodory outer measure approach to construction of measures.

Notes and Historical Remarks. Our development of measure theory in this chapter for general compact spaces, rather than only compact metric spaces, is inconsistent with our normal attitude that the only interesting spaces are separable. If X is a compact Hausdorff space and μ a Baire measure with $\mu(A) > 0$ for all open Baire sets A, then $L^p(X, d\mu)$ ($1 \le p < \infty$) is separable if and only if X is second countable, and that happens (see Theorem 2.3.7) if and only if X is metrizable. Our reason for doing this is mainly to show that the Lax approach applies even in the nonmetrizable case so long as one distinguished between Baire and Borel sets.

There is, however, one resulting awkwardness in these inconsistent attitudes. In proving the Radon–Nikodym and Lebesgue decomposition theorems, we'll exploit the Riesz representation theorem (that describes the dual of a Hilbert space) but, given that we require Hilbert spaces to be separable, $L^2(X, d\mu)$ is, in general, only separable if X is metrizable. One can prove the Riesz representation theorem for the nonseparable case (by the same proof we used!) and apply it or else restrict Theorem 4.7.6 to the metrizable case.

4.1. Riemann–Stieltjes Integrals

Here we want to construct Stieltjes integrals on continuous functions by a modification of the standard construction of the Riemann integral. We'll show the procedure is so flexible that it allows constructions of integrals on continuous functions on arbitrary compact Hausdorff spaces. We begin by recalling the procedure for ordinary Riemann integrals via limits of Riemann sums—we'll provide an alternate construction in Problem 1.

Theorem 4.1.1. Let $f \in C([0,1])$. Define

$$R_n(f) = \sum_{j=0}^{n-1} f\left(\frac{j}{n}\right)\frac{1}{n} \tag{4.1.1}$$

Then for any $n < m$,

$$|R_n(f) - R_m(f)| \leq 2\Big[\sup_{|x-y|\leq 1/n} |f(x) - f(y)|\Big] \qquad (4.1.2)$$

In particular, for any such f,

$$\int_0^1 f(x)\, dx \equiv \lim_{n\to\infty} R_n(f) \qquad (4.1.3)$$

exists.

Proof. The final statement follows from uniform continuity of f (see Theorem 2.3.10). (4.1.2) follows from

$$|R_n(f) - R_{nm}(f)| \leq \sup_{|x-y|\leq 1/n} |f(x) - f(y)| \qquad (4.1.4)$$

and this is immediate from

$$R_{nm}(f) - R_n(f) = \sum_{j=0}^{n-1} \frac{1}{nm} \sum_{k=0}^{m-1} \Big[f\Big(\frac{j}{n} + \frac{k}{nm}\Big) - f\Big(\frac{j}{n}\Big) \Big] \qquad (4.1.5)$$

$\square$

There are a number of simple extensions of this argument:

(1) If $\{x_j^{(n)}\}_{j=0}^{n-1}$ is a set of points with $x_j^{(n)} \in [\frac{j}{n}, \frac{j+1}{n}]$ and

$$R_n(f; \{x_j^{(n)}\})_{j=0}^{n-1} = \sum_{j=0}^{n-1} f(x_j^{(n)}) \frac{1}{n} \qquad (4.1.6)$$

then

$$|R_n(f; \{x_j^{(n)}\})_{j=0}^{n-1} - R_n(f)| \leq \sup_{|x-y|\leq 1/n} |f(x) - f(y)| \qquad (4.1.7)$$

so for any choice of $\{x_j^{(n)}\}_{j=0, n=1,2,\dots}^{n-1}$,

$$\lim_{n\to\infty} R_n(f; \{x_j^{(n)}\}_{j=0}^{n-1}) = \int_0^1 f(x)\, dx \qquad (4.1.8)$$

(2) A partition of $[0,1]$ is $\{p_j\}_{j=0}^n$ with $0 = p_0 < p_1 < \cdots < p_n = 1$ with $\#(p) \equiv n$ and $\Delta(p) = \sup_{j=1,\dots,n} |p_j - p_{j-1}|$. Define

$$\tilde{R}_n(f; p) = \sum_{j=0}^{n-1} (p_{j+1} - p_j) f(p_j) \qquad (4.1.9)$$

Then an easy estimate (Problem 4) shows that

$$\Big| \tilde{R}_n(f; p) - \int_0^1 f(x)\, dx \Big| \leq \sup_{|x-y|\leq \Delta(p)} |f(x) - f(y)| \qquad (4.1.10)$$

so that for any choice of $p^{(n)}$ with $\#(p^{(n)}) = n$ and $\Delta(p^{(n)}) \to 0$, we have

$$\lim_{n\to\infty} R_n(f;p) = \int_0^1 f(x)\,dx \qquad (4.1.11)$$

(3) Most importantly for our purposes, we can replace dx by a more general object. Suppose α is a monotone function from $[0,1]$ to $\mathbb{R}$ (so, in particular, $\alpha(0), \alpha(1)$ are finite, so $\alpha(1) - \alpha(0)$ is). Define

$$R_n^\sharp(f;\alpha) = \sum_{j=0}^{n-1} f\left(\frac{j}{n}\right)\left[\alpha\left(\frac{j+1}{n}\right) - \alpha\left(\frac{j}{n}\right)\right] \qquad (4.1.12)$$

Then by the same argument that led to (4.1.2) for $n < m$,

$$|R_n^\sharp(f;\alpha) - R_m^\sharp(f;\alpha)| \le 2[\alpha(1) - \alpha(0)] \sup_{|x-y|\le 1/n} |f(x) - f(y)|$$

so that

$$\int_0^1 f(x)\,d\alpha \equiv \lim_{n\to\infty} R_n^\sharp(f;\alpha) \qquad (4.1.13)$$

called the *Riemann–Stieltjes integral*, exists. As in (1) and (2), we can change the points at which f is evaluated or the partition.

(4) Given a partition, p, and a function, α, on $[0,1]$, define

$$V_p(\alpha) = \sum_{j=1}^{n} |\alpha(p_j) - \alpha(p_{j-1})| \qquad (4.1.14)$$

Then one can still define $R_n^\sharp(f;\alpha)$ by (4.1.12), and the argument that led to (4.1.5) implies

$$|R_n^\sharp(f;\alpha) - R_{nm}^\sharp(f;\alpha)| \le V_{p_{nm}}(\alpha) \sup_{|x-y|\le n^{-1}} |f(x) - f(y)| \qquad (4.1.15)$$

where p_{nm} is the partition with $\#(p_{nm}) = nm$ and $p_j - p_{j-1} = 1/nm$.

This suggests we single out functions, α, called functions of *bounded variation*, that obey

$$\sup_p V_p(\alpha) \equiv \mathrm{Var}(\alpha) < \infty \qquad (4.1.16)$$

For any such function, we can form a Riemann–Stieltjes integral by (4.1.13) which obeys

$$\left|\int_0^1 f(x)\,d\alpha\right| \le \|f\|_\infty \mathrm{Var}(\alpha) \qquad (4.1.17)$$

Once we have have measure theory under our belts, we'll be able to say a lot about functions of bounded variation (see Section 4.15), for example, every such function is a difference of monotone increasing functions.

Example 4.1.2. Let $x_0 \in (0,1)$ and $a < c < b$. Let α be the monotone function that is

$$\alpha(x) = \begin{cases} a, & x < x_0 \\ c, & x = x_0 \\ b, & x > x_0 \end{cases} \tag{4.1.18}$$

It is easy to see that, independently of c for any continuous function, f, we have

$$\int f \, d\alpha = (b-a)f(x_0) \tag{4.1.19}$$

More generally (Problem 5), for any monotone α, we have for all but countably many $\{x_n\}_{n=1}^N$ that α is continuous at x. We set $k_n = \lim_{\varepsilon \downarrow 0} \alpha(x_n + \varepsilon) - \alpha(x_n - \varepsilon)$. We can write

$$\alpha = \alpha_{\text{cont}} + \alpha_{\text{pp}} \tag{4.1.20}$$

where α_{cont} is monotone and continuous and

$$\int f \, d\alpha_{\text{pp}} = \sum_{n=1}^N k_n f(x_n) \tag{4.1.21}$$

$\square$

Example 4.1.3. If α is a C^1 monotone function, it is easy to see (Problem 6) that

$$\int_0^1 f(x) \, d\alpha(x) = \int_0^1 f(x)\alpha'(x) \, dx \tag{4.1.22}$$

where the right side is a standard Riemann integral. This suggests the following, which is easy to see: if α and β are continuous monotone functions on $[0,1]$, then

$$\int_0^1 \alpha \, d\beta + \int_0^1 \beta \, d\alpha = \alpha(1)\beta(1) - \alpha(0)\beta(0) \tag{4.1.23}$$

(see Problem 3 of Section 4.15). $\square$

Finally, we turn to general compact sets. The key will be to find a suitable notion of partition that allows refinement and into finer partitions.

Definition. An *algebra* of sets in a "space," X, is a family, $\mathfrak{A}$, of subsets of X so that $A, B \in \mathfrak{A} \Rightarrow A \cup B$, $A \cap B$, and $X \setminus A$ are in $\mathfrak{A}$.

The reason for the name is made clear by Problem 7.

Definition. Given an algebra, $\mathfrak{A}$, a *partition* associated to $\mathfrak{A}$, is a finite subset $\mathcal{P} \subset \mathfrak{A}$ so that

(i) All sets in $\mathcal{P}$ are nonempty
(ii) $P_1, P_2 \in \mathcal{P} \Rightarrow P_1 \cap P_2 = \emptyset$
(iii) $\bigcup_{P \in \mathcal{P}} P = X$

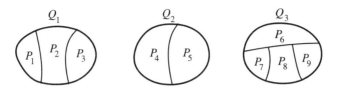

Figure 4.1.1. Refinement of a partition.

We say one partition $\mathcal{P}_1$ is a *refinement* of $\mathcal{P}_2$, another partition, if $\forall P \in \mathcal{P}_1$, $\exists Q \in \mathcal{P}_2$, so $P \subset Q$.

Thus, if $\mathcal{P}_1$ is a refinement of $\mathcal{P}_2$, each Q in $\mathcal{P}_2$ is a finite union of sets in $\mathcal{P}_1$ (see Figure 4.1.1). If $\mathcal{P}_1$ and $\mathcal{P}_2$ are partitions, we define $\mathcal{P}_1 \triangle \mathcal{P}_2 = \{P \cap Q \mid P \in \mathcal{P}_1, Q \in \mathcal{P}_2, P \cap Q \neq \emptyset\}$. This is a common refinement of $\mathcal{P}_1$ and $\mathcal{P}_2$. Given any finite family $\mathfrak{A}_1 \subset \mathfrak{A}$, we can form all nonempty intersections of the sets in $\mathfrak{A}_1$ and their complements, and keep the minimal elements in this collection and get a partition $\mathcal{P}$ with two properties (Problem 8):

(1) Any $A \in \mathfrak{A}_1$ is a finite union of sets in $\mathcal{P}$.
(2) Any $\mathcal{P}_1$ that obeys (a) is a refinement of $\mathcal{P}$.

Given a cover, $\mathcal{U}$, of X, a partition, P, is called *subordinate* to $\mathcal{U}$ if every $P \in \mathcal{P}$ lies in some element of $\mathcal{U}$.

Definition. Given an algebra, $\mathfrak{A}$, of sets, a *finitely additive set function* on $\mathfrak{A}$ is a function $\alpha \colon \mathfrak{A} \to [0, \infty)$ so that if $A_1, A_2 \in \mathfrak{A}$ and $A_1 \cap A_2 = \emptyset$, then $\alpha(A_1 \cup A_2) = \alpha(A_1) + \alpha(A_2)$.

Thus, if $\mathcal{P}$ is a partition,

$$\sum_{P \in \mathcal{P}} \alpha(P) = \alpha(X) \tag{4.1.24}$$

Given a finitely additive set function, α, on an algebra, $\mathfrak{A}$, and function $f \colon X \to \mathbb{R}$, any partition, $\mathcal{P} = \{P_1, \ldots, P_\ell\}$, and choice of $x_j \in P_j$, we define

$$R_\mathcal{P}(f; \alpha, \{x_j\}_{j=1}^\ell) = \sum_{j=1}^\ell f(x_j)\alpha(P_j) \tag{4.1.25}$$

the Riemann sum associated to α.

Now let X be a compact Hausdorff space. We say an algebra, $\mathfrak{A}$, has *arbitrarily fine refinements* if for any open cover $\mathcal{U}$ of X, there is a partition, P, associated to $\mathfrak{A}$ and subordinate to $\mathcal{U}$.

Example 4.1.4. Let X be a compact Hausdorff space. Let $\mathfrak{A}$ consist of all finite unions $\bigcup_{j=1}^\ell U_j \cap A_j$, where U_j is open and A_j is closed. This is an algebra with arbitrarily fine refinements (Problem 9). $\qquad\square$

Example 4.1.5. In $[0,1]$, let $\mathfrak{A}$ consist of all finite unions of sets of the form $[c,d)$ where c,d are rational, or $[c,1]$ where c is rational. $\mathfrak{A}$ is an algebra with arbitrarily fine refinements (Problem 10). $\qquad\square$

Here is an abstraction of Riemann–Stieltjes integrals.

Theorem 4.1.6. *Let X be a compact Hausdorff space, $\mathfrak{A}$, an algebra with arbitrarily fine refinements, and α a finitely additive set function. For each partition, $\mathcal{P} = \{P_1, \ldots, P_\ell\}$ associated to $\mathfrak{A}$, make a choice $(x_1^{(\mathcal{P})}, \ldots, x_\ell^{(\mathcal{P})})$ of points $x_j^{(\mathcal{P})} \in P_j$. Then the set of partitions, $\mathbb{P}$, ordered by $\mathcal{P}_1 > \mathcal{P}_2$ if $\mathcal{P}_1$ is a refinement of $\mathcal{P}_2$, is a directed set, and for each $f \in C(X)$, the net $\mathcal{P} \to R_\mathcal{P}(f; \alpha, \{x_j^{(\mathcal{P})}\}_{j=1}^\ell)$ has a limit $\int f\, d\alpha$ independent of the choices of $\{x_j^{(\mathcal{P})}\}$ which obeys*

(a) $$\int (\lambda f + g)\, d\alpha = \lambda \int f\, d\alpha + \int g\, d\alpha \qquad (4.1.26)$$

> *for all $f, g \in C(X)$ and $\lambda \in \mathbb{C}$*

(b) $$f \geq 0 \Rightarrow \int f\, d\alpha \geq 0 \qquad (4.1.27)$$

(c) $$\left| \int f\, d\alpha \right| \leq \|f\|_\infty\, \alpha(X) \qquad (4.1.28)$$

Proof. Since $R_\mathcal{P}$ obeys (a)–(c), it is easy to see the limit does also. Thus, we need only show that $R_\mathcal{P}$ is Cauchy and that the limit is $\{x_j\}$-independent.

Fix ε. For each $x \in X$, there is an open U_x containing x, so if $y \in U_x$, then $|f(y) - f(x)| \leq \varepsilon/2$. $\mathcal{U} = \{U_x\}_{x \in X}$ is an open cover, so find a refinement, $\mathcal{P}_\varepsilon$, associated to $\mathfrak{A}$, subordinate to $\mathcal{U}$.

Then if $y, z \in P_1 \in \mathcal{P}_\varepsilon$, we have $|f(y) - f(x)| \leq \varepsilon$. Thus, if $\mathcal{P}$ is a refinement of $\mathcal{P}_\varepsilon$, for any two choices of $\{x_j^{(\mathcal{P})}\}$, say $\{x_j^{(\mathcal{P})}\}$ and $\{y_j^{(\mathcal{P})}\}$, we have

$$|R_\mathcal{P}(f; \alpha, \{x_j^{(\mathcal{P})}\}) - R_\mathcal{P}(f; \alpha, \{y_j^{(\mathcal{P})}\})| \leq \varepsilon\, \alpha(X) \qquad (4.1.29)$$

and

$$|R_\mathcal{P}(f; \alpha, \{x_j^{(\mathcal{P})}\}) - R_{\mathcal{P}_\varepsilon}(f; \alpha, x_j^{(\mathcal{P}_\varepsilon)})| \leq \varepsilon\, \alpha(X) \qquad (4.1.30)$$

The second of these shows the limit exists (see Problem 3 of Section 2.6) and the first the independence of choice. $\qquad\square$

Example 4.1.7. Given a monotone function $\tilde{\alpha}$, if $\{[c_j, d_j)\}_{j=1}^\ell$ is a disjoint finite family of half-open intervals (every union can be rewritten as a disjoint union),

$$\alpha\left(\bigcup_{j=1}^\ell [c_j, d_j) \right) = \sum_{j=1}^\ell \tilde{\alpha}(d_j) - \tilde{\alpha}(c_j) \qquad (4.1.31)$$

is finitely additive, and Theorem 4.1.6 is essentially the same as Theorem 4.1.1 extended to Riemann–Stieltjes integrals. $\qquad\square$

The argument that proves $\int f(x)\,d\alpha(x)$ exists for continuous f extends without change to Banach space-valued functions—one only replaces $|\cdot|$ in (4.1.2) by $\|\cdot\|$. Thus,

Theorem 4.1.8. *Let $f\colon [0,1] \to X$, a Banach space, be continuous and let α be of bounded variation. Define $R_n(f;\alpha) \in X$ by*

$$R_n(f;\alpha) = \sum_{j=0}^{n-1} f\left(\frac{j}{n}\right)\left[\alpha\left(\frac{j+1}{n}\right) - \alpha\left(\frac{j}{n}\right)\right] \qquad (4.1.32)$$

Then for any $n < m$, we have

$$\|R_n(f;\alpha) - R_m(f;\alpha)\| \leq 2\operatorname{Var}(\alpha)\sup_{|x-y|\leq\frac{1}{n}} \|f(x) - f(y)\|$$

In particular, for any such f, $\int_0^1 f(x)\,dx \equiv \lim_{n\to\infty} R_n(f)$ exists.

Notes and Historical Remarks. It was Cauchy who first realized that it was necessary to actually prove integrals exist, and in 1823 [**170**], he essentially proved Theorem 4.1.1 (although he wasn't clear on the notion of uniform continuity). In 1854, Riemann [**772**], in consideration of not necessarily continuous functions, realized the significance of being able to change which points are used within the intervals. Bressoud [**129**] discusses the history of the nineteenth-century developments in connection with extending Riemann's idea to not continuous functions, an issue we return to in the Notes to Section 4.4.

In his work on the moment problem, Stieltjes [**881**] defined the Riemann–Stieltjes integral. As we discuss in the Notes to Section 3.5, Jordan [**455**] first defined functions of bounded variation in connection with work on convergence of Fourier series—it was later tailor-made for defining Riemann–Stieltjes integrals for nonmonotone functions, a step taken by F. Riesz [**779**].

Thomas Jan Stieltjes (1856–94) was a Dutch mathematician whose father was a famous engineer known for his work on Rotterdam's harbor. Despite his interest in mathematics, he was trained as an astronomer, and becoming active in mathematics was difficult. Without question, the most important influence on his mathematics was his correspondence with Charles Hermite (1822–1901) of over four hundred letters, starting in 1882 and ending twelve years later with Stieltjes' untimely death at age only 38. He had problems getting a position in mathematics, smoothed over by his getting an honorary degree under Hermite's influence. He spent the last eight years of his life as a professor in Toulouse. If one notes that Picard, Hermite's student and son-in-law also spent time in Toulouse, it is natural to assume that Hermite played a role in this.

Stieltjes would have warranted at most a minor footnote, except for the masterpiece [881], in which the introduction of Stieltjes integrals was a small part. The key developments of that paper were convergence of continued fractions and the related issue of the moment problem. We'll return to these in Sections 4.17 and 5.6 of this Part, Section 7.5 of Part 2A and Section 7.7 of Part 4.

As we'll see in Problem 2, there is no problem extending Riemann-Stieltjes integrals to situations where α is a finite-dimensional (real) vector-valued function, say $\alpha \in \mathbb{R}^\nu$. Then $\alpha\colon [0,1] \to \mathbb{R}^\nu$ is a curve and α's of bounded variation obeying

$$\sup_{0=t_0<t_1<\cdots<t_{n-1}<t_n=1} \sum_{j=1}^n |\alpha(t_j) - \alpha(t_{j-1})| < \infty \qquad (4.1.33)$$

are called *rectifiable*. If the vector space is an algebra (i.e., there are products with a distributive law, e.g., $\mathbb{C}$), one can even form $\int f(t)\, d\alpha(t)$, where both f and α take values in the vector space. For example, this is how we'll define contour integrals in Section 2.2 of Part 2A. One can also study the case where α takes values in a Banach space (Problem 3), although the norm convergence required there is sometimes too much, and for operator-valued α's, one often wants only weak convergence.

While this chapter is on integration and we are assuming familiarity with the differential calculus, we'd be remiss if we defined the Riemann integral and didn't mention the connection to the antiderivative. The fundamental theorem of calculus has two forms. They rely on the ability to define $\int_a^b f\, dx$, not just $\int_0^1 f(x)\, dx$.

Theorem 4.1.9 (Fundamental Theorem of Calculus, First Form). *Let*

$$F(x) = \int_0^x f(y)\, dy \qquad (4.1.34)$$

for a continuous function f on $[0,1]$. Then F is C^1 and $F' = f$.

Theorem 4.1.10 (Fundamental Theorem of Calculus, Second Form). *Let F be a continuous function on $[0,1]$, C^1 on $(0,1)$ with $F(0) = 0$, and let $F' = f$. Then (4.1.34) holds.*

The first theorem implies the second if one knows

Theorem 4.1.11 (Fundamental Theorem of ODEs). *Let f be a function of $(0,1)$ which is differentiable at every point in $(0,1)$ and obeys $f'(x) = 0$ for all x. Then f is constant.*

We are used to thinking of this as trivial since

$$f(b) - f(a) = \int_a^b f'(x)\, dx \tag{4.1.35}$$

but that argument won't work since we want to use this theorem to prove (4.1.35). The argument is surprisingly subtle and given in Problem 12. Theorems 4.1.9 and 4.1.10 are proven in Problems 11 and 13, respectively. We'll return to issues that illuminate the fundamental theorem of calculus when f is not continuous or F is not differentiable at all x in Problem 8 of Section 4.4.

Problems

1. A function, f, on $[0,1]$ is called piecewise constant if there is $y_0 \equiv 0 < y_1 < \cdots < y_{n-1} < y_n = 1$ so f is constant on each interval (y_{j-1}, y_j), $j = 1, \ldots, n$. $PC([0,1])$ is the space of all piecewise constant functions on $[0,1]$. $B_\infty([0,1])$ is the space of all bounded functions on $[0,1]$ with $\|f\|_\infty = \sup_{x \in [0,1]} |f(x)|$ (huge since f is not restricted to be continuous or even measurable).

   (a) Prove that $C(X) \subset \overline{PC([0,1])}$, closure in B_∞ in the $\|\cdot\|_\infty$.

   (b) If α is of bounded variation and $f \in PC([0,1])$ is constant on each (y_{j-1}, y_j) with $0 = y_0 < y_1 < \cdots < y_n = 1$, define

   $$L_\alpha(f) = \sum_{j=1}^n f\left(\frac{y_{j-1} + y_j}{2}\right)[\alpha(y_j) - \alpha(y_{j-1})] \tag{4.1.36}$$

   Prove that $PC([0,1])$ is a vector space, L_α is linear, and

   $$|L_\alpha(f)| \le \|f\|_\infty \mathrm{Var}(\alpha) \tag{4.1.37}$$

   (c) By (4.1.37) and general principles, L_α has a unique continuation to $\overline{PC([0,1])}$ obeying (4.1.37). This defines $L_\alpha(f)$ on $C(X)$. Prove that it is the same as $\int_0^1 f\, d\alpha$.

2. Show that either the proof of Theorem 4.1.1 in the text or the proof in Problem 1 extends to the case where α takes values in $\mathbb{R}^\nu$. If $\mathbb{R}^\nu$ has a distributive and associative jointly continuous product, show that one can define $\int_0^1 f(s)\, d\alpha(s)$ when f is also $\mathbb{R}^\nu$-valued.

3. Show that either the proof of Theorem 4.1.1 in the text or the proof in Problem 1 extends to the case where f takes values in $\mathbb{R}$ (or $\mathbb{C}$) and α takes values in a Banach space over $\mathbb{R}$ (or $\mathbb{C}$), where bounded variation means

   $$\sup_{0 = t_0 < \cdots < t_{n-1} < t_n = 1} \sum_{j=0}^n \|\alpha(t_j) - \alpha(t_{j-1})\| < \infty \tag{4.1.38}$$

4. Verify (4.1.10). (*Hint*: For any a, b and $a < x_0 < b$, prove $|\int_a^b f(x)\,dx - (b-a)f(x_0)| \leq |b-a|\sup_{x,y\in[a,b]}|f(x) - f(y)|$.)

5. Let α be monotone on $[0,1]$.

   (a) Prove that $\lim_{\varepsilon\downarrow 0}\alpha(x\pm\varepsilon) = \alpha(x\pm 0)$ exists for any x and that $\alpha(x-0) \leq \alpha(x) \leq \alpha(x+0)$.

   (b) Prove for any distinct $x_1,\ldots,x_n$ in $[0,1]$ that $\sum_{j=1}^n \alpha(x_j+0)-\alpha(x_j-0) \leq \alpha(1) - \alpha(0)$, so that

   $$\#\left(x \,\Big|\, \alpha(x+0) - \alpha(x-0) \geq \frac{\alpha(1) - \alpha(0)}{n}\right) \leq n$$

   (c) Prove that $P \equiv \{x \mid \alpha(x+0) \neq \alpha(x-0)\}$ is countable.

   (d) Define $\tilde{\alpha}_{\mathrm{pp}}(x)$ by

   $$\tilde{\alpha}_{\mathrm{pp}}(x) = \sum_{\substack{y<x\\y\in P}}[\alpha(y+0) - \alpha(y-0)]$$

   Prove $\tilde{\alpha}_{\mathrm{pp}}$ is monotone.

   (e) Define

   $$\alpha_{\mathrm{pp}}(x) = \begin{cases} \tilde{\alpha}_{\mathrm{pp}}(x) & \text{if } x \notin P \\ \alpha(x) - \alpha(x-0) + \tilde{\alpha}_{\mathrm{pp}}(x-0) & \text{if } x \in P \end{cases}$$

   Prove that α_{pp} is monotone and $\alpha - \alpha_{\mathrm{pp}}$ is continuous.

   (f) Prove that for $f \in C([0,1])$,

   $$\int f\,d\alpha_{\mathrm{pp}} = \int f\,d\tilde{\alpha}_{\mathrm{pp}} = \sum_{x\in P}[\alpha(x+0) - \alpha(x-0)]f(x)$$

6. Prove (4.1.22).

7. Let $\mathfrak{A}$ be an algebra of sets in X. For $A, B \in \mathfrak{A}$, define

   $$A + B = (A \setminus B) \cup (B \setminus A)$$
   $$A \cdot B = A \cap B$$

   (a) Prove that $+$ and $\cdot$ are associative and commutative.

   (b) Prove that $A \cdot (B + C) = A \cdot B + A \cdot C$.

   (c) Prove that $\emptyset \in \mathfrak{A}$ and $A + \emptyset = A$.

   (d) Prove that $X \in \mathfrak{A}$ and $X \cdot A = A$.

   (e) What is the additive inverse of $A \in \mathfrak{A}$?

   (f) Which A's have multiplicative inverses?

(g) Let $\mathfrak{A}$ be the set of all subsets of X. Let $\mathcal{B} = 2^X$, that is, functions from X to $\{0,1\}$ with coordinate addition and multiplication. Let $\rho\colon \mathfrak{A} \to B$ by

$$\rho(A)_x = \begin{cases} 0, & x \notin A \\ 1, & x \in A \end{cases}$$

Prove that ρ is a homeomorphism and bijection.

8. If $\mathfrak{A}$ is an algebra of sets in a space X, $\mathfrak{A}_1 \subset \mathfrak{A}$ is finite, and $\mathcal{P}$ is the set of minimal elements in nonempty intersections of $\{A \mid A \in \mathfrak{A}_1$ or $X \setminus A \in \mathfrak{A}_1\}$, prove that $\mathcal{P}$ is a partition, that any $A \in \mathfrak{A}_1$ is a union of sets in $\mathcal{P}$, and any $\mathcal{P}_1$ with this property is a refinement of $\mathcal{P}$. (*Hint*: Use induction in $\#(\mathfrak{A}_1)$.)

9. (a) Prove that if X is a compact Hausdorff space and $\mathfrak{A}$ is the family of finite unions of $U \cap A$ with U and A closed, then $\mathfrak{A}$ is an algebra. (*Hint*: $X \setminus U \cap A$ is a union of an open and closed set.)

   (b) Show that the $\mathfrak{A}$ of (a) has arbitrarily fine refinements.

10. Let $\mathfrak{A}$ consist of finite unions of the form $[c,d)$ with c,d rational or $[c,1]$ with c rational. Prove that $\mathfrak{A}$ is an algebra of sets with arbitrarily fine refinements.

11. (a) For any $x \in (a,b)$ and any monotone α on (a,b), prove that

$$\left| \int_a^b f(y)\, d\alpha(y) - f(x)[\alpha(b) - \alpha(a)] \right| \le \left[\sup_{x,y \in [a,b]} |f(x) - f(y)| \right](\alpha(b) - \alpha(a)) \tag{4.1.39}$$

   (b) Suppose α is strictly monotone on (a,b) and f is continuous there. For all $x \in (a,b)$, prove that (this includes Theorem 4.1.9)

$$\lim_{\substack{y \downarrow x \\ z \uparrow x}} \frac{1}{\alpha(y) - \alpha(z)} \int_z^y f(u)\, d\alpha(u) = f(x) \tag{4.1.40}$$

   uniformly in x on each interval $[a + \delta, b - \delta]$ with $\delta > 0$.

12. This problem will prove Theorem 4.1.11.

   (a) Let f be continuous on $[a,b]$ and suppose f' exists at $c \in [a,b]$, and for some ε, $f(c) \ge f(y)$ for all $y \in (c - \varepsilon, c + \varepsilon)$. Prove that $f'(c) = 0$.

   (b) Prove *Rolle's theorem*, that if f is continuous on $[a,b]$, C^1 on (a,b), and $f(a) = f(b)$, then for some $c \in [a,b]$, $f'(c) = 0$. (*Hint*: This is trivial if f is constant on $[a,b]$. Otherwise, show that f has a maximum or minimum in (a,b).)

(c) Prove the *mean value theorem*, that if f is continuous on $[a, b)$ and C^1 on (a, b), there exists $c \in (a, b)$ so that

$$f'(c) = \frac{f(b) - f(a)}{b - a} \qquad (4.1.41)$$

(d) Prove Theorem 4.1.11.

13. Knowing Theorems 4.1.9 and 4.1.11, prove Theorem 4.1.10.

4.2. The Cantor Set, Function, and Measure

In this section, we present a closely related set and monotone function and the Riemann–Stieltjes integral associated to the function.

In $[0, 1]$, define open sets, $U_{1,1}, U_{2,1}, U_{2,2}, U_{3,1}, \ldots, U_{n,1}, \ldots, U_{n,2^{n-1}}$, $U_{n+1,1}, \ldots$, as follows: $U_{1,1} = (\frac{1}{3}, \frac{2}{3})$, $U_{2,1} = (\frac{1}{9}, \frac{2}{9})$, $U_{2,2} = (\frac{7}{9}, \frac{8}{9}), \ldots$, $U_{n,1} = (\frac{1}{3^n}, \frac{2}{3^n}), \ldots, U_{n,2^{n-1}} = (1 - \frac{2}{3^n}, 1 - \frac{1}{3^n}), \ldots$. Thus, $\{U_{n,j}\}_{j=1}^{2^{n-1}}$ is 2^{n-1} sets of size 3^{-n} and these sets are all disjoint and of total size

$$\sum_{n=1}^{\infty} \frac{2^{n-1}}{3^n} = \frac{\frac{1}{3}}{1 - \frac{2}{3}} = 1 \qquad (4.2.1)$$

Basically, after removing $U_{1,1}, \ldots, U_{n,2^{n-1}}$, there are 2^n connected closed sets left, each of size 3^{-n}, and at stage $n + 1$, we remove the middle third of each closed interval that is left (Figure 4.2.1). If C_n is the closed set,

$$C_n = [0, 1] \setminus \bigcup_{k=1}^{n} \bigcup_{j=1}^{2^{n-1}} U_{k,j} \qquad (4.2.2)$$

then

$$|C_{n+1}| = \tfrac{2}{3} |C_n|, \qquad |C_n| = \frac{2^n}{3^n} \qquad (4.2.3)$$

Figure 4.2.1. C_n for $n = 2, 3, 4, 5$.

The *Cantor set* is defined by

$$C = \bigcap_n C_n \tag{4.2.4}$$

which by the f.i.p. of $[0,1]$ is nonempty. Naively, one might think that C only consists of the endpoints of the $U_{k,j}$, that is,

$$Q = \{\tfrac{1}{3}, \tfrac{2}{3}, \tfrac{1}{9}, \tfrac{2}{9}, \tfrac{7}{9}, \tfrac{8}{9}, \tfrac{1}{27}, \dots\} \tag{4.2.5}$$

which is a countable set. In fact, C is much bigger and is uncountable! Here is a simple way of seeing this. We consider base-three expansions. Let

$$Z = \mathop{\times}_{n=1}^{\infty} \{0,1,2\} \tag{4.2.6}$$

as a product space in the discrete topology. Map $Z \xrightarrow{f} [0,1]$ by

$$f(\{a_n\}_{n=1}^{\infty}) = \sum_{n=1}^{\infty} \frac{a_n}{3^n} \tag{4.2.7}$$

f is onto $[0,1]$ (Problem 1(a)) but it is not one-one. Indeed (Problem 1(b)), $f^{-1}(y)$ has two points if and only if $y \in Q$ (the set of (4.2.5)), and otherwise $f^{-1}(y)$ is a single point. For example,

$$\tfrac{1}{3} = f((1,0,0,\dots)) = f((0,2,2,2,\dots)) \tag{4.2.8}$$

In particular (Problem 1(c)),

$$\bigcup_{j=1}^{2^{k-1}} \overline{U}_{k,j} = \{y = f(\{a_n\}_{n=1}^{\infty}) \mid a_k = 1, a_1, \dots, a_{k-1} \in \{0,2\}\} \tag{4.2.9}$$

with the 2^{k-1} pieces coming from the 2^{k-1} choices of $a_1, \dots, a_{k-1}$ among 0 or 2. Thus (Problem 1(d)),

$$C = \{f(\{a_n\}_{n=1}^{\infty}) \mid \text{each } a_n \text{ is 0 or 2}\} \tag{4.2.10}$$

and f is a bijection of $\times_{n=1}^{\infty}\{0,2\}$ and C. In fact, f is a homeomorphism of the infinite product and C (Problem 1(e)). This, of course, proves that C is uncountable. In $[0,1]$, C is a perfect set and is totally disconnected (Problems 1(f) and 1(g)). It is *nowhere dense* in the sense that $(\overline{C})^{\mathrm{int}} = \emptyset$ (Problem 1(h)). C is *the* Cantor set. Modeling some of its critical properties, we define *a* Cantor set by:

Definition. A *Cantor set* is a perfect subset of $\mathbb{R}$ that is nowhere dense.

Somewhat surprisingly, there are positive measure Cantor sets; see the Notes and Problem 9.

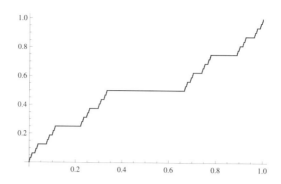

Figure 4.2.2. The Cantor function.

The *Cantor function*, c, is defined by $c(x) = \frac{1}{2}$ on $U_{1,1}$, $c(x) = \frac{1}{4}$ on $U_{2,1}$, $c(x) = \frac{3}{4}$ on $U_{2,2}$, $c(x) = \frac{2j-1}{2^k}$ on $U_{k,j}$ (see Figure 4.2.2). There is a unique continuous extension of c to all of $[0,1]$, given by (Problem 7)

$$c\left(\sum_{n=1}^{\infty} \frac{a_n}{3^n}\right) = \sum_{n=1}^{m} \frac{\frac{1}{2}a_n}{2^n} + \frac{1}{2^{m+1}}; \quad m = \max(n \mid a_n \neq 1) \qquad (4.2.11)$$

with an obvious meaning if $m = \infty$. Thus, if $x \in C$, $c(x)$ is defined by writing x in a base-three expansion as 0 and 2's, changing all 2 to 1's and interpreting as base two.

c, shown in Figure 4.2.2, has the following properties:

(i) c is continuous on $[0,1]$ (Problem 7).
(ii) c is C^1 on $[0,1] \setminus C$ with $c'(x) = 0$ there.
(iii) For $x \in C$, $\lim_{\varepsilon \downarrow 0} \frac{c(x+\varepsilon) - c(x-\varepsilon)}{2\varepsilon} = \infty$ (Problem 8).
(iv) $c(1) - c(0) = 1$.

Thus, even though $c'(x) = 0$ on an open set whose total size in $[0,1]$ is 1, it is not constant! It is sometimes called the *devil's staircase* (Figure 4.2.3).

Figure 4.2.3. The devil's staircase.

For now, the Cantor function is a wondrous but rather pathological-looking monotone function which, of course, defines a Riemann–Stieltjes integral. Once we use this integral to define a measure in Section 4.4, we'll have a remarkable object, the *Cantor measure*, the paradigm of singular continuous measures to be discussed starting in Section 4.7. Cantor measures are discussed further in Problem 4 of Section 4.12, Section 6.7, and Section 8.2.

The Problems will explore various aspects of the classical Cantor set and modifications of the Cantor construction. In particular, the reader will prove (Problem 5) the following universality result.

Theorem 4.2.1 (Alexandroff–Hausdorff Theorem). *Let X be a compact metric space. Then there is a continuous map $\varphi\colon C \to X$ with $\mathrm{Ran}(\varphi) = X$.*

This theorem will be the key to a later result (see Theorem 5.0.1 and Problem 14 of Section 5.5) that any separable Banach space is isometric to a closed subset of $C\big([0,1]\big)$ and to the construction of space-filling curves.

Notes and Historical Remarks. Cantor's name is associated with the Cantor set because he mentions this example in passing in an 1883 paper [153], the fifth in a series on point sets in $\mathbb{R}$. In fact, the British mathematician, Henry John Stephen Smith (1826–83), already found the set in 1875 [863], but his paper went unnoticed, and between the two, Paul du Bois-Reymond (1831–89) [258] and Vito Volterra (1860–1940) [952] also found the set. Cantor, though, was the first to construct the Cantor function [154] as a way to show the integral of the derivative of a function might not recover the function.

Georg Ferdinand Ludwig Philippe Cantor (1845–1918) was born in St. Petersburg, spent most of his life in Germany, and has been described variously as Russian, German, Danish, and Jewish. His paternal grandparents were Danish Jews, but unobservant enough that his grandfather gave all his children names of Christian saints. Cantor's father was a Lutheran and his mother was raised as a Russian Roman Catholic. Despite this, Cantor suffered from anti-Jewish prejudice during parts of his career.

For his education, Cantor spent some time at the ETH in Zurich and in Göttingen, but was mainly at Berlin where he wrote a thesis in number theory in 1867. A major change occurred in 1869 when he moved to Halle, where he spent the remainder of his career. Spurred by his colleague Heine, Cantor shifted to analysis, originally tackling the question of uniqueness of Fourier series representation.

He then shifted to what came to be called set theory, starting with spectacular papers on countable and uncountable sets in 1873–74. He showed the algebraic numbers are countable but the reals uncountable, thereby indirectly establishing the existence of transcendental numbers (see Section 1.6). Particularly disturbing to some contemporaries were Cantor's proof that $\mathbb{R}$ and $\mathbb{R}^n$ could be put in one-one correspondence and his concept of transfinite numbers. While these ideas are now commonplace, they were very controversial, with especially strong opposition from Kronecker (who blocked Cantor's hopes for a position in Berlin), Poincaré, and Weyl, and strong support from Dedekind, Klein, and Hilbert.

This initial burst of activity ended about 1885, with his discovery of the Cantor function. There was a second few years around 1891. In between and in the later years of his life, Cantor was incapacitated by depression, now believed to be caused by bipolar disorder.

The nearly simultaneous discovery of the Cantor set is connected with some work of Hermann Hankel (1839–73) in 1870 [**391**] which attempted to prove that certain functions were Riemann integrable (see the Notes to Section 4.4 for the definition of Riemann integrability of discontinuous functions). Hankel made the error of thinking nowhere dense sets are thin; they can have positive size as seen in the following variant of the Cantor set, called the *Smith–Volterra–Cantor set*, S.

Instead of removing the middle $\frac{1}{3}$, that is, $(\frac{1}{3}, \frac{2}{3})$, initially, remove the middle $\frac{1}{4}$, that is, $(\frac{3}{8}, \frac{5}{8})$. At the next stage, remove the middle piece of the two remaining parts but only of size $\frac{1}{16}$. At stage n, remove 2^{n-1} pieces of size $\frac{1}{4^n}$. Thus, the total amount removed is an open set of size

$$\frac{1}{4} + \frac{2}{16} + \frac{4}{64} + \cdots = \frac{\frac{1}{4}}{1 - \frac{1}{2}} = \frac{1}{2} \tag{4.2.12}$$

The Cantor-like remainder, S, is a Cantor set, but of size $\frac{1}{2}$.

Motivated in part by Dini [**246**], Volterra [**952**], then a twenty-year-old student, went further and constructed a function, f, which is continuous, $f \upharpoonright S = 0$, $f'(x)$ exists at every point, $f' \upharpoonright S = 0$, f' is bounded but arbitrarily close to any $x \in S$, f' takes the values $+1$ and also -1. These oscillations near a fat set, S, show f' is not Riemann integrable. Thus, the fundamental theorem of calculus doesn't make sense for this function if the integral is a Riemann integral! We'll see later (Problem 8 of Section 4.4) that by allowing the Lebesgue integral, this difficulty is surmounted.

The basic building block of Volterra is the following function on $[-1, 1]$:

$$g(x) = \begin{cases} 0, & x \leq 0 \\ x^2 \sin(\frac{1}{x}), & x > 0 \end{cases} \tag{4.2.13}$$

Then $g'(x)$ exists at all x and

$$g'(x) = \begin{cases} 0, & x \le 0 \\ -\cos(\frac{1}{x}) + 2x\sin(\frac{1}{x}), & x > 0 \end{cases} \qquad (4.2.14)$$

so g' is discontinuous with strong oscillations near $x = 0$. f is formed by putting scaled copies of g (cut off and reflected about the middle of the intervals) in each interval of $[0,1] \setminus S$. For details, see Bressoud's book [**129**].

The Alexandroff–Hausdorff theorem, Theorem 4.2.1, was proven by them independently [**14, 405**] in 1927. Benyamini [**70**] has a number of application of the theorem.

The Cantor set is characterized, up to homeomorphism, as the only totally disconnected, perfect compact metric space.

Problems

In Problems 1–5, C denotes the clasical Cantor set given by (4.2.4).

1. (a) Prove the map (4.2.7) has range $[0,1]$. (*Hint*: Divide in three.)

   (b) Prove that $y \in [0,1]$ fails to have a unique expansion of the form (4.2.7) if and only if y has an expansion that ends in $\cdots \times 222\ldots2\ldots$, where x is 0 or 1, and that these are precisely the points in Q, the set (4.2.5).

   (c) Verify (4.2.9).

   (d) Verify each point in C has an expansion (4.2.7) with each a_n equal to 0 or 2, and that this expansion is unique and every such expansion defines a point in C.

   (e) Prove $f \restriction \{0,2\}^{\mathbb{Z}_+}$ is a homeomorphism of this product and C. (*Hint*: Theorem 2.3.11.)

   (f) Prove that C is perfect.

   (g) Prove that C is totally disconnected.

   (h) Prove that C is nowhere dense.

   (i) Let $g = c \restriction C$, that is the restriction of the Cantor function to the Cantor set. Prove that g is a continuous surjection of C to $[0,1]$.

   The next few problems will explore properties of the Cantor set. For clarity, we'll use P for the infinite product $\{0,1\}^{\mathbb{Z}_+}$ which, by Problem 1 is homeomorphic to C.

2. (a) Prove that for any $m \in \mathbb{Z}_+$ or $m = \infty$ (countable infinity), P^m is homeomorphic to P.

   (b) Prove that there is a continuous map of P onto $[0,1]^2$, the square. (*Hint*: See Problem 1(i).)

(c) Prove that there is a continuous map of P onto $H = [0,1]^\infty$, the Hilbert cube.

3. (a) Let $\Omega \subset \mathbb{R}^\nu$ be a convex set and $f\colon C \to \Omega$ continuous. Prove that f has a continuous extension (with values in Ω) to $[0,1]$. (*Hint*: Make it affine on each connected component of $[0,1] \setminus C$.)

(b) Construct a space-filling curve, i.e., a map $g\colon [0,1] \to [0,1] \times [0,1]$ which is surjective. (*Hint*: Use Problem 2(b).)

Remark. This is called the Lebesgue space-filling curve after Lebesgue [**562**, p. 44–45]. Sagan [**808**] is a book on space-filling curves.

4. This problem will construct for each closed set A in C, a continuous map $f\colon C \to A$ with $\mathrm{Ran}\, f = A$, indeed f will be a retraction, i.e., $f(x) = x$ for all $x \in A$. We start with maps $f_n\colon C \to \{0,1\}^n$ constructed inductively as follows. If $x \in C$ and there is $a_1(x) \in A$ with $\big(a_1(x)\big)_1 = x_1$, set $f_1(x) = x_1$; otherwise, set $f_1(x) = 1 - x_1$. Having constructed $f_n(x)$, given $x \in C$, set $f_{n+1}(x) = \big(f_n(x), x_{n+1}\big)$ if there is $a_{n+1}(x) \in A$ with $\big(a_{n+1}(x)\big)_j = f_n(x)_j$ for $j = 1, \ldots, n$ and $\big(a_{n+1}(x)\big)_{n+1} = x_{n+1}$; otherwise, set $f_{n+1}(x) = \big(f_n(x), (1 - x_{n+1})\big)$.

(a) Prove that for each n, there is $a_n(x) \in A$ so $\big(a_n(x)\big)_j = f_n(x)_j$ for $j = 1, \ldots, n$.

(b) Define $f(x)_j = f_n(x)_j$ for $j = 1, \ldots, n$. Prove that $f(x) \in A$. (*Hint*: $a_n(x) \to f(x)$ and A is closed.)

(c) Prove $f(x)_j$ for $j = 1, \ldots, n$ only depends on $(x_1, \ldots, x_n)$ and conclude that f is continuous from C to A.

(d) If $a \in A$, prove that $f(a) = a$ and, in particular, that $\mathrm{Ran}\, f = A$.

The remaining parts of this problem will construct a retraction $g\colon C \to A$ geometrically.

(e) Prove that between any two gaps of C of the same size, there is a larger gap. Conclude that if $\alpha, \beta \in C$, that there is a unique largest gap of C in (α, β).

(f) Let (α, β) be a gap of A (i.e., bounded connected component of $\mathbb{R} \setminus A$). Let G be the largest gap of C in (α, β). Define $g(x) = \alpha$ if $x \in C \cap (\alpha, \beta)$ and $x \le \inf G$ and $g(x) = \beta$ if $x \in C \cap (\alpha, \beta)$ and $x \ge \sup G$. Let $g(x) = \sup A$ if $x \in C$ and $x > \sup A$ and similarly for $\inf A$. Let $g \restriction A = \mathrm{id}$. Prove that g is continuous and is a retraction.

5. This will prove the Alexandroff–Hausdorff theorem (Theorem 4.2.1).

(a) If X is a compact metric space, prove that X is homeomorphic to a subset, Y, of the Hilbert cube, H. (*Hint*: See the proof of Theorem 2.2.1.)

(b) Let $h\colon C \to H$ be the surjective map constructed in Problem 2(c) and $A = h^{-1}[Y]$. Let f be the map of $f\colon C \to A$ constructed in Problem 4. Prove that $h \circ f$ is a surjective map of C to Y and conclude the Alexandroff–Hausdorff theorem.

6. (This problem assumes familiarity with locally convex spaces as discussed in Section 5.8). Let B be a separable compact convex subset of a locally convex space, X. Prove there is a continuous map $f\colon [0,1] \to B$ so $\operatorname{Ran} f = B$. (*Hint*: See Problem 3.)

   Remark. This is the ultimate space-filling curve theorem! It is a theorem of Hahn [**381, 385**] and Mazurkiewicz [**644**] that a Hausdorff topological space, B, is a continuous image of $[0,1]$ if and only if B is compact, connected, and locally connected (see Willard [**1004**] for a proof).

7. Prove that c given by (4.2.11) is continuous, is equal to $\frac{2j-1}{2^k}$ on $U_{k,j}$, and is the unique continuous function with those values on the $U_{k,j}$. (*Hint*: C is nowhere dense.)

8. For all $x \in C$, prove that $\lim_{\varepsilon \downarrow 0} \frac{c(x+\varepsilon)-c(x-\varepsilon)}{2\varepsilon} = \infty$.

9. Let $n_1, n_2, \dots$ be a sequence of odd integers at least 3. Define

$$\widetilde{C} = \left\{ \sum_{j=1}^{\infty} \frac{a_j}{n_1 n_2 \dots n_j} \;\middle|\; a_j \neq \tfrac{1}{2}(n_j - 1) \right\} \tag{4.2.15}$$

   (a) Prove that $\widetilde{C}$ is nowhere dense.

   (b) Prove that $\widetilde{C}$ is perfect.

   (c) Prove that $\widetilde{C}$ is totally disconnected.

   (d) Prove $|\widetilde{C}| = \prod_{j=1}^{\infty}(1 - \frac{1}{n_j})$, so if $\sum_{j=1}^{\infty} \frac{1}{n_j} < \infty$, then $|\widetilde{C}| > 0$.

4.3. Bad Sets and Good Sets

In Section 4.1, we saw finitely additive set functions on certain classes of sets were natural; we'll shortly discuss countably additive set functions. In this section, we'll first see that one doesn't want to define these set functions on all sets and then we'll turn to specifying the class of sets where we do want to define them. The examples below rely on the axiom of choice.

Example 4.3.1 (Vitali Set). Let $\partial \mathbb{D} = \{e^{2\pi i \theta} \mid \theta \in [0,1)\}$, where for $z_0 \in \partial \mathbb{D}$, M_{z_0} is a map of $\partial \mathbb{D}$ to itself, the rotation given by $M_{z_0}(z) = z z_0$. A nonnegative function, μ, on all subsets of $\partial \mathbb{D}$ is called *rotationally invariant* if for every set A and all $z_0 \in \partial \mathbb{D}$, we have that $\mu(M_{z_0}^{-1}[A]) = \mu(A)$. It is called *countably additive* if for all sets $\{A_j\}_{j=1}^{\infty}$,

$$A_j \cap A_k = \emptyset \text{ for } j \neq k \Rightarrow \mu\left(\bigcup_{j=1}^{\infty} A_j\right) = \sum_{j=1}^{\infty} \mu(A_j) \qquad (4.3.1)$$

We will show here that there is no nontrivial countably additive, rotationally invariant set function defined for *all* sets, $A \subset \partial \mathbb{D}$.

Put an equivalence relation on $\partial \mathbb{D}$, $e^{2\pi i \theta} \sim e^{2\pi i \psi} \Leftrightarrow \theta = \psi + q$ for $q \in \mathbb{Q}$. Let V be a set obtained by choosing exactly one point from each equivalence class, possible by the axiom of choice. V is called the *Vitali set*. If $z_0 = e^{2\pi i q_0}$ with $q_0 \in \mathbb{Q}$, $q_0 \neq 0$, then $M_{z_0}^{-1}[V] \cap V = \emptyset$. Moreover, for any other distinct $z_1 = e^{2\pi i q_1}$, $M_{z_1}^{-1}[V] \cap M_{z_0}^{-1}[V] = \emptyset$. Therefore, if μ were a countably additive set function on all sets, $\mu(\bigcup_{q \in \mathbb{Q}} M_{e^{2\pi i q}}^{-1}[V]) = \infty \mu(V)$. If $\mu(\partial \mathbb{D}) < \infty$, we see $\infty \mu(V) \leq \mu(\partial \mathbb{D})$, so $\mu(V) = 0$. But then, since $\partial \mathbb{D} = \bigcup_{q \in \mathbb{Q}} M_{e^{2\pi i q}}^{-1}[V]$, $\mu(\partial \mathbb{D}) \equiv 0$. It follows that we cannot define a nontrivial rotationally invariant set function from *all* sets of $\partial \mathbb{D}$ to $[0, \infty)$. $\qquad \square$

Example 4.3.2 (Banach–Tarski Paradox). Let B, D be any two closed balls in $\mathbb{R}^3$. Banach and Tarski have used the axiom of choice to show there exist m and $\{B_j\}_{j=1}^m$, $\{D_j\}_{j=1}^m$, subsets of $\mathbb{R}^3$, and Euclidean maps (i.e., rotations and translations), $\{R_j\}_{j=1}^m$ so that (i) $B_j \cap B_k = \emptyset = D_j \cap D_k$ if $j \neq k$; (ii) $\bigcup_{j=1}^m B_j = B$, $\bigcup_{j=1}^m D_j = D$; (iii) $R_j^{-1}[B_j] = D_j$. In picturesque terms, the sun and a peanut would have the same volume if I could split them arbitrarily. This implies there cannot be a nonzero finitely additive set function on the bounded subsets of $\mathbb{R}^3$ invariant under rotations and translations. $\qquad \square$

The moral of these two examples is that one should not try to define measures on all sets, but only on a rich family, $\mathfrak{A}$, of all sets. In order to talk about countable additivity, $\mathfrak{A}$ has to be closed under countable unions. To go from general sets to disjoint sets, we need $\mathfrak{A}$ to be closed under complements. Since $A \cup (X \setminus A) = X$, it will contain X, and since $\bigcap_{j=1}^{\infty} A_j = X \setminus \bigcup_{j=1}^{\infty} (X \setminus A_j)$, it will be closed under countable intersection.

Definition. A σ-*algebra* (or *sigma-algebra*) is a nonempty family of subsets, $\mathfrak{A}$, of a set X, that obeys

(a) $\{A_j\}_{j=1}^{\infty} \subset \mathfrak{A} \Rightarrow \bigcup_{j=1}^{\infty} A_j \in \mathfrak{A}$
(b) $\{A_j\}_{j=1}^{\infty} \subset \mathfrak{A} \Rightarrow \bigcap_{j=1}^{\infty} A_j \in \mathfrak{A}$
(c) $A \in \mathfrak{A} \Rightarrow X \setminus A \in \mathfrak{A}$
(d) $X, \emptyset \in \mathfrak{A}$

As we've seen, (a)+(c) imply the others. This has a little of the flavor of topological space, except for the countability and, most importantly, the complements. As with topology, the intersection of an arbitrary collection of σ-algebras is a σ-algebra. Thus, given any collection, $\mathcal{C}$, of subsets of X, there is a smallest σ-algebra containing $\mathcal{C}$ called the *σ-algebra generated by $\mathcal{C}$*.

There are several definitions close to that of σ-algebra. If (a), (b) are replaced by finite, rather than countable, union and intersection, we get an *algebra of sets*. If $X \in \mathfrak{A}$ is dropped and (c) replaced by $A, B \in \mathfrak{A} \Rightarrow B \setminus A \in \mathfrak{A}$, we get a *$\sigma$-ring of sets*. If, in addition, we replace countable by finite, we get a *ring of sets*. For rings, an elegant rephrasing is to demand that $\mathfrak{A}$ is nonempty and

$$A, B \in \mathfrak{A} \Rightarrow A \cap B, \quad A \Delta B \in \mathfrak{A}$$

where $A \Delta B = (A \setminus B) \cup (B \setminus A)$ for $A \Delta A = \phi$, $\phi \in \mathfrak{A}$. Since

$$A \cup B = (A \Delta B) \Delta (A \cap B)$$

$\mathfrak{A}$ is closed under finite unions.

Definition. Let X and Y be sets with σ-algebras $\mathfrak{A}$ and $\mathcal{B}$, respectively. A function $f \colon X \to Y$ is called $\mathfrak{A} - \mathcal{B}$ *measurable* if and only if for all $B \in \mathcal{B}$, $f^{-1}[B] \in \mathfrak{A}$.

As with continuity, f^{-1} is natural because it preserves Boolean operators. For that reason, it is sufficient that $f^{-1}[B] \in \mathfrak{A}$ for $B \in \mathcal{C}$, a family that generates $\mathcal{B}$. On $\mathbb{R}$, it will be natural to take the σ-algebra generated by $\{(a, b) \mid a, b \in \mathbb{R}\}$. This leads to

Definition. In any topological space, X, the *Borel sets* are the σ-algebra generated by the family of all open sets.

If X is second countable, we can replace the generating family by any countable base. Clearly,

Proposition 4.3.3. *Let X, Y be two topological spaces. Any continuous function $f \colon X \to Y$ is Borel measurable, that is, measurable with respect to the Borel σ-algebra on each space.*

You might think this is the end of the story, but recall from the same argument that led to Proposition 2.2.8 that if X is a topological space and $f \colon X \to \mathbb{R}$ is continuous, then $f^{-1}([a, b])$ is not merely closed—it is a closed G_δ, and from Example 2.7.2, there are in very big spaces closed sets which are not G_δ's. This suggests:

Definition. Let X be a compact Hausdorff space. The *Baire sets* are the smallest σ-algebra containing all compact G_δ's.

Of course, in any compact metric space, the Baire and Borel sets are the same.

Proposition 4.3.4. *Let X be a compact Hausdorff space and $f: X \to \mathbb{R}$ a continuous function. Then f is measurable if the Baire σ-algebras are put on X and $\mathbb{R}$.*

Remark. As we saw in Theorem 2.2.9, if X is a compact Hausdorff space and $A \subset X$ is a compact G_δ, then there exists $f \in C_{\mathbb{R}}(X)$, so $\mathrm{Ran}(f) \subset [0,1]$ and $f^{-1}(\{0\}) = A$. Thus, any σ-algebra in which every continuous $f \in C_{\mathbb{R}}(X)$ is measurable contains all Baire sets. Combining this with Proposition 4.3.4 shows the following which, for some, is the definition of the Baire sets.

Proposition 4.3.5. *The Baire σ-algebra is the smallest σ-algebra in which every $f \in C(X)$ is measurable.*

We already defined G_δ and their complements, F_σ sets. G_δ's are closed under countable intersections, but not under unions. Just as a G_δ is a countable intersection of open sets and an F_σ is a countable union of closed sets, we define $G_{\delta\sigma}$ as countable unions of G_δ's. We can also form $G_{\delta\sigma\delta}, G_{\delta\sigma\delta\sigma}, \dots$, but that isn't all. We need to take the union or intersection of one open G_δ, one $G_{\delta\sigma}, \dots$. In the end, a constructive approach to all Borel or Baire sets requires transfinite induction. We'll instead rely on the implicit definition as the smallest σ-algebra containing all open sets (for Borel) or all compact G_δ's (for Baire).

There is one extremely important feature of Baire (or Borel) functions: closure under pointwise limits.

Theorem 4.3.6. *Let X be a space with a distinguished σ-algebra, $\mathcal{B}$. Let $\{f_n\}_{n=1}^{\infty}$ be a family of functions from X to $\mathbb{R}$, each of which is $\mathcal{B}$-measurable. Then the following functions are all $\mathcal{B}$-measurable as functions with values in $\mathbb{R} \cup \{\pm\infty\}$:*

$$\sup f_n(x), \quad \inf f_n(x), \quad \limsup f_n(x), \quad \liminf f_n(y)$$

Proof. For a sequence $\{y_n\}_{n=1}^{\infty}$ of real numbers, we have

$$\limsup y_n = \inf_{m \geq 1}\left[\sup_{n \geq m} y_n\right], \qquad \liminf y_n = \sup_{m \geq 1}\left[\inf_{n \geq m} y_n\right]$$

so the results for sup and inf imply the results for $\limsup$ and $\liminf$. Since $\inf y_n = -[\sup(-y_n)]$, we need only prove the result for sup. Let $f(x) = \sup f_n(x)$.

We have that

$$f(x) > \alpha \Leftrightarrow \exists n \; f_n(x) > \alpha \tag{4.3.2}$$

$$f(x) < \alpha \Leftrightarrow \exists m \, \forall n \; f_n(x) < \alpha - \frac{1}{m} \tag{4.3.3}$$

$$f(x) = +\infty \Leftrightarrow \forall N \, \exists n \; f_n(x) > N \tag{4.3.4}$$

Thus,

$$f^{-1}((\alpha, \infty]) = \bigcup_{n=1}^{\infty} f_n^{-1}((\alpha, \infty)) \qquad (4.3.5)$$

$$f^{-1}((-\infty, \alpha)) = \bigcup_{m=1}^{\infty} \bigcap_{n=1}^{\infty} f_n^{-1}\left(\left(-\infty, \alpha - \frac{1}{m}\right)\right) \qquad (4.3.6)$$

$$f^{-1}((\infty)) = \bigcap_{N=1}^{\infty} \bigcup_{n=1}^{\infty} f_n^{-1}((N, \infty)) \qquad (4.3.7)$$

proving that if each f_n is $\mathcal{B}$-measurable, so is f. $\square$

In Theorem 4.4.12, we'll see that the bounded Baire functions are the smallest class of functions, including the continuous functions, that is closed under bounded limits and sums and products.

We note that it is easy to see (Problem 1) that if $f, g \colon X \to \mathbb{R}$ are Baire or Borel, so are $f + g$ and fg.

The moral of this section is that we don't want to consider all sets or all functions, but only the Baire sets and Borel functions. We want to emphasize that, in this book, we will never consider so-called Lebesgue measurable functions. Those who aren't going to worry about this issue can skip the diatribe below and jump to the Notes.

Suppose $\mu \colon \mathcal{B} \to [0, \infty]$ is a countably additive set function on a σ-algebra, $\mathcal{B}$. Let

$$\mathcal{I} = \{B \in \mathcal{B} \mid \mu(B) = 0\}$$

$\mathcal{I}$ has two properties:

(a) $\{A_n\}_{n=1}^{\infty} \subset \mathcal{I} \Rightarrow \bigcup_{n=1}^{\infty} A_n \in \mathcal{I}$

(b) $A \in \mathcal{I}, B \in \mathcal{B} = A \cap B \in \mathcal{I}$

Such subsets of a σ-algebra, $\mathcal{B}$, are called a σ-ideal or sigma-ideal (see the Notes).

Now let

$$\mathcal{J} = \{C \subset B \text{ for some } B \text{ in } \mathcal{I}\}$$

Here C need not lie in $\mathcal{B}$. Let

$$\mathcal{C} = \{A \triangle C \mid A \in \mathcal{B}, C \in \mathcal{J}\}$$

sets which differ from a $\mathcal{B}$ set by adding or subtracting subsets of $\mathcal{B}$ sets of measure 0. It is easy to see that if μ is extended to $\mathcal{C}$ by setting

$$\tilde{\mu}(A \triangle C) = \mu(A) \quad \text{if } C \in \mathcal{J}, A \in \mathcal{B}$$

then $\tilde{\mu}$ is also a countably additive set function. It is called the *completion* of μ and if $\mu = \tilde{\mu}$ (and, e.g., $\tilde{\tilde{\mu}} = \tilde{\mu}$), then μ is called a *complete measure*.

When this is done for the Baire–Lebesgue measure we'll construct in Section 4.4, the σ-algebra $\mathcal{C}$ is called the Lebesgue measurable sets and the functions, measurable with respect to $\mathcal{C}$, are called Lebesgue measurable. We want to emphasize this does *not* mean what you think. If $f\colon \mathbb{R} \to \mathbb{R}$, we mean $f^{-1}([a,b]) \in \mathcal{C}$ for each $[a,b]$, that is, f is *Lebesgue measurable* if we use the σ-algebra, $\mathcal{C}$, on the domain, but the Borel sets on the range.

Traditional literature discusses Lebesgue measurable sets and functions because that is what Lebesgue does and what comes naturally from the Carathéodory construction of Section 8.1.

This has several disadvantages:

(1) Because of the asymmetry of σ-algebras on domain and range, compositions of Borel functions from $\mathbb{R}$ to $\mathbb{R}$ are Borel, but compositions of Lebesgue measurable functions are not necessarily Lebesgue measurable!

(2) Product σ-algebras require an extra completion. If V is the Vitali set moved to $[0,1]$ and $\widetilde{V} = \{(0,y) \mid y \in V\} \subset \mathbb{R}^2$, $\widetilde{V}$ is not in the σ-algebra generated by products of Lebesgue measurable sets, but it is a two-dimensional Lebesgue measurable set.

(3) Since every Lebesgue measurable function is equal Lebesgue a.e. to a Borel function, and it is really equivalence classes that matter, there is no gain by enlarging the class of Borel functions.

The only advantages are that it is faithful to history and to most books, that some authors say it is natural to pass to completions (hah!) and it forces some crazy gymnastics. In summary, passing from Borel to Lebesgue measurable functions is the work of the devil. Don't even consider it!

Notes and Historical Remarks. The Vitali set was found by Giuseppe Vitali in 1905 [**948**]. In 1914, Hausdorff [**401**] (and in his book [**402**]) showed that the two-dimensional sphere could be decomposed into four sets A, B, C, D so that D is countable, and there are rotations R_1, R_2, R_3 so $R_1[A] = B$, $R_2[A] = C$, and $R_3[A] = B \cup C$. Thus, if S^2 had a finitely additive, rotationally invariant set function, η, with $\eta(S^2) = 1$, then $\eta(A)$ is both $\frac{1}{2}$ and $\frac{1}{3}$! Hausdorff's ideas were critical to the 1924 construction of Banach and Tarski [**58**]. Von Neumann [**963**] related their constructions to the nonabelian nature of the rotation group and, in particular, to the fact that it contains a subgroup isomorphic to the free nonabelian group on two generators. In particular, in Example 5.12.15, we'll show that S^1 has a rotation invariant, finitely additive set function on all sets. One can use that to construct a translation invariant, finite additive nontrivial set function on all subsets of $\mathbb{R}$. For a book on the Banach–Tarski paradox and related examples, see Wagon [**973**]. For a pedagogic presentation, see Stromberg

[**890**]. The constructions of the Vitali set and the Banach–Tarski paradox depend critically on the axiom of choice. This is illustrated dramatically by a paper of Solovay [**868**] that there is a model of set theory with all the usual axioms of set theory except for the axiom of choice, in which there exists a countably additive, translation invariant measure on all subsets of $\mathbb{R}^{\nu}$!

Borel and Baire sets are named after these mathematicians in honor of their studies on the foundations of measure theory; see Sections 2.3 and 5.4 for their capsule biographies. Borel constructed sets [**112**]; Baire, limits of functions [**47**]. Lebesgue eventually showed on $\mathbb{R}$ that their notions were equivalent. The importance of compact G_δ's and the name "Baire set" go back to Kakutani–Kodaira [**473**].

It is a theorem of Halmos [**386**] that every compact Baire set is a G_δ, that is, the process of using countable unions and complements leads to no new compact sets other than the compact G_δ's we started with; see Problem 2.

The name "ring" in σ-ring is connected with the fact that if "$A + B$" is $A \triangle B$ and "$A \cdot B$"$= A \cap B$, then we have the usual properties of a ring; see Problem 7 of Section 4.1. From this point of view, the condition $A \in \mathcal{I}$, $B \in \mathcal{B} \Rightarrow A \cap B \in \mathcal{I}$ is exactly what one would expect from an ideal.

Problems

1. (a) Show that $F_1(x,y) = x + y$ and $F_2(x,y) = xy$ are Borel maps of $\mathbb{R}^2$ to $\mathbb{R}$.

   (b) If X is given a σ-field $\mathcal{B}$ and $f, g \colon X \to \mathbb{R}$ are $\mathcal{B}$-measurable (when $\mathbb{R}$ is given the Borel σ-field), prove that $f \# g \colon X \to \mathbb{R}^2$ by $(f \# g)(x) = (f(x), g(x))$ is $\mathcal{B}$-measurable.

   (c) If $f, g \colon X \to \mathbb{R}$ are $\mathcal{B}$-measurable (when $\mathbb{R}$ is given the Borel σ-field), prove that $f + g$ and fg are $\mathcal{B}$-measurable.

2. This problem will prove Halmos' theorem that every compact Baire set is a G_δ.

   (a) Let $\mathcal{B}$ be a σ-algebra generated by a set, S, of sets. Show that any $A \in \mathcal{B}$ is in the σ-algebra generated by a countable number of elements of S. (*Hint*: For each countable $C \subset S$, let $\mathcal{B}(C)$ be the σ-algebra generated by C. Prove that $\cup_{C \subset S, \text{countable}} \mathcal{B}(C)$ is a σ-algebra, and so conclude it is $\mathcal{B}(S)$.)

   (b) Let X be a compact Hausdorff space, K a compact Baire set, and $\{A_j\}_{j=1}^{\infty}$ a countable family of compact G_δ's, so K is in the σ-algebra generated by them. Let $f_j \colon X \to [0,1)$ be such that $f_j^{-1}[\{0\}] = A_j$ (see Theorem 2.2.9). Define

$$\rho(x,y) = \sum_{n=1}^{\infty} 2^{-n} |f_j(x) - f_j(y)|$$

Prove that ρ is a semimetric on X (i.e., all the properties of a metric except $\rho(x,y) = 0$ need not imply $x = y$).

(c) Say $x \sim y$ if and only if $\rho(x,y) = 0$. Prove this is an equivalence relation and that if $\widetilde{X} = X/\sim$ is the class of equivalence classes, $\tilde{\rho}(\sim x, \sim y) \equiv \rho(x,y)$ is well defined and a metric on $\widetilde{X}$. Here $\sim x \equiv \{y \mid y \sim x\}$.

(d) Prove that $G\colon X \to \widetilde{X}$ by $x \mapsto \sim x$ is continuous if X has the given topology and $\widetilde{X}$ the metric topology.

(e) Prove that $G^{-1}[G[A_j]] = A_j$. (*Hint*: Prove that $x \in A_j$ and $\rho(x,y) = 0 \Rightarrow y \in A_j$.)

(f) Prove that $\{G^{-1}[B] \mid B$ a Baire set in $\widetilde{X}\}$ is a σ-algebra, and then that $K = G^{-1}[G[K]]$.

(g) Prove that $G[K]$ is a G_δ in $\widetilde{X}$. (*Hint*: What do you know about compact sets in metric spaces?)

(h) Prove that K is a G_δ.

4.4. Positive Functionals and Measures via $L^1(X)$

This is the central section of this chapter. In it, we'll provide a general procedure, pioneered by Peter Lax, for going from an "integral" defined for functions in $C_{\mathbb{R}}(X)$ to bounded Baire functions (and some unbounded ones) and then, by integrating characteristic functions, a general measure. We'll go from positive functionals to L^1 as an abstract completion. We'll then show how to define $(\ )_+$ and $|\ |$ on the abstract space, and use that to state and prove our first version of the monotone convergence theorem. With that and a partition of unity tool in hand, we'll be able to define the measure of open sets and the notion of negligible Baire set. That will allow us to show that each element of the abstract L^1 is a Baire function, or rather an equivalence class of Baire functions equal almost everywhere, that is, up to a negligible set. We'll show that every bounded Baire function lies in L^1 and, in particular, define a measure on all Baire sets.

Definition. Let X be a compact Hausdorff space. A *positive functional* on $C_{\mathbb{R}}(X)$ is a linear map $\ell\colon C_{\mathbb{R}}(X) \to \mathbb{R}$ so that

$$c(x) \geq 0 \text{ for all } x \Rightarrow \ell(c) \geq 0 \tag{4.4.1}$$

We call it *normalized* if $\ell(\mathbb{1}) = 1$, where $\mathbb{1}$ is the function $\mathbb{1}(x) \equiv 1$. We call it *strictly positive* if $\ell(c) > 0$ for any nonnegative function c not identically zero.

Henceforth we'll suppose ℓ is normalized and strictly positive. Problem 1 will describe the simple changes needed to accommodate positive but not necessarily strictly positive ℓ's.

Since $|c| \pm c \geq 0$, $|c| \leq \|c\|_\infty \mathbb{1}$, and $\ell(\mathbb{1}) = 1$, (4.4.1) implies

$$|\ell(c)| \leq \ell(|c|) \tag{4.4.2}$$

$$\leq \|c\|_\infty \tag{4.4.3}$$

so that any positive functional is a BLT on $C_\mathbb{R}(X)$ with the $\|\cdot\|_\infty$-norm. Define

$$\|c\|_\ell \equiv \ell(|c|) \tag{4.4.4}$$

Since $|c+d| \leq |c|+|d|$, $\|\cdot\|_\ell$ obeys the triangle inequality, and by the assumed strict positivity of ℓ, $\|\cdot\|_\ell$ is a norm on $C_\mathbb{R}(X)$.

Definition. $L^1(X, \ell)$ denotes the abstract completion of $C_\mathbb{R}(X)$ in $\|\cdot\|_\ell$. Thus, an element of L^1 is an equivalence class of Cauchy sequences of elements in $C_\mathbb{R}(X)$. Shortly, after the reader has gotten used to these notions, we'll start using $L^1(\ell)$ as a shorthand for $L^1(X, \ell)$.

For a while, we'll use f, g for elements of L^1 and c, d for elements of $C_\mathbb{R}(X)$. Thus, $f = [\{c_n\}_{n=1}^\infty]$ is an equivalence class of certain sequences of continuous functions, c_n.

(4.4.2) implies that for any c, d,

$$|\ell(c) - \ell(d)| \leq \|c - d\|_\ell \tag{4.4.5}$$

so ℓ extends to a linear functional on L^1 obeying

$$|\ell(f)| \leq \|f\|_\ell \tag{4.4.6}$$

Recall that a Lipschitz function, $\Phi \colon \mathbb{R} \to \mathbb{R}$ obeys

$$|\Phi(x) - \Phi(y)| \leq N(\Phi)|x - y| \tag{4.4.7}$$

where we use $N(\Phi)$ for the minimal constant that works. Examples are

$$\Phi(x) = |x|, \qquad \Phi(x) = x_+ = \tfrac{1}{2}(|x| + x) \tag{4.4.8}$$

$$\Phi(x) = \Phi_a^b(x) \equiv \begin{cases} b, & x > b \\ x, & a \leq x \leq b \\ a, & x < a \end{cases} \tag{4.4.9}$$

for $a < b$. We abuse notation: if $\Phi \colon \mathbb{R} \to \mathbb{R}$, we define a map of $C_\mathbb{R}(X) \to C_\mathbb{R}(X)$ by requiring for all $x \in X$ that

$$\Phi(c)(x) = \Phi(c(x)) \tag{4.4.10}$$

Proposition 4.4.1. *Let $\{c_n\}_{n=1}^\infty$ be a Cauchy sequence of $C_\mathbb{R}(X)$ functions in $\|\cdot\|_\ell$. Then for any Lipschitz, Φ, $\Phi(c_n)$ is also Cauchy, and if $\{c_n\}_{n=1}^\infty \equiv \{d_n\}_{n=1}^\infty$ in the sense that $\|c_n - d_n\|_\ell \to 0$ as $n \to \infty$, then $\Phi(c_n) \equiv \Phi(d_n)$. Thus, we can define $\Phi(f)$ in L^1 for any f in L^1 as the equivalence class of $\{\Phi(c_n)\}_{n=1}^\infty$ for any $\{c_n\}_{n=1}^\infty \in f$.*

Proof. By (4.4.7), for any $c, d \in C_{\mathbb{R}}(X)$ pointwise,

$$|\Phi(c) - \Phi(d)| \leq N(\Phi)|c - d| \tag{4.4.11}$$

and, so by positivity of ℓ,

$$\|\Phi(c) - \Phi(d)\|_\ell \leq N(\Phi)\|c - d\|_\ell \tag{4.4.12}$$

From this, all the results follow. $\square$

Thus, for $f \in L^1$, we can use the appropriate $\Phi(f)$ to define f_+, $|f|$, and $\Phi_a^b(f) \equiv f_a^b$.

Definition. We say $f \in L^1$ is *positive* (written) $f \geq 0$ if and only if $f = f_+$. We say $f \in L^1$ is *bounded* if for some $a < b$ in $\mathbb{R}$, $\Phi_a^b(f) = f$.

This lets us place an order on L^1 by

$$f \leq g \Leftrightarrow g - f \geq 0 \tag{4.4.13}$$

It is easy to see L^1 is a lattice in that

$$f \vee g = \tfrac{1}{2}\left(f + g + |f - g|\right), \quad f \wedge g = \tfrac{1}{2}\left(f + g - |f - g|\right) \tag{4.4.14}$$

define a lub and glb. Since $\ell(c) \geq 0$ if $c \geq 0$ and $f \geq 0 \Rightarrow f = f_+ = \lim(c_n)_+$, so $\ell(f) = \lim \ell(c_n)_+ \geq 0$, we have that

$$f \geq 0 \Rightarrow \ell(f) \geq 0 \tag{4.4.15}$$

Similarly, (4.4.11) and (4.4.12) imply that, for $f, g \in L^1$,

$$|\Phi(f) - \Phi(g)| \leq N(\Phi)|f - g| \tag{4.4.16}$$

$$\|\Phi(f) - \Phi(g)\|_\ell \leq N(\Phi)\|f - g\|_\ell \tag{4.4.17}$$

Theorem 4.4.2 (Monotone Convergence Theorem, First Half). *Let $\{f_n\}_{n=1}^\infty$ be a sequence in $L^1(X, \ell)$ so that*

(i) $f_{n+1} \geq f_n$ *for all n*
(ii) $\sup_n \ell(f_n) < \infty$.

Then there exists $f \in L^1(X, \ell)$ so that $\|f_n - f\|_\ell \to 0$.

Remark. We call this first half because once we know that f_n's are given by functions, we'll be able to identify f as $f(x) = \sup f_n(x)$ (for a.e. x).

Proof. By replacing f_n by $f_n - f_1$, we can suppose $f_1 = 0$, so $f_n \geq 0$. Thus, $\ell(f_{n+1}) \geq \ell(f_n)$, and if $n \leq m$,

$$\|f_m - f_n\|_\ell = \ell(f_m - f_n) \leq \left[\sup_m \ell(f_m)\right] - \ell(f_n) \tag{4.4.18}$$

Since $\ell(f_n) \uparrow \sup_m \ell(f_m)$, we conclude $\{f_m\}_{m=1}^\infty$ is Cauchy, so the limit exists. $\square$

Proposition 4.4.3. *For any $f \in L^1(X, \ell)$, we have*

$$\underset{\substack{b \to \infty \\ a \to -\infty}}{L^1\text{-lim}} f_a^b = f \tag{4.4.19}$$

so the bounded f's are dense in L^1.

Proof. Given ε, find $c \in C_{\mathbb{R}}(X)$ so

$$\|f - c\|_\ell < \frac{\varepsilon}{2} \tag{4.4.20}$$

Let $A = \|c\|_\infty$. Thus, if $b > A$ and $a < -A$,

$$c = c_a^b \tag{4.4.21}$$

By (4.4.20) and (4.4.17) (plus $N(\Phi_a^b) = 1$),

$$\|f_a^b - c_a^b\|_\ell < \frac{\varepsilon}{2} \tag{4.4.22}$$

The triangle inequality and (4.4.20)–(4.4.22) imply

$$a < -A \text{ and } b > A \Rightarrow \|f - f_a^b\|_\ell < \varepsilon \tag{4.4.23}$$

$\square$

So far, we have used only very soft arguments that haven't used the structure of X or $C_{\mathbb{R}}(X)$. We next need a simple but technical fact that uses what we know about $C_{\mathbb{R}}(X)$. Recall that

Definition. Let $f \colon X \to \mathbb{R}$ be a continuous function from a topological space X to $\mathbb{R}$. We define the *support of f* by

$$\operatorname{supp}(f) = \overline{\{x \mid f(x) \neq 0\}} \tag{4.4.24}$$

Theorem 4.4.4 ($C_{\mathbb{R}}(X)$ Partition of Unity). *Let X be a compact Hausdorff space and $\{U_\alpha\}_{\alpha \in I}$ an open cover of X. Then there exist $\alpha_1, \ldots, \alpha_n$ and functions $c_1, \ldots, c_n$ in $C_{\mathbb{R}}(X)$, so that*

(i) $c_j(x) \geq 0$ $\qquad\qquad\qquad\qquad\qquad\qquad\qquad\qquad$ (4.4.25)

(ii) $\displaystyle\sum_{j=1}^n c_j(x) \equiv 1$ $\qquad\qquad\qquad\qquad\qquad\qquad\quad$ (4.4.26)

(iii) $\operatorname{supp}(c_j) \subset U_{\alpha_j}$ $\qquad\qquad\qquad\qquad\qquad\qquad\quad$ (4.4.27)

Remark. $\{c_j\}_{j=1}^n$ is called a partition of unity subordinate to $\{U_\alpha\}_{\alpha \in I}$.

Proof. This is Theorem 2.3.16. $\qquad\qquad\qquad\qquad\qquad\qquad\qquad$ $\square$

We are going to define a notion of size for open F_σ sets. Eventually, this will turn out to be the measure associated to ℓ restricted to open sets, but for now, it is not defined on a σ-algebra. We'll use the symbol μ_ℓ.

Definition. Let G be an open F_σ set. $\mathcal{F}_G$ is the set of *admissible functions* for G, defined to be those functions $c \in C_\mathbb{R}(X)$ that obey:

(i) $0 \leq c(y) \leq 1$ on X

(ii) $\text{supp}(c) \subset G$

We define

$$\mu_\ell(G) = \sup_{c \in \mathcal{F}_G} \ell(c) \tag{4.4.28}$$

Since $\ell(\mathbb{1}) = 1$ and $c \leq \mathbb{1}$ for any admissible c, $\mu_\ell(G) \leq 1$.

Theorem 4.4.5. μ_ℓ *on open* F_σ*'s has the following properties:*

(a) $\mu_\ell(\emptyset) = 0$

(b) $F \subset G \Rightarrow \mu_\ell(F) \leq \mu_\ell(G)$ $\qquad\qquad\qquad\qquad\qquad\qquad\qquad$ (4.4.29)

(c) μ_ℓ *is countably subadditive, that is, for any* $\{F_j\}_{j=1}^\infty$,

$$\mu_\ell\left(\bigcup_{j=1}^\infty F_j\right) \leq \sum_{j=1}^\infty \mu_\ell(F_j) \tag{4.4.30}$$

(d) μ_ℓ *is countably additive, that is, for any* $\{F_j\}_{j=1}^\infty$ *with* $F_j \cap F_k = \emptyset$ *for all* $j \neq k$, *we have*

$$\mu_\ell\left(\bigcup_{j=1}^\infty F_j\right) = \sum_{j=1}^\infty \mu_\ell(F_j) \tag{4.4.31}$$

Proof. (a) $F_\emptyset = \{0\}$.

(b) $\mathcal{F}_F \subset \mathcal{F}_G$.

(c) Let $d \in \mathcal{F}_{\cup_{j=1}^\infty F_j}$ and let $K = \text{supp}(d)$. $\{F_j\}_{j=1}^\infty \cup X \setminus K$ cover X, so by Theorem 4.4.4, we can find $\{c_j\}_{j=1}^n$ obeying (4.4.25), (4.4.26), and

$$\text{supp}(c_j) \subset F_j, \quad j = 1, \ldots, n-1, \qquad \text{supp}(c_n) \subset X \setminus K$$

Since $dc_n = 0$, we have $\sum_{j=1}^{n-1} dc_j = d$. Thus,

$$\ell(d) = \sum_{j=1}^{n-1} \ell(dc_j) \leq \sum_{j=1}^{n-1} \mu_\ell(F_j) \tag{4.4.32}$$

since dc_j is admissible for F_j. Taking the sup over all $d \in \mathcal{F}_{\cup_{j=1}^\infty F_j}$, we get (4.4.30).

(d) Fix N. For each $j = 1, \ldots, N$, pick $c_j \in \mathcal{F}_{F_j}$, so

$$\ell(c_j) \geq \mu_\ell(F_j) - \frac{1}{N^2} \tag{4.4.33}$$

Since $\sum_{j=1}^{N} c_j$ is admissible for $\bigcup_{j=1}^{N} F_j$ (since the F_j's are disjoint),

$$\mu_\ell\left(\bigcup_{j=1}^{\infty} F_j\right) \geq \mu_\ell\left(\bigcup_{j=1}^{N} F_j\right) \geq \sum_{n=1}^{N} \ell(c_j)$$

$$\geq \left[\sum_{j=1}^{N} \mu_\ell(F_j)\right] - \frac{1}{N} \qquad (4.4.34)$$

Taking $N \to \infty$ yields

$$\sum_{j=1}^{\infty} \mu_\ell(F_j) \leq \mu\left(\bigcup_{j=1}^{\infty} F_j\right) \qquad (4.4.35)$$

which, together with (4.4.30), implies (4.4.31). □

Theorem 4.4.6 (Markov's Inequality for $C_{\mathbb{R}}(X)$). *Let $h \in C_{\mathbb{R}}(X)$ be non-negative. Then for any $a > 0$,*

$$\mu_\ell(\{x \mid h(x) > a\}) \leq \frac{1}{a}\ell(h) \qquad (4.4.36)$$

Remark. As we've seen, $\{x \mid h(x) > a\} = \bigcup_{n=1}^{\infty}\{x \mid h(x) \geq a + \frac{1}{n}\}$ is an open F_σ.

Proof. Let c be admissible for $\{x \mid h(x) > a\}$. Then for all x, $ac(x) \leq h(x)$. For on $\mathrm{supp}(c)$, $ac(x) \leq a < h(x)$ since $\mathrm{supp}(c) \subset \{x \mid h(x) > a\}$, and on $X \setminus \mathrm{supp}(c)$, $c(x) = 0$ and $h(x) \geq 0$. Thus, $a\ell(c) \leq \ell(h)$. Taking the sup over admissible c's yields (4.4.36). □

Definition. A Baire set, S, is called *negligible* if and only if for any $\varepsilon > 0$, there is an open F_σ, G, so that $S \subset G$ and $\mu_\ell(G) \leq \varepsilon$. If $Q(x)$ is an x-dependent statement, we say Q holds *almost everywhere* (a.e.) if $\{x \mid Q(x)$ is false$\}$ is a negligible Baire set.

Notice that if $\{S_n\}_{n=1}^{\infty}$ is a family of negligible sets, given ε, we can find open F_σ's, G_n so $\mu_\ell(G_n) < \varepsilon/2^n$ and $S_n \subset G_n$. Thus, $\mu_\ell(\bigcup_{n=1}^{\infty} G_n) < \varepsilon$ and $\bigcup_{n=1}^{\infty} S_n \subset \bigcup_{n=1}^{\infty} G_n$, so

$$\{S_n\}_{n=1}^{\infty} \text{ negligible} \Rightarrow \bigcup_{n=1}^{\infty} S_n \text{ is negligible} \qquad (4.4.37)$$

We are now prepared to realize L^1 as a set of (equivalence classes of) functions:

Theorem 4.4.7 (Riesz–Fischer Theorem). *Let $f \in L^1(X, \ell)$. Then there exists a Cauchy sequence $\{c_n\}_{n=1}^{\infty} \in f$ and a negligible Baire set, S, so that*

$$\lim_{n \to \infty} c_n(x) \equiv c_\infty(x) \qquad (4.4.38)$$

exists for all $x \notin S$. *If* $\tilde{c}_\infty(x)$ *is the limit of another such convergent* $\{\tilde{c}_n\}_{n=1}^\infty \in f$ *for* $x \notin \tilde{S}$, *then* $\{x \in X \setminus (S \cup \tilde{S}) \mid c_\infty(x) \neq \tilde{c}_\infty(x)\}$ *is a negligible set.*

Remarks. 1. This doesn't look like what anyone else calls the Riesz–Fischer theorem; see the Notes for why we give it this name.

2. If c_∞ is defined on X by setting it to 0 on S, then c_∞ is a Baire function by Theorem 4.3.6. We call a negligible set, S, and such a limit, c_∞, defined on $X \setminus S$ a *representative of* f.

Proof. Given any Cauchy sequence, $\{d_m\}_{m=1}^\infty$, you can always find a subsequence $\{c_n\}_{n=1}^\infty$ so that

$$\|c_{n+1} - c_n\|_\ell \leq \frac{1}{n^4} \tag{4.4.39}$$

(for pick $m(n)$ inductively so $m(n+1) \geq m(n)$ and $\|d_j - d_k\|_\ell \leq 1/(n+1)^4$ if $j, k \geq m(n+1)$. Let $c_n = d_{m(n)}$.) Let

$$G_n = \left\{ x \ \middle| \ |c_{n+1}(x) - c_n(x)| > \frac{1}{n^2} \right\} \tag{4.4.40}$$

which is an open F_σ since $|c_{n+1} - c_n|$ is continuous.

By Markov's inequality, (4.4.36), and (4.4.40),

$$\mu_\ell(G_n) \leq \frac{1}{n^2} \tag{4.4.41}$$

Let

$$S = \bigcap_{m=1}^\infty \left(\bigcup_{n=m}^\infty G_n \right) \tag{4.4.42}$$

If $x \notin S$, then for some m, $x \in \bigcap_{n=m}^\infty (X \setminus G_n)$, that is,

$$|c_{n+1}(x) - c_n(x)| \leq \frac{1}{n^2}, \qquad n = m, m+1, \ldots \tag{4.4.43}$$

Thus, on $X \setminus S$,

$$\sum_{n=1}^\infty |c_{n+1}(x) - c_n(x)| < \infty \tag{4.4.44}$$

so

$$c_N = c_1 + \sum_{j=1}^{N-1} (c_{j+1} - c_j)$$

converges, that is, (4.4.38) holds for $x \notin S$.

We need to show that S is negligible. By definition,

$$S \subset \bigcup_{n=m}^\infty G_n \tag{4.4.45}$$

and, by (4.4.41) and (4.4.30),

$$\mu_\ell\left(\bigcup_{n=m}^{\infty} G_n\right) \leq \sum_{n=m}^{\infty} \frac{1}{n^2} \to 0 \quad \text{as } m \to \infty \qquad (4.4.46)$$

Thus, S is negligible.

Let $\{c_n\}_{n=1}^{\infty}$ and $\{\tilde{c}_n\}_{n=1}^{\infty}$ be two Cauchy sequences in f that each have a limit off negligible sets S and $\widetilde{S}$. Then $(c_1, \tilde{c}_1, c_2, \tilde{c}_2, \dots)$ is also a Cauchy sequence, and by the construction above, we can find a subsequence d_n obeying (4.4.40) so that d_{2k} is a c_n and d_{2k+1} is a $\tilde{c}_n$. Except for a negligible set, $S^\sharp$, $\lim d_n(x)$ exists, and on $X \setminus S^\sharp \cup S \cup \widetilde{S}$, $c_\infty(x) = \tilde{c}_\infty(x)$ as required. $\qquad \square$

The proof shows more:

Theorem 4.4.8. *Let $f \in L^1(\ell)$. Then*

(a) *There is a sequence $c_n \in C_{\mathbb{R}}(X)$ so $\|c_n - f\|_\ell \to 0$, and for any $\varepsilon > 0$, there is an open F_σ, G_ε with $\mu_\ell(G_\varepsilon) < \varepsilon$ so that $c_n \to F$, a representative of f, uniformly on $X \setminus G_\varepsilon$.*

(b) *(Lusin's Theorem). There is a representative, $F = (S, c_\infty)$ of f, and for any ε, a compact $K_\varepsilon \subset X$ with $\mu_\ell(X \setminus K_\varepsilon) < \varepsilon$ so $c_\infty \restriction K_\varepsilon$ is continuous.*

Proof. (a) Pick c_n and G_n as in the proof. If $x \notin \bigcap_{n=m}^{\infty} G_n$ and $j, k \geq m$, then

$$|c_j(x) - c_k(x)| \leq \sum_{n=\min(j,k)}^{\max(j,k)-1} |c_{n+1}(x) - c_n(x)|$$

$$\leq \sum_{n=\min(j,k)}^{\infty} \frac{1}{n^2} \qquad (4.4.47)$$

Thus, given ε, pick m so $\sum_m^{\infty} 1/n^2 < \varepsilon$ and let $G_\varepsilon = \bigcup_{n=m}^{\infty} G_n$. Then $\mu_\ell(G_\varepsilon) < \varepsilon$ and on $X \setminus G_\varepsilon$, $c_j \to c_\infty$ uniformly by (4.4.47).

(b) Define c_∞, S as in the proof of the last theorem and let $F = S, c_\infty$. By (a), on each $X \setminus G_\varepsilon \equiv K_\varepsilon$, c_∞ is a uniform limit of continuous functions, so continuous and $\mu_\ell(X \setminus K_\varepsilon) < \varepsilon$. $\qquad \square$

After the next theorem, we'll stop thinking of $f \in L^1(\ell)$ as an equivalence class of Cauchy sequences and start thinking of f as an equivalence class of representatives. Indeed, by setting F to 0 on S, we'll even forget about S and only think of Baire functions equal a.e. But until we establish the following connections between f's in L^1 and their representatives, we'll need to distinguish, so we'll use capital letters for the representatives.

220 4. Measure Theory

Theorem 4.4.9. *Let $f, g \in L^1(\ell)$ and let (S, F) and (T, G) be representatives for f and g, respectively. Then*

(a) *$(S \cup T, F + G)$ is a representative of $f + g$, and for any $\lambda \in \mathbb{R}$, $(S, \lambda F)$ is a representative of λf.*

(b) *If g is bounded, then $fg \in L^1(\ell)$ also and $(S \cup T, FG)$ is a representative of fg.*

(c) *If Φ is Lipschitz, $(S, \Phi(F))$ is a representative of $\Phi(f)$.*

(d) *If $F(x) = G(x)$ for a.e. $x \in X \setminus (S \cup T)$, then $f = g$.*

(e) *If $f_n \to f$ in $\|\cdot\|_\ell$ and if there are representatives (S_n, F_n) of f_n and a function, F, and negligible set $S \supset \bigcup_{n=1}^\infty S_n$ so that $F_n(x) \to F(x)$ for $x \notin S$, then there is a negligible set, S_0, so that $(S \cup S_0, F)$ is a representative of f.*

(f) *$f \geq 0$ if and only if for a.e. x, $F(x) \geq 0$.*

(g) *$f \geq g$ if and only if for a.e. x, $F(x) \geq G(x)$.*

(h) *$(S \cup T, \max(F(x), G(x))$ is a representative of $F \vee G$ (and similarly for $F \wedge G$ pointwise and $\min$).*

Proof. (a)–(c) If $c_n \xrightarrow{\ell} f$, $c_n \in C_\mathbb{R}(X)$, $c_n(x) \to F(x)$, $x \notin S$, and similarly for d_n, then $c_n + d_n$ and λc_n work for $f + g$ and λf, proving (a). To get (c), use $\Phi(c_n)$.

For (b), note that for some a, b, $\Phi_a^b(g) = g$ and we can replace d_n by $\Phi_a^b(d_n)$, that is, suppose $\{d_n\}$ are uniformly bounded. With this in place, we get $c_n d_n$ as a sequence for fg.

(d) This involves a little fiddling. By replacing f, g by $f - g, 0$, we are reduced to showing that if f has $(S, F \equiv 0)$ as representative, then $f = 0$. By (c), if f has zero representative, so does f_a^b. So by (4.4.19), we can suppose f is bounded. Replacing f by $|f|$, we can also suppose $f \geq 0$, and by multiplying by a constant, we can suppose $0 \leq f \leq 1$. Thus, without loss, the Cauchy sequence $c_n \to f$ in L^1 obeys $0 \leq c_N \leq 1$.

Since $F = 0$, Theorem 4.4.8 implies that, given ε, we can suppose $c_n \to 0$ uniformly on $X \setminus G_\varepsilon$, where $\mu_\ell(G_\varepsilon) < \varepsilon$. Thus, picking N large, we can suppose c_N exists with

$$\mu_\ell(G_\varepsilon) < \varepsilon, \quad \|f - c_N\|_\ell < \varepsilon, \quad 0 < c_N(x) < \varepsilon \text{ on } X \setminus G_\varepsilon \quad (4.4.48)$$

Let $K_\varepsilon = \{x \mid c_N(x) \geq 2\varepsilon\}$. Then K_ε is closed and lies in G_ε by (4.4.48). Let $d = (c_N - 2\varepsilon\mathbb{1})_+$. Then $\text{supp}(d) \subset K_\varepsilon \subset G_\varepsilon$ and $0 \leq d \leq 1$ since $0 \leq c_N \leq 1$. It follows that d is admissible for G_ε so

$$\ell(d) \leq \mu_\ell(G_\varepsilon) < \varepsilon \quad (4.4.49)$$

Clearly, for all x,

$$c_N \leq d + 2\varepsilon\mathbb{1} \quad (4.4.50)$$

since this is trivial if $c_N \leq 2\varepsilon$ (since $d \geq 0$) and $d = c_N - 2\varepsilon$ if $c_N \geq 2\varepsilon$. Thus, since $c_n, d \geq 0$,

$$\|c_N\|_\ell \leq \ell(d) + 2\varepsilon < 3\varepsilon \tag{4.4.51}$$

so by (4.4.48),

$$\|f\|_\ell < 4\varepsilon \tag{4.4.52}$$

Since ε is arbitrary, $f = 0$ in L^1.

(e) First pass to a subsequence, still denoted f_n, so that $\|f_n - f_{n+1}\|_\ell \leq 1/n^4$. It follows that if $S_0 = [\bigcap_{m=1}^\infty (\bigcup_{n=m}^\infty G_n)] \cup \bigcup_{n=1}^\infty S_n$, then

$$\|f_n - f\|_\ell \to 0, \qquad S_0 \text{ is negligible}, \qquad F_n \to F \text{ for } x \notin S_0$$

Thus, $(S_0 \cup S, F)$ is a representative of f.

(f) If $f \geq 0$, F_+ is a representative of f_+, by (c), so $f_+ = f$ implies that f has a positive representative. So every representative is positive a.e.

Conversely, if a.e. $F \geq 0$, f_+ and f have a.e. equal representatives. So, by (d), $f = f_+$, so $f \geq 0$.

(g) is immediate from (f).

(h) By (c), $|F - G|$ is a representative of $|f - g|$, so $\frac{1}{2}(f + g + |f - g|)$ has $\max(F, G)$ as a representative. $\qquad\square$

Remark. The proof of (e) shows that if $f_n \to f$ in L^1, there is a subsequence, f_{n_j}, so that $F_{n_j}(x)$ converges to a limit $F_\infty(x)$ which is a.e. finite. Thus, if we know a priori only that F_n converges a.e. to a function, F, which might be infinite, the limit is finite for a.e. x.

Henceforth, we will consider elements of $L^1(\ell)$ as sets of Baire functions equal a.e. We can now complete the monotone convergence theorem.

Theorem 4.4.10 (Monotone Convergence Theorem). *Under the hypothesis of Theorem 4.4.2, for a.e. x, $f_n(x)$ is monotone in x, and for such x, $f_\infty(x) \equiv \lim f_n(x) = \sup f_n(x)$ is a.e. finite and represents the L^1 limit f. Put differently, if f_n is monotone in x with $f_n \in L^1$, then*

$$\sup_n \ell(f_n) < \infty \text{ (plus } f_n \uparrow)$$
$$\Rightarrow \ell(\sup f_n) = \sup \ell(f_n) \text{ and } \|f_n - \sup_m f_m\|_\ell \to 0 \tag{4.4.53}$$

Proof. By (g) of the last theorem, $f_n(x)$ is monotone in x for a.e. x, so $f_\infty(x) = \sup_n f_n(x) = \lim_n f_n(x)$ exists for a.e. x, although it may be infinity. By the remark after the theorem, by $f_n \to f$ for $f \in L^1$, we see f_∞ is a.e. finite and is the limit f. $\qquad\square$

We proved that any $f \in L^1(\ell)$ has a representative which is a Baire function. The following shows first that any bounded Baire function is in $L^1(\ell)$ and specifies exactly which Baire functions lie in $L^1(\ell)$.

Theorem 4.4.11. (a) *For every open F_σ, A, its characteristic function, χ_A, lies in L^1 (i.e., there is $f \in L^1$ which has χ_A as a representative). Moreover,*

$$\ell(\chi_A) = \mu_\ell(A) \qquad (4.4.54)$$

(b) *For every Baire set, A, χ_A lies in L^1.*
(c) *Every bounded Baire function lies in L^1.*
(d) *If $f \geq 0$ is a Baire function, then $f \in L^1(\ell)$ if and only if*

$$\sup_n \|\min(n, f)\|_\ell < \infty \qquad (4.4.55)$$

(e) *If f is a Baire function, $f \in L^1(\ell)$ if and only if $|f| \in L^1(\ell)$.*

Remarks. 1. Writing μ for μ_ℓ, we define for $f \in L^1$,

$$\int f(x)\, d\mu(x) \equiv \ell(f) \qquad (4.4.56)$$

If f is Baire and $f \geq 0$, we set

$$\int f(x)\, d\mu(x) \equiv \sup_n \int \min(f(x), n)\, d\mu(x) \qquad (4.4.57)$$

which may be $+\infty$. (e) is then written as

$$f \text{ Baire lies in } L^1 \Leftrightarrow \int |f(x)|\, d\mu(x) < \infty \qquad (4.4.58)$$

2. The proof sheds some light on why we use Baire and not Borel functions. If A is an open F_σ, we realize χ_A as a monotone limit of continuous functions at *all* $x \in X$. Since the Baire functions are closed under pointwise limits and all $f \in C(X)$ are Baire, only Baire sets, A, can be such pointwise limits at all x. Of course, it might be that we could define negligible sets and get pointwise limits at all x but a negligible set. Indeed, as we'll discuss in the Notes to the next section, one can do this, although the approximating sequence will depend on the functional, ℓ. As an example of a space so big that not all Borel sets are Baire, consider $\{0,1\}^{[0,1]}$, that is, all functions $g: [0,1] \to \{0,1\}$ (with no continuity or measurability restrictions). Put the product topology on this space so it is compact. Baire functions, $f(g)$, can only depend on the values of g on a countable set. The characteristic function of the point $g = 0$ is Borel, but not Baire.

Proof. (a) Let $A = \bigcup_{n=1}^\infty K_n$ with K_n closed. By replacing K_n by $\bigcup_{j=1}^n K_j$, we can suppose $K_n \subset K_{n+1}$. By normality, we can find $K_n \subset U_n \subset C_n \subset A$, where U_n is open and C_n is closed, and by Urysohn's lemma, find $f_n \in$

$C_{\mathbb{R}}(x)$, $\mathrm{Ran}(f_n) \subset [0,1]$, and so that $f_n \equiv 1$ on K_n and $f_n \equiv 0$ on $X \setminus U_n$, so $\mathrm{supp}(f_n) \subset C_n \subset A$. Thus, each f_n is admissible for A. Let $g_n = \max(f_1, \ldots, f_n)$. Then g_n is admissible and $g_n \leq g_{n+1} \leq \ldots$. Clearly, since $g_n \leq \chi_A$ and $g_n \equiv 1$ on K_n, $\sup_n g_n = \lim_n g_n = \chi_A$. Thus, by the monotone convergence theorem, $\chi_A \in L^1$ and

$$\ell(\chi_A) = \sup_n \ell(g_n) \leq \mu_\ell(A) \qquad (4.4.59)$$

On the other hand, if h is admissible, $h \leq \chi_A$, so $\ell(h) \leq \ell(\chi_A)$. So taking the sup over h,

$$\mu_\ell(A) \leq \ell(\chi_A) \qquad (4.4.60)$$

proving (4.4.54).

(b) Let $\mathcal{B} = \{B \text{ Baire} \mid \chi_B \in L^1(\ell)\}$. By (a), $\mathcal{B}$ contains the open F_σ's. If $B \in \mathcal{B}$, then $X \setminus B \in \mathcal{B}$ since $\chi_{X \setminus B} = 1 - \chi_B$. Moreover, if $B_1, B_2 \in \mathcal{B}$, so is $B_1 \cap B_2$ since $\chi_{B_1 \cap B_2} = \chi_{B_1} \chi_{B_2}$, and we have (b) of Theorem 4.4.9. Thus, $B_1 \cup B_2 = X \setminus [(X \setminus B_1) \cap (X \setminus B_2)] \in \mathcal{B}$. If $\{B_j\}_{j=1}^\infty \subset \mathcal{B}$, let $C_j = B_1 \cup \cdots \cup B_j$, so $\chi_{\cup_1^\infty B_j} = $ monotone limit of $\chi_{C_j} \in L^1$ by the monotone convergence theorem. It follows that $\mathcal{B}$ is a σ-algebra containing the open F_σ's, so $\mathcal{B}$ is all the Baire sets.

(c) Let f be a bounded Baire function, say $\sup_x |f(x)| \leq 1$. Then let

$$f_n(x) = \sum_{j=-2^n}^{2^n - 1} \frac{j}{2^n} \chi_{\{x \mid \frac{j}{2^n} \leq f(x) < \frac{j+1}{2^n}\}} \qquad (4.4.61)$$

with the $< \frac{j+1}{2^n}$ replaced by $\leq \frac{j+1}{2^n}$ if $j = 2^n - 1$. Then each f_n is a finite linear combination of elements of L^1 by (b), so $f_n \in L^1$. Moreover, $f_n \uparrow f$, so by the monotone convergence theorem, $f \in L^1$.

(d) If the sup is finite, $f = \sup(\min(n, f)) \in L^1$ by the monotone convergence theorem. On the other hand, if $f \in L^1$, $\|\min(n, f)\|_\ell \leq \ell(f)$, so the sup is finite.

(e) If $f \in L^1$, then $f_\pm \in L^1$ by Theorem 4.4.9(c), so $|f| = f_+ + f_- \in L^1$. Conversely, if $|f| \in L^1$, $\min(n, f_\pm) \leq |f|$, so by (d), $f_\pm \in L^1$, so $f = f_+ - f_- \in L^1$. $\qquad \square$

The ideas of this proof provide a general result about Baire functions.

Theorem 4.4.12. *Let $\mathcal{F}$ be an algebra of bounded functions $f \colon X \to \mathbb{R}$ for X a compact Hausdorff space. Suppose that $C_{\mathbb{R}}(X) \subset \mathcal{F}$ and that $\mathcal{F}$ has the property*

$$f_n \in \mathcal{F} \text{ and } f_n(x) \to f_\infty(x) \text{ for all } x \in X \Rightarrow f_\infty \in \mathcal{F} \qquad (4.4.62)$$

Then $\mathcal{F}$ contains the class of all bounded Baire functions.

Remark. As we've seen, the set of all bounded Baire functions obeys (4.4.62), so this theorem says that the smallest algebra obeying (4.4.62) and containing $C_{\mathbb{R}}(X)$ is the set of all bounded Baire functions.

Proof. If A is an open F_σ, the g_n constructed in the proof of (a) of Theorem 4.4.11 are in $C_{\mathbb{R}}(X)$ and have $g_n \to \chi_A$, so $\chi_A \in \mathcal{F}$.

Let $\mathcal{B} = \{A \mid \chi_A \in \mathcal{F}\}$. Then $\chi_{X \setminus B} = 1 - \chi_B$ and $\chi_{A \cup B} = \chi_A + \chi_B - \chi_A \chi_B$ shows $\mathcal{B}$ is closed under complements and finite unions. If $\{B_j\}_{j=1}^\infty \subset \mathcal{B}$,

$$\chi_{\cup_{j=1}^\infty B_j} = \lim \chi_{\cup_{j=1}^n B_j} \tag{4.4.63}$$

so $\mathcal{B}$ is a σ-ring and so contains all Baire sets.

By (4.4.61), $\mathcal{F}$ contains every bounded Baire function. $\qquad\square$

We saw in (4.4.54) that $\mu_\ell(A) = \ell(\chi_A) = \|\chi_A\|_\ell$. This allows the extension of μ_ℓ to a countably additive set function on all Baire sets.

Definition. Let X be a compact Hausdorff space. Given any normalized positive functional, ℓ, on $C(X)$, define $\mu_\ell(\cdot)$ on the Baire sets by

$$\mu_\ell(A) = \|\chi_A\|_\ell = \ell(\chi_A) \tag{4.4.64}$$

Theorem 4.4.13. (a) *For any* A, $0 \le \mu_\ell(A) \le 1$.

(b) $\mu_\ell(X \setminus A) = 1 - \mu_\ell(A)$ $\qquad\qquad\qquad\qquad\qquad\qquad\qquad$ (4.4.65)

(c) *If* $\{A_j\}_{j=1}^\infty$ *are pairwise disjoint Baire sets, then*

$$\mu_\ell\left(\bigcup_{j=1}^\infty A_j\right) = \sum_{j=1}^\infty \mu_\ell(A_j) \tag{4.4.66}$$

(d) *For any* $f \in L^1(\ell)$,

$$\ell(f) = \lim_{n \to \infty} \sum_{j=-\infty}^\infty \frac{j}{2^n}\, \mu_\ell\left(\left\{x \,\middle|\, \frac{j}{2^n} \le f(x) < \frac{j+1}{2^n}\right\}\right) \tag{4.4.67}$$

Proof. (a) and (b) are trivial.

(c) follows from (4.4.63) and the monotone convergence theorem.

(d) Let f_n be given by (4.4.61) with the sum from $-\infty$ to ∞. Since $f - 1 \le f_n \le f$ for all n, all f_n lie in L^1 and $f_n \uparrow f$. So (4.4.67) follows from the monotone convergence theorem. $\qquad\square$

We will start writing $L^1(X, d\mu_\ell)$ rather than $L^1(\ell)$ and $\int f(x)\, d\mu_\ell(x)$ instead of $\ell(f)$. We will also use $\|\cdot\|_1$ rather than $\|\cdot\|_\ell$ for the norm on $L^1(X, d\mu_\ell)$.

As a final aside, we define:

Definition. Given a positive Baire measure, μ, on a compact Hausdorff space, we define its *support*, supp(μ), by

$$\text{supp}(\mu) = \{x \in X \mid \text{all open } F_\sigma \text{ sets, } U, \text{ with } x \in U \text{ have } \mu(U) > 0\} \tag{4.4.68}$$

It is easy to see this set is closed (Problem 10). Moreover,

Proposition 4.4.14. *For every nonzero, positive Baire measure μ, supp(μ) is nonempty.*

Proof. Suppose supp(μ) = $\emptyset$. Then for all x, there is an open F_σ, U_x with $x \in U_x$, and $\mu(U_x) = 0$. Since $\{U_x\}_{x \in X}$ cover X, we can find $x_1, \ldots, x_n$ with $X \subset \cup_{j=1}^n U_{x_j}$. But then

$$\mu(X) \leq \sum_{j=1}^{n} \mu(U_{x_j}) = 0 \tag{4.4.69}$$

so supp(μ) is nonempty. $\square$

Notes and Historical Remarks. I learned this approach to the construction of measures from an appendix of Lax's book [**553**] and we follow him fairly closely. He only considered compact metric spaces, but so long as one restricts to Baire functions, the general case is easy, as we've seen.

There are basically two usual approaches to go from $|[a,b]| = b - a$ to a general theory of Lebesgue integral and measure. One approach first constructs a measure on general sets and then an integral via something like (4.4.67) (see our discussion in Section 8.1 which shows how to get the measure and Section 4.13 which goes from measure to integral). The other approach first constructs an integral from the Riemann integral of continuous functions by a two-step process and then forms the measure as the integral of characteristic functions. See [**122, 122**] for presentations of this approach. In a sense, the Lax approach is a variant on the integral-first construction.

One defect in the Lax approach is that it obscures Lebesgue's great insight that the key to extending integration was to break up the range (as the right side of (4.4.67) does!) rather than breaking up the domain as Cauchy and Riemann did. We will rectify this defect somewhat by the historical discussion below; see Bressoud [**128, 129**], Chae [**179**], and Hawkins [**406**] for historically-based discussions of the Lebesgue integral.

The history of convergence theorems for integrals is discussed in the Notes to Section 4.6. We emphasize that it is false in general for nets (Problem 5) but true for nets if $f_\alpha \uparrow f$ and all functions, including the limit,

f, are continuous (Problem 6). This is because of a theorem of Dini [**246**] (who proved it for sequences and $X = [a, b]$) that monotone convergence to a continuous limit implies uniform convergence (Problem 6) and that ℓ is a $\|\cdot\|_\infty$-continuous function on L^1 (Problem 4).

The Riesz–Fischer theorem is named after their 1907 papers [**305, 775**] (see Section 4.5 for a capsule biography of F. Riesz). There are two results from their works called the Riesz–Fischer theorem in the literature and neither is Theorem 4.4.7! One is the fact that the Fourier series for a function in $L^2([0, 2\pi], dx)$ converges in L^2-sense. We already discussed this result in Section 3.5 and its Notes. More generally, they dealt with L^2 convergence of abstract Fourier series. It was this that their contemporaries focused on and that the authors were after. Riesz's work was motivated by the work of Fatou [**295**] applying Lebesgue's theory to trigonometric series.

But, in time, it was realized that the key technical fact that led to the Fourier series result was that $L^2([0, 2\pi], dx)$ was complete. From one point of view, the whole point of the Lebesgue integral is this completeness result, and many books use the name "Riesz–Fischer theorem" for the proof of completeness of L^p either for general $p < \infty$ or for $p = 1$ or $p = 2$ or for both $p = 1$ and 2.

The proof in standard textbooks goes from a Cauchy sequence in L^p-norm, passes to a subsequence with $\|f_{n+1} - f_n\|_p \leq n^{-4}$, and by a Markov estimate, shows for a.e. x that $\sum_{n=1}^\infty |f_{n+1}(x) - f_n(x)| < \infty$. That yields a pointwise limit of $f_n(x)$, which one shows is the L^p limit of the original Cauchy sequence.

In the Lax approach, completeness is obtained at the very first step by appealing to an abstract metric space completion theorem. So it might appear that the Riesz–Fischer argument has become irrelevant. But a glance at the above argument and the proof of Theorem 4.4.7 shows that the argument is still very much needed, not to prove completeness but to show that the elements of the abstract completion are given by (equivalence classes of) functions. It explains why we have chosen to call Theorem 4.4.7 the Riesz–Fischer theorem.

Lusin's theorem is usually stated not for L^1 functions but for any a.e. finite Baire function. Problem 7 shows how to get this from the L^1 case we prove. We'll return to Lusin's theorem when we discuss Littlewood's three principles in Section 4.6.

Lusin's theorem was proven in 1912 by the Russian analyst, Nikolai Nikolayevich Luzin (1883–1950) [**610**]. The theorem is written Lusin after the name on the French paper; the usual transliteration from Russian is Luzin. Luzin was a student of Egorov and his students include Alexandroff,

Keldysh, Khinchin, Kolmogorov, Lyusternik, Menshov, Shnirelman, Souslin, and Urysohn .

Like his teacher, Egorov, Luzin suffered during the time of the Stalin purges. In particular, in the summer of 1936, he was the defendant in the scientific equivalent of a show trial—consideration of his crimes by a commission of the Academy (see, e.g., Lorentz [**606**]). During its proceedings, he was attacked by some of his former students, including Alexandroff, Khinchin, and Kolmogorov. For unclear reasons, his punishment was mild— he was neither imprisoned nor dismissed from the Academy, but his influence within the Academy was diminished and he lost almost all his former considerable influence on Moscow mathematics. On January 17, 2012 (more than seventy-five years after the trial), the Russian Academy officially rescinded its motion condemning Lusin.

Markov's inequality is essentially equivalent to a result known as *Chebyshev's inequality*. Chebyshev stated his inequality in the form

$$\mathbb{E}(|f - \mathbb{E}(f)| > \varepsilon) \leq \varepsilon^{-2}[\mathbb{E}(f^2) - \mathbb{E}(f)^2] \qquad (4.4.70)$$

for real f (and $\mathbb{E}(\cdot) = \int \cdot \, d\mu$ for a probability measure) which can be seen to be equivalent to the L^2 version (see Theorem 4.6.10 and Problem 9), but the idea is the same. The inequality appeared implicitly in an 1853 paper of Irénée-Jules Bienaymé (1796–1878) [**89**], but published in a more explicit form in 1867 by Chebyshev [**183**]. It appeared in Liouville's Journal and Liouville arranged Bienyamé's paper to appear again immediately before Chebyshev's paper. Despite this and Chebyshev's acknowledgement of Bienaymé, the inequality is almost universally called Chebyshev's inequality or occasionally the Bienaymé–Chebyshev inequality. Bienaymé's paper concerned defending Laplace's least square approximation, while it was Chebyshev who realized its power, using (4.4.70) in his proof of the weak law of large numbers (see Section 7.2).

Markov's inequality is named after its appearance in his book, *The Calculus of Probabilities* [**632**]; most often, the 1913 edition is mentioned but it may have already appeared in this 1900 edition. Andrei Andreyevich Markov (1856–1922) was a student of Pafnuty Chebyshev (1821–94; his capsule biography is in the Notes to Section 7.2) whose inequality is a variant, so this is a case of Arnol'd's principle.

We turn now to some comments on the history of Lebesgue and more general measures. As we explained in the Notes to Section 4.1, Cauchy already understood that for continuous functions, what we now call Riemann sums converge and give a satisfactory integral. There were some obscure points involving uniform continuity that were cleaned up later with the understanding of uniform continuity and uniform convergence.

The crisis that was eventually resolved by Lebesgue began with consid-erations by Dirichlet and Riemann concerning integrals of not necessarily continuous functions. This was not engendered by abstract thought but in the context of understanding Fourier series. A key contribution was Rie-mann's paper [**772**] where he considered Riemann sums with a fixed $1/n$ decomposition but allowed variable points in these intervals. A bounded function $f \colon [0,1] \to \mathbb{R}$ came to be called *Riemann integrable* if and only if

$$\lim_{n \to \infty} \frac{1}{n} \sum_{j=1}^{n} \left[\sup \left\{ f(x) \,\middle|\, x \in \left[\frac{j}{n}, \frac{j-1}{n} \right] \right\} \right.$$
$$\left. - \inf \left\{ f(x) \,\middle|\, x \in \left[\frac{j}{n}, \frac{j-1}{n} \right] \right\} \right] = 0 \tag{4.4.71}$$

In that case, one can prove (see Problem 2) that the Riemann sums converge independently of the choices made in the intervals.

Dirichlet already discussed the function $f(x)$ which was 1 if $x \in \mathbb{Q}$ and 0 if $x \notin \mathbb{Q}$ and noted that despite the convergence of the Cauchy sums (when the points are taken at j/n), it didn't really have a good integral in the Riemann sense (in the Lebesgue theory, the integral is 0). Another example which raised critical questions was

$$f(x) = \begin{cases} 0, & x \notin \mathbb{Q} \\ \frac{1}{q} & \text{if } x = \frac{p}{q} \text{ with } p, q \text{ relatively prime} \end{cases} \tag{4.4.72}$$

This function is discontinuous at every rational but continuous at the irrationals. It is not hard to see (Problem 3) that it is Riemann integrable and that $\int_0^1 f(x)\,dx = 0$. It raised the issue of what sets could be points of discontinuity—eventually answered (see Problem 3 in Section 5.4) by the theorem that if the points of continuity are dense, then the points of discontinuity are of first Baire category.

We will not try to give a blow-by-blow history (see [**128, 129, 179, 406**] for that), but mention that some of the key figures in these develop-ments were Cesare Arzelà (1847–1912), Giulio Ascoli (1843–96), Emile Borel (1871–1956), Georg Cantor (1845–1918), Gaston Darboux (1842–1917), Richard Dedekind (1831–1916), Ulisse Dini (1845–1918), Paul du Bois-Reymond (1831–89), Hermann Hankel (1839–73), Axel Harnack (1851–88), Eduard Heine (1821–81), Otto Hölder (1859–1937), Camille Jordan (1838–1922), William Osgood (1864–1943), Giuseppe Peano (1858–1932), Herman Schwarz (1843–1921), Otto Stolz (1842–1905), and Karl Weierstrass (1815–97). Among the puzzles and issues that were finally clarified by Lebesgue's theory were

(1) Exactly which bounded functions are Riemann integrable? (Lebesgue eventually proved they were the bounded Baire functions whose points of discontinuity had zero Lebesgue measure.)

(2) If u_n, u_∞ are uniformly bounded Riemann integrable functions and $u_n(x) \to u_\infty(x)$ for all x in $[0,1]$, does

$$\int_0^1 u_\infty(x)\, dx = \lim_{n\to\infty} \int_0^1 u_n(x)\, dx \qquad (4.4.73)$$

(This is true but decidedly difficult to prove within the context of the Riemann integral—it was done by Arzelà [37] and Osgood [694], but their proofs are involved; see Luxemburg [612] for historical notes. We'll see it is easy with the Lebesgue integral; see Theorem 4.6.3.)

(3) Exactly when does a convergent Fourier series determine the Fourier coefficients? (Because Fourier coefficients are given by integrals, this is a question of integration theory—in the Lebesgue context, it was settled by Fatou and Lebesgue.)

(4) For discontinuous derivatives, does the fundamental theory of calculus hold? (As Volterra showed and we discussed in the Notes to Section 4.2, there exist functions with everywhere defined bounded derivatives for which f' isn't Riemann integrable, but f' is always Borel measurable as a pointwise limit of $[f(x + \frac{1}{n}) - f(x)]/\frac{1}{n}$ and if bounded, Lebesgue proved that $\int_a^b f'(x)\, dx = f(b) - f(a)$ for the Lebesgue integral; see Problem 8. Lebesgue himself also considered the fact that for a.e. x, if $f \in L^1$, then $\frac{d}{dx} \int_a^x f(y)\, dy = f(x)$; see Section 2.4 of Part 3.)

Lebesgue's theory is discussed in his five papers in 1899–1901 [556, 557, 558, 559, 560] and presented in full in his 1902 thesis [561] and 1904 book [562]. Lebesgue's breakthrough depended on two ideas that went beyond earlier work on the Riemann integral: even those, like Jordan, who went beyond decompositions into intervals, only considered sets covered by finitely many intervals, while Lebesgue used countable covers. More importantly, as we noted earlier, Lebesgue partitioned the range, not the domain. Despite the fact that we now think of this work as clarifying, it met with some resistance (e.g., from Hermite)—even Lebesgue was unsure of its importance. But the work of Fatou, Riesz, and Fischer established the theory.

The first and a very significant extension beyond the Lebesgue measure is Riesz's construction in 1909 [779, 781] of the Lebesgue–Stieltjes integral in the context of his determining the dual space of $C([0,1])$ (see the next section). In 1913, Radon [753] abstracted to a general theory of measures as countably additive set functions on Borel sets in $\mathbb{R}^\nu$, and Fréchet [318] noted the further abstraction beyond $\mathbb{R}^\nu$.

There is an approach to axiomatically defining the properties of an integral that puts the integral first that was pioneered by Percy John Daniell (1889–1946) in 1918 [214]. (He was born in Chile, educated in England,

and did this work while a professor in what is now Rice University in Houston.) It was especially pioneered by Bourbaki [**122, 122**] who, like this book (before Section 4.13), restrict their integration to the locally compact case.

There is a different extension of the Lebesgue integral, allowing one to integrate something like $x^{-1}\sin(x^{-1})$, which is not in L^1 and is not integrable. This is due to Denjoy [**235**], Perron [**714**], Kurzweil [**538**], and Henstock [**417**].

For textbook discussions of measure theory, see [**41, 62, 64, 104, 181, 202, 255, 314, 386, 530, 624, 750, 759, 892, 907, 911, 1002**].

Henri Léon Lebesgue (1875–1941) was a student of Borel. He made his discoveries on the integral while teaching in a lycée at Nancy. He was influenced by Baire, Borel, and Jordan. His work was opposed by some, and while his lectures in Paris in 1903 and 1905 were well received, his initial university appointments were only at Rennes. He moved to the Sorbonne in 1910 and Collège de France in 1921. While he didn't do anything of the significance of Lebesgue measure, in his later career, he made important contributions to dimension theory (see the Notes to Section 8.2) and potential theory (see Section 3.4 of Part 3). From 1922 on, he focused on pedagogy.

Problems

1. (a) A *semimetric* on a set Y is a function $\rho\colon Y \times Y$ to $[0,\infty)$ that obeys all the axioms of a metric except that $\rho(x,y)=0$ need not imply that $x=y$. In that case, say $x \sim y \Leftrightarrow \rho(x,y)=0$. Prove that $\sim$ is an equivalence relation.

   (b) Let $Y/\sim$ be the set of equivalence classes and if $\sim x = \{y \mid x \sim y\}$ and if $\tilde{\rho}(\sim x, \sim y)=\rho(x,y)$, prove that $\tilde{\rho}$ is well defined on $Y/\sim$ and defines a metric there.

   (c) If ℓ is a normalized positive functional on a compact Hausdorff space, X, not necessarily a strictly positive function, prove that (4.4.4) defines a semimetric on $C_{\mathbb{R}}(X)$ by $\rho(c,d)=\ell(|c-d|)$ and that by passing to the quotient, one can push through the entire theory of this section.

2. Prove that for a function f on $[0,1]$, $\lim_{n\to\infty}\frac{1}{n}\sum_{j=1}^{n}f(x_j^{(n)})$, for any choice of $x_j^{(n)} \in [\frac{j}{n},\frac{j-1}{n}]$ (and the limit is then independent of choice) if and only if (4.4.71) holds.

3. Prove that the function f of (4.4.72) is Riemann integrable with integral 0.

   The next three problems explore convergence theorems, a subject we study in depth in Section 4.6.

4. (a) For any bounded Baire function, f, on a compact Hausdorff space, X, prove that $\|f\|_\infty \equiv \inf\{\sup_x |g(x)| \mid f - g = 0 \text{ for a.e. } x\}$ exists, defines a seminorm, and equals $\sup_x |f(x)|$ if $f \in C(X)$. Prove that

$$\|f\|_\infty = \sup\{a \mid \mu(\{x \mid |f(x)| > a\}) > 0\}$$

(b) For any bounded Baire function f and any μ_ℓ for a normalized positive functional ℓ, we have that

$$|\ell(f)| \leq \|f\|_\infty \qquad (4.4.74)$$

(c) If f_n, f are bounded Baire functions and $\|f_n - f\|_\infty \to 0$, prove that $\ell(f) \to \ell(f_n)$.

5. (a) Let $\mathcal{F}$ be the directed set of all finite subsets $F \subset [0, 1]$ ordered by $F > F'$ if $F' \subset F$. Let f_F be the characteristic function for F. Prove that as a net, $f_F \uparrow 1$ but $\int f_F \, dx \nrightarrow \int 1 \, dx$. Thus, the monotone convergence theorem is false for nets!

(b) Find a uniformly bounded monotone net f_α of Baire functions for which $\sup_\alpha f_\alpha$ is not a Baire function. (*Hint*: Take a Vitali subset in (a).)

6. (a) Let f_α be a monotone net (i.e., $\alpha < \beta \Rightarrow f_\alpha(x) \leq f_\beta(x)$ for all x) of continuous functions on a compact Hausdorff space, X. Suppose $f = \sup_\alpha f_\alpha$ is also continuous. Prove that $f_\alpha \to f$ in $\| \ \|_\infty$. This is known as Dini's theorem[**246**], usually stated for sequences. (*Hint*: For each $\varepsilon > 0$ and x, show there exists α_x and U_x, an open neighborhood of x, so that if $\alpha > \alpha_x$, $|f_\alpha(y) - f(y)| < \varepsilon$ for all $y \in U_x$. Then use compactness.)

(b) For every positive functional, ℓ, on $C_{\mathbb{R}}(X)$ and f_α, f as in (a), prove that $\ell(f_\alpha) \to \ell(f)$.

7. This will extend Lusin's theorem (Theorem 4.4.8(b)) to a Baire f which is a.e. finite. X is a compact Hausdorff space and μ_ℓ a measure defined by a positive normalized functional.

(a) Suppose $\sum_{n=0}^\infty a_n < \infty$ for $a_n > 0$. Prove there exists $b_n > 0$ so $b_{n+1} > b_n$ and $b_n \to \infty$ so $\sum_{n=0}^\infty a_n b_n < \infty$. (*Hint*: Pick $N(j)$ so that $N(j+1) > N(j)$ and so that $\sum_{n=N(j)}^\infty a_n < 4^{-N(j)}$. Then pick b_n so $b_{N(j)} = 2^N$ and is linear between $N(j)$ and $N(j+1)$.)

(b) For any Baire f which is a.e. finite, prove there is a strictly monotone function on $[0, \infty)$ with $F(y) \to \infty$ as $y \to \infty$ so that $\int F(f(x)) \, d\mu_\ell(x) < \infty$. (*Hint*: Let $a_n = \mu_\ell(\{x \mid n \leq f(x) < n+1\})$ and use (a).)

(c) For any a.e. finite Baire function and ε, prove that there is K_ε compact so $\mu_\ell(X \setminus K_\varepsilon) < \varepsilon$ and $f \upharpoonright K_\varepsilon$ is continuous. (*Hint*: Use the L^1-Lusin theorem for $F(f(\cdot))$.)

8. This problem will show that if f' exists for all $x \in [0, 1]$ and some continuous $f \colon [0, 1] \to \mathbb{R}$ and if

$$\sup_{x \in [0,1]} |f'(x)| = B < \infty \tag{4.4.75}$$

and $f(0) = 0$, then f' is a Baire function, and for all $y \in [0, 1]$,

$$f(y) = \int_0^y f'(x), dx \tag{4.4.76}$$

This is a result of Lebesgue, especially interesting since there are such f''s which are not Riemann integrable (see the discussion in the Notes to Section 4.2). It will need the following special case of the Lebesgue dominated convergence theorem that if g_n are Baire functions with $\sup_{n,x} |g_n(x)| = C < \infty$, and $\lim g_n(x) = g_\infty(x)$ exists (so g_∞ is Baire), then

$$\lim_{n \to \infty} \int_0^1 g_n(x)\, dx = \int_0^1 g_\infty(x)\, dx \tag{4.4.77}$$

(a) Prove the mean value theorem that, for all $x, y \in [0, 1]$ with $x \neq y$, there exists z between them so that

$$\frac{f(x) - f(y)}{x - y} = f'(z) \tag{4.4.78}$$

(*Hint*: Follow Problem 12 of Section 4.1.)

(b) Let

$$g_n(x) = \frac{f(x + \frac{1}{n}) - f(x)}{\frac{1}{n}}$$

Prove that $\sup_{n,x} |g_n(x)| \leq B$, given by (4.4.75), so by the dominated convergence theorem,

$$\int_0^y f'(x)\, dx = \lim_{n \to \infty} \int_0^y g_n(x)\, dx \tag{4.4.79}$$

(c) By the continuity of f, prove that for any $x_0 \in [0, 1]$,

$$\lim_{n \to \infty} \left(\frac{1}{n}\right)^{-1} \int_0^{1/n} [f(x_0 + x)]\, dx = f(x_0) \tag{4.4.80}$$

(d) Conclude (4.4.76) if $f(0) = 0$.

9. (a) Let $g \in L^2(\Omega, d\mu)$. Let $\widetilde{\Omega} = \Omega \times \{0, 1\}$ and $f(x, 0) = g(x)$, $f(x, 1) = -g(x)$ and $\tilde{\mu} \upharpoonright \Omega \times \{0\} = \frac{1}{2}\mu$, $\tilde{\mu} \upharpoonright \Omega \times \{1\} \equiv \frac{1}{2}\mu$. Prove that (4.4.70) for f implies

$$\mathbb{E}(|g| > \varepsilon) \leq \varepsilon^{-2}\mathbb{E}(g^2) \qquad (4.4.81)$$

(b) Prove that (4.4.81) for $g = \sqrt{|f|}$ implies Markov's inequality

$$\mathbb{E}(|f| > \varepsilon) \leq \varepsilon^{-1}\mathbb{E}(|f|) \qquad (4.4.82)$$

(c) Let G be even and monotone on $[0, \infty)$. Prove that (4.4.81) implies (also called Markov's inequality)

$$\mathbb{E}(|f| > \varepsilon) \leq G(\varepsilon)^{-1}\mathbb{E}(G(|f|)) \qquad (4.4.83)$$

(d) Prove that (4.4.83) for $G(x) = x^2$ and $f = g - \mathbb{E}(g)$ implies (4.4.70).

10. Let μ be a positive Baire measure.

(a) Let $x \in \overline{\operatorname{supp}(\mu)}$. Let $x \in U$, an open F_σ, prove that $\mu(U) > 0$ and conclude that $\operatorname{supp}(\mu)$ is closed.

(b) If $\operatorname{supp}(\mu)$ is a G_δ, prove that $U = X \setminus \operatorname{supp}(\mu)$ is the largest open set, U, with $\mu(U) = 0$.

Remark. In a space so big that single point sets are not Baire sets, supports may not be G_δ's.

4.5. The Riesz–Markov Theorem

Definition. Given a set, X, with σ-algebra, $\mathcal{B}$, a *measure* is a map $\mu \colon \mathcal{B} \to [0, \infty]$ which is *countably additive*, that is,

$$\{B_j\}_{j=1}^\infty \subset \mathcal{B}, \quad B_i \cap B_j = \emptyset \text{ if } i \neq j \Rightarrow \mu\left(\bigcup_{j=1}^\infty B_j\right) = \sum_{j=1}^\infty \mu(B_j) \qquad (4.5.1)$$

A measure is *finite* if $\mu(X) < \infty$, *σ-finite* if there exist $\{B_j\}_{j=1}^\infty \subset \mathcal{B}$ so $\mu(B_j) < \infty$ for all j and $X = \bigcup_{j=1}^\infty B_j$, and a *probability measure* if $\mu(X) = 1$.

Definition. Let X be a compact Hausdorff space. The *Baire probability measures*, $\mathcal{M}_{+,1}(X)$, are the probability measures on the Baire sets.

Let $C(X)^*_{+,1}$ be the normalized positive linear functionals on $C_{\mathbb{R}}(X)$. In the last section, we found a map, $\ell \mapsto \mu_\ell$ of $C(X)^*_{+,1}$ to $\mathcal{M}_{+,1}(X)$. Using the Riemann–Stieltjes–type construction of Theorem 4.1.6, we can find a map $\mu \mapsto L(\mu)$ of $\mathcal{M}_{+,1}(X)$ to $C(X)^*_{+,1}$ (it is easy to see—Problem 1—that the Baire sets have arbitrarily fine refinements.) Our main goal in this section will be to show that these two constructions are inverses, that is, $L(\mu_\ell) = \ell$ and $\mu_{L(\nu)} = \nu$, a result known as the Riesz–Markov theorem. We also prove that all Baire probability measures, μ, have the following regularity property for all Baire sets, A,

$$\sup\{\mu(K) \mid K \subset A,\ K\text{ compact}\} = \mu(A) = \inf\{\mu(U) \mid A \subset U,\ U\text{ open}\} \tag{4.5.2}$$

and we'll explore the connection between Baire and Borel measures.

Remark. Our Baire and Borel measures here are countably additive maps from the Baire (respectively, Borel) sets to $[0, A]$ for some $A < \infty$. Eventually (see Sections 4.10, 4.12 and Chapter 8) we'll allow Borel measures to take the value ∞ even when X is compact but on compact sets we'll reserve "Baire measures" to be finite (and, even in the σ-compact case, like $\mathbb{R}^\nu$, we'll require $\mu(K) < \infty$ for compact G_δ, K). Some authors allow Baire measures to be infinite and use the term *Radon measure* for measures on the Baire sets with $\mu(K) < \infty$ for K compact.

Proposition 4.5.1. $L(\mu_\ell) = \ell$

Proof. Fix $f \in C_\mathbb{R}(X)$. Given a partition, $\mathcal{P} = \{P_1, \ldots, P_k\}$, and $\{x_j\}_{j=1}^k$ with $x_j \in P_j$, the object in (4.1.25) is given by

$$R_\mathcal{P}(f, \mu_\ell, \{x_j\}_{j=1}^k) = \ell(F(f, \mathcal{P}, \{x_j\}_{j=1}^k))$$

where F is the simple function

$$F(f, \mathcal{P}, \{x_j\}_{j=1}^k)(y) = \sum_{j=1}^k f(x_j)\chi_{P_j}(y) \tag{4.5.3}$$

Clearly,

$$\|F(f, \mathcal{P}, \{x_j\}_{j=1}^k) - f\|_\infty \leq \sup_{j=1,\ldots,k}\ \sup_{x,y\in P_j} |f(x) - f(y)| \tag{4.5.4}$$

$$\equiv \delta_\mathcal{P}(f) \tag{4.5.5}$$

By a compactness argument (Problem 2), for any ε, we can find a Baire partition $\mathcal{P}_\varepsilon$ so $\delta_{\mathcal{P}_\varepsilon}(f) \leq \varepsilon$, and thus, if $\mathcal{P}' \rhd \mathcal{P}_\varepsilon$, $\delta_{\mathcal{P}'}(f) \leq \varepsilon$. It follows that the net $F(f, \mathcal{P}, \{x_j\}_{j=1}^k) \to f$ uniformly in the natural order of refinement in $\mathcal{P}$ for any x's. By $|\ell(f - g)| \leq \|f - g\|_\infty$ for all $f, g \in L^1(\ell)$ (see (4.4.74)), we obtain

$$\lim_\mathcal{P} \ell(F(f, \mathcal{P}, \{x_j\}_{j=1}^k)) = \ell(f) \tag{4.5.6}$$

By definition, the left side of (4.5.6) is $L(\mu_\ell)(f)$. $\qquad\square$

Lemma 4.5.2. *Let A be an open F_σ in a compact Hausdorff space, X. Then there exist compact sets $\{K_j\}_{j=1}^\infty$ with*

$$K_j \subset K_{j+1}^{\mathrm{int}} \tag{4.5.7}$$

$$\bigcup_{j=1}^\infty K_j = A \tag{4.5.8}$$

In particular, in any Baire probability measure, μ,

$$\mu(A) = \sup \mu(K_j) = \lim \mu(K_j) \tag{4.5.9}$$

and

$$\mu(A) = \sup\{\mu(K) \mid K \subset A, \, K \, compact\} \tag{4.5.10}$$

Proof. By hypothesis, $A = \bigcup_{j=1}^{\infty} C_j$ with C_j closed. Define K_j inductively as follows. $K_1 = C_1$. Given K_j, by Urysohn's lemma, find $f \colon X \to [0,1]$ so $f \restriction K_j = 1$, $f \restriction X \setminus A = 0$. Define

$$K_{j+1} = C_{j+1} \cup \{x \mid f(x) \geq \tfrac{1}{2}\} \tag{4.5.11}$$

so it is easy to see that (4.5.7) and (4.5.8) hold.

Since μ is countably additive, if $K_0 \equiv \emptyset$,

$$\mu(A) = \sum_{j=1}^{\infty} \mu(K_j \setminus K_{j-1})$$

$$= \lim_n \sum_{j=1}^{n} \mu(K_j \setminus K_{j-1})$$

$$= \lim_n \mu(K_j)$$

proving (4.5.9).

By (4.5.9), $\mu(A) \leq \sup_K \mu(K)$. Since $K \subset A$ implies $\mu(K) \leq \mu(A)$, $\sup_K \mu(K) \leq \mu(A)$ is trivial. $\qquad\square$

Proposition 4.5.3. *For any $\nu \in \mathcal{M}_{+,1}(X)$,*

$$\mu_{L(\nu)} = \nu \tag{4.5.12}$$

Proof. Let $\mu \equiv \mu_{L(\nu)}$. Since μ and ν are countably additive, $\{A \text{ Baire} \mid \mu(A) = \nu(A)\}$ is a σ-algebra, so it suffices to show $\mu(A) = \nu(A)$ if A is an open F_σ.

Let $\mathcal{F}$ be the admissible functions for A. Then, by the construction in Section 4.4,

$$\mu(A) = \sup_{f \in \mathcal{F}} L(\nu)(f) \tag{4.5.13}$$

Let K_j be the sequence of compacts in the lemma and $g_j \colon X \to [0,1]$ continuous, so $g_j \restriction K_j \equiv 1$, $g_j \restriction X \setminus K_{j+1}^{\mathrm{int}} = 0$. Then

$$\nu(K_j) \leq L(\nu)(g_j) \leq \nu(K_{j+1}) \tag{4.5.14}$$

by considering a subnet of partitions where K_j and $X \setminus K_{j+1}^{\mathrm{int}}$ are unions of sets in the partitions. By (4.5.9),

$$\nu(A) = \sup_j L(\nu)(g_j) \tag{4.5.15}$$

On the other hand, each g_j is admissible, and if f is admissible, $Q = \mathrm{supp}(f)$ is covered by $\{K_j^{\mathrm{int}}\}$. So, by compactness, $Q \subset K_{j_0}$ for some j_0, and thus, $f \leq g_{j_0}$. We conclude, by (4.5.13), that $\mu(A) = \nu(A)$ for open F_σ's. $\qquad\square$

We can combine these two propositions to see

Theorem 4.5.4 (Riesz–Markov Theorem, First Form). *The map $\ell \mapsto \mu_\ell$ sets up a bijection of $C(X)^*_{+,1}$ and $\mathcal{M}_{+,1}(X)$, that is, every normalized positive functional is the Riemann–Stieltjes-type integral associated to a unique Baire probability measure.*

Remarks. 1. Henceforth, we won't distinguish between the two sets and objects and just write $\mathcal{M}_{+,1}(X)$.

2. The second form of the Riesz–Markov theorem will identify $C(X)^*$ with the set of all complex measures, $\mathcal{M}(X)$. We'll discuss it as Theorem 4.8.8 in Section 4.8.

We turn next to the issue of regularity of Baire measures.

Definition. Let $\mathcal{B}$ be a σ-algebra of sets in a compact Hausdorff space and μ a finite measure. We say $A \in \mathcal{B}$ is *inner regular* if and only if

$$\mu(A) = \sup_{K \subset A,\, K \in \mathcal{B},\, K\,\mathrm{compact}} \mu(K) \qquad (4.5.16)$$

and *outer regular* if

$$\mu(A) = \inf_{A \subset U,\, U \in \mathcal{B},\, U\,\mathrm{open}} \mu(U) \qquad (4.5.17)$$

If all $A \in \mathcal{B}$ are both inner and outer regular, we say that μ is a *regular measure*.

Note. Since μ is finite, $\mu(A) = \mu(X) - \mu(X \setminus A)$, so

$$A \text{ is inner regular} \Leftrightarrow X \setminus A \text{ is outer regular} \qquad (4.5.18)$$

and so μ is regular if and only if every set is inner regular.

Lemma 4.5.5. *If μ is a finite measure on a σ-algebra, $\mathcal{B}$, then $\mathcal{S} = \{B \in \mathcal{B} \mid B \text{ is both inner and outer regular for } \mu\}$ is a σ-algebra.*

Proof. (4.5.18) implies the set $\mathcal{S}$ is closed under $B \to X \setminus B$, so we need only prove $\{B_n\}_{n=1}^\infty \subset \mathcal{S} \Rightarrow B \equiv \bigcup_{n=1}^\infty B_n \in \mathcal{S}$.

Given ε, find K_n compact with $K_n \subset B_n$ and $\mu(B_n \setminus K_n) < \varepsilon/3^n$. Also, find M (possible since $\mu(X) < \infty$) so that $\mu(B \setminus \bigcup_{n=1}^M B_n) < \varepsilon/2$. Then

$$\mu\left(B \setminus \bigcup_{n=1}^M K_n\right) \leq \mu\left(B \setminus \bigcup_{n=1}^M B_n\right) + \sum_{n=1}^M \mu(B_n \setminus K_n)$$

$$< \frac{\varepsilon}{2} + \sum_{n=1}^{\infty} \frac{\varepsilon}{3^n} \leq \varepsilon$$

so $\bigcup_{n=1}^{\infty} B_n$ is inner regular.

Given ε, find U_n open with $B_n \subset U_n$ and $\mu(U_n \setminus B_n) < \varepsilon/2^n$. Then $\bigcup_{n=1}^{\infty} U_n = U$ is open and

$$\mu(U \setminus B) \leq \sum_{n=1}^{\infty} \mu(U_n \setminus B_n) < \varepsilon$$

so B is outer regular. □

Theorem 4.5.6. *Every Baire measure, μ, is regular.*

Proof. Let A be an open F_σ. Trivially, A is outer regular and, by Lemma 4.5.2, A is inner regular. By Lemma 4.5.5, all sets in the σ-algebra generated by the open F_σ's are regular but that is all Baire sets. □

The following facts will not be proven since we'll only consider Baire measures on compact Hausdorff spaces, but they answer natural questions (see the reference in the Notes):

(1) Let $\mathcal{B}_0$ be the Baire σ-algebra and $\mathcal{B}_1$ the Borel σ-algebra. Let μ be a measure on $\mathcal{B}_0$. There is a unique *regular measure*, $\tilde{\mu}$, on $\mathcal{B}_1$ so that $\tilde{\mu} \restriction \mathcal{B}_0 = \mu$. In some cases, there are multiple nonregular measures and, in particular, Borel measures on general compact Hausdorff spaces may not be regular.

(2) For the measure $\tilde{\mu}$ of (1), for any $A \in \mathcal{B}_1$, there is a $B \in \mathcal{B}_0$ so $\tilde{\mu}(A \triangle B) = 0$. In particular, every equivalence class in $L^1(X, d\tilde{\mu})$ contains a Baire function, so $L^1(X, d\tilde{\mu}) = L^1(X, d\mu)$.

Closely related to regularity is the following:

Theorem 4.5.7. *Let $\{\mu_n\}_{n=1}^{\infty}$, μ_∞ be probability measures on a compact Hausdorff space, X, so that for all $f \in C(X)$,*

$$\int f(x) \, d\mu_n(x) \to \int f(x) \, d\mu_\infty(x) \tag{4.5.19}$$

Suppose A is a Baire set with A^{int} and $\bar{A}$ Baire sets and with $\mu_\infty(\partial A) = 0$. Then

$$\lim_{n \to \infty} \mu_n(A) = \mu_\infty(A) \tag{4.5.20}$$

Remarks. 1. (4.5.19) is called *vague* or *weak convergence*.

2. Once we have finite measures on locally compact spaces, this result extends.

3. This result fails for signed measures; see Example 4.8.6.

Proof. Let $f \in C_{\mathbb{R}}(X)$, $0 \leq f \leq 1$, with $f = 0$ on $X \setminus A^{\text{int}}$ (i.e., f is admissible for A^{int}). Then

$$\liminf \mu_n(A) \geq \liminf \mu_n(f) = \mu_\infty(f) \qquad (4.5.21)$$

Thus, by (4.4.28),

$$\liminf \mu_n(A) \geq \mu_\infty(A^{\text{int}}) \qquad (4.5.22)$$

Taking complements,

$$\limsup \mu_n(A) \leq \mu_\infty(\bar{A}) \qquad (4.5.23)$$

Clearly, $\limsup \mu_n(A) \geq \liminf \mu_n(A)$, so if $\mu_\infty(\bar{A}) = \mu_\infty(A^{\text{int}})$ (i.e., if $\mu_\infty(\partial A) = 0$), then the limit exists and equals $\mu_\infty(A)$. $\qquad \square$

Notes and Historical Remarks. Here is the history of the Riesz–Markov theorem. In 1911, F. Riesz [**781**] showed that the dual of $C([a, b])$ was the Riemann–Stieltjes integrals on $[a, b]$. In doing this, he first extended Stieltjes integrals to allow functions of bounded variation, rather than just monotone functions, used the fact that it was known since Jordan's work that such functions were differences of monotone functions, and identified positive functionals and monotone function Stieltjes integrals. The last result used ideas in Hadamard's earlier work [**378**] on $C([a, b])$ as a space. Without knowing of Riesz's work, Helly [**412**] proved similar results, along the way proving an earlier version of the Hahn–Banach theorem (see the Notes to Section 5.5).

In the 1937 version of his book on integration, Saks [**810**] stated the Riesz–Markov theorem for compact metric spaces, attributing it to Banach. The theorem for general compact Hausdorff spaces was found independently by Markov [**635**] and Kakutani [**469**]. This Markov is not the Markov of Markov processes and Markov's inequality, but his son. What we call the Riesz–Markov theorem is also called the Riesz–Kakutani theorem, or even the Riesz representation theorem. Since Riesz found the duals of $C(X)$, $\mathcal{H}$, and L^p spaces, this last term is overused!

Frigyes Riesz (1880–1956), the Hungarian mathematician, was a giant of twentieth-century analysis, with key contributions in virtually all areas of abstract analysis with dominant contributions from 1905–35. He got his degree from Budapest in 1902 and, in 1911, was appointed to chair at the University of Kolozsvar (now Cluj, Romania). In the aftermath of World War I, that city became part of Romania, so the Hungarian University moved to Szeged, a city without a university until then. Riesz spent the next twenty-five years as professor in Szeged, including time as rector. He moved to the University of Budapest in 1945. Marcel Riesz (see the Notes to Section 5.7 of Part 3 for a capsule biography) was his younger brother.

F. Riesz's contributions are vast. He was a pioneer in the early theory of normed linear spaces, including finding the duals of Hilbert spaces, L^p spaces (which he invented and named after Lebesgue), and $C([a,b])$. He had central results in orthogonal expansions (Riesz–Fischer theorem). He also named H^p spaces (after Hardy) and found the factorization that allows the reduction of H^p to H^2 for many results. He was an innovator in operator theory, both with the earliest definitions and the general spectral theory for compact operators (Riesz–Schauder theory; see Section 3.3 of Part 4), and had some of the earliest results on rearrangement inequalities. He made important progress in ergodic theory and in the theory of maximal inequalities; see Section 2.3 of Part 3. He also was the first to define general subharmonic functions; see Section 3.2 of Part 3.

I want to warn about a possible misimpression the reader might get from the constructions we use in this section and Section 4.1. Since one only needs a finitely additive set function, α_0, on an algebra, $\mathfrak{A}_0$, to construct a Riemann–Stieltjes-type integral on $C(X)$, one might think by $\alpha_0 \to L(\alpha_0) \to \mu_{L(\alpha_0)}$, one proves any such finitely additive set function is the restriction of a countable additive Baire measure to $\mathfrak{A}_0$. This is false, as Problem 3 shows. The issue is that proof that $\mu_{L(\nu)} = \nu$ depended on the countable additivity of ν.

For a discussion of the relation between Baire and Borel measures, including the results mentioned in the text, see Dudley [**259**].

We can return to the remark after Theorem 4.4.11 about extending the construction there to Borel functions and sets on spaces so big that not all Borel sets are Baire sets. By the fact that Baire measures have regular extensions with the property (2) listed at the end of this section, one can define a Borel set as negligible by the same definition as we used for Baire sets and then define Borel representatives. This will construct the regular extension, and while we'll get all bounded Borel functions this way, as noted in property (2), we'll get the same equivalence classes, that is, every Borel function will be a.e. equal to a Baire function.

Problems

1. Given any open cover, $\{U_\alpha\}_{\alpha \in I}$, of a compact Hausdorff space, X, prove that one can find a partition $\{P_j\}_{j=1}^n$ into Baire sets so that each P_j lies in some single U_α. (*Hint*: First find an open cover by Baire sets, $\{V_\ell\}_{\ell=1}^m$, so each V_ℓ is in some U_α.)

2. Given any continuous function, f, on a compact Hausdorff space and any $\varepsilon > 0$, find a Baire partition $\{P_j\}_{j=1}^n$ so that $\sup_j \sup_{x,y \in P_j} |f(x) - f(y)| < \varepsilon$. (*Hint*: First find an open cover by Baire sets, $\{U_\ell\}_{\ell=1}^n$, so that for each ℓ, $\sup_{x,y \in U_\ell} |f(x) - f(y)| < \varepsilon$.)

3. Let $\mathfrak{A}_0$ be the algebra of all finite unions as in Example 4.1.5 with α given by (4.1.31), where

$$\tilde{\alpha}(x) = \begin{cases} 0, & x < \frac{1}{2} \\ 1, & x \geq \frac{1}{2} \end{cases}$$

(a) Prove that $\alpha([0, \frac{1}{2})) = 1$, $\alpha([\frac{1}{2}, 1]) = 0$, and that α is finitely additive on $\mathfrak{A}_0$, the ring of finite unions of $[c, d)$ or $[c, 1]$.

(b) Prove that the associated Lebesgue–Stieltjes measure, μ, has

$$\mu(A) = \begin{cases} 0, & \frac{1}{2} \notin A \\ 1, & \frac{1}{2} \in A \end{cases}$$

for any Baire set A.

(c) Note that $\mu \restriction \mathfrak{A}_0$ is not α.

4. Let X be a compact metric space. Prove that $C(X)$ is separable. Then prove that the weak topology on $\mathcal{M}_{+,1}(X)$ given by the maps $L_f(\mu) = \mu(f)$ is metrizable.

Remark. This is sometimes called the *vague topology* and convergence in it is called *vague convergence*.

4.6. Convergence Theorems; L^p Spaces

We saw the basic monotone convergence theorem in Section 4.4. Here we'll consider theorems that deal with the case where f_n are not necessarily monotone in n. As in the monotone case, these theorems only hold for sequences, *not*, in general, for nets. We then turn to Littlewood's three principles, including Egorov's theorem. Finally, we give the definition of $L^p(X, d\mu)$ and extend the convergence theorems to L^p.

Example 4.6.1. Define

$$f_n(x) = \begin{cases} n, & 0 < x < \frac{1}{n} \\ 0, & x = 0 \text{ or } x \geq \frac{1}{n} \end{cases}$$

Then $f_n(x) \to 0$ for every x, but $\lim \int_0^1 f_n(x)\, dx = 1$, not 0. Thus, something more than pointwise convergence is needed. $\quad\square$

Theorem 4.6.2 (Fatou's Lemma). *Let $\{f_n\}_{n=1}^\infty$ be a sequence of nonnegative functions in $L^1(X, d\mu)$ for μ a probability measure on some compact Hausdorff space, X. Then*

$$\int \liminf_{n\to\infty} f_n(x)\, d\mu(x) \leq \liminf_{n\to\infty} \int f_n(x)\, d\mu(x) \qquad (4.6.1)$$

Remarks. 1. This appeared as a technical lemma in work of Fatou so it is universally called Fatou's lemma, but is useful enough to be thought of as a theorem. (Indeed, like Schur's lemma, it is more useful than most theorems.)

2. In Example 4.6.1, $\liminf f_n = 0$ so (4.6.1) has $0 \leq 1$. This shows one may not have equality but only inequality. Of course, as the monotone convergence theorem demonstrates, one can have equality.

3. If f_n is the negative of the functions in Example 4.6.1, then $\int \liminf f_n(x)\, d\mu(x) = 0$, but $\liminf \int f_n(x)\, d\mu(x) = -1$. This shows that the nonnegativity hypothesis on f_n is essential.

Proof. Define

$$h_n(x) = \inf_{m \geq n} f_m(x) = \lim_{k \to \infty} \left(\inf_{n \leq m \leq k} f_m(x) \right) \qquad (4.6.2)$$

which is Baire measurable by Theorem 4.3.6. Moreover, since

$$0 \leq h_n(x) \leq f_n(x) \qquad (4.6.3)$$

each h_n lies in $L^1(x)$.

Clearly, for each $m \geq n$, $0 \leq h_n \leq f_m$, so

$$0 \leq \int h_n(x)\, d\mu(x) \leq \int f_m(x)\, d\mu(x) \qquad (4.6.4)$$

and thus,

$$0 \leq \int h_n(x)\, d\mu(x) \leq \inf_{m \geq n} \int f_m(x)\, d\mu(x) \qquad (4.6.5)$$

Since h_{n+1} is an inf over a smaller set than h_n, we have $h_n(x) \nearrow$, so by the monotone convergence theorem,

$$\int \sup_n h_n(x)\, d\mu(x) \leq \sup_n \inf_{m \geq n} \int f_m(x)\, d\mu(x) \qquad (4.6.6)$$

For any sequence $\{c_n\}_{n=1}^\infty$ of reals, it is easy to see (Problem 1) that

$$\sup_n \inf_{m \geq n} c_m = \liminf_{n \to \infty} c_n \qquad (4.6.7)$$

which implies that $\sup_n h_n(x) = \liminf f_n(x)$ and that the right side of (4.6.6) is $\liminf \int f_m(x)\, d\mu(x)$. □

Remark. In the proof, the positivity for f_n enters only in (4.6.3), that is, in being sure that h_n is bounded from below by an L^1 function. If there is an L^1 function g, so $h_n \geq g$ for all x and n, then Fatou's lemma still holds (as can also be seen by using Fatou's lemma on $h_n - g$). It is interesting to note that in Example 4.6.1, $\inf_n(-f_n(x)) = -\sup_n f_n(x)$ is not in L^1.

Theorem 4.6.3 (Dominated Convergence Theorem). *Let $\{f_n\}_{n=1}^{\infty}$ be a sequence in $L^1(X, d\mu)$ for μ, a Baire probability measure on X, a compact Hausdorff space. Suppose that for a.e. x,*

$$\lim_{n \to \infty} f_n(x) = f_{\infty}(x) \tag{4.6.8}$$

and that for some $g \in L^1(X, d\mu)$, we have for all n and a.e. x that

$$|f_n(x)| \leq g(x) \tag{4.6.9}$$

Then $\lim_{n \to \infty} \int f_n(x) \, d\mu$ exists,

$$\int f_{\infty} \, d\mu(x) = \lim_{n \to \infty} \int f_n(x) \, d\mu(x) \tag{4.6.10}$$

and

$$\lim_{n \to \infty} \int |f_n(x) - f_{\infty}(x)| \, d\mu(x) = 0 \tag{4.6.11}$$

Remarks. 1. Thus, counterexamples like Example 4.6.1 depend on the fact that (Problem 2) in that example, $\sup_n f_n(x) \notin L^1$.

2. (4.6.9) is paraphrased by saying g *dominates* f_n—and is where the name of the theorem comes from.

3. f_{∞} is only defined for a.e. x and is a Baire function on the Baire set where $\limsup f_n(x) = \liminf f_n(x)$. We imagine extending f_{∞} in any Baire measurable way on the complement of the set which, by hypothesis, is negligible.

Proof. Let $h_n^{\pm} = g \pm f_n \geq 0$ by (4.6.9) and is in L^1 since g is. Moreover, for a.e. x,

$$\liminf h_n^{\pm}(x) = g(x) \pm f_{\infty}(x) \tag{4.6.12}$$

Thus, Fatou's lemma implies

$$\int (g(x) \pm f_{\infty}(x)) \, d\mu(x) \leq \liminf \int (g(x) \pm f_n(x)) \, d\mu(x) \tag{4.6.13}$$

which says, subtracting $\int g(x) \, d\mu(x)$, that

$$\pm \int f_{\infty}(x) \, d\mu(x) \leq \liminf \left[\pm \int f_n(x) \, d\mu(x) \right] \tag{4.6.14}$$

or

$$\limsup \int f_n(x) \, d\mu(x) \leq \int f_{\infty}(x) \, d\mu \leq \liminf \int f_n(x) \, d\mu(x) \tag{4.6.15}$$

which implies that the limit exists and that (4.6.10) holds. (4.6.11) follows by applying (4.6.10) to $h_n(x) = |f_n(x) - f_{\infty}(x)|$ since $|h_n(x)| \leq 2g(x)$. □

We've already seen the usefulness of the dominated convergence theorem in Lebesgue's version of the second form of the fundamental theorem of calculus (see Problem 8 of Section 4.4). The dominated convergence theorem is among the most significant tools in analysis.

There is a quantitative version of the error in Fatou's lemma, at least when $\lim f_n$ exists.

Theorem 4.6.4 (Brézis–Lieb Theorem). *Let f_n, f be measurable L^1 functions with values in $[0, \infty]$. Suppose $f_n(x) \to f(x)$ pointwise for a.e. x. Then, as $n \to \infty$,*

$$\|f_n\|_1 - \|f - f_n\|_1 \to \|f\|_1 \qquad (4.6.16)$$

Remark. In particular, $\liminf \|f_n\|_1 \geq \|f\|_1$, which is Fatou's lemma in this case.

Proof. For any $a, b \in [0, \infty)$,

$$a + b - |a - b| = 2\min(a, b) \qquad (4.6.17)$$

Thus,

$$f + |f - f_n| - f_n = 2f - 2\min(f, f_n) \qquad (4.6.18)$$

Since $f_n \to f$ pointwise a.e., we have that the right side of (4.6.18) goes pointwise to zero. It is nonnegative and bounded by $2f$. Thus, by the dominated convergence theorem, its integral goes to zero. But the integral of the left side is $\|f\|_1 + \|f - f_n\|_1 - \|f_n\|_1$, so we have proven (4.6.16). $\square$

The following says that if (4.6.8) holds, then (4.6.10) $\Leftrightarrow$ (4.6.11).

Theorem 4.6.5 (Scheffé's Lemma). *Suppose $\{f_n\}_{n=1}^\infty$, f_∞ are functions in $L^1(X, d\mu)$ for μ a Baire probability measure on X, a compact Hausdorff space. Suppose (4.6.8) holds for a.e. $x \in X$. Then*

$$\lim_{n \to \infty} \|f_n - f_\infty\|_1 = 0 \Leftrightarrow \lim_{n \to \infty} \|f_n\|_1 = \|f_\infty\|_1 \qquad (4.6.19)$$

Proof. By the triangle inequality, $\Rightarrow$ in (4.6.19) is trivial.

Suppose first $f_n(x) \geq 0$ for a.e. x. Then (4.6.16) shows the right side implies the left. Now let f_n be a general real-valued sequence so $\|f_n\|_1 \to \|f_\infty\|_1$ and (4.6.9) hold. Then, by Fatou's lemma, using $f^\pm(x) = \max(0, \pm f(x))$

$$\int f_\infty^+(x) \, d\mu(x) \leq \liminf \int f_n^+(x) \, d\mu(x)$$

$$\leq \limsup \int f_n^+(x) \, d\mu(x)$$

$$= \lim \int |f_n(x)| \, d\mu(x) - \liminf \int f_n^-(x) \, d\mu(x)$$

$$\leq \int |f_\infty(x)| \, d\mu(x) - \int f_\infty^-(x) \, d\mu(x)$$

$$= \int f_\infty^+(x) \, d\mu(x)$$

by the hypothesis and Fatou's lemma again. Thus, $\lim \int f_n^+(x) \, d\mu(x) = \int f_\infty^+(x) \, d\mu(x)$ and so also $\lim \int f_n^-(x) \, d\mu(x) = \int f_\infty^-(x) \, d\mu(x)$. By the special case proven above, we get $\|f_n^+ - f_\infty^+\|_1 + \|f_n^- - f_\infty^-\|_1 \to 0$, so $\|f_n - f_\infty\|_1 \to 0$. □

We turn next to Egorov's theorem, a result on convergence and measure that can be used to provide another proof of the dominated convergence theorem (see Problem 3) and of Lusin's theorem (see Problem 5), which illuminates what pointwise convergence means in a measure theoretic context. We'll put this in context by listing what are known as "Littlewood's three principles of real analysis"[1]:

(1) Every Borel subset of $[0,1]$ is almost a finite union of intervals.
(2) Every measurable function is almost a continuous function.
(3) Every pointwise convergent sequence of functions is almost a uniformly convergent sequence.

(2) is, of course, a pithy restatement of Lusin's theorem. For (1), we prove a slightly more general statement:

Theorem 4.6.6. *Let $\mathcal{U}$ be a base of the open sets of X, a compact Hausdorff space, so that each $U \in \mathcal{U}$ is a Baire set. Let μ be a finite Baire measure on X and A a Baire set. Then for any $\varepsilon > 0$, there exist finitely many $U_1, \ldots, U_\ell \in \mathcal{U}$ so that*

$$\mu\left(A \triangle \bigcup_{j=1}^\ell U_j\right) < \varepsilon \qquad (4.6.20)$$

Proof. By outer regularity (see Theorem 4.5.6), it suffices to prove the result for A open. In that case, since $\mathcal{U}$ is a base, we can find $\mathcal{I} \subset \mathcal{U}$ so $A = \bigcup_{U \in \mathcal{I}} U$. Given ε, by inner regularity, find $K \subset A$ compact so $\mu(A \setminus K) < \varepsilon$. Since $\mathcal{I}$ is an open cover of K, we can find $U_1, \ldots, U_\ell$ covering K. Since $K \subset \bigcup_{j=1}^\ell U_j \subset A$, we have $\mu(A \triangle \bigcup_{j=1}^\ell U_j) \leq \mu(A \triangle K) < \varepsilon$. □

As for (3):

Theorem 4.6.7 (Egorov's Theorem). *Let μ be a finite positive Baire measure on a compact Hausdorff space, X. Let $\{f_n\}_{n=1}^\infty$ and f_∞ be a.e. finite Baire functions on X, so that for a.e. x, we have that*

$$f_n(x) \to f_\infty(x) \qquad (4.6.21)$$

[1] Cf "Simon's Three Kvetches" discussed in the preface to this Part.

Then for any ε, there exists a compact Baire set K_ε with $\mu(X \setminus K_\varepsilon) < \varepsilon$ and so that $f_n \to f$ uniformly on K_ε.

Proof. We first claim that for any $\alpha, \beta > 0$, there exist a Baire set $E(\alpha, \beta)$ and integer $N(\alpha, \beta)$ so that

$$\mu(X \setminus E(\alpha, \beta)) < \alpha, \qquad \sup_{\substack{n \geq N(\alpha,\beta) \\ x \in E(\alpha,\beta)}} |f_n(x) - f_\infty(x)| < \beta \qquad (4.6.22)$$

For let

$$F_{n,k} = \bigcup_{m \geq n} \left\{ x \ \middle| \ |f_n(x) - f_\infty(x)| > \frac{1}{2^k} \right\} \qquad (4.6.23)$$

Fix k. Then (4.6.21) for a.e. x implies that for a.e. x, $\exists n$ so $x \notin F_{n,k}$, that is,

$$\mu\left(\bigcap_{n=1}^\infty F_{n,k} \right) = 0 \qquad (4.6.24)$$

Since $F_{n+1,k} \subset F_{n,k}$, we see that (4.6.24) implies

$$\lim_{N \to \infty} \mu\left(\bigcup_{n=1}^N (X \setminus F_{n,k}) \right) = \lim_{N \to \infty} \mu(X \setminus F_{N,k}) = \mu(X) \qquad (4.6.25)$$

and thus, for each fixed k, $\lim_{n \to \infty} \mu(F_{n,k}) = 0$. Thus, pick k so $\frac{1}{2^k} < \beta$ and then pick $N(\alpha, \beta)$ so $\mu(F_{N(\alpha,\beta),k}) < \alpha$ and take $E_{\alpha,\beta} = X \setminus F_{N(\alpha,\beta),k}$ so find (4.6.22).

Given ε, let $B_\varepsilon = \bigcap_{\ell=1}^\infty E(\frac{\varepsilon}{3^\ell}, \frac{1}{2^\ell})$. Clearly,

$$\mu(X \setminus B_\varepsilon) \leq \sum_{\ell=1}^\infty \mu\left(X \setminus E\left(\frac{\varepsilon}{3^\ell}, \frac{1}{2^\ell} \right) \right) < \frac{\varepsilon}{2} \qquad (4.6.26)$$

and on B_ε, we have uniform convergence since, if $n \geq N(\frac{\varepsilon}{2^\ell}, \frac{1}{2^\ell})$, then $|f_n(x) - f_\infty(x)| < \frac{1}{2^\ell}$ on B_ε.

Finally, by inner regularity, pick a compact Baire K_ε so $K_\varepsilon \subset B_\varepsilon$ and $\mu(B_\varepsilon \setminus K_\varepsilon) < \frac{\varepsilon}{2}$, so $\mu(X \setminus K_\varepsilon) < \varepsilon$. $\qquad \square$

Next, we want to complexify L^1 and define L^p for $p \in (1, \infty]$.

Definition. Let X be a compact Hausdorff space with finite Baire measure, μ. Let V be a finite-dimensional real or complex vector space with a basis $\{v_j\}_{j=1}^n$ and norm $\||\cdot\||$. A function $f \colon X \to V$ is called *Baire (measurable)* if and only if $f(x) = \sum_{j=1}^n \alpha_j(x) v_j$, where each α_j is Baire in the real case and where $\mathrm{Re}\,\alpha_j$ and $\mathrm{Im}\,\alpha_j$ are Baire in the complex case. Define

$$L^1(X, d\mu; V) = \left\{ f \colon X \to V \ \text{Baire} \ \middle| \ \|f\| \equiv \int \||f(x)\|| \, d\mu(x) < \infty \right\}$$

Remarks. 1. We only restrict to the finite-dimensional case because of not wanting to deal with the issue of when f is Baire; see Section 4.18.

2. It is not hard to see that $\|f(\cdot)\|$ is a Baire function (Problem 6).

It is easy to see that L^1 is a vector space and that $f \mapsto \|f\|$ is a norm. It is not hard to prove completeness and that the continuous V-valued functions are dense. Henceforth, when we write $L^1(X, d\mu)$, we will mean complex-valued functions. By applying the dominated convergence theorem to $\operatorname{Re} f_n$ and $\operatorname{Im} f_n$ (or to the basis components in the V-valued case), it is easy to see that the dominated convergence theorem extends to the complex (or vector-valued) case. Of course, the g in (4.6.9) is still real-valued.

Now let $1 \leq p < \infty$.

Definition. Let μ be a finite Baire measure on a compact Hausdorff space, X.

$$L^p(X, d\mu) =$$

$$\left\{ f \text{ complex-valued and Baire measurable} \,\middle|\, \int |f(x)|^p \, d\mu(x) < \infty \right\}$$

We define

$$\|f\|_p = \left(\int |f(x)|^p \, d\mu(x) \right)^{1/p} \tag{4.6.27}$$

Since $1 \leq p < r \Rightarrow |x|^p \leq 1 + |x|^r$, we see that

$$1 \leq p < r \Rightarrow L^r(X, d\mu) \subset L^p(X, d\mu) \qquad (\mu(X) < \infty \text{ is important}) \tag{4.6.28}$$

Since

$$|f + g|^p \leq 2^p \max(|f|, |g|)^p \leq 2^p(|f|^p + |g|^p)$$

we see that L^p is a vector space. In the development of L^p, two inequalities are exceedingly useful:

– *Minkowski's inequality*:

$$\|f + g\|_p \leq \|f\|_p + \|g\|_p \tag{4.6.29}$$

– *Hölder's inequality*:

$$\frac{1}{p} + \frac{1}{q} = 1, \qquad f \in L^p, g \in L^q \Rightarrow fg \in L^1 \text{ and } \|fg\|_1 \leq \|f\|_p \|g\|_q \tag{4.6.30}$$

Since the proofs fit into the convexity theme of part of the next chapter, we defer the proofs. Section 5.2 has a very quick proof of (4.6.30) and then uses that to prove (4.6.29). Section 5.3 has several additional proofs emphasizing the convexity connection. We'll use these inequalities freely in the rest of this chapter. They are among the most useful inequalities in analysis.

The import of Minkowski's inequality is that it says $\|\cdot\|_p$ is a norm and L^p an NLS.

Since $|fg| \leq \frac{1}{2}(|f|^2 + |g|^2)$, we can define an inner product on $L^2(X, d\mu)$ by

$$\langle f, g \rangle = \int \overline{f(x)}\, g(x)\, d\mu \tag{4.6.31}$$

Since L^2 is complete, we see it is a Hilbert space if X is a compact metric space (and, in general, only a nonseparable Hilbert space).

The monotone and dominated convergence theorems extend to L^p and are very useful (we'll define L^∞ shortly; they do not extend to L^∞ as we'll see).

Theorem 4.6.8 (Dominated Convergence for L^p). *Let μ be a finite Baire measure on X, a compact Hausdorff space, and $1 \leq p < \infty$. Suppose $\{f_n\}_{n=1}^\infty$ and g lie in $L^p(X, d\mu)$ and that*

$$\text{for a.e. } x, \qquad\qquad f_n(x) \to f_\infty(x) \tag{4.6.32}$$
$$\text{for all } n \text{ and a.e. } x, \quad |f_n(x)| \leq g(x) \tag{4.6.33}$$

Then $f_\infty \in L^p$ and $\|f_\infty - f_n\|_p \to 0$.

Proof. (4.6.32)/(4.6.33) prove for a.e. x, $|f_\infty(x)| \leq g(x)$, so $f_\infty \in L^p$. Since

$$|f_n(x) - f_\infty(x)|^p \leq 2^p(|f_n(x)|^p + |f_\infty(x)|^p) \leq 4^p |g(x)|^p$$

and $|g(x)|^p \in L^1$, and since $f_n - f_\infty \to 0$, the L^1 dominated convergence theorem proves that $\int |f_n - f_\infty|^p \, d\mu \to 0$. $\qquad\square$

Theorem 4.6.9 (Monotone Convergence for L^p). *Let $\{f_n\}_{n=1}^\infty$ be a sequence of real-valued Baire functions in $L^p(X, d\mu)$ for some $1 \leq p < \infty$. Suppose $f_n(x) \leq f_{n+1}(x)$ for all n and a.e. x, and that $\sup_n \|f_n\|_p < \infty$. Then $f_\infty(x) \equiv \sup_n f_n(x)$ is in L^p and $\|f_n - f_\infty\|_p \to 0$.*

Proof. By replacing f_n by $f_n - f_1$, we can suppose $f_n(x) \geq 0$ for a.e. x and all n. Let $g_n = |f_n|^p$. Then g_n is monotone and $\sup_n \|g_n\|_1 < \infty$, so by the L^1 monotone convergence theorem,

$$g_\infty \equiv \sup_n g_n(x) = |f_\infty(x)|^p \tag{4.6.34}$$

lies in L^1, that is, $f_\infty \in L^p$. Now apply the dominated convergence theorem for L^p to f_n, f_∞. $\qquad\square$

We'll also need an extension of Markov's inequality to L^p:

Theorem 4.6.10 (Markov's Inequality for $L^p(X, d\mu)$). *Let μ be a finite Baire measure on a compact Hausdorff space, X, and $1 \leq p < \infty$. Let $h \in L^p(X, d\mu)$. Then for any $a > 0$,*

$$\mu(\{x \mid |h(x)| > a\}) \leq \frac{1}{a^p} \|h\|_p^p \qquad (4.6.35)$$

Proof. Let χ be the characteristic function of $\{x \mid |h(x)| \geq a\}$. Then $|h(x)|^p \geq a^p \chi$. Integrating yields (4.6.35). $\qquad \square$

Here are the key facts about L^p.

Theorem 4.6.11. *Let μ be a Baire measure on a compact Hausdorff space, X. Then $L^p(X, d\mu)$ is a complete metric space and $C(X)$ is dense in L^p.*

Proof. Completeness follows the proof of the Riesz–Fischer theorem (Theorem 4.4.7) (see Problem 7).

Let h be a positive bounded Baire function. Let $f_n \in C(X)$ so that $f_n \to h$ in $L^1(X, d\mu)$. By replacing f_n by $\min(\max(0, f_n(x)), \|h\|_\infty)$, we can suppose $0 \leq f_n \leq \|h\|_\infty$. Since $|f_n - h|^p \leq |f_n - h| \|h\|_\infty^{p-1}$, L^1 convergence of f_n to h implies L^p convergence.

If h is a positive L^p function, $h_m \equiv \min(h, m)$ are bounded Baire functions and, by the dominated convergence theorem, $h_m \to h$ in L^p. Thus, h lies in the L^p closure of $C(X)$.

Any $f \in L^p$ is a combination of positive L^p functions since $f = (\operatorname{Re} f)_+ - (\operatorname{Re} f)_- + i(\operatorname{Im} f)_+ - i(\operatorname{Im} f)_-$, so $C(X)$ is dense in L^p. $\qquad \square$

Finally, we define $L^\infty(X, d\mu)$ to be the set of Baire functions f for which $\mu(\{x \mid |f(x)| > a\}) = 0$ for some a. $\|f\|_\infty$ is the inf over all such a's. It is easy to see $\|\cdot\|_\infty$ is a norm, that Hölder's inequality in the form $\|fg\|_1 \leq \|f\|_1 \|g\|_\infty$ holds, that L^∞ is complete, and that if $\mu(X) = 1$, for all $p < \infty$, $L^\infty \subset L^p$ and $\|f\|_p \leq \|f\|_\infty$. However, the dominated and monotone convergence theorems fail (Problem 8) and $C(X)$ is not dense in $L^\infty(X, d\mu)$.

The last theorem lets us realize the space which we called $L^2([0,1], dx)$ in Example 3.1.9 as an L^2 space of equivalence classes of Baire functions equal a.e. For general X and μ, if $f, g \in L^2(X, d\mu)$, $|fg| \leq \frac{1}{2}|f|^2 + \frac{1}{2}|g|^2$, so the integral in $\langle f, g \rangle = \int \overline{f(x)} \, g(x) \, d\mu(x)$ converges and $L^2(X, d\mu)$ is a Hilbert space with $\|\cdot\|_2$ its norm.

A topological space, X, is called *function separable* if $C(X)$ is separable in $\|\cdot\|_\infty$. If X is compact and function separable, we have:

Theorem 4.6.12. *If μ is a finite measure on X a compact, function separable space, then for all $p < \infty$, $L^p(X, d\mu)$ is separable.*

Proof. Let $Y \subset C(X)$ be a countable dense set in $\|\cdot\|_\infty$. Since $\|\cdot\|_\infty$-convergence implies L^p convergence for all p, $C(X) \subset \overline{Y}^{\|\cdot\|_p}$. By Theorem 4.6.11, Y is dense in L^p.   □

Notes and Historical Remarks. Lebesgue [**560, 562**] proved the dominated convergence theorem for the special case $g(x) \equiv c$, a constant (actually, if we know this for all measures, it implies the general result; (see Problem 4), but Lebesgue only considered dx on $[0, 1]$). In 1906, Pierre Fatou (1878–1929) [**295**] stated and proved his lemma, and Beppo Levi (1875–1961) [**574**] stated and proved the monotone convergence theorem which some books call the Beppo Levi lemma. Fatou's paper was his thesis. The general dominated convergence theorem was announced by Lebesgue in 1908 [**563**] with a complete proof in 1910 [**564**]. In 1907, Vitali [**949**] had a related result.

Scheffé's lemma was proven in 1947 [**817**]; the result is named after this paper. Vitali [**949**] already had the result forty years earlier! Scheffé did only the case $f_n \geq 0$. I'm not sure who first noted the general case. Given its simplicity and elegance, I'm surprised the result isn't much better known. It seems to be known primarily in the probability/statistics community. Since Henry Scheffé proved many facts about probabilistic convergence, I note that there are other results called Scheffé's lemma or Scheffé's theorem.

The Brézis–Lieb theorem is from their 1983 paper [**130**]. They seem to have been unaware of Scheffé's earlier, related work. Moreover, they prove the same for L^p norms. This immediately implies an L^p version of Scheffé's lemma.

Littlewood's three principles were formulated in his 1944 monograph [**597**]. The Notes to Section 2.3 of Part 3 have a capsule biography of Littlewood.

Egorov's theorem is named after his 1911 paper [**272**]. In an application of Arnold's principle, the theorem was found a year earlier by Severini [**839**], but went largely unnoticed outside of Italy. Some authors call it the Egorov–Severini theorem. These authors stated it for $L^1([a, b], dx)$. The general measure theoretic result was noted by Riesz [**784**].

Dmitri Egorov (1869–1931), like his student, Luzin, ran afoul of the Stalin purges. He objected to the Soviet treatment of the Russian Orthodox Church (both Egorov and Lusin as discussed in Graham–Kantor [**358**] were impacted by a strong religious mystic tradition in Moscow mathematics), was dismissed from his academic position in 1929, arrested and imprisoned in 1930, and died from the impact of a hunger strike in 1931.

While we use "convergence" in pointwise a.e. convergence, we emphasize that there is no underlying topology in which this is true convergence; see Problem 9 of Section 7.1.

The space $L^p([a,b], dx)$, including the duality theorem to be discussed in Section 4.9, is due to F. Riesz in 1910 [**780**]. The "L" Riesz picked was in honor of Lebesgue. It is interesting that H^p (also named by Riesz!) are called Hardy spaces, but L^p is hardly ever called a Lebesgue space.

Since $F(x) = x^p$ is a positive convex function on $[0, \infty)$ with $F(0) = 0$, one might expect that for a general such F, one might define a norm via

$$F^{-1}\left(\int F(f(x)) \, d\mu(x)\right) \qquad (4.6.36)$$

but this is not homogeneous. Indeed, if, for example, $F(x) = e^x - 1$, it can happen the integral above is finite for f but not for $2f$, so this doesn't even define a vector space. That said, there is a space and norm (called Orlicz space) associated to such an F—we discuss this further in the Notes and Problems to Section 5.3; see (5.3.82) and (5.3.86) for two choices of norm.

For the history of Hölder's and Minkowski's inequality, see the Notes to Section 5.2.

Problems

1. For any sequence of reals $\{c_n\}_{n=1}^\infty$, prove that we have

$$\liminf_{n\to\infty} c_n = \sup_n \inf_{m \ge n} c_m$$
$$\limsup_{n\to\infty} c_n = \inf_n \sup_{m \ge n} c_m$$

2. For the functions f_n in Example 4.6.1, prove that $\sup_n f_n \notin L^1$.

3. This problem will use Egorov's theorem to provide another proof of the dominated convergence theorem. μ is a finite Baire measure on a compact Hausdorff space, X.

(a) Let G_n be a sequence of sets with $G_{n+1} \subset G_n$ and $\mu(\cap_n G_n) = 0$. Let χ_n be the characteristic function of G_n. For any $g \in L^1$, prove that $\lim \int |g\chi_n| \, d\mu = 0$. (*Hint*: Use monotone convergence.)

(b) Prove that if $f_n \to f_\infty$ pointwise a.e. for Baire functions $\{f_n\}_{n=1}^\infty$ and f_∞, then one can find sets G_n inductively so that $G_{n+1} \subset G_n$, $\mu(G_n) < \frac{1}{n}$, and on $X \setminus G_n$, we have $f_n \to f_\infty$ uniformly.

(c) Prove the dominated convergence theorem.

4. Show that the special case of the dominated convergence theorem, where $\mu(X) < \infty$ and $\sup_n|f_n(x)| < \infty$, implies the general theorem. (*Hint*: Let $d\nu = g \, d\mu$ and $\tilde{f}_n = f_n/g$.)

5. This problem will use Egorov's theorem and inner regularity to prove Lusin's theorem. Let f be an a.e. finite, positive Baire function on a compact Hausdorff space, X, with finite Baire measure, μ.

   (a) For any ε, show there exists M so that $\mu(\{x \mid f(x) > M\}) < \varepsilon/3$. Prove that there exists a compact set $K_\varepsilon^{(1)}$ with $\mu(X \setminus K_\varepsilon^{(1)}) < \varepsilon/2$ and $|f(x)| \le M$ on K_ε.

   (b) For any M, prove that there exists a sequence $f_n \in C(X)$ so that $f_n(x) \to \min(M, f(x))$ for a.e. x. (*Hint*: Use Riesz–Fischer.)

   (c) Prove Lusin's theorem for $f \ge 0$, given Egorov's theorem.

   (d) Prove Lusin's theorem for general a.e. finite Baire functions.

6. (a) Let V be a finite-dimensional vector space with norm $\|\cdot\|$. Let V^* be the dual of V with the dual norm $\|\cdot\|^*$ given by (3.3.3). Prove that $\|x\| = \sup_{\ell \in V^*} \{|\ell(x)| \mid \|\ell\|^* \le 1\}$.

   (b) Prove that it suffices to take a dense set of ℓ's in V^*.

   (c) Prove that if $f \colon X \to V$ is Baire measurable, then $x \mapsto \|f(x)\|$ is a Baire measurable real-valued function.

7. Show that L^p is complete. (*Hint*: If f_n is a sequence obeying $\|f_{n+1} - f_n\|_p \le n^{-4}$, prove that $\sup_N \|\sum_{j=1}^{N} |f_{j+1} - f_j|\|_p < \infty$ and use monotone convergence in L^p to show that a pointwise limit exists, and then dominated convergence to get an L^p limit.)

8. (a) Show that monotone and dominated convergence fail in $L^\infty([0,1], dx)$. (*Hint*: Let f_n be the characteristic function of $[0, 1 - \frac{1}{n}]$.)

   (b) What is the closure of $C([0,1])$ in $L^\infty([0,1], dx)$?

9. (a) Prove a version of Scheffé's lemma for complex-valued f's.

   (b) Prove a version for f's in L^p, $1 \le p < \infty$.

10. This will explore what the pointwise convergence theorems tell us about vague convergence of measures. We consider $\mathcal{M}_+([0,1])$, although any compact Hausdorff space, X, and any reference measure will do. Suppose that $d\mu_n = f_n(x)\, dx$, for a.e. x, $f_n(x) \to f_\infty(x)$, and $d\mu_n \to d\mu(x) = f(x)\, dx$ vaguely.

    (a) Prove $f_\infty(x) \le f(x)$ for a.e. x. (*Hint*: Apply Fatou's lemma to $\int g(x) f_n(x)\, dx$ for $g \ge 0$, $g \in C(X)$.)

    (b) If $\sup_{n,x} f_n(x) < \infty$, prove that $f_\infty(x) = f(x)$ for a.e. x.

(c) Let A_n be the union of intervals centered about $\{\frac{j}{2^n} \mid 1 \le j \le 2^n - 1\}$, each of size 4^{-n}. Let

$$f_n(x) = \begin{cases} \frac{1}{2}, & x \notin A_n \\ \frac{1}{2} 2^n, & x \in A_n \end{cases}$$

Prove that $f_n(x)\, d\mu(x) \to dx$, while $f_n(x) \to \frac{1}{2}$ for a.e. x, showing $f_\infty < f$ is possible.

4.7. Comparison of Measures

In this section, we'll consider two positive Baire measures, μ and ν, on the same compact Hausdorff space, X (which we fix throughout). We define the important notions of mutually singular and absolutely continuous, and prove two big theorems about these notions: the Lebesgue decomposition theorem and the Radon–Nikodym theorem.

On $[0, 1]$, consider $d\mu = dx$, Lebesgue measure, and $d\nu =$ the Cantor measure, the measure associated to the Lebesgue–Stieltjes integral of the Cantor function. Let C be the Cantor set. Since $[0, 1] \setminus C$ is a union of open sets of (Lebesgue) size $\frac{1}{3}, \frac{2}{9}, \frac{4}{27}, \ldots$, which sum to 1, $\mu(C) = 0$. On the other hand, since the Cantor function is constant on each of the connected open sets in $[0, 1] \setminus C$, we have $\nu([0, 1] \setminus C) = 0$, so μ and ν live on different sets. They are the paradigm for the following definition:

Definition. We say two positive Baire measures, μ and ν, are *mutually singular* (written $\mu \perp \nu$) if and only if there exists a Baire set $A \subset X$ so $\mu(A) = 0$, $\nu(X \setminus A) = 0$. We will sometimes say that ν is μ-singular.

One can derive mutual singularity from apparently weaker conditions:

Proposition 4.7.1. *Let μ, ν be two Baire measures.*

(a) *Suppose there are exist Baire sets, A_n, so that*

$$\lim_{n \to \infty} \mu(A_n) = 0, \qquad \lim_{n \to \infty} \nu(X \setminus A_n) = 0$$

Then $\mu \perp \nu$.

(b) *Suppose there are nonnegative Baire functions, $\{g_n\}_{n=1}^\infty$, so that $g_n(x) > 0$ for ν-a.e. x and*

$$\lim_{n \to \infty} \int g_n(x)\, d\mu(x) = 0 \qquad \lim_{n \to \infty} \int g_n(x)^{-1}\, d\nu(x) = 0$$

Then $\mu \perp \nu$.

Proof. (a) By passing to a subsequence, we can suppose $\mu(A_n) \le 2^{-n}$. Let $A = \bigcap_{m=1}^\infty \bigcup_{n=m}^\infty A_m$. Then $\mu(\bigcup_{n=m}^\infty A_m) \le \sum_{n=m}^\infty 2^{-n} = 2^{1-n}$, so

$\mu(A) \leq \inf 2^{1-n} = 0$. Since $X \setminus A = \bigcup_{m=1}^{\infty} \bigcap_{n=m}^{\infty} (X \setminus A_n)$ and $\nu(\bigcap_{n=m}^{\infty}(X \setminus A_n)) \leq \inf \nu(X \setminus A_n) = 0$, $\nu(X \setminus A) = 0$. Thus, $\mu \perp \nu$.

(b) If $A_n = \{x \mid g_n(x) \geq 1\}$, then

$$\mu(A_n) \leq \int g_n(x)\, d\mu(x) \to 0$$

Since $X \setminus A_n = \{x \mid g_n(x)^{-1} > 1\}$, so

$$\nu(X \setminus A_n) \leq \int g_n(x)^{-1}\, d\nu(x) \to 0$$

Thus, by (a), $\mu \perp \nu$. □

Something that looks close to the opposite of mutually singular is:

Definition. Let μ, ν be two positive Baire measures. We say ν is *absolutely continuous* (a.c.) with respect to μ, written $\nu \ll \mu$, if and only for all Baire sets $A \subset X$,

$$\mu(A) = 0 \Rightarrow \nu(A) = 0 \tag{4.7.1}$$

Here's another condition that seems to capture "continuity" more:

Definition. Let μ, ν be two positive measures. We say ν is *strongly absolutely continuous* (s.a.c.) with respect to μ if and only if

$$\forall \varepsilon\ \exists \delta\ \forall A \text{ Baire sets, } \mu(A) < \delta \Rightarrow \nu(A) < \varepsilon \tag{4.7.2}$$

Clearly, s.a.c. $\Rightarrow$ a.c. Surprisingly, we'll prove the converse in this section.

Example 4.7.2. Let μ be a positive Baire measure, $f \in L^1(X, d\mu)$, with $f \geq 0$. For any Baire set A, define

$$\nu(A) = \int \chi_A(x) f(x)\, d\mu(x) \tag{4.7.3}$$

which we'll write in shorthand as

$$d\nu = f\, d\mu \tag{4.7.4}$$

It is easy to see (Problem 1) that ν is a Baire measure, the one associated to the functional on $C(X)$,

$$\ell_\nu(g) = \int g(x) f(x)\, d\mu(x) \tag{4.7.5}$$

We claim ν is s.a.c. with respect to μ, for given ε, first find M so that

$$\int f(x) \chi_{\{y \mid f(y) > M\}}(x)\, d\mu(x) < \frac{\varepsilon}{2} \tag{4.7.6}$$

(Problem 2(a)) and then set $\delta = \varepsilon/2M$ (Problem 2(b)). □

Here are the two main theorems on these notions:

Theorem 4.7.3 (Lebesgue Decomposition Theorem). *Let μ, ν be two positive measures. Then*

$$\nu = \nu_{\mathrm{ac}} + \nu_{\mathrm{s}} \qquad (4.7.7)$$

where $\nu_{\mathrm{s}} \perp \mu$ and $\nu_{\mathrm{ac}} \ll \mu$.

Remark. It is easy to see (Problem 3) that the decomposition is unique.

Theorem 4.7.4 (Radon–Nikodym Theorem). *Let μ, ν be two positive Baire measures. Suppose $\nu \ll \mu$. Then there exists $f \in L^1(X, d\mu)$, $f \geq 0$, so that ν is given by (4.7.3).*

Because of the analysis in Example 4.7.2/Problem 2, we immediately have:

Corollary 4.7.5. *Every a.c. measure is s.a.c.*

Remarkably, we'll prove these two theorems as one by an elegant argument relying on the Riesz representation theorem for Hilbert spaces!

Theorem 4.7.6 (von Neumann). *If μ, ν are two positive Baire measures on X, there exists $f \in L^1(X, d\mu)$, $f \geq 0$, so*

$$d\nu = f \, d\mu + d\nu_{\mathrm{s}} \qquad (4.7.8)$$

with $\nu_{\mathrm{s}} \perp \mu$.

Remarks. 1. Since $f \, d\mu$ is a.c. wrt $d\mu$, this clearly implies the Lebesgue decomposition theorem. Suppose $\nu \ll \mu$ and ν_{s} is given by (4.7.8) with $\nu_{\mathrm{s}}(X \setminus A) = 0$ and $\mu(A) = 0$. Since $\nu \ll \mu$, $\nu(A) = 0$, but then, by (4.7.8), $\nu_{\mathrm{s}}(A) \leq \nu(A) = 0$, so $\nu_{\mathrm{s}}(X) = 0$, that is, $d\nu = f \, d\mu$, and we conclude the Radon–Nikodym theorem.

2. Below we'll use that $L^2(X, d\mu + d\nu)$ is a Hilbert space because we use the Riesz representation theorem. This requires L^2 to be separable (which is true if X is a compact metric space) or else to extend the Riesz representation theorem to the nonseparable case; see the Notes to Section 4.0.

Proof. Let $\eta = \mu + \nu$, and for g a bounded Baire function, define

$$\ell(g) = \int g(x) \, d\mu(x) \qquad (4.7.9)$$

Then

$$|\ell(g)| \leq \int |g(x)| \, d\mu(x)$$

$$\leq \int |g(x)| \, d\eta(x) \qquad (4.7.10)$$

$$\leq \left(\int |g(x)|^2 \, d\eta(x) \right)^{1/2} \eta(X)^{1/2} \qquad (4.7.11)$$

(4.7.10) comes from $\int |g(x)| \, d\nu \geq 0$ and (4.7.11) from the Schwarz inequality and $g = g\mathbb{1}$.

(4.7.11) says that first ℓ is constant on the $d\eta$ a.e. equivalence classes and that ℓ extends to a BLF on $L^2(X, d\eta)$. Thus, by the Riesz representation theorem, there exists $F \in L^2(X, d\eta)$ so

$$\int g \, d\mu = \int g \, F \, (d\mu + d\nu) \qquad (4.7.12)$$

or, for any $g \in L^2(d\eta)$,

$$\int g(1 - F) \, d\mu = \int g \, F \, d\nu \qquad (4.7.13)$$

or formally,

$$(1 - F) \, d\mu = F \, d\nu \qquad (4.7.14)$$

We need to avoid the temptation to divide by F, but instead, we will be more careful.

Since g real $\Rightarrow \ell(g)$ is real, F is real-valued by uniqueness of the representing function. Let $A_m = \{x \mid F(x) < -\frac{1}{m}\}$. Then, integrating (4.7.13) for $g = \chi_{A_m}$, we find

$$-\frac{1}{m} \nu(A_m) \geq \int F\chi_{A_m} \, d\nu = \int (1 - F)\chi_{A_m} \, d\mu \geq \mu(A_m) \geq 0$$

so $\mu(A_m) = \nu(A_m) = 0$. Thus, $\eta(\bigcup_{m=1}^{\infty} A_m) = 0$, that is, $F \geq 0$ for η a.e. x. Similarly, $F \leq 1$ for η a.e. x.

Let $B = \{x \mid F(x) = 0\}$. By (4.7.13) with $g = \chi_B$,

$$\mu(B) = 0 \qquad (4.7.15)$$

Let

$$f(x) = \begin{cases} 0, & x \in B \\ F(x)^{-1} - 1, & x \notin B \end{cases}$$

We claim that

$$f \in L^1(d\mu) \qquad (4.7.16)$$

and if ν_{s} is given by $d\nu_{\mathrm{s}} = \chi_B \, d\nu$, then (4.7.8) holds, proving the theorem.

For $m = 1, 2, 3, \ldots$, let

$$C_m = \{x \mid F(x) \geq (m+1)^{-1}\} = \{x \mid f(x) \leq m\} \qquad (4.7.17)$$

Let h be a bounded Baire function. In (4.7.13), pick

$$g = hF^{-1}\chi_{C_m} \qquad (4.7.18)$$

so

$$g(1 - F) = hf\chi_{C_m} \tag{4.7.19}$$

We see that

$$\int_{C_m} hf \, d\mu = \int_{C_m} h \, d\nu \tag{4.7.20}$$

Picking $h = 1$, we get

$$\int_{C_m} f \, d\mu = \nu(C_m) \leq \nu(X \setminus B) \tag{4.7.21}$$

with convergence as $m \to \infty$. Thus, by the monotone convergence theorem, $f \in L^1(X, d\mu)$ and

$$\int f \, d\mu = \nu(X \setminus B) \tag{4.7.22}$$

By the dominated convergence theorem, we can take $m \to \infty$ in (4.7.20) and get

$$\int_{X \setminus B} hf \, d\mu = \int_{X \setminus B} h \, d\nu \tag{4.7.23}$$

which proves (4.7.8). □

An interesting application of the Radon–Nikodym theorem is to see that $\mathcal{M}_+(X)$, the positive measures, are a lattice. In the next section, we'll see this from an abstract point of view, since $\mathcal{M}_+(X)$ is the positive cone of the dual space to a Banach lattice. Here we note that if μ, ν are two positive measures, each is a.c. wrt $\mu + \nu$, so

$$d\mu = f\,(d\mu + d\nu), \qquad d\nu = g\,(d\mu + d\nu) \tag{4.7.24}$$

If $(f \vee g)(x) = \max(f(x), g(x))$, $(f \wedge g)(x) = \min(f(x), g(x))$, then one can show that $\mu \vee \nu$, $\mu \wedge \nu$ given by

$$d(\mu \vee \nu) = (f \vee g)(d\mu + d\nu), \qquad d(\mu \wedge \nu) = (f \wedge g)(d\mu + d\nu) \tag{4.7.25}$$

are the lub and glb of μ and ν (Problem 4).

Finally, we want to say something about another decomposition complementary to the Lebesgue decomposition. We'll suppose in the rest of this section that X is a space in which $\{x\}$ is a Baire set (e.g., a compact metric space).

Definition. A *pure point* (aka *mass point* or *point mass*) of a measure μ is a point $x \in X$ with $\mu(\{x\}) > 0$. A measure is called a *pure point measure* if and only if $\mu(A) \neq 0 \Rightarrow \exists x \in A$ so that $\mu(\{x\}) > 0$.

Definition. A measure, μ is called *continuous* if $\mu(\{x\}) = 0$ for all x.

Remark. This may seem a strange name. It came from the fact that a positive Lebesgue–Stieltjes measure, $d\alpha$, on $[0,1]$ is continuous if and only if the monotone function, α, is continuous. The decomposition (4.7.27) below is a generalization of the decomposition (4.7.23) for monotone functions.

The following is easy to prove and left to the Problems (see Problems 5 and 6):

Theorem 4.7.7. (a) *For any positive Baire measure, $\{x \mid \mu(\{x\}) > 0\}$ is countable.*

(b) *μ is a pure point measure if and only if for every A,*

$$\mu(A) = \sum_{x \in A} \mu(\{x\}) \tag{4.7.26}$$

(c) *Any measure μ has a unique decomposition*

$$\mu = \mu_c + \mu_{pp} \tag{4.7.27}$$

where μ_{pp} is pure point and μ_c is continuous.

Suppose μ has no pure points. Then ν_{ac} has no pure points. Thus, $\nu_{pp} = (\nu_s)_{pp}$. We can decompose

$$\nu = \nu_{ac} + \nu_{pp} + \nu_{sc} \tag{4.7.28}$$

where ν_{pp} is pure point, ν_{ac} is μ-a.c., and ν_{sc} is continuous and μ-singular. For $d\mu = dx$ on $[a,b]$ or on $\mathbb{R}$, one often uses this decomposition.

Notes and Historical Remarks. In his initial book on integration [**562**], Lebesgue proved that any monotone function had a three-fold decomposition: $\alpha = \alpha_{ac} + \alpha_{sc} + \alpha_{pp}$, where α_{pp} is a pure jump function, and the others are continuous. α_{ac} is an integral of its derivative, and α_{sc} has an dx-a.e. 0 derivative. The general theorem has been given Lebesgue's name because it generalizes this.

The Radon–Nikodym theorem for measures on $\mathbb{R}^\nu$ was proven by Radon [**753**] in 1913 and for general measures by Nikodym [**685**] in 1930. In a footnote to his 1936 paper [**968**] on uniqueness of Haar measure, von Neumann indicated he had a new proof of the Radon–Nikodym theorem. His 1940 paper [**970**] was (in the words of Halmos [**387**]) "devoted to the construction of algebras of operators with peculiar properties. When in the course of the construction von Neumann found that he needed some measure theory, he cheerfully waded in and started writing a quick textbook on the subject. In six pages we get definitions of all the basic concepts (e.g., measure and measurable function) and a motivation, statement, and proof of the Radon–Nikodym theorem."

In a general measure-theoretic context, where single points need not lie in the σ-algebra, the analog of a pure point is an *atom*: a measurable set A with $\mu(A) > 0$ and the property that $B \subset A$ measurable implies either $\mu(B) = 0$ or $\mu(A \setminus B) = 0$. A measure without atoms (called *nonatomic*) is *continuous* in the sense that for any measurable set, A, with $0 < \mu(A) < \infty$ and any $\theta \in (0,1)$, there is $B \subset A$ with $\mu(B) = \theta\mu(A)$.

Problems

1. If ν is the Baire measure given by (4.7.3), prove that the associated functional on $C(X)$ is given by (4.7.5).

2. (a) Let $f \in L^1(X, d\mu)$. Prove that

$$\lim_{M \to \infty} \int f(x)\chi_{\{y \mid f(y) > M\}}(x) \, d\mu(x) = 0$$

   (b) Complete the proof of s.a.c. for ν's of the form (4.7.1).

3. Let μ be a Baire measure and suppose $\lambda_{\mathrm{ac}} + \lambda_{\mathrm{s}} = \nu_{\mathrm{ac}} + \nu_{\mathrm{s}}$, where $\nu_{\mathrm{s}} \perp \mu$, $\lambda_{\mathrm{s}} \perp \mu$, $\nu_{\mathrm{ac}} \ll \mu$, $\lambda_{\mathrm{ac}} \ll \mu$.

   (a) Prove if A, B are such that $\mu(A) = \mu(B) = 0$, $\lambda_{\mathrm{s}}(X \setminus A) = 0 = \nu_{\mathrm{s}}(X \setminus B)$, then $\lambda_{\mathrm{s}}(C) = \lambda_{\mathrm{s}}(C \cap A \cap B) = \nu_{\mathrm{s}}(C \cap A \cap B) = \nu_{\mathrm{s}}(C)$, so $\nu_{\mathrm{s}} = \lambda_{\mathrm{s}}$.

   (b) Prove that $\lambda_{\mathrm{ac}} = \nu_{\mathrm{ac}}$.

4. Let $\mu \vee \nu$ be given by (4.7.25). Prove that $\mu \vee \nu$ is the lub of μ and ν in that $\mu \vee \nu \geq \mu$, $\mu \vee \nu \geq \nu$, and if $\kappa \geq \mu$ and $\kappa \geq \nu$, then $\kappa \geq \mu \vee \nu$.

5. Let X be a compact Hausdorff space in which every $\{x\}$ is a Baire set and let μ be a Baire measure. Prove that $\{x \mid \mu(\{x\}) > 0\}$ is a countable set.

6. Let X, μ be as in Problem 5. Define

$$\mu_{\mathrm{pp}}(A) \equiv \sum_{x \in A} \mu(\{x\}) \qquad (4.7.29)$$

   (a) Prove that μ_{pp} is a pure point measure.

   (b) Prove that $\mu_{\mathrm{c}} \equiv \mu - \mu_{\mathrm{pp}}$ is a nonnegative continuous measure.

   (c) If $\mu = \nu_{\mathrm{c}} + \nu_{\mathrm{pp}}$ with ν_{pp} and ν_{c} continuous, prove that $\nu_{\mathrm{pp}} = \mu_{\mathrm{pp}}$ and so $\nu_{\mathrm{c}} = \mu_{\mathrm{c}}$.

4.8. Duality for Banach Lattices; Hahn and Jordan Decomposition

One of our main goals in this section is to find the dual, $C(X)^*$, of the continuous functions on a compact Hausdorff space, X, and the closely related dual of $C_{\mathbb{R}}(X)$. One result will be that any $\ell \in C_{\mathbb{R}}(X)^*$ can be written

$$\ell = \ell_+ - \ell_- \tag{4.8.1}$$

where ℓ_+ and ℓ_- are positive linear functionals. This will allow us to associate $C_{\mathbb{R}}(X)^*$ with a suitably defined space of signed measures and $C(X)$ with a space of complex measures, providing extensions of the Riesz–Markov theorem.

But we'll prove much more than (4.8.1)—we'll prove there is a unique decomposition in which

$$\|\ell_+ - \ell_-\| = \|\ell_+\| + \|\ell_-\| \tag{4.8.2}$$

This, in turn, will show that the associated positive measures, $\mu_\pm$, are mutually singular (Jordan Decomposition Theorem) and, indeed, for some Baire set A, we have

$$\mu_+(C) = \mu(C \cap A), \qquad \mu_-(C) = -\mu(C \cap (X \setminus A)) \tag{4.8.3}$$

(Hahn decomposition theorem). Finally, we prove extensions of the Lebesgue decomposition and Radon–Nikodym theorems to signed and complex measures.

We want to emphasize how strong (4.8.2) is. Of course, the triangle inequality says $\|\ell_+ - \ell_-\| \le \|\ell_+\| + \|\ell_-\|$, but equality is rare. For example, if f_+, f_- are two $L^p(X, d\mu)$ with $1 < p \le \infty$, then $\|f_+ - f_-\|_p = \|f_+\|_p + \|f_-\|_p \Rightarrow \|f_+\|_p = 0$ or $\|f_-\|_p = 0$ (see Problem 6). For $p = 1$, it can happen—not surprising since $L^1(X, d\mu)$ with $\mu \in \mathcal{M}_{+,1}(X)$ is isometrically embedded in $C(X)^*$ by $f \mapsto L(f \, d\mu)$.

Our approach to decomposing ℓ into $\ell_+ - \ell_-$ will be abstract, depending on the lattice structure of $C(X)$.

Definition. A *lattice* is a partially ordered set, $\mathcal{L}$ (see Section 1.4), so that every $a, b \in \mathcal{L}$ has a *greatest lower bound* (glb), $a \wedge b$ (i.e., $a \wedge b \le a$, $a \wedge b \le b$, and $(c \le a) + (c \le b) \Rightarrow c \le a \wedge b$) and *least upper bound* (lub), $a \vee b$.

Definition. A *vector lattice* or *Riesz space*, V, is a real vector space, which has an order in which it is a lattice, with the properties that

$$a \le b \Rightarrow x + a \le x + b, \qquad \lambda \in [0, \infty) \text{ and } a \le b \Rightarrow \lambda a \le \lambda b \tag{4.8.4}$$

Definition. In a vector lattice, set

$$x_+ = x \vee 0, \qquad x_- = (-x) \vee 0, \qquad |x| = x_+ + x_- \tag{4.8.5}$$

Proposition 4.8.1. *Let X be a vector lattice with $x, y \in X$.*

(a) *Multiplication by -1 is order-reversing, that is,*

$$x \leq y \Leftrightarrow -y \leq -x \qquad (4.8.6)$$

(b) $x \wedge y = -[(-x) \vee (-y)]$ (4.8.7)

(c) $x \wedge y + y \vee x = x + y$ (4.8.8)

(d) $x_+ - x_- = x$ (4.8.9)

(e) *If*

$$V_+ = \{x \mid x \geq 0\}, \qquad V_- = \{x \mid x \leq 0\} \qquad (4.8.10)$$

then

$$V_+ \cap V_- = \{0\}, \qquad V_- = -V_+, \qquad V_+ + V_- = X \qquad (4.8.11)$$

(f) $x_+ \wedge x_- = 0$ (4.8.12)

(g) $x_+ \vee x_- = |x|$ (4.8.13)

(h) *If $x = a_+ - a_-$ and $a_\pm \geq 0$, then $x_\pm \leq a_\pm$.*

(i) $-x \leq y \leq x \Rightarrow |y| \leq x$ (4.8.14)

Proof. (a) $x \leq y$ and $a = -y - x \Rightarrow a + x = -y \leq a + y = -x$.

(b) Immediate from the order reversal of multiplication by -1.

(c) In any vector lattice,

$$a + (x \vee y) = (a + x) \vee (a + y) \qquad (4.8.15)$$

so

$$(x + y) + [(-x) \vee (-y)] = y \vee x \qquad (4.8.16)$$

implies (4.8.8) by (4.8.7).

(d) By (4.8.15), $x_+ - x = -x + (x \vee 0) = 0 \vee (-x) = x_-$.

(e) If $x \in V_+ \cap V_-$, then $x \geq 0$ and $-x \geq 0$, so by (4.8.6), $x \leq 0$, so by antisymmetry of $\leq$, $x = 0$. $V_+ + V_- = X$ is (4.8.9) and $V_- = -V_+$ follows from (4.8.6).

(f) $x_- = (-x) \vee 0 \Rightarrow -x_- = x \wedge 0$, so $0 = -x_- + x_- = (x \wedge 0) + x_- = x_+ \wedge x_-$.

(g) (See also Problem 1.) By (4.8.8),

$$|x| \equiv x_+ + x_- = (x_- \wedge x_+) + (x_+ \vee x_-) = x_+ \vee x_-$$

by (4.8.12).

(h) Since $a_+ = x + a_-$, we have $a_+ \geq x$ and, by hypothesis, $a_+ \geq 0$, so $a_+ \geq x_+$. Similarly, $a_- \geq x_-$.

(i) $-x \leq x \Rightarrow 2x \geq 0 \Rightarrow x \geq 0$. $x \geq y$ and $x \geq 0 \Rightarrow x \geq y_+$. Similarly, $x \geq -y$, so $x \geq (-y)_+ = y_-$. Thus, $x \geq y_+ \vee y_- = |y|$. $\square$

Definition. A *Banach lattice* is a vector lattice, X, which is a Banach space in a norm, $\|\cdot\|$, that obeys $|x| \leq |y| \Rightarrow \|x\| \leq \|y\|$. Since $||x|| = |x|$, notice that in a Banach lattice,

$$\||x|\| = \|x\| \tag{4.8.17}$$

Example 4.8.2. If X is a compact Hausdorff space, $C_{\mathbb{R}}(X)$ is a Banach lattice with the pointwise order (i.e., $f \leq g \Leftrightarrow$ all x, $f(x) \leq g(x)$) and $\|\cdot\|_\infty$-norm. Similarly, $L^p_{\mathbb{R}}(X, d\mu)$, the real-valued L^p functions, are a Banach lattice in $\|\cdot\|_p$ for any $1 \leq p \leq \infty$. $\square$

The main theorem of the abstract part of this section is:

Theorem 4.8.3 (Duality for Banach Lattices). *Let X be a Banach lattice. Define*

$$X^*_+ = \{\ell \in X^* \mid \ell(x) \geq 0 \ for \ all \ x \geq 0\} \tag{4.8.18}$$

Then

(a) *X^* is partially ordered by*

$$\ell \geq k \Leftrightarrow \ell - k \in X^*_+ \tag{4.8.19}$$

Moreover,

$$\ell \leq k \Leftrightarrow \ell + m \leq k + m \tag{4.8.20}$$

(b) *Any $\ell \in X^*$ can be decomposed as*

$$\ell = \ell_+ - \ell_- \tag{4.8.21}$$

with $\ell_+, \ell_- \in X^*_+$ in such a way that if $\ell = k_+ - k_-$ with $k_\pm$, then $k_\pm \geq \ell_\pm$.

(c) *For all $x \geq 0$, we have that*

$$\ell_+(x) + \ell_-(x) \leq \|\ell\| \, \|x\| \tag{4.8.22}$$

(d) *X^* with the order $\geq$ is a vector lattice in which*

$$\ell_\pm = 0 \vee (\pm \ell) \tag{4.8.23}$$

(e) *X^* with the dual norm is a Banach lattice.*

We need a decomposition lemma:

Lemma 4.8.4. *In a vector lattice, if $x, y, z \geq 0$ and $x \leq y + z$, then there exist y_1 and z_1 so that $0 \leq y_1 \leq y$ and $0 \leq z_1 \leq z$ and so that*

$$x = y_1 + z_1 \tag{4.8.24}$$

Proof. Let $y_1 = x \wedge y$ so $0 \le y_1 \le y$. Let $z_1 = x - y_1$, so (4.8.24) is obvious. All we need is $0 \le z_1 \le z$. Since $y_1 \le x$, $z_1 \ge 0$ is immediate. Moreover, since $z \ge 0$,

$$y_1 + z = (x + z) \wedge (y + z) \ge (x + z) \wedge x \ge x$$

so $z_1 = x - y_1 \le z$. □

Proof of Theorem 4.8.3. (a) $\ell \ge k \ge j \Rightarrow \ell \ge j$ is trivial. If $\ell \ge 0$ and $\ell \le 0$, then $\ell(x) = 0$ for all $x \ge 0$, and so, since any $x = x_+ - x_-$, $\ell(x) = 0$ for all x, so $\ell = 0$. (4.8.20) is immediate from (4.8.19).

(b) For $x \ge 0$, define

$$\ell_+(x) = \sup(\ell(y) \mid 0 \le y \le x) \qquad (4.8.25)$$

We are heading towards showing ℓ_+ is the restriction of a linear functional. Taking $y = 0$ in (4.8.25), we see that $\ell_+(x) \ge 0$. By the Banach lattice property,

$$|\ell(y)| \le \|\ell\| \, \|y\| \le \|\ell\| \, \|x\| \qquad (4.8.26)$$

so

$$|\ell_+(x)| = \ell_+(x) \le \|\ell\| \, \|x\| \qquad (4.8.27)$$

We claim (and here the lemma is essential) that for $y, z \ge 0$,

$$\ell_+(y + z) = \ell_+(y) + \ell_+(z) \qquad (4.8.28)$$

for

$$\begin{aligned}
\ell_+(y + z) &= \sup(\ell(x) \mid 0 \le x \le y + z) \\
&= \sup(\ell(y_1 + z_1) \mid 0 \le y_1 \le y, 0 \le z_1 \le z) \quad \text{(by the lemma)} \\
&= \ell_+(y) + \ell_+(z)
\end{aligned}$$

proving (4.8.28).

Now, define for any $x \in X$,

$$\ell_+(x) = \ell_+(x_+) - \ell_+(x_-) \qquad (4.8.29)$$

If $x = y_+ - y_-$ with $y_+, y_- \ge 0$, then $y_+ + x_- = y_- + x_+$. So by (4.8.28),

$$\ell_+(x) = \ell_+(y_+) - \ell_+(y_-) \qquad (4.8.30)$$

In particular, since $y + z = (y_+ + z_+) - (y_- + z_-)$, we see

$$\begin{aligned}
\ell_+(y + z) &= \ell_+(y_+ + z_+) - \ell_+(y_- + z_-) & \text{(by (4.8.30))} \\
&= \ell_+(y_+) - \ell_+(y_-) + \ell_+(z_+) - \ell_+(z_-) & \text{(by (4.8.28))} \\
&= \ell_+(y) + \ell_+(z) & (4.8.31)
\end{aligned}$$

by (4.8.29). Thus, ℓ_+ is additive.

If $\lambda > 0$ is real,

$$\ell_+(\lambda x_\pm) = \lambda \ell(x_\pm) \qquad (4.8.32)$$

by (4.8.25). So by (4.8.29),

$$\ell_+(\lambda x) = \lambda \ell_+(x) \tag{4.8.33}$$

for any $x \in X$, $\lambda \geq 0$. Since $(-x)_\pm = x_\mp$, we see that

$$\ell_+(-x) = -\ell_+(x) \tag{4.8.34}$$

This implies (4.8.33) for all $\lambda \in \mathbb{R}$, so ℓ_+ is a linear functional.

Clearly, $\ell_+(x) \geq \ell(x)$, so

$$\ell_- \equiv \ell_+ - \ell \geq 0 \tag{4.8.35}$$

and $\ell = \ell_+ - \ell_-$ is a difference of elements of X_+^*. Note next that

$$\ell_-(x) = \sup(\ell(y-x) \mid 0 \leq y \leq x)$$
$$= \sup(-\ell(z) \mid 0 \leq z \leq x) \tag{4.8.36}$$

since $x - y$ runs between 0 to x as y runs between x and 0. Thus,

$$\ell_- = (-\ell)_+ \tag{4.8.37}$$

If $\ell = k_+ - k_-$ with $k_\pm \in X_+^*$ and $0 \leq y \leq x$, then $\ell(y) = k_+(y) - k_-(y) \leq k_+(y) = k_+(x) - k_+(x-y) \leq k_+(x)$. Taking sups over y, $\ell_+ \leq k_+$. The same argument with (4.8.36) shows $\ell_- \leq k_-$.

(c) Suppose $x \geq 0$ and $0 \leq y \leq x$, $0 \leq z \leq x$. Then $-x \leq y - z \leq x$. So, by Proposition 4.8.1(i), $|y - z| \leq x$ and, by the Banach lattice property, $\|y - z\| \leq \|x\|$. Thus,

$$|\ell(y) - \ell(z)| = |\ell(y-z)| \leq \|\ell\| \, \|y-z\| \leq \|\ell\| \, \|x\| \tag{4.8.38}$$

y and z are arbitrary in between 0 and x, so taking sups and using (4.8.36), we obtain (4.8.22).

(d) By (a), we need only show X^* is a lattice to see that it is a vector lattice. Define

$$\ell \vee k = \ell + (k - \ell)_+ \tag{4.8.39}$$

Then, clearly, $\ell \vee k \geq \ell$ since $(k+\ell)_+ \geq 0$. Since $(k-\ell)_+ = (k-\ell) + (k-\ell)_-$, we see

$$\ell \vee k = k + (k - \ell)_- \tag{4.8.40}$$

so $\ell \vee k \geq k$ also.

If $m \geq \ell$, $m \geq k$, we have $m - \ell \geq k - \ell$ and $m - \ell = (m - \ell)_+$, so $m - \ell = (m - \ell)_+ \geq (k - \ell)_+$ and $m \geq \ell + (k - \ell)_+$, so $m \geq \ell \vee k$. Thus, $\ell \vee k$ is an lub.

Since our order obeys $\ell \geq k \Leftrightarrow -\ell \leq -k$, we see $-((-\ell) \vee (-k)) = \ell \wedge k$ so X^* has glbs's also.

Taking $\ell = 0$ and then $k \to \ell$ in (4.8.39) yields (4.8.23).

(e) We first claim that (of course, $|\ell| = \ell_+ + \ell_-$)

$$|||\ell||| = \|\ell\| \tag{4.8.41}$$

for, on the one hand, (4.8.22) says, for $x > 0$, $||\ell|(x)| = |\ell|(x) \leq \|\ell\| \, \|x\|$, and for any x,

$$||\ell|(x)| = ||\ell|(x_+) - |\ell|(x_-)| \leq \max(|\ell|(x_+), |\ell|(x_-)) \leq |\ell|(x)$$

so $||\ell|(x)| \leq \|\ell\| \, |||x||| = \|\ell\| \, \|x\| \Rightarrow |||\ell||| \leq \|\ell\|$.

On the other hand, if x is positive

$$-|\ell|(x) \leq \pm\ell(x) \leq |\ell|(x) \tag{4.8.42}$$

so

$$-|\ell|(|x|) \leq \pm(\ell(x_+) - \ell(x_-)) \leq |\ell|(|x|) \tag{4.8.43}$$

and thus,

$$|\ell(x)| \leq |\ell|(|x|) \tag{4.8.44}$$

so

$$|\ell(x)| \leq |||\ell||| \, |||x||| = |||\ell||| \, \|x\| \tag{4.8.45}$$

that is, $\|\ell\| \leq |||\ell|||$, proving (4.8.41).

Now suppose $\ell, k \in X^*$ and $|\ell| \leq |k|$. By (4.8.44), $|\ell(x)| \leq |\ell|(|x|) \leq |k|(|x|) \leq \|k\| \, \|x\|$ since $|||k||| = \|k\|$. Thus, $\|\ell\| \leq \|k\|$. $\qquad\square$

We now return to the special case of $C_{\mathbb{R}}(X)^*$. Here is something special about $C_{\mathbb{R}}(X)$, not true in general Banach lattices:

Proposition 4.8.5. *If $\ell \in C_{\mathbb{R}}(X)^*$ and $\ell = \ell_+ - \ell_-$ is the canonical decomposition, then*

$$\|\ell_+\| + \|\ell_-\| = \|\ell\| \tag{4.8.46}$$

Proof. Clearly, $\|\ell\| = \|\ell_+ - \ell_-\| \leq \|\ell_+\| + \|\ell_-\|$ by the triangle inequality.

On the other hand, what is special to $C_{\mathbb{R}}(X)$ is $\|\ell\| = \ell(\mathbb{1})$ if $\ell \geq 0$. Thus, by (4.8.22),

$$\|\ell_+\| + \|\ell_-\| = \ell_+(\mathbb{1}) + \ell_-(\mathbb{1}) \leq \|\ell\| \, \|\mathbb{1}\| = \|\ell\|$$

proving (4.8.25). $\qquad\square$

Having finished the abstract theory and an important consequence for $C_{\mathbb{R}}(X)^*$, we turn to the general Riesz–Markov theorem which uses that any ℓ can be written as a difference of positive functionals (we'll use (4.8.46) later).

Definition. Let X be a compact Hausdorff space. A *signed Baire measure* (respectively, *complex Baire measure*) is a function, μ, from the Baire sets to $\mathbb{R}$ (respectively, $\mathbb{C}$) that obeys:

(i) There is a constant, C, so that for all *countable Baire partitions* of X (i.e., Baire sets $\{A_j\}_{j=1}^\infty$ with $\bigcup_{j=1}^\infty A_j = X$ and $A_j \cap A_k = \emptyset$ for all $j \neq k$), we have

$$\sum_{j=1}^\infty |\mu(A_j)| \leq C \qquad (4.8.47)$$

(ii) If $\{A_j\}_{j=1}^\infty$ are Baire sets with $A_j \cap A_k = \emptyset$ if $j \neq k$, then

$$\mu\left(\bigcup_{j=1}^\infty A_j\right) = \sum_{j=1}^\infty \mu(A_j) \qquad (4.8.48)$$

Remarks. 1. The minimal C in (4.8.47) is called $\|\mu\|$.

2. If μ is a positive measure, (4.8.47) is automatic with $\|\mu\| = \mu(X)$.

3. (4.8.47) is needed for the sum in (4.8.48) to be well defined and finite.

4. It is not hard to see that (4.8.47) is implied by $\sum_{j=1}^n |\mu(P_j)| \leq C$ for all finite partitions (Problem 2).

Example 4.8.6. On $[0,1]$, let δ_x be the measure $\delta_x(f) = f(x)$. Let $\mu_n = \delta_1 - \delta_{1-\frac{1}{n}}$. Then for all $f \in C([0,1])$, $\int f \, d\mu_n \to 0$, and if $A = [0,1)$, $\mu_\infty = 0$, then $\mu_\infty(\partial A) = 0$ but $\mu_n(A) = -1 \nrightarrow \mu_\infty(A) = 0$. Thus, Theorem 4.5.7 fails for signed measures. $\qquad \square$

If (4.8.47) holds, it is easy to see for each $f \in C(X)$, we can define a Riemann–Stieltjes-type integral, $L(\mu)(f)$, for the sum in (4.1.25) (with α replaced by μ) is bounded by $\|f\|_\infty \|\mu\|$ and the analog of (4.1.29) holds with $\alpha(X)$ replaced by $\|\mu\|$.

On the other hand, any $\ell \in C_{\mathbb{R}}(X)^*$ (respectively, $C(X)^*$) is a difference of two (respectively, linear combinations of four) positive functionals, so can be extended to a countably additive set function, μ_ℓ, by doing that for the positive pieces. We have

Lemma 4.8.7. *Let μ be a signed measure. Then there is a positive measure, $\mu_{|\cdot|}$, so that*

(a)

$$|\mu(A)| \leq \mu_{|\cdot|}(A) \qquad \textit{for any Baire set } A \qquad (4.8.49)$$

(b) *For any finite family $\{B_j\}_{j=1}^\ell$ of disjoint Baire sets,*

$$\left|\sum_{j=1}^\ell \alpha_j \mu(B_j)\right| \leq \sup_j |\alpha_j| \mu_{|\cdot|}\left(\bigcup_{j=1}^\ell B_j\right) \qquad (4.8.50)$$

Proof. Let

$$\mu_+(A) = \sup_{B \subset A} \mu(B), \qquad \mu_-(A) = -\inf_{B \subset A} \mu(B) \qquad (4.8.51)$$

sup and inf being over all Baire subsets. Since $B = \emptyset$ is a choice, $\mu_\pm(A) \geq 0$, and it is easy see (Problem 3) that μ_+, μ_- are measures of total mass at most $\|\mu\|$. Define

$$\mu_{|\cdot|} = \mu_+ + \mu_- \tag{4.8.52}$$

Then (4.8.49) is immediate and (4.8.50) comes from (4.8.49) and additivity of $\mu_{|\cdot|}$. $\qquad\square$

Remark. The explicit form for $\mu_\pm$ is interesting but one can instead define $\mu_{|\cdot|}$ as the measure associated to $|\ell|$, where ℓ is the Riemann–Stieltjes-type integral associated to μ.

Theorem 4.8.8 (Riesz–Markov Theorem, Second Form). *The maps L from signed (respectively, complex) measures to $C_\mathbb{R}(X)^*$ (respectively, $C(X)^*$) and $\ell \mapsto \mu_\ell$ are inverse to each other and set up a one-one correspondence between measures and norm-bounded linear functionals.*

Remark. We'll see below for the real case (and the complex case in Problem 4) that it is a norm isometry also.

Proof. We'll do the real case. The complex case is similar. If $\ell = \ell_+ - \ell_-$, then $\mu_\ell = \mu_{\ell_+} - \mu_{\ell_-}$ by construction, so $L(\mu_\ell) = L(\mu_{\ell_+}) - L(\mu_{\ell_-}) = \ell_+ - \ell_- = \ell$.

For the converse, let μ be a signed measure, $\ell = L(\mu)$, $\nu = \mu_\ell$. $\nu(X) = \ell(\mathbb{1}) = \mu(X)$. Thus, the $\{A \mid \text{Baire sets with } \mu(A) = \nu(A)\}$ is closed under countable unions and complements, and so a σ-ring. Thus, it suffices to prove $\mu(A) = \nu(A)$ for each open F_σ set, A. Thus, we can suppose A is open and there exist compact sets, K_n, with

$$K_n \subset K_{n+1}^{\text{int}}, \qquad \bigcup_n K_n = A \tag{4.8.53}$$

Let f_n be a continuous function with $f_n \equiv 1$ on K_n, $\text{supp}(f_n) \subset K_{n+1}$, and $0 \leq f_n \leq 1$. We claim that in terms of the measure $\mu_{|\cdot|}$ of Lemma 4.8.7,

$$|\ell(f_n) - \mu(K_n)| \leq \mu_{|\cdot|}(A \setminus K_n) \tag{4.8.54}$$

For Riemann sums converging to $L(\mu)(f_n)$ have the form $\mu(K_n) + \sum_{j=1}^K \alpha_j \mu(B_j)$, where $\bigcup B_j = K_{j+1} \setminus K_n$ and $0 < \alpha_j < 1$. Thus, (4.8.54) follows from (4.8.50).

As $n \to \infty$, $\ell_+(f_n) \to \nu_+(A)$ and $\ell_-(f_n) \to \nu_-(A)$ by the monotone convergence theorem, so

$$\ell(f_n) \to \nu(A) \tag{4.8.55}$$

On the other hand, by countable additivity of μ and of $\mu_{|\cdot|}$, $\mu(K_n) \to \mu(A)$ and $\mu_{|\cdot|}(K_n) \to \mu_{|\cdot|}(A)$, so $\mu_{|\cdot|}(A \setminus K_n) \to 0$. Thus, by (4.8.54), $\mu(A) = \nu(A)$, that is, $\ell_{L(\mu)} = \mu$. $\qquad\square$

We turn to exploiting (4.8.46) and its consequences.

Theorem 4.8.9. *Let ℓ be in $C_\mathbb{R}(X)^*$ and let $|\ell| = \ell_+ + \ell_-$. Let $\mu, |\mu|$ be the associated measures. Then there exists a real-valued Baire function, g, with*

$$g(x) = \pm 1, \qquad |\mu| \text{ a.e. } x \tag{4.8.56}$$

so that

$$d\mu(x) = g(x)\, d|\mu|(x) \tag{4.8.57}$$

In particular, for any bounded Baire function, f,

$$\left| \int f(x)\, d\mu(x) \right| \leq \int |f(x)|\, d|\mu|(x) \tag{4.8.58}$$

Remark. Problem 4 has a kind of analog for complex functionals. Given a complex measure, μ, there is a unique positive measure, $|\mu|$, and Baire function, h, with $|h(x)| = 1$ so that $d\mu = h\, d|\mu|$.

Proof.

$$\mu_\pm \leq |\mu| \tag{4.8.59}$$

so, by the Radon–Nikodym theorem,

$$d\mu_\pm(x) = g_\pm(x)\, d|\mu|(x) \tag{4.8.60}$$

for nonnegative functions $g_\pm$ in $L^1(X, d|\mu|)$.

Let $B_\varepsilon^\pm = \{x \mid g_\pm(x) \geq 1 + \varepsilon\}$. Then, by (4.8.60) and (4.8.59),

$$\mu_\pm(B_\varepsilon^\pm) \geq (1 + \varepsilon)|\mu|(B_\varepsilon^\pm) \geq (1 + \varepsilon)\mu_\pm(B_\varepsilon^\pm) \tag{4.8.61}$$

so $\mu_\pm(B_\varepsilon^\pm) = 0$ and then, by (4.8.61), $|\mu|(B_\varepsilon^\pm) = 0$. So for a.e. x,

$$0 \leq g_\pm(x) \leq 1 \tag{4.8.62}$$

Since

$$\ell(f) = \ell_+(f) - \ell_-(f) = \int (g_+ - g_-)(x) f(x)\, d|\mu|(x) \tag{4.8.63}$$

we see

$$\|\ell\| \leq \int |g_+(x) - g_-(x)|\, d|\mu|(x) \tag{4.8.64}$$

On the other hand,

$$\|\ell_\pm\| = \ell_\pm(\mathbb{1}) = \int g_\pm(x)\, d|\mu|(x) \tag{4.8.65}$$

The last two equations and (4.8.46) imply that

$$\int [g_+(x) + g_-(x)]\, d|\mu|(x) \leq \int |g_+(x) - g_-(x)|\, d|\mu|(x)$$

which can only happen if g_+ and g_- have disjoint supports.

On the other hand, since $\|\ell\| = \|\|\ell\|\|$, (4.8.46) implies

$$\int (g_+(x) + g_-(x)) \, d|\mu|(x) = |\mu|(X) \qquad (4.8.66)$$

The disjoint supports implies $0 \le g_+ + g_- \le 1$, so (4.8.66) implies $g_+(x) + g_-(x) = 1$ a.e. Thus,

$$g(x) = g_+(x) - g_-(x) \qquad (4.8.67)$$

is $|\mu|$-a.e. ± 1. $\square$

The next two corollaries are standard theorems:

Theorem 4.8.10 (Hahn Decomposition Theorem). *If μ is a signed Baire measure, there exists a Baire set $A \subset X$ so that*

$$\mu(B) \ge 0 \qquad \text{for all } B \subset A \qquad (4.8.68)$$
$$\mu(B) \le 0 \qquad \text{for all } B \subset X \setminus A \qquad (4.8.69)$$

Remark. Put differently, $\chi_A \, d\mu$ is a positive measure and so is $-\chi_{X \setminus A} \, d\mu$.

Proof. Let $A = \{x \mid g(x) = 1\}$, so up to sets of $|\mu|$-measure zero, $X \setminus A = \{x \mid g(x) = -1\}$, and if $B \subset A$, $\mu(B) = |\mu|(B)$, and if $B \subset X \setminus A$, $\mu(B) = -|\mu|(B)$. $\square$

Theorem 4.8.11 (Jordan Decomposition Theorem). *Any signed measure μ can be written $\mu = \mu_+ - \mu_-$, where μ_+ and μ_- are mutually singular.*

Remark. In terms of the lattice structure, this says $\mu_+ \wedge \mu_- = 0$ (see Problem 5).

Proof. If $A = \{x \mid g(x) = 1\}$, then $d\mu_+ = \chi_A \, d|\mu|$, $d\mu_- = \chi_{X \setminus A} \, d|\mu|$, $\mu_+(X \setminus A) = 0$, $\mu_-(A) = 0$, so these measures are mutually singular. $\square$

Finally, we note that by using the decomposition into a linear combination of positive functions and the Lebesgue decomposition and Radon–Nikodym theorems for the pieces, we get:

Theorem 4.8.12. (Radon–Nikodym Theorem for Signed or Complex Measures). *Let μ be a signed or complex measure on X, a compact Hausdorff space, and ν a positive measure. If $\nu(A) = 0 \Rightarrow \mu(A) = 0$, then there exists $f \in L^1(X, d\nu)$ so that $d\mu = f \, d\nu$.*

Proof. We'll consider the signed case (the complex follows by writing $\mu = \mu_r + i\mu_i$, where μ_r, μ_i are signed measures). If B is the set with $\mu_+(\cdot) = \mu(\cdot \cap B)$, $\mu_-(\cdot) = -\mu(\cdot \cap (X \setminus B))$, and if $\nu(A) = 0$, then $\nu(A \cap B) = 0 = \nu(A \cap (X \setminus B)) = \mu_\pm(A) = 0$. Thus, we can apply the Radon–Nikodym theorem to $\mu_\pm$. $\square$

Theorem 4.8.13. (Lebesgue Decomposition Theorem for Signed Measures). *Let μ be a signed measure on X, a compact Hausdorff space, and ν a positive Baire measure. Then*

$$d\mu = f \, d\nu + d\mu_s \tag{4.8.70}$$

where $f \in L^1(X, d\nu)$ and μ_s is ν-singular in the sense that there exists A so $|\mu_s|(A) = 0$ and $\nu(X \setminus A) = 0$.

Notes and Historical Remarks. The decomposition into positive and negative parts goes back to the dual of $C([a, b])$ (see the discussion of the Jordan decomposition theorem below) and not to the context of general lattices, which, as mathematical objects, goes back to work in the 1930s by Albert Bennett, Garrett Birkhoff, Fritz Klein, and Øystein Ore. For an exposition of the history of lattices, see Mehrtens [**649**].

The term "Riesz space" goes back to work of Riesz using the lattice and vector structure to prove that $\ell \in C([a, b])^*$ has a decomposition $\ell_+ - \ell_-$ based on the decomposition lemma, Lemma 4.8.4. He announced this at a 1928 International Congress [**786**] and published the details in [**788**]. Riesz mentioned Daniell's work [**214**] on the use of sup and inf in function spaces. A key early work on Riesz spaces is Freudenthal [**326**]. There is an enormous literature on Banach lattices; see [**20, 21, 93, 228, 325, 613, 614, 652, 811, 1013, 1014**].

Two heavily studied classes of Banach lattices are the L- and M-spaces. An L-space obeys

$$x \geq 0, \, y \geq 0 \Rightarrow \|x + y\| = \|x\| + \|y\|$$

while an M-space obeys

$$x, y \geq 0 \Rightarrow \|x \vee y\| = \max(\|x\|, \|y\|)$$

L-spaces include $L^1(M, d\mu)$ and $\mathcal{M}(X)$. M-spaces include $C(X)$ and $L^\infty(M, d\mu)$. The dual of an L- or M-space is an M- or L-space.

The Hahn decomposition is named after their early introduction in Hahn [**382**]. The formulae (4.8.50) for their decomposition go back at least to Alexandroff [**10**].

In the first paper on functions of bounded variation, C. Jordan [**455**] proved any bounded variation function, α, could be written as $\alpha_+ - \alpha_-$, where $\alpha_\pm$ are monotone, and $\text{Var}(\alpha) = \text{Var}(\alpha_+) + \text{Var}(\alpha_-)$; see Theorem 4.15.2. The Jordan decomposition theorem is named after this work.

Problems

1. Give a second proof of (4.8.13) using part (b) of Proposition 4.8.1.

2. Let μ be a set function on Baire sets for which there is C with $X = P_1 \cup \cdots \cup P_k$ and $P_i \cap P_j = \emptyset$ for $i \neq j \Rightarrow \sum_{j=1}^{k} |\mu(P_j)| \leq C$. Prove that (4.8.47) holds.

3. Let μ be a signed measure and define $\mu_{\pm}$ by (4.8.51). Prove that $\mu_{\pm}$ are positive measures with $\mu_{\pm}(X) \leq \|\mu\|$.

4. Let μ be a complex measure $\mu = \mu_r + i\mu_i$.

   (a) Let $\nu = |\mu_r| + |\mu_i|$. Prove that there is a function $g \in L^1(X, d\nu)$ so $d\mu = g\,d\nu$.

   (b) Define $|\mu|$ by $d|\mu| = |g|\,d\nu$. Prove that there is h with $|h(x)| = 1$ for $|\mu|$-a.e. x so $d\mu = h\,d|\mu|$.

   (c) Prove that $|\int g\,d\mu| \leq \int |g|\,d|\mu|$ for all bounded Baire g.

   (d) Prove that (b) uniquely determines $|\mu|$.

5. Let μ, ν be positive Baire measures on X, a compact Hausdorff space. Prove that μ and ν are mutually singular if and only if $\mu \wedge \nu = 0$.

6. (a) If $p \in (1, \infty)$ and $(a^p + b^p)^{1/p} = a + b$ for $a, b \in [0, \infty)$, prove that either $a = 0$ or $b = 0$. If $\max(a, b) = a + b$, prove $a = 0$ or $b = 0$.

   (b) If $p \in (1, \infty)$ and f, g in L^p have disjoint supports and if $\|f + g\|_p = \|f\|_p + \|g\|_p$, prove that either $f = 0$ or $g = 0$.

4.9. Duality for L^p

Let $p \in [1, \infty)$ and $q \in (1, \infty]$ be related by the following equivalent conditions (if $p = 1$, then $q = \infty$; in that case not all the conditions are meaningful):

$$\frac{1}{p} + \frac{1}{q} = 1, \quad pq = p + q, \quad (p-1)(q-1) = 1, \quad q = \frac{p}{p-1} \tag{4.9.1}$$

Our goal in this section is to prove the following:

Theorem 4.9.1 (Riesz L^p Duality Theorem). *Let X be a compact Hausdorff space, μ a (positive) Baire measure and $p \in [1, \infty)$. Then*

$$L^p(X, d\mu)^* = L^q(X, d\mu) \tag{4.9.2}$$

in the following sense. Given $g \in L^q$, the map

$$f \mapsto L_g(f) \equiv \int g(x) f(x)\,d\mu \tag{4.9.3}$$

defines an element of $L^p(X, d\mu)^*$ with

$$\|L_g\|_{(L^p)^*} = \|g\|_q \tag{4.9.4}$$

and every element of $(L^p)^*$ is an L_g for a unique element, g, of L^q.

Remark. Notice $p = \infty$ is not included. $L^\infty(X, d\mu)^*$ is much bigger than L^1; see Example 5.5.15.

We'll prove this in a sequence of propositions:

Proposition 4.9.2. *For every $g \in L^q$, $f \in L^p$, the integrand in (4.9.3) is in L^1 and the integral defines a linear functional in $(L^p)^*$ with $\|L_g\|_{(L^p)^*} \leq \|g\|_q$.*

Proof. This is just a restatement of Hölder's inequality; see (4.6.30). $\quad\square$

Given any a.e. finite Baire measurable function g, define the *sgn of g*, sgn g, by

$$(\operatorname{sgn} g)(x) = \begin{cases} 0, & g(x) = 0 \text{ or } \infty \\ \frac{g(x)}{|g(x)|} & \text{if } 0 < |g(x)| < \infty \end{cases} \tag{4.9.5}$$

Proposition 4.9.3. *Let $g \in L^q$ with $q \in (1, \infty)$. Then $f = |g|^{q-1}(\operatorname{sgn} g)(x)$ is in L^p,*

$$\|f\|_p^p = \|g\|_q^q \quad and \quad L_g(f) = \|g\|_q^q \tag{4.9.6}$$

In particular, $\|L_g\|_{(L^p)^*} \geq \|g\|_q$.

Proof. Since $p(q - 1) = q$, we have

$$\int |f(x)|^p \, d\mu(x) = \int |g(x)|^{p(q-1)} \, d\mu(x) = \int |g(x)|^q \, d\mu(x)$$

proving the first equality in (4.9.6) and that $f \in L^p$. The second comes from $g[(\operatorname{sgn} g)] = |g|$, so $\int g(x) f(x) \, d\mu(x) = \int |g(x)|^q \, d\mu$.

The final assertion comes from noting that since $f \in L^p$,

$$\|L_g\|_{(L^p)^*} \geq \frac{|L_g(f)|}{\|f\|_p} = \|g\|_q^{q-q/p} = \|g\|_q$$

since $q - \frac{q}{p} = q(1 - \frac{1}{p}) = 1$. $\quad\square$

Proposition 4.9.4. *If $g \in L^\infty$, $\|L_g\|_{(L^1)^*} \geq \|g\|_\infty$.*

Proof. Let $a = \|g\|_\infty$. Given ε, we have $\mu(A_\varepsilon) > 0$, where $A_\varepsilon = \{x \mid |g(x)| \geq a - \varepsilon\}$. Let $f_\varepsilon = (\operatorname{sgn} g)\chi_{A_\varepsilon}$. Then

$$L_g(f_\varepsilon) = \int_{A_\varepsilon} (\operatorname{sgn} g)g(x) \, d\mu(x) = \int_{A_\varepsilon} |g(x)| \, d\mu(x) \geq (a - \varepsilon)\mu(A_\varepsilon)$$

Since $\|f_\varepsilon\|_{L^1} = \mu(A_\varepsilon)$, $f_\varepsilon \neq 0$, we see $|L_g(f_\varepsilon)|/\|f_\varepsilon\| \geq a - \varepsilon$, so for all ε, $\|L_g\|_{(L^1)^*} \geq \|g\|_\infty - \varepsilon$. Since ε is arbitrary, we have the claim. $\quad\square$

We've thus proven for any $g \in L^q$, $L_g \in (L^p)^*$ and (4.9.4) holds. Since $L_g = L_h \Rightarrow L_{g-h} = 0 \Rightarrow \|g - h\|_q = 0$, we have uniqueness. All that remains is to prove that every $L \in (L^p)^*$ is an L_g for some $g \in L^q$. We start with positive functionals.

Proposition 4.9.5. *Let* $L \in (L^p)^*$ *be a positive functional, that is,* $f \geq 0 \Rightarrow L(f) \geq 0$. *Then there exists* $g \in L^q$ *so* $L = L_g$.

Proof. Define a set function, ν, on Baire sets by

$$\nu(A) = L(\chi_A) \tag{4.9.7}$$

For any $\{A_j\}_{j=1}^\infty$ disjoint, $\sum_{j=1}^n \chi_{A_j} \to \chi_{\cup_{j=1}^\infty A_j}$ monotonically, and the limit lies in L^p. So by the monotone convergence theorem (valid since $p < \infty$), the convergence is in L^p. Since L is continuous,

$$\nu\left(\bigcup_{j=1}^\infty A_j\right) = \lim_{N \to \infty} \sum_{j=1}^N \nu(A_j) = \sum_{j=1}^\infty \nu(A_j)$$

Thus, ν is a (positive) Baire measure.

Clearly, if $\mu(A) = 0$, $\chi_A = 0$ in $L^p(X, d\mu)$, so $\nu(A) = L(\chi_A) = 0$. Thus, ν is a.c. wrt μ. By the Radon–Nikodym theorem (Theorem 4.7.4), for some $g \in L^1$,

$$L(\chi_A) = \int \chi_A(x) g(x) \, d\mu(x) \tag{4.9.8}$$

If $A = \{x \mid g(x) < 0\}$, $L(\chi_A) \geq 0$, but the right-hand side of (4.9.8) is ≤ 0, so $\mu(A) = 0$, that is, $g(x) \geq 0$ for a.e. x.

By taking finite linear combinations and using the dominated convergence theorem (in L^p and L^1), we see for any bounded Baire f, we have that

$$L(f) = \int f(x) g(x) \, d\mu(x) \tag{4.9.9}$$

Fix M, let $B = \{x \mid 0 \leq g(x) < M\}$ and $f = g^{q-1}(x)\chi_B(x)$. Then f is bounded, so

$$L(f) = \int_B g^q(x) \, d\mu(x) \tag{4.9.10}$$

On the other hand, as in the proof of (4.9.6),

$$\|f\|_p = \left(\int_B g^q(x) \, d\mu(x)\right)^{1/p} \tag{4.9.11}$$

Since $L(f) \leq \|L\| \, \|f\|_p$, we see that

$$\left(\int_B g^q(x) \, d\mu\right)^{1-1/p} \leq \|L\| \tag{4.9.12}$$

By the monotone convergence theorem in L^1, since $g^{q-1}\chi_B$ is monotone in M, we conclude $g \in L^q$ and $\|g\|_q \le \|L\|$. Thus, (4.9.9) extends to all $f \in L^p$ and $L = L_g$. □

Proof of Theorem 4.9.1. Any $L \in (L^p)^*$ can be written $L = L_r + iL_i$ with L_r and L_i real on $L^p_{\mathbb{R}}$. Since $L^p_{\mathbb{R}}$ is a Banach lattice, by Theorem 4.8.3, we have

$$L = L_{r+} - L_{r-} + iL_{i+} - iL_{i-} \tag{4.9.13}$$

By Proposition 4.9.5, each positive functional is an L_g, so

$$L = L_{g_{r+}} - L_{g_{r-}} + iL_{g_{i+}} - iL_{g_{i-}} = L_g$$

where $g = g_{r+} - g_{r-} + ig_{i+} - ig_{i-}$, that is, L is an L_g. This completes the proof. □

We can use the Riesz L^p duality result to prove that operators from L^p to L^∞ have an integral kernel. Operators with integral kernels will be a recurrent theme (See the Notes). $T : L^p(M, d\mu) \to L^r(N, d\nu)$ is said to have integral kernel, $K(n, m)$, a function on $N \times M$ if $K(n, \cdot)$ is measurable for a.e. n, $\int K(n, m)f(m)d\mu(m)$ is absolutely convergent for all $f \in L^p(M, d\mu)$ and a.e. n and

$$(Tf)(n) = \int K(n, m)f(m)d\mu(m) \tag{4.9.14}$$

We'll need separability of $L^p(M, d\mu)$ in our construction of K. The key is a technical issue. Let (N, Σ, ν) be a measure space (or to limit to the setup before Sections 4.10 and 4.13, a compact metric space with the Baire sets and a Baire measure). Let $\mathcal{B}^\infty(N, \Sigma)$ be the bounded Σ-measurable functions on N. Let $\pi : \mathcal{B}^\infty(N, \Sigma) \to L^\infty(N, d\mu)$ by letting $\pi(f)$ be the L^∞ equivalence class of f. If $g \in L^\infty$, we say $f \in \mathcal{B}^\infty$ is a *lift* of g if $\pi(f) = g$. It is easy to see that any $g \in L^\infty$ has a lift f with $\|f\|_{\mathcal{B}^\infty} = \|g\|_{L^\infty}$. Here is the technical fact we'll need:

Lemma 4.9.6. *Let $Y \subset L^\infty(N, d\mu)$ be a separable subspace. Then there exists $\tau : Y \to \mathcal{B}^\infty(N, \Sigma)$ so that $\pi(\tau(g)) = g$ for all $g \in Y$ and so that*

$$\|\tau(g)\|_{\mathcal{B}^\infty} = \|g\|_{L^\infty} \tag{4.9.15}$$

Proof. Let $\widetilde{Y} \subset Y$ be the vector space over the rationals generated by a countable dense subset of Y (i.e., finite linear combinations from the countable Y dense subsets with rational coefficients) so $\widetilde{Y}$ is countable. By picking an algebraic basis for $\widetilde{Y}$ and lifting each of them, we get a lift $\sigma : \widetilde{Y} \to \mathcal{B}^\infty(N, \Sigma)$ which is linear but for which (4.9.15) may fail.

For each $\tilde{g} \in \widetilde{Y}$, let $S_{\tilde{g}} \subset N$ be the set of measure zero so $|\sigma(\tilde{g})(m)| \geq \|\tilde{g}\|_{L^\infty}$. Let

$$S = \bigcup_{\tilde{g} \in \widetilde{Y}} S_{\tilde{g}} \tag{4.9.16}$$

and let

$$\tau(\tilde{g})(n) = \begin{cases} \sigma(\tilde{g})(n), & n \in N \setminus S \\ 0, & n \in S \end{cases} \tag{4.9.17}$$

Then, by construction,

$$\|\tau(\tilde{g})\|_{\mathcal{B}^\infty} = \|g\|_{L^\infty} \tag{4.9.18}$$

and τ is linear since σ is.

Since τ is a rational linear isometry on $\widetilde{Y}$, it extends to a rational linear isometry on Y. It is easy to see it is automatically real linear by taking limits of rationals. $\qquad \square$

Theorem 4.9.7 (Dunford–Pettis Theorem). *Let X be a separable Banach space and $(N, \Sigma, d\mu)$ a measure space. Let $T : X \to L^\infty(N, d\mu)$ be a bounded linear map. Then there is a function $\eta : N \to X^*$ so that $n \mapsto \eta(n)(x)$ is measurable for each $x \in X$ and so that*

$$(Tx)(\cdot) = \pi\big(\eta(\cdot)(x)\big) \tag{4.9.19}$$

and, for all $n \in N$

$$\|\eta(n)\|_{X^*} \leq \|T\| \tag{4.9.20}$$

Proof. Since X is separable and T continuous, $Y = \mathrm{Ran}(T)$ is separable, so by the Lemma, there is an isometric lift $\tau : \mathrm{Ran}\, T \to \mathcal{B}^\infty(N)$. Define η by

$$\eta(n)(x) = [\tau(Tx)](n) \tag{4.9.21}$$

It is easy to see that η obeys (4.9.19) and (4.9.20). $\qquad \square$

Corollary 4.9.8. *Let $1 \leq p < \infty$. Let $(M, d\mu)$ be a measure space so that $L^p(M, d\mu)$ is separable (e.g., M is a locally compact, σ-compact metric space with a Baire measure). Let $T : L^p(M, d\mu) \to L^\infty(N, d\nu)$. Then there exists a function $K(n, m)$ on $N \times M$ so $K(n, \cdot)$ is measurable in $\cdot$ for all n fixed*

$$\sup_n \Big(\int |K(n, m)|^q d\mu(m) \Big)^{1/q} \leq \|T\| \tag{4.9.22}$$

(where $q = p/p - 1$) if $p > 1$, and $\sup_{m,n} |K(n, m)| \leq \|T\|$ if $p = 1$ so that

$$(Tf)(n) = \int K(n, m) f(m) d\mu(m) \tag{4.9.23}$$

for all $f \in L^p(M, d\mu)$.

Proof. Follows immediately from Theorems 4.9.7 and 4.9.1 $\qquad \square$

Notes and Historical Remarks. That the dual of L^p is L^q for $1 \leq p < \infty$ is a 1909 result of Riesz [**780**].

Just as our proof that $(L^2)^* = L^2$ relied on a minimization result for closed convex sets, there is an alternate proof that $(L^p)^* = L^q$ for $1 < p < \infty$ that relies on a minimization result; see Lieb–Loss [**587**, Thm. 1.4].

There is an interesting approach to this duality result for $1 < p < \infty$ that replaces the Radon–Nikodym theorem with some substantial abstract Banach space theory as follows: By Hölder's inequality, $L^q \subset (L^p)^*$ and $L^p \subset (L^q)^*$ as closed subspaces. If $(L^p)^*$ were strictly bigger than L^q, then by the Hahn–Banach theorem, L^p would be strictly smaller than $(L^p)^{**}$. Clarkson's inequality (see the Notes to Section 5.3) and the Milman–Pettis theorem (Theorem 5.7.12) imply L^p, $1 < p < \infty$, is reflexive, which implies L^q must be all of $(L^p)^*$.

The Dunford–Pettis theorem is named after their 1939 paper [**261**] where the result appeared. Operators with integral kernels will reappear in Section 6.4 (distributional kernels), Section 6.6 of Part 3 (ultracontractive semigroups), Section 4.3 of Part 3 (pseudodifferential operators), and Chapter 3 of Part 4 (Hilbert–Schmidt operators).

Problems

1. Use the complex Radon–Nikodym theorem (Theorem 4.8.12) to prove that any $L \in (L^p)^*$ is an L_g for some $g \in L^q$.

4.10. Measures on Locally Compact and σ-Compact Spaces

In this section, we extend measure theory to some topological spaces that are not compact but have lots of compact subsets. We'll first develop the theory of *finite* measures for locally compact spaces. Then we'll introduce a class of spaces called σ-compact that naturally support some positive measures of infinite total mass. The most important case is $\mathbb{R}^\nu$ and the most important measure of totally infinite mass is $d^\nu x$, Lebesgue measure on $\mathbb{R}^\nu$.

We begin with a compact Hausdorff space, X, where $\{a\}$ is a Baire set for some $a \in X$ (e.g., compact metric spaces). Recall from Theorem 2.5.4 that

$$C_a(X) = \{f \in C_\mathbb{R}(X) \mid f(a) = 0\} \tag{4.10.1}$$

Theorem 4.10.1. *Let ℓ be a positive linear functional on $C_a(X)$ (i.e., $f \geq 0 \Rightarrow \ell(f) \geq 0$). Then there exists a unique positive Baire measure, μ, on X so that*

$$\mu(\{a\}) = 0 \tag{4.10.2}$$

and

$$\ell(f) = \int f(x)\, d\mu(x) \tag{4.10.3}$$

for all $f \in C_a(X)$. General functionals in $C_a(X)^*$ have the form (4.10.3)
where μ is a unique signed Baire measure with $\mu(\{a\}) = 0$.

Proof. Since $\{a\}$ is a Baire set, we can find compact sets $K_n \subset K_{n+1}^{\mathrm{int}}$
so $\bigcup_{n=1}^{\infty} K_n = X \setminus \{a\}$ (see the construction in Theorem 4.4.11) and then
functions f_n so

$$f_n \upharpoonright K_n \equiv 1, \qquad \mathrm{supp}(f_n) \subset K_{n+1}, \qquad 1 \geq f_{n+1} \geq f_n \geq 0 \qquad (4.10.4)$$

We want to sketch a proof that

$$L \equiv \sup_n \ell(f_n) < \infty \qquad (4.10.5)$$

leaving the details to the reader (Problem 1). Suppose (4.10.5) is false. Then
if

$$\alpha_n = \ell(f_{n+1}) - \ell(f_n), \qquad \alpha_0 = \ell(f_1) \qquad (4.10.6)$$

we have that

$$0 \leq \alpha_n, \qquad \sum_{n=0}^{\infty} \alpha_n = \infty \qquad (4.10.7)$$

Then there exists $\beta_n \geq 0$, $\beta_n \to 0$, so

$$\sum_{n=0}^{\infty} \alpha_n \beta_n = \infty \qquad (4.10.8)$$

Let $(f_0 \equiv 0)$

$$g = \sum_{n=0}^{\infty} \beta_n(f_{n+1} - f_n) \qquad (4.10.9)$$

This sum is finite at each $x \in X$, so g is well defined and g is an element of
$C_a(X)$. But $g \geq \sum_{n=1}^{N} \beta_n(f_{n+1} - f_n)$, so

$$\ell(g) \geq \sum_{n=1}^{N} \beta_n \alpha_n$$

(4.10.8) is inconsistent with $\ell(g) \in \mathbb{R}$. This contradiction proves that (4.10.5)
holds.

Now define $\tilde{\ell}$ on $C_{\mathbb{R}}(X)$ by

$$\tilde{\ell}(f) = Lf(a) + \ell(f - f(a)1) \qquad (4.10.10)$$

It is not hard to see (Problem 2) that $\tilde{\ell}$ is a positive on $C_{\mathbb{R}}(X)$ of the form

$$\tilde{\ell}(f) = \int f(x) \, d\mu(x) \qquad (4.10.11)$$

for a positive Baire measure, μ, on X.

Since $f_n \uparrow \chi_{X \setminus \{a\}}$, by the monotone convergence theorem,

$$\mu(X \setminus \{a\}) = L \qquad (4.10.12)$$

but, by (4.10.10), $\mu(X) = \tilde{\ell}(\mathbb{1}) = L$, so (4.10.2) holds.

The signed measure result follows from the fact that $C_a(X)$ is a Banach lattice, so any ℓ has the form $\ell_+ - \ell_-$ by Theorem 4.8.3. Uniqueness is left to the reader (Problem 3). $\qquad \square$

Now let X be a locally compact Hausdorff space, $C_\infty(X)$ the continuous functions going to zero at infinity, and $X_\infty = X \cup \{\infty\}$ the one-point compactification. Suppose X is such that $\{\infty\}$ is a Baire set (in terms of the definition below, this is equivalent to X being σ-compact). Then we can think of $C_\infty(X)$ as $C_{a=\infty}(X_\infty)$ and translate Theorem 4.10.1 to

Theorem 4.10.2. *Let X be a locally compact Hausdorff space where $\{\infty\}$ is a Baire set in X_∞. Then any positive functional, ℓ, on $C_\infty(X)$ uniquely has the form (4.10.3), where μ is a unique positive Baire measure of X_∞ with $\mu(\{\infty\}) = 0$. Every element of $C_\infty(X)^*$ is of the form (4.10.3) with a unique signed measure with $\mu(\{\infty\}) = 0$.*

For general locally compact spaces, X, by considering regular Borel extensions, one can extend these last two theorems even if $\{a\}$ is not Baire.

Next we want to consider an extension that will allow measures of totally infinite mass like Lebesgue measure on $\mathbb{R}^\nu$.

Definition. A *σ-compact space* is a topological space, X, for which there exists a countable family of subsets $\{K_n\}_{n=1}^\infty$ obeying

(a) Each K_n is compact.
(b) $K_n \subset K_{n+1}^{\text{int}}$
(c) $\bigcup_{n=1}^\infty K_n = X$.

By a simple compactness argument (see Problem 4), if $\{L_n\}_{n=1}^\infty$ is another family with the same properties, $\forall m \, \exists n$ so that $K_m \subset L_n$, and $\forall n \, \exists m$ so that $L_n \subset K_m$. An example is $\mathbb{R}^\nu$ with

$$K_n = \{x \mid |x| \leq n\} \qquad (4.10.13)$$

Note that by using Urysohn's lemma, one can find a family $\{K_n\}_{n=1}^\infty$ obeying (a)–(c) so that each K_n is a compact G_δ.

If $L_n = \overline{K_n^{\text{int}}}$, then $L_n^{\text{int}} = K_n^{\text{int}}$ and L_n has all the properties (a)–(c) plus

(d) $\overline{L_n^{\text{int}}} = L_n$

which we'll henceforth assume also. The K_n of (4.10.13) obeys (d).

Definition. A Baire measure on a σ-compact space, X, is a countably additive set function from the Baire sets to $[0, \infty]$ so that $\mu(K) < \infty$ for any compact G_δ, $K \subset X$.

We recall that some authors use the term *Radon measure* for what we just called a Baire measure and use Baire measure for any countably additive set function to $[0, \infty]$ without requiring $\mu(K) < \infty$ for compact G_δ, K. That said, we will use Borel measure for arbitrary countably additive set functions to $[0, \infty]$ even if $\mu(K) = \infty$ for some compact K's. This will be relevant when we discuss Hausdorff s-dimensional measures.

Notice that any Baire measure is σ-finite (defined after (4.5.1)) by the assumed σ-compactness of X.

Definition. Let X be a locally compact Hausdorff space. $C_0(X)$ will denote the set of continuous functions, $f \colon X \to \mathbb{C}$, so that $\mathrm{supp}(f) = \overline{\{x \mid f(x) \neq 0\}}$ is compact. This is the space of functions of *compact support*.

If $K \subset X$ is compact, let $C_0(K) = \{f \in C_0(X) \mid \mathrm{supp}(f) \subset K\}$. Then if $\{K_n\}_{n=1}^\infty$ is a sequence of compact G_δ's for X,

$$C_0(X) = \bigcup_{n=1}^{\infty} C_0(K_n) \qquad (4.10.14)$$

Notice that if $\overline{K_n^{\mathrm{int}}} = K_n$, then $C_0(K_n)$ can be identified with $C_\infty(K_n^{\mathrm{int}})$, that is,

$$C_0(K_n) = C_\infty(K_n^{\mathrm{int}}) \qquad (4.10.15)$$

Theorem 4.10.3. *Let X be a σ-compact Hausdorff space. Then there is a one-one correspondence between positive linear functionals, ℓ, on $C_0(X)$ and Baire measures, μ, on X given by*

$$\ell(f) = \int f(x)\, d\mu(x) \qquad (4.10.16)$$

Remark. If $\mathrm{supp}(f) = K$, then $\mu \restriction K$ is a (positive) Baire measure on the compact set K and (4.10.16) is the usual compact integral, discussed in Sections 4.4–4.5.

Proof. If μ is a Baire measure, (4.10.16) defines a positive linear functional on $C_0(K_n)$ and there is a consistency that if $f \in C_0(K_n)$ and $m \geq n$, the functional on $C(K_m)$ restricted to $C_0(K_n)$ is still given by (4.10.16). Thus, μ defines a positive linear functional on $C_0(X)$ by (4.10.14).

Conversely, let ℓ be a positive functional on $C_0(X)$ and K_n a set of compact G_δ's which obey properties (a)–(d). Then by Theorem 4.10.2 and

(4.10.14)/(4.10.15), there are measures, μ_n, on K_n^{int} so that if $f \in C_0(K_n)$, then

$$\ell(f) = \int f(x)\,d\mu_n(x) \tag{4.10.17}$$

It is not hard to see (Problem 5) that if A is a Baire set in K_n^{int} and $m \geq n$, then

$$\mu_m(A) = \mu_n(A) \tag{4.10.18}$$

and then, if

$$\mu(A) = \lim_{n\to\infty} \mu_n(A \cap K_n^{\text{int}}) \tag{4.10.19}$$

which exists by (4.10.18) and a monotonicity argument, then μ is a Baire measure on X which generates ℓ (Problem 6). $\qquad\square$

Basically, the above proof shows measures on X are given by sequences of finite measures, μ_n, on K_n^{int} that obey (4.10.18). Lebesgue measure on $\mathbb{R}^\nu$ is defined by piecing together Lebesgue measure on $(-n,n)^\nu$ defined by iterated integrals (see the next section).

Given a Baire measure, μ, on X, a σ-compact space, one defines $L^1(X, d\mu)$ by first defining $\int_{K_n^{\text{int}}} f(x)\,d\mu$ for any bounded Baire function as $\int f(x)\chi_{K_n^{\text{int}}}(x)\,d\mu_n(x)$ and then

$$L^1(X, d\mu) = \left\{ f \,\middle|\, \sup_{n,m} \int_{K_n^{\text{int}}} \min(|f(x)|, m)\,d\mu(x) \right\} \tag{4.10.20}$$

for any Baire measurable f. For $p \in [1, \infty)$,

$$L^p(X, d\mu) = \{f \mid |f|^p \in L^1\} \tag{4.10.21}$$

One can extend the convergence theorems to L^p and then prove completeness (Problems 7 and 8). The Lebesgue decomposition and Radon–Nikodym theorems extend (Problem 9).

One can define a signed measure to be a difference of positive Baire measures defined only on sets A with compact closure. Associating these with continuous linear functionals requires putting together a topology on $C_0(X)$. The "right" topology is not metrizable and uses inductive limits. It will be discussed in Section 9.2.

Problems

1. This will provide the details of the proof of (4.10.5).

    (a) Prove (4.10.7) if $L = \infty$.

    (b) If $\{\alpha_n\}_{n=0}^\infty$ is an arbitrary sequence of positive reals with $\sum_{n=0}^\infty \alpha_n = \infty$, prove there exists $\beta_n \geq 0$, $\beta_n \to 0$, so $\sum_{n=0}^\infty \alpha_n\beta_n = \infty$. (*Hint*: Pick N_j so $\sum_{n=N_j+1}^{N_{j+1}} \alpha_n \geq 4^j$ and let $\beta_n = 2^{-j}$ if $N_{j+1} \leq n \leq N_{j+1}$.)

(c) Show that g given by (4.10.9) lies in $C_a(X)$ but $\ell(g)$ is not in $\mathbb{R}$. Conclude that $L < \infty$.

2. (a) Prove that $\tilde{\ell}$ given by (4.10.10) is a positive linear functional on $C_{\mathbb{R}}(X)$.

(b) If $\ell^{\sharp}$ is another positive linear functional on $C_{\mathbb{R}}(X)$ with $\ell^{\sharp}(f) = \ell(f)$ for $f \in C_a(X)$, prove that

$$\ell^{\sharp}(f) = \tilde{\ell}(f) + \alpha f(a) \qquad (4.10.22)$$

for some $\alpha \in [0, \infty)$.

3. (a) Let μ, ν be two signed measures on X, a compact Hausdorff space. Suppose $\int f \, d\mu = \int f \, d\nu$ for all $f \in C_a(X)$. Prove that $\mu - \nu = \alpha\delta_a$ where δ_a is the measure $\delta_a(A) = 0$ (respectively, 1) if $a \notin A$ (respectively, $a \in A$).

(b) Let ℓ be a functional on $C_a(X)$. Prove there is at most one signed measure μ so that $\mu(\{a\}) = 0$ and $\ell(f) = \int f(x) \, d\mu(x)$.

4. Let L_n, K_n be two families obeying (a)–(c) in the definition of σ-compact space. For all m, prove that there is an n with $K_m \subset L_n$. (*Hint*: $\{L_n^{\text{int}}\}$ is an open cover of K_m.)

5. Let ℓ be a positive functional on $C_0(X)$, K_n a sequence of compact G_δ's obeying properties (a)–(d) in the definition of σ-compact spaces, X. Let μ_n be the measure on K_n^{int} given by (4.10.17) for $f \in C_0(K_n) = C_\infty(K_n^{\text{int}})$. If $m \geq n$, prove that $\mu_m(A) = \mu_n(A)$ for all Baire sets $A \subset K_n^{\text{int}}$. (*Hint*: First show the A's for which (4.10.18) are a σ-algebra and then, using the relation of measures to admissible functions, prove (4.10.18) for open F_σ's in K_n^{int}.)

6. (a) Prove that μ defined by (4.10.19) is a Baire measure on X. (*Hint*: Use monotone convergence for sums.)

(b) Prove that μ generates ℓ.

7. (a) If $\{f_n\}_{n=1}^\infty \subset L^p(X, d\mu)$ for some $1 \leq p \leq \infty$, μ a Baire measure on the σ-compact set X, and $f_{n+1} \geq f_n \geq 0$, prove that $f_\infty = \sup_n f_n \in L^p$ if and only if $\sup_n \|f_n\|_p < \infty$, and in that case, $\|f_n - f_\infty\|_p \to 0$. (*Hint*: Look at the restriction of f_n to K_m.)

(b) Prove Fatou's lemma for $L^1(X, d\mu)$.

(c) Explain the following by giving an example for $L^1(\mathbb{R}^\nu, d^\nu x)$: Equality can fail for Fatou's lemma on compact spaces because $f_n \to \infty$ on a smaller and smaller set, but it can also fail in the σ-compact case by the support of f going off to infinity.

(d) Prove the dominated convergence theorem for $L^p(X, d\mu)$, $1 \leq p < \infty$.

8. Prove that $L^p(X, d\mu)$ is complete for μ a Baire measure on a σ-compact set, X.

9. Let μ, ν be positive Baire measures on a σ-compact space. Prove that

$$d\nu = f \, d\mu + d\nu_{\text{sc}} \tag{4.10.23}$$

for $f \in L^1(K, d\mu)$ for each compact $K \subset X$ and $\nu_{\text{sc}} \perp \mu$. (*Hint*: Look at the corresponding decompositions for $\mu \upharpoonright K_m$ and $\nu \upharpoonright K_m$.)

4.11. Product Measures and Fubini's Theorem

In this section, we'll see that by focusing on measures on (locally) compact spaces, we get an almost effortless proof of Fubini's theorem. One aspect of this theorem is the equality of iterated integrals independently of the order of integration. We'll start with two examples that delimit the scope of this equality of iterated integrals, then we'll discuss product measures on compact spaces and σ-compact spaces proving Fubini's theorem, and finally, we'll say something about Gaussian integrals on $\mathbb{R}^\nu$.

For $\mathbb{R}^2$, equality of iterated integrals means that for a Borel function, f, on $\mathbb{R}^2$, we have

$$\int_0^\infty \left(\int_0^\infty f(x, y) \, dx \right) dy = \int_0^\infty \left(\int_0^\infty f(x, y) \, dy \right) dx \tag{4.11.1}$$

Example 4.11.1. Consider f which is $+1$ on S_+ and -1 on S_-, where (see Figure 4.11.1)

$$S_+ = \bigcup_{n=0}^\infty [n, n+1) \times [n, n+1) \tag{4.11.2}$$

$$S_- = \bigcup_{n=0}^\infty [n+1, n+2) \times [n, n+1) \tag{4.11.3}$$

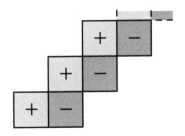

Figure 4.11.1. An example with unequal iterated slices.

Then

$$\int f(x, y)\,dx = 0, \quad \text{all } y \tag{4.11.4}$$

$$\int f(x, y)\,dy = \begin{cases} 1, & 0 \le x < 1 \\ 0, & \text{otherwise} \end{cases} \tag{4.11.5}$$

so (4.11.1) fails. Note that

$$\int |f(x, y)|\,dx dy = \infty \tag{4.11.6}$$

$\square$

This example clearly exploits the fact that dx on $\mathbb{R}$ is an infinite measure and, indeed, if f is bounded and measures are finite, we'll see (4.11.1) always holds. But if we allow unbounded f's, (4.11.1) can fail, even if we are dealing with Baire measures on compact spaces.

Example 4.11.2. Let $\Omega = [0, 1] \times [0, 1]$ and let $f \colon \Omega \to \mathbb{R}$ by (see Figure 4.11.2)

$$f(x, y) = \begin{cases} y^{-2} & 0 < x \le \tfrac{1}{2}\,y;\ y \le 1 \\ -y^{-2} & \tfrac{1}{2}\,y < x \le y;\ y \le 1 \\ 0 & x > y;\ x \le 1 \end{cases} \tag{4.11.7}$$

Clearly, $\int_0^1 f(x, y)\,dx = 0$ for all y, so

$$\int_0^1 \left(\int_0^1 f(x, y)\,dx \right) dy = 0 \tag{4.11.8}$$

On the other hand, an easy calculation (Problem 1) proves that

$$\int_0^1 \left(\int_0^1 f(x, y)\,dy \right) dx = -\log(2) \tag{4.11.9}$$

so (4.11.1) fails. Notice that in this case also (4.11.6) holds. See Problem 3 for another example. $\square$

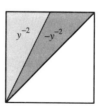

Figure 4.11.2. An example with unequal iterated integrals.

We turn to $C(X \times Y)$. Given two compact Hausdorff spaces, X and Y, define $\mathcal{P}(X, Y)$ to be the set of finite sums of the form

$$\sum_{j=1}^{N} f_j(x)g_j(y), \qquad f_j \in C(X), \quad g_j \in C(Y) \tag{4.11.10}$$

We write $\sum_{j=1}^{N} f_j \otimes g_j$ as shorthand for this function.

Lemma 4.11.3. *$\mathcal{P}(X, Y)$ is $\|\cdot\|_\infty$-dense in $C(X \times Y)$.*

Proof. $\mathcal{P}$ is an algebra, closed under $h(x, y) \to \overline{h(x, y)}$ with $\mathbb{1} \in \mathcal{P}$, and given $(x_1, y_1) \neq (x_2, y_2)$, there in $h \in \mathcal{P}$ with $h(x_1, y_1) \neq h(x_2, y_2)$ (if $x_1 \neq x_2$, pick $h(x, y) = f(x)$ where $f(x_1) \neq f(x_2)$, and if $x_1 = x_2$, we must have $y_1 \neq y_2$ so there is g with $g(y_1) \neq g(y_2)$ and we pick $h(x, y) = g(y)$). Thus, by the Stone–Weierstrass theorem (Theorem 2.5.7), $\overline{\mathcal{P}}^{\|\ \|_\infty} = C(X \times Y)$. $\quad\square$

Theorem 4.11.4. *Let X and Y be compact Hausdorff spaces and $d\mu, d\nu$ (positive) Baire measures on X and Y, respectively. Then for any $h \in C(X \times Y)$, we have*

$$y \mapsto \int h(x, y)\, d\mu(x), \qquad x \mapsto \int h(x, y)\, d\nu(y) \tag{4.11.11}$$

are continuous in y (respectively, x) and

$$\int \left(\int h(x, y)\, d\mu(x) \right) d\nu(y) = \int \left(\int h(x, y)\, d\nu(y) \right) d\mu(x) \tag{4.11.12}$$

There is a unique Baire measure $d\kappa$ on $X \times Y$ so that for any $h \in C(X \times Y)$,

$$\int h(x, y)\, d\kappa(x, y) = \int \left(\int h(x, y)\, d\mu(x) \right) d\nu(y) \tag{4.11.13}$$

Proof. Let $I_\mu(h)$ (respectively, $I_\nu(h)$) denote the functions of y (respectively, x) in (4.11.11). Clearly,

$$\|I_\mu(h)\|_\infty \leq \|h\|_\infty \mu(X), \qquad \|I_\nu(h)\|_\infty \leq \|h\|_\infty \nu(Y) \tag{4.11.14}$$

Moreover,

$$I_\mu \left(\sum_{j=1}^{N} f_j \otimes g_j \right) = \sum_{j=1}^{N} \left(\int f_j(x)\, d\mu(x) \right) g_j \tag{4.11.15}$$

so I_μ of such an h is continuous. By density of $\mathcal{P}$, we deduce $I_\mu(h)$ is continuous in y for any h. Similarly, $I_\nu(h)$ is continuous in x for any h.

By density, it suffices to prove (4.11.12) for $h \in \mathcal{P}(X, Y)$ where both sides are $\sum_{j=1}^{N} (\int f_j(x)\, d\mu(x))(\int g_j(y)\, d\nu(y))$ and so equal.

Clearly, $h \to \int (\int h(x, y)\, d\mu(x))\, d\nu(y)$ defines a positive linear functional, so a unique measure. $\quad\square$

κ is called the *product measure*, written

$$d\kappa = d\mu \otimes d\nu \qquad \text{or} \qquad \kappa = \mu \otimes \nu \qquad (4.11.16)$$

Theorem 4.11.5. *Let X, Y be compact Hausdorff spaces and μ, ν Baire measures on X and Y, respectively. Let $\kappa = \mu \otimes \nu$. Then for any bounded Baire function, h, we have that*

$$y \mapsto \int h(x,y)\,d\mu(x), \qquad x \mapsto \int h(x,y)\,d\nu(y) \qquad (4.11.17)$$

are bounded Baire functions and (4.11.12) holds and so does (4.11.13).

Remark. In particular (taking $h = \chi_A$), if A is a Baire set and $A_x = \{y \mid (x,y) \in A\}$, $_yA = \{x \mid (x,y) \in A\}$ are the slices of A, these slices are Baire sets and

$$\kappa(A) = \int \nu(A_x)\,d\mu(x) = \int \mu(_yA)\,d\nu(y) \qquad (4.11.18)$$

Proof. We use the by now standard song-and-dance, leaving the details to Problem 2. Since the characteristic function of an open F_σ, A is a monotone limit of a sequence of continuous functions, we get measurability and (4.11.18) for such A. One then proves the set of A for which $\nu(A_x)$ and $\mu(_yA)$ are measurable and (4.11.18) holds is a σ-algebra, so it contains all Baire sets. Since any bounded Baire function is a monotone limit of simple functions, we get the general result. $\square$

Theorem 4.11.6 (Fubini's Theorem for Positive Functions). *Let X, Y be compact Hausdorff spaces and μ, ν Baire measures on X and Y, respectively. Let $\kappa = \mu \otimes \nu$. Then for any nonnegative Baire function, h, the functions in (4.11.17) are Baire measurable and (4.11.12) and (4.11.13) hold in the sense that all their integrals are either infinite or are all finite and equal.*

Proof. Let $h_n = \min(h, n)$. Then $h_n \to h$ monotonically, proving the measurability and, by the repeated use of the monotone convergence theorem, this theorem. $\square$

Theorem 4.11.7 (Fubini's Theorem). *Let X, Y be compact Hausdorff spaces and μ, ν Baire measures on X and Y, respectively. Let $\kappa = \mu \otimes \nu$ and h a Baire function. Then*

(a) *$h \in L^1(X \times Y, d\kappa)$ if and only if either of the integrals*

$$\int \left(\int |h(x,y)|\,d\mu(x) \right) d\nu(y), \qquad \int \left(\int |h(x,y)|\,d\nu(y) \right) d\mu(x)$$

are finite.

(b) *If $h \in L^1(X \times Y, d\kappa)$, then the functions in the integrands in (4.1.17) are integrable for a.e. y (respectively, x). The functions defined by the integrals are a.e. finite and integrable in x (respectively, y).*

(c) *(4.11.12) and (4.11.13) hold.*

Remark. While we intend this for the real-valued case, it trivially extends to the complex-valued case by considering $\operatorname{Re} h$ and $\operatorname{Im} h$.

Proof. (a) is a special case of Theorem 4.11.6. (b) is immediate from the finiteness of the iterated integrals. (c) follows by writing $h = h_+ - h_-$ and using Theorem 4.11.6 on h_+ and h_-. $\qquad\square$

Product measures are related to tensor products of Hilbert spaces (see Section 3.8):

Theorem 4.11.8. *Let μ, ν be probability measures on compact metric spaces, X and Y. If $\{\varphi_j\}_{j=1}^{\infty}$ and $\{\psi_j\}_{j=1}^{\infty}$ are orthonormal bases of $L^2(X, d\mu)$ and $L^2(Y, d\nu)$, respectively, then $\{\varphi_j(x)\psi_k(y)\}_{j,k=1}^{\infty}$ is an orthonormal basis of $L^2(X \times Y, d(\mu \otimes \nu))$.*

Proof. Orthonormality is immediate. To check completeness, suppose that for all j, k,

$$\iint f(x,y)\bar{\varphi}_j(x)\bar{\psi}_k(y)\, d\mu(x)d\nu(y) = 0 \qquad (4.11.19)$$

Fix k. By the Schwarz inequality, $\int f(x,y)\bar{\psi}_k(y)\, d\nu(y)$ converges for a.e. x and defines a function $g_k(x)$. Since $g_k \perp \varphi_j$ for all j, $g_k(x) = 0$ for a.e. x. Thus, for a.e. x, $f(x, \cdot) \in L^2(Y, d\nu)$ and is orthogonal to each ψ_k. Thus, $f(x,y) = 0$ for a.e. x, y, that is, $f = 0$, so we have completeness. $\qquad\square$

Corollary 4.11.9. $L^2(X \times Y, d(\mu \otimes \nu))$ *is naturally isomorphic to* $L^2(X, d\mu) \otimes L^2(Y, d\nu)$.

There are two extensions of what we've done so far in this section that are immediate:

(1) Theorems 4.11.6 and 4.11.7 extend to Baire measures on σ-compact spaces (and finite measures on locally compact spaces). One lets $\ldots \subset K_n \subset K_{n+1}^{\mathrm{int}} \subset \ldots$ be a sequence of compact sets with $\bigcup K_n = X$ and L_n for Y and χ_n the characteristic function of $K_n \times L_n$ and applies the monotone or dominated convergence theorem to $h\chi_n$.

(2) Instead of two spaces, one can consider $X_1, \ldots, X_k$, Baire measures μ_j on X_j, and $\kappa = \mu_1 \otimes \cdots \otimes \mu_k$ on $X_1 \times \cdots \times X_k$. The proofs are all virtually identical. We have that

$$L^2(X_1 \times \cdots \times X_k, d(\mu \otimes \cdots \otimes \mu_k)) = \bigotimes_{j=1}^{k} L^2(X_j, d\mu_j) \qquad (4.11.20)$$

As a final topic in this section, we want to consider Gaussian measures on $\mathbb{R}^\nu$ which are sometimes, but not always, product measures. We first need to know the Gaussian integral.

Proposition 4.11.10. *We have that*

$$\int_{-\infty}^{\infty} \exp(-\tfrac{1}{2}\,x^2)\,dx = (2\pi)^{1/2} \tag{4.11.21}$$

Remarks. 1. For other proofs, see Problem 7 and the following in Part 2A: Example 5.7.11, Problems 26 and 28 of Section 5.7, Corollary 9.6.5, and Theorem 9.6.6.

2. This can be used to compute the surface area and volume of the unit ball in $\mathbb{R}^\nu$; see Problem 5.

Proof. We assume the reader is familiar with coordinate changes in $d^\nu x$ integrals and, in particular, with 2d polar coordinates. Let I be the integral in (4.11.21). Then

$$I^2 = \int_{-\infty}^{\infty} dx \int_{-\infty}^{\infty} dy\,\exp(-\tfrac{1}{2}\,x^2 - \tfrac{1}{2}\,y^2)$$
$$= \int_0^{2\pi} d\theta \int_0^{\infty} \exp(-\tfrac{1}{2}\,r^2) r\,dr \tag{4.11.22}$$

by using $x = r\cos\theta$, $y = r\sin\theta$ coordinates. If $u = \tfrac{1}{2}r^2$, we get

$$I^2 = 2\pi \int_0^{\infty} e^{-u}\,du = 2\pi \tag{4.11.23}$$

$\square$

From that, we can do many other integrals:

Theorem 4.11.11. *Let $a > 0$. Then*

(a) $\displaystyle \int \exp\left(-\frac{x^2}{2a}\right) dx = (2\pi a)^{1/2}$ $\qquad\qquad$ (4.11.24)

Let

$$d\mu_a(x) = (2\pi a)^{-1/2} \exp\left(-\frac{x^2}{2a}\right) dx \tag{4.11.25}$$

Then

(b) $\displaystyle \int_{-\infty}^{\infty} e^{tx}\,d\mu_a(x) = \exp(\tfrac{1}{2}\,at^2)$ $\qquad\qquad$ (4.11.26)

(c) $\displaystyle \int_{-\infty}^{\infty} x^{2\ell+1}\,d\mu_a = 0, \quad \ell = 0, 1, 2, \ldots$ $\qquad$ (4.11.27)

(d) $\displaystyle\int_{-\infty}^{\infty} x^{2\ell}\, d\mu_a(x) = 2^{-\ell}\,\frac{(2\ell)!}{\ell!}\,a^{\ell}$ \hfill (4.11.28)

(e) $\displaystyle\int_{-\infty}^{\infty} e^{itx}\, d\mu_a(x) = \exp(-\tfrac{1}{2}\,at^2)$ \hfill (4.11.29)

Remarks. 1. Once one knows about analytic functions, one can use Weierstrass' theorem (Theorem 3.1.6 of Part 2A) to see the left side of (4.11.26) is entire analytic in t and then get (c)–(e) from (b) for t real.

2. The use of $\exp(-x^2/2a)$ and not $\exp(-bx^2/2)$ may seem strange but the a^{ℓ} in (4.11.28) is convenient, and we'll want to take $a = 0$ below with $d\mu_{a=0}(x) = \delta_{\{0\}}$.

Proof. (a) Change variables to $y = x/\sqrt{a}$ so $dx = \sqrt{a}\, dy$.

(b) $e^{tx}e^{-x^2/2a} = \exp\left(-\dfrac{(x-ta)^2}{2a}\right)\exp(\tfrac{1}{2}\,at^2)$ \hfill (4.11.30)

so change x to $y = x - ta$, $dy = dx$.

(c) Immediate under $x \to -x$ symmetry.

(d) Let $F(t)$ be the integral in (4.11.26). By the dominated convergence theorem, $F(t)$ is C^1 with derivative $\int_{-\infty}^{\infty} xe^{tx}\, d\mu_a(x)$ and then, by iteration, it is C^{∞} and

$$F^{(\ell)}(t) = \int_{-\infty}^{\infty} x^{\ell} e^{tx}\, d\mu_a(x) \tag{4.11.31}$$

Thus, (4.11.28) follows from (4.11.26) by using

$$\exp(\tfrac{1}{2}\,at^2) = \sum_{\ell=0}^{\infty} 2^{-\ell} a^{\ell}\, \frac{t^{2\ell}}{\ell!} \tag{4.11.32}$$

and the Taylor series

$$F(t) = \sum_{\ell=0}^{\infty} F^{(\ell)}(0)\,\frac{t^{\ell}}{\ell!} = \sum_{\ell=0}^{\infty} F^{(2\ell)}(0)\,\frac{t^{2\ell}}{(2\ell)!} \tag{4.11.33}$$

(e) For $t > 0$,

$$\sum_{n=0}^{\infty} \frac{t^n}{n!}\, |x|^n = \exp(t|x|) \leq \exp(tx) + \exp(-tx) \tag{4.11.34}$$

for x real. By the dominated convergence theorem, it follows that for any $z \in \mathbb{C}$,

$$\int_{-\infty}^{\infty} \exp(zx)\, d\mu_a(x) = \sum_{n=0}^{\infty} \frac{z^n}{n!} \int_{-\infty}^{\infty} x^n\, d\mu_a(x) \tag{4.11.35}$$

so (c), (d) $\Rightarrow$ (e). $\qquad\square$

Recall that we use "positive matrix" on an inner product space to mean a Hermitian matrix with $\langle \varphi, A\varphi \rangle \geq 0$ for all φ (and "strictly positive" if $\langle \varphi, A\varphi \rangle > 0$ for all $\varphi \neq 0$); that is, "positive matrices" can have a nontrivial kernel.

Theorem 4.11.12. *Let* $A = (a_{ij})_{1 \leq i, j \leq \nu}$ *be a positive real matrix on* $\mathbb{R}^\nu$. *Then the Gaussian measure with covariance* A *is the unique measure,* $d\mu_A$, *on* $\mathbb{R}^\nu$ *with*

$$\int \exp(i\mathbf{t} \cdot \mathbf{x}) \, d\mu_A(\mathbf{x}) = \exp(-\tfrac{1}{2} \langle \mathbf{t}, A\mathbf{t} \rangle) \qquad (4.11.36)$$

for all $\mathbf{t} \in \mathbb{R}^\nu$. *Moreover,*

(a) $\displaystyle \int x_i x_j \, d\mu_A(\mathbf{x}) = a_{ij}$ \hfill (4.11.37)

(b) *If* $\mathrm{Ker}(A) \neq 0$ *and* $(b_{ij}) = B$ *is* A^{-1}, *then*

$$d\mu_A(\mathbf{x}) = (2\pi)^{-\nu} \det(A)^{-1/2} \exp\left(-\tfrac{1}{2} \sum_{i,j} x_i x_j b_{ij}\right) d^\nu x \qquad (4.11.38)$$

Proof. Uniqueness follows from the theory of the Fourier transform (see Theorem 6.2.12). For existence, suppose first that A is diagonal, $a_{ij} = \delta_{ij}\alpha_j$ with $\alpha_1, \ldots, \alpha_\ell$ nonzero and $\alpha_{\ell+1}, \ldots, \alpha_\nu = 0$. Let $\delta(\mathbf{x})$ be the point mass at $x = 0$ in $\mathbb{R}^{\nu - \ell}$. Then, taking

$$d\mu_A(x) = \delta(x_{\ell+1}, \ldots, x_\nu) \prod_{j=1}^{\ell} d\mu_{\alpha_j}(x_j) \qquad (4.11.39)$$

with $d\mu_\alpha$ the measure in (4.11.25), we get a measure obeying (4.11.36) by (4.11.29).

For general A, we use the fact that $A = ODO^{-1}$, where O is orthogonal and D is diagonal. Taking $\frac{\partial^2}{\partial t_i \partial t_j}\big|_{t=0}$ in (4.11.36) implies (4.11.37).

For diagonal A, (4.11.38) is just (4.11.39). An orthogonal change of variables gets the formula for general A with $\det(A) \neq 0$. $\qquad \square$

Notes and Historical Remarks. Fubini's theorem is named after a 1907 paper [**334**] of Guido Fubini (1879–1943). This genre of theorems is also associated with Leonida Tonelli (1885–1946) after his 1909 paper [**925**]. Some authors refer to the Fubini–Tonelli theorem and some use Fubini's theorem for Theorem 4.11.7 (for L^1 functions) and Tonelli's theorem for Theorem 4.11.6 (for positive functions even where all the integrals may be infinite).

An important precursor of Fubini's theorem is a result of Bonaventura Cavalieri (1598–1647) who, in a 1635 book [**175**], stated *Cavalieri's principle*: that if two two-dimensional (respectively, two three-dimensional) bodies had equal cross-sections at every height, their areas (respectively, volumes) are equal (see also Evans [**287**]). This, of course, follows from (4.11.18).

The Gaussian integral (4.11.21) was certainly known to Euler who computed $\Gamma\left(\frac{1}{2}\right)$ using a product formula of Wallis (see (5.7.80) of Part 2A). Laplace [**547**] computed the integral via a different iterated integral. The double integral in the text goes back to Poisson [**739**] and Jacobi [**448**]. The next section will say more about multidimensional Gaussian integrals.

Problems

1. Let f be given by (4.11.7).

   (a) Prove that $g(x) = \int_0^1 f(x,y)\,dy$ is given by

$$g(x) = \begin{cases} 1 - x^{-1}, & \frac{1}{2} \le x < 1 \\ -1, & 0 < x \le \frac{1}{2} \end{cases} \tag{4.11.40}$$

   (b) Prove that $\int_0^1 g(x)\,dx = -\log(2)$.

2. Prove the details of the proof of Theorem 4.11.5.

3. Compute

$$\int_0^1 \int_0^1 \frac{x^2 - y^2}{(x^2 + y^2)^2}\,dx dy \tag{4.11.41}$$

   as iterated integrals in two ways and get another counterexample to Fubini's theorem if $|f| \notin L^1$. (*Hint:* Show first that $\int_0^1 dy \ldots$ is $(1+x^2)^{-1}$.)

4. (Wick powers) Let $d\mu_a$ be the measure (4.11.25) and let x be the function $f(x) = x$ on $\mathbb{R}$. For any $f \in L^1(\mathbb{R}, d\mu_a)$, let $\langle f \rangle = \int f(x)\,d\mu_a(x)$.

   (a) Prove there are polynomials, $: x^n :$, of degree n in x uniquely determined by

$$: x^0 := 1, \qquad \frac{d}{dx} : x^n := n : x^{n-1} :, \qquad \langle : x^n : \rangle = \delta_{n0} \tag{4.11.42}$$

   (b) Prove that if $: \exp(tx) :$ is defined by

$$: \exp(tx) := \sum_{n=0}^{\infty} \frac{t^n : x^n :}{n!} \tag{4.11.43}$$

   then $: \exp(tx) :$ is determined by

$$\frac{d}{dx} : \exp(tx) := t : \exp(tx) :, \qquad \langle : \exp(tx) : \rangle = 1 \tag{4.11.44}$$

   (c) Conclude that

$$: \exp(tx) := \exp(tx - \tfrac{1}{2}t^2 a) \tag{4.11.45}$$

Note. There is a convergence issue in (4.11.43), so after getting (4.11.45) formally, it is better to *define* $: \exp(tx):$ by (4.11.45), confirm it obeys (4.11.44), and then that the series in (4.11.43) converges in $L^1(\mathbb{R}, d\mu_a)$.

(d) Prove that

$$\langle : \exp(tx) :: \exp(sx) : \rangle = \exp(ast) \qquad (4.11.46)$$

(e) Prove that

$$\langle : x^n :: x^m : \rangle = \delta_{nm} n! \, a^n \qquad (4.11.47)$$

Note. Thus, $: x^n : /[a^{n/2}(n!)^{1/2}]$ are orthonormal polynomials in $L^2(\mathbb{R}, d\mu_a)$, that is, the result of applying Gram–Schmidt to $\{x^n\}_{n=0}^{\infty}$. These are thus essentially Hermite polynomials. See the further discussion in Section 6.4.

(f) For $0 < c < 1$, define $\Gamma(c) \colon L^2(\mathbb{R}, d\mu_a) \to L^2(\mathbb{R}, d\mu_a)$ by

$$\Gamma(c) : x^n : = c^n : x^n : \qquad (4.11.48)$$

Prove that

$$\Gamma(c) : \exp(tx) : =: \exp(ctx) : \qquad (4.11.49)$$

and that

$$\Gamma(c) \exp(tx) = \exp(\tfrac{1}{4} t^2 (1 - c^2)) \exp(ctx) \qquad (4.11.50)$$

(g) For $f \in C_0^{\infty}(\mathbb{R})$, prove that

$$(\Gamma(c)f)(x) = \int K_c(x, y) f(y) \, dy \qquad (4.11.51)$$

where

$$K_c(x, y) = \pi^{-1/2} (1 - c^2)^{-1/2} \exp\left(\frac{-(y - cx)^2}{1 - c}\right) \qquad (4.11.52)$$

Remarks. 1. To prove (g), you'll use $\exp(ikx)$ and you'll need to know that the Fourier transform of a product is a convolution.

2. (4.11.51)/(4.11.52) is called *Mehler's formula* and, as a formula for $\exp(-t^2(-\frac{d^2}{dx^2} + x^2))$, goes back to the nineteenth century. The proof here is from Simon–Høegh-Krohn [**429**].

5. Let σ_{ν} be the surface area of $\{x \in \mathbb{R}^{\nu} \mid |x| = 1\}$ and τ_{ν} the volume of $\{x \in \mathbb{R}^{\nu} \mid |x| \leq 1\}$. This problem will compute σ_{ν} and τ_{ν}. It will be useful to consider

$$\Gamma(s) = \int_0^{\infty} x^{s-1} e^{-x} \, dx \qquad (4.11.53)$$

the Euler gamma function studied heavily in Sections 9.6 and 9.7 of Part 2A.

(a) Prove that
$$(2\pi)^{\nu/2} = \sigma_\nu \int_0^\infty r^{\nu-1} e^{-\frac{1}{2}r^2} \, dr \qquad (4.11.54)$$

(*Hint*: Mimic (4.11.23).)

(b) Prove that
$$\sigma_\nu = \frac{2\pi^{\nu/2}}{\Gamma(\frac{\nu}{2})} \qquad (4.11.55)$$

(*Hint*: $u = \frac{1}{2}r^2$.)

(c) Prove that $\sigma_1 = 2$ and conclude that
$$\Gamma(\tfrac{1}{2}) = \sqrt{\pi} \qquad (4.11.56)$$

(d) Prove that
$$\Gamma(s+1) = s\Gamma(s) \qquad (4.11.57)$$

(*Hint*: Integrate by parts.)

(e) Prove $\Gamma(1) = 1$ and then that for $k = 1, 2, \ldots$ (here $0! = 1$),
$$\sigma_{2k} = \frac{2\pi^k}{(k-1)!} \qquad (4.11.58)$$

(f) Prove that
$$\Gamma(k + \tfrac{1}{2}) = \frac{(2k)!}{4^k k!} \Gamma(\tfrac{1}{2}) \qquad (4.11.59)$$

and then that for $k = 1, 2, \ldots$,
$$\sigma_{2k+1} = \frac{2\pi^k 4^k k!}{(2k)!} \qquad (4.11.60)$$

(*Remark*: Check σ_3.)

(g) Prove that $\tau_\nu = \sigma_\nu / \nu$.

6. This will provide another proof of (4.11.55) using simple geometry and the following facts about the gamma function proven in Section 9.6 of Part 2A:
$$B(\alpha, \beta) \equiv \int_0^1 y^{\alpha-1}(1-y)^{\beta-1} \, dy = \frac{\Gamma(\alpha)\Gamma(\beta)}{\Gamma(\alpha+\beta)} \qquad (4.11.61)$$
$$\Gamma(\tfrac{1}{2}) = \sqrt{\pi} \qquad (4.11.62)$$
$$\Gamma(x+1) = x\Gamma(x) \qquad (4.11.63)$$

(a) By slicing the unit ball in $\mathbb{R}^\nu$ into constant x_n slices, prove that
$$\frac{\tau_\nu}{\tau_{\nu-1}} = \int_{-1}^1 (1-x^2)^{(\nu-1)/2} \, dx \qquad (4.11.64)$$

(b) Prove that the integral in (4.11.64) is $B(\frac{1}{2}, \frac{\nu+1}{2})$. (*Hint*: Use $\int_{-1}^1 = 2\int_0^1$ and change variable via $y = x^2$.)

(c) Prove that

$$\frac{\tau_\nu}{\tau_{\nu-1}} = \frac{\sqrt{\pi}\,\Gamma(\frac{\nu+1}{2})}{\Gamma(\frac{\nu}{2}+1)} \tag{4.11.65}$$

(*Note:* $\tau_1 = 2$.)

(d) Prove by induction that

$$\tau_\nu = \frac{(\sqrt{\pi})^\nu}{\Gamma(\frac{\nu}{2}+1)} \tag{4.11.66}$$

(e) Prove $\sigma_\nu = \nu\tau_\nu$ and conclude that

$$\sigma_\nu = \frac{2(\sqrt{\pi})^\nu}{\Gamma(\frac{\nu}{2})} \tag{4.11.67}$$

7. This problem will lead the reader through Laplace's original calculation of the Gaussian integral [**547**]. Let

$$A = \int_0^\infty e^{-x^2}\,dx \tag{4.11.68}$$

(a) Prove that

$$\int_0^\infty s^{-\frac{1}{2}}\,e^{-s}\,ds = 2A \tag{4.11.69}$$

(*Hint:* $s = x^2$.)

(b) Let $I = \int_0^\infty ds \int_0^\infty e^{-s(1+x^2)}\,dx$. Integrating first ds, prove that

$$I = \frac{\pi}{2} \tag{4.11.70}$$

(c) Iterating first ds, prove that

$$I = 2A^2 \tag{4.11.71}$$

(d) Conclude that

$$A = \frac{1}{2}\sqrt{\pi} \tag{4.11.72}$$

4.12. Infinite Product Measures and Gaussian Processes

Let $X_1, \ldots, X_n, \ldots$ be a sequence of compact Hausdorff spaces and $\mu_1, \ldots, \mu_n, \ldots$ Baire measures on X_j. We want to try to define the infinite product measure $\otimes_{j=1}^\infty \mu_j$ on $X = \times_{n=1}^\infty X_j$. Clearly, one way is as some kind of limit of $\otimes_{j=1}^N \mu_j = \mu^{(N)}$. For this to work, notice that if $f \in C(X)$ is only a function of $(x_1, \ldots, x_\ell)$ and $N > \ell$, then

$$\int f\,d\mu^{(N)} = \prod_{j=\ell+1}^N \mu_j(X_j) \int f\,d\mu^{(\ell)} \tag{4.12.1}$$

so for any hope of limits existing, one needs $\prod_{j=1}^\infty \mu_j(X_j)$ to converge.

While we could define an infinite product measure in such generality, there is no real loss (since we can replace μ_j by $\mu_j(X_j)^{-1}\mu_j$) to suppose each $\mu_j \in \mathcal{M}_{+,1}(X_j)$ is a probability measure. Our goal then is to first define such infinite product mesaures on products of compact spaces, then consider locally compact spaces and illustrate this by considering Gaussian processes. Along the way, we'll also define more general measures on products than product measures. We'll also see that product measures provide a model for independent, identically distributed random variables, which makes them central to some of the most important questions in probability theory. Thus, we return to this subject several times in Chapter 7.

Lemma 4.12.1. *Let $X = \times_{j=1}^{\infty} X_j$ be an infinite product of compact Hausdorff spaces. Let $\mathcal{P}(X)$ denote linear combinations of all functions of the form*

$$f(\{x_j\}_{j=1}^{\infty}) = f_1(x_1)\dots f_n(x_n) \tag{4.12.2}$$

where $n = 1, 2, \dots$ and f_j runs through all of $C(X_j)$. Then $\mathcal{P}(X)$ is dense in $C(X)$ in $\|\cdot\|_\infty$.

Proof. By Tychonoff's theorem (Theorem 2.7.1), X is compact. The proof of this lemma follows from the Stone–Weierstrass theorem (Theorem 2.5.7) as in the proof of Lemma 4.11.3. $\qquad\square$

Recall that X is called function separable if $C(X)$ is separable when given the $\|\cdot\|_\infty$-norm. We have:

Proposition 4.12.2. *Let $X = \times_{j=1}^{\infty} X_j$ be an infinite product of compact Hausdorff spaces. If each X_j is function separable, so is X.*

Proof. Let $Y_j \subset C(X_j)$ be a countable dense set. As $n = 1, 2, 3\dots$ and $f_j \in Y_j$, (4.12.2) runs through a countable set whose rational (finite) linear combinations are dense in $\mathcal{P}$, and so in $C(X)$. $\qquad\square$

In particular, the Hilbert cube, $X = [0, 1]^\infty$, of Example 2.2.11 is function separable.

Theorem 4.12.3. *Let $\{X_j\}_{j=1}^{\infty}$ be a collection of compact Hausdorff spaces and $\mu_j \in \mathcal{M}_{+,1}(X_j)$ probability measures on X_j. Then there is a unique measure, $\mu^{(\infty)} \equiv \otimes_{j=1}^{\infty} \mu_j$, on $C(X)$, where $X = \times_{j=1}^{\infty} X_j$, so that for all n and $(f_1, \dots, f_n)$ in $C(X_1) \times \cdots \times C(X_n)$, we have*

$$\int (f_1 \otimes \cdots \otimes f_n)(x)\, d\mu^{(\infty)}(x) = \prod_{j=1}^{n} \int f_j(x_1)\, d\mu_j(x_j) \tag{4.12.3}$$

Moreover, $\mu^{(\infty)} \in \mathcal{M}_{+,1}(X)$.

Proof. (4.12.3) determines $\int g\,d\mu^{(\infty)}$ for $g \in \mathcal{P}(X)$, so by the lemma, $\mu^{(\infty)}$ is unique.

Now let $g \in \mathcal{P}(X)$. Then g is a finite sum of products of functions of finitely many variables, so for some n, g is a function of $(x_1, \ldots, x_n)$. Thus, using the iterated integral construct of Section 4.11, we can define

$$L(g) = \int_{X_1 \times \cdots \times X_n} g(x)\,d^{(n)}\mu(x) \tag{4.12.4}$$

L is linear on $\mathcal{P}(X)$ because if g is a function of $(x_1, \ldots, x_n)$ and f of $(x_1, \ldots, x_m)$ with $m \geq n$, we have

$$L(g) = \int_{X_1 \times \cdots \times X_m} g(x)\,d^{(m)}\mu(x) \tag{4.12.5}$$

since $\mu_{n+1}(X_{n+1}) = \cdots = \mu_m(X_m) = 1$.

By (4.12.4) and $\mu^{(n)}(X_1 \times \cdots \times X_n) = \prod_{j=1}^n \mu_j(X_j) = 1$, we have

$$|L(g)| \leq \|g\|_\infty \tag{4.12.6}$$

for all $g \in \mathcal{P}(X)$. Since $\mathcal{P}(X)$ is dense, L extends to all of $C(X)$. Since $L(g) \geq 0$ if $g \geq 0$, L is positive and so defines a measure $d\mu^{(\infty)}$. Since $L(\mathbb{1}) = 1$, $\mu_\infty \in \mathcal{M}_{+,1}$. $\square$

Example 4.12.4 (Coin flips). Suppose we want a mathematical model of repeated coin flips. That is, we flip a coin N times with results $x_1, \ldots, x_N$, where $x_j = 1$ (heads) or $= 0$ (tails). The notion that the results of the flips don't depend on each other is modeled by a product measure. So if $x_j = 1$ occurs with probability $p\ (\in (0,1))$ and 0 with probability $q = 1-p$, we take the measure $d\mu_0(x) = q\delta_0 + p\delta_1$ on $\{0,1\}$ and model N flips as a $d\mu_0(x_1) \otimes \cdots \otimes d\mu_0(x_N)$ on $\{0,1\}^N$. To understand what happens as $N \to \infty$, we consider the infinite product measure.

Thus, we let

$$S_N = \sum_{j=1}^N x_j \tag{4.12.7}$$

and expect

$$\frac{1}{N} S_N \to p \tag{4.12.8}$$

in some sense as $N \to \infty$. Here is one realization of that. Note that

$$\int x_j\,d\mu_\infty = p \tag{4.12.9}$$

so that for $j \neq k$,

$$\int x_j x_k\,d\mu_\infty = \left(\int x_j\,d\mu_\infty\right)^2 = p^2 \tag{4.12.10}$$

Thus, for $j \neq k$,

$$\int (x_j - p)(x_k - p) \, d\mu_\infty = p^2 - 2p^2 + p^2 = 0 \qquad (4.12.11)$$

and

$$\left\| \frac{1}{N} S_n - p \right\|^2 = \frac{1}{N^2} \int d\mu_\infty \left(\sum_{j=1}^N (x_j - p) \right)^2$$

$$= \frac{1}{N^2} \sum_{j=1}^N \int (x_j - p)^2 \, d\mu_\infty$$

$$= \frac{1}{N} \, (p - p^2)$$

goes to zero as $N \to \infty$, an expression of (4.12.8). This is a version of the weak law of large numbers, discussed further (as well as the strong law) in Sections 7.2 and 7.3. $\qquad \square$

Example 4.12.5 (Lebesgue and Cantor Measures). Let $X_j = \{0, 1, 2\}$, $X_\infty = \times_{j=1}^\infty X_j$, $d\mu_j = \frac{1}{3}(\delta_{j0} + \delta_{j1} + \delta_{j2})$, and $d\nu_j = \frac{1}{2}(\delta_{j0} + \delta_{j2})$, $d\mu = \otimes_{j=1}^\infty d\mu_j$, $d\nu = \otimes_{j=1}^\infty d\nu_j$. Let $T \colon X \to [0, 1]$ by $T(x_j) = \sum_{j=1}^\infty x_j/3_j$, the base three decimal expansion of $x \in [0, 1]$. X has a countable set, S (namely, those x with either $x_j \equiv 0$ for all $j > J$ or with $x_j \equiv 2$ for all $j \in x$), so T is one-one on $X \setminus S$ and T is two-one on S. It it easy to see (Problem 2) that $\tilde{\mu} = T^*(\mu)$ (i.e., $\tilde{\mu}[A] = \mu(T^{-1}[A])$) is a Lebesgue measure and $\tilde{\nu} = T^*(\nu)$ is a Cantor measure. Given the criterion of Kakutani (Problem 1), this provides another proof that μ and ν are mutually singular. It also allows the calculation of the Fourier transform of the Cantor measure (Problem 4). $\qquad \square$

For the construction in Theorem 4.12.3 to work, we didn't need the $\mu^{(n)}$ to be successive products. Given $X_1, \ldots, X_n, \ldots$, if $X^{(n)} = \times_{j=1}^n X_j$, we define $\pi^\sharp_{(n,m)}$ for $n \geq m$ to be the map $\pi^\sharp_{(n,m)} \colon X^{(n)} \to X^{(m)}$ by

$$\pi^\sharp_{(n,m)}((x_1 \ldots, x_n)) = (x_1, \ldots, x_m) \qquad (4.12.12)$$

that drops $(x_{m+1}, \ldots, x_n)$. We define $\tilde{\pi}_{(n,m)} \colon C(X^{(m)}) \to C(X^{(n)})$ by

$$(\tilde{\pi}_{(n,m)} f)((x_1, \ldots, x_n)) = f(\pi^\sharp_{(n,m)}((x_1, \ldots, x_n))) \qquad (4.12.13)$$

that is, that takes a function of m-variables and views it as a function of n-variables. Duality then lets us define $\pi_{(n,m)} \colon C(X^{(n)})^* \to C(X^{(m)})^*$, called the *projection* of $\mu \in \mathcal{M}(X^{(n)})$ to $\mathcal{M}(X^{(m)})$, obtained by "integrating out" $(x_{m+1}, \ldots, x_n)$. It is easy to see that if $\mu \in \mathcal{M}_{+,1}(X^{(n)})$, then $\pi_{(n,m)}(\mu) \in$

$\mathcal{M}_{+,1}(X^{(m)})$. Notice we can take $n = \infty$ and define first $\pi_{(\infty,m)}^{\sharp} : X^{(\infty)} \rightarrow X^{(n)}$ and then $\tilde{\pi}_{(\infty,m)}$ and $\pi_{(\infty,m)}$.

Definition. Let $X_1, \ldots, X_n, \ldots$, be a sequence of compact Hausdorff spaces and $X^{(n)} = X_1 \times \cdots \times X_n$. A sequence of measures $\mu^{(n)} \in \mathcal{M}_{+,1}(X^{(n)})$ is called *consistent* if and only if for all $n \geq m$, $\pi_{(n,m)}(\mu^{(n)}) = \mu^{(m)}$.

Theorem 4.12.6 (Kolmogorov Consistency Theorem). *If $\{\mu^{(n)}\}_{n=1}^{\infty}$ is a family of consistent measures, there is a unique measure $\mu^{(\infty)}$ on $X^{(\infty)}$ so that for all n, $\pi_{(\infty,n)}(\mu^{(\infty)}) = \mu^{(n)}$.*

Proof. Uniqueness follows from density of $\mathcal{P}(X^{(\infty)})$ in $C(X^{(\infty)})$. Existence follows as in the proof of Theorem 4.12.3; the analog of (4.12.5) follows from consistency. $\qquad\square$

Remark. We don't even need that $\pi_{(n,m)}(\mu^{(n)}) = \mu^{(m)}$, but only that as measures on $X^{(m)}$, $\pi_{(n,m)}(\mu^{(n)})$ have a limit $\nu^{(m)}$. Then, automatically, $\pi_{(n,m)}(\nu^{(n)}) = \nu^{(m)}$ and we can form $\nu^{(\infty)}$ and, in an obvious sense, $\mu^{(n)}$ converges to $\nu^{(\infty)}$.

Example 4.12.7 (Discrete Gaussian Free Field). Let $J^{(N)}$ be the $N \times N$ matrix

$$J_{jk}^{(N)} = \tfrac{1}{2} \exp(-|j - k|), \qquad 1 \leq j, k \leq N \qquad (4.12.14)$$

It can be seen (Problem 5) that for any $\{t_j\}_{j=1}^{N} \in \mathbb{R}^N \setminus \{0\}$, we have

$$\sum_{j,k=1}^{N} t_j t_k J_{jk}^{(N)} > 0 \qquad (4.12.15)$$

Thus, we can let $d\mu^{(N)}$ be the Gaussian measure on $\mathbb{R}^N$ with covariance $J^{(N)}$.

By (4.11.36), for any $M \geq N$, we have

$$\int \exp\left(i \sum_{j=1}^{N} t_j x_j\right) d\mu^{(M)}(x) = \exp\left(-\tfrac{1}{2} \sum_{j,k=1}^{N} t_j t_k J_{ij}^{(M)}\right)$$

$$= \exp\left(-\tfrac{1}{2} \sum_{j,k=1}^{N} t_j t_k J_{ij}^{(N)}\right) \qquad (4.12.16)$$

We see $\pi_{(M,N)}(\mu^{(M)}) = \mu^{(N)}$. These measures are consistent and we can form an infinite product measure in which $\{x_j\}_{j=1}^{\infty}$ are Gaussian random variables with

$$\int x_j x_k \, d\mu_{\infty}(x) = \tfrac{1}{2} \exp(-|j - k|) \qquad (4.12.17)$$

The observant reader may be spluttering at this point: "But wait, you only constructed product measures on products of compact spaces and $\mathbb{R}$ is not compact. Indeed, $\mathbb{R}^\infty$ in the product topology isn't even locally compact (Problem 6) so you can't discuss measures on it at all!" Precisely. So we next turn to infinite products of probability measures on locally compact spaces. $\qquad \square$

Now let $X_1, X_2, \dots$ be a sequence of locally compact Hausdorff spaces and $\mu_1, \mu_2, \dots$ probability measures on X_j. Let $Y_j = X_j \cup \{\infty_j\}$ be the one-point compactifications of X_j, as discussed in Theorem 2.3.17. Then there are probability measures $\tilde\mu_j$ on Y_j defined by

$$\tilde\mu_j(A) = \mu_j(A \cap X_j) \tag{4.12.18}$$

that is,

$$\tilde\mu_j(\{\infty_j\}) = 0 \tag{4.12.19}$$

We can, as above, define $\tilde\mu^{(\infty)}$ on $Y^{(\infty)}$. Here is the basic point:

Theorem 4.12.8. $X^{(\infty)} = \times_{j=1}^\infty X_j$ *is a* G_δ *in* $Y^{(\infty)}$ *and* $\tilde\mu^{(\infty)}(Y^{(\infty)} \setminus X^{(\infty)}) = 0$.

Proof. Let $I_j = \{y \in Y^{(\infty)} \mid y_j = \infty_j\}$. Then I_j is closed, and since $\mu_j(\{\infty_j\}) = 0$, $\mu^{(\infty)}(I_j) = 0$. It follows that $\bigcup_{j=1}^\infty I_j$ is on F_σ and $\mu^{(\infty)}(\bigcup_{j=1}^\infty I_j) = 0$. But $X^{(\infty)} = Y^{(\infty)} \setminus \bigcup_{j=1}^\infty I_j$. $\qquad \square$

In essence, we can define a measure $\mu^{(\infty)}$ which is the restriction to $X^{(\infty)}$. If Σ is the set of Baire subsets of $X^{(\infty)}$, $(X^{(\infty)}, \Sigma^{(\infty)}, \mu^{(\infty)})$ is a measure space in the sense we'll discuss in the next section. So we've succeeded in defining an infinite product measure in this case also. For now, we add $Y^{(\infty)} \setminus X^{(\infty)}$ to apply the theory of integration we've developed but, as we'll see in the next section, we can do that directly.

We are now able to define the Gaussian process associated to $\ell_{\mathbb{R}}^2$, the real-valued sequences. Let μ_∞ be the measure on $\Omega_\infty \equiv \mathbb{R}^\infty$ (or $(\mathbb{R} \cup \{\infty\})^\infty$ if one doesn't want to use the theory of the next section!), which is the infinite product of $(2\pi)^{-1/2} \exp(-\frac{1}{2}x_j^2)\, dx_j$. Let x_j be the coordinate functions, viewed as elements of $L^2(\Omega_\infty, d\mu_\infty)$. Then

$$\int x_j x_k \, d\mu_\infty = \delta_{jk} \tag{4.12.20}$$

For any finite real sequence, $\{a_j\}_{j=1}^J$,

$$\left\| \sum_{j=1}^J a_j x_j \right\|^2 = \sum_{j=1}^J |a_j|^2 \tag{4.12.21}$$

by (4.12.20). Thus, if $a \equiv \{a_j\}_{j=1}^\infty \in \ell_{\mathbb{R}}^2$, we have $\sum_{j=1}^J a_j x_j$ converges in $L^2(\Omega_\infty, d\mu_\Omega)$ to a function we call $\phi(a)$. The $\phi(a)$ are determined by

$$\phi(a+b) = \phi(a) + \phi(b), \qquad \phi(\lambda a) = \lambda \phi(a) \quad \text{for } \lambda \in \mathbb{R},$$
$$\|\exp(i\phi(a))\| = \exp(-\tfrac{1}{2} \|a\|^2) \tag{4.12.22}$$

Definition. *The Gaussian process indexed by* $\ell_{\mathbb{R}}^2$ *is a probability measure space* (Ω, Σ, μ) *and map,* ϕ, *of* $\ell_{\mathbb{R}}^2 \to L^2(\Omega, d\mu)$ *so that* ϕ *obeys* (4.12.22) *and polynomials in* $\phi(a_1), \dots, \phi(a_\ell)$ *are dense in* L^2.

We should really say "a Gaussian process" but, in a sense, all such processes are the same, for if $\widetilde{\phi}$ is another such process on $(\widetilde{\Omega}, \widetilde{\Sigma}, \widetilde{\mu})$, there is a unitary $U \colon L^2(\Omega, d\mu) \to L^2(\widetilde{\Omega}, d\widetilde{\mu})$ so that

$$U\phi(a)U^{-1} = \widetilde{\phi}(a) \tag{4.12.23}$$

for all a, and so that if $F \in L^\infty(\Omega, d\mu)$, then $UF \in L^\infty(\widetilde{\Omega}, d\widetilde{\mu})$, and for all $g \in L^2$, $U(Fg) = (UF)(Ug)$. In particular, if $F = \chi_A$, $(UF)^2 = UF$, so $UF = \chi_B$ for some $B \in \widetilde{\Omega}$.

Above we proved existence of this Gaussian process. Given any separable real inner product space, $\mathcal{H}_0$, we can complete $\mathcal{H}_0$, pick an orthonormal basis for the completion, and realize $\mathcal{H}_0$ as a dense subspace of ℓ^2. The *Gaussian process indexed by* $\mathcal{H}_0$ then obeys (4.12.22), where $\|\cdot\|$ is the norm in $\mathcal{H}_0$. Indeed, we can do this even if the inner product is only semidefinite.

Example 4.12.7 is a realization of the Gaussian process with inner product on finite sequences $\{a_j\}_{j=1}^J$, $\{b_j\}_{j=1}^K$ given by

$$\langle a, b \rangle = \sum_{j,k=1}^{\max(J,K)} a_j J_{jk}^{\max(J,K)} b_k \tag{4.12.24}$$

Later (see Section 4.15), we will define Brownian motion as a Gaussian process.

Notes and Historical Remarks.

In his foundational work on probability, Kolmogorov [**507**] proved that if μ_j were probability measures on $\times_{j=1}^n X_j$ which were consistent in an obvious sense, then there was an induced measure on the infinite product space, the induced infinite product measure.

In Problem 1, the reader will prove a famous criterion of Kakutani [**472**] for mutual singularity of infinite product measures:

Theorem 4.12.9 (Kakutani's Dichotomy). *Let* $\{X_j\}_{j=1}^\infty$ *be a sequence of compact Hausdorff spaces,* $\{d\mu_j\}_{j=1}^\infty$ *and* $\{d\nu_j\}_{j=1}^\infty$ *two sequences of probability measures, and* $d\mu = \otimes_{j=1}^\infty d\mu_j$, $d\nu = \otimes_{j=1}^\infty d\nu_j$. *Suppose each* $d\nu_j$ *is* $d\mu_j$

a.c., that is,

$$dv_j = f_j \, d\mu_j \tag{4.12.25}$$

Let

$$\gamma_j = \int \sqrt{f_j} \, d\mu_j \tag{4.12.26}$$

Then

(a) *If* $\prod_{j=1}^{\infty} \gamma_j > 0$, dv *is a.c. wrt* $d\mu$.
(b) *If* $\prod_{j=1}^{\infty} \gamma_j = 0$, *then* dv *is singular wrt* dv.

Remark. Since $0 < \gamma_j \leq 1$ (by the Schwarz inequality), the finite products $\prod_{j=1}^{J} \gamma_j$ are monotone, so the infinite product $\prod_{j=1}^{\infty} \gamma_j$ always has a limit.

Problems

1. This problem will prove Kakutani's dichotomy (Theorem 4.12.9). Let $F_J = \prod_{j=1}^{J} \sqrt{f_j}$.

(a) If $J \leq K$, prove that in $L^2(X, d\mu)$,

$$\|F_J - F_K\|^2 = 2 - 2 \sum_{j=J+1}^{K} \gamma_j \tag{4.12.27}$$

(b) If $\prod_{j=1}^{\infty} \gamma_j > 0$, prove that $F_J \to F_\infty$ in $L^2(X, d\mu)$ (for some $F_\infty \in L^2$) and that $dv = F_\infty \, d\mu$, so dv is a.c. wrt $d\mu$.

(c) If $\prod_{j=1}^{\infty} \gamma_j = 0$, prove that

$$\lim_{J \to \infty} \int F_J \, d\mu = 0, \qquad \lim_{J \to \infty} \int F_J^{-1} \, dv = 0 \tag{4.12.28}$$

(d) Conclude that if $\prod_{j=1}^{\infty} \gamma_j = 0$, then dv is singular wrt $d\mu$. (*Hint*: See Proposition 4.7.1.)

2. (a) If η, κ are two measures on $[0,1]$ without any pure points and $\eta([\frac{j}{3^k}, \frac{j+1}{3^k}]) = \kappa([\frac{j}{3^k}, \frac{j+1}{3^k}])$ for all $k, j \in \{0, 1, 2, \dots\}$, prove that $\eta = \kappa$.

(b) In Example 4.12.5, verify that $T^*(\mu)$ is Lebesgue measure and $T^*(\nu)$ is the classical Cantor measure.

(c) Use the Kakutani dichotomy to see ν is singular wrt μ.

3. On $\{0, 1\}$, let $dv_p = p\delta_0 + (1-p)\delta_1$. On $\{0,1\}^\infty = X$, let $d\mu = \otimes_{j=1}^{\infty} d\mu_{1/2}$ and $dv = \otimes_{j=1}^{\infty} d\mu_{p_j}$, where $p_j = \frac{1}{2} + \alpha_j$. Prove that dv is a.c. wrt $d\mu$ if and only if $\sum_{j=1}^{\infty} \alpha_j^2 < \infty$.

4. Let $d\mu$ be Cantor measure translated to lie on $[-\frac{1}{2}, \frac{1}{2}]$ so $d\mu$ is invariant under $x \to -x$.

(a) Let

$$\tilde{\mu}(k) = \int e^{ikx} \, d\mu(x) \tag{4.12.29}$$

Prove that (including that the product converges)

$$\tilde{\mu}(k) = \prod_{n=1}^{\infty} \cos\left(\frac{k}{3^n}\right) \tag{4.12.30}$$

(b) Prove that $\tilde{\mu}(2\pi 3^m) = c \neq 0$ for $m = 1, 2, \ldots$ so, in particular, $\lim_{k\to\infty} \tilde{\mu}(k)$ is not 0.

5. Verify (4.12.15) for the matrix in (4.12.14)

6. Prove that $\mathbb{R}^\infty$ is not locally compact.

4.13. General Measure Theory

The most common construct of the Lebesgue integral is in two steps: first, go from $\|[a, b]\| = |b - a|$ to a measure on the Borel sets; second, construct an integral from the measure. Our approach in Section 4.4 has the advantage (and disadvantage, given its restriction to the compact case) of doing both steps at once. In this section, we'll provide the general framework to construct an integral from a measure. This will allow us to directly discuss examples like $\mathbb{R}^\infty$ relevant to the last section and $C([0, 1])$ relevant to Section 4.16, which are not locally compact. The steps are only a slight reordering from what we did earlier, so most of this section will be "the same as the last time." The passage from $\|[a, b]\| = |b - a|$ to Lebesgue measure will be discussed in Section 8.1.

Definition. A *measure space* is a triple (Ω, Σ, μ), where Ω is a set, Σ is a σ-algebra of subsets of Ω, and μ is a *measure*, that is, a map $\mu \colon \Sigma \to [0, \infty]$ (∞ included) which obeys

   (i)   (Countable additivity) $\{A_n\}_{n=1}^{\infty} \subset \Sigma$, disjoint

$$\Rightarrow \mu\left(\bigcup_{n=1}^{\infty} A_n\right) = \sum_{n=1}^{\infty} \mu(A_n) \tag{4.13.1}$$

   (ii) $\mu(\phi) = 0$ \tag{4.13.2}

If $\mu(\Omega) < \infty$, we say the measure is *finite*. If $\Omega = \bigcup_{n=1}^{\infty} A_n$ with $\mu(A_n) < \infty$, we say μ is *σ-finite*.

Remarks. 1. In (4.13.1), the sum of nonnegative numbers is always "convergent" although it may be to infinity.

2. (4.13.2) is just to eliminate the trivial case $\mu(A) = \infty$ for all A.

We begin by discussing the integral and L^p when $\mu(\Omega) < \infty$. Here are the steps:

Step 1. One defines a number of sets. $\mathcal{B}(\Omega, \Sigma)$ is the set of $f \colon \Omega \to \mathbb{R} \cup \{\infty\} \cup \{-\infty\}$ which are measurable, that is, for any Borel set $A \subset \mathbb{R}$, $f^{-1}[A] \in \Sigma$ and both of the sets $f^{-1}(\{\pm\infty\}) \in \Sigma$. There are the bounded measurable functions $\mathcal{B}_\infty(\Omega, \Sigma) = \{f \in \mathcal{B}(\Omega, \Sigma) \mid \|f\|_\infty \equiv \sup_{\omega \in \Omega} |f(\omega)| < \infty\}$. There are the positive measurable functions $\mathcal{B}^+(\Omega, \Sigma) = \{f \in \mathcal{B}(\Omega, \Sigma) \mid \forall \omega, \, f(\omega) \in [0, \infty]\}$, $\mathcal{B}_\infty^+(\Omega, \Sigma) = \mathcal{B}^+ \cap \mathcal{B}_\infty$. $\mathcal{S}(\Omega, \Sigma)$, the set of *simple functions*, is f's of the form

$$f = \sum_{j=1}^{n} c_j \chi_{A_j} \qquad (4.13.3)$$

where $A_j \in \Sigma$, $c_j \in \mathbb{R}$. $\mathcal{B}_\infty$ and $\mathcal{S}$ are vector spaces. It is easy to see that $\mathcal{S}$ is $\|\cdot\|_\infty$-dense in $\mathcal{B}_\infty$ (by approximating f by $f_n < f$, so $|f(\omega) - f_n(\omega)| < 2^{-n}$ at all ω, and $\mathrm{Ran}(f_n) \in \{\frac{j}{2^n}\}_{j \in \mathbb{Z}}$). It is also easy to see that every $f \in \mathcal{S}$ has a unique expression (4.13.3) if we demand $A_j \cap A_k = \emptyset$ for $j \neq k$ and the c_j are distinct and nonzero. We'll call this the *canonical decomposition*. Notice that for such a decomposition,

$$\|f\|_\infty = \max_j |c_j| \qquad (4.13.4)$$

Step 2. Given a measure, we define the integral, I, first on $\mathcal{S}$ by

$$I\left(\sum_{j=1}^{n} c_j \chi_{A_j}\right) = \sum_{j=1}^{n} c_j \mu(A_j) \qquad (4.13.5)$$

It is easy to see that the value of $I(f)$ is independent of the choices of c_j and A_j for which (4.13.3) holds, that I is linear, and by (4.13.4), that

$$|I(f)| \leq \mu(\Omega) \|f\|_\infty \qquad (4.13.6)$$

Thus, by density of $\mathcal{S}$ in $\mathcal{B}_\infty$, I can be defined uniquely on $\mathcal{B}_\infty$ by demanding that (4.13.6) continue to hold. I is linear and

$$f \geq g \Rightarrow I(f) \geq I(g) \qquad (4.13.7)$$

Step 3. For any $f \in \mathcal{B}^+$, we let

$$f^{(N)}(\omega) = \min(f(\omega), N) \qquad (4.13.8)$$

so $I(f^{(N+1)}) \geq I(f^{(N)})$ by (4.13.7). Thus, we can define $I(f) \in [0, \infty]$ by

$$I(f) = \sup_N I(f^{(N)}) = \lim_N I(f^{(N)}) \qquad (4.13.9)$$

(4.13.7) holds for $f, g \in \mathcal{B}^+$.

Step 4. We define $\mathcal{L}^1(\Omega, \Sigma, d\mu)$ to be those $f \in \mathcal{B}$ so that $I(|f|) < \infty$. If $f, g \in \mathcal{L}^1$, $f(\omega)$ and $g(\omega)$ are in $\mathbb{R}$ for a.e. ω. We can define $f - g$ for a.e. ω

and set it to 0 if $f(\omega) = \pm\infty$ or $g(\omega) = \pm\infty$. This $f - g$ is measurable and $|f - g| \leq |f| + |g|$, so $I(|f - g|) < \infty$ and defines a seminorm on $\mathcal{L}^1$. L^1, the set of equivalence classes of functions in $\mathcal{L}^1$ equal a.e., is easily seen to be a vector space on which $\|\cdot\|$ is norm.

Step 5. Here, we must deviate from the analysis in Section 4.4. There we deduced a monotone convergence theorem using completeness. Here, we'll need, following the more usual use of the Riesz–Fischer argument, to prove completeness already knowing a monotone convergence theorem. One needs the following: if $0 \leq g_1 \leq g_2 \leq \dots$ and $g_\infty = \sup_n g_n$ and if $g_j \in L^1$ with $\sup_j \|g_j\|_1 < \infty$, then $g_\infty \in L^1$ and $\|g_j - g_\infty\|_1 \to 0$. The reader will prove this in Problem 2 (using a preliminary monotone decreasing theorem proven in Problem 1).

Step 6. Once we have the monotone convergence theorem, by following Section 4.6 without change, we can prove Fatou's lemma and the dominated convergence theorem.

Step 7. By the argument in the proof of Theorem 4.4.7, $L^1(\Omega, \Sigma, d\mu)$ is complete—if f_n is a Cauchy sequence, we pass to a subsequence $f_{n(j)}$, so $\sum_{j=1}^{\infty} \|f_{n(j+1)} - f_{n(j)}\|_1 < \infty$. We set

$$g_m = |f_{n(1)}| + \sum_{j=1}^{m-1} |f_{n(j+1)} - f_{n(j)}| \tag{4.13.10}$$

$$g_\infty = |f_{n(1)}| + \sum_{j=1}^{\infty} |f_{n(j+1)} - f_{n(j)}| \tag{4.13.11}$$

and apply the monotone convergence theorem to see that $g_\infty \in L^1$. Thus

$$f_\infty = f_{n(1)} + \sum_{j=1}^{\infty} \left(f_{n(j+1)} - f_{n(j)} \right) = \lim_{j \to \infty} f_{n(j)} \tag{4.13.12}$$

exists for a.e. ω, $|f_\infty| \leq g_\infty \in L^1$ and

$$\|f_{n(j)} - f_\infty\|_1 \leq \|g_j - g_\infty\| \to 0 \tag{4.13.13}$$

proving the Cauchy sequence has f_∞ as an L^1-limit.

Step 8. For $1 \leq p \leq \infty$, one defines L^p as the set of $f \in \mathcal{B}$ with $|f|^p \in L^1$ and $\|f\|_p = \||f|^p\|_1^{1/p}$. The proofs of Minkowski's and Hölder's inequalities in the next chapter work in this general context, so L^p is a Banach space.

Step 9. The von Neumann proof of the Radon–Nikodym and Lebesgue decomposition theorems only depended on the Riesz representation theorem for L^2, which is still valid (at least if $L^2(\Omega, d\mu)$ and $L^2(\Omega, d\nu)$ are separable or if we prove the Riesz representation theorem for nonseparable spaces) since it is a Hilbert space result. So we get these results in this generality.

Step 10. The Riesz proof that $(L^p)^* = L^q$ only depended on the Radon–Nikodym theorem and Hölder's inequality, so we get that for general finite measure spaces.

Step 11. $\mathcal{B}_\infty$ is a Banach lattice with the property that if $\ell \geq 0$, then $\|\ell\| = \ell(\mathbb{1})$, so any bounded linear functional, ℓ, on $\mathcal{B}_\infty$ can be written as $\ell_+ - \ell_-$ uniquely if we demand $\|\ell\| = \|\ell_+\| + \|\ell_-\|$. If $\mu\colon \Sigma \to \mathbb{R}$ is a set function and there is a $c > 0$ so that if $\{A_j\}_{j=1}^\infty$ disjoint, then

$$\sum_{j=1}^\infty |\mu(A_j)| \leq c \tag{4.13.14}$$

then I defined on $\mathcal{S}$ by (4.13.5) obeys

$$|I(f)| \leq c\|f\|_\infty \tag{4.13.15}$$

Thus, it extends to an element of $\mathcal{B}_\infty^*$ and we can decompose it. This leads to the Hahn and Jordan decomposition theorems for signed measures obeying (4.13.14).

Step 12. Given two finite measure spaces, $(\Omega_1, \Sigma_1, \mu_1)$ and $(\Omega_2, \Sigma_2, \mu_2)$, we can define a product σ-algebra, Σ_{12}, on $\Omega_1 \times \Omega_2$ and product measure $\mu_1 \otimes \mu_2$ as follows. Σ_{12} is the σ-algebra generated by all sets of the form $A \times B$ with $A \in \Sigma_1$ and $B \in \Sigma_2$. For any $C \subset \Omega_1 \times \Omega_1$, define $C_{\omega_1} = \{\omega_2 \in \Omega_2 \mid (\omega_1, \omega_2) \in C\}$ and $_{\omega_2}C = \{\omega_1 \in \Omega_1 \mid (\omega_1, \omega_2) \in C\}$. The set of C with $C_{\omega_1} \in \Sigma_2$ and $\mu_2(C_{\omega_1}) \in \mathcal{B}(\Omega_1, \Sigma_1)$ is easily seen to be a σ-algebra and it contains any $A \times B$, $A \in \Sigma_1$, $B \in \Sigma_2$, so every $C \in \Sigma_{12}$ has this property. We need to prove that

$$\int \mu_2(C_{\omega_1}) \, d\mu_1(\omega_1) = \int \mu_1(_{\omega_2}C) \, d\mu_2(\omega_2) \tag{4.13.16}$$

for then we have the analog of (4.11.18) and we can define $\mu_1 \otimes \mu_2$ with $\mu_1 \otimes \mu_2(C)$ as the common value of (4.13.16).

That (4.13.16) requires some argumentation is an indication of the advantage of the Lax approach where the direct construction of $\mu_1 \otimes \mu_2$ and proof of (4.11.18) only relied on the Stone–Weierstrass theorem. Of course, our arguments here work on any finite (and then σ-finite) measure spaces.

A *monotone class* of sets is a family Ξ of sets so that if $\{A_j\}_{j=1}^\infty$ and $\{B_j\}_{j=1}^\infty \subset \Xi$ and $A_1 \subset \ldots \subset A_n \subset \ldots$ and $B_1 \supset \ldots B_n \supset \ldots$, then $\bigcup_{j=1}^\infty A_j$ and $\bigcap_{j=1}^\infty B_j$ lie in Ξ.

Let $\mathcal{E}$ be the set of finite unions of disjoint rectangles, $A \times B$, with $A \in \Sigma_1, B \in \Sigma_2$. We claim that if $P, Q \in \mathcal{E}$, then $P \cap Q$, $P \setminus Q$, and $P \cup Q$

all lie in $\mathcal{E}$. For rectangles, we note that

$$(A_1 \times B_1) \cap (A_2 \times B_2) = (A_1 \cap A_2) \times (B_1 \cap B_2) \qquad (4.13.17)$$

$$(A_1 \times B_1) \setminus (A_2 \times B_2) = \big[(A_1 \setminus A_2) \times B_1\big] \cup \big[(A_1 \cap A_2) \times (B_1 - B_2)\big]$$
$$(4.13.18)$$

(drawing pictures might help). This immediately implies that $P, Q \in \mathcal{E} \Rightarrow P \cap Q, P \setminus Q \in \mathcal{E}$ and then $P \cup Q = (P \cap Q) \cup (P \setminus Q)(Q \setminus P) \in \mathcal{E}$ since disjoint unions of two sets in $\mathcal{E}$ lies in $\mathcal{E}$.

We claim that Σ_{12} is the smallest monotone class, Ξ, which contains $\mathcal{E}$. For any set $P \subset \Omega_1 \times \Omega_2$, define

$$S(P) = \{Q \subset \Omega_1 \times \Omega_2 \mid P \setminus Q, \, Q \setminus P, \, P \cap Q \in \Xi\} \qquad (4.13.19)$$

Since Ξ is a monotone class, so is each $S(P)$. Let $P \in \mathcal{E}$. By the above argument $\mathcal{E} \subset S(P)$ so since $S(P)$ is a monotone class, $\Xi \subset S(P)$. From (4.13.19), $P \in S(Q) \Leftrightarrow Q \in S(P)$. Thus for any $Q \in \Xi$, $\mathcal{E} \subset S(Q)$, so $\Xi \subset S(Q)$ and we have that $P, Q \in \Xi \Rightarrow P \setminus Q, \, Q \setminus P, \, P \cap Q \in \Xi$.

Since $\Omega_1 \times \Omega_2 \in \mathcal{E} \subset \Xi$, we see $P \in \Xi \Rightarrow P^c \in \Xi$. Thus, $P, Q \in \Xi \Rightarrow P \cup Q = (P^c \cap Q^c)^c \in \Xi$ so Ξ is closed under finite unions and so by monotonicity applied to $\bigcup_{j=1}^{n} P_j$, we see that Ξ is a σ-algebra and thus $\Sigma_{12} \subset \Xi$. But any σ-algebra is a monotone class so $\Sigma_{12} = \Xi$. We have thus proven our claim that Σ_{12} is the smallest monotone class containing $\mathcal{E}$.

Let Ξ be the set of $C \in \Sigma_{12}$ obeying (4.13.16). Any rectangle $A \times B$ with $A \in \Sigma_1$, $B \in \Sigma_2$ has $(A \times B)_{\omega_1} = \mu_2(B)\chi_A$ so $A \times B \in \Xi$. It is easy to see Ξ is closed under finite disjoint unions so $\mathcal{E} \subset \Xi$. By the monotone convergence theorem, Ξ is a monotone class, so by the above argument any $C \in \Sigma_{12}$ obeys (4.13.16).

(4.13.16) is Fubini's theorem for χ_C and so we get Fubini, first for simple functions, then for $\mathcal{B}(\Omega_1 \times \Omega_2, \Sigma_{12})$, then for positive functions, and finally for L^1 functions.

It is straightforward to get from finite to σ-finite measures for all the above. Just find $A_1 \subset A_2 \subset \ldots$ so $\bigcup A_n = \Omega$ and $\mu(A_n) < \infty$ and study $f\chi_n$, where χ_n is the characteristic function of A_n. For example, if $f > 0$, $I(f) = \lim_n I(f\chi_n)$. L^p is $\{f \mid I(|f|^p) < \infty\}$. As for the non σ-finite case, with one exception, they arise about as often as nonseparable Hilbert spaces—namely, Hausdorff s-dimensional measures on $\mathbb{R}^\nu$ with $s < \nu$, which we construct in Section 8.2, is not σ-finite. While that measure is useful, I've never seen integration with respect to that measure used so we'll stick to the σ-finite case.

The main example we've seen is Ω, compact, locally compact, or σ-compact. $\mathbb{R}^\infty$ and $C([0, 1])$ are two cases that don't fit into that framework, but they do in a slightly larger framework that captures almost all examples of interest: A *Polish space* is a complete, separable metric space, Ω. Σ is the set of Borel subsets of Ω, and one studies probability measures on (Ω, Σ). Automatically, $L^p(\Omega, \Sigma, d\mu)$ is separable for $p < \infty$. We'll discuss measures on Polish spaces in the next section.

Notes and Historical Remarks. We discussed the history of general measure theory in the Notes to Section 4.4.

Problems

1. This problem and the next will have you prove two monotone convergence theorems after Step 4 in the analysis of the section. In this problem, we will look at a sequence $f_1 \geq f_2 \ldots \geq 0$ with $f_1 \in L^1(\Omega, \Sigma, d\mu)$ and $f_j(\omega) \to 0$ for a.e. ω and you will prove that

$$\lim_{j \to \infty} \|f_j\|_1 = 0 \tag{4.13.20}$$

(a) With $f^{(N)}$ given by (4.13.8), prove that given $\varepsilon > 0$, there is N so that

$$\|f_1 - f_1^{(N)}\|_1 \leq \varepsilon \tag{4.13.21}$$

   Let

$$B = \{\omega \mid f_1(\omega) > N\} \tag{4.13.22}$$

(b) Fix $\delta > 0$. Let

$$A_n = \{\omega \mid f_n(\omega) > \delta\} \tag{4.13.23}$$

   Prove that $A_{n+1} \subset A_n$ and that $\mu(\bigcap_n A_n) = 0$ and conclude that

$$\mu(A_n) \to 0 \text{ as } n \to \infty \tag{4.13.24}$$

(c) Prove that, with χ_C the characteristic function of C,

$$f_n(\omega) \leq \delta \chi_{A_n^c} + N\chi_{A_n} + (f_1 - N)\chi_B \tag{4.13.25}$$

and conclude that

$$\|f_n\|_1 \leq \delta\mu(\Omega) + N\mu(A_n) + \frac{\varepsilon}{2} \tag{4.13.26}$$

(d) By taking $n \to \infty$, then $\delta \downarrow 0$ and then $\varepsilon \downarrow 0$, prove that $\limsup \|f_n\|_1 = 0$.

2. In this problem, the reader will prove that if $0 \leq f_1 \leq f_2 \leq \ldots$ and $f_\infty(\omega) = \sup_n f_n(\omega)$ and if $f_j \in L^1$ with

$$\sup_n \|f_n\|_1 < \infty \tag{4.13.27}$$

then $f_\infty \in L^1$ and $\|f_n - f_\infty\|_1 \to 0$.

(a) By using Problem 1, prove that for each N,

$$\|f_n^{(N)} - f_\infty^{(N)}\|_1 \to 0 \tag{4.13.28}$$

(b) Prove that $\|f_\infty^{(N)}\|_1 \le \sup_n \|f_n\|_1$ and conclude that $f_\infty \in L^1$.

(c) Prove that $\|f_n - f_\infty\|_1 \to 0$.

4.14. Measures on Polish Spaces

Definition. A *Polish space* is a topological space, X, which is separable and has a topology generated by a complete metric.

Separable is intrinsic to the topology, but as the case $X = (0,1)$ (where $\mathbb{R}$ is complete and homeomorphic to $(0,1)$ but $(0,1)$ is not complete in its usual metric) shows, completeness is metric-dependent, and we will shift metric as needed.

On any metric space, the Borel sets are the smallest σ-algebra containing the open (and closed) sets. $\mathcal{M}_{+,1}(X)$ will denote the probability measures (positive Borel measures with $\mu(X) = 1$) on X. We'll have three layers of discussion: First, we prove every Borel probability measure on a metric space is (weakly) regular and give several equivalent notions to weak convergence. Then we add separability and show that this implies X is homeomorphic to a subset of the Hilbert cube, $H = [0,1]^\infty$ (not unrelated to the discussion of metrizability in Section 2.2). Finally, we turn to Polish spaces proper— first, in that case, the homomorphism we construct to a subset of H is onto a G_δ, so Borel, which will imply $L^p(X, d\mu)$ is separable for any $p < \infty$ and $\mu \in \mathcal{M}_{+,1}(X)$ and that weak convergence is defined by a metric. We'll then turn to the notion of tightness and describe precompact subsets of $\mathcal{M}_{+,1}(X)$.

We define *weakly regular* measures in the metric space case by (4.5.2), but with inner approximation (i.e., closed rather than compact) via the condition

$$\sup\{\mu(C) \mid C \subset A, \, C \text{ closed}\} = \mu(A) \qquad (4.14.1)$$

Lemma 4.14.1. *Let $C \subset X$, a metric space, be closed and let d be the metric on X. Define*

$$A_n = \{y \in X \mid d(y, C) < n^{-1}\}, \qquad f_n(x) = \max(0, 1 - nd(x, C)) \quad (4.14.2)$$

Then

(a) *A_n is open.*

(b) *$C = \bigcap_n A_n$; in particular, C is a G_δ.*

(c) *f_n is uniformly continuous with $f_n = 0$ on $X \setminus A_n$.*

(d) *$f_n(x) \downarrow \chi_C(t)$, the characteristic function of C.*

Remark. As usual

$$d(y, C) = \min_{x \in C} d(x, y) \qquad (4.14.3)$$

Proof. (a) If $y \in A_n$ and $r_n(y) = n^{-1} - d(y, c)$, then $B_{r_n(y)}(y) \subset A_n$, so A_n is open.

(b) Clearly, $C \subset A_n$ and if $x \in \bigcap A_n$, $\exists y_n \in C$, so $d(y_n, x) < 2n^{-1}$, so $y_n \to x$, so $x \in C$.

(c) $|f_n(x) - f_n(y)| \leq nd(x, y)$, so f_n is Lipschitz and thus, uniformly continuous. Obviously, $f_n(x) > 0 \Rightarrow d(x, c) < n^{-1}$.

(d) $f_n \downarrow$ is obvious. Since $f_n = 0$ on $X \backslash A_n$, $f_n(x) \to 0$ on $X \backslash \bigcap_n A_n = X \backslash C$. $f_n \equiv 1$ on C. $\qquad \square$

Theorem 4.14.2. *If X is a metric space, any $\mu \in \mathcal{M}_{+,1}(X)$ is weakly regular.*

Remark. In the Polish space case, we'll eventually prove regularity.

Proof. Lemma 4.5.5 is valid in this setting, so it suffices to prove that any closed set C is weakly inner and outer regular. Inner regularity is easy. To get outer regularity, notice $C \subset A_{n+1} \subset A_n \subset \cdots \subset A_1$, so $\sum_{j=1}^{\infty} \mu(A_j \backslash A_{j-1}) \leq \mu(A_1) < \infty$. Thus, $\mu(A_n \backslash C) = \sum_{j=n}^{\infty} \mu(A_j \backslash A_{j-1}) \to 0$ since $\bigcap_n A_n = C$. Thus, C is outer regular. $\qquad \square$

Theorem 4.14.3. *Let X be a metric space. Then for $\mu, \nu \in \mathcal{M}_{+,1}(X)$, the following are equivalent:*

(1) $\mu = \nu$
(2) *For every uniformly continuous function,*

$$\int f(x) \, d\mu(x) = \int f(x) \, d\nu(x) \tag{4.14.4}$$

(3) $\mu(C) = \nu(C)$ *for all closed sets C.*

Proof. (1) $\Rightarrow$ (2) is trivial. (2) $\Rightarrow$ (3) follows from Lemma 4.14.1(d) and the monotone convergence theorem. (3) $\Rightarrow$ (1) by weak regularity. $\qquad \square$

Remark. In the Polish space case, we'll see that (3) need only hold for all compact subsets of X.

Definition. If $\{\mu_n\}_{n=1}^{\infty}$ is a sequence in $\mathcal{M}_{+,1}(X)$, we say μ_n converges to $\mu_\infty \in \mathcal{M}_{+,1}(X)$ weakly if

$$\int f(x) \, d\mu_n(x) \to \int f(x) \, d\mu_\infty(x) \tag{4.14.5}$$

for all $f \in C(X)$, the bounded continuous functions on X.

Theorem 4.14.4 (Portmanteau Theorem). *Let X be a metric space. For $\{\mu_n\}_{n=1}^{\infty}$ and $\mu_\infty \in \mathcal{M}_{+,1}(X)$, the following are equivalent:*

(1) $\mu_n \to \mu_\infty$ *weakly.*

(2) *(4.14.5) holds for all uniformly continuous functions on* X.

(3) *For any closed set,* C,

$$\limsup_{n \to \infty} \mu_n(C) \leq \mu_\infty(C) \tag{4.14.6}$$

(4) *For any open set,* U,

$$\liminf_{n \to \infty} \mu_n(U) \geq \mu_\infty(U) \tag{4.14.7}$$

(5) *For any Borel set,* A, *with* $\mu_\infty(\partial A) = 0$,

$$\lim_{n \to \infty} \mu_n(A) = \mu_\infty(A) \tag{4.14.8}$$

Proof. $\underline{(1) \Rightarrow (2)}$ is trivial.

$\underline{(2) \Rightarrow (3)}$. Let f_m be given by (4.14.2). Then $\chi_C \leq f_m$ implies that for any m,

$$\limsup_{n \to \infty} \mu_n(C) \leq \lim_{n \to \infty} \int f_m(x)\, d\mu_n(x) = \int f_m(x)\, d\mu_\infty(x) \tag{4.14.9}$$

Since this holds for all m and $f_m \downarrow \chi_C$, the monotone convergence theorem implies (4.14.6).

$\underline{(3) \Leftrightarrow (4)}$ is trivial by $\mu_n(U) = 1 - \mu_n(X \setminus U)$.

$\underline{(3) + (4) \Rightarrow (5)}$. Let $U = A^{\text{int}}$, $C = \bar{A}$. Then

$$\limsup_{n \to \infty} \mu_n(A) \leq \lim_{n \to \infty} \mu_n(C) \leq \mu_\infty(C)$$

$$= \mu_\infty(A) = \mu_\infty(U)$$

$$\leq \liminf_{n \to \infty} \mu_n(U) \leq \liminf_{n \to \infty} \mu_n(A)$$

since $\mu_\infty(\partial A) = \emptyset \Rightarrow \mu_\infty(C) = \mu_\infty(A) = \mu_\infty(U)$.

$\underline{(5) \Rightarrow (1)}$. Let $f \in C(X)$, the bounded continuous functions. Suppose for all x, $a < f(x) < b$. Then

$$\{c \in (a, b) \mid \mu_\infty(\{x \mid f(x) = c\}) > 0\} \tag{4.14.10}$$

is countable. So for any m, we can find

$$a \equiv c_0^{(m)} < c_j^{(m)} < \cdots < c_{2m}^{(m)} \equiv b$$

so that no $c_j^{(m)}$ lies in the set (4.14.10) and so that for all j,

$$c_{j+1}^{(m)} - c_j^{(m)} \leq \frac{b - a}{m} \tag{4.14.11}$$

Let

$$A_j^{(m)} = \{x \mid c_j^{(m)} < f(x) \leq c_{j+1}^{(m)}\} \tag{4.14.12}$$

Because f is continuous, $\partial A_j^{(m)} \subset \{x \mid f(x) = c_j^{(m)}$ or $c_{j+1}^{(m)}\}$, and therefore,

$$\mu_\infty(\partial A_j^{(m)}) = 0 \qquad (4.14.13)$$

It follows from (5) that

$$\sum_{j=0}^{2m-1} c_j^{(m)} \mu_n(A_j^{(m)}) \to \sum_{j=0}^{2m-1} c_j^{(m)} \mu_\infty(A_j^{(m)}) \qquad (4.14.14)$$

By (4.14.10), for any $\nu \in \mathcal{M}_{+,1}(X)$,

$$\left| \int f(x)\, d\nu(x) - \sum_{j=0}^{2m-1} c_j^{(m)} \nu(A_j^{(m)}) \right| \le \frac{b-a}{m} \qquad (4.14.15)$$

so if $L_+ = \limsup_{n\to\infty} \int f\, d\mu_n$, $L_- = \liminf_{n\to\infty} \int f\, d\mu_n$, then

$$\left| L_\pm - \int f\, d\mu_\infty \right| \le \frac{2(b-a)}{m} \qquad (4.14.16)$$

Taking $m \to \infty$, we get (4.14.5) for f. $\qquad\square$

Now we add the assumption that X is separable. Let $\{x_n\}_{n=1}^\infty$ be a countable dense subset and let

$$\varphi\colon X \to H, \text{ the Hilbert cube}, \qquad \varphi(x)_n = \min(1, d(x, x_n)) \qquad (4.14.17)$$

Theorem 4.14.5. φ *is a homeomorphism of X and* $\mathrm{Ran}(\varphi)$.

Proof. We first prove that φ is one-one. Suppose $x \neq y$. Since $\{x_n\}_{n=1}^\infty$ is dense, find x_k with $d(x, x_k) < \min\left(1, \frac{1}{2}d(x,y)\right)$. Then $d(x_k, y) > \frac{1}{2}d(x,y)$, so $\varphi(x)_k \neq \varphi(y)_k$ and $\varphi(x) \neq \varphi(y)$.

φ is obviously continuous. Suppose $\{z_m\}_{m=1}^\infty$, $z_\infty \in X$, and $\varphi(z_m) \to \varphi(z_\infty)$. Given $\varepsilon < \frac{1}{2}$, find x_k so $d(z_\infty, x_k) < \varepsilon$ and then M, so for $m > M$, $|\varphi(z_m)_k - \varphi(z_\infty)_k| < \varepsilon$. Then $d(z_m, x_k) < 2\varepsilon$ and $d(z_\infty, z_m) < 3\varepsilon$. Thus, $z_m \to z_\infty$ in X, that is, φ^{-1} is continuous. $\qquad\square$

Finally, we pass to the Polish case.

Theorem 4.14.6. *Let X be a complete separable metric space with metric, d. Let φ be given by (4.14.17). Then $\mathrm{Ran}(\varphi)$ is a G_δ and so a Borel subset of H.*

Proof. Since φ^{-1} is continuous, for each m and k in $\{1, 2, \dots\}$, $\varphi[B_{1/k}(x_m)]$ is relatively open, so there is $V_{k,m}$ open in H so that

$$\varphi[B_{1/k}(x_m)] = V_{k,m} \cap \mathrm{Ran}(\varphi) \qquad (4.14.18)$$

We claim

$$\text{Ran}(\varphi) = \overline{\text{Ran}(\varphi)} \cap \left[\bigcap_{k=1}^{\infty} \left(\bigcup_{m=1}^{\infty} V_{k,m} \right) \right] \qquad (4.14.19)$$

which is a G_δ since closed sets are G_δ's (see Lemma 4.14.1(b)).

Since x_m is dense, $\bigcup_{m=1}^{\infty} \varphi[B_{1/k}(x_m)] = \text{Ran}(\varphi)$, so by (4.14.18), $\text{Ran}(\varphi) \subset \bigcup_{m=1}^{\infty} V_{k,m}$ and thus, $\text{Ran}(\varphi)$ is contained in the set on the right of (4.14.19). We need only show any point in the set on the right lies in $\text{Ran}(\varphi)$.

So let $v \in$ rhs of (4.14.19). Then, since for each k, $v \in \bigcup_{m=1}^{\infty} V_{k.m}$, for each k, there is m_k so

$$v \in V_{k,m_k} \qquad (4.14.20)$$

Fix k. Since $v \in \bigcap_{j=1}^{k} V_{j,m_j}$ which is open and $v \in \overline{\text{Ran}(\varphi)}$, there exists $z_k \in X$ so (with ρ the metric (2.2.18) on H)

$$\rho(\varphi(z_k), v) < \frac{1}{k}, \qquad \varphi(z_k) \in \bigcap_{j=1}^{k} V_{j,m_j} \qquad (4.14.21)$$

By (4.14.18) and the fact that φ is a bijection, we conclude

$$z_k \in \bigcap_{j=1}^{k} B_{1/j}(x_{m_j}) \qquad (4.14.22)$$

If $k > \ell$, (4.14.22) implies z_k and z_ℓ both lie in $B_{1/\ell}(x_{m_\ell})$, so $d(z_k, z_\ell) < 2/\ell$, that is, $\{z_k\}$ is Cauchy. Since X is complete, $z_\ell \to z_\infty$ for some $z_\infty \in X$. Since φ is continuous, $\varphi(z_\ell) \to \varphi(z_\infty)$. By (4.14.21), $\varphi(z_\ell) \to v$. Thus, $v = \varphi(z_\infty) \in \text{Ran}(\varphi)$, as we needed to prove. $\qquad \square$

If μ is a Borel measure on X, we can define ν on H by

$$\nu(A) = \mu(\varphi^{-1}[\text{Ran}(\varphi) \cap A]) \qquad (4.14.23)$$

which defines a Borel measure on H. We have seen (Proposition 4.12.2) that $C(H)$ has a countable dense set in $\|\cdot\|_\infty$ which is thus dense in each $L^p(H, d\nu)$, $p < \infty$. But since $\text{Ran}(\varphi)$ has ν-measure one and φ is a bijection, $f \mapsto f \circ \varphi$ is an isometry of $L^p(H, d\nu)$ to $L^p(X, d\mu)$. We have thus proven:

Theorem 4.14.7. *Let X be a Polish space. There is a countable set, $\mathcal{F}$, of functions in $C(X)$ which is dense in each $L^p(X, d\mu)$, $p < \infty$, for all $\mu \in \mathcal{M}_{+,1}(X)$.*

If we put the metric

$$\tilde{\rho}(x, y) = \rho(\varphi(x), \varphi(y)) \qquad (4.14.24)$$

on X, the functions f_n of (4.14.2) needed to get convergence are restrictions of functions on H, so in this metric there is a $\|\cdot\|_\infty$-dense family, $\{g_m\}_{=1}^{\infty}$, of functions that works for all C. By replacing g_m by $2^{-m} g_m / \|g_m\|_\infty$, we see that

$$D(\mu, \nu) = \sum_{m=1}^{\infty} \left| \int g_m \, d\mu - \int g_m \, d\nu \right| \qquad (4.14.25)$$

defines a convergent sum and a metric on $\mathcal{M}_{+,1}(X)$ in which convergence is weak convergence. Thus,

Theorem 4.14.8. *Let X be a Polish space. There is a metric on $\mathcal{M}_{+,1}(X)$ for which convergence is weak convergence of measures.*

Note $\mathcal{F}$ is *not* claimed to be $\|\cdot\|_\infty$-dense $C(X)$ (in fact, it is dense in those $g \in C(X)$ for which there is $f \in C(H)$ with $g = f \circ \varphi$).

Our final topic concerns the notion of tightness.

Definition. A Borel measure, μ, on a Polish space, X, is called *tight* if and only if for all $\varepsilon > 0$, there is a compact K_ε with

$$\mu(K_\varepsilon) \geq 1 - \varepsilon \qquad (4.14.26)$$

Theorem 4.14.9. *Every measure, μ, on a Polish space is tight.*

Proof. Pick a metric, d, in which X is complete, and let $\{x_m\}_{m=1}^\infty$ be dense. By the density, for any $k = 1, 2, \dots$, $\bigcup_{m=1}^\infty B_{1/k}(x_m) = X$, so $\bigcup_{m=1}^M B_{1/k}(x_m)$ is an increasing family, which implies

$$\lim_{M \to \infty} \mu \left(\bigcup_{m=1}^M B_{1/k}(x_m) \right) = 1 \qquad (4.14.27)$$

Thus, we can find $M_1 \leq M_2 \leq \dots$ so

$$\mu \left(\bigcup_{m=1}^{M_k} B_{1/k}(x_m) \right) \geq 1 - \frac{\varepsilon}{2^k} \qquad (4.14.28)$$

Let

$$S_\varepsilon = \bigcap_{k=1}^\infty \left(\bigcup_{m=1}^{M_k} B_{1/k}(x_m) \right), \qquad K_\varepsilon = \bar{S}_\varepsilon \qquad (4.14.29)$$

S_ε is totally bounded since it is covered by M_k balls of radius $1/k$. Thus, by Theorem 2.3.8, K_ε is compact.

Moreover,

$$\mu(K_\varepsilon) \geq \mu(S_\varepsilon) \geq 1 - \sum_{k=1}^\infty \left(1 - \mu \left(\bigcup_{m=1}^{M_k} B_{1/k}(x_m) \right) \right) \geq 1 - \varepsilon \qquad (4.14.30)$$

$\square$

Corollary 4.14.10. *Any probability measure on a Polish space is regular.*

Proof. Let $\mu \in \mathcal{M}_{+,1}(X)$ and let A be a Borel set. Fix $\varepsilon > 0$. By Theorem 4.14.2, find C closed so $C \subset A$ and $\mu(A \setminus C) < \varepsilon$. By Theorem 4.14.9, find K_1 compact so $\mu(X \setminus K_1) < \varepsilon$. Then $K = K_1 \cap C$ is compact, $K \subset A$, and $\mu(A \setminus K) < 2\varepsilon$. Thus, $\mu(A) = \sup_{K \subset A, K \text{ compact}} \mu(K)$. $\qquad\square$

Finally,

Definition. A family, $\mathcal{F} \subset \mathcal{M}_{+,1}(X)$, is called *tight* if and only if for all ε, there is a compact K so for all $\mu \in \mathcal{F}$, $\mu(K) > 1 - \varepsilon$.

Theorem 4.14.11 (Prokhorov's Theorem). *Let X be a Polish space. A family, $\mathcal{F} \subset \mathcal{M}_{+,1}(X)$ is (weakly) precompact if and only if it is tight.*

Remark. On $\mathbb{R}$, let μ_n be the point mass at $x = n$. Then $\mathcal{F} = \{\mu_n\}_{n=1}^\infty$ is not precompact; showing some condition for precompactness is needed if X is not compact. Of course, $\mathcal{F}$ is not tight either.

Proof. Suppose first that $\mathcal{F}$ is tight and $\{\mu_n\}_{n=1}^\infty$ is a sequence of measures in $\mathcal{F}$. By tightness, for each m, find K_m compact so for all n,

$$\mu_n(K_m) \geq 1 - (m+1)^{-1} \qquad (4.14.31)$$

By the compactness of $\mathcal{M}_{+,1}(K_1)$, we can find a measure ν_1 on K_1 and sequence $n_1(j)$ so $\mu_{n_1(j)} \upharpoonright K_1 \to \nu_1$ and $\nu_1(K_1) \geq \frac{1}{2}$. By successively passing to subsequences and using the diagonalization trick (see Section 1.5), we find a subsequence $n_\infty(j)$ so for all m, $\mu_{n_\infty(j)} \upharpoonright K_m \to \nu_m$ and $\nu_m(K_m) \geq 1 - (m+1)^{-1}$. It is then easy to see (Problem 1) that $\mu_{n_\infty(j)}$ has a weak limit in $\mathcal{M}_{+,1}(X)$.

For the converse, suppose $\mathcal{F}$ is precompact. Let d be a metric in which X is separable and complete and let $\{x_m\}_{m=1}^\infty$ be a dense subset. We claim that for each $\delta > 0$, there is M_δ so that for all $\mu \in \mathcal{F}$,

$$\mu\left(\bigcup_{m=1}^{M_\delta} B_\delta(x_m) \right) > 1 - \delta \qquad (4.14.32)$$

For if not, find δ so that for each M, there is $\mu_M \in \mathcal{F}$ with

$$\mu_M\left(\bigcup_{m=1}^{M} B_\delta(x_m) \right) \leq 1 - \delta \qquad (4.14.33)$$

In particular, that means for each M and all $N \geq M$,

$$\mu_N\left(\bigcup_{m=1}^{M} B_\delta(x_m) \right) \leq 1 - \delta \qquad (4.14.34)$$

By precompactness of $\mathcal{F}$, find $N(j)$, so $\mu_{N(j)} \to \mu_\infty$ weakly. By Theorem 4.14.4(d) and the fact that $\bigcup_{m=1}^M B_\delta(x_m)$ is open,

$$\mu_\infty\left(\bigcup_{m=1}^M B_\delta(x_m)\right) \leq 1 - \delta \qquad (4.14.35)$$

Since M is arbitrary and $\cup_{m=1}^\infty B_\delta(x_m) = X$, we see $\mu(X) \leq 1 - \delta$, contradicting $\mu \in \mathcal{M}_{+,1}(X)$. Thus, our claim is proven that for every $\delta > 0$, there is M_δ so (4.14.32) holds for all $\mu \in \mathcal{F}$.

Given ε, let $S_\varepsilon = \bigcap_{k=1}^\infty \bigcup_{m=1}^{M_{\varepsilon/2^k}} B_{\varepsilon/2^k}(x_m)$. By (4.14.32), $\mu(S_\varepsilon) \geq 1 - \varepsilon$ for all $\mu \in \mathcal{F}$ and S_ε is totally bounded, so precompact. Thus, $K_\varepsilon = \overline{S_\varepsilon}$ is compact and $\mu(K_\varepsilon) \geq 1 - \varepsilon$, implying that $\mathcal{F}$ is tight. $\qquad \square$

Notes and Historical Remarks. French mathematicians invented the term Polish space in homage to the Polish School of topology led especially by Kuratowski—initially for their use in descriptive set theory; the use in measure theory is later. Because most stochastic processes are described by measures on function spaces which are Polish, measure theory on Polish spaces is especially beloved by probabilists.

For references on measure theory of Polish spaces, see Albeverio et al. [8], Bauer [63], Billlingsley [90], Dudley [259], Fristedt–Gray [329], Mushtari [673], and the appendix in Varadhan [946].

A portmanteau is a large French traveling trunk. The name applied to Theorem 4.14.4 was pushed by Billingsley who, in the second edition of his book [90], includes the following reference in his bibliography: Jean-Pierre Portmanteau, *Espoir pour l'ensemble vide?*, Annales de l'Université de Felletin CXLI (1915), 322–325. This reference, which is nowhere quoted in the text, is an elaborate joke: the title translates to "Hope for the empty set?", Felletin is a small town in France with no university, abstract measure theory and even metric spaces barely existed in 1915, and no journal had volume 141 in 1915.

Prokhorov's theorem appeared first in [751] where it was also first noted that the weak topology on $\mathcal{M}_{+,1}(X)$ for a Polish space is given by a metric.

The set theoretic aspects of Polish spaces have been extensively studied because of their relevance to logic—a good reference is Kechris [480]. An important result in the theory is Alexandroff's theorem: A subset of a Polish space is a Polish space in the induced topology if and only if it is a G_δ. In Theorem 4.14.6, we saw an explicit example of this.

A subset of a Polish space which is a continuous image of a Polish space is called an *analytic set* (sometimes a Souslin or Suslin set).

Problems

1. If μ_n is a family of probabilistic measures on a Polish space, X, so there are compact sets K_m and $\nu_m \in \mathcal{M}_+(K_m)$ so $\mu_n \upharpoonright K_m \to \nu_m$ weakly (i.e., in $\sigma(\mathcal{M}_+(K_m), C(K_m))$-topology in the language of Section 5.7) and $\nu_m(K_m) \geq 1 - (m+1)^{-1}$, prove that there is a probability measure, ν, on X so $\nu \upharpoonright K_m = \nu_m$ and $\mu_n \to \nu$ weakly.

4.15. Another Look at Functions of Bounded Variation

In Section 4.1, we defined a function, α, on bounded variation as follows: A partition, $\mathbf{t}$, of $[0,1]$ is an $(n+1)$-tuple, $(t_0, \ldots, t_n)$ with $0 = t_0 < t_1 < \cdots < t_n = 1$. Given $\alpha \colon [0,1] \to \mathbb{R}$,

$$V_{\mathbf{t}}(\alpha) = \sum_{j=1}^{n} |\alpha(t_j) - \alpha(t_{j-1})| \qquad (4.15.1)$$

and the *total variation*,

$$\mathrm{Var}(\alpha) = \sup_{\mathbf{t}} V_{\mathbf{t}}(\alpha) \qquad (4.15.2)$$

We defined a (signed) Riemann–Stieltjes integral for α's of *bounded variation*, that is, $\mathrm{Var}(\alpha) < \infty$. Since then we have developed a Lebesgue–Stieltjes integral and measure and learned how to analyze general measures. In this section, we use these insights to return to the study of functions on bounded variation. We'll find translations of the basic decompositions for measures.

We say $\mathbf{s}$ is a *refinement* of $\mathbf{t}$ if the set of values in $\mathbf{t}$ is a subset of values in $\mathbf{s}$. Thus, the intervals $[s_{j-1}, s_j)$ are subsets of some $[t_{k-1}, t_k)$. If we order partitions by $\mathbf{s} \triangleright \mathbf{t}$ if s is a refinement of t, they are a directed set, since any s, t have a common refinement—indeed, a minimal common refinement (Problem 1). Since

$$\mathbf{s} \triangleright \mathbf{t} \Rightarrow V_{\mathbf{s}}(\alpha) \geq V_{\mathbf{t}}(\alpha) \qquad (4.15.3)$$

We have

Proposition 4.15.1. *For any function, α, of bounded variation, there exists a sequence of partitions $\mathbf{t}_j$ so that $\mathbf{t}_{j+1} \triangleright \mathbf{t}_j$ and*

$$V_{\mathbf{t}_j}(\alpha) \uparrow \mathrm{Var}(\alpha) \qquad (4.15.4)$$

Proof. Pick partitions $\mathbf{s}_j$ so $V_{\mathbf{s}_j}(\alpha) \geq \mathrm{Var}(\alpha) - 1/j$. Define $\mathbf{t}_j$ inductively so $\mathbf{t}_1 = \mathbf{s}_1$ and $\mathbf{t}_{j+1}$ is a common refinement of $\mathbf{t}_j$ and $\mathbf{s}_{j+1}$. Then $\mathbf{t}_{j+1} \triangleright \mathbf{t}_j$ by construction and $V_{\mathbf{s}_j}(\alpha) \leq V_{\mathbf{t}_j}(\alpha) \leq \mathrm{Var}(\alpha)$, so (4.15.4) holds. $\square$

If $x_0 \in [0,1)$ and $a = \limsup_{x\downarrow x_0} \alpha(x)$, $b = \liminf_{x\downarrow x_0} \alpha(x)$, we can find $x_1 > x_2 > \cdots > x_0$ with $x_n \to x_0$ so $\alpha(x_{2n}) \to a$, $\alpha(x_{2n+1}) \to b$. If $a > b$, $\lim_{N\to\infty} \sum_{n=1}^{N} (\alpha(x_{2n}) - \alpha(x_{2n+1})) \to \infty$, so bounded variation implies $a = b$, that is, $\lim_{x \downarrow x_0} \alpha(x)$ exists, and similarly, $\lim_{x \uparrow x_0} \alpha(x)$ exists for $x_0 \in (0, 1]$, so we can talk of $\alpha(x_0 \pm 0)$.

Clearly, the set of functions of bounded variation is a vector space with

$$\text{Var}(\alpha_1 + \alpha_2) \le \text{Var}(\alpha_1) + \text{Var}(\alpha_2), \qquad \text{Var}(c\alpha) = |c|\text{Var}(\alpha) \qquad (4.15.5)$$

Moreover, if α is a monotone function,

$$\alpha \text{ monotone} \Rightarrow \forall \mathbf{t}, \quad V_{\mathbf{t}}(\alpha) = \alpha(1) - \alpha(0) \Rightarrow \text{Var}(\alpha) = \alpha(1) - \alpha(0)$$

The following illustrates what the general function of bounded variation is:

Theorem 4.15.2 (Jordan's Theorem). *Any function, α, of bounded variation has the form*

$$\alpha = \alpha_+ - \alpha_- \qquad (4.15.6)$$

where $\alpha_\pm$ are monotone and

$$\text{Var}(\alpha) = \text{Var}(\alpha_+) + \text{Var}(\alpha_-) \qquad (4.15.7)$$

Remarks. 1. It can be seen that up to a single constant, the decomposition obeying (4.15.7) is unique (Problem 2).

2. The proof shows that the positive measures $d\alpha_+$ and $d\alpha_-$ are mutually singular.

Proof. Without loss, we suppose $\alpha(0) = 0$. Let μ_α be the Stieltjes measure associated to α. By (4.1.17),

$$\|\mu_\alpha\| \le \text{Var}(\alpha) \qquad (4.15.8)$$

By Proposition 4.8.5, we have that

$$\mu_\alpha = \mu_+ - \mu_-, \qquad \|\mu_+\| + \|\mu_-\| = \mu_+([0,1]) + \mu_-([0,1]) = \|\mu_\alpha\| \quad (4.15.9)$$

Since $\mu_\pm$ are positive measure, $\mu_\pm = \mu_{\alpha_\pm}$, where $\alpha_\pm(x) = \mu_\pm([0,x])$ (for $x > 0$, $\alpha_\pm(0) = 0$) is monotone. Thus,

$$\mu_\pm([0,1]) = \alpha_\pm(1) - \alpha_\pm(0) = \text{Var}(\alpha_\pm) \qquad (4.15.10)$$

By $\mu_+ - \mu_- = \mu_\alpha$, we have (since $\alpha(0) = \alpha_\pm(0) = 0$),

$$\alpha(x) = \alpha_+(x) - \alpha_-(x) \qquad (4.15.11)$$

and, by (4.15.9),

$$\|\mu_\alpha\| = \text{Var}(\alpha_+) + \text{Var}(\alpha_-) \qquad (4.15.12)$$

By (4.15.5),

$$\text{Var}(\alpha) \le \text{Var}(\alpha_+) + \text{Var}(\alpha_-) \qquad (4.15.13)$$

On the other hand, (4.15.6) and (4.15.12) imply

$$\text{Var}(\alpha_+) + \text{Var}(\alpha_-) \le \text{Var}(\alpha) \qquad (4.15.14)$$

Thus, (4.15.7) holds. $\qquad \square$

Next we turn to differentiability properties of α. There are three main theorems:

Theorem 4.15.3. *Every α has the form*

$$\alpha = \alpha_{\mathrm{ac}} + \alpha_{\mathrm{sing}} \qquad (4.15.15)$$

where $\alpha_{\mathrm{ac}}(x) = \int_0^x f(x)\,dx$ for some $f \in L^1([0,1], dx)$ and α_{sing} is such that $d\alpha_{\mathrm{sing}}$ is singular to dx.

Theorem 4.15.4 (Lebesgue's Theorem on Differentiation of the Integral). *Let $f \in L^1([0,1], dx)$. Then for dx-a.e. x_0, we have*

$$\lim_{\varepsilon \downarrow 0} \frac{1}{2\varepsilon} \int_{x_0 - \varepsilon}^{x_0 + \varepsilon} f(x)\,dx = f(x_0) \qquad (4.15.16)$$

Remark. There are also results for $\frac{1}{\varepsilon} \int_{x_0}^{x_0+\varepsilon}$ and $\frac{1}{\varepsilon} \int_{x_0 - \varepsilon}^{\varepsilon}$; see Section 2.4 of Part 3.

Theorem 4.15.5. *If α is a singular function of bounded variation in the sense that $d\alpha$ is singular to dx, then for dx-a.e. x_0,*

$$\frac{\alpha(x_0 + \varepsilon) - \alpha(x_0 - \varepsilon)}{2\varepsilon} \to 0 \qquad (4.15.17)$$

and for $d\alpha$-a.e. x,

$$\frac{|\alpha(x_0 + \varepsilon) - \alpha(x_0 - \varepsilon)|}{2\varepsilon} \to \infty \qquad (4.15.18)$$

Theorem 4.15.3 is just Theorem 4.7.6 for the Lebesgue–Stieltjes measure, $d\alpha$. Theorems 4.15.4 and 4.15.5 involve pointwise limits, a subject of some subtlety. The modern approach to such limits involve maximal functions and will be the subject of Chapter 2 of Part 3. In particular, we'll prove Theorems 4.15.4 and 4.15.5 as Theorem 2.5.1 of Part 3.

Putting together these two theorems yields:

Theorem 4.15.6. *Let $\alpha\colon [0,1] \to \mathbb{R}$ have bounded variation. Then for dx-a.e. $x \in [0,1]$,*

$$\alpha'(x) = \lim_{\varepsilon \downarrow 0} \frac{\alpha(x + \varepsilon) - \alpha(x - \varepsilon)}{2\varepsilon}$$

exists and $\alpha' \in L^1([0,1], dx)$ and $\alpha(x) - \int_0^x \alpha'(y)\,dy = \alpha_{\mathrm{sing}}(x)$ is a singular function in the sense that $d\alpha_{\mathrm{sing}}$ and dx are mutually singular.

Finally, we want to prove an interesting formula of Banach for the total variation of a continuous function of (a, b), a formula we'll use in Section 4.6 of Part 2A.

Definition. Let $f\colon (a,b)$ be a bounded continuous function. The *indicatrix* of f is the map $N_f\colon \mathbb{R} \to \mathbb{N} \cup \{\infty\}$ by

$$N_f(s) = \#\{x \mid f(x) = s\} \tag{4.15.19}$$

the cardinality of $f^{-1}[\{s\}]$.

Theorem 4.15.7 (Banach Indicatrix Theorem). *Let f be a bounded continuous function on (a,b). Then N_f is measurable and*

$$\mathrm{Var}(f) = \int_{-\infty}^{\infty} N_f(s)\,ds \tag{4.15.20}$$

Remarks. 1. To get a feel for why this is true, the reader should prove it for piecewise linear f's.

2. The integral can obviously be taken from $\inf(f)$ to $\sup(f)$.

3. In particular, if $\mathrm{Var}(f) < \infty$, then $N_f(s) < \infty$ for Lebesgue a.e. s.

4. If f has right and left limits at each point and N_f is defined by

$$N_f(t) = \#\{x \mid f(x-0) \le t \le f(x+0) \text{ or } f(x+0) \le t \le f(x-0)\} \tag{4.15.21}$$

then (4.15.20) still holds (Problem 6).

Proof. By Proposition 4.15.1, we can pick a sequence of partitions $\mathbf{t}^j = \{t_0^j = 0 < t_1^j < \cdots < t_{n_j}^j = 1\}$ so that $\mathbf{t}^{j+1} \rhd \mathbf{t}^j$, so

$$V_{\mathbf{t}^j}(f) = \sum_{k=1}^{n_j} |f(t_k^j) - f(t_{k-1}^j)| \tag{4.15.22}$$

obeys

$$V_{\mathbf{t}^j}(f) \uparrow \mathrm{Var}(f) \tag{4.15.23}$$

and for all j and $k = 1, \ldots, n_j$,

$$|t_k^j - t_{k-1}^j| \le j^{-1} \tag{4.15.24}$$

For any s and $j = 1, 2, \ldots$, define

$$N_f^{(j)}(s) = \#\Big\{k \in (1, \ldots, n_j) \;\Big|\; \min_{t_k^j \le x < t_k^j} f(x) \le s \le \max_{t_k^j \le x \le t_k^j} f(x)\Big\} \tag{4.15.25}$$

We will prove that for $s \notin \{f(t_k^j) \mid j = 1, 2, \ldots, \; k = 0, \ldots n_j\} \equiv Q$,

$$N_f^{(j)}(s) \uparrow N_f(s) \tag{4.15.26}$$

that

$$V_{\mathbf{t}^j}(f) \le \int N_f^{(j)}(s)\,ds \tag{4.15.27}$$

and that for all j,

$$\int N_f^{(j)}(s)\,ds \le \mathrm{Var}(f) \tag{4.15.28}$$

We claim these three statements imply the theorem. For, if I_k^j (respectively, S_k^j) are $\min_{t_{k-1}^j \leq x \leq t_k^j} f(x)$ (respectively, max), then

$$N_f^{(j)}(s) = \sum_{k=1}^{n_j} \chi_{[I_k^j, S_k^j]}(s) \qquad (4.15.29)$$

is a Borel function, so (4.15.26) and Q countable imply that N_f is Borel and (4.15.23), (4.15.28), and (4.15.29) plus the monotone convergence theorem imply (4.15.22). Thus, we need only prove the three formulae.

Since $\mathbf{t}^{j+1}$ is a refinement of $\mathbf{t}^j$, each interval defined by $\mathbf{t}^j$ is a union of intervals defined by $\mathbf{t}^{j+1}$, so the corresponding $[I_k^j, S_k^j]$ is a union of $[I_{\tilde{k}}^{j+1}, S_{\tilde{k}}^{j+1}]$, showing $N_f^{(j)} \leq N_f^{(j+1)}$. If $s \notin Q$, then $N_j^{(j)}(s)$ counts distinct points, where $f(x) = s$, so $N_f^{(j)}(s) \leq N_f(s)$. If there are at least m distinct points $x_1, \ldots, x_m$, where $f(x) = s$, pick j so $\lim_{\ell \neq n}|x_\ell - x_n| \geq j^{-1}$, so by (4.15.20), $N_f^{(j)}(s) \geq m$. This proves that $N_f^{(j)}(s) \to N_f(s)$. Thus, (4.15.26) holds.

Since $f(t_{k-1}^j), f(t_k^j) \in [I_k^j, S_k^j]$, we have

$$|f(t_{k-1}^j) - f(t_k^j)| \leq S_k^j - I_k^j \qquad (4.15.30)$$

which, given (4.15.29), implies (4.15.27). Finally, for each j, there are points. $y_1^- < y_1^+ \leq y_2^- < y_2^+ \leq \cdots < y_k^+$ with $y_k^\pm \in [t_{k-1}^j, t_k^j]$, so $\{f(y_j^-), f(y_j^+)\} = \{I_k^j, S_k^j\}$, which implies (4.15.28) given (4.15.29). $\qquad \square$

Notes and Historical Remarks. Theorem 4.15.2 is from Jordan [**455**], the first paper to define functions of bounded variation. Theorems 4.15.3–4.15.5 are due to Lebesgue [**562**]. Theorem 4.15.7 is from Banach [**50**].

Problems

1. Let $\mathbf{s}$ and $\mathbf{t}$ be two partitions. Show there is a partition $\mathbf{u}$ so $\mathbf{u} \triangleright \mathbf{s}$, $\mathbf{u} \triangleright \mathbf{t}$, and if $\mathbf{v} \triangleright \mathbf{s}$, $\mathbf{v} \triangleright \mathbf{t}$, then $\mathbf{v} \triangleright \mathbf{u}$ (i.e., $\mathbf{u}$ is a glb of $\mathbf{s}$ and $\mathbf{t}$).

2. If $\alpha = \alpha_+ - \alpha_- = \beta_+ - \beta_-$, where $\beta_\pm, \alpha_\pm$ are all monotone, and $\mathrm{Var}(\alpha) = \mathrm{Var}(\alpha_+) + \mathrm{Var}(\alpha_-) = \mathrm{Var}(\beta_+) + \mathrm{Var}(\beta_-)$, prove for some constant, c, that $\beta_\pm = \alpha_\pm + c$. (*Hint*: First prove $d\beta_\pm = d\alpha_\pm$.)

3. Let f, g be two functions of bounded variation on $[a, b]$, both continuous from above at a and from below at b (so the Stieltjes measures df and dg do not have pure points at a or b. Suppose g is continuous. Prove that

$$\int_a^b f \, dg + \int_a^b g \, df = f(b)g(b) - f(a)g(a) \qquad (4.15.31)$$

(*Hint*: Look at the Riemann sums.)

4. Let g be a monotone function and f a bounded Borel function on $[a, b]$.

   (a) Prove the *first mean value theorem*, that for some $d \in [\inf f, \sup f]$, we have

$$\int_a^b f(x)\, dg(x) = d[g(b) - g(a)] \qquad (4.15.32)$$

   (a) If, in addition, f is continuous, prove there is $c \in [a, b]$ so that

$$\int_a^b f(x)\, dg(x) = f(c)[g(b) - g(a)] \qquad (4.15.33)$$

5. Let f be a bounded Borel function on $[a, b]$ and g monotone so g is continuous from above at a and from below at b. The *second mean value theorem* says that there is a $c \in [a, b]$ so that

$$\int_a^b f(x)g(x)\, dx = g(a) \int_a^c f(x)\, dx + g(b) \int_c^b f(x)\, dx \qquad (4.15.34)$$

   (a) Let $h(y) = \int_a^y f(x)\, dx$. Prove that

$$\int_a^b f(x)g(x)\, dx = g(b)h(b) - \int_a^b h(x)\, dg(x) \qquad (4.15.35)$$

   (*Hint:* $\int_a^b f(x)g(x)\, dx = \int_a^b g(x)\, dh(x)$.)

   (b) Prove (4.15.34). (*Hint:* Pick c, via (4.15.33), so that $\int_a^b h(x)\, dg(x) = h(c)(g(b) - g(a))$.)

6. Prove that if (4.15.21) is used to define $N_f(t)$, then Theorem 4.15.7 extends to f with right and left limits at every point.

7. Let $\{f_j\}_{j=1}^\infty$ be a family of monotone functions on $[0, 1]$ with $f_j(0) = 0$ for all j and $\sum_{j=1}^\infty f_j(1) < \infty$. Prove that $s(x) = \sum_{j=1}^\infty f_j(x)$ has a derivative for Lebesgue a.e. x given by $\sum_{j=1}^\infty f_j'(x)$.

   Remark. This is a theorem of Fubini [**335**].

4.16. Bonus Section: Brownian Motion

Basically, Brownian motion is the Gaussian process, $\{b(s)\}_{0 \le s}$, indexed by $\mathbb{R}^+$, with covariance (using $\mathbb{E}(\cdot)$ for the integral with respect to a probability measure)

$$\mathbb{E}(b(s)b(t)) = \min(s, t) \qquad (4.16.1)$$

This has the novel feature that there are uncountably many b's. The continuity of $\min(s, t)$ will imply the underlying Hilbert space is separable, so, at least for defining L^2 functions, this will present no problem. For pointwise behavior, we'll have to exercise some care, but eventually, we'll show for a.e. ω, $b(s)(\omega)$ is continuous in s, which will enable us to define an underlying measure on $\mathbb{C}(\mathbb{R}^+)$ so that $b(s)$ is just a random function on $\mathbb{R}^+$.

But first, we want to discuss where the strange-looking $\min(s,t)$ comes from. Let $\{x_n\}_{n=1}^{\infty}$ be independent random variables, each with ± 1 values and each with probability $\frac{1}{2}$, that is, the coordinate functions on $\{-1,1\}^{\mathbb{Z}_+}$ with the product measure.

$$S_n = \sum_{j=1}^{n} x_j \tag{4.16.2}$$

is called *simple random walk.* Notice that (with $\mathbb{E}$ the integral)

$$\mathbb{E}(S_n S_m) = \min(n, m) \tag{4.16.3}$$

The central limit theorem asserts $S_n/\sqrt{n}$ approaches the Gaussian random variable with variance 1 (in a suitable sense discussed in Sections 7.1 and 7.3). Notice that (4.16.3) says

$$\mathbb{E}\left(\left(\frac{S_{[sn]}}{\sqrt{n}}\right)\left(\frac{S_{[tn]}}{\sqrt{n}}\right)\right) = \min\left(\frac{[sn]}{n}, \frac{[tn]}{n}\right) \tag{4.16.4}$$

so in some sense, $S_{[sn]}/\sqrt{n}$ approaches $b(s)$ (we make this precise in the Notes). Thus, the function $\min(s,t)$ has an explanation if we want $b(s)$ to be a limit of scaled random walk.

While on the subject of the form of (4.16.1), we note that for t fixed, $\min(s,t)$ is not C^1 in s. Indeed, if $s > t$,

$$\mathbb{E}(|b(s) - b(t)|^2) = s + t - 2t = s - t \tag{4.16.5}$$

so for all s, t,

$$\mathbb{E}(|b(s) - b(t)|^2) = |s - t| \tag{4.16.6}$$

Thus, as L^1 functions, $s \mapsto b(s)$ is not smooth; indeed, (4.16.6) says $|b(s) - b(t)|$ is $O(|s-t|^{1/2})$. In fact, we'll see that, modulo issues of proper definition, $b(s)(\omega)$ is Hölder-continuous of any order $\alpha < \frac{1}{2}$, but because of fluctuations, not of order $\alpha > \frac{1}{2}$ at any point and, in particular, it is nowhere differentiable. This complements our discussion of nowhere differentiable functions in Sections 3.5 and 5.4.

There is another aspect of $\min(s,t) \equiv g(s,t)$ we should mention. If t is fixed, then $\frac{d}{ds}g(s,t) = 1$ (if $s < t$), 0 (if $s > t$), so in a formal sense, $-\frac{d^2}{ds^2}g(s,t) = \delta(s-t)$. g is a Green's function for $-\frac{d^2}{ds^2}$. We'll explore this further in the Notes.

With these preliminaries, we turn to defining $b(s)$ formally. We begin with

Lemma 4.16.1. *Fix $t_0 \equiv 0 < t_1 < t_2 < \cdots < t_\ell$. Then for any $(c_1, \ldots, c_\ell) \in \mathbb{R}^\ell$, we have that*

$$\sum_{j,k=1}^{\ell} c_j c_k \min(t_j, t_k) \geq 0 \tag{4.16.7}$$

Proof. We claim that

$$\sum_{j,k=1}^{\ell} c_j c_k \min(t_j, t_k) = \sum_{j=1}^{\ell} (t_j - t_{j-1})(c_1 + \cdots + c_j)^2 \tag{4.16.8}$$

because for $j \leq k$, $c_j c_k$ occurs in $(t_1 - t_0) + \cdots + (t_j - t_{j-1}) = \min(t_j, t_k)$. From this, (4.16.7) is immediate. □

Remark. (4.16.8) realizes the idea that $\{b(s_j) - b(s_{j-1})\}_{j=0}^{\ell}$ are orthogonal and $\sum_{j=1}^{\ell} c_j b(s_j) = \sum_{j=1}^{\ell} [b(s_j) - b(s_{j-1})](\sum_{k=1}^{j} c_j)$.

Theorem 4.16.2. *Let V be the vector space of all finite sums $\{\sum_{j=1}^{n} c_j \delta_{t_j}\}$ with $0 < t_1 < \cdots < t_j$ and $c_j \in \mathbb{R}$. Put the inner product*

$$\left\langle \sum_{j=1}^{n} c_j \delta_{t_j}, \sum_{k=1}^{\ell} d_k \delta_{s_k} \right\rangle = \sum_{\substack{j=1,\ldots,n \\ k=1,\ldots,\ell}} c_j d_j \min(t_j, s_\ell) \tag{4.16.9}$$

Then the completion of V is a (separable) Hilbert space.

Proof. If $s_n \to s$, then $\|\delta_s - \delta_{s_n}\|^2 = |s - s_n| \to 0$, so $\{\delta_q\}_{q \in \mathbb{Q}}$ is dense in $\{\delta_t\}$ and thus, V is separable. □

This allows us to set up a Gaussian process, that is, an L^2 space $L^2(\Omega, d\mu)$ with a family of L^2 functions $\{b(s)\}_{s>0}$ so that $(b(s_1), \ldots, b(s_\ell))$ are jointly Gaussian with covariance $\min(s_j, s_k)$. This is called *Brownian motion*. Here is the basic continuity result:

Theorem 4.16.3 (Kolmogorov Continuity Theorem). *Let $\mathbb{Q}_D$ be the dyadic rationals (i.e., $j/2^n$, $j \in \mathbb{Z}$, $n = 0, 1, 2, \ldots$) and let $\{x(q)\}_{q \in \mathbb{Q}_D \cap (0,1)}$ be a family of measurable functions on a probability measure space, (Ω, Σ, μ). Suppose for some $0 < r < p$, we have, for all $t, h \in \mathbb{Q}_D$ with $t, t+h \in (0,1)$, that*

$$\mathbb{E}(|x(t+h) - x(t)|^p) \leq K|h|^{1+r} \tag{4.16.10}$$

for some $K < \infty$. Fix

$$0 < \alpha < \frac{r}{p} \tag{4.16.11}$$

Then for a.e. $\omega \in \Omega$, we have $C(\omega)$ so that

$$|x(t)(\omega) - x(s)(\omega)| \le C(\omega)|t - s|^\alpha \qquad (4.16.12)$$

for all $t, s \in \mathbb{Q}_D \cap (0, 1)$.

Remark. In essence, the last part of the proof below is proving the first Borel–Cantelli lemma (see Theorem 7.2.1)

Proof. For $n = 1, 2, \ldots$, $k = 0, 1, 2, \ldots, 2^n - 1$, let $\chi_{k,n}(\omega)$ be the characteristic function of

$$\left\{ \omega \,\middle|\, \left|x\left(\frac{k+1}{2^n}\right) - x\left(\frac{k}{2^n}\right)\right| \ge 2^{-n\alpha} \right\} \qquad (4.16.13)$$

Letting

$$\varepsilon = r - \alpha p \qquad (4.16.14)$$

Markov's inequality (Theorem 4.6.10) implies that

$$\mathbb{E}(\chi_{k,n}) \le K \, 2^{+n\alpha p} 2^{-n(1+r)} = K \, 2^{-n} 2^{-n\varepsilon} \qquad (4.16.15)$$

Therefore,

$$\sum_{n,k} \mathbb{E}(\chi_{k,n}) \le K \sum_{n=1}^{\infty} 2^n (2^{-n} 2^{-n\varepsilon}) < \infty \qquad (4.16.16)$$

Thus, for a.e. ω, $\sum_{n,k} \chi_{k,n}(\omega) < \infty$, and therefore, for a.e. ω, $\exists N(\omega)$ so that for $n \ge N(\omega)$ and all k, $\chi_{k,n}(\omega) = 0$, that is,

$$s = \frac{k}{2^n}, \quad t = s + \frac{1}{2^n}, \quad n \ge N(\omega) \Rightarrow |x(s)(\omega) - x(t)(\omega)| \le |t-s|^\alpha \ (4.16.17)$$

If $s = k/2^n$, $t = s + 1/2^n$ but $n \le N(\omega)$, we can write $s - t$ as $2^{N(\omega)-n}$ basic $2^{-N(\omega)}$ intervals so

$$|x(s)(\omega) - x(t)(\omega)| \le 2^{N(\omega)-n} 2^{-N(\omega)\alpha}$$
$$\le 2^{(1-\alpha)(N(\omega)-n)} 2^{-n\alpha}$$
$$\le 2^{N(\omega)(1-\alpha)}|s-t|^\alpha \qquad (4.16.18)$$

If now s and t are arbitrary dyadic rationals, with $s < t$, suppose

$$2^{-m-1} \le |s - t| \le 2^{-m} \qquad (4.16.19)$$

If $s \in [\frac{k}{2^m}, \frac{k+1}{2^m}]$, then $t \in [\frac{k}{2^m}, \frac{k+2}{2^m}]$ and we can write

$$s = \frac{k}{2^m} + \sum_{n=m+1}^{S} \frac{\gamma_n}{2^n}, \qquad t = \frac{k}{2^m} + \sum_{n=m}^{T} \frac{\eta_m}{2^n} \qquad (4.16.20)$$

where each γ_n and each η_n is 0 or 1. Thus, we can get from s to t by adding or subtracting at most one basic interval of size $2^{-m}, 2^{-m-1}, \ldots, 2^{-\max(S,T)}$. It follows from (4.16.17) and (4.16.18) that

$$
\begin{aligned}
|x(s)(\omega) - x(t)(\omega)| &\leq 2^{N(\omega)(1-\alpha)} \sum_{n=m}^{\infty} 2^{-n\alpha} \\
&= 2^{N(\omega)(1-\alpha)}(1 - 2^{-\alpha})2^{-m\alpha} \\
&\leq 2^{N(\omega)(1-\alpha)}2^{\alpha}(1 - 2^{-\alpha})|s - t|^{\alpha} \qquad (4.16.21)
\end{aligned}
$$

which is (4.16.12) with $C(\omega) = 2^{N(\omega)(1-\alpha)}2^{\alpha}(1 - 2^{-\alpha})$. $\qquad\square$

Example 4.16.4. Let (Ω, Σ, μ) be $\Omega = [0, 1]$, the Borel sets and Lebesgue measure. Let

$$q(t)(\omega) = 0 \quad \text{for all } \omega \in [0, 1], \, 0 \leq t \leq 1 \qquad (4.16.22)$$

$$\tilde{q}(t)(\omega) = \begin{cases} 1, & t - \omega \in \mathbb{Q} \\ 0, & t - \omega \notin \mathbb{Q} \end{cases} \qquad (4.16.23)$$

Then for each ω, $t \mapsto q(t)$ is continuous, but $t \mapsto \tilde{q}$ is never continuous. However, for every t, $q(t)(\omega) = \tilde{q}(t)(\omega)$ for a.e. ω.

The moral is that if $\{f(t)\}_{t \in [0,1]}$ is a family of functions on Ω with the minimal σ-algebra making each $f(t)$ measurable, the statement, "for a.e. ω, $f(t)(\omega)$ is continuous" is not a measurable function! This is because uncountably many t are involved. $\qquad\square$

This example forces us to speak of specific choices of $f(t)(\omega)$. In the context of Theorem 4.16.3, if (4.16.10) holds, then if $t \in [0, 1]$ and $t_n \in \mathbb{Q}_D$ has $t_n \to t$, then $x(t_n)$ is Cauchy in L^p and $x(t_n)(\omega)$ is Cauchy in $\mathbb{R}$. Thus, we *define* the realization of $x(t)(\omega)$ as the limit of $x(t_n)(\omega)$, and with this choice, $t \mapsto x(t)(\omega)$ is continuous for a.e. ω. Moreover, if m is fixed, $F \in C_{\infty}(\mathbb{R}^m)$ and if $t_n^{(k)} \to t^{(k)}$, $k = 1, \ldots, m$ with $t_n^{(k)} \in \mathbb{Q}_D$, then $F(x(t_n^{(1)}), \ldots, x(t_n^{(m)})) \to F(x(t^{(k)}), \ldots, x(t^{(m)}))$ for a.e. ω. So, by the dominated convergence theorem, $\mathbb{E}(f(x_n^{(1)}, \ldots, x_n^{(m)})) \to \mathbb{E}(f(x(t^{(1)}), \ldots, x(t^{(m)})))$. We conclude:

Theorem 4.16.5. *Let $\{x(t)\}_{t \in [0,1]}$ be a family of measurable functions on a probability measure space, (Ω, Σ, μ). Suppose for some $0 < r < p$, we have for all $t, s \in [0, 1]$ that*

$$\mathbb{E}(|x(t) - x(s)|^p) \leq K|t - s|^{1+r} \qquad (4.16.24)$$

for some $K < \infty$. Fix $0 < \alpha < r/p$. Then there is a representative $x(t)(\omega)$ of $x(t)$ for each $t \in [0, 1]$ so that for a.e. ω,

$$|x(t)(\omega) - x(s)(\omega)| \leq C(\omega)|t - s|^{\alpha} \qquad (4.16.25)$$

and all $t, s, \in [0, 1]$. *For these representatives, the joint probability distributions of* $x(t_1), \dots, x(t_n))$ *are given by the original* x's.

With this in hand, one can move the measure to one on the Polish space $(C([0,1]), \Sigma)$, where Σ is the Borel algebra. Returning to Brownian motion, for any integer k,

$$\mathbb{E}(|b(s) - b(t)|^{2k}) \leq C_k |t - s|^k \qquad (4.16.26)$$

so (4.16.24) holds with $r = k - 1$, and so $\frac{r}{p} = \frac{k-1}{2k} = \frac{1}{2} - \frac{1}{2k}$. We conclude:

Theorem 4.16.6. *Brownian motion has a realization in which* $b(s)(\omega)$ *is Hölder-continuous of every order* $\alpha < \frac{1}{2}$.

The flip side of this is:

Theorem 4.16.7. *Fix* $\alpha > \frac{1}{2}$. *Then for a.e.* ω, $b(s)(\omega)$ *is nowhere Hölder-continuous of order* α, *that is, for a.e.* ω,

$$\inf_{0 \leq t \leq 1} \left[\limsup_{h \to 0} |h|^{-\alpha} |b(t+h)(\omega) - b(t)(\omega)| \right] = \infty \qquad (4.16.27)$$

Remark. The intuition behind the proof is that if $b(t)(\omega)$ is Hölder-continuous of order α at some t, then for large n, there will need to be some i, with $|b(\frac{i}{n})(\omega) - b(\frac{i-1}{n})(\omega)|$ bounded by $n^{-\alpha}$ for many successive i's. These differences are independent, so the probability of this will be a large power of the probability that $|b(\frac{1}{n})(\omega)|$ is order $n^{-\alpha}$. But $b(\frac{1}{n})(\omega)$ is of order $(\frac{1}{n})^{1/2}$, so if $\alpha > \frac{1}{2}$, this probability will be $o(n^{-(\alpha - \frac{1}{2})})$. Thus, we'll be able to show for each i, the probability is $o(n^{-1})$. There are n choices of i and $no(n^{-1}) \to 0$.

Proof. Fix an integer k with

$$k(\alpha - \tfrac{1}{2}) > 1 \qquad (4.16.28)$$

Suppose the left side of (4.16.27) is finite. Then there is $t \in [0, 1]$, $C < \infty$, and $h_0 > 0$, so if $|h| < h_0$, then

$$|b(t+h)(\omega) - b(t)(\omega)| \leq C|h|^\alpha \qquad (4.16.29)$$

Pick m so $(k+1)/m < h_0$. For $n \geq m$, let $i = [tn] + 1$. Then for all $n \geq m$, $i/n, (i+1)/n, \dots, (i+k)/n \in [t, t+h]$, so

$$\left| b\left(\frac{i+j}{n}\right)(\omega) - b\left(\frac{i+j-1}{n}\right)(\omega) \right| \leq C n^{-\alpha} [|k|^\alpha + |k+1|^\alpha] \qquad (4.16.30)$$

for $j = 1, \dots, k$ (since $|b(s)(\omega) - b(u)(\omega)| \leq C[|s - t|^\alpha + |u - t|^\alpha]$). Thus,

$$\{\omega \mid b(s)(\omega) \text{ is somewhere Hölder-continuous of order } \alpha\}$$

$$\subset \left\{ \omega \,\middle|\, \exists D \in \{1, 2, \dots\}, \exists m \geq 1, \forall n \geq m, \exists i \in \{0, \dots, n - k - 1\} \right.$$

$$\forall j \in \{i+1, \dots, i+k\}, \left| b\left(\frac{j}{n}\right)(\omega) - b\left(\frac{j-1}{n}\right)(\omega) \right| \leq Dn^{-\alpha} \Big\}$$

$$= \bigcup_{D=1}^{\infty} \bigcup_{m=1}^{\infty} \bigcap_{n \geq m} \bigcup_{0 \leq i \leq n-k+1} \bigcap_{j=k+1}^{i+k} \left\{ \omega \,\Big|\, \left| b\left(\frac{j}{n}\right)(\omega) - b\left(\frac{j-1}{n}\right)(\omega) \right| \leq Dn^{-\alpha} \right\}$$

$$(4.16.31)$$

Since the $b(\frac{j}{n}) - b(\frac{j-1}{n})$ are independent random variables with distribution the same as $b(\frac{1}{n})$, we see that

$$\mathbb{E}\left(\bigcap_{j=i+1}^{i+k} \left\{ \omega \,\Big|\, \left| b\left(\frac{j}{n}\right)(\omega) - b\left(\frac{j-1}{n}\right)(\omega) \right| \leq D_n^{-\alpha} \right\} \right)$$

$$= \mathbb{E}\left(\omega \,\Big|\, \left| b\left(\frac{1}{n}\right)(\omega) \right| \leq Dn^{-\alpha} \right)^k$$

$$= O(n^{-(\alpha-\frac{1}{2})k}) \qquad (4.16.32)$$

by scaling since

$$\mathbb{E}\left(\left(\omega \,\Big|\, \left| b\left(\frac{1}{n}\right)(\omega) \right| \leq Dn^{-\alpha} \right) \right) = \mathbb{E}(\omega \mid |b(1)(\omega)| \leq Dn^{-(\alpha-\frac{1}{2})}) \quad (4.16.33)$$

and $b(1)$ has bounded, absolutely continuous density and $(\alpha - \frac{1}{2}) > 0$.

By (4.16.28), k is chosen so $n(\text{LHS of } (4.16.32)) \to 0$, which implies for each D, m,

$$\mathbb{E}\left(\bigcap_{n \geq m} \bigcup_{0 \leq i \leq n-k+1} \bigcap_{j=i+1}^{i+k} \left\{ \omega \,\Big|\, \left| b\left(\frac{j}{n}\right)(\omega) - b\left(\frac{j-1}{n}\right)(\omega) \right| \leq Dn^{-\alpha} \right\} \right) = 0$$

$$(4.16.34)$$

Thus, by (4.16.31), the probability that $b(s)(\omega)$ is somewhere Hölder-continuous of order α is 0. $\qquad\square$

This completes our construction of one-dimensional Brownian motion and the proof that Brownian paths are Hölder-continuous of any order $\alpha < \frac{1}{2}$ and not Hölder-continuous anywhere for any order $\alpha > \frac{1}{2}$. We note that Brownian motion in $\mathbb{R}^\nu$ is just ν-independent copies of one-dimensional Brownian motion, $\vec{b}(t) = (b_1(t), \dots, b_\nu(t))$; equivalently, the $b_j(t)$ is the Gaussian process with

$$\mathbb{E}(b_j(t)b_k(s)) = \delta_{jk} \min(t, s) \qquad (4.16.35)$$

A key further development is the connection to diffusion. As we'll see in Section 6.9, if Δ is the Laplacian in ν dimensions, then $\exp(-\frac{t}{2}\Delta)$ is an integral operator with integral kernel,

$$P_t(\vec{x}, \vec{y}) = (2\pi t)^{-\nu/2} \exp\left(-\frac{|\vec{x} - \vec{y}|^2}{2t}\right) \tag{4.16.36}$$

from which it follows (Problem 1) that

$$\exp\left(\frac{t}{2}\Delta\right)f(x) = \mathbb{E}(f(x + \vec{b}(t))) \tag{4.16.37}$$

for ν-dimensional Brownian motion.

Two other developments we'll briefly explore in the Notes are:

(1) The *Feynman–Kac formula*: For reasonable functions $V(x)$, one can define $H = -\frac{1}{2}\Delta + V(x)$ and one has

$$(\exp(-tH)f)(x) = \mathbb{E}\left(\exp\left(-\int_0^t V(x + \vec{b}(s))\,ds\right)f(x + \vec{b}(t))\right) \tag{4.16.38}$$

(2) If Ω is an open region, one can define a Laplacian $-\Delta_\Omega$ on $L^2(\Omega, d^\nu x)$ with Dirichlet boundary conditions (i.e., $u(0) = 0$ on $\partial\Omega$) and show that

$$\exp\left(-\frac{t}{2}\Delta_\Omega\right)f(x) = \mathbb{E}\big(\chi(\omega \mid \vec{b}(s)(\omega) \in \Omega, \text{ all } s \in (0, t))f(x + \vec{b}(t))\big) \tag{4.16.39}$$

Notes and Historical Remarks.

> ...this study introduced me to the theory of probability. Moreover, it led me very directly to the periodogram, and to the study of forms of harmonic analysis more general than the classical Fourier series and Fourier integral. All these concepts have combined with the engineering preoccupations of a professor of the Massachusetts Institute of Technology to lead me to make both theoretical and practical advances in the theory of communication, and ultimately to found the discipline of cybernetics, which is in essence a statistical approach to the theory of communication. Thus, varied as my scientific interests seem to be, there has been a single thread connecting all of them from my first mature work ...
>
> —*Norbert Wiener* in [**997**], discussing his
> continuing interest in Brownian motion

The term Brownian motion is after Robert Brown (1773–1858), a British botanist, who in 1827 [**136**] discussed the motion of specks of pollen grains in water. It was raised to considerable importance to physicists by a 1905 paper [**274**] of Albert Einstein (1879–1955) who used the phenomenon as proof of the atomic hypothesis, linked it to the diffusion equation, and exploited its physical parameters to compute atomic sizes (essentially to find Avogadro's number). Interestingly enough, in about 60 BC, in his poem *De rerum natura* (On the nature of things) [**608**], the Roman philosopher Lucretius (estimated dates 99 BC–55 BC) claimed to prove the existence of atoms via the jerky motion of dust particles in air! While Einstein's work was, in retrospect, spectacular, it was only one of three signal accomplishments in the miraculous year 1905—the other two being his discovery of special relativity and his introduction of photons and their use to explain the photoelectric effect.

The mathematical model was invented by Norbert Wiener (1894–1964) in 1923 [**994**]. It was a subject he returned to often. Wiener was a child prodigy, essentially home-schooled by his father, an eccentric immigrant who became a professor of Slavic languages at Harvard. Norbert entered Tufts in 1906, at age only eleven, and graduated with an undergraduate degree in mathematics at age 14. In 1913, he got a Ph.D. in mathematical logic and went off to Europe where he was influenced by Russell, Hilbert, Landau, and especially, Hardy.

After several years of war work, including a very short period as an enlisted soldier, he wound up at M.I.T. where he spent the rest of his career. Wiener suffered from anti-Semitism for much of his career. He always felt that this was the reason he didn't get a position at Harvard (where Birkhoff opposed him) and when he wanted to move to Caltech in the 1930s, Millikan prevented it, commenting, in essence, that in an important area like physics (where Caltech had hired Paul Epstein), Millikan would hire a Jew, but not a Jewish mathematician.

While Brownian motion was probably his most significant achievement, Wiener also came up with the axiomatic scheme for Banach spaces (independently of Banach), made important contributions to harmonic analysis (especially the Wiener tauberian theorem), ergodic theory, stochastic processes, and founded cybernetics, a mathematical theory of communication.

For books on mathematical Brownian motion, see [**115, 196, 197, 254, 264, 478, 552, 589, 629, 641, 667, 770, 797, 849, 891, 893, 911**].

The construction of Brownian motion as a measure on the continuous functions, $C([0,\infty))$, can be done by a variety of methods:

(1) As a process on $\mathbb{R}^\infty$ via $\{b(t)\}_{t\in\mathbb{Q}}$ and then a Kolmogorov regularity argument and transfer to $C([0,\infty))$. This is sketched in this section and fleshed out in Simon [**849**].

(2) Directly on $C([0,\infty))$; see, for example, Billingsley [**90**].

(3) A construction of Ciesielski [**199**] and Lévy [**582**] (see also McKean [**646**]) that, in essence, constructs a measure on distributions and then shows it is supported on the distributions which are continuous functions.

(4) An approach of Nelson [**679**] that works on $(\mathbb{R} \cup \{\infty\})^{[0,1]}$ where, as we noted, the Hölder-continuous functions are not Baire measurable. But they are Borel measurable and the measure we construct has a

unique regular Borel extension. In this extension, the Hölder-continuous functions have measure 1.

The realization of Brownian motion as a limit of random walks is codified in a beautiful theorem of Donsker [**253**]: If one linearly interpolates $S_{[sn]}/\sqrt{n}$, one gets a set of measures on $C([0,\infty))$, and Donsker shows these measures converge in a suitable topology to Brownian motion. See, for example, [**849**, Sect. 17].

Kolmogorov's continuity theorem (Theorem 4.16.3) is from his famous 1933 book [**507**] on the foundations of probability theory. The nondifferentiability of Brownian paths (indeed, the stronger Theorem 4.16.7) is due to Paley, Wiener, and Zygmund [**698**]; the proof we give is due to Dvoretzky, Erdős, and Kakutani [**266**]. The regularity properties of ν-dimensional Brownian motion, including the Hausdorff dimension of $\mathrm{Ran}(b)$ and double and triple points, have been heavily studied; see, for example, [**667**] and [**849**, Sect. 5 and 7].

There is a form of the law of the iterated logarithm (a subject discussed in detail in Section 7.2) for Brownian motion that says, with probability 1, for any t,

$$\limsup_{h\to 0}\frac{|b(t+h)-b(t)|}{h^{1/2}\log(\log h^{-1})}=1 \tag{4.16.40}$$

so that b is not Hölder-continuous of order $\frac{1}{2}$. For a proof of (4.16.40), see [**849**, Sect. 5].

The arguments in the proofs of Theorems 4.16.3 and 4.16.7 are, in essence, special cases of the Borel–Cantelli lemmas of Section 7.2.

Simon's book [**849**] has extensive discussion of the Feynman–Kac formula and the Dirichlet boundary condition semigroup results. If V_n is 0 on Ω and n on $\mathbb{R}^\nu\setminus\Omega$, one can show $\exp(-t(-\frac{1}{2}\Delta+V_n))$ converges as $n\to\infty$ in a suitable sense to $\exp(-\frac{t}{2}\Delta_\Omega)$, which shows the relation between the two. We also discuss these questions in Section 7.6 of Part 4.

The Feynman–Kac formula was found by Kac [**462**] after he heard Feynman talk about his path integral ideas in quantum mechanics. Kac realized that by going from $\exp(-itH)$ to $\exp(-tH)$ and using the Wiener process, one could turn Feynman's poetry into rigorous mathematics.

There are several other natural Gaussian processes that are connected to semigroups the way Brownian motion is to $\exp(-\frac{t}{2}\Delta)$. The Gaussian process $\{q(t)\}_{t\in\mathbb{R}}$ with $\mathbb{E}(q(s)q(t))=\frac{1}{2}\exp(-|t-s|)$ (closely related to Example 4.12.7) is associated to $\exp(-tH)$, where $H=-\frac{1}{2}\frac{d^2}{dx^2}+\frac{1}{2}x^2-\frac{1}{2}$ (see Section 6.6 of Part 3). Simon [**849**] calls it the *oscillator process*. It is often called the Ornstein–Uhlenbeck process. The process $\{b(s)\}_{0\le x\le 1}$, where $\mathbb{E}(b(s)b(t))=\min(s,t)(1-\max(s,t))$ is called the *Brownian bridge* and describes "Brownian motion conditioned to have $b(1) = 0$." These are discussed in Simon's book [**849**].

The fact that the covariance matrix for Brownian motion is the inverse to $-\frac{d^2}{dx^2}$, that the inverse of the covariance matrix appears in the exponential, and that $\langle u, -\frac{d^2}{dx^2} u \rangle = \langle \frac{d}{dx} u, \frac{d}{dx} u \rangle$ says that formally, the measure in the Gaussian integral is

$$\exp\left(-\tfrac{1}{2} \int_0^\infty \left(\frac{db}{ds}\right)^2 ds\right) d^\infty b$$

In the same way, the oscillator process is

$$\exp\left(-\tfrac{1}{2} \int_{-\infty}^\infty \left[\left(\frac{dq}{ds}\right)^2 + q(s)^2\right] ds\right) d^\infty q$$

There are higher-dimensional (i.e., "s" is replaced by a higher-dimensional object) analogs called free Euclidean quantum field theories, originally written down by Symanzik [**900**] and Nelson [**680, 681**]. You can learn more about them in the books of Simon [**848**] and Glimm–Jaffe [**350**].

By using Lévy processes (see the Notes to Section 7.3) instead of Brownian motion, there are analogs of the Feynman–Kac formula for $(-\Delta + m^2)^\alpha + V(x)$, $0 < \alpha < 1$; see Carmona, Masters, and Simon [**163**].

Problems

1. (a) Find the joint probability distribution of $\{x_j + b_j(t)\}_{j=1}^\nu$.

   (b) Given (4.16.36), prove (4.16.37).

4.17. Bonus Section: The Hausdorff Moment Problem

Given a measure, μ, on $\mathbb{R}$, its *moments* are defined by

$$c_n = \int x^n \, d\mu(x) \tag{4.17.1}$$

Of course, for this to make sense, one needs for all n that $c_{2n} < \infty$. We will always normalize so that μ is a probability measure, that is,

$$c_0 = 1 \tag{4.17.2}$$

We'll call μ *nontrivial* if it is not supported at finitely many points.

The *moment problem* is to ask which c_n's are the weights of a measure, and if they are, is the measure unique. These two halves are called the existence and the uniqueness problems. If μ is unique, the problem is called *determinate* and if not, *indeterminate*.

There are several flavors of the moment problem, depending on whether one restricts μ to have support on a particular set:

(1) If we allow μ to be any measure on $\mathbb{R}$ with $c_{2n} < \infty$, the problems are called the *Hamburger moment problem*.
(2) If we require $\operatorname{supp}(\mu) \subset [0, \infty)$, the problems are called the *Stieltjes moment problem*.
(3) If we require $\operatorname{supp}(\mu) \subset [0, 1]$, the problems are called the *Hausdorff moment problem*.

The first two cases, where $\operatorname{supp}(\mu)$ is not necessarily compact, are essentially problems in extension of linear functionals and will be studied (except for one step here) in the next chapter, in Section 5.6 and also in Section 7.7 of Part 4. The Hausdorff problem has a different flavor because, by the Weierstrass approximation theorem, the polynomials are dense. Typically, one demands nontriviality in the Hamburger and Stieltjes cases, but not in the Hausdorff case. It is the Hausdorff moment problem we study here. We begin with the elementary:

Theorem 4.17.1. *The Hausdorff moment problem is always determinate, that is, given $\{c_n\}_{n=0}^{\infty}$, there is at most one measure μ on $[0, 1]$ obeying (4.17.1).*

Remarks. 1. After seeing the proof, the reader might think all moment problems are determinate, but we'll see in Example 5.6.5 that there are many indeterminate problems. A simple one is

$$c_n = \exp(\tfrac{1}{4}(n+1)^2) \tag{4.17.3}$$

where the Stieltjes (and so also the Hamburger) problem are solvable but indeterminate.

2. It is easy to show the stronger result that if μ is supported on $[0, 1]$ and ν is a priori any measure with finite moments, then $\mu = \nu$ (Problem 1).

Proof. If μ and ν both obey (4.17.1),

$$\int f(x)\,d\mu(x) = \int f(x)\,d\nu(x) \tag{4.17.4}$$

for any polynomial f. Since the polynomials are $\|\cdot\|_\infty$-dense in $C([0, 1])$ and μ, ν are both supported on $[0, 1]$, (4.17.4) holds for all $f \in C([0, 1])$, so $\mu = \nu$. $\qquad\square$

Thus, the key question is existence. We'll need some notation. Given $\{a_j\}_{j=0}^{2n-2}$, the $n \times n$ *Hankel matrix*, H, determined by their a's is the one with

$$h_{ij} = a_{i+j-2} \qquad i, j = 1, \ldots, n \tag{4.17.5}$$

that is,

$$H_n = \begin{pmatrix} a_0 & a_1 & a_2 & \cdots \\ a_1 & a_2 & a_3 & \ddots \\ a_2 & a_3 & a_4 & \ddots \\ \vdots & \ddots & \ddots & a_{2n-2} \end{pmatrix} \tag{4.17.6}$$

We write this as $H_n(\{a_j\}_{j=0}^{2n-2})$. Its determinant, which we'll write as $h_n(\{a_n\}_{j=0}^{2n-2})$, is called a *Hankel determinant*.

Hankel matrices arise because if μ obeys (4.17.1) and $P_{n-1}(x) = \sum_{j=0}^{n-1} \alpha_j x^j$ is a general polynomial of degree $n-1$, then

$$\int |P_{n-1}(x)|^2 \, d\mu(x) = \sum_{j,k=0}^{n-1} \bar{\alpha}_j \alpha_k \int x^{j+k} \, d\mu(x)$$

$$= \sum_{j,k=0}^{n-1} \bar{\alpha}_j \alpha_k c_{j+k} \tag{4.17.7}$$

$$= \sum_{j,k=1}^{n} \bar{\alpha}_{j-1} \alpha_{k-1} H_n(\{c_\ell\}_{\ell=0}^{2n-2})_{jk} \tag{4.17.8}$$

We'll now need a lemma in linear algebra that we leave to the reader (Problem 2):

Lemma 4.17.2. *Let A be an $n \times n$ self-adjoint matrix and let d_j, $j = 1, 2, \ldots$, be the determinants of the $j \times j$ matrix, $\{a_{k,\ell}\}_{k,\ell=1}^{j}$. Then A is strictly positive definite if and only if $d_1 > 0, \ldots, d_n > 0$.*

Remark. The proof is by induction, depending on the important fact that B is $n \times n$ (and self-adjoint) and C is the $(n-1) \times (n-1)$ matrix obtained by removing the right-most and bottom row of B, then the eigenvalues of B and C interlace. Thus, knowing the lemma, by induction, the matrix $\widetilde{A}$ obtained by dropping the bottom row and last column has all strictly positive eigenvalues. So by the interlacing, A has its $n-1$ largest eigenvalues strictly positive. The lowest eigenvalue is strictly positive if and only if $d_n > 0$.

We thus have the following:

Theorem 4.17.3. *If μ is nontrivial and obeys (4.17.1), then*

(a) *For all n,*
$$h_n(\{c_\ell\}_{\ell=0}^{2n-2}) > 0 \tag{4.17.9}$$

(b) *If also $\mathrm{supp}(\mu) \subset [0, \infty)$, then also, for all n*
$$h_n(\{c_\ell\}_{\ell=1}^{2n-1}) > 0 \tag{4.17.10}$$

Proof. By (4.17.8) and the lemma, (4.17.9) is equivalent to

$$\int |P(x)|^2 \, d\mu(x) > 0 \tag{4.17.11}$$

for all nonzero polynomials. Since μ is nontrivial and P can vanish at only finitely many points, we have strict positivity.

Similarly, (4.17.10) is equivalent to

$$\int |P(x)|^2 x \, d\mu(x) > 0 \tag{4.17.12}$$

which holds if $\operatorname{supp}(\mu) \subset [0, \infty)$ and μ is nontrivial. $\qquad\square$

Thus, (4.17.9) is necessary for the Hamburger moment problem to have a solution and both (4.17.9) and (4.17.10) are necessary for the Stieltjes moment problem to have a solution. The big result of Section 5.6 is that these conditions are also sufficient (and we'll use that fact below in one place).

Given a sequence $\{a_n\}_{n=0}^\infty$, we define a new sequence δa by

$$(\delta a)_n = a_n - a_{n+1} \tag{4.17.13}$$

Here is the main theorem of this section:

Theorem 4.17.4 (Hausdorff Moment Theorem). *Let $\{c_n\}_{n=0}^\infty$ be a sequence of reals obeying (4.17.2). Consider the following:*

(1) *There is a measure μ on $[0,1]$ obeying (4.17.1), that is, the Hausdorff moment problem is soluble.*
(1$'$) $\equiv$ (1) *plus the measure is nontrivial.*
(2) *For all $n, k = 0, 1, 2, 3, \ldots,$*

$$(\delta^k c) \geq 0 \tag{4.17.14}$$

(3) *For all n,*

$$h_n(\{c_\ell\}_{\ell=0}^{2n-2}) > 0, \qquad h_n(\{c_\ell\}_{\ell=1}^{2n-1}) > 0 \tag{4.17.15}$$
$$\sup_n |c_n| < \infty \tag{4.17.16}$$

(4) *For all n, (4.17.15) holds and*

$$h_n(\{\delta c_\ell\}_{\ell=0}^{2n-2}) > 0, \qquad h_n(\{\delta c_\ell\}_{\ell=1}^{2n-1}) > 0 \tag{4.17.17}$$

Then (1) $\Leftrightarrow$ (2) *and* (1$'$) $\Leftrightarrow$ (3) $\Leftrightarrow$ (4).

Remarks. 1. We'll prove each of (2), (3), and (4) are equivalent to (1$'$) (or for (2), to (1)). Of course, this implies that any two of them are related (i.e., (3) $\Leftrightarrow$ (4) $\Rightarrow$ (2)). The remarkable thing is without going through the equivalence to (1), it is not clear how to see these direct conditions on the

c's are equivalent. In particular, it is striking that (2) is a condition linear in the c's while (3) and (4) are nonlinear.

2. (4.17.16) can be replaced by $\limsup |c_n|^{1/n} \leq 1$ and, in turn (given (4.17.15)), it implies $\sup_n |c_n| = 1$.

3. If one replaces (4.17.15)/(4.17.17) by nonstrict positivity of the Hankel matrices (not just Hankel determinants), one gets conditions equivalent to (1).

4. We'll prove the steps through some propositions.

Proposition 4.17.5. $(1') \Rightarrow (3), (4)$ *and* $(1) \Rightarrow (2)$.

Proof. We've already noted that

$$(4.17.15) \Leftrightarrow \forall \text{ polynomials } P,$$

$$\int |P(x)|^2 \, d\mu(x) > 0, \quad \int x |P(x)|^2 \, d\mu(x) > 0$$

so clearly, $(4.17.1) \Rightarrow (4.17.15)$. Similarly,

$$(4.17.14) \Leftrightarrow \int x^n (1-x)^k \, d\mu(x) \geq 0$$

$$(4.17.17) \Leftrightarrow \forall \text{ polynomials } P,$$

$$\int (1-x)|P(x)|^2 \, d\mu, \quad \int x(1-x)|P(x)|^2 \, d\mu(x) > 0$$

so that $(4.17.1) \Rightarrow (4.17.14)$ and $(4.17.1) + \text{nontriviality} \Rightarrow (4.17.17)$.

All that remains is (4.17.6). $\operatorname{supp}(\mu) \subset [0,1]$ clearly implies $c_n \leq 1$. Indeed, $(4.17.14) \Rightarrow \delta c_n \geq 0 \Rightarrow c_n \leq c_{n-1} \leq \cdots \leq c_0 = 1$. $\square$

To show $(3) \Rightarrow (1')$, we'll need that $(4.17.15) \Rightarrow$ there exists μ supported on $[0, \infty)$ so that (4.17.1) holds for a nontrivial μ—that is the result of Section 5.6 (see Theorem 5.6.2).

Proposition 4.17.6. $(3) \Rightarrow (1')$.

Proof. By the results from Section 5.6, (4.17.15) implies there is a measure μ on $[0, \infty)$ so (4.17.1) holds. If $\operatorname{supp}(\mu)$ is not inside $[0,1]$, there is $\varepsilon > 0$ so that $\mu([1 + \varepsilon, \infty)) = \delta > 0$. Then $c_n \geq \delta(1 + \varepsilon)^n$, violating (4.17.6), so (4.17.6) implies $\operatorname{supp}(\mu) \subset [0,1]$. $\square$

For $(4) \Rightarrow (1)$ and $(2) \Rightarrow (1')$, we need to exploit the fact that on $[0,1]$, polynomials are bounded and dense in $C([0,1])$. Let $\mathcal{P}$ denote the set of all real polynomials and

$$\mathcal{P}_+ = \{P \in \mathcal{P} \mid P(x) \geq 0 \text{ if } x \in [0,1], P \not\equiv 0\} \tag{4.17.18}$$

Given potential moments, $\{c_n\}_{n=0}^\infty$, we define $\ell\colon \mathcal{P} \to \mathbb{R}$ by

$$\ell\left(\sum_{j=0}^{n} a_j x^j\right) = \sum_{j=0}^{n} a_j c_j \tag{4.17.19}$$

Proposition 4.17.7. *There is a nontrivial measure μ on $[0,1]$ solving (4.17.1) if and only if for all $P \in \mathcal{P}$, we have $\ell(P) \geq 0$. If $\ell(P) > 0$ for all $P \in \mathcal{P}$, then μ is nontrivial.*

Proof. If μ exists,

$$\ell(P) = \int P(x)\, d\mu(x) \tag{4.17.20}$$

so $\ell(P) \geq 0$. If μ is nontrivial, since P has only finitely many zeros, $\ell(P) > 0$.

Conversely, if $\ell(P) \geq 0$, since $\|P\|_\infty \mathbb{1} \pm P \geq 0$ on $[0,1]$ (where $\|\cdot\|_\infty$ is on $C([0,1])$), we have

$$|\ell(P)| \leq \|P\|_\infty \ell(\mathbb{1}) = \|P\|_\infty c_0 = \|P\|_\infty \tag{4.17.21}$$

Thus, ℓ extends to a linear functional on $C([0,1])$ with

$$|\ell(f)| \leq \|f\|_\infty, \qquad \ell(\mathbb{1}) = 1 \tag{4.17.22}$$

which corresponds to a positive measure (see the proof of Proposition 4.8.5). If the measure is trivial, it is supported at $\{x_j\}_{j=1}^N$, and then if $P = \prod_{j=1}^{N}(x - x_j)^2$, $\ell(P) = 0$ and $P \in \mathcal{P}_+$. Thus, μ solves (4.17.1) and is nontrivial if $\ell(P) > 0$ for all $P \in \mathcal{P}$. $\qquad\square$

The proof that $(2) \Rightarrow (1)$ will depend on the use of Bernstein polynomials, as discussed in Section 2.4. Recall (2.4.10), the definition of $\mathbb{E}_{x,n}$ for a finite sequence $\{f_j\}_{j=0}^n$ given $n \in \mathbb{Z}_+$ and $x \in [0,1]$:

$$\mathbb{E}_{x,n}(f) = \sum_{j=0}^{n} f_j \binom{n}{j} x^j (1-x)^{n-j} \tag{4.17.23}$$

For $\ell = 0, 1, 2\ldots$, let

$$Q_\ell(x) = x(x-1)\ldots(x-\ell+1) \tag{4.17.24}$$

(if $\ell = 0$, $Q_\ell(x) \equiv 1$). In Problem 3, the reader will prove: For $\ell = 0, 1, 2, \ldots$,

$$\mathbb{E}_{x,n}(Q_\ell(j)) = x^\ell Q_\ell(n) \tag{4.17.25}$$

This is proven for $\ell = 0, 1, 2$ in Lemma 2.4.6 and the proof is the same.

Recall that, given $f \in C([0,1])$, the Bernstein polynomials of degree n, $B_n(f)$, are defined by ((2.4.4))

$$B_n(f) = \sum_{j=0}^{n} f\left(\frac{j}{n}\right)\left[\binom{n}{j} x^j (1-x)^{n-j}\right] \tag{4.17.26}$$

Lemma 4.17.8. *Let P be a polynomial of degree ℓ. Then for every $n \geq \ell$, $B_n(P)$ is a polynomial of degree precisely ℓ. The coefficients of $B_n(P)$ differ from those of P by an amount bounded by C/n, where C is a P-dependent constant.*

Proof. $\{x^j\}_{j=0}^{\ell}$ and $\{Q_j(x)\}_{j=0}^{\ell}$ are sets with exactly one polynomial of degree exactly j for $j = 0, \ldots, \ell$, so they both span all polynomials of degree ℓ. Since they are monic, there exist constants $\{a_{\ell,k}\}_{k=0}^{\ell-1}$ so that

$$x^\ell = Q_\ell(x) + \sum_{j=1}^{\ell} a_{\ell,\ell-j} Q_{\ell-j}(x) \tag{4.17.27}$$

Thus, by (4.17.25),

$$B_n(x^\ell) = n^{-\ell}\left[x^\ell Q_\ell(n) + \sum_{j=1}^{\ell} a_{\ell,\ell-j} x^{\ell-j} Q_{\ell-j}(n)\right] \tag{4.17.28}$$

If $n \geq \ell$, $Q_\ell(n) = n(n-1)\ldots(n-\ell+1) \neq 0$, so $B_n(x^\ell)$ is a polynomial of degree exactly ℓ. Since

$$n^{-\ell} Q_\ell(n) = 1 + O(n^{-1}), \qquad n^{-\ell} Q_{\ell-j} = Q(n^{-j})$$

we get the C/n bound for $P(x) = x^\ell$. Since any polynomial is a linear combination of these P's and $f \mapsto B_n(f)$ is linear, we have the result for all polynomials. $\square$

Proposition 4.17.9. (2) $\Rightarrow$ (1).

Proof. If $P \in \mathcal{P}_+$, since $\ell(x^j(1-x)^{n-j}) \geq 0$ by (2), we have $\ell(B_n(P)) \geq 0$. Since ℓ is continuous on polynomials of degree at most k, $\ell(P) \geq 0$. By Proposition 4.17.7, (4.17.1) is solvable. $\square$

Lemma 4.17.10. *Let $\mathcal{P}_\mathbb{R}$ be the set of real polynomials and*

$$\mathcal{R}_1 = \{P(x)^2 \mid P \in \mathcal{P}_\mathbb{R}, P \not\equiv 0\}$$
$$\mathcal{R}_2 = \{xP(x)^2 \mid P \in \mathcal{P}_\mathbb{R}, P \not\equiv 0\}$$
$$\mathcal{R}_3 = \{(1-x)P(x)^2 \mid P \in \mathcal{P}_\mathbb{R}, P \not\equiv 0\}$$
$$\mathcal{R}_4 = \{x(1-x)P(x)^2 \mid P \in \mathcal{P}_\mathbb{R}, P \not\equiv 0\}$$

Then any $P \in \mathcal{P}_+$ if and only if P is a sum of polynomials in $\mathcal{R}_1 \cup \mathcal{R}_2 \cup \mathcal{R}_3 \cup \mathcal{R}_4$.

Proof. Since P is real on $[0,1]$, $\overline{P(\bar{x})} - P(x)$ is zero on $[0,1]$, and so a polynomial identically zero, that is, $\overline{P(\bar{x})} = P(x)$. Thus, P has only real zeros or complex conjugate pairs. Thus,

$$P(x) = \prod_{j=1}^{J}[(x - a_j)^2 + b_j^2]Q(x) \qquad (4.17.29)$$

where $Q \in \mathcal{P}_+$ and has only real zeros. By expanding the product, we see P is a sum of polynomials in $\mathcal{P}_+$, all of whose zeros are on $\mathbb{R}$, so we restrict to that case.

If P has a zero x_0 in $[0,1]$, it must be of even order for P not to have both signs near x_0. Thus,

$$P(x) = \prod_{k=1}^{K}(x - x_k)^2 Q(x) \qquad (4.17.30)$$

with $x_k \in (0,1)$ and $Q \in \mathcal{P}_+$ with a zero in $\mathbb{R} \setminus [0,1]$, so it suffices to consider such Q's which have the form

$$Q(x) = c \prod_{\ell=1}^{L}(x - x_\ell) \prod_{n=1}^{N}(y_n - x)$$

where $c > 0$ and $x_\ell \leq 0$, $y_n \geq 1$. Writing

$$x - x_\ell = x + |x_\ell|, \qquad y_n - x = (y_n - 1) + (1 - x)$$

we see $Q(x)$ is a sum of positive numbers times terms of the form $x^p(1-x)^q$. Writing $p = 2P$ or $2P + 1$, $q = 2Q$ or $2Q + 1$, we see that every such term lies in one of $\mathcal{R}_1, \mathcal{R}_2, \mathcal{R}_3, \mathcal{R}_4$. $\square$

The following completes the proof of Theorem 4.17.4:

Proposition 4.17.11. $(4) \Rightarrow (1')$.

Proof. By Lemma 4.17.2, strict positivity of the Hankel determinants implies strict positivity of the Hankel matrices. As in the proof of Theorem 4.17.3, (4.17.15) implies $\ell(P) > 0$ for P in $\mathcal{R}_1$ or $\mathcal{R}_2$ and (4.17.17) for $\mathcal{R}_3$ and $\mathcal{R}_4$. By Lemma 4.17.10, $\ell(P) > 0$ for $P \in \mathcal{P}_+$, so by Proposition 4.17.7, $(1')$ holds. $\square$

Notes and Historical Remarks. We'll discuss in detail the history of the moment problem in the Notes to Section 5.6. Here we note only the central role of Stieltjes in formulating such problems and that the main result of this section, namely, that $(1) \Leftrightarrow (2)$ in Theorem 4.17.4, is due to Hausdorff [**404**].

Problems

1. Suppose μ, ν are two measures on $\mathbb{R}$ with equal moments and with μ supported on $[0,1]$. Prove that

   (a) $c_{2n} \le 1$

   (b) ν is supported on $[-1,1]$

   (c) $\mu = \nu$

2. Let A be an $n \times n$ self-adjoint matrix. Let C be the matrix obtained by dropping the bottom row and right-most column. Suppose C has eigenvalues $\mu_1 \le \mu_2 \le \cdots \le \mu_{n-1}$ and A has eigenvalues $\lambda_1 \le \lambda_2 \le \cdots \le \lambda_n$.

   (a) For each k, find a space, V_k, of dimension k so that for $\varphi \in V_k$, $\langle \varphi, A\varphi \rangle = \langle \varphi, C\varphi \rangle \le \mu_k$.

   (b) Conclude that $\lambda_k \le \mu_k$.

   (c) Prove that $\mu_k \le \lambda_{k+1}$.

   (d) Suppose $0 < \mu_1$ and that $\lambda_1 \ldots \lambda_n > 0$. Prove that $\lambda_1 > 0$.

   (e) Prove Lemma 4.17.2.

3. Verify (4.17.25).

4.18. Bonus Section: Integration of Banach Space-Valued Functions

In this brief bonus section, we'll discuss some aspects of integrating functions with values in a Banach space touching on the two main theorems. We'll see there are two natural notions of measurability, weak and strong, and prove Pettis' theorem that they agree in the separable case. We'll also prove Bochner's theorem that a Banach space-valued function is an L^1-limit of simple functions if and only if it is strongly measurable and its norm is L^1. We will not discuss the related issue where the measure—rather than the functions—takes Banach space values. We'll freely use results from the theory of Banach spaces only proven in the next chapter.

Definition. Let (Ω, Σ, μ) be a σ-finite measure space, X a Banach space over $\mathbb{K} = \mathbb{R}$ or $\mathbb{C}$, and X^* its dual. A function $f \colon \Omega \to X$ is called *weakly measurable* if and only if for all $\ell \in X^*$, $\ell(f(\cdot))$ is a measurable $\mathbb{K}$-valued function. If $\ell(f(\cdot)) \in L^1(\Omega, d\mu)$ for all ℓ and there exists $x \in X$ so for all $\ell \in X^*$ we have

$$\ell(x) = \int \ell(f(\omega)) \, d\mu(\omega) \qquad (4.18.1)$$

we call x the *Pettis integral* of f (sometimes called the Gel'fand–Pettis integral).

Remark. By the Hahn–Banach theorem (see Theorem 5.5.9), if x exists obeying (4.18.1), it is unique.

Theorem 4.18.1. (a) *If X^* is separable and f is* weakly measurable, *then* $\|f(\cdot)\|$ *is measurable.*

(b) *If X is reflexive and X^* is separable, the Pettis integral exists if*

$$\|f(\cdot)\| \in L^1(X, d\mu) \tag{4.18.2}$$

Proof. (a) Let $\{\ell_n\}_{n=1}^\infty$ be a dense subset of $(X^*)_1$, the unit ball in X^*. By (5.5.36),

$$\|f(\omega)\| = \sup_n |\ell_n(f(\omega))| \tag{4.18.3}$$

Measurability follows from Theorem 4.3.6.

(b) By (4.18.2), if

$$\lambda(\ell) = \int \ell(f(\omega)) \, d\mu(\omega) \tag{4.18.4}$$

then

$$|\lambda(\ell)| \le \|\ell\| \int \|f(\omega)\| \, d\mu(\omega) \tag{4.18.5}$$

so $\ell \mapsto \lambda(\ell)$ is a BLT. Since X is reflexive, there exists $x \in X$ obeying (4.18.1). □

Definition. A *simple function* (with values in X) is one of the form $\sum_{n=1}^N \alpha_n \chi_{A_n}$, where N is finite, $\{\alpha_n\}_{n=1}^N \subset X$ and $\{A_n\}_{n=1}^N$ are sets with $\mu(A_n) < \infty$.

Definition. A *strongly measurable function* (aka *Bochner measurable*), $f \colon \Omega \to X$, is one for which there is a sequence of simple functions, f_n, with $f_n(\omega) \to f(\omega)$ for a.e. $\omega \in \Omega$.

We are heading towards a characterization of strongly measurable functions. We need the following lemma:

Lemma 4.18.2. *Let X be a separable Banach space. Then there exists a countable subset in $(X^*)_1$ which is dense in $(X^*)_1$ in the $\sigma(X^*, X)$-topology.*

Proof. By the Banach–Alaoglu theorem (Theorem 5.8.1), $(X^*)_1$ is compact and, by the separability, the $\sigma(X^*, X)$-topology is metrizable (see Theorem 5.7.2). Compact metric spaces are separable (see Proposition 2.3.5 and Theorem 2.3.6). □

One of the basic results on measurability of Banach space-valued functions is:

Theorem 4.18.3 (Pettis' Theorem). *Let (Ω, Σ, μ) be a σ-finite measure space and let X be a Banach space. Let $f : \Omega \to X$. Then f is strongly measurable if and only if f is weakly measurable and $\mathrm{Ran}(f)$ is almost separable in that there exists $\Omega' \subset \Omega$ so $\mu(\Omega \setminus \Omega') = 0$ and $f[\Omega']$ is separable.*

Remark. In particular, if X is separable, f is strongly measurable if and only if it is weakly measurable.

Proof. If f is strongly measurable, for every $\ell \in X^*$, $\ell(f(\cdot))$ is a pointwise a.e. limit of simple scalar functions, so measurable, and thus, f is weakly measurable. If $f_n(\omega) = \sum_{j=1}^{N_n} a_{n,j} \chi_{A_{n,j}}$ and $\widetilde{X}$ is the closure of the span of $\{a_{n,j}\}_{n=1, j=1}^{\infty, \ N_n}$, then $\widetilde{X}$ is separable and $\mathrm{Ran}(f)$ is a.e. in $\widetilde{X}$, so $\mathrm{Ran}(f)$ is a.e. separable.

Conversely, suppose f is weakly measurable and a.e. separable. By setting f to 0 on $\Omega \setminus \widetilde{\Omega}$, we can suppose f is separably valued, which means we need to prove that if X is separable and weakly measurable, it is strongly measurable.

In that case, we claim, for any α, $\{\omega \mid \|f(\omega)\| \leq \alpha\}$ is measurable. For by the Hahn–Banach theorem,

$$\|f(\omega)\| \leq \alpha \Leftrightarrow \forall \ell \in (X^*)_1, \ |\ell(f(\omega))| \leq \alpha \qquad (4.18.6)$$

and by the lemma, $(X^*)_1$ contains a $\sigma(X^*, X)$-dense set $\{\ell_m\}_{m=1}^{\infty}$ so that

$$\forall \ell \in (X^*)_1, \ |\ell(f(\omega))| \leq \alpha \Leftrightarrow \forall m \ |\ell_m(f(\omega))| \leq \alpha \qquad (4.18.7)$$

Thus,

$$\{\omega \mid \|f(\omega)\| \leq \alpha\} = \bigcap_{m=1}^{\infty} \{\omega \mid |\ell_m(f(\omega))| \leq \alpha\} \qquad (4.18.8)$$

is measurable.

An easy argument (Problem 1) shows that a pointwise a.e. limit of a sequence of strongly measurable functions is strongly measurable. Thus, if we can show each $f \chi_{\{\omega \mid \|f(\omega)\| \leq N\}}$ is strongly measurable, f is strongly measurable, that is, we can suppose $\|f(\cdot)\|$ is bounded, so for simplicity of notation, we can suppose $\|f(\omega)\| \leq 1$ for all ω.

Applying the above argument to $f(\omega) - x_0$, for any $x_0 \in X$ and α, $B_f(x_0, \alpha) \equiv \{\omega \mid \|f(\omega) - x_0\| \leq \alpha\}$ is measurable.

Let $\{x_j\}_{j=1}^{\infty}$ be a dense subset of $\{x \mid \|x\| \leq 1\}$. Let

$$B_{n,j} = B_f\left(x_j, \frac{1}{n}\right) \qquad (4.18.9)$$

and

$$A_{n,j} = B_{n,j} \setminus \bigcup_{k=1}^{j-1} B_{n,k} \tag{4.18.10}$$

Let

$$f_n(x) = \sum_{j=1}^{\infty} x_j \chi_{A_{n,j}} \tag{4.18.11}$$

Since $\operatorname{Ran}(f) \subset \bigcup_j A_{n,j}$ (since $\|f\|_\infty \leq 1$) and the $A_{n,j}$ are a disjoint cover of $\operatorname{Ran}(f)$,

$$\|f_n - f\|_\infty \leq \frac{1}{n} \tag{4.18.12}$$

Clearly, if $\Omega = \bigcup_{m=1}^{\infty} \Omega_m$ with $\mu(\Omega_m) < \infty$ and $\Omega_m \subset \Omega_{m+1}$,

$$f_{n,N}(\omega) = \sum_{j=1}^{N} x_j \chi_{A_{n,j} \cap \Omega_n}(\omega) \tag{4.18.13}$$

then $f_{n,N}$ is simple, as $N \to \infty$, and $f_{n,N} \to f_n$ at all ω, so each f_n is strongly measurable. By (4.18.12), f is a pointwise limit of f_n's. So by Problem 1, f is strongly measurable. $\square$

Definition. Let (Ω, Σ, μ) be a σ-finite measure space and X a Banach space. $f \colon \Omega \to X$ is called *Bochner integrable* if and only if f is strongly measurable and there is a sequence, f_n, of simple functions with

$$\lim_{n \to \infty} \int \|f(\omega) - f_n(\omega)\| \, d\mu(\omega) = 0 \tag{4.18.14}$$

By the argument in the last theorem, $\|f - f_n\|$ is measurable, so the integral exists, although it may be ∞. (4.18.14) means it is eventually finite and goes to zero. If

$$f_n = \sum_{j=1}^{N_n} x_{j,n} \chi_{A_{n,j}} \tag{4.18.15}$$

we define $\int f_n \, d\mu = \sum_{j=1}^{N_n} x_{j,n} \mu(A_{n,j})$. (4.18.14) implies these elements of X are Cauchy, so we can define the Bochner integral as

$$\lim_{n \to \infty} \int f_n(\omega) \, d\mu(\omega) \equiv \int f(\omega) \, d\mu(\omega) \tag{4.18.16}$$

The set of all Bochner integrable functions is denoted $L^1(\Omega, d\mu; X)$. By a simple diagonalization argument, if $g_n(\omega) \in L^1(\Omega, d\mu; X)$ and

$$\lim_{n \to \infty} \int \|g(\omega) - g_n(\omega)\| \, d\mu(\omega) = 0 \tag{4.18.17}$$

then $g \in L^1(\Omega, d\mu; X)$.

Here is the second main theorem we'll prove:

Theorem 4.18.4 (Bochner's Integrability Theorem). *A function is Bochner integrable if and only if it is strongly measurable and*

$$\int \|f(\omega)\| \, d\mu(\omega) < \infty \tag{4.18.18}$$

Remark. As in the proof of the last theorem, if f is strongly measurable, $\|f(\cdot)\|$ is measurable as a scalar function.

Proof. For any simple function, f_n, of the form (4.18.15),

$$\int \|f_n(\omega)\| \, d\mu(\omega) \leq \sum_{j=1}^{N_n} \|x_{j,n}\| \mu(A_{n,j}) < \infty \tag{4.18.19}$$

so (4.18.14) implies (4.18.18).

Conversely, let f be strongly measurable and obey (4.18.18). By using the remark connected to (4.18.17) and the σ-finiteness of μ, we can restrict to the case $\mu(\Omega) < \infty$. By this same remark and (by the dominated convergence theorem)

$$(4.18.18) \Rightarrow \lim_{M \to \infty} \int_{\{\omega \mid \|f(\omega)\| \geq M\}} \|f(\omega)\| \, d\mu(\omega) = 0$$

we can reduce to the case $\|f(\omega)\| \leq K$ for all ω and some K.

By the argument in Pettis' theorem, we can suppose X is separable. Given all that, the argument in the proof of Pettis' theorem (supplemented by $\mu(\Omega) < \infty$ which implies $\lim_{M \to \infty} \mu(\bigcup_{j=M}^{\infty} A_{n,j}) = 0$ for each n) shows first that f_n (of the form (4.18.11)) lies in L^1 and then that f does. □

Notes and Historical Remarks. Weak measurability and the weak integral was developed by Gel'fand [**343**] for $\Omega = [a, b]$ in 1936 and by Pettis [**715**] for general Ω in 1938. Pettis, in particular, had Theorem 4.18.3. The Bochner integral, including Theorem 4.18.4, is from Bochner [**102**] in 1933.

Problems

1. (a) Suppose $\mu(\Omega) < \infty$. Let g_n, g be functions with $\|g_n - g\|$, $\|g_n - g_k\|$ measurable for all k, n. Suppose for a.e. ω, $\|g_n(\omega) - g(\omega)\| \to 0$. For any ε, prove that $\exists N$ so that $\mu(\{\omega \mid \|g_n(\omega) - g(\omega)\| > \varepsilon\}) < \varepsilon$ if $n > N$.

   (b) Using (a), prove that if $\mu(\Omega) < \infty$ and g_n are strongly measurable and $\|g_n(\omega) - g(\omega)\| \to 0$ for a.e. ω, then g is strongly measurable.

   (c) Extend to the σ-finite case.

4.19. Bonus Section: Haar Measure on σ-Compact Groups

In this section, we'll discuss invariant measures on topological groups. A *topological group* is a topological space, G, which is also a group, so that $(x, y) \mapsto xy$ from $G \times G \to G$ and $x \to x^{-1}$ from $G \to G$ are continuous functions ($G \times G$ is given the product topology). We'll consider here only the σ-compact case (but see the Notes).

A Baire measure, μ, on G is called a *Haar measure* (more precisely, a *left-invariant Haar measure*) if and only if μ is nonzero, and for all $f \in C_0(G)$, the continuous functions of compact support, we have that for all $x \in G$,

$$\int f(xy)\, d\mu(y) = \int f(y)\, d\mu(y) \tag{4.19.1}$$

This definition depends on the easy fact (Problem 1) that if $f \in C_0(G)$, then for every x, $\tau_x f$ defined by

$$(\tau_x f)(y) = f(xy) \tag{4.19.2}$$

is also in $C_0(G)$ and the general fact that for any Baire measure, μ, $C_0(G) \subset L^1(G, d\mu)$. By considering limits, if (4.19.1) holds for all $f \in C_0(G)$, then $\tau_x f \in L^1$ if $f \in L^1$ and (4.19.1) holds for all $f \in L^1$. By considering $f = \chi_A$, one sees that if A is a Baire set with compact closure, then

$$\mu(xA) = \mu(A) \tag{4.19.3}$$

for all x (since $\chi_{xA}(y) = \chi_A(x^{-1}y)$). Conversely (Problem 2), if (4.19.3) holds, for all such A and x, (4.19.1) holds for all $f \in C_0(G)$.

The main result in this section is

Theorem 4.19.1. *Every σ-compact group has a Haar measure which is unique up to normalization. That is, if μ, ν are two Haar measures, then for some c, $d\mu = c\, d\nu$.*

Once we have existence and uniqueness, one consequence is the existence of a function, $\Delta(x)$, on G that measures how far a Haar measure is from being right-invariant. For a function, $f(x)$, and for $x \in G$, define

$$(\sigma_x f)(y) = f(yx^{-1}) \tag{4.19.4}$$

We use x^{-1} rather than x so that

$$\sigma_{xy} = \sigma_x \sigma_y \tag{4.19.5}$$

Left-invariance of μ says $\tau_x^*(\mu) = \mu$. Since each τ_y commutes with each σ_x, $\sigma_x^*(\mu)$ is also left-invariant. Thus, since Haar measure is unique up to a constant, we know that

$$\sigma_x^*(\mu) = \Delta(x)\mu \tag{4.19.6}$$

Theorem 4.19.2. *Let μ be a nonzero Haar measure on G. Then*

(a) *There is a continuous function, $\Delta(x)$, from G to $(0,\infty)$ so that* (4.19.6)
   holds.

(b) $\Delta(xy) = \Delta(x)\Delta(y)$ $\qquad\qquad\qquad\qquad\qquad\qquad$ (4.19.7)

(c) *For every $f \in C_0(G)$,*

$$\int f(x)\,d\mu(x) = \int f(x^{-1})\Delta(x^{-1})\,d\mu(x) \qquad (4.19.8)$$

Remarks. 1. $\Delta(x)$ is called the *modular function* of G. Haar measure is also right-invariant if and only if $\Delta(x) \equiv 1$, in which case G is called *unimodular*. Every abelian group and every compact group (see Problem 3) is unimodular and $\mathbb{GL}(n,\mathbb{C})$, $\mathbb{SL}(n,\mathbb{C})$, $\mathbb{GL}(n,\mathbb{R})$, $\mathbb{SL}(n,\mathbb{R})$ are all unimodular (Problem 4). The affine group in one dimension, that is, the maps $T_{a,\lambda}\colon \mathbb{R} \to \mathbb{R}$ of the form $x \mapsto a + \lambda x$, $a \in \mathbb{R}$, $\lambda \in (0,\infty)$ is not unimodular (Problem 5).

2. If μ is Haar measure, $f \mapsto \int f(x^{-1})\,d\mu(x)$ is right-invariant measure, $d\mu_R(x)$. It follows from (4.19.8) that

$$d\mu_R(x) = \Delta(x^{-1})\,d\mu(x) \qquad (4.19.9)$$

which can be checked directly (Problem 6).

Proof. (a) We've already shown that uniqueness of Haar measure implies $\Delta(x)$ exists, and clearly, $\Delta(x) \in (0,\infty)$. Let $f \in C_0(G)$ with $\int f(x)\,d\mu(x) \neq 0$ (shortly, we'll see that any nonnegative, not identically zero, f has that property). Then by definition of σ_x,

$$\Delta(x) = \frac{\int f(yx^{-1})\,d\mu(y)}{\int f(y)\,d\mu(y)} \qquad (4.19.10)$$

from which continuity of Δ is immediate (Problem 7).

(b) Immediate from $\sigma_{xy} = \sigma_x\sigma_y$ and (4.19.9).

(c) Fix $g \in C_0(G)$ with $\int g(x)\,d\mu(x) = 1$. Let $f \in C_0(G)$ and $h(x) = f(x^{-1})$. Then

$$\int g(y)f(y^{-1}x)\,d\mu(y) = \int g(y)h(x^{-1}y)\,d\mu(y)$$

$$= \int g(xy)h(y)\,d\mu(y)$$

$$= \int g(xy)f(y^{-1})\,d\mu(y) \qquad (4.19.11)$$

(this provides two expressions for the convolution of g and f).

Integrate this $d\mu(x)$. Since $\int f(y^{-1}x)\,d\mu(x) = \int f(x)\,d\mu(x)$ and $\int g(y)\,d\mu(y) = 1$, we get

$$\int\left(\int g(y)f(y^{-1}x)\,d\mu(y)\right)d\mu(x) = \int f(x)\,d\mu(x) \qquad (4.19.12)$$

On the other hand,

$$\int\left(\int g(xy)f(y^{-1})\,d\mu(y)\right)d\mu(x) = \int\left(\int g(xy)\,d\mu(x)\right)f(y^{-1})\,d\mu(y)$$

$$= \int \Delta(y^{-1})f(y^{-1})\,d\mu(y)$$

which proves (4.19.8). $\qquad\qquad\qquad\qquad\qquad\qquad\qquad\qquad\qquad\qquad\quad\square$

We'll separately prove uniqueness and existence. The following preliminary is useful:

Proposition 4.19.3. *If μ is a nonzero Haar measure, then*

(a) *For any nonempty open set, A, $\mu(A) > 0$.*
(b) *For any $f \in C_0(G)$, $f \geq 0$, and $f \not\equiv 0$, we have*

$$\int f(x)\,d\mu(x) > 0 \qquad (4.19.13)$$

Proof. (a) Let $\tau_x(A) = \{xy \mid y \in A\}$. If $\mu(A) = 0$, by (4.19.3), $\mu(\tau_x A) = 0$. Suppose $y \in A$. Let K be compact. Since $x \in \tau_{xy^{-1}}(A)$,

$$K \subset \bigcup_{x \in G} \tau_x(A) \qquad (4.19.14)$$

Since K is compact, for some $x_1,\ldots,x_n \in G$,

$$K \subset \bigcup_{j=1}^n \tau_{x_j}(A) \qquad (4.19.15)$$

so $\mu(K) = 0$. Since G is σ-compact, $\mu(G) = 0$. Thus, $\mu(A) \neq 0$.

(b) For some $\varepsilon > 0$, $A = \{x \mid f(x) > \varepsilon\}$ is open and nonempty. Since

$$\int f(x)\,d\mu(x) \geq \varepsilon\mu(A) \neq 0 \qquad (4.19.16)$$

we have (4.19.13). $\qquad\qquad\qquad\qquad\qquad\qquad\qquad\qquad\qquad\qquad\qquad\quad\square$

We now give von Neumann's elegant proof of uniqueness of Haar measure. First, we need a lemma:

Lemma 4.19.4. *If μ is a Haar measure and $\mu[A] = 0$ for a Baire set, A, then with $A^{-1} = \{x^{-1} \mid x \in A\}$, we have that $\mu[A^{-1}] = 0$.*

Proof. Fix $g \geq 0$ in $C_0(G)$ with

$$\int g(x)\, d\mu(x) = 1 \tag{4.19.17}$$

Define $\Delta \colon G \to (0, \infty)$ by

$$\Delta(s) = \int g(xs^{-1})\, d\mu(x) \tag{4.19.18}$$

Since we don't know yet that μ is unique, we cannot conclude (4.19.7), but the proofs of continuity near e and positivity of Δ in Theorem 4.19.2 go through, as does the proof of (4.19.8). So we have

$$\int f(x)\Delta(x)^{-1}\, d\mu(x) = \int f(x)\, d\mu(x^{-1}) \tag{4.19.19}$$

(by replacing f by $f\Delta^{-1}$ and changing variables). This implies for any A with compact closure that

$$\mu(A^{-1}) = \int_A \Delta(x)^{-1}\, d\mu(x) \tag{4.19.20}$$

so $\mu(A) = 0 \Rightarrow \mu(A^{-1}) = 0$. Since G is σ-compact, we get this for any A. $\square$

Theorem 4.19.5. *Let μ, ν be two nonzero Haar measures on G. Then for some $c \in (0, \infty)$,*

$$d\mu = c\, d\nu \tag{4.19.21}$$

Proof. Let $\eta = \mu + \nu$, which is also a Haar measure. If we prove $d\mu = k\, d\eta$ for a constant k, necessarily $d\nu = (1-k)\, d\eta$, so $0 < k < 1$ and $d\mu = k(1-k)^{-1}\, d\nu$, proving (4.19.21).

Since $\mu \leq \eta$, μ is η-a.c. and so, by the Radon–Nikodym theorem, for an $h \in L^1(G, d\eta)$,

$$d\mu(x) = h(x)\, d\eta(x) \tag{4.19.22}$$

As in the proof of Theorem 4.7.6,

$$0 \leq h(x) \leq 1 \tag{4.19.23}$$

Let $f \in C_0(G)$. Then for any $y \in G$,

$$\int f(x)h(x)\, d\eta(x) = \int f(x)\, d\mu(x)$$
$$= \int f(yx)\, d\mu(x)$$
$$= \int f(yx)h(x)\, d\eta(x)$$
$$= \int f(x)h(y^{-1}x)\, d\eta(x) \tag{4.19.24}$$

where we used left-invariance of both μ and η. Thus,

$$\int f(x)[h(x) - h(y^{-1}x)]\, d\eta(x) = 0 \qquad (4.19.25)$$

Since $h \in L^\infty$ and $C_0(G)$ is dense in L^1, this extends to all $f \in L^1(G, d\eta)$. So for every y and η-a.e. x,

$$h(x) - h(y^{-1}x) = 0 \qquad (4.19.26)$$

Thus, by Fubini's theorem,

$$\int \left[\int |h(x) - h((x^{-1}y)^{-1})|\, d\eta(y) \right] d\eta(x) = 0 \qquad (4.19.27)$$

By the left-invariance of η, this says

$$\int \left[\int |h(x) - h(y^{-1})|\, d\eta(y) \right] d\eta(x) = 0 \qquad (4.19.28)$$

so for η-a.e. x, we have for η-a.e. y that

$$h(y^{-1}) = h(x) \qquad (4.19.29)$$

Picking x_0 so (4.19.29) holds for a.e. y, we get that $h(y^{-1})$ is a.e. $h(x_0) \equiv k$ and then, by the lemma, that for a.e. y, $h(y) = k$. Thus, $d\mu = k\, d\eta$, as we needed to prove. □

We now turn to the proof of existence. We want to begin by noting that it suffices to define $\ell(f) = \int f(x)\, d\mu$ for $C_+(G)$, the nonnegative f's in $C_0(G)$:

Lemma 4.19.6. *Suppose we have a map* $\ell: C_+(G) \to [0, \infty)$ *obeying*

(a) *For all* $\lambda \in [0, \infty)$, $f \in C_+(G)$, *we have*

$$\ell(\lambda f) = \lambda \ell(f) \qquad (4.19.30)$$

(b) *For all* $f, g \in C_+(G)$,

$$\ell(f + g) = \ell(f) + \ell(g) \qquad (4.19.31)$$

(c) *For all* $f \in C_+(G)$ *and* $x \in G$,

$$\ell(\tau_x(f)) = \ell(f) \qquad (4.19.32)$$

Then there is a Baire measure, μ, *on* G *so that* $\tau_x^*(\mu) = \mu$ *for all* x *and*

$$\ell(f) = \int f(x)\, d\mu(x) \qquad (4.19.33)$$

Thus, if $\ell \not\equiv 0$, μ *is a (nonzero) Haar measure.*

Proof. Let $f_\pm, g_\pm \in C_+(G)$ with

$$f_+ - f_- = g_+ - g_- \tag{4.19.34}$$

Then $f_+ + g_- = g_+ + f_-$, so $\ell(f_+) + \ell(g_-) = \ell(g_+) + \ell(f_-)$, so

$$\ell(f_+) - \ell(f_-) = \ell(g_+) - \ell(g_-) \tag{4.19.35}$$

Since any $f \in C_0(G)$ is an $f_+ - f_-$, this shows we can extend ℓ to $C_0(G)$ in a consistent way. This consistency implies the extended ℓ is linear. It is positive, and so defines a Baire measure, μ.

(4.19.32) extends to ℓ on $C_0(G)$ and then implies $\tau_x^*(\mu) = \mu$. $\qquad\square$

We are going to approximate $\ell(f)$ by seeing how many copies of a g and its translates fit over f. By shrinking the support of g, we'll get a limit which obeys (a)–(c) above.

Lemma 4.19.7. *Let $f, g \in C_+(G)$ with $g \not\equiv 0$. Then there exists $n \in \mathbb{Z}^+$, $\{x_j\}_{j=1}^n$ in G and $t_1, \ldots, t_n > 0$ so that*

$$0 \le f \le \sum_{j=1}^n t_j \tau_{x_j}(g) \tag{4.19.36}$$

Proof. Since $g \not\equiv 0$, find y with $g(y) > 0$ and then an open neighborhood, U, of y and $\varepsilon > 0$ so

$$z \in U \Rightarrow g(z) > \varepsilon \tag{4.19.37}$$

Since $xy \in \tau_x(U)$, the $\{\tau_x(U)\}_{x \in G}$ cover supp(f). By compactness of supp(f), we find $\{x_j\}_{j=1}^n$, so supp$(f) \subset \cup_{j=1}^n \tau_{x_j}(U)$. Then

$$f \le \varepsilon^{-1} \|f\|_\infty \sum_{j=1}^n \tau_{x_j}(g) \tag{4.19.38}$$

proving the desired result. $\qquad\square$

For $f, g \in C_+(G)$ with $g \not\equiv 0$, we define

$$(f : g) = \inf\left\{ \sum_{j=1}^n t_j \,\middle|\, t_j \ge 0 \text{ and } (4.19.36) \text{ holds for some } \{x_j\}_{j=1}^n \right\}$$

Here are the basic properties of this object:

Proposition 4.19.8. *Let $h, g \in C_+(G)$ with $h, g \not\equiv 0$, $f, f_1, f_2 \in C_+(G)$, $x \in G$, $\lambda \in [0, \infty)$. Then*

(a) $\forall x, (\tau_x f : g) = (f : g)$
(b) $(f_1 + f_2 : g) \le (f_1 : g) + (f_2 : g)$
(c) *For all $\lambda \ge 0$, $(\lambda f : g) = \lambda(f : g)$ and if $\lambda \ne 0$, $(f : \lambda^{-1} g) = \lambda(f : g)$*

(d) $(f\colon h) \le (f\colon g)(g\colon h)$

(e) $(f\colon g) \ge \|f\|_\infty \|g\|_\infty^{-1}$.

Proof. Since this is straightforward (only (d) and (e) aren't immediate), we leave the proof to the reader (Problem 8). $\square$

Thus, $(f\colon g)$ is almost what we need—only subadditivity (b) holds rather than additivity. The key is that if $\operatorname{supp}(g)$ is small enough, then $(\,\cdot\,\colon g)$ is almost linear.

Lemma 4.19.9. *For each triple (f_0, f_1, f_2) of nonzero functions in $C_+(G)$ and $\varepsilon > 0$, there is a neighborhood, N, of e (the identity) in G so that for all $g \in C_+(G)$, $g \not\equiv 0$, with*

$$\operatorname{supp}(g) \subset N \tag{4.19.39}$$

we have

$$(f_1\colon g) + (f_2\colon g) \le (f_1 + f_2\colon g) + \varepsilon(f_0\colon g) \tag{4.19.40}$$

Proof. Let $K = \operatorname{supp}(f_1) \cup \operatorname{supp}(f_2)$ and $h \in C_+(G)$ so $h \equiv 1$ on K. Pick $\delta > 0$ (we'll fix δ below to get the desired ε) and let

$$f = f_1 + f_2 + \delta h, \qquad h_i = \frac{f_i}{f} \qquad (i = 1, 2) \tag{4.19.41}$$

Since $f > 0$ in a neighborhood of $\operatorname{supp}(f_i)$, h_i lies in $C_+(G)$ and $f_i = f h_i$.

For each δ_1, by a compactness argument (Problem 7), we can find a neighborhood, N, of e so that

$$x^{-1}y \in N \Rightarrow |h_i(x) - h_i(y)| < \delta_1 \quad \text{for } i = 1, 2 \tag{4.19.42}$$

Suppose now that (4.19.41) holds, that $\operatorname{supp}(g) \subset N$, and that

$$f \le \sum_{\ell=1}^{n} c_\ell \tau_{y_\ell^{-1}}(g) \tag{4.19.43}$$

Then

$$f_j(x) = f(x)h_j(x) \le \sum_{\ell=1}^{n} c_\ell g(y_\ell^{-1}x) h_j(x)$$

$$\le \sum_{\ell=1}^{n} c_\ell g(y_\ell^{-1}x)(h_j(y_\ell) + \delta_1) \tag{4.19.44}$$

since $g(y_\ell^{-1}x) \ne 0 \Rightarrow y_\ell^{-1}x \in N \Rightarrow h_j(x) \le h_j(y_\ell) + \delta_1$ by (4.19.42). It follows that

$$(f_j\colon g) \le \sum_{\ell=1}^{n} c_\ell(h_j(y_\ell) + \delta_1) \tag{4.19.45}$$

By (4.19.41), $h_1 + h_2 \leq 1$, so

$$(f_1 : g) + (f_2 : g) \leq \sum_{\ell=1}^{n} c_\ell(1 + 2\delta_1)$$

so taking the inf of all c_ℓ's and y_ℓ's for which (4.19.43) holds, we get

$$(f_1 : g) + (f_2 : g) \leq (f : g)(1 + 2\delta_1) \qquad (4.19.46)$$
$$\leq [(f_1 + f_2 : g) + \delta(h : g)](1 + 2\delta_1) \qquad (4.19.47)$$

by (4.19.41) and subadditivity. By (d) of the proposition,

$$(h : g) \leq (h : f_0)(f_0 : g)$$
$$(f_1 + f_2 : g) \leq (f_1 + f_2 : f_0)(f_0 : g)$$

so (4.19.47) implies that

$$(f_1 : g) + (f_2 : g) \leq (f_1 + f_2 : g) + q(f_0 : g) \qquad (4.19.48)$$

where

$$q = \delta(h : f_0)(1 + 2\delta_1) + 2\delta_1(f_1 + f_2 : f_0) \qquad (4.19.49)$$

This tells us how to choose δ and δ_1. Since f_1, f_2, f_0 are fixed, we can choose δ_1 so

$$2\delta_1(f_1 + f_2 : f_0) \leq \frac{\varepsilon}{2} \qquad (4.19.50)$$

and then δ so that

$$\delta(h : f_0)(1 + 2\delta_1) \leq \frac{\varepsilon}{2} \qquad (4.19.51)$$

$\square$

Pick a nonzero reference function $f_0 \in C_+(G)$ and define

$$\ell_g(f) = \frac{(f : g)}{(f_0 : g)} \qquad (4.19.52)$$

We can now complete the proof of Theorem 4.19.1.

Theorem 4.19.10. *There exists a nonzero Haar measure.*

Proof. Since $(f : g) \leq (f : f_0)(f_0 : g)$ and $(f_0 : g) \leq (f_0 : f)(f : g)$, we see

$$\ell_g(f) \subset I_f \equiv [(f_0 : f)^{-1}, (f : f_0)] \qquad (4.19.53)$$

Let $\mathcal{I} = \times_{f \in C_0(G)} I_f$, which is compact by Tychonoff's theorem. Each ℓ_g defines a point in $\mathcal{I}$ by (4.19.53). For each open neighborhood, N of e, let $g_N \in C_+(G)$ have $\mathrm{supp}(g_N) \subset N$. Order the N's by $N_1 \triangleright N_2$ if and only if $N_1 \subset N_2$. $\{\ell_{g_N}\}_N$ is a net in $\mathcal{I}$, so by compactness, it has a limit point $\{\ell(f)\}_{f \in C_+(G)}$ in $\mathcal{I}$.

ℓ clearly obeys (a), (c) of Lemma 4.19.6 and

$$\ell(f_1 + f_2) \leq \ell(f_1) + \ell(f_2) \qquad (4.19.54)$$

By Lemma 4.19.9 and $\ell_g(f_0) = 1$, we have for all ε that

$$\ell(f_1) + \ell(f_2) \le \ell(f_1 + f_2) + \varepsilon \qquad (4.19.55)$$

Thus, ℓ obeys (b) of Lemma 4.19.6, and thus, ℓ defines a Haar measure. $\ell \ne 0$ since $\ell(f_0) = 1$. $\qquad\qquad\qquad\qquad\qquad\qquad\qquad\qquad\qquad\qquad\qquad\square$

Notes and Historical Remarks. Prior to Haar's 1933 work on the construction of invariant measures on general (separable) locally compact groups, invariant measures were constructed on explicit matrix groups. This earlier work was motivated by problems in classical invariant theory and the representation theory of the classical compact continuous groups ($\mathbb{SO}(n)$, $\mathbb{SU}(n)$, $\mathbb{SL}(n)$). In 1897, in order to construct orthogonally invariant polynomials in n real variables by averaging over rotations, Hurwitz [**439**] constructed an integral over $\mathbb{SO}(n)$, the orthogonal matrices on $\mathbb{R}^n$, by an explicit formula in terms of Euler angles. During the next thirty years, in their work on group representations, Schur (starting in [**825**]) and Weyl [**983, 984**] pushed the Hurwitz integral into other contexts. (See the Notes to Sections 6.4, 7.5, and 7.1 of Part 2A, respectively, for capsule biographies of Hurwitz, Schur, and Weyl.)

In modern notation, given any Lie group, G (a C^∞-manifold with a group structure), for any ω_1 in the dual Lie algebra, g^*, that is, the cotangent space at the identity, $e \in G$, there is a unique left-invariant 1-form, $\tilde{\omega}_1$, on G (obtained by using left translation). If $\omega_1, \dots, \omega_m$ is a basis for g^*, $\tilde{\omega}_1 \wedge \cdots \wedge \tilde{\omega}_m$ defines a left-invariant measure on the Lie group; see also Problem 4.

While virtually all groups of interest are either discrete or Lie groups, the existence of an invariant measure on general locally compact groups is of great theoretical interest, but it was regarded as very hard until constructed by Alfred Haar (1885–1933) [**375**] in 1933. Shortly after, von Neumann [**965**] found a simpler proof for the compact case, and in 1935, von Neumann [**967**] and Weil (only reported in his 1940 book [**980**]) proved uniqueness.

Haar's argument is based on the idea we exploit for existence in this section, but he used a diagonalization argument to get a limit and so was restricted to the separable case. By using the axiom of choice (i.e., essentially Tychonoff's theorem), Weil (in the book cited above) found the general argument we give in this section. Cartan [**167**] found a way to combine the Haar idea with a uniqueness argument to get convergence without a subnet and thereby construct an integral without recourse to the axiom of choice.

For textbook discussions of this subject, see Bourbaki [**122**], Dieudonné [**242**], Lang [**545**], Loomis [**602**], Nachbin [**675**], or the notes of Alfsen [**17**] and Pedersen [**710**]. But be wary of subtle errors; for example, in his book,

Nachbin uses $\Delta(xy) = \Delta(x)\Delta(y)$ in his proof of uniqueness, referring back to an argument he gave for this that relied on uniqueness! (We use Δ but avoid the use of $\Delta(xy) = \Delta(x)\Delta(y)$.) And Pedersen has a gap in his presentation of von Neumann's proof since he doesn't state or prove Lemma 4.19.4 but he does use it!

In a general locally compact group, G, there exists (see, e.g., [**545**, Lemma XII.2.1] or Problem 9) H, a subgroup which is open and closed, so that H is σ-compact. Thus, $G = \bigcup_{x \in I} xH$ for a discrete subset $I \subset G$. Haar measure on G is just counting measure on I and Haar measure on H, that is,

$$\mu_G(A) = \sum_{x \in I} \mu_H(x^{-1}A \cap H)$$

Thus, it is easy to go from the σ-compact case we study to the general locally compact case.

Problems

1. If G is a topological group and $(\tau_x f)(y) = f(xy)$, prove that $f \in C_0(G) \Rightarrow \tau_x f \in C_0(G)$.

2. Prove that if μ is a measure obeying (4.19.3) for all Baire A and $x \in G$, then (4.19.1) holds for all $f \in C_0(G)$. (*Hint*: Approximate f by simple functions from below.)

3. Prove that every compact group is unimodular. (*Hint*: What is $\int f(yx^{-1}) \, d\mu(y)$ if $f \equiv 1$?)

4. Let $(a_1, \ldots, a_n)$ be a set of coordinates on a dense open subset of a matrix group, G (i.e., $V \subset \mathbb{R}^n$ is open and $A \colon (a_1, \ldots, a_n) \mapsto G$ maps V bijectively to an open dense subset of G). Let m_b be the left multiplication by b written in coordinates $(a_1, \ldots, a_n)$. Define

$$J_b = \det\left(\frac{[m_b(a)]_i}{\partial a_j}\right) \tag{4.19.56}$$

be the Jacobian of m_b.

(a) Prove that

$$J_{bc}(a) = J_b(m_c(a))J_c(a) \tag{4.19.57}$$

(*Hint*: Chain rule.)

(b) With $e = $ identity, prove that

$$d\mu(a) = \frac{da_1 \ldots da_n}{J_a(e)} \tag{4.19.58}$$

is Haar measure on G.

352 4. Measure Theory

(c) For $\mathbb{GL}(n, \mathbb{R})$ and $\mathbb{GL}(n, \mathbb{C})$, use $\{a_{ij}\}_{1 \leq i,j \leq n}$ as local coordinates (Re a_{ij} and Im a_{ij} in the case of $\mathbb{C}$). Prove that ($2n$ for $\mathbb{C}$)

$$J_A(B) = [\det(A)]^n \tag{4.19.59}$$

for all B and that the same is true for right multiplication so that ($d^2(a_{ij})$) and $|\det(A)|^{2n}$ in the case of $\mathbb{C}$)

$$d\mu(A) = \frac{\prod_{i,j} da_{ij}}{\det(A)^n} \tag{4.19.60}$$

(d) Prove that $\mathbb{GL}(n, \mathbb{R})$ and $\mathbb{GL}(n, \mathbb{C})$ are unimodular.

(e) In $\mathbb{SL}(n, \mathbb{R})$ and $\mathbb{SL}(n, \mathbb{C})$, prove that one can use $\{a_{ij}\}_{1 \leq i,j \leq n; (i,j) \neq (n,n)}$ as local coordinates and that $\prod_{i,j} da_{ij}$ is both left and right Haar measure and that these groups are unimodular.

5. Let $\mathbb{R} \times \mathbb{R}_+$ ($\mathbb{R}_+ = (0, \infty)$) act on $\mathbb{R}$ by

$$T_{a,\lambda}(x) = (a + \lambda x) \tag{4.19.61}$$

(a) Prove that the multiplication law is

$$(a, \lambda)(b, \kappa) = (a + \lambda b, \lambda \kappa) \tag{4.19.62}$$

(b) If $J(\cdot)$ is given by the Jacobian, (4.19.56), of left multiplication, prove that

$$J_{(a,\lambda)}(b, \kappa) = \det \begin{pmatrix} \lambda & 0 \\ 0 & \lambda \end{pmatrix} = \lambda^2 \tag{4.19.63}$$

and if R is the Jacobian of right multiplication, then

$$R_{(b,\kappa)}(a, \lambda) = \det \begin{pmatrix} 1 & b \\ 0 & \kappa \end{pmatrix} = \kappa \tag{4.19.64}$$

(c) For this group, prove that (left) Haar measure is

$$d\mu(a, \lambda) = \frac{da \, d\lambda}{\lambda^2} \tag{4.19.65}$$

(d) Prove that

$$\Delta(a, \lambda) = \lambda \tag{4.19.66}$$

so this group is not unimodular.

(e) Prove right-invariant Haar measure is given by

$$d\rho(a, \lambda) = \frac{da \, d\lambda}{\lambda} \tag{4.19.67}$$

6. Use (4.19.21) to prove that (4.19.22) is right-invariant Haar measure.

7. This problem will prove that for every $f \in C_0(G)$, then for all δ, there exists N, a neighborhood of $e \in G$, so that

$$yx^{-1} \text{ or } x^{-1}y \in N \Rightarrow |f(x) - f(y)| < \delta \qquad (4.19.68)$$

(a) Prove that this uniform continuity implies $\Delta(x)$ given by (4.19.23) is continuous near $x = 0$.

(b) Show continuity of Δ near $x = 0$ implies continuity on G.

(c) Given δ, prove that for each x, there is U_x, an open neighborhood of x, so $y \in U_x \Rightarrow |f(x) - f(y)| < \delta/2$.

(d) For each x, show there is a neighborhood V_x of e and a neighborhood W_x of x so $V_x W_x \cup W_x V_x \subset U_x$. Then there are $x_1, \ldots, x_n$ so that $\text{supp}(f) \subset \bigcup_{j=1}^{n} W_{x_j}$.

(e) Let $N_1 = (\bigcap_{j=1}^{n} V_{x_j}) \cap (\bigcap_{j=1}^{n} x_j^{-1} W_{x_j}) \cap (\bigcap_{j=1}^{n} W_{x_j} x_j^{-1})$ and $N = N_1 \cap N_1^{-1}$. If $x^{-1}y$ or yx^{-1} is in N, prove either $f(x) = f(y) = 0$ or else there is j with both x and y in U_{x_j} so that $|f(x) - f(y)| < \delta$.

8. Provide the details of the proof of Proposition 4.19.8.

9. Let G be a locally compact group and U an open neighborhood of e so that $U^{-1} = U$ and $\overline{U}$ is compact. Let $U_n = \{x_1 \ldots x_n \mid x_j \in U\}$. Let $H = \bigcup_{n=1}^{\infty} U_n$. Prove that U is a σ-compact subgroup of G that is both open and closed and that G/H in the quotient topology is discrete.

Chapter 5

Convexity
and Banach Spaces

We have seen a rabble of functions arise whose only job, it seems, is to look as little as possible like decent and useful functions. No more continuity, or perhaps continuity but no derivatives... Yesterday, if a new function was invented it was to serve some practical end; today they are specially invented only to show up the arguments of our fathers, and they will never have any other use.

—*H. Poincaré* [**733**], as translated in [**512**]

Big Notions and Theorems: Seminorm, Norm, NLS, TVS, Unique TVS of Dimension $\ell < \infty$, Direct Sum, Quotient, Fréchet Derivative, Hölder's Inequality, Minkowski Inequality, Young's Inequality, Convex Set, Convex Function, Jensen Inequality, Relation of Triangle Inequality and Convexity, Gauge of a Convex Absorbing Set, Baire Category Theorem, Baire Generic, Lebesgue Generic, Diophantine Approximation, Principle of Uniform Boundedness, Open Mapping Theorem, Inverse Mapping Theorem, Closed Graph Theorem, Knaster–Kuratowski Fan, Hahn–Banach Theorem, Banach–Mazur Theorem, $\sigma(X, Y)$-Topology, Weak-$*$ Topology, L^p $(0 < p < 1)$, Locally Convex Space, Uniformly Convex Space, Milman–Pettis Theorem, Banach–Alaoglu Theorem, Potential, Equilibrium Measure, Separating Hyperplane Theorem, Hamburger Moment Problem, Stieltjes Moment Problem, Extreme Point, Carathéodory–Minkowski Theorem, Face, Krein–Milman Theorem, Strong Krein–Milman Theorem, Choquet Theory, Contraction Mapping Theorem, Picard Iteration, Gronwall's Method, Inverse Mapping Theorem, Implicit Function Theorem, Markov–Kakutani Theorem, Banach Limit, Brouwer Fixed Point Theorem, Schauder–Tychonoff Fixed Point Theorem, Hilbert Cube, Peano's ODE Theorem, Invariant Subspace, Lomonosov's Theorem, Aronszajn–Smith Theorem

This chapter focuses on two intertwined topics already alluded to in Chapter 3: the theory of Banach spaces, defined but barely studied in that earlier chapter, and the theory of convex sets and functions (the former was defined earlier but convex functions will only be formally defined in Section 5.3).

We start with the finite-dimensional theory and notion of direct sums in Section 5.1. Then we fill in some details of $L^p(X, d\mu)$, quoted but not proven in the last chapter, namely, Minkowski's and Hölder's inequalities. Section 5.2 has short, elegant proofs of both. These are quick, but obscure the fact that, at their hearts, both are statements about convex functions, an issue we turn to in Section 5.3.

The general theory of Banach spaces is the subject of the remaining parts of the chapter, except for three bonus sections with applications of this general theory. Section 5.4 begins with a basic fact that a countable intersection of dense open sets in a complete metric space is dense, and then some deep consequences for Banach spaces. Section 5.5 proves a general result, the Hahn–Banach theorem, about extending linear functionals that implies any NLS has lots of linear functions. By stating it in terms of a convex function rather than norm, we'll have a form that is useful in Sections 5.7, 5.10, and 5.11.

The existence of lots of linear functionals is relevant for the weak topology and, more generally, the discussion of a larger class of topological vector spaces, the locally convex spaces, which are required to have lots of open convex sets. These issues are discussed in Section 5.5 and recur in Section 5.10, where geometric facts about slipping hyperplanes between convex sets are presented. As an application of these notions, Bonus Section 5.8 discusses the issue of for which sequences $\{a_n\}_{n=0}^{\infty}$ there is a measure, $d\mu$, so $a_n = \int_{-\infty}^{\infty} x^n \, d\mu(x)$. This extends to $\mathbb{R}$ the discussion in Section 4.15 for measures on $[0, 1]$.

Having discussed the weak topology, Section 5.8 has the important theorem that the unit ball of the dual of any Banach space is compact in the weak-$*$ topology. An application in Bonus Section 5.9 discusses potential theory and proves the existence of so-called equilibrium measures. Convexity is a critical part of this application. Uniqueness of equilibrium measures is discussed in Section 6.8 (Corollary 6.8.5). Chapter 3 of Part 3 has much more about potential theory.

The geometry of convex sets is the subject of Section 5.11 on extreme points in compact convex sets. As an application, we'll see that neither $L^1([0, 1], dx)$ nor $C([0, 1])$ is the dual space of some NLS. Finally, Section 5.12 explores the specialized question of fixed point theorems.

While we will not discuss the structure of general Banach spaces much, we note that in Problem 14 of Section 5.5, the reader will prove

Theorem 5.0.1 (Banach–Mazur Theorem). *Every separable Banach space is isometric to a closed subspace of $C([0,1])$ in the $\|\cdot\|_\infty$.*

Remarks. 1. This theorem appeared first in Banach–Mazur [**56**].

2. In contradistinction to this, we note that Bessaga [**87**] has proven that no finite-dimensional NLS has the property that every two-dimensional Banach space is isometric to one of its subspaces!

    I should emphasize that virtually all the results of this chapter are pre-1950. This has been an active and vibrant area since then in the hands of (among other) J. Bourgain, T. Gowers, A. Grothendieck, W. Johnson, J. Lindenstrauss, A. Pelczynski, and G. Piser. Much of this involves the zoology of Banach spaces—special classes, their structure, and tools to analyze them. The unifying element is the underlying geometry. Johnson–Lindenstrauss [**453**] is a collection of review articles and [**9, 71, 292**] are three textbooks on advanced aspects of Banach space theory.

5.1. Some Preliminaries

Here we give some general background on Banach spaces and topological vector spaces (defined in Sections 3.1 and 3.3). Part of this section will put in one place definitions given in passing in the chapter on Hilbert space. We'll define the important notion of equivalent norms and prove the result that in the finite-dimensional case, all norms are equivalent—indeed, we'll prove the stronger result that in the finite-dimensional case, there is only one topology making the space into a topological vector space.

    We remind the reader that our vector spaces are over $\mathbb{R}$ or $\mathbb{C}$ and that we use $\mathbb{K}$ to stand for one or the other. A *seminorm* is a nonnegative function, $\|\cdot\|$, on a vector space, V, which is scalar homogeneous (i.e., $\lambda \in \mathbb{K}$, $x \in V \Rightarrow \|\lambda x\| = |\lambda| \|x\|$) and which obeys the triangle inequality ($x, y \in V \Rightarrow \|x + y\| \le \|x\| + \|y\|$). A *norm* also obeys $\|x\| = 0 \Leftrightarrow x = 0$. An NLS (aka *normed linear space*) is a vector space with a norm.

    A *topological vector space* (TVS) is a vector space, V, with a Hausdorff topology in which $(x, y) \mapsto x + y$ from $V \times V \to V$ and $(\lambda, x) \mapsto \lambda x$ from $\mathbb{K} \times X \to X$ are continuous when the product topology is used. Every NLS has a metric, ρ, given by

$$\rho(x, y) = \|x - y\| \tag{5.1.1}$$

and the NLS is a TVS in the *metric topology*. A *Banach space* is an NLS which is complete in the metric topology.

As proven in Theorem 3.3.1, a linear map between NLS over the same $\mathbb{K}$, $T: (X, \|\cdot\|_X) \to (Y, \|\cdot\|_Y)$ is continuous if and only if for some C, we have

$$\|Tx\|_Y \leq C\|x\|_X \tag{5.1.2}$$

for all $x \in X$. The smallest such constant C is given by

$$\|T\| = \sup_{x \neq 0} \frac{\|Tx\|_Y}{\|x\|_X} = \sup_{\|x\|_X = 1} \|Tx\|_Y \tag{5.1.3}$$

Maps obeying (5.1.2) are called BLTs (aka *bounded linear transformations*) and the set of all such maps is denoted $\mathrm{BLT}(X, Y)$. $\|\cdot\|$, given by (5.1.3), is a norm on $\mathrm{BLT}(X, Y)$, and if Y is a Banach space, so is $\mathrm{BLT}(X, Y)$. If $\widetilde{X}$ is the completion of X, any $T \in \mathrm{BLT}(X, Y)$ has a unique extension to $\widetilde{T} \in \mathrm{BLT}(\widetilde{X}, Y)$ so that under restriction, $\mathrm{BLT}(\widetilde{X}, Y) \cong \mathrm{BLT}(X, Y)$.

If $Y = \mathbb{K}$, $\mathrm{BLT}(X, \mathbb{K})$ is called the *dual space* of X, denoted X^*. It is always a Banach space. As above, $\widetilde{X}^* \cong X^*$. We will often write $\mathcal{L}(X)$ for $\mathrm{BLT}(X, X)$.

If $\|\cdot\|_1$ and $\|\cdot\|_2$ are two norms on a vector space, V, they generate the same norm topology if and only if $T: (X, \|\cdot\|_1) \to (X, \|\cdot\|_2)$ by $Tx = x$ is continuous with continuous inverse. By Theorem 3.3.1, this happens if and only if for $c_1, c_2 \in (0, \infty)$ and all $x \in X$, we have

$$c_1\|x\|_2 \leq \|x\|_1 \leq c_2\|x\|_2 \tag{5.1.4}$$

If that happens, we say $\|\cdot\|_1$ and $\|\cdot\|_2$ are *equivalent norms*. We have thus proven

Theorem 5.1.1. *Two norms on a vector space, X, generate the same metric topology if and only if the norms are equivalent.*

Notice that, as the name implies, equivalent norms is an equivalence relation. We are heading towards a proof that all norms on a finite-dimensional space are equivalent. We do this by an approach that also says something about topologies making a finite-dimensional space into a TVS. If X is a finite-dimensional space, there is a finite basis $\{x_j\}_{j=1}^d$ so $T: \mathbb{K}^d \to X$ by

$$T(\alpha_1, \ldots, \alpha_d) = \sum_{j=1}^d \alpha_j x_j \tag{5.1.5}$$

is a bijection. Moreover, by the continuity of scalar multiplication and of addition, if X is given a topology, τ, turning it into a TVS, T is continuous when X is given the τ-topology and $\mathbb{K}^d$ the product topology. The following is the key to the finite-dimensional results.

Proposition 5.1.2. *Let X be a finite-dimensional TVS with topology, τ, and basis $\{x_j\}_{j=1}^d$. Then*

$$S = \left\{ \sum_{j=1}^d \alpha_j x_j \;\middle|\; \sum_{j=1}^d |\alpha_j|^2 = 1 \right\} \tag{5.1.6}$$

is compact in the τ-topology.

Proof. Let $\widetilde{S} = \{\{\alpha\} \in \mathbb{K}^d \mid \sum_{j=1}^d |\alpha_j|^2 = 1\}$. Then $\widetilde{S}$ is compact in the product topology on $\mathbb{K}^d$. Since T is a continuous bijection, $S = T[\widetilde{S}]$ is compact by Theorem 2.3.11. $\qquad\square$

Theorem 5.1.3. *All norms on a finite-dimensional vector space, X, are equivalent.*

Proof. Let $\|\cdot\|_1$ be some norm and $\|\cdot\|_2$ the Euclidean norm in some basis $\{x_j\}_{j=1}^d$ for X (i.e., in the inner product making this basis orthonormal). Since, by the triangle inequality, $\|\cdot\|_1$ is continuous in the topology, τ, defined by $\|\cdot\|_1$ and the set S of (5.1.6) is τ-compact, there are points $y_1, y_2 \in S$ so $\|y_1\|_1 = c_1 \equiv \inf_{y \in S} \|y\|_1$ and $\|y_2\|_1 = c_2 \equiv \sup_{y \in S} \|y\|_1$. In particular, $0 < c_1 \leq c_2 < \infty$.

Thus since, $y/\|y\|_2 \in S$ for any $y \neq 0$, we have (5.1.4). Therefore, any norm is equivalent to $\|\cdot\|_2$, so by the fact that equivalent norms is an equivalence relation, all norms are equivalent. $\qquad\square$

Theorem 5.1.4. *Let X be a finite-dimensional vector space. Let τ_1 be the topology generated by the Euclidean norm in some basis $\{x_j\}_{j=1}^d$. Let τ_2 be a topology in which X is a TVS. Then $\tau_2 = \tau_1$.*

Remark. See Problem 10 for another proof.

Proof. That the map T of (5.1.5) is continuous says that every τ_2-open set is τ_1-open. Let $B = \{\sum_{j=1}^{\infty} \alpha_j x_j \mid \sum_{j=1}^d |\alpha_j|^2 < 1\}$. If we show B is τ_2-open, then it is easy to see that every τ_1-open set is τ_2-open (Problem 1(a)). If we show B is a τ_2-neighborhood of 0, it is easy to see that B is τ_2-open (Problem 1(b)). Thus, we need to show that B is a τ_2-neighborhood of 0.

Since S is τ_2-closed, $X \setminus S \equiv Q$ is τ_2-open. Since $(\alpha, x) \overset{G}{\mapsto} \alpha x$ is τ_2-continuous and $G(0,0) = 0 \in Q$, there are $N_1 = \{\alpha \mid |\alpha| < r\} \subset \mathbb{K}$ and N_2 a τ_2-open neighborhood of 0 so that $N_1 \times N_2 \subset G^{-1}[Q]$, that is, $|\alpha| < r$ and $x \in N_2 \Rightarrow \alpha x \in Q$. This implies $\frac{r}{2} x \in B$ since $\beta \frac{r}{2} x \in Q$ for all $\beta \in [0, 1]$. Thus, $\frac{r}{2} N_2 \subset B$. Since $\frac{r}{2} N_2$ is τ_2-open (by continuity of multiplication by $\frac{2}{r}$), B is a τ_2-neighborhood of 0. $\qquad\square$

Corollary 5.1.5. *Every finite-dimensional subspace, E, of a TVS, X, is closed.*

Proof. Let $\{x_j\}_{j=1}^d$ be a basis for E. Suppose $\{y_\alpha\}_{\alpha \in I}$ is a net in E so $y_\alpha \to y_\infty$ in X. Let $\widetilde{E}$ be the space generated by $\{x_j\}_{j=1}^d \cup \{y_\infty\}$. Then $y_\alpha \to y_\infty$ in the relative topology on $\widetilde{E}$. In this topology, $\widetilde{E}$ is isomorphic to $\mathbb{K}^{\tilde{d}}$ for $\tilde{d} = \dim(\widetilde{E}) = d + 1$ or d. Since every subspace of $\mathbb{K}^{\tilde{d}}$ is closed, E is closed in $\widetilde{E}$, so $y_\infty \in E$.   □

While on the subject of finite-dimensional Banach spaces, let us prove that any locally compact NLS is finite-dimensional. The key is

Lemma 5.1.6 (Riesz's Geometric Lemma). *Let Y be a closed, proper subspace of an NLS, X. Then for any $\varepsilon > 0$, there exists $x \in X$ with*

$$\|x\| = 1, \qquad \text{dist}(x, Y) \geq (1 - \varepsilon) \tag{5.1.7}$$

Remarks. 1. In case X is finite-dimensional, one can take (Problem 7) $\varepsilon = 0$, but not, in general, in infinite dimension.

2. Problem 8 has a proof using quotient spaces.

Proof. Pick $x_0 \in X \setminus Y$. Pick $y_0 \in Y$ so

$$\|x_0 - y_0\| \leq (1 - \varepsilon)^{-1} \min_{y \in Y} \|x_0 - y\| \tag{5.1.8}$$

Let $x = (x_0 - y_0)/\|x_0 - y_0\|$ so $\|x\| = 1$. For any $y_1 \in Y$, let $y_2 = y_0 + \|x_0 - y_0\| y_1$. Then by (5.1.8),

$$\|x - y_1\| = \frac{\|x_0 - y_2\|}{\|x_0 - y_0\|} \geq \frac{\min_{y \in Y} \|x_0 - y\|}{\|x_0 - y_0\|} \geq 1 - \varepsilon \tag{5.1.9}$$

proving (5.1.8).   □

Theorem 5.1.7. *Let X be an NLS. Suppose $\{x \mid \|x\| \leq 1\}$ is compact. Then $\dim(X) < \infty$. In particular, an infinite-dimensional X is not locally compact.*

Remark. See Problem 11 for an alternate proof that handles TVS.

Proof. If $\dim(X) = \infty$, pick $Y_1 \subset Y_2 \subset \ldots$, with $\dim(Y_\ell) = \ell$. By Corollary 5.1.5, each Y_ℓ is closed. By the lemma, pick $y_\ell \in Y_\ell$, so $\|y_\ell\| = 1$ and $\text{dist}(y_\ell, Y_{\ell-1}) \geq \frac{1}{2}$. Then $\{y_\ell\}_{\ell=1}^\infty$ is a sequence in $\{x \mid \|x\| \leq 1\}$ by $\|y_\ell - y_j\| \geq \frac{1}{2}$ for all $j \neq \ell$. Thus, there is no convergent subsequence.

If X were locally compact, 0 would have a compact neighborhood, N. For some ε, $\{x \mid \|x\| \leq \varepsilon\}$ is a closed subset of N, so compact. But then, the unit ball is compact since multiplication by ε^{-1} is continuous.   □

Next, we turn to direct sums and quotients. Let $X_1, \ldots, X_\ell$ be NLS with norms $\|\cdot\|_1, \ldots, \|\cdot\|_\ell$. Let $X = X_1 \times \cdots \times X_\ell$ be the Cartesian product, which is a vector space under coordinate operators and clearly a TVS under the product topology. If we put the norm on X,

$$\|(x_1, \ldots, x_\ell)\| = \sum_{j=1}^{\ell} \|x_j\|_j \qquad (5.1.10)$$

it is easy to see this is a norm whose topology is the product topology (Problem 2). X with this norm is called the *direct sum* of $X_1, \ldots, X_\ell$, written $X_1 \oplus \cdots \oplus X_\ell$. If each X_j is a Banach space, so is $X_1 \oplus \cdots \oplus X_\ell$, since a Cauchy sequence $\{(x_1^{(n)}, \ldots, x_\ell^{(n)})\}$ has each $x_j^{(n)}$ Cauchy.

If the X_j are all Hilbert spaces, one normally uses the equivalent norm

$$\|(x_1, \ldots, x_\ell)\|_2 = \left(\sum_{j=1}^{\ell} \|x_j\|^2 \right)^{1/2} \qquad (5.1.11)$$

associated to the inner product

$$\langle (x_1, \ldots, x_\ell), (y_1, \ldots, y_\ell) \rangle = \sum_{j=1}^{\ell} \langle x_j, y_j \rangle \qquad (5.1.12)$$

If X is an NLS and $Y \subset X$ a subspace, then the *quotient space*, X/Y (equivalence classes with $x \sim z \Leftrightarrow x - z \in Y$), has a seminorm

$$\|[x]\|^\sim = \inf\{\|z\| \mid z \sim x\} \qquad (5.1.13)$$

It is easy to see (Problem 4) $\|[x]\|^\sim = 0$ if and only if $x \in \overline{Y}$, so $\|[x]\|^\sim$ is a norm if and only if Y is closed. In that case, X/Y is called the *quotient NLS* and $\|\cdot\|^\sim$ the *quotient norm*. If X is a Banach space, so is X/Y for any closed Y (Problem 5). If X_1 and X_2 are two NLS, then X_2 is closed in $X_1 \oplus X_2$ and $X_1 \oplus X_2/X_2$ is naturally isomorphic to X_1 (Problem 6).

We want to discuss the relation of quotients, dual spaces, and annihilators, where if $Y \subset X$ with X a normed linear space we define $Y^\perp$, the *annihilator* of Y, by

$$Y^\perp = \{\ell \in X^* \mid \ell(y) = 0 \text{ for all } y \in Y\} \qquad (5.1.14)$$

We will need one result, a form of the Hahn–Banach theorem, only proved later (see Corollary 5.5.2 and Theorem 5.5.5): given $Y \subset X$ with X a real or complex normed linear space and $\ell \in Y^*$, there is $L \in X^*$ so $L \restriction Y = \ell$ and $\|L\| = \|\ell\|$.

Theorem 5.1.8. *Let X be a Banach space and $Y \subset X$ a closed subspace. Then,*

$$(X/Y)^* \cong Y^\perp, \quad Y^* \cong X^*/Y^\perp \qquad (5.1.15)$$

as isometric isomorphisms in the following sense: for $\ell \in Y^\perp$ define $\varphi(\ell)$ on X/Y by

$$\varphi(\ell)([x]) = \ell(x) \tag{5.1.16}$$

Then φ is a well-defined isometric isomorphism of $Y^\perp$ and $(X/Y)^*$.

For $[L] \in X^*/Y^\perp$, define $\psi(L) \in Y^*$ by

$$\psi([L]) = L \upharpoonright Y \tag{5.1.17}$$

Then ψ is well-defined and ψ is an isometric isomorphism of $X^*/Y^\perp$ and Y^*.

Remark. Corollary 5.5.11 has further important results about annihilators.

Proof. If $\ell \in Y^\perp$, then $\ell(x) = \ell(x')$ if $[x] = [x']$ so φ is well-defined from $Y^\perp$ to functionals on X/Y. Since

$$|\varphi(\ell)([x])| \leq \|\ell\|\,\|x\| \tag{5.1.18}$$

for all x, we see $\varphi(\ell) \in (X/Y)^*$, i.e.,

$$\|\varphi(\ell)\|_{(X/Y)^*} \leq \|\ell\|_{Y^*} \tag{5.1.19}$$

On the other hand,

$$|\ell(x)| = |\varphi(\ell)([x])| \leq \|\varphi(\ell)\|\,\|[x]\|$$
$$\leq \|\varphi(\ell)\|\,\|x\| \tag{5.1.20}$$

so

$$\|\ell\|_{Y^*} \leq \|\varphi(\ell)\|_{(X/Y)^*} \tag{5.1.21}$$

proving φ is an isometry. If $L \in (X/Y)^*$, $\ell(x) = L([x])$ defines an element of $Y^\perp$, so φ is onto $(X/Y)^*$.

If $\ell \in Y^\perp$, $(L + \ell) \upharpoonright Y = L \upharpoonright Y$, so ψ is well-defined. By calculations similar to the above, one can show that

$$\|\psi([L])\| \leq \|[L]\| \tag{5.1.22}$$

On the other hand, given $\ell \in Y^*$, there is by the Hahn–Banach result quoted above, $L \in X^*$ with $\|L\| = \|\ell\|$ and $L \upharpoonright Y = \ell$. Thus, $\psi([L]) = \ell$ and

$$\|\psi([L])\| = \|L\| \geq \|[L]\| \tag{5.1.23}$$

proving ψ is onto and an isometry. $\square$

Given a closed subspace Y in X, it is natural to ask when is there another closed subspace, Z, so that if $\pi : X \to X/Y$ is the canonical map $\pi(x) = [x]$, then $\pi \upharpoonright Z$ is a bijection. If there is, one can show (using the inverse mapping theorem, Theorem 5.4.14) that X with its norm is equivalent to $Y \oplus Z$ (and conversely). This is equivalent (if Z is closed) to $Y + Z = X$ and $Y \cap Z = \{0\}$. It is also equivalent to there existing a bounded linear transformation, P, from X to itself with $P^2 = P$ and $\operatorname{Ran} P = Y$. Such projections are studied in Section 2.1 of Part 4. If such a Z exists, we say Y is *complemented*. If no such Z exists, it is *uncomplemented*. All closed subspaces of a Hilbert space are complemented as are all finite-dimensional Y and all finite codimensional Y (i.e., X/Y is finite-dimensional). Problems 7–9 of Section 2.1 of Part 4 provide examples of uncomplemented subspaces.

A subset, T of a Banach space, X, is called *total* if the finite linear combinations of elements of T are dense in X.

A function $f\colon U \to Y$, where $U \subset X$, X and Y are Banach spaces, and U is open, is called *differentiable* (or *Fréchet differentiable*) at $x_0 \in U$ if there is a linear mapping $Df_{x_0}\colon X \to Y$ so that

$$\|f(x_0 + z) - f(x_0) - Df_{x_0}(z)\|_Y = o(\|z\|_X) \qquad (5.1.24)$$

Df_{x_0} is called the *derivative* or *Fréchet derivative*.

If $X = X_1 \oplus X_2$ and f as above is differentiable at $x_0 = (x_0^{(1)}, x_0^{(2)}) \in U$, then there are linear maps $D^{(j)}f_{x_0}\colon X_j \to Y$ for $j = 1, 2$ so that

$$Df_{x_0}(z_1, z_2) = D^{(1)}f_{x_0}(z_1) + D^{(2)}f_{x_0}(z_2) \qquad (5.1.25)$$

We'll sometimes call $D^{(j)}f_{x_0}$ the *partial derivative*.

Finally, we want to note that any real Banach space, X, can be complexified, that is, we can find a complex Banach space, $X_{\mathbb{C}}$, with X as a real subspace (i.e., subspace if we think of $X_{\mathbb{C}}$ as a real vector space), so that if $x \in X$, $\|x\|_{\mathbb{C}} = \|x\|$, and so that $X_{\mathbb{C}} = X + iX$ and $\|x + iy\|_{\mathbb{C}} = \|x - iy\|_{\mathbb{C}}$. Explicitly, take the algebraic direct sum $X \oplus X = \{(x, y) \mid x, y \in X\}$ and write (x, y) as $x + iy$. Do *not* put the standard direct sum norm on, but instead

$$\|x + iy\|_{\mathbb{C}} = \sup_{0 \le s \le 2\pi} \|x \cos s + y \sin s\| \qquad (5.1.26)$$

It is not hard to see (Problem 9) that this makes $X_{\mathbb{C}}$ into a Banach space obeying

$$\|x\|_{\mathbb{C}} = \|x\|, \qquad \|x + iy\|_{\mathbb{C}} = \|x - iy\|_{\mathbb{C}} \qquad (5.1.27)$$

Notes and Historical Remarks.

> It is my aim to show the dominating role of Stefan Banach, who is the father of the theory of complete normed linear spaces, which now bear his name with full right. But at the same time, I refer to Frigyes Riesz as the grandfather and to Eduard Helly as the (sometimes underestimated) godfather.
>
> —A. Pietsch [**727**]

The term Banach space goes back to Fréchet's 1928 book [**322**] which coined the term Espace de Banach. It is an homage to Stefan Banach who introduced an axiom scheme for them in his 1920 thesis [**49**] published in

1922 and who wrote the first comprehensive book [**55**]. As we will see, he had many fundamental results in the general theory for the abstract spaces.

Given Riesz's work around 1910 on concrete Banach spaces and the basic metric space notions of Fréchet (1906) and Hausdorff (1914), it is surprising that the abstraction took so long. In fact, there were some earlier partial definitions by Bennett [**68**] and Lamson [**541**] and approximately simultaneous papers by Hahn [**383**], Helly [**413**], and Wiener [**993**], but Banach was more extensive and only he developed a comprehensive theory.

Stefan Banach (1892–1945) was a Polish mathematician and founder of a flourishing school of Polish functional analysis. His parents weren't married and he had the last name of his mother who disappeared shortly after his birth. He was raised first by his paternal grandparents and then by friends of his father. Largely self-taught in basic mathematics and without a college degree, his life took a dramatic turn in 1916. Hugo Steinhaus (1887–1972), already established, was strolling in Cracow when he overheard the words "Lebesgue measure." He stopped to meet the young Banach and his friend, Otto Nikodym (1887–1974). Steinhaus became Banach's mentor and eventual collaborator in research and in the founding of the journal *Studia Mathematica*. Stienhaus took Banach to Lwów when he took up a position and, despite Banach's lack of a first degree, arranged for him to submit a thesis and get a second degree.

Banach stayed in Lwów and became a professor. He and Steinhaus were the center of what came to be called the Lwów School of Mathematics, which included Kac, Mazur, Orlicz, Saks, Schauder, and Ulam. Banach died at the end of the Second World War due to health problems exacerbated by his treatment during the Nazi occupation.

Riesz's geometric lemma was proven by him [**783**] as part of his analysis of compact operators on $C([a, b])$; we'll discuss this further in Section 3.3 of Part 4.

Theorem 5.1.7 has the following extension (see Problem 11):

Theorem 5.1.9. *If X is a TVS and $\emptyset \neq U \subset K \subset C$ with U open and K compact, then* $\dim(X) < \infty$.

TVS were defined by Kolmogorov [**508**] and von Neumann [**966**] about 1935.

The Fréchet derivative, Df_{x_0}, is to be distinguished from the *Gateaux derivative* or directional derivative

$$\mathcal{D}f_{x_0}(z) = \lim_{t\downarrow 0} \frac{[f(x_0 + tz) - f(x_0)]}{t} \tag{5.1.28}$$

Clearly, f Fréchet differentiable $\Rightarrow f$ Gateaux differentiable with

$$\mathcal{D}f_{x_0}(z) = Df_{x_0}(z) \qquad (5.1.29)$$

but as is true even if $\dim(X) = 1$, if f is only Gateaux differentiable, $\mathcal{D}f_{x_0}(z)$ need not be linear in z (consider $f(x) = |x|$ on $\mathbb{R}$); and even if it is linear in z, f need not be Fréchet differentiable at x_0.

The Fréchet derivative was introduced by Fréchet [**317**] in the infinite-dimensional case. He thought his definition was new even if $\dim(X) < \infty$ but, in a note added in proof, pointed out that W. H. Young [**1008**] had the definition earlier. In fact, Weierstrass had used a similar idea on $\mathbb{R}^\nu$. The Gateaux derivative is named after his 1913 paper [**340**] that introduced it.

Complexification with a norm equivalent to (5.1.26) is due to Michal–Wyman [**654**]. For forty years, there was an open question if any complex Banach space was a complexification of a real Banach space with norm obeying (5.1.27). In 1986, Bourgain [**123**] found a counterexample; see also Kalton [**475**].

Problems

1. (a) Let B be the open unit ball in Euclidean norm in the coordinates defined by a basis of a finite-dimensional space, X. Let τ_1 be the norm topology in which this is the unit ball and τ_2 a TVS topology. Prove that if B is open in the τ_2-topology, then every τ_1-open set is open in the τ_2-topology. (*Hint*: Scaling plus basis.)

   (b) Prove that if B is an open τ_2-neighborhood of 0, then B is open in the τ_1-topology. (*Hint*: If $0 \in U \subset B$, then for any $x \in B$, $x + (1 - \|x\|_2)U \subset B$.)

2. Prove convergence in the norm (5.1.10) is equivalent to coordinate-wise convergence.

3. Let η be a norm on $\mathbb{K}^\ell$ with $\eta(\alpha_1 x_1, \ldots, \alpha_\ell x_\ell) = \eta(x_1, \ldots, x_\ell)$ if $|\alpha_j| = 1$. Define $\|\cdot\|_\eta$ on $X_1 \times \cdots \times X_\ell$ by

   $$\|(x_1, \ldots, x_\ell)\|_\eta = \eta(\|x_1\|_1, \ldots, \|x_\ell\|_\ell)$$

   Prove $\|\cdot\|_\eta$ is a norm and is equivalent to the norm of (5.1.10).

   Remark. In particular, one can take $\eta(\alpha_1, \ldots, \eta_\ell) = (\sum_{j=1}^\ell |\alpha_j|^p)^{1/p}$ for $1 \le p < \infty$.

4. With the definition (5.1.12), prove that $\|[x]\|^\sim = 0 \Leftrightarrow x \in \overline{Y}$.

5. Prove that the quotient space of any Banach space by a closed subspace is a Banach space in the quotient norm. (*Hint*: First show that an NLS, X, is complete if and only if $\left(\sum_{n=1}^\infty \|x_n\| < \infty \Rightarrow \sum_{n=1}^N x_n \text{ converges}\right)$ for

any sequence $\{x_n\}_{n=1}^\infty \subset X$. For such a sequence $\{[x_n]\}_{n=1}^\infty$ in X/Y, pick $y_n \sim x_n$ so that $\|y_n\| \leq \|[x_n]\|^\sim + 2^{-n}$ and use the above completeness result.)

6. Prove that $X_1 \oplus X_2/X_2$ is isomorphic to X_1.

7. If $\|\cdot\|$ is a norm on $\mathbb{C}^n$ and Y is a closed subspace, prove there is $x \in \mathbb{C}^n$, $\|x\| = 1$, and $\operatorname{dist}(x, Y) = 1$. (*Hint*: Compactness plus the Riesz lemma.)

8. Phrase our proof of the Riesz lemma in the language of the quotient space X/Y.

9. Prove that $X_\mathbb{C}$ with the norm (5.1.27) and complex multiplication $(re^{i\theta})(x + iy) = (r\cos\theta)x - (r\sin\theta)y + i((r\cos\theta)y + (r\sin\theta)x)$ makes $X_\mathbb{C}$ into a complex Banach space obeying (5.1.27).

10. This will provide an alternate proof of Theorem 5.1.4. So let X be a finite-dimensional TVS, $\{e_j\}_{j=1}^n$ a basis, $f \colon \mathbb{K}^\nu \to X$ by $f(\lambda_1, \dots, \lambda_n) = \sum_{j=1}^n \lambda_j e_j$, and g its inverse. Let $\|\cdot\|$ be the Euclidean norm on $\mathbb{K}^\nu$.

    (a) Prove that f is continuous.

    (b) Suppose $\{x_\alpha\}_{\alpha \in I}$ is a net in X so that in the topology of X, x_α has a limit. Show that to prove $g(x_\alpha) \to g(x_\infty)$, you can suppose $x_\infty = e_1$.

    (c) Suppose $\|g(x_\alpha)\|$ is unbounded. Prove you can find a subnet y_β so $\|g(y_\beta)\| \geq 2$ and $y_\beta \to e_1$ and $\|g(y_\beta)\|^{-1} \to \mu \leq \frac{1}{2}$.

    (d) Let $z_\beta = y_\beta/\|g(y_\beta)\|$. Prove that by passing to a further subnet, you can suppose $g(z_\beta) \to z_\infty \in \mathbb{K}^\nu$ with $\|z_\infty\| = 1$.

    (e) Prove $f(z_\infty) = \mu e_1$ so $z_\infty = (\mu, 0, \dots)$, contradicting $\|z_\infty\| = 1$. Conclude $\|g(z_j)\|$ is bounded.

    (f) Let λ_∞ be a limit point of $g(x_\alpha)$. Prove $f(\lambda_\infty) = e_1$ so $\lambda_\infty = (1, 0, \dots, 0)$.

    (g) Using compactness of balls in $\mathbb{K}^\nu$, prove that $g(x_\alpha) \to (1, 0, \dots)$ so g is continuous.

11. This will prove Theorem 5.1.9. So suppose X is a TVS with $\emptyset \neq U \subset K \subset X$ with U open, $0 \in U$, and K compact.

    (a) Prove that there exist $\{x_j\}_{j=1}^k \subset X$ so $K \subset \cup_{j=1}^k (x_j + \frac{1}{2}U)$.

    (b) Let $Y \subset X$ be the subspace spanned by $\{x_j\}_{j=1}^k$. Prove $U \subset Y + \frac{1}{2}U$ and then that $U \subset Y + \frac{1}{2^n}U$.

    (c) If z_α is a net in K and $n(\alpha) \in \mathbb{N}$ so $n(\alpha) \to \infty$, prove that $2^{-n(\alpha)}z_\alpha \to 0$.

(d) If $u \in U$, prove that there is a net $y_\alpha \in Y$ and $u_\alpha \in \cup_{0 \le \lambda \le 1} \lambda K$ so $u = y_\alpha + u_\alpha$ with $u_\alpha \to 0$. Conclude $U \subset \overline{Y} = Y$.

(e) Prove that $X = Y$ so $\dim(X) \le k$.

12. This problem will prove an analog of the Dirichlet–Heine theorem (Theorem 2.3.10), namely, if K is a compact subset of a topological vector space, X, and a continuous function $f \colon K \to Y$, a metric space (with metric, ρ), then for any ε, there is a neighborhood, U, of 0 so that $x, y \in K$ and $x - y \in U \Rightarrow \rho(f(x), f(y)) < \varepsilon$. This is called *uniform continuity*.

(a) Prove there exist neighborhoods $U_1, \ldots, U_n$ of 0, $V_1, \ldots, V_n$ of 0 with $V_j = -V_j$ and $V_j + V_j \subset U_j$, and $x_1, \ldots, x_n$ in K so that $\bigcup_{i=1}^{n}(x_i + V_i)$ cover K and $y \in x_i + U_i \Rightarrow \rho(f(x_i), f(y)) < \varepsilon/2$.

(b) Show $U = \bigcap_{i=1}^{n} V_j$ has the required property.

Remark. The natural framework for this are *uniform spaces*, topological spaces, X, with a family $\mathcal{U}$ of subsets of $X \times X$ obeying:
 (i) $\forall U \in \mathcal{U}$, $\Delta \equiv \{(x, x)\} \subset U$
 (ii) $U \in \mathcal{U}$ and $U \subset V \Rightarrow V \in \mathcal{U}$
 (iii) $U, V \in \mathcal{U} \Rightarrow U \cap V \in \mathcal{U}$
 (iv) $\forall U \in \mathcal{U}$, $\exists V \in \mathcal{U}$ so that $(x, y), (y, z) \in V \Rightarrow (x, z) \in \mathcal{U}$
 (v) $U \in \mathcal{U} \Rightarrow U^{-1} \equiv \{(x, y) \mid (y, x) \in U\} \in \mathcal{U}$
 (vi) $\forall x \in X$, $\{U(x) \equiv \{y \mid (x, y) \in U\}\}$ is a neighborhood base for x.

The canonical examples are $U = \{(x, y) \mid \rho(x, y) < \varepsilon\}$ and all supersets for a metric space and $U = \{x^{-1}y \in V\}$, V a neighborhood of the identity in a topological group. For more on uniform spaces, see Kelley [**484**, Ch. 6], Willard [**1004**, Ch. 9], or James [**449**]. The notion is due to Weil [**980**]. In particular, the argument in this problem extends to topological groups.

5.2. Hölder's and Minkowski's Inequalities: A Lightning Look

In this section, we'll first prove Hölder's and then Minkowski's inequality. The key will be:

Theorem 5.2.1 (Young's Inequality). *Let $1 < p, q < \infty$ with*

$$\frac{1}{p} + \frac{1}{q} = 1 \tag{5.2.1}$$

Then for all $x, y \ge 0$,

$$xy \le \frac{x^p}{p} + \frac{y^q}{q} \tag{5.2.2}$$

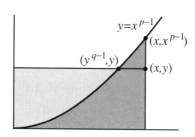

Figure 5.2.1. Geometric proof of Young's inequality.

Proof. (5.2.1) is equivalent to

$$(p-1)(q-1) = 1 \tag{5.2.3}$$

so the following curves are the same (for $x, y \geq 0$):

$$y = x^{p-1}, \qquad x = y^{q-1} \tag{5.2.4}$$

Suppose first $y \leq x^{p-1}$. The rectangle with corners (x, y) and $(0, 0)$ is broken by the curve (5.2.4) into two pieces (see Figure 5.2.1). One is exactly the area between the curve and the y-axis as cut by a line $y =$ constant. The other is less than the area under the curve up to the x-axis and a line $x =$ constant.

The areas in question are $\int_0^y y^{q-1}\, dy = \frac{y^q}{q}$ and $\int_0^x x^{p-1}\, dx = \frac{x^p}{p}$. Thus, (5.2.2) is geometrically obvious. If $x \leq y^{q-1}$, the argument is very similar. $\qquad\square$

Theorem 5.2.2 (Hölder's Inequality). *Let $1 \leq p, q, r \leq \infty$ with*

$$\frac{1}{p} + \frac{1}{q} = \frac{1}{r} \tag{5.2.5}$$

Let μ be a Baire measure on a locally compact, σ-compact space, X (see Section 4.10). If $f \in L^p(X, d\mu)$, $g \in L^q(X, d\mu)$, then $fg \in L^r(X, d\mu)$ and

$$\|fg\|_r \leq \|f\|_p \|g\|_q \tag{5.2.6}$$

Proof. $p = q = r = \infty$ is obvious, so we can suppose that $r < \infty$. By letting

$$\tilde{f} = \frac{|f|^r}{\|f\|_p^r}, \qquad \tilde{g} = \frac{|g|^r}{\|g\|_q^r}$$

$\tilde{p} = \frac{p}{r}$, $\tilde{q} = \frac{q}{r}$, so $\|\tilde{f}\|_{\tilde{p}} = \|\tilde{g}\|_{\tilde{q}} = 1$ and $\frac{1}{\tilde{p}} + \frac{1}{\tilde{q}} = 1$, we are reduced to the special case where

$$\|f\|_p = \|g\|_q = 1, \qquad \frac{1}{p} + \frac{1}{q} = 1 \tag{5.2.7}$$

By Theorem 5.2.1, for all x,

$$|f(x)g(x)| \leq \frac{|f(x)|^p}{p} + \frac{|g(x)|^q}{q} \tag{5.2.8}$$

Integrating this shows $fg \in L^1$ and $\|fg\|_1 \leq 1$. $\qquad\square$

Theorem 5.2.3. *Let μ be a Baire measure on a locally compact, σ-compact space, X. Let $\mathcal{B}$ be the set of bounded measurable functions which vanish off some compact G_δ set, A. Then for $1 < p < \infty$ and $q = \frac{p}{p-1}$,*

$$\|f\|_p = \sup_g \left\{ \left| \int fg \, d\mu \right| \, \middle| \, g \in \mathcal{B}, \|g\|_q = 1 \right\} \tag{5.2.9}$$

with the interpretation $\|f\|_p = \infty$ if $f \notin L^p$.

Proof. By Hölder's inequality (noting if $f \notin L^p$, (5.2.10) is immediate),

$$\text{RHS of (5.2.9)} \leq \|f\|_p \tag{5.2.10}$$

Fix a compact set A with

$$\mu(\{x \mid x \in A, \, f(x) \neq 0\}) > 0 \tag{5.2.11}$$

and $M < \infty$. Define

$$g(x) = \begin{cases} 0 & \text{if } f(x) = 0 \text{ or } x \notin A \\ c\,\overline{f(x)}\,|f(x)|^{p-2}, & \text{otherwise and } |f(x)| \leq M \\ c\,M^p\,\dfrac{f(x)}{|f(x)|} & \text{if } x \in A \text{ and } |f(x)| \geq M \end{cases} \tag{5.2.12}$$

where

$$c = \left(\int_{x \in A} |\min(M, |f(x)|)|^p \, d\mu \right)^{-1/q} \tag{5.2.13}$$

c is chosen to arrange

$$\int |g(x)|^q \, d\mu = 1 \tag{5.2.14}$$

since $(p-1)q = p$, so $g \in \mathcal{B}$ with $\|g\|_q = 1$. Moreover,

$$\int f(x)g(x) \, d\mu \geq c \int_A |\min(M, |f(x)|)|^p \, d\mu = \left(\int_A |\min(M, |f(x)|)|^p \, d\mu \right)^{1/p}$$

Taking $M \to \infty$ using the monotone convergence theorem shows

$$\text{RHS of (5.2.9)} \geq \left(\int |\chi_A f|^p \, d\mu \right)^{1/p} \tag{5.2.15}$$

Picking compacts A_n so $A_n \subset A_{n+1} \subset \ldots$ and $\cup A_n = X$, we use monotone convergence again to get

$$\text{RHS of (5.2.9)} \geq \|f\|_p \tag{5.2.16}$$

This and (5.2.10) prove (5.2.9). $\qquad\square$

As an immediate consequence, we get

Theorem 5.2.4 (Minkowski's Inequality). *Let* $1 \leq p \leq \infty$. *If* $f, g \in L^p(X, d\mu)$, *so is* $f + g$, *and*

$$\|f + g\|_p \leq \|f\|_p + \|g\|_p \tag{5.2.17}$$

Proof. This is immediate if $p = 1$ or ∞, so suppose $1 < p < \infty$. By (5.2.9),

$$\|f + g\|_p = \sup_h \left\{ \left| \int [(f + g)h] \, d\mu \right| \; \middle| \; h \in \mathcal{B}, \|h\|_q = 1 \right\} \tag{5.2.18}$$
$$\leq \|f\|_p + \|g\|_p$$

since $|\int [(f + g)h] \, d\mu| \leq |\int fh \, d\mu| + |\int gh \, d\mu|$ and a sup of sums is less than a sum of sups. $\qquad\square$

One useful consequence of Hölder's inequality is to allow us to control $\|\cdot\|_p$ in terms of $\|\cdot\|_{p_0}$ and $\|\cdot\|_{p_1}$ if $p_0 \leq p \leq p_1$.

Theorem 5.2.5. *Let* $1 \leq p_0 \leq p_1 \leq \infty$. *Let* p *obey*

$$\frac{1}{p} = \frac{1 - \theta}{p_0} + \frac{\theta}{p_1} \tag{5.2.19}$$

Then $L^p \supset L^{p_0} \cap L^{p_1}$ *and for* $f \in L^{p_0} \cap L^{p_1}$, *we have*

$$\|f\|_p \leq \|f\|_{p_0}^{1-\theta} \|f\|_{p_1}^{\theta} \tag{5.2.20}$$
$$\leq (1 - \theta)\|f\|_{p_0} + \theta\|f\|_{p_1} \tag{5.2.21}$$

Proof. Let $r_0 = p_0/(1-\theta)$, $r_1 = p_1/\theta$. Then $r_0^{-1} + r_1^{-1} = p^{-1}$ so by Holder's inequality

$$\|f\|_p = \| \, |f|^{1-\theta} \, |f|^{\theta} \, \|_p = \| \, |f|^{1-\theta} \, \|_{r_0} \| \, |f|^{\theta} \, \|_{r_1} \tag{5.2.22}$$

Noting that $\| \, |f|^{1-\theta} \, \|_{r_0} = \left(\int |f|^{(1-\theta)/r_0} \right)^{1/r_0} = \|f\|_{p_0}^{1-\theta}$ and similarly for p_1, we get (5.2.20).

If $s = \theta^{-1}$, $t = (1 - \theta)^{-1}$, then $s^{-1} + t^{-1} = 1$, so (5.2.2) says

$$x^{1-\theta} y^{\theta} \leq \frac{x^{(1-\theta)t}}{t} + \frac{y^{\theta s}}{s} = (1 - \theta)x + \theta y \tag{5.2.23}$$

showing that (5.2.20) implies (5.2.21). $\qquad\square$

While, in general, $p < r < q$ implies $L^r \supset L^p \cap L^q$, there are stronger results in two special cases:

Theorem 5.2.6. (a) *If* $1 \leq q < p \leq \infty$, *and* $\mu(X) = 1$, *then* $L^p(X, d\mu) \subset L^q(X, d\mu)$ *and*

$$\|f\|_q \leq \|f\|_p \tag{5.2.24}$$

(b) *If* $1 \leq q < p \leq \infty$, *then* $\ell^q \subset \ell^p$ *and*

$$\|f\|_p \leq \|f\|_q \tag{5.2.25}$$

Remarks. 1. (5.2.24)/(5.2.25) are intended for all f with $\|f\|_p$ or $\|f\|_q = \infty$ allowed.

2. The inclusion in (a) holds if $\mu(X) < \infty$ with the inequality including a power of $\mu(X)$ as constant.

3. While we intend (b) for one-sided sequences, i.e., $\ell^p(\mathbb{Z}_+)$, it is true for counting measure on any set. The inclusion holds for any measure on a discrete set with $\inf \mu(\{x\}) > 0$ and $\sup \mu(\{x\}) < \infty$.

Proof. (a) Let r be defined by $p^{-1} + r^{-1} = q^{-1}$. Then, $f = f\mathbb{1}$ and, by Hölder's inequality,

$$\|f\|_q \leq \|\mathbb{1}\|_r \|f\|_p = \|f\|_p$$

(b) By Theorem 5.2.5, it suffices to handle the case $p = \infty$ which is obvious!
□

Notes and Historical Remarks. Minkowski's inequality for sums (i.e., that $\|a\|_p = (\sum_{n=1}^{\infty} |a_n|^p)^{1/p}$ is a norm on ℓ_p) is due to Minkowski [**658, 659**]. Hermann Minkowski (1864–1909) was a German mathematician of Lithuanian Jewish descent. He died suddenly of a burst appendix at age 44. His friend and colleague, David Hilbert, pulled together his work on convexity, much of it unpublished, in the 1911 book [**659**] mentioned above. His inequality appeared already in his 1896 book on the geometry of numbers [**658**]. Closely related to Minkowski's inequalities are Clarkson's inequalities, discussed in the Notes to Section 5.3. The proof of Minkowski's inequality from Hölder's inequality appeared first in Riesz [**782**].

Minkowski has been described as German, Polish, Lithuanian, or Russian. His German Jewish parents had moved to a small village near Kovno, then considered to be in the Polish part of Russia, now in Lithuania. In 1872, to escape persecution, the family moved to Königsberg where Hermann received his education through a Ph.D. with von Lindemann. He became lifelong friends with Hilbert and Hurwitz, later his colleagues at Göttingen and at the ETH, Zurich.

Undoubtedly, Minkowski is best known for his geometric reformation of special relativity in terms of indefinite metric. As a sidelight, we note that Einstein took classes with Minkowski when both were at the ETH. Initially, Einstein was skeptical that Minkowski's rephrasing was useful, but, of course, he eventually embraced it and used it as a springboard to general relativity.

Besides this work and his deep contributions to convexity, Minkowski made significant contributions to number theory. Constantin Carathéodory (whose capsule biography can be found in Section 5.6 of Part 2A) was Minkowski's student.

Minkowski's inequality extends to functions f on $X \times Y$ with measures $d\nu$ on Y and $d\mu$ on X to

$$\left(\int \left| \int f(x,y)\, d\nu(y) \right|^p d\mu(x) \right)^{1/p} \leq \int \left(\int |f(x,y)|^p\, d\mu(x) \right)^{1/p} d\nu(y) \quad (5.2.26)$$

which we interpret as

$$\left\| \int f_y \, d\nu \right\|_{L^p(X,d\mu)} \leq \int \| f_y \|_{L^p(X,d\mu)} \, d\nu \qquad (5.2.27)$$

and can prove by approximating integrals by sums.

Hölder's inequality for sums first appeared in Rogers [802] and a year later in Hölder [430], and for integrals in Riesz [780]. Maligranda [623] writes a plea for changing the name to Rogers' inequality or Rogers–Hölder and presents the history of the naming.

Young's inequality in a more general form appeared in Young [1009]: namely, if f is a convex function on $\mathbb{R}$ with $\lim_{|x|\to\infty} f(x)/|x| = \infty$, then the conjugate convex function is defined by $f^*(y) = \sup_{x\in\mathbb{R}}[xy - f(x)]$. Young's inequality says that $xy \leq f(x) + f^*(y)$ (immediate from the definition!) and (5.2.2) comes from $f(x) = |x|^p/p \Rightarrow f^*(y) = |y|^q/q$, as follows from computing derivatives to find the sup (see Problem 1). There are persistent rumors that some of the work of William Henry Young (1863–1942) was actually done by or joint with his wife, Grace Chisholm Young (1868–1944), whom he first met when he was her tutor at Girton College, Cambridge. In any event, she had considerable mathematical influence on her husband. She went on to get a Ph.D. under Felix Klein. At one point Young wrote:

> The fact is that our papers ought to be published under our joint names, but if this were done neither of us get the benefit of it. No. Mine the laurels now and the knowledge. Yours the knowledge only. Everything under my name now, and later when the loaves and fishes are no more procurable in that way, everything or much under your name. At present you cannot undertake a public career. You have your children.
>
> —*William Young*, letter to his wife, as quoted in [363]

Young's contributions to mathematics include a discovery of a theory equivalent to the Lebesgue integral two years after Lebesgue and his work on inequalities, including the convolution inequality that we'll discuss in Section 6.6. He has often been confused with the clergyman and amateur mathematician, Alfred Young (1873–1940), the inventor of Young tableaux in the theory of the symmetric group.

Problems

1. This will provide another proof of (5.2.2).

   (a) Let $1 < p < \infty$. Fix $y > 0$. On $[0, \infty)$, let $f(x) = xy - x^p/p$. Prove that $\lim_{x \to \infty} f(x) = -\infty$ and $f(x) > 0$ for x small and conclude $\sup f(x) = f(x_0)$ for an $x_0 \in (0, \infty)$ with $f'(x_0) = 0$.

   (b) Compute x_0 and then $f(x_0)$ as a function of y and conclude that $f(x) \leq y^q/q$, where $q^{-1} = 1 - p^{-1}$.

2. Use

$$|f + g|^p \leq |f||f + g|^{p-1} + |g||f + g|^{p-1}$$

and Hölder's inequality to obtain Minkowski's inequality directly, i.e., without going through (5.2.9).

5.3. Convex Functions and Inequalities

> There are three great pillars of the theory of inequalities: positivity, monotonicity, and convexity.
>
> —*J. Michael Steele* [**873**]

In this section, we recall the notion of convex set defined and used in Section 3.2 and define the closely related notion of convex function. These notions will play a key role later in the chapter—we put them here to provide alternate proofs of Minkowski's and Hölder's inequality. While the reader can skip these alternative proofs, the basic notions and the final general Jensen inequality should not be skipped.

Given $x, y \in V$ a real or complex vector space, $[xy]$ denotes the line segment between x and y, that is,

$$[xy] = \{(1 - \theta)x + \theta y \mid 0 \leq \theta \leq 1\} \qquad (5.3.1)$$

A *convex set* is a subset $A \subset V$ that obeys

$$x, y \in A \Rightarrow [xy] \subset A \qquad (5.3.2)$$

Thus, Figure 5.3.1 shows some convex and some nonconvex sets in $\mathbb{R}^2$.

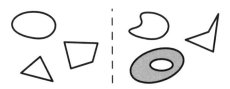

Figure 5.3.1. Some convex and nonconvex sets.

A map $T\colon A \to W$ from a convex set $A \subset V$ to another vector space W is called *affine* if and only if

$$T((1-\theta)x + \theta y) = (1-\theta)T(x) + \theta T(y) \qquad (5.3.3)$$

Restrictions of linear maps to A are affine, and if $A = V$, a real vector space, the affine maps all have the form $T(x) = a + L(x)$ with $a = T(0) \in W$ and L linear.

Notice that if A is convex, then writing

$$\sum_{j=1}^{N} \theta_j x_j = (1-\eta) \sum_{j=1}^{N-1} \psi_j x_j + \eta x_N \qquad (5.3.4)$$

where $\eta = \theta_N$ and $\psi_j = \theta_j/(1-\theta_N)$, proves inductively that if A is convex, then

$$x_1, \ldots, x_N \in A, \quad \theta_j \geq 0, \quad \sum_{j=1}^{N} \theta_j = 1 \Rightarrow \sum_{j=1}^{N} \theta_j x_j \in A \qquad (5.3.5)$$

The left side of (5.3.4) is called a *convex combination* of $\{x_j\}_{j=1}^{N}$.

In $\mathbb{R}^N$,

$$S_{N-1} \equiv \left\{ (\theta_1, \ldots, \theta_N) \mid \theta_j \geq 0, \sum_{j=1}^{N} \theta_j = 1 \right\} \qquad (5.3.6)$$

is called the $N-1$ *simplex* (it has dimension $N-1$). Clearly,

$$T((\theta_1, \ldots, \theta_N)) = \sum_{j=1}^{N} \theta_j x_j \qquad (5.3.7)$$

is an affine map of S_{N-1} into A. Its range is called the *convex hull* of $\{x_1, \ldots, x_N\}$. If this T is a bijection to its range, we say that $\{x_1, \ldots, x_N\}$ are *affinely independent* and T is called an *affine bijection* if the range is all of A. Notice that if $x \neq y$, $\theta \mapsto (1-\theta)x + \theta y$ is an affine bijection of $[0,1]$ and $[xy]$.

For any set, S, in a vector space, V, the union over all N and all $\{x_1, \ldots, x_N\}$ of the convex hull of $\{x_1, \ldots, x_N\}$ is called the *convex hull* of S, written $\mathrm{ch}(S)$. It is easy to see that it is the smallest convex set containing S. If V has a topology, the closure of $\mathrm{ch}(S)$ is called the *closed convex hull* of S, written $\mathrm{cch}(S)$. It is the smallest closed convex set containing S.

While we will not use it much, the notion of circled convex sets are useful, especially in the case of complex vector spaces. A set, A, in a vector space, V, over a field $\mathbb{K} = \mathbb{R}$ or $\mathbb{C}$ is *circled* if and only if $\lambda \in \mathbb{K}$, $x \in A$ and $|\lambda| = 1 \Rightarrow \lambda x \in A$. *Circled convex sets* are sets that are convex and circled.

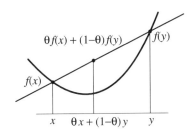

Figure 5.3.2. A convex function.

They obey $\lambda \in \mathbb{K}$, $x \in A$ and $|\lambda| \leq 1 \Rightarrow \lambda x \in A$. The circled simplex is the set in $\mathbb{K}^N$

$$\Sigma_{N-1}^{(\mathbb{K})} = \{(\theta_1, \ldots, \theta_N) \mid \sum_{j=1}^{N} |\theta_j| \leq 1\} \tag{5.3.8}$$

Using T as in (5.3.7) but with $(\theta_1, \ldots, \theta_N) \in \Sigma_{N-1}^{(\mathbb{K})}$, we get the *circled convex hull* of $\{x_1, \ldots, x_N\}$ and of a set A. Notice since $0 = \frac{1}{2}x + \left(-\frac{1}{2}\right)x$, we have for circled convex sets, A, that $\sum_{j=1}^{N} \theta_j x_j \in A$ if $\{x_1, \ldots, x_j\} \subset A$ and $\sum_{j=1}^{N} |\theta_j| \leq 1$. We can also talk about the circled closed convex hull.

Let $A \subset V$ be a convex set. A function $f \colon A \to \mathbb{R}$ is called *convex* if and only if for all $x, y \in A$ and $\theta \in [0, 1]$, we have

$$f((1 - \theta)x + \theta y) \leq (1 - \theta)f(x) + \theta f(y) \tag{5.3.9}$$

see Figure 5.3.2 for the case $A = [a, b]$.

If $-f$ is convex, that is,

$$f((1 - \theta)x + \theta y) \geq (1 - \theta)f(x) + \theta f(y) \tag{5.3.10}$$

we call f *concave*. Notice that if f is both convex and concave, it is an *affine* function to $\mathbb{R}$, that is,

$$f((1 - \theta)x + \theta y) = (1 - \theta)f(x) + \theta f(y) \tag{5.3.11}$$

It is easy to see (Problem 1) that f is convex if and only if

$$\{(x, t) \in V \times \mathbb{R} \mid x \in A, \ t \geq f(x)\} \tag{5.3.12}$$

is a convex set in $V \times \mathbb{R}$ viewed as a direct sum vector space.

We now want to focus on the case $A = [a, b]$. This is not only illustrative but, because $f \colon A \to \mathbb{R}$ is convex if and only it is convex on each $[xy]$ with $x, y \in A$ and $[xy]$ is affinely equivalent to $[0, 1]$, the general theory is impacted by the special case. We say $f \colon A \to \mathbb{R}$ is *midpoint convex* if and only if for all $x, y \in A$,

$$f(\tfrac{1}{2}x + \tfrac{1}{2}y) \leq \tfrac{1}{2}f(x) + \tfrac{1}{2}f(y) \tag{5.3.13}$$

Theorem 5.3.1. *Let $f\colon (a,b) \to \mathbb{R}$. Then the following are equivalent:*
(1) *f is convex on (a,b).*
(2) *f is continuous and midpoint convex.*
In particular, any convex function on (a,b) is continuous. If f is C^2, (1) and (2) are equivalent to

(3) *$f''(x) \geq 0$ for all x in (a,b)* $\qquad\qquad$ (5.3.14)

Remark. It can be shown (Problem 2) that midpoint convexity and measurability implies convexity.

Proof. $\underline{(1) \Rightarrow f \text{ continuous}}$. Fix $x \in (a,b)$ and $x_n \downarrow x$, so $f(x_n) \to c$. Fix $y \in (x,b)$, and for n large, find $\theta_n \in (0,1)$ so $x_n = (1 - \theta_n)x + \theta_n y$. Since $x_n \downarrow x$, $\theta_n \downarrow 0$, so $f(x_n) \leq (1 - \theta_n)f(x) + \theta_n f(y)$ implies

$$c \leq f(x) \qquad\qquad (5.3.15)$$

Fix $z \in (a,x)$ and $\psi_n \in [0,1]$, so

$$x = (1 - \psi_n)z + \psi_n x_n \qquad\qquad (5.3.16)$$

Since $x_n \downarrow x$, $\psi_n \to 1$, and $f(x) \leq (1 - \psi_n)f(z) + \psi_n f(x_n)$ implies

$$f(x) \leq c \qquad\qquad (5.3.17)$$

Thus, $c = f(x)$. Since x_n is arbitrary, $\lim_{y\downarrow x} f(y) = f(x)$. Similarly, f is continuous from below.

$\underline{(1) \Rightarrow (2)}$. We have just proven continuity and, clearly, (5.3.9) for all $\theta \in [0,1]$ implies it for $\theta = \frac{1}{2}$.

$\underline{(2) \Rightarrow (1)}$. Assume midpoint convexity. That gives us (5.3.9) for $\theta = \frac{1}{2}$. Consider $\theta = \frac{1}{4}$. By midpoint convexity,

$$f(\tfrac{3}{4}x + \tfrac{1}{4}y) \leq \tfrac{1}{2}f(x) + \tfrac{1}{2}f(\tfrac{1}{2}x + \tfrac{1}{2}y)$$

(since $\frac{1}{2}x + \frac{1}{2}(\frac{1}{2}x + \frac{1}{2}y) = \frac{3}{4}x + \frac{1}{4}y$)

$$\leq \tfrac{1}{2}f(x) + \tfrac{1}{2}[\tfrac{1}{2}f(x) + \tfrac{1}{2}f(y)]$$
$$= \tfrac{3}{4}f(x) + \tfrac{1}{4}f(y)$$

proving (5.3.9) for $\theta = \frac{1}{4}$. Similarly, we get $\theta = \frac{3}{4}$. By induction, we get (5.3.9) for all $j/2^n$, $n = 1, 2, \ldots$; j odd in $1, 2, \ldots, 2^{n-1}$. Continuity gets the result for all θ.

$\underline{(2) \Leftrightarrow (3) \text{ if } f \text{ is } C^2}$. Since f is C^2, Taylor's theorem with remainder shows for $x \in (a,b)$ and δx such that $x \pm \delta x \in (a,b)$, we have

$$f(x \pm \delta x) = f(x) \pm \delta x f'(x) + \int_0^{\delta x} (\delta x - y) f''(x \pm y) \, dy \qquad (5.3.18)$$

so

$$\tfrac{1}{2}\left[f(x + \delta x) + f(x - \delta x)\right] - f(x) = \tfrac{1}{2} \int_0^{\delta x} (\delta x - y)[f''(x + y) + f''(x - y)]\, dy$$
(5.3.19)

If $f''(z) \geq 0$, (5.3.19) implies midpoint convexity (and C^2 implies continuity).

Conversely, midpoint convexity implies the integral is nonnegative for all small δx, so

$$f''(x) = \lim_{\delta x \downarrow 0}\left[\frac{2}{(\delta x)^2}\,\text{LHS of (5.3.19)}\right]$$

is nonnegative. $\square$

The next three results are straightforward consequences of this last theorem and of the basic definition and are left to the Problems (Problems 3–6).

Theorem 5.3.2. *Let A be an open convex subset of $\mathbb{R}^\nu$ and $F\colon A \to \mathbb{R}$ a C^2 function. Then F is convex if and only if for all $x_0 \in A$, the Hessian matrix, $\frac{\partial^2 F}{\partial x_i \partial x_j}(x_0)$, is positive definite (but not necessarily strictly positive definite).*

Theorem 5.3.3. *If $f\colon (a,b) \to \mathbb{R}$ is convex, then $f(a+) = \lim_{t \downarrow 0} f(a + t)$ and $f(b-) = \lim_{t \uparrow 0} f(b - t)$ exist in $(-\infty, \infty]$ ($+\infty$ allowed). $f\colon [a,b] \to \mathbb{R}$ is convex if and only if $f \restriction (a,b)$ is convex and $f(a) \geq f(a+)$, $f(b) \geq f(b-)$.*

Theorem 5.3.4. *Let $f\colon \mathbb{R} \to \mathbb{R}$ obey*

$$f(-x) = f(x)$$
(5.3.20)

Then f is convex on $\mathbb{R}$ if and only if f is convex on $(0, \infty)$, f is monotone nondecreasing on $(0, \infty)$, and $f(0) = \lim_{x \downarrow 0} f(x)$. In this case, $g(z) = f(|z|)$ is convex on $\mathbb{C}$.

Example 5.3.5. Let $f(x) = x^p$ on $(0, \infty)$ for $p \geq 1$. Then f is C^2 and $f''(x) = p(p-1)x^{p-2} \geq 0$, so f is convex. Since f is monotone, $f(x) = |x|^p$ on $\mathbb{R}$ or $\mathbb{C}$ is convex by Theorem 5.3.4. $\square$

Theorem 5.3.6 (Discrete Jensen Inequality). *If $A \subset V$ is a convex set, $F\colon A \to \mathbb{R}$ a convex function, $\{x_j\}_{j=1}^N \subset A$, and $\theta_1, \ldots, \theta_N \in [0,1]$ with $\sum_{j=1}^N \theta_j = 1$, then*

$$F\left(\sum_{j=1}^N \theta_j x_j\right) \leq \sum_{j=1}^N \theta_j F(x_j)$$
(5.3.21)

Proof. We use (5.3.4) and induction. $N = 2$ is the definition of convex function. Suppose (5.3.21) holds for N replaced by $N - 1$. By (5.3.4) and convexity,

$$F\left(\sum_{j=1}^{N} \theta_j x_j\right) \le (1 - \eta)F\left(\sum_{j=1}^{N-1} \psi_j x_j\right) + \eta F(x_N) \le \sum_{j=1}^{N} \theta_j F(x_j)$$

by the $(N - 1)$ result. $\square$

Example 5.3.7 (Arithmetic-Geometric Mean and Generalizations).   If $a, b \ge 0$, then $\frac{1}{2}(\sqrt{a} - \sqrt{b})^2 \ge 0$, so

$$\sqrt{ab} \le \tfrac{1}{2}(a + b) \tag{5.3.22}$$

the well-known *arithmetic-geometric mean* inequality (see Problem 7 for a geometric proof). If $a = e^t$, $b = e^s$, (5.3.22) is equivalent to

$$e^{\frac{1}{2}(t+s)} \le \tfrac{1}{2}e^t + \tfrac{1}{2}e^s \tag{5.3.23}$$

for all $t, s, \in \mathbb{R}$. Thus, if $f \colon \mathbb{R} \to (0, \infty)$ by

$$f(t) = e^t \tag{5.3.24}$$

(5.3.22) says f is midpoint convex. Since f is continuous, (5.3.22) is equivalent to convexity of $t \mapsto e^t$, something that also follows from $f''(t) = e^t > 0$. Notice that Jensen's inequality with $\theta_j = 1/N$ implies (if $a_j = e^{x_j}$)

$$\sqrt[N]{a_1 \dots a_n} \le \frac{1}{N} \sum_{j=1}^{N} a_j \tag{5.3.25}$$

$\square$

With these definitions and examples under our belt, we return to Minkowski's and Hölder's inequality. We first want to show that the triangle inequality is a convexity statement.

Definition. Let V be a vector space over the reals or complex numbers ($\mathbb{K}$ is $\mathbb{R}$ or $\mathbb{C}$). $p \colon V \to [0, \infty)$ is called *homogeneous symmetric of degree* 1 (*homogeneous* for short) if and only if

$$\forall x \in V, \lambda \in \mathbb{K} \Rightarrow p(\lambda x) = |\lambda| p(x) \tag{5.3.26}$$

Theorem 5.3.8. *Let V be a vector space over $\mathbb{K} = \mathbb{R}$ or $\mathbb{C}$ and p a positive homogeneous function on V. Then the following are equivalent:*

(1) *(Triangle inequality)*

$$p(x + y) \le p(x) + p(y) \tag{5.3.27}$$

(2) *(Convexity of p) p is a convex function.*

(3) (Convexity of the unit ball)

$$B_p = \{x \mid p(x) \leq 1\} \qquad (5.3.28)$$

is a convex set.

Proof. $(1) \Rightarrow (2)$. By (5.3.27), if $x, y \in V$ and $\theta \in [0, 1)$,

$$p((1 - \theta)x + \theta y) \leq p((1 - \theta)x) + p(\theta y) = (1 - \theta)p(x) + \theta p(y) \qquad (5.3.29)$$

by (5.3.26), so p is convex.

$(2) \Rightarrow (3)$. For any convex function, F, if $F(x) \leq 1$ and $F(y) \leq 1$, then $F((1 - \theta)x + \theta y) \leq (1 - \theta)F(x) + \theta F(y) \leq 1$, so $\{x \mid F(x) \leq 1\}$ is convex.

$(3) \Rightarrow (1)$. Given x, y, suppose $p(x) > 0$, $p(y) > 0$. Let

$$x_1 = \frac{x}{p(x)}, \qquad y_1 = \frac{y}{p(y)} \qquad (5.3.30)$$

Pick $\theta = p(y)/(p(x) + p(y))$ so $1 - \theta = p(x)/(p(x) + p(y))$ and

$$(1 - \theta)x_1 + \theta y_1 = \frac{x + y}{p(x) + p(y)} \qquad (5.3.31)$$

$x_1, y_1 \in B_p$, so by convexity of B_p, so is $(x + y)/(p(x) + p(y))$, that is,

$$\frac{p(x + y)}{p(x) + p(y)} \leq 1 \qquad (5.3.32)$$

which is (5.3.27).

In general, when $p(x)$ or $p(y)$ might be 0, pick

$$\varepsilon > 0, \quad x_{1,\varepsilon} = \frac{x}{p(x) + \varepsilon}, \quad y_{1,\varepsilon} = \frac{y}{p(y) + \varepsilon}, \quad \theta = \frac{p(y) + \varepsilon}{p(x) + p(y) + 2\varepsilon}$$

and find that $p(x + y) \leq p(x) + p(y) + 2\varepsilon$ and then take $\varepsilon \downarrow 0$. $\qquad \square$

This allows our second proof of Minkowski's inequality:

Theorem 5.3.9 ($\equiv$ Theorem 5.2.4). *Let $1 \leq p \leq \infty$. If $f, g \in L^p(X, d\mu)$, so is $f + g$, and*

$$\|f + g\|_p \leq \|f\|_p + \|g\|_p \qquad (5.3.33)$$

Proof. $p = \infty$ is easy, so suppose $p < \infty$. Since $|f + g|^p \leq 2^p \max(|f|^p, |g|^p) \leq 2^p(|f|^p + |g|^p)$, L^p is a vector space. The function, $\Psi(f) = \|f\|_p$, on L^p is homogeneous. Thus, (5.3.33) is equivalent to B_Ψ being convex. Since $\alpha \to \alpha^{1/p}$ is monotone on $[0, \infty)$,

$$B_\Psi = \left\{ f \,\middle|\, \int |f(x)|^p \, d\mu(x) \leq 1 \right\}$$

If $f, g \in B_\Psi$, then since $y \mapsto |y|^p$ is convex,

$$|(1 - \theta)f + \theta g|^p \leq (1 - \theta)|f|^p + \theta|g|^p$$

Thus, integrating

$$\int |(1-\theta)f + \theta g|^p \, d\mu \le (1-\theta)\|f\|_p^p + \theta\|g\|_p^p \le 1$$

showing that B_Ψ is convex. $\square$

It seems that all that matters here is that $y \to |y|^p$ is convex and monotone on $[0, \infty)$ with $|0|^p = 0$. That if $\varphi(x)$ is such a function, then $\varphi^{-1}(\int \varphi(|f(x)|) \, d\mu(x))$ on the set of f's for which the integral is bounded should be a norm. The situation is close to this, but more subtle—for example, if $\varphi(y) = e^{|y|} - 1$, $\{f \mid \int \varphi(|f(x)|) \, d\mu(x) < \infty\}$ isn't even a vector space since the integral may be finite for f but not for $2f$! We'll say more about this in the Notes and Problem 16.

There is a part of Theorem 5.3.8 that doesn't require $p(\lambda x) = p(x)$ for $|\lambda| = 1$ and which will play a role in Section 5.10.

Definition. Let V be a vector space over $\mathbb{K}$ which is $\mathbb{R}$ or $\mathbb{C}$. A set $A \subset V$ is called *absorbing* if and only if $0 \in A$ and $\bigcup_{\lambda \in (0,\infty)} \lambda A = V$. A is called *pseudo-open* if for any $x \in V$ and $y \in A$, $\{\lambda > 0 \mid y + \lambda x \in A\}$ is a nonempty interval. A is called *balanced* if $\lambda \in \mathbb{K}$ with $|\lambda| = 1$ and $x \in A$ implies $\lambda x \in A$.

It is easy to see that if V is a TVS and A is open, it is pseudo-open. It is also easy to see that any pseudo-open set containing 0 is absorbing.

Theorem 5.3.10. *Let A be a convex absorbing subset of V, a vector space over $\mathbb{K}$. Define*

$$p(x) = \inf\{\lambda \in (0, \infty) \mid \lambda^{-1} x \in A\} \tag{5.3.34}$$

Then p is a convex function with

$$\{x \mid p(x) < 1\} \subset A \subset \{x \mid p(x) \le 1\} \tag{5.3.35}$$

Moreover, for all x and $\mu \ge 0$,

$$p(\mu x) = \mu p(x) \tag{5.3.36}$$

If A is pseudo-open,

$$A = \{x \mid p(x) < 1\} \tag{5.3.37}$$

If A is balanced, then p is a seminorm.

Remarks. 1. p is called the *gauge* or *Minkowski gauge* of A.

2. If A is pseudo-open and p is a seminorm, then conversely, A is balanced. But it can happen if (5.3.37) fails that p is a seminorm but A is not balanced.

Proof. We sketch the proof, leaving the details to Problem 27. If $\lambda^{-1}x \in A$ and $\mu^{-1}y \in A$ and $\psi = \lambda(1-\theta)/(\lambda(1-\theta)+\theta\mu)$, then $\psi\lambda^{-1}x+(1-\psi)\mu^{-1}y = (\lambda(1-\theta)+\theta\mu)^{-1}((1-\theta)x+\theta y)$, which shows $p((1-\theta)x+\theta y) \le (1-\theta)p(x)+\theta p(y)$.

If $x \in A$, by (5.3.34), $1 \in \{\lambda \in (0,\infty) \mid \lambda^{-1}x \in A\}$, so $p(x) \le 1$. On the other hand, if $p(x) < 1$, $1 \in \{\lambda \in (0,\infty) \mid \lambda^{-1}x \in A\}$, that is, $x \in A$. The last statement is easy.

If A is balanced, then $|\lambda| = 1$ implies $p(\lambda x) = p(x)$, so for any $\lambda \in \mathbb{K}$, $p(\lambda x) = |\lambda|p(x)$. Thus, p is a seminorm by Theorem 5.3.8. $\square$

Having discussed the relation of Minkowski's inequality to convexity, we turn to Hölder's inequality. A key role will be played by the following functional on real-valued bounded Baire functions, F, on a compact Hausdorff space, X, with positive Baire measure, μ:

$$\Phi(F) = \log \int \exp(F(x))\, d\mu(x) \tag{5.3.38}$$

Meta Theorem 5.3.11. *Hölder's inequality in the form*

$$\|fg\|_r \le \|f\|_p\|g\|_q \tag{5.3.39}$$

for all $f \in L^p(X, d\mu)$, $g \in L^q(X, d\mu)$, where

$$r^{-1} = p^{-1} + q^{-1} \tag{5.3.40}$$

with $p, q, r \in [1, \infty]$ is equivalent to $F \mapsto \Phi(F)$ being a convex function of F.

Remarks. 1. Logically speaking, any two true statements are equivalent. We mean this in the colloquial sense that either can be easily used to prove the other. That's why we add "Meta" before "Theorem."

2. We state this for μ a positive Baire measure on a compact Hausdorff space, but by a simple approximation theorem (Problem 8), it then holds for any (even unbounded) positive Baire measure on a σ-compact space.

Meta Proof. Fix p, q, r obeying (5.3.40) with $p, q, r < \infty$ (since Hölder is trivial if p, q, or r is ∞). Given F, G bounded real-valued Baire functions, let

$$f = e^{F/p}, \qquad g = e^{G/q}, \qquad \theta = \frac{r}{q}, \qquad 1-\theta = \frac{r}{p} \tag{5.3.41}$$

so

$$e^{(1-\theta)F+\theta G} = (fg)^r \tag{5.3.42}$$

Thus,

$$e^{\Phi((1-\theta)F+\theta G)} = \|fg\|_r^r, \qquad e^{(1-\theta)\Phi(F)+\theta\Phi(G)} = \|f\|_p^r\|g\|_q^r \tag{5.3.43}$$

which means

$$\Phi((1-\theta)F+\theta G) \le (1-\theta)\Phi(F)+\theta\Phi(G) \Leftrightarrow \|fg\|_r \le \|f\|_p\|g\|_q \tag{5.3.44}$$

This shows that convexity of Φ is equivalent to Hölder's inequality for f, g obeying $\varepsilon \leq f \leq \varepsilon^{-1}$, $\varepsilon \leq g \leq \varepsilon^{-1}$ for some $\varepsilon > 0$. A limiting argument (Problem 9) goes from this special case of Hölder to the general case. $\quad\square$

We will give several proofs of convexity of Φ. Each such proof is a new proof of Hölder's inequality.

First Proof of Convexity of Φ. It is sufficient to prove convexity on each line segment. So, for F, G real-valued bounded Baire functions, let

$$\Psi(t) = \Phi((1-t)F + tG) \tag{5.3.45}$$

so we only need convexity of Ψ. By dominated convergence, Ψ is continuous in t, so we only need $\frac{1}{2}$-convexity which, by changing F, G is implied by

$$\Psi(\tfrac{1}{2}) \leq \tfrac{1}{2}\Psi(0) + \tfrac{1}{2}\Psi(1) \tag{5.3.46}$$

that is, that

$$\int e^{\frac{1}{2}(F+G)} \, d\mu \leq \left(\int e^F \, d\mu \right)^{1/2} \left(\int e^G \, d\mu \right)^{1/2} \tag{5.3.47}$$

which is just the Cauchy–Schwarz inequality! $\quad\square$

Remark. Of course, one can just repeat the proof that $\frac{1}{2}$-convexity implies convexity. For example,

$$\int |fg| \, d\mu = \int |f|^{2/3} |f^{1/3}g| \, d\mu$$

$$\leq \left(\int |f|^{4/3} \, d\mu \right)^{1/2} \left(\int |f^{2/3}g^2| \, d\mu \right)^{1/2}$$

$$\leq \left(\int |f|^{4/3} \, d\mu \right)^{1/2} \left(\int |f|^{4/3} \, d\mu \right)^{1/4} \left(\int |g|^4 \, d\mu \right)^{1/4}$$

$$\leq \left(\int |f|^{4/3} \, d\mu \right)^{3/4} \left(\int |g|^4 \, d\mu \right)^{1/4} \tag{5.3.48}$$

proving Hölder for $p = \frac{1}{4}$.

Remarkably enough, there is another proof using the Schwarz inequality!

Second Proof of Convexity of Φ. It suffices to show that Ψ given by (5.3.45) is convex. Since it is C^2 (by dominated convergence), we only need $\Psi''(t) \geq 0$.

Making the F, G, μ dependence explicit, we see

$$\Psi(t + t_0; F, G, \mu) = \Psi(t; 0, G - F, \mu_{t_0}) \tag{5.3.49}$$

where $d\mu_{t_0}(x) = e^{(1-t_0)F(x) + t_0 G(x)} \, d\mu(x)$, so it suffices to prove $\Psi''(t; 0, G, \mu)|_{t=0} \geq 0$ for all G, μ.

Since
$$\Psi(t; 0, G, c\mu) = \log(c) + \Psi(t; 0, G, \mu) \tag{5.3.50}$$
we can also suppose $\int d\mu(x) = 1$. In that case,
$$\Psi'(t; 0, G, \mu) = \frac{\int Ge^{tG}\, d\mu}{\int e^{tG}\, d\mu} \tag{5.3.51}$$
and
$$\Psi''(t; 0, G, \mu)\big|_{t=0} = \int G^2\, d\mu - \left(\int G\, d\mu\right)^2 \tag{5.3.52}$$
which is nonnegative by the Schwarz inequality since $\int d\mu = 1$. $\quad\square$

Finally, we will prove Φ convex as a special case of a continuum Jensen inequality. We need a preliminary:

Theorem 5.3.12. *Let $F\colon (a, b) \to \mathbb{R}$ be convex. Then for any $c \in (a, b)$,*
$$(D^+ F)(c) = \lim_{t\downarrow 0} \frac{F(c + t) - F(c)}{t} \tag{5.3.53}$$
exists, and for all $d \in (a, b)$,
$$F(d) - F(c) \geq (d - c)(D^+ F)(c) \tag{5.3.54}$$
Moreover, if $a < c < d < b$, then
$$(D^+ F)(c) \leq (D^+ F)(d) \tag{5.3.55}$$
and
$$\left(D^+ F\right)(c) = \lim_{\varepsilon \downarrow 0} D^+ F(c + \varepsilon) \tag{5.3.56}$$

Remarks. 1. This says F lies above its tangent at c; see Figure 5.3.3.

2. (5.3.55) implies if F is convex on (a, ∞), then $\lim_{x \to \infty} F(x)/x$ exists (it may be $+\infty$); see Problem 5.

Figure 5.3.3. Tangent to a convex function.

Proof. Let $a < d_1 < c < q < d_2 < b$. Then convexity implies (Problem 10; see Figure 5.3.4)
$$\frac{F(c) - F(d_1)}{c - d_1} \leq \frac{F(q) - F(c)}{q - c} \leq \frac{F(d_2) - F(c)}{d_2 - c} \tag{5.3.57}$$

Figure 5.3.4. Comparison of slopes.

This implies for $t \in (0, b-c)$, $[F(c+t) - F(c)]/t$ is monotone nondecreasing in t and bounded from below (by $((F(c) - F(d_1))/(c - d_1))$), so the limit in (5.3.53) exists.

(5.3.57) then implies that

$$\frac{F(c) - F(d_1)}{c - d_1} \leq (D^+ F)(c) \leq \frac{F(d_2) - F(c)}{d_2 - c} \qquad (5.3.58)$$

which is equivalent to (5.3.54). This in turn implies

$$(D^+ F)(c) \leq \frac{F(d) - F(c)}{d - c} \leq (D^+ F)(d) \qquad (5.3.59)$$

To see the continuity of D^+ on the right (i.e., (5.3.56)), (5.3.58) says $(D^+ F)(x)$ is monotone in x so

$$\alpha = \lim_{\varepsilon \downarrow 0} (D^+ F)(c + \varepsilon) \qquad (5.3.60)$$

exists and

$$(D^+ F)(c) \leq \alpha \qquad (5.3.61)$$

Fix $d > c$ and note that (5.3.59) implies, for $\varepsilon < d - c$, that

$$(D^+ F)(c + \varepsilon) \leq \frac{F(d) - F(c + \varepsilon)}{d - c - \varepsilon} \qquad (5.3.62)$$

Since F is continuous, we can take $\varepsilon \downarrow 0$ to get

$$\alpha \leq \frac{F(d) - F(c)}{d - c} \qquad (5.3.63)$$

Now take $d < c$ so that

$$\alpha \leq (D^+ F)(c) \qquad (5.3.64)$$

proving equality.   □

Theorem 5.3.13. *Let $F \colon (a, b) \to \mathbb{R}$. Then F is convex if and only if there is a $g(c)$ for all $c \in (a, b)$ so that for all $c, d \in (a, b)$,*

$$F(d) - F(c) \geq g(c)(d - c) \qquad (5.3.65)$$

Proof. If F is convex, take $g(c) = (D^+F)(c)$ and use (5.3.54).

For the converse (see Problem 11 for a geometric proof), fix $c, d \in (a, b)$, $e = (1 - \theta)c + \theta d$. By (5.3.65),

$$F(c) - F(e) \geq g(e)(c - d)\theta \tag{5.3.66}$$

$$F(d) - F(e) \geq g(e)(d - c)(1 - \theta) \tag{5.3.67}$$

Multiply (5.3.66) by $(1 - \theta)$ and (5.3.67) by θ and add to get

$$(1 - \theta)F(c) + \theta F(d) - F(e) \geq 0 \tag{5.3.68}$$

which is convexity. $\square$

With these tools, we can prove:

Theorem 5.3.14 (Jensen's Inequality, General Form). *Let μ be a Baire probability measure on a compact Hausdorff space, X. Let $f \in L^1(X, d\mu)$ and let F be a convex function on an interval (α, β) with $f(x) \in (\alpha, \beta)$ for a.e. x. Then*

$$F\left(\int f(x)\, d\mu(x)\right) \leq \int F(f(x))\, d\mu(x) \tag{5.3.69}$$

Remarks. 1. If $X = [\alpha, \beta]$, $d\mu = \sum_{j=1}^N \theta_j \delta_{t_j}$ with all $t_j \in (\alpha, \beta)$ and $f(x) \equiv x$, then (5.3.69) is (5.3.21), so this really is a generalization of the discrete Jensen inequality. Indeed, there is a proof of (5.3.69) as a limit of the discrete case (Problem 12).

2. There is a generalization to ν-tuples of f's and F convex on a subset of $\mathbb{R}^\nu$ (see Problem 13).

Proof. Since $f(x) \in (\alpha, \beta)$ for a.e. x and μ is a probability measure

$$\gamma = \int f(x)\, d\mu(x) \tag{5.3.70}$$

lies in (α, β). Thus, we have

$$F(f(x)) - F(\gamma) \geq (D^+F)(\gamma)(f(x) - \gamma) \tag{5.3.71}$$

for a.e. x. By (5.3.70), the $d\mu$ integral of the right side of (5.3.71) is 0, so

$$\int (F(f(x)) - F(\gamma))\, d\mu(x) \geq 0 \tag{5.3.72}$$

which is (5.3.69). $\square$

Example 5.3.15. The following special case of (5.3.69) is sometimes called Jensen's inequality. As we've seen, $x \mapsto e^x$ is convex. Thus,

$$\exp\left(\int f(x)\, d\mu(x)\right) \leq \int \exp(f(x))\, d\mu(x) \tag{5.3.73}$$

$\square$

Third Proof of Convexity of Φ. Using the notation of the second proof, let

$$\nu_{t_0} = \frac{\mu_{t_0}}{\int_X d\mu_{t_0}} \tag{5.3.74}$$

Then (5.3.49) and (5.3.50) imply that

$$\Psi(t + t_0; f, g, \mu) = \Psi(t_0; f, g, \mu) + \Psi(t; 0, g - f, \nu_{t_0}) \tag{5.3.75}$$

The special case, (5.3.73), of Jensen's inequality says that

$$\Psi(t; 0, g - f, d\nu_{t_0}) \geq G(t_0)t \tag{5.3.76}$$

where

$$G(t_0) = \int (g(x) - f(x)) \, d\nu_{t_0}(x) \tag{5.3.77}$$

By Theorem 5.3.13, (5.3.75)/(5.3.76) implies $\Psi(t)$ is convex. $\square$

Example 5.3.16. If $f \colon (a, b) \to \mathbb{R}$ is convex and $x_0 \in (a, b)$, the above constructions show that $f(x) \geq f(x_0) + (x - x_0)f'(x)$ and if f is concave, then $f(x) \leq f(x_0) + (x - x_0)f'(x)$. $f_\alpha(x) = (1 + x)^\alpha$ is convex (respectively, concave) if $\alpha \in (-\infty, 0] \cup [1, \infty)$ (respectively, $[0, 1]$). We thus get *Bernoulli's inequality*

$$\alpha \geq 1 \text{ or } \alpha \leq 0, \, x \in (-1, \infty) \Rightarrow (1 + x)^\alpha \geq 1 + \alpha x \tag{5.3.78}$$

$$\alpha \in [0, 1], \, x \in (-1, \infty) \Rightarrow (1 + x)^\alpha \leq 1 + \alpha x \tag{5.3.79}$$

We end with a result about compact, convex sets.

Theorem 5.3.17 (Mazur's Theorem). *Let K be a compact subset of a Banach space X. Then $\mathrm{cch}(K)$ is compact.*

Remark. The same proof shows in the complex case that the circled closed convex hull of K is compact (Problem 23).

Proof. By Theorem 2.3.6 (and the fact that since $\mathrm{cch}(K)$ is a closed subset of a complete space, it is complete), it suffices to prove that $\mathrm{ch}(K)$ is totally bounded. Given ε, let B_ε be the unit ball about 0. Since $\bigcup_{x \in K} B_\varepsilon(x)$ covers K, we can find a finite set $F = \{x_1, \dots, x_N\} \subset K$ with $K \subset \bigcup_{j=1}^N B_\varepsilon(x_j) = F + B_\varepsilon$.

We claim that $G \equiv \mathrm{cch}(F)$ is compact since G is the range under T (given by (5.3.7)) of $\Sigma_{N-1} \times F^N$ and T is continuous. Since G is compact, G is covered by finitely many $B_\varepsilon(y)$ balls, so $G + B_\varepsilon$ is covered by finitely many $B_{2\varepsilon}(y)$ balls. Since $G + B_\varepsilon$ is convex and contains $F + B_\varepsilon$, we see $\mathrm{ch}(K)$ is covered by finitely many $B_{2\varepsilon}$ balls and is thus totally bounded. $\square$

Remark. Totally bounded is defined by $A \subset \bigcup_{i=1}^{n} B_\varepsilon(x_i)$ for $x_i \in A$ and in the above, we only have $A \subset \bigcup_{i=1}^{n} B_\varepsilon(y_i)$ for $y_i \in X$. However, if $B_\varepsilon(y) \cap A \neq \emptyset$, we pick x in the intersection and note that $x \in B_\varepsilon(y) \Rightarrow B_\varepsilon(y) \subset B_{2\varepsilon}(x)$ to see we get the more restrictive notion.

Notes and Historical Remarks.

> Since my student years Minkowski was my best, most dependable friend who supported me with all the depth and loyalty that was so characteristic of him. Our science, which we loved above all else, brought us together; it seemed to us a garden full of flowers. In it, we enjoyed looking for hidden pathways and discovered many a new perspective that appealed to our sense of beauty, and when one of us showed it to the other and we marveled over it together, our joy was complete. He was for me a rare gift from heaven and I must be grateful to have possessed that gift for so long. Now death has suddenly torn him from our midst. However, what death cannot take away is his noble image in our hearts and the knowledge that his spirit continues to be active in us.
>
> —D. Hilbert, obituary for Minkowski [**427**]

The modern theory of convex sets was initiated by Minkowski in a series of works summarized in the posthumous work [**659**] discussed in the Notes to Section 5.2. In particular, he proved Minkowski's inequality for sums using an approach close to the one in this section and developed the notion of gauge. Another pioneer in convex sets was Carathéodory, whose work we return to in Section 5.4 of Part 3; there is a capsule biography in Section 5.6 of Part 2A.

The modern theory of convex functions is often credited to a 1906 paper of Jensen [**451**], who focused on $\frac{1}{2}$-convexity and also stated the discrete Jensen inequality. Johan Ludwig Jensen (1859–1925) was a Danish mathematician who spent his life as the top engineer of the Danish telephone company (head of their technical department from 1890 to 1925), doing his mathematics as an amateur. Even though he is one of Denmark's most influential mathematicians, he was never made a member of the Danish Academy because he had no advanced degrees! For a time, the Danish post office used the discrete Jensen inequality as their postmark! Despite the name, the discrete Jensen inequality for $\theta_n = 1/n$ appeared earlier than Jensen in Grolous [**371**] and the general discrete inequality in Hölder [**430**] and Henderson [**416**]. In discussing the early history of convexity, one should mention three remarkable papers [**345, 346, 347**] from 1873–78 of Josiah Willard Gibbs (1839–1903) who spent his career as a chemist and physicist at Yale.

For book presentations of convexity, see [**271, 554, 709, 720, 793, 796**] and my personal favorite, Simon [**856**]. In particular, Simon [**856**] has three chapters on inequalities that come from convexity; see also Garling [**339**].

We will not have space to discuss many of these useful inequalities, but see Problems 24–26 on rearrangement inequalities.

The inequality (5.3.25) is sometimes called Cauchy's inequality after its first appearance in Cauchy [168]. Bullen et al. [139] have fifty-two proofs of it! Maligranda [623] shows that it is equivalent to Hölder's inequality for sums (akin to our argument in (5.3.47) for the integral version).

As we've seen, Minkowski's inequality is intimately connected to convexity of the unit ball of L^p. For $1 < p < \infty$, the balls have a stronger property, namely, a norm on a Banach space is called *uniformly convex* if and only if $\forall \varepsilon\, \exists \delta\, \forall x, y$ with $\|x\| \leq 1$, $\|y\| \leq 1$, $\|\frac{1}{2}(x+y)\| > 1 - \delta \Rightarrow \|x - y\| < \varepsilon$. This notion was introduced by Clarkson [200]. In Theorem 5.7.12, we'll see that every uniformly convex space is reflexive. Clarkson [200] proved if $2 \leq p < \infty$, then

$$\left\| \frac{f+g}{2} \right\|_p^p + \left\| \frac{f-g}{2} \right\|_p^p \leq \tfrac{1}{2}\left(\|f\|_p^p + \|g\|_p^p \right) \tag{5.3.80}$$

(see Problem 19), and if $1 < p < 2$ and $q = p/(p-1)$, then

$$\left\| \frac{f+g}{2} \right\|_p^q + \left\| \frac{f-g}{2} \right\|_p^q \leq \left(\tfrac{1}{2}\|f\|_p^p + \tfrac{1}{2}\|g\|_p^p \right)^{q/p} \tag{5.3.81}$$

which implies uniform convexity (Problem 20). Hanner [392] determined the optimal $\delta(\varepsilon)$ for L^p, $1 < p < \infty$.

Orlicz [690] and Birnbaum–Orlicz [94] developed an extension of L^p spaces. If F is a function on $\mathbb{R}$, with $F(-x) = F(x)$, $F(0) = 0$, and F monotone and convex on $(0, \infty)$, and if G is the conjugate convex function $G(y) = \sup_x[xy - F(x)]$, Orlicz defined the *Orlicz space* as those f's with

$$\|f\|_F^{(\mathrm{Or})} = \sup\left\{ \left| \int f(x)g(x)\, d\mu(x) \right| \,\middle|\, \int G(|g(x)|)\, d\mu(x) \leq 1 \right\} \tag{5.3.82}$$

finite. An alternate definition and norm is due to Luxemburg [611] and discussed in Problem 16. For book discussions of Orlicz spaces, see Krasnosel'skiĭ–Rutickiĭ [522], Simon [856], and Zaanen [1012].

Mazur's theorem (Theorem 5.3.17) is from Mazur [642]. In Section 5.12, we'll prove an analog (the Krein–Šmulin theorem) for the weak topology.

Problems

1. (a) Prove that $f \colon A \to \mathbb{R}$ is convex if and only if $\{(x, z) \mid z \geq f(x)\} \subset A \times \mathbb{R}$ is a convex set.

(b) If $f \colon A \to \mathbb{R}$ is convex, prove that for any α, $\{x \mid f(x) \geq \alpha\}$ is a convex set.

2. Let f be a bounded measurable function on (a, b) which is midpoint convex. Prove that f is equal a.e. to a continuous, and so convex. (*Hint:* Pick an approximate identity, j_n, supported on $(-\frac{1}{n}, \frac{1}{n})$. Let $f_n = j_n * f$ on $(a + \frac{1}{n}, b - \frac{1}{n})$. Prove that $\{f_n\}_{n=1}^\infty$ are equicontinuous on each $(a + \delta, b - \delta)$ by using the idea behind Theorem 5.3.12 and conclude that $\lim f_n$ exists, is continuous, and equals f a.e.)

3. (a) Let F be a C^2 function on an open set A in $\mathbb{R}^\nu$. Fix $x_0 \in A$, and for $v \in \mathbb{R}^\nu$, let $f_v(t) = f(x_0 + tv)$ for small t. Prove that $f_v''(0) \geq 0$ for all v if and only if $\frac{\partial^2 F}{\partial x_i \partial x_j}(x_0)$ is a positive matrix.

   (b) Prove Theorem 5.3.2.

4. This will use Theorem 5.3.12 to prove Theorem 5.3.3.

   (a) If $c \in (a, b)$ and f is convex on (a, b), prove that $f(x) - (x - c)(D^* f)(x)$ is monotone increasing in (c, b) and monotone decreasing in (a, c).

   (b) Prove that $f(a+)$ and $f(b-)$ exist (although they could be infinite).

   (c) If $f : [a, b]$ is convex on (a, b), prove it is convex on $[a, b]$ if and only if $f(a) \geq f(a+)$, $f(b) \geq f(b-)$.

5. Let F be a convex function in (a, ∞).

   (a) Prove that $x \mapsto (D^+ F)(x)$ is measurable. (*Hint:* Monotonicity.)

   (b) For $x > y > a$, prove that

   $$F(x) - F(y) = \int_y^x (D^+ F)(u)\, du \qquad (5.3.83)$$

   (c) Prove that $\lim_{x \to \infty} (D^+ F)(x) = \alpha$ exists (α may be $+\infty$).

   (d) Prove that

   $$\lim_{x \to \infty} \frac{F(x)}{x} = \alpha \qquad (5.3.84)$$

6. (a) If f is convex on $\mathbb{R}$ and (5.3.20) holds, prove first that $f(0) \leq f(x)$ for all x and then that $0 < x < y \Rightarrow f(x) \leq f(y)$.

   (b) If f defined on $\mathbb{R}$ obeys (5.3.20) and is convex on $(0, \infty)$, continuous at $x = 0$, and monotone on $(0, \infty)$, prove that f is convex on $\mathbb{R}$.

   (c) If f obeys (b), prove that $g(z) = f(|z|)$ is convex on $\mathbb{C}$.

7. This will provide a geometric proof of the arithmetic-geometric mean, (5.3.22). Figure 5.3.5 shows a semicircle with diameter broken into two parts of size b and a and an embedded right triangle.

   (a) Prove that altitude, c, has length $\sqrt{ab}$. (*Hint:* Similar triangles.)

   (b) Show $c \leq$ radius of circle $= \frac{1}{2}(a + b)$ and conclude (5.3.22).

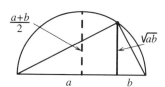

Figure 5.3.5. Geometric proof of arithmetic-geometric inequality.

8. Suppose one has Hölder's inequality for any positive Baire μ on a compact Hausdorff space, X. Prove it for positive Baire measures on σ-compact spaces. (*Hint*: Let K_n be a set of compacts as specified in the definition of σ-compact and apply Hölder to $(f\chi_{K_n})(g\chi_{K_n})$.)

9. Suppose μ is a Baire measure on a compact Hausdorff space, X. Given f, a Baire measure on X, let

$$f_{\alpha\beta}(x) = \begin{cases} f(x) & \text{if } \alpha \le |f(x)| \le \beta \\ 0 & \text{if } |f(x)| < \alpha \text{ or } |f(x)| > \beta \end{cases}$$

Prove that $\|f\|_p = \lim_{\beta\uparrow\infty} \lim_{\alpha\downarrow 0} \|f_{\alpha\beta}\|_p$ and conclude Hölder's inequality for general f, g from the result for f, g of the form e^F, e^G for bounded Baire F and G.

10. Prove (5.3.57).

11. Suppose F obeys (5.3.65). For any c, let

$$\pi_c = \{(x, y) \mid x \in (a, b), y \ge F(c) + g(c)(x - c)\}$$

Prove that $\bigcap_{c\in(a,b)} \pi_c = \{(x, y) \mid x \in (a, b), g \ge F(x)\}$ and use this to conclude that F is convex.

12. (a) Prove that Jensen's inequality for continuous f's implies it for general f's.

(b) For any finite number of continuous functions, $f_1, \ldots, f_\ell$, and any probability measure $d\mu$ on X, a compact Hausdorff space, show there is a sequence $d\nu_1, d\nu_2, \ldots$ of probability measures where each $d\nu_j$ is a finite combination of point masses, so for $k = 1, \ldots, \ell$, $\int f_k \, d\mu = \lim_{j\to\infty} \int f_k \, d\nu_j$.

(c) Prove that Jensen's inequality for f continuous and $d\mu$ a finite combination of point masses is just the discrete Jensen inequality.

(d) Deduce the general Jensen inequality from the discrete one.

13. Let $A \subset \mathbb{R}^\nu$ be an open convex set and $F\colon A \to \mathbb{R}$ a convex function. Let $f_1, \ldots, f_\nu \in L^1(X, d\mu)$, with $d\mu$ a probability measure, so that for a.e. x,

$(f_1(x), \dots, f_\nu(x)) \in A$. Prove that

$$F\left(\int f_1(x)\,d\mu(x), \dots, \int f_\nu(x)\,d\mu(x)\right) \leq \int F(f_1(x), \dots, f_\nu(x))\,d\mu(x)$$

14. Let $f\colon (a,b) \to \mathbb{R}$. Prove that f is convex if and only if for all $a < x < y < z < b$, we have the determinant

$$\begin{vmatrix} x & f(x) & 1 \\ y & f(y) & 1 \\ z & f(z) & 1 \end{vmatrix} \geq 0$$

15. A cone, K, is a subset of V, a real vector space, so that $\lambda \geq 0$ and $x \in K \Rightarrow \lambda x \in K$. Prove that a cone is convex if and only if $x, y \in K \Rightarrow x + y \in K$. How is this related to Theorem 5.3.8?

16. Let $F\colon [0,\infty)$ be convex with $F(0) = 0$ and $F(y) > 0$ for $y > 0$. For f a Baire function on a compact Hausdorff space, X, with Baire probability measure, μ, define (the value may be $+\infty$)

$$Q_F(f) = \int F(|f(x)|)\,d\mu(x) \tag{5.3.85}$$

Let $L^{(F)}(X, d\mu)$ be the equivalence classes equal a.e. of those f with $Q_F(\alpha f) < \infty$ for some $\alpha > 0$. Define the *Luxemburg norm* on $L^{(F)}$ by

$$\|f\|_F = \inf\{\lambda > 0 \mid Q_F(\lambda^{-1} f) \leq 1\} \tag{5.3.86}$$

Prove that this is a norm and that $L^{(F)}$ is complete. This is called the *Orlicz space* associated to F. See the Notes for references to this subject.

17. Let F be real-valued and defined and be convex on an open convex set, A, of normed linear space, X.

(a) Prove that if $\{x \mid \|x - x_0\| \leq r\} \subset A$, then for such x,

$$|F(x) - F(x_0)| \leq 2\|x - x_0\|r^{-1} \sup_{\|y - x_0\| \leq r} |F(y)|$$

(b) Prove that if $A = \{x \mid \|x\| < 1\}$ and F is bounded there, then F is continuous on each $\{x \mid \|x\| < 1 - \varepsilon\}$ for $\varepsilon > 0$.

18. Let $\mathbb{R}$ be viewed as a vector space over $\mathbb{Q}$. Let $\{e_j\}_{j \in J}$ be an algebraic basis and $f(\lambda_0 e_{j_0} + \sum_{k=1}^n \lambda_{j_k} e_{j_k}) = \lambda_0$ for a fixed $j_0 \in I$. Prove that for θ rational in $(0, 1)$, we have

$$f((1 - \theta)x + \theta y) = (1 - \theta)f(x) + \theta f(y)$$

but that f is not continuous.

19. This will have the reader prove (5.3.80) following Boas [**96**]. Let $\alpha, \beta \in \mathbb{C}$. Let $2 \leq p < \infty$.

    (a) Prove that $(|\alpha + \beta|^p + |\alpha - \beta|^p)^{1/p} \leq (|\alpha + \beta|^2 + |\alpha - \beta|^2)^{1/2}$.

    (b) Prove that $(|\alpha + \beta|)^2 + |\alpha - \beta|^2)^{1/2} \leq \sqrt{2}\,(|\alpha|^2 + |\beta|^2)^{1/2}$.

    (c) Prove that $(|\alpha|^2 + |\beta|^2)^{1/2} \leq 2^{\frac{1}{2} - \frac{1}{p}}(|\alpha|^p + |\beta|^p)^{1/p}$.

    (d) Prove that $(|\alpha + \beta|^p + |\alpha - \beta|^p)^{1/p} \leq 2^{1 - \frac{1}{p}}(|\alpha|^p + |\beta|^p)^{1/p}$.

    (e) Prove (5.3.80).

20. Show that (5.3.80)/(5.3.81) imply uniform convexity of L^p for $1 < p < \infty$.

21. Are L^1 or L^∞ uniformly convex?

22. Let $\mathrm{Conv}(A)$ be the nonnegative convex continuous functions on a convex set, A, in X, an NLS. Suppose A is a compact Hausdorff space in the induced topology.

    (a) If $f, g \in \mathrm{Conv}(A)$, prove that $f + g$ and f^2 are in $\mathrm{Conv}(A)$.

    (b) Let $Q = \mathrm{Conv}(A) - \mathrm{Conv}(A)$. Prove that is an algebra.

    (c) Suppose you know (as we'll prove in Section 5.5) that the continuous linear functions on X separate points. Prove that $\overline{Q}^{\|\cdot\|_\infty} = C_{\mathbb{R}}(X)$.

23. (a) If $F = \{x_j\}_{j=1}^N$ is a finite subset of a Banach space over $\mathbb{K}$, prove that the circled convex hull (which is $\{\sum_{j=1}^N \theta_j x_j \mid \theta_j \in \mathbb{K}, \sum_{j=1}^N |\theta_j| \leq 1\}$) is compact.

    (b) Prove Mazur's theorem for a circled closed convex hull.

    The next three problems introduce some ideas of convexity and rearrangement inequalities. Let $a_1, a_2, \ldots, a_\nu \in \mathbb{R}_+^\nu = [0, \infty)^\nu$. We define a^* to be that permutation of $a_1, \ldots, a_\nu$ so that

    $$a_1^* \geq \ldots \geq a_\nu^* \tag{5.3.87}$$

    called the *symmetric decreasing rearrangement* of a. Given a permutation $\pi \in \Sigma_\nu$, we define a_π by

    $$(a_\pi)_j = a_{\pi^{-1}(j)} \tag{5.3.88}$$

    We define $S_k(a)$ for $k = 1, \ldots, \nu$ by

    $$S_k(a) = \sum_{j=1}^k a_j^* \tag{5.3.89}$$

    We say that a *majorizes* b *in the Hardy–Littlewood–Pólya sense* and write $b \prec_{\mathrm{HLP}} a$ if and only if $a, b \in \mathbb{R}_+^\nu$ and

    $$S_k(b) \leq S_k(a); \quad k = 1, 2, \ldots, \nu - 1 \tag{5.3.90}$$
    $$S_k(b) = S_k(a); \quad k = \nu \tag{5.3.91}$$

24. In this problem the reader will prove the *HLP theorem*: a majorizes b if and only if b is in the convex hull, $K(a)$, of $\{a_\pi \mid \pi \in \Sigma\}$. You will need to use the separating hyperplane theorems of Section 5.11

(a) Prove that on $\mathbb{R}_\nu^+$

$$S_k(a) = \sup_{j_1,\ldots,j_k \text{ distinct}} a_{j_1} + \ldots + a_{j_k} \tag{5.3.92}$$

and conclude that on $\mathbb{R}_\nu^+$, $a \mapsto S_k(a)$ is convex so that $b \in K(a) \Rightarrow b \prec_{\text{HLP}} a$.

(b) If $b \notin K(a)$, prove there is $\ell \in \mathbb{R}^\nu$ so that

$$\ell(b^*) \geq \max_{\pi \in \Sigma_\nu} \ell(a_\pi) \tag{5.3.93}$$

Without loss, prove one can take $\ell_1 \geq \ell_2 \geq \ldots \geq \ell_\nu$.

(c) Prove that for any $\ell_j \subset \mathbb{R}^\nu$:

$$\sum_{j=1}^{\nu} \ell_j(c_j) = \ell_\nu(c_1 + \ldots + c_\nu) + \sum_{j=1}^{\nu-1}(\ell_{\nu-j} - \ell_{\nu-j+1})\left(\sum_{k=1}^{\nu-j} c_k\right) \tag{5.3.94}$$

(d) If $b \prec_{\text{HLP}} a$ and $\ell_1 \geq \ell_2 \geq \ldots \geq \ell_\nu$ prove that

$$\ell(b^*) \leq \ell(a^*) \tag{5.3.95}$$

(e) Conclude that $b \notin K(a) \Rightarrow \sim (b \prec_{\text{HLP}} a)$.

25. Let $a, b \in \mathbb{R}^\nu$ and let $|a| \in \mathbb{R}^\nu$ be given by $|a|_j = |a_j|$. We say a *majorizes* b *in the Markus sense* and write $b \prec_M a$ if and only if

$$S_k(|b|) \leq S_k(|a|), \quad k = 1, \ldots, \nu \tag{5.3.96}$$

Let $\widetilde{\Sigma}_\nu$ be the group of $2^\nu \nu!$ elements that acts on $\mathbb{R}^\nu$ by permuting the indices and flipping a subset of the signs. By mimicking the arguments in Problem 24, prove *Markus' theorem* that $b \prec_M a$ if and only if b is in the convex hull of $\{a_\pi \mid \pi \in \widetilde{\Sigma}_\nu\}$.

26. Let φ be a function on $(0, \infty)$ so that $t \mapsto \varphi(e^t)$ is a monotone increasing positive convex function of t. This problem will prove a theorem of Weyl that for $a, b \in \mathbb{R}_\nu^+$

$$\prod_{j=1}^{k} b_j^* \leq \prod_{j=1}^{k} a_j^*, j = 1, \ldots, \nu \Rightarrow \sum_{j=1}^{\nu} \varphi(b_j) \leq \sum_{j=1}^{\nu} \varphi(a_j) \tag{5.3.97}$$

(a) Show it suffices to consider the case $b_\nu \geq 1$, $a_\nu \geq 1$. (*Hint:* For $\zeta = \min(a_\nu, b_\nu)$ replace a, b, by $\zeta^{-1} a, \zeta^{-1} b$.)

(b) Prove that $\Phi(c_1, \ldots, c_\nu) = \sum_{j=1}^{\nu} \varphi(e^{|c_j|})$ is convex in $\mathbb{R}^\nu$.

(c) Define $c_j = \log a_j$, $d_j = \log b_j$. Prove that in terms of the Markus majorization of Problem 25, we have $d \prec_M c$ if LHS of (5.3.97) holds.

(d) Prove (5.3.97). (You'll need Problem 25.)

(e) Prove that for any $\alpha > 0$

$$\text{LHS of } (5.3.97) \Rightarrow \sum_{j=1}^{\nu} |b_j|^\alpha \leq \sum_{j=1}^{\nu} |a_j|^\alpha$$

Remarks. 1. Majorization has its roots in a 1902 paper of Muirhead [**669**] that deduced a consequence of what we call $b \prec_{\text{HLP}} a$ and was raised to high art in Hardy–Littlewood–Pólya [**397**] who, in particular, proved the theorem in Problem 24. One can also apply majorization to functions more complicated than those in Problem 26 and, in particular, to a family of functions studied by Schur [**828**].

2. $b \prec_M a$ goes back to Markus [**636**] although the idea appeared earlier in Weyl [**985**] who proved the result in Problem 26.

3. Weyl's theorem is useful to obtain results on singular values, $\mu_n(A)$, (defined in Section 3.5 of Part 4) and eigenvalues, $\lambda_n(A)$, of a compact operator, A. One shows that $\prod_{j=1}^k |\lambda_j(A)| \leq \prod_{j=1}^k |\mu_j(A)|$ and from that deduces (using (5.3.97)), for all $p > 0$, that $\sum_{j=1}^\infty |\lambda_j(A)|^p \leq \sum_{j=1}^\infty |\mu_j(A)|^p$. For $p \geq 1$, we have a different proof of this in Section 3.9 of Part 3. Since $\prod_{j=1}^k \mu_j(AB) \leq \prod_{j=1}^k \mu_j(A)\mu_j(B)$ is easy, one obtains from (5.3.97) Horn's inequality [**435**] that $\sum_{j=1}^\infty \mu_j(AB)^p \leq \sum_{j=1}^\alpha \mu_j(A)^p \mu_j(B)^p$ for all $p > 0$.

4. Marshall–Olkin [**638**] is a whole book on majorization while Simon [**856**] has a chapter on the subject.

5. The other major rearrangement inequalities are those of Brascamp–Lieb–Luttinger [**126**] which we discuss briefly in the Notes to Section 6.2 of Part 3.

6. Section 2.2 of Part 3 discusses decreasing rearrangements of functions.

27. Provide the details of the proof to Theorem 5.3.10.

5.4. The Baire Category Theorem and Applications

In this section, we prove a basic fact about complete metric spaces and discuss several kinds of applications—to a notion of genericity that provides a "nonconstructive" way of showing certain apparently singular objects exist, to various applications in the theory of linear functionals and linear operators on a Banach space, and as part of a construction of certain interesting sets.

Theorem 5.4.1 (Baire Category Theorem). *A countable intersection of dense open subsets of a complete metric space is dense.*

Remarks. 1. The end of the section discusses "category," where the theorem takes its name from and gives the more common form of this theorem.

2. Problem 1 shows this result can be false in a metric space that is not complete.

Proof. Let (X, ρ) be a complete metric space and let $\{A_n\}_{n=1}^\infty$ be a sequence of dense open sets. Let $x \in X$ and $\varepsilon > 0$ be given. We'll construct $x_\infty \in \bigcap_{n=1}^\infty A_n$ with $\rho(x, x_\infty) < \varepsilon$, proving the required density.

Since A_1 is dense, find $x_1 \in A_1$ so $\rho(x, x_1) < \varepsilon/3$. Since A_1 is open, find $\delta_1 > 0$ with $2\delta_1 < \varepsilon/3$ so that $B_{2\delta_1}(x_1) \subset A_1$. We now pick $x_2, \delta_2, x_3, \delta_3, \ldots$ inductively so $\rho(x_{n-1}, x_n) < \delta_{n-1}$, $x_n \in A_n$, and δ_n so $2\delta_n < \varepsilon/3^n$ and $B_{2\delta_n}(x_n) \subset A_n \cap B_{\delta_{n-1}}(x_{n-1})$. Because A_n is dense, we can pick x_n with the required property, and since $x_n \in A_n \cap B_{\delta_{n-1}}(x_{n-1})$, which is open, we can pick δ_n.

By construction, $\rho(x_{n-1}, x_n) < \varepsilon/2(3^{n-1})$, so for $k = 1, 2, \ldots$, $\rho(x_n, x_{n+k}) < \frac{1}{2}\varepsilon[\frac{1}{3^n} + \frac{1}{3^{n+1}} + \ldots] = \frac{3}{4}\frac{\varepsilon}{3^n}$ is Cauchy. Thus, $x_n \to x_\infty$ for some $x_\infty \in X$. Also, by construction, $\overline{B_{\delta_n}(x_n)} \subset A_n \cap B_{\delta_{n-1}}(x_{n-1})$. Thus, $x_n, x_{n+1}, \ldots, x_{n+k}, \ldots \in \overline{B_{\delta_n}(x_n)}$, so $x_\infty \in \overline{B_{\delta_n}(x_n)} \subset A_n$, that is, $x_\infty \in \bigcap_{n=1}^\infty A_n$.

Finally, by construction,

$$\rho(x, x_\infty) \leq \frac{\varepsilon}{3} + \frac{1}{2}\left(\frac{\varepsilon}{3} + \frac{\varepsilon}{3^2} + \ldots\right) \leq \frac{\varepsilon}{3} + \frac{\varepsilon}{4} < \varepsilon$$

completing the construction. □

Corollary 5.4.2. *A countable intersection of dense G_δ's in a complete metric space is a dense G_δ.*

Corollary 5.4.3. *Every dense G_δ in a complete metric space with no isolated points is uncountable.*

Proof. If A is a dense G_δ and $A = \{x_n\}_{n=1}^\infty$ is countable, note that $X \setminus \{x_n\}$ is a dense open set, so $A \cap \bigcap_{n=0}^\infty (X \setminus \{x_n\}) = \emptyset$, and so not dense. □

It is easy to see such G_δ's are locally uncountable (see Problem 2). There is a connection between Cantor's original proof that $\mathbb{R}$ is uncountable and Corollary 5.4.3. (The standard textbook proof of uncountability—see Section 1.6—is Cantor's second and later proof of the fact.) Indeed, the proof of Theorem 5.4.1 in Problem 22 is a refinement of a proof of Cantor's result.

Definition. Let X be a metric space. A family, $\mathcal{F}$, of *generic sets* is a family of dense subsets of X closed under countable intersections.

The family of dense G_δ's of a complete metric space is a generic family. If some property holds on a dense G_δ, we say it is *Baire generic*.

The family of Borel subsets $A \subset [0,1]$ (or $A \subset \mathbb{R}^\nu$) with $|[0,1] \setminus A| = 0$, where $|\cdot|$ is Lebesgue measure, is a generic family. If a property holds Lebesgue a.e., we say it is *Lebesgue generic*.

Example 5.4.4. This will construct a set, S, in $[0,1]$ which is Baire generic, while its complement in $[0,1]$ is Lebesgue generic, showing that these notions can be very different. Let $\{q_n\}_{n=1}^\infty$ be a counting of the rationals. Let

$$S_{n,m} = \left\{ x \in [0,1] \mid |x - q_n| < \frac{1}{2^{m+n+1}} \right\} \tag{5.4.1}$$

which is open with ($|\cdot| =$ Lebesgue measure)

$$|S_{n,m}| \leq \frac{1}{2^{n+m}} \tag{5.4.2}$$

Let

$$S_m = \bigcup_{n=1}^\infty S_{n,m} \tag{5.4.3}$$

so S_m is a dense open set (since $\mathbb{Q} \cap [0,1] \subset S_m$) with

$$|S_m| \leq \sum_{n=1}^\infty 2^{-m-n} = 2^{-m} \tag{5.4.4}$$

Thus, $S = \cap S_m$ is a dense G_δ (so Baire generic) with

$$|S| = 0 \tag{5.4.5}$$

so $[0,1] \setminus S$ is Lebesgue generic. $\qquad\qquad\qquad\qquad\qquad\qquad\qquad\square$

Example 5.4.5 (Diophantine Approximation). This will provide less artificial disjoint Lebesgue and Baire generic sets. It often happens that in iterative procedures, one comes across division by $(q\alpha - p)$, where p and q are integers and α is irrational. Thus, we care about real numbers, α, that obey

$$\left| \alpha - \frac{p}{q} \right| \geq \frac{C}{q^\beta} \tag{5.4.6}$$

for some $C > 0$ and β and all p and q. In Problem 4, the reader will show for each $\beta > 2$,

$$D_\beta = \{\alpha \in [0,1] \mid \exists C > 0, \forall p, q \in \mathbb{Z}, (5.4.6) \text{ holds}\} \tag{5.4.7}$$

is Lebesgue generic.

A *Liouville number* is an α so that for all $n = 1, 2, \ldots$, there is $p, q \in \mathbb{Z}$ so

$$\left| \alpha - \frac{p}{q} \right| < \frac{1}{q^n} \tag{5.4.8}$$

Often one considers even better approximation by rationals, like for all $n = 1, 2, \ldots$, there is $p, q \in \mathbb{Z}$ so that $|\alpha - \frac{p}{q}| < e^{-nq}$. In Problem 5, the reader will show that if $C_{p,q,n}$, defined for $0 \le p \le q$ and $q > 1$ in $\mathbb{Z}$, are arbitrary nonnegative reals

$$L_C = \left\{ \alpha \in [0, 1] \, \middle| \, \forall n, \exists p, q \, \left| \alpha - \frac{p}{q} \right| < C_{p,q,n} \right\} \tag{5.4.9}$$

is a dense G_δ, and that if

$$\inf_n \sum_{\substack{0 \le p \le q \\ q \ge 2}} C_{p,q,n} = 0 \tag{5.4.10}$$

then L_C has Lebesgue measure zero (Problem 5). The case of (5.4.8), where $C_{p,q,n} = q^{-n}$ has $\sum_{0 \le p \le q; \, q \ge 2} C_{p,q,n} = \sum_{q=2}^{\infty} (q+1) q^{-n} \to 0$ as $n \to \infty$, showing that the α's obeying (5.4.8), is a Baire generic set disjoint from a Lebesgue generic set of the form (5.4.7) for $\beta > 2$. Liouville numbers originally entered in mathematics because they are all transcendental—Liouville proved this for $\sum_{j=1}^{\infty} 10^{-j!}$ (see Problem 6). $\qquad \square$

Example 5.4.6 (Nowhere Differentiable Functions). In Problem 7, the reader will show that in $C([0, 1])$, the set of nowhere differentiable functions contains a dense G_δ. This will be a "nonconstructive" way of showing there are lots of such functions to be distinguished from the more explicit construction we gave in Theorem 3.5.15. We say "nonconstructive" in quotes because, while the method doesn't provide an explicit function, the proof of the Baire category theorem, in principle, tells you how to construct such a function. $\qquad \square$

Example 5.4.7. In Problem 4 of Section 4.5, we noted that the weak topology on $\mathcal{M}_{+,1}([0, 1])$ is metrizable. In Problem 8, the reader will show that a Baire generic measure is purely singular continuous. Again, this nonconstructive approach should be distinguished from providing explicit examples like the Cantor measure. Unlike the Cantor measure, a Baire generic measure also has all of $[0, 1]$ as support (Problem 9). $\qquad \square$

Having discussed the use of the Baire category theorem to show that interesting sets are nonempty, we turn to applications in the theory of Banach spaces. We'll first prove two main theorems (the principle of uniform boundedness and the open mapping theorem) and then look at their consequences. For both proofs, the key will be showing that some set has nonempty interior, so the Baire category theorem will enter because it implies that

Lemma 5.4.8. *Let X be a complete metric space and $\{C_n\}_{n=1}^\infty$ a sequence of closed sets with $\cup_{n=1}^\infty C_n = X$. Then some C_n has nonempty interior.*

Proof. If not, with $A_n = X \backslash C_n$, each A_n is open and dense (since $C_n^{\text{int}} = \emptyset$). Thus, $\bigcap_{n=1}^\infty A_n$ is dense and so, not empty. Thus, $\bigcup_{n=1}^\infty C_n = X \backslash \bigcap_{n=1}^\infty A_n$ is not all of X. This contradiction shows that some C_n has $C_n^{\text{int}} \neq \emptyset$. $\square$

Theorem 5.4.9 (Principle of Uniform Boundedness). *Let $\mathcal{F}$ be a subset of bounded linear maps from one Banach space, X, to another one, Y. Suppose that for each $x \in X$,*

$$\sup_{T \in \mathcal{F}} \{\|Tx\|_Y\} < \infty \tag{5.4.11}$$

Then

$$\sup_{T \in \mathcal{F}} \{\|T\|_{\mathcal{L}(X,Y)}\} < \infty \tag{5.4.12}$$

Remarks. 1. This is also called the *Banach–Steinhaus theorem.*

2. In many applications, $Y = \mathbb{R}$ or $\mathbb{C}$, and we are dealing with $\mathcal{F} \subset X^*$.

Proof. Let

$$C_n = \left\{ x \in X \mid \sup_{T \in \mathcal{F}} \|Tx\| \leq n \right\} \tag{5.4.13}$$

If $x_m \to x$ and $x_m \in C_n$, then for $T \in \mathcal{F}$,

$$\|Tx\| = \lim_m \|Tx_m\| \leq n$$

so $x \in C_n$, that is, C_n is closed. (Alternatively, $C_n = \bigcap_{T \in \mathcal{F}} T^{-1}[\{y \mid \|y\|_Y \leq n\}]$ is an intersection of closed sets.) By (5.4.11), $\bigcup_{n=1}^\infty C_n = X$. By Lemma 5.4.8, for some n, $C_n^{\text{int}} \neq \emptyset$, that is, there exist x_0, δ, and n so $B_\delta(x_0) \subset C_n$, that is,

$$\|x - x_0\| < \delta \text{ and } T \in \mathcal{F} \Rightarrow \|Tx\| \leq n \tag{5.4.14}$$

Letting $y = x - x_0$, we see

$$\|y\| < \delta \text{ and } T \in \mathcal{F} \Rightarrow \|Ty\| \leq n + \sup_{T \in \mathcal{F}} \|Tx_0\| \equiv C \tag{5.4.15}$$

Replacing y by $y/(1+\varepsilon)$ and taking $\varepsilon \downarrow 0$, we see that we can change $\|y\| < \delta$ to $\|y\| \leq \delta$. Thus,

$$T \in \mathcal{F} \Rightarrow \|T\| \leq \delta^{-1} C \tag{5.4.16}$$

proving (5.4.12). $\square$

The contrapositive of this says that if $\sup_{T \in \mathcal{F}} \|T\| = \infty$, then for some x, $\sup_{T \in \mathcal{F}} \|Tx\| = \infty$ but we've proven more.

Theorem 5.4.10. (Strong Contrapositive of Uniform Boundedness Principle). *Let $\mathcal{F}$ be a family of maps from one Banach space to another. If*

$$\sup_{T \in \mathcal{F}} \|T\| = \infty \tag{5.4.17}$$

then

$$\{x \mid \sup_{T \in \mathcal{F}} \|Tx\| < \infty\} \tag{5.4.18}$$

is a countable union of closed nowhere dense sets.

Remark. Equivalently $\{x \mid \sup_{T \in \mathcal{F}} \|Tx\| = \infty\}$ is a dense G_δ.

Proof. As in the last proof, C_n is closed. If some C_n had $C_n^{\text{int}} \neq \emptyset$, as in that proof, (5.4.17) would fail, so each C_n is nowhere dense. But the set in (5.4.18) is $\cup_{n=1}^\infty C_n$. $\quad\square$

Theorem 5.4.11 (Open Mapping Theorem). *Let $T\colon X \to Y$ be a bounded linear map between Banach spaces. If $\mathrm{Ran}(T)$ is all of Y, then T is open, that is, if $A \subset X$ is open in X, then $T[A]$ is open in Y.*

Proof. Since we'll need balls in both X and Y, we use $B_r^X(x_0)$ and $B_r^Y(y_0)$. The key will be proving that for some r, $T[B_r^X]$ has a nonempty interior. The Baire category theorem will imply some $\overline{T[B_r^X]}$ has nonempty interior, and we'll need a little song-and-dance to show this implies that some $T[B_r^X]$ has nonempty interior.

For each integer, n, let
$$C_n = \overline{T[B_n^X]} \tag{5.4.19}$$
Each C_n is closed, and since $\bigcup_{n=1}^\infty T[B_n^X] = Y$, we have $\bigcup_{n=1}^\infty C_n = Y$. Thus, by Lemma 5.4.8, some C_n has nonempty interior, that is, for some n, some $y_0 \in Y$, and $\rho > 0$,
$$B_\rho^Y(y_0) \subset \overline{T[B_n^X]} \tag{5.4.20}$$

Given $y \in B_\rho^Y(0)$, find $x_m \in B_n^X$ so $T(x_m) \to y_0 + y$. Find $z_m \in B_n^X$ so that $T(z_m) \to y_0$. Then $T(x_m - z_m) \to y$, proving that
$$B_\rho^Y(0) \subset \overline{T[B_{2n}^X]} \tag{5.4.21}$$

Since
$$T[B_{\lambda\alpha}^X] = \lambda T[B_\alpha^X] \tag{5.4.22}$$
for $\lambda, \alpha > 0$, we conclude that there is $\varepsilon > 0$ so that
$$B_\varepsilon^Y \subset \overline{T[B_{1/2}^X]} \tag{5.4.23}$$

Then, by (5.4.22), for each $n = 0, 1, 2, \ldots$,
$$B_{\varepsilon/2^n}^Y \subset \overline{T[B_{1/2^{n+1}}^X]} \tag{5.4.24}$$

We'll use this to prove that

$$B_\varepsilon^Y \subset T[B_1^X] \tag{5.4.25}$$

Given $y \in B_\varepsilon^Y$, pick $x_0, x_1, \ldots$ inductively so that

$$x_j \in B_{1/2^{j+1}}^X \text{ and } \|y - T(x_0 + \cdots + x_j)\| < \frac{\varepsilon}{2^{j+1}} \tag{5.4.26}$$

We can first pick $x_0 \in B_{1/2}$ so $\|y - Tx_0\| < \varepsilon/2$ by (5.4.23), and then x_j inductively since $y - T(x_0 + \cdots + x_{j-1}) \in B_{\varepsilon/2^j}^Y$, and we have (5.4.24). Since $\sum_{j=0}^n x_j$ is Cauchy, it has a limit $x \in B_1^X$, so $Tx = y$. This proves (5.4.25).

Having completed the song-and-dance to get rid of the need to take closure, we can complete the proof. Let U be open and $y \in T[U]$, so there is $x \in U$ with $Tx = y$. Find δ so $B_\delta^X(x) \subset U$. By (5.4.25) and (5.4.22),

$$T[B_\delta^X(0)] \supset B_{\varepsilon\delta}^Y \tag{5.4.27}$$

which implies that

$$T[U] \supset T[B_\delta^X(x)] \supset B_{\varepsilon\delta}^Y(y) \tag{5.4.28}$$

so $T[U]$ is open. $\square$

Again, as with the uniform boundedness principle, the proof gives more information. It shows that if some $\overline{T[B_n^X]}$ has nonempty interior, then for some ε,

$$T_\varepsilon^Y \subset T[B_1^X]$$

which implies $\operatorname{Ran} T$ is all of Y. We have thus proven

Theorem 5.4.12. *Let $T : X \to Y$ be a bounded linear transformation. Then either $\operatorname{Ran} T = Y$ or else $Y \setminus \operatorname{Ran} T$ contains a dense G_δ.*

For example, if (Ω, Σ, μ) is a measure space with $\mu(\Omega) < \infty$ and $p_1 < p_2$, then $L^{p_2}(\Omega, d\mu) \subseteq L^{p_1}(\Omega, d\mu)$ but (unless Ω doesn't have sets of arbitrary small measure), L^{p_2} is a small set and $L^{p_1} \setminus L^{p_2}$ contains a dense G_δ.

Having proven the two main direct consequences of the Baire category theorem, we turn to their applications—a sequence of more specialized corollaries of the open mapping theorem and then a significant consequence of the principle of uniform boundedness.

Theorem 5.4.13. *Let $T: X \to Y$ be a one-one bounded linear map between Banach spaces. Suppose $\operatorname{Ran}(T)$ is closed in Y. Then there exists $\varepsilon > 0$ so that for all $x \in X$,*

$$\|Tx\| \geq \varepsilon\|x\| \tag{5.4.29}$$

Proof. Let $\widetilde{Y} = \operatorname{Ran}(T)$ so $\widetilde{Y}$ is a Banach space and $T: X \to \widetilde{Y}$ is onto. The open mapping theorem implies that for some $\varepsilon > 0$,

$$B_\varepsilon^{\widetilde{Y}} \subset T[B_1^X] \tag{5.4.30}$$

Thus, for any $0 < \delta < 1$, $T[(1-\delta)\varepsilon x / \|Tx\|] \in B_\varepsilon^{\widetilde{Y}} \subset T[B_1^X]$. Since T is one-one, we conclude that for all $\delta \in [0,1]$,

$$\left\| \frac{(1-\delta)\varepsilon x}{\|Tx\|} \right\| \leq 1 \qquad (5.4.31)$$

Since δ is arbitrarily small, this implies (5.4.29). $\qquad\square$

Theorem 5.4.14 (Inverse Mapping Theorem). *Let T be a continuous linear bijection between Banach spaces, X and Y. Then T^{-1} is continuous.*

Proof. By (5.4.29) for $x = T^{-1}y$, $\|T^{-1}y\| \leq \varepsilon^{-1}\|y\|$. $\qquad\square$

Corollary 5.4.15 (Norm Equivalence). *Let X be a vector space and $\|\cdot\|_1, \|\cdot\|_2$ two norms in which X is a Banach space. If there is C_1 so that for all $x \in X$, $\|x\|_1 \leq C_1\|x\|_2$, then there is C_2 so that for all $x \in X$, $\|x\|_2 \leq C_2\|x\|_1$.*

If X is any vector space, the subspaces X_1 and X_2 are called *complementary* if and only if

$$X_1 + X_2 = X, \qquad X_1 \cap X_2 = \{0\} \qquad (5.4.32)$$

Equivalently, any $x \in X$ can be uniquely written $x = x_1 + x_2$ with $x_j \in X_j$. We also say X_2 is a *complementary subspace* or *complement* to X_1. An important corollary to Theorem 5.4.14 is

Corollary 5.4.16. *Let X be a Banach space and X_1, X_2 complementary subspaces, each of which is closed. Then for some $\delta > 0$ and all $x_j \in X_j$, we have*

$$\delta(\|x_1\| + \|x_2\|) \leq \|x_1 + x_2\| \leq \|x_1\| + \|x_2\| \qquad (5.4.33)$$

Equivalently, the direct sum norm on $X_1 \oplus X_2$ is equivalent to $\|\cdot\|_X$.

Proof. If $T\colon X_1 \oplus X_2 \to X$ by $T(x_1 \oplus x_2) = x_1 + x_2$, then T is continuous (since the triangle inequality implies the second inequality in (5.4.33)). Thus, T^{-1} is bounded which implies that the first inequality holds. $\qquad\square$

Remark. By a Zornification, any subspace has a complement, but a closed subspace need not have a closed complement (see Problem 9 of Section 5.7 and Problems 7–9 of Section 2.1 of Part 4). If X_1 is a closed subspace of a Banach space, usually we will reserve the name complement to mean *closed* complement.

We need a preliminary for the next result. In Section 5.1 we defined the direct sum $X \oplus Y$ of the Banach spaces. The *graph*, $\Gamma(T)$, of a linear map $T\colon X \to Y$ is a subset of $X \oplus Y$ given by

$$\Gamma(T) = \{(x, Tx) \mid x \in X\} \qquad (5.4.34)$$

It is always a subspace of $X \oplus Y$ even if T is a priori not assumed continuous.

Theorem 5.4.17 (Closed Graph Theorem). *Let T be a (not a priori bounded) linear map from a Banach space, X, to another Banach space, Y. If the graph of T is closed in $X \oplus Y$, then T is a bounded linear transformation.*

Proof. By definition of direct sum, $\pi_1 \colon X \oplus Y \to X$ and $\pi_2 \colon X \oplus Y \to Y$ by $\pi_1((x,y)) = x$, $\pi_2((x,y)) = y$ are both continuous. Clearly, $\pi_1 \restriction \Gamma(T)$ is a bijection of $\Gamma(T)$ and X. Since $\Gamma(T)$ is closed, it is a Banach space, so by the inverse mapping theorem, $\pi_1^{-1} \colon X \to \Gamma(X)$ by $\pi_1^{-1}(x) = (x, Tx)$ is continuous. Since $T = \pi_2 \circ \pi_1^{-1}$, T is continuous. $\square$

To understand the depth of this result, consider three statements for convergent sequences $\{x_n\}_{n=1}^{\infty} \subset X$:

(a) $x_n \to x$
(b) Tx_n has a limit y
(c) $y = Tx$

Continuity says (a) $\Rightarrow$ (b) + (c) for every such convergent sequence. $\Gamma(T)$ closed says (a) + (b) $\Rightarrow$ (c). Theorem 5.4.17 says that one can assume (b) in trying to prove (c) to get continuity.

As a final consequence of the open mapping theorem:

Theorem 5.4.18 (Hellinger–Toeplitz Theorem). *Let $A \colon \mathcal{H} \to \mathcal{H}$ be a linear map from a Hilbert space to itself. Suppose for all $\varphi, \psi \in \mathcal{H}$, we have*

$$\langle \varphi, A\psi \rangle = \langle A\varphi, \psi \rangle \tag{5.4.35}$$

Then A is continuous.

Remark. If A obeys (5.4.35), we say that A is *Hermitian*.

Proof. We'll prove that (5.4.35) implies that $\Gamma(A)$ is closed. If $\varphi_n \to \varphi$ and $A\varphi_n \to \psi$, then

$$\begin{aligned}
\langle \eta, A\varphi \rangle &= \langle A\eta, \varphi \rangle \\
&= \lim \langle A\eta, \varphi_n \rangle \\
&= \lim \langle \eta, A\varphi_n \rangle \\
&= \langle \eta, \psi \rangle
\end{aligned}$$

Picking $\eta = A\varphi - \psi$, we see $\|A\varphi - \psi\| = 0$, so $\psi = A\varphi$. Thus, $\Gamma(A)$ is closed. $\square$

Here is an especially significant consequence of the uniform boundedness principle:

Theorem 5.4.19. *Let T and $\{T_n\}_{n=1}^{\infty}$ be a sequence of bounded linear transformations from one Banach space, X, to another one, Y. Suppose for each*

$x \in X$, $T_n x \to Tx$. *Then*

$$\sup_n \|T_n\| < \infty \qquad (5.4.36)$$

Remark. In terms of the topology we'll define later (see Section 5.7), which parallels the one for Hilbert space discussed in Section 3.7, this says that strong operator convergence *of sequences* implies uniform boundedness. If we take $Y = \mathbb{C}$, so $T, T_n \in X^*$, this says weak convergence *of sequences* implies norm boundedness. We emphasize "of sequences" because Example 3.6.9 (which easily extends to the general Banach space case) shows the result is false for general nets.

Proof. Given x, pick N so that $n > N \Rightarrow \|T_n x - Tx\| \leq 1$. Then

$$\sup_n \|T_n x\| \leq \max(1 + \|Tx\|, \{\|T_j x\|\}_{j=1}^N) \qquad (5.4.37)$$

$$< \infty$$

Thus, by Theorem 5.4.9, we have (5.4.36). $\square$

The principle of uniform boundedness is very versatile. In Problem 10, the reader will show that it implies a divergence result for Fourier series. In Problem 14, the reader will prove that it implies separate continuity of bilinear maps implies joint continuity. In Section 3.1 of Part 2A (Theorem 3.1.12), it will be used to prove Dunford's theorem that weak analyticity implies norm analyticity of Banach space-valued analytic functions.

Here is a final application of the Baire category theorem to the structure of Banach spaces.

Theorem 5.4.20. *Every Banach space, X, which is not finite-dimensional has an uncountable algebraic dimension, that is, for no countable family $\{x_j\}_{j=1}^\infty \subset X$ is*

$$\left\{ \sum_{j=1}^N \alpha_j x_j \;\middle|\; N = 1, 2, \ldots; \alpha_j \in \mathbb{K} \right\} \qquad (5.4.38)$$

all of X.

Proof. If not, let $\{x_j\}_{j=1}^\infty$ be such that (5.4.38) is all of X. Let

$$X_N = \left\{ \sum_{j=1}^N \alpha_j x_j \;\middle|\; \alpha_1, \ldots, \alpha_N \in \mathbb{K} \right\} \qquad (5.4.39)$$

By assumption, $\bigcup_{N=1}^\infty X_N = X$ and, by Corollary 5.1.5, each X_N is closed. Thus, by Lemma 5.4.8, some X_N has no empty interior.

Let $y \in X_N^{\text{int}}$, $x \in X$. Then by continuity of multiplication, $A = \{\lambda \mid y + \lambda x \in X_N^{\text{int}}\}$ is open. Since nonempty open sets of $\mathbb{K}$ have multiple points and $0 \in A$, $y + \lambda_1 x \in X_N$ for some $\lambda_1 \neq 0$. Thus, $x = \lambda_1^{-1}(y + \lambda_1 x - y) \in X_N$. Since x is arbitrary, $X = X_N$, that is, X is finite-dimensional. This contradiction proves the result. $\qquad\square$

Finally, we want to rephrase Theorem 5.4.1 in terms of "category" and make an application. A subset, A, of a metric space, X, is called *nowhere dense in X* if and only if $(\bar{A})^{\mathrm{int}} = \emptyset$. For example, the Cantor set is nowhere dense in $[0, 1]$. A countable union of nowhere dense sets is called *meager* or of *first category*. Any set not of first category is called of *second category*.

Let $\{A_n\}_{n=1}^{\infty}$ be a family of nowhere dense sets in a metric space, X. Note that a set B is dense in X if and only if $X \setminus B$ has empty interior. Thus, $B_n = X \setminus \bar{A}_n$ is a dense open set. Thus, by Theorem 5.4.1, $\bigcap B_n$ is a dense G_δ, and its complement, $\bigcup_{n=1}^{\infty} \bar{A}_n$, and so $\bigcup_{n=1}^{\infty} A_n$, has empty interior. Therefore, Theorem 5.4.1 implies and—it is easy to see—is equivalent to:

Theorem 5.4.21 (Baire Category Theorem–Strong Category Form). *A first category subset of a complete metric space has empty interior.*

Remark. If $X = \mathbb{Q} \cap [0, 1]$, each $\{x\}$ for $x \in X$ is nowhere dense, so X is first category. This shows completeness is essential for the Baire category theorem.

Obviously, since X has nonempty interior, we have

Theorem 5.4.22 (Baire Category Theorem–Weak Category Form). *Every complete metric space is second category.*

It is not hard to prove the general result from this special case (Problem 21). Here is a fascinating example one can analyze with the notion of category.

Example 5.4.23 (Knaster–Kuratowski Fan). Let C be the classical Cantor set in $[0, 1]$ (see Section 4.2). Let $K \subset C$ be those points which are endpoints of intervals in $\mathbb{R} \setminus C$, that is, $x \in K$ if and only if $x \in [0, 1]$ and $x = p/q$ with $q = 3^n$, $n = 0, 1, 2, \dots$ and $p \in \mathbb{Z}$ with $3 \nmid p$, so $K = \{0, 1, \frac{1}{3}, \frac{2}{3}, \frac{1}{9}, \frac{2}{9}, \frac{4}{9}, \frac{5}{9}, \dots\}$. In particular, K is countable.

For each $x \in [0, 1]$, let L_x be the line segment in $\mathbb{R}^2$ with endpoints $(x, 0)$ and $(\frac{1}{2}, 1)$. Let B_1 be $\mathbb{Q} \cap [0, 1]$ and $B_2 = [0, 1] \setminus B_1$, the rationals and irrationals, respectively, in $[0, 1]$. Define ($w = (w_1, w_2)$)

$$F = \bigcup_{x \in K} \{w \in L_x \mid w_2 \in B_1\} \cup \bigcup_{x \in C \setminus K} \{w \in L_x \mid w_2 \in B_2\} \qquad (5.4.40)$$

F is called the *Knaster–Kuratowski fan*. We will prove that F has the following properties:

(a) $\mathbb{R}^2 \setminus F$ is connected.

(b) $F \setminus (\frac{1}{2}, 1)$ is totally disconnected, that is, its components are single points.

(c) F is connected.

The first two are easy; the third is subtle and, perhaps, unexpected—we'll use the Baire category theorem to prove it.

Because $\mathbb{R} \setminus C$ is open, it is easy to see that $\mathbb{R}^2 \setminus \bigcup_{x \in C} L_x$ is connected. The closure of this set in $\mathbb{R}^2 \setminus F$ is all of $\mathbb{R}^2 \setminus F$, so $\mathbb{R}^2 \setminus F$ is connected by Theorem 2.1.13. This shows (a).

Let T be a component of $F \setminus (\frac{1}{2}, 1)$ and suppose T has two distinct points, w, t. If $w \in L_{x_1}$, $t \in L_{x_2}$ with $x_1 \neq x_2$, find $x \in (x_1, x_2) \setminus C$ and note that $\widetilde{L}_x$, the extension of L_x to a full line, is disjoint from $F \setminus (\frac{1}{2}, 1)$ and w, t are on opposite sides of that line. So T cannot be connected. Thus, T must lie in a single L_x. But $F \cap L_x$ is totally disconnected for any x, so T can only contain single points. This proves (b).

If F is not connected, we can find disjoint A, B with $(\frac{1}{2}, 1)$ in A so that $A \cup B = F$ and both are closed in F. In particular, if $w_n \in A$ converges to $w \in \mathbb{R}^2$, then either $w \notin F$ or $w \in A$ (and similarly for B). We'll call this the convergence property.

For each $x \in C \setminus K$, define $h(x) = \sup\{y \mid (w, y) \in B \cap L_x\}$, with the convention that $h(x) = 0$ if $B \cap L_x = \emptyset$. For each x with $h(x) > 0$, there exist $(w_n, y_n) \in B \cap L_x$ so $y_n \uparrow h(x)$. Since $(\frac{1}{2}, 1) \in A$, we must have $h(x) < 1$ by the convergence property. On the other hand, all points in $F \cap L_x$ with $y > h(x)$ lie in A. Thus, the point in $B \cap L_x$ with $y = h(x)$ is a limit in $\mathbb{R}^2$ of points in A and of points in B. Thus, by the convergence property, it must lie in $\mathbb{R}^2 \setminus F$, that is, each $h(y)$ is rational.

Let $q_1, q_2, \ldots$ be a counting of rationals in $(0, 1)$ and let $M_j = \{x \in C \setminus K \mid h(x) = q_j\}$. Suppose $x_n \to x \in C$ with $x_n \in M_j$. Then the point in L_x with $y = q_j$ is a limit of points in A and of points in B, so by the convergence property, it is not in F. So $L_x \cap F$ cannot contain the rationals, that is, $x \in C \setminus K$ also. Thus, $\overline{M}_j \subset C \setminus K$. Since K is dense in C, each M_j is nowhere dense in C. Since K is countable and all its points are not isolated in C, K is first category. Thus, $M_0 \equiv C \setminus (\bigcup_{j=1}^{\infty} M_j \cup K) = \{x \mid h(x) = 0\}$ is dense in C by the Baire category theorem in the form Theorem 5.4.21. Thus, $A \supset \bigcup_{x \in M_0} L_x$ is dense in F, so B is empty since A is closed. This contradiction proves that F is connected, and proves (c). $\square$

To put this last example in context, we want to show it could not happen if F were closed: we'll prove that if a metric space is compact and connected, then removing a single point cannot make it totally disconnected. The stronger result we'll prove will also be needed in Section 4.5 of Part 2A.

We need a definition: A *continuum* (pl. *continua*) is a nonempty, compact, connected metric space.

Theorem 5.4.24. *Let $\widehat{X}$ be a continuum and x_∞ a point in $\widehat{X}$. Let $\Omega \subset X \equiv \widehat{X} \setminus \{x_\infty\}$ be an open connected set. Then $\widehat{X} \setminus \Omega$ is connected if and only if every component of $X \setminus \Omega$ is noncompact.*

In particular, if $\Omega = \emptyset$, every component of $\widehat{X} \setminus \{x_\infty\}$ is noncompact, and so more than a single point. We begin with:

Lemma 5.4.25. *Let X be a continuum and $\{X_\alpha\}_{\alpha \in I}$ a nested set of subsets which are continua. Then $\bigcap_{\alpha \in I} X_\alpha$ is a continuum.*

Remark. By nested, we mean that, for any α, β, either $X_\alpha \subset X_\beta$ or $X_\beta \subset X_\alpha$.

Proof. By the finite intersection property (see Theorem 2.3.1), $X_\infty = \bigcap_{\alpha \in I} X_\alpha$ is nonempty and compact, so we only need to show that X_∞ is connected. If not, there are U, V closed in X and nonempty so that $U \cup V = X_\infty$. By Urysohn's lemma (see Theorem 2.2.4), there is a continuous function, f, from X to $[0,1]$ so $f \restriction U = 0$ and $f \restriction V = 1$.

Since $f[X_\alpha]$ is connected and contains 0 and 1 (since $U, V \subset X_\infty \subset X_\alpha$), $f[X_\alpha] = [0,1]$, so there exists $x_\alpha \in X_\alpha$ with $f(x_\alpha) = \frac{1}{2}$. Turn I into a directed set by $\alpha > \beta$ if $X_\alpha \subset X_\beta$ so $\{x_\alpha\}_{\alpha \in I}$ is a net in X. It has a limit point, x_∞, which lies in each X_α since the X_α are closed and nested. Therefore, $x_\infty \in X_\infty$, so in $U \cup V$, so $f(x_\infty) \in \{0,1\}$. But, by continuity of f, $f(x_\infty) = \frac{1}{2}$, a contradiction. $\qquad\square$

Lemma 5.4.26. *Let X be a continuum and $Q \subset X$ an arbitrary subset. Then there exists a continuum, Y, with $Q \subset Y \subset X$ so that if Z is a continuum, with $Q \subset Z \subset Y$, then $Z = Y$.*

Proof. The set of continua, W, with $Q \subset W \subset X$ is a partially ordered set with $W \triangleright Z$ if $W \subset Z$. By Lemma 5.4.25, every chain has an upper bound, so by Zorn's lemma, there exists Y's maximal in this order. $\qquad\square$

Proof of Theorem 5.4.24. We begin by noting that a closed set, $F \subset X$, is compact if and only if $\bar{F}$, the closure of F in $\widehat{X}$, does not contain x_∞. For suppose that $\{x_\alpha\}$, a net in F, has a limit point y in $\widehat{X}$. If $x_\infty \notin \bar{F}$, then $y \neq x_\infty$, so $y \in F$ and F is compact. On the other hand, if $x_\infty \in \bar{F}$, there is a net, $\{x_\alpha\}$, in F with x_∞ the limit in $\widehat{X}$, and so $\{x_\alpha\}$ has no limit point in F.

Suppose first that every component of $X \setminus \Omega$ is noncompact and $\widehat{X} \setminus \Omega = U \cup V$ with U, V disjoint and closed in $\widehat{X}$ with $x_\infty \in U$. Since any component, F, of $X \setminus \Omega$ is connected, either $F \cap U$ or $F \cap V$ is empty, that is, $F \subset U$

or $F \subset V$. If $F \subset V$, then $x_\infty \notin \bar{F}$, so F is compact. By assumption, this is false, so $F \subset U$. Thus, V is empty, and we have shown that $\widehat{X} \setminus \Omega$ is connected.

Next suppose that $\widehat{X} \setminus \Omega$ is connected and that F is a component of $X \setminus \Omega$. Let $\widetilde{X}$ be a minimal continuum containing $F \cup \{x_\infty\}$, which exists by Lemma 5.4.26. We will prove that $\widetilde{X} = \bar{F}$ so, in particular, $x_\infty \in \bar{F}$, and thus, F is not compact (by the first paragraph of this proof), completing the proof of the theorem.

Let $X^\sharp = \widetilde{X} \setminus \{x_\infty\}$ and suppose $X^\sharp = U \cup V$ with U, V closed (in $X^\sharp$) and $U \cap V = \emptyset$. As above, either $F \subset U$ or $F \subset V$, so we can suppose $F \subset U$. If $x_\infty \notin \bar{U}$, then U is closed in $\widetilde{X}$ and $V \cup \{x_\infty\}$ is also closed and disjoint, violating the connectedness of $\widetilde{X}$ (since both U and $V \cup \{x_\infty\}$ are nonempty). Thus, $x_\infty \in \bar{U}$.

Next, we claim $\bar{U}$ is connected, for if $\bar{U} = A \cup B$, with A, B closed and disjoint, and $x_\infty \in A$, then $A \cup V$ is closed in $\widetilde{X}$, so by connectedness of $\widetilde{X}$, $B = \emptyset$.

Since $\bar{U}$ is connected and compact, it is a continuum, so by minimality, $\bar{U} = \widetilde{X}$ and $V = \emptyset$.

We have thus proven that $X^\sharp$ is connected. But F is a maximal connected set, so $F = X^\sharp$ and, as a bonus, $x_\infty \in \bar{F}$. Thus, $\bar{F} = \widetilde{X}$, as we needed to prove. $\qquad\square$

Notes and Historical Remarks. In 1897, Osgood [**694**] proved a result equivalent to the Baire category theorem for subsets of $\mathbb{R}$. Two years later, Baire [**48**] proved the result for $\mathbb{R}^\nu$ and gave his name to the theorem. The form in general metric spaces is due to Kuratowski [**535**] and Banach [**53**].

In (4.4.72), we saw there exist functions, $f \colon [0,1] \to [0,1]$, whose set of discontinuities is exactly $\mathbb{Q} \cap [0,1]$. It was a long-standing open problem if one could find a function discontinuous exactly at the irrational numbers in $[0,1]$. Baire invented the notion of first category in showing no such example existed; see Problem 3.

René-Louis Baire (1874–1932) was a French analyst. He came from a background of poverty and was only able to get higher education via a scholarship. For financial reasons, he initially taught in lycée, where he did his fundamental work on pointwise limits of continuous functions (from which the names Baire function and Baire set come) and on the Baire category theorem. He later got his degree and eventually a professorship—his most famous student was Arnaud Denjoy. Baire suffered from ill health his entire life and was bitter because he felt that Lebesgue got credit for his ideas on pointwise limits.

A topological space in which the Baire category theorem (in the form Theorem 5.4.1) holds is called a *Baire space*. Every locally compact space is a Baire space (Problem 22), so for example, an uncountable product of $[0, 1]$ is a space which is a Baire space but not metrizable. So are nonparacompact manifolds.

Oxtoby [696] has extensive discussions of Baire category and of the analogy between Baire generic and Lebesgue generic.

During the period 1903–27, a series of results that we now recognize as a special case of the principle of uniform boundedness were proven by Lebesgue, Hellinger–Toeplitz, Helly, Hahn, Banach, and Hildebrandt, culminating in a paper of Banach and Steinhaus [57]. The earlier papers and the preliminary version of the Banach–Steinhaus paper relied on a method called the *gliding hump method* (see Problem 18). Saks suggested the use of the Baire category theorem to Banach and Steinhaus and they took his suggestion! Some authors call Theorem 5.4.9 the Banach–Steinhaus principle and others use that name for Theorem 5.4.19.

The first of the open/inverse mapping/closed graph theorems was the inverse mapping theorem proven in 1929 by Banach [52], using an involved argument that depended on weak convergence. The now standard Baire category approach is due to Schauder in 1930 [814], who also proved the open mapping theorem. The closed graph theorem appeared at least as early as Banach's great monograph on Banach spaces [55].

The arguments in Theorems 5.4.9 and 5.4.11 have a similar look. One can organize things by first proving an elegant lemma of Zabreĭko [1015] that a countably subadditive seminorm (i.e., $\rho\left(\sum_1^\infty x_j\right) \leq \sum_1^\infty \rho(x_j)$) is continuous. Megginson's book [648] is a good reference for this and a lot more on the Banach space structure theorems of this section.

The applications to Banach space theory are reasonable and powerful, but it seems difficult to obtain them with our bare hands. But we can with our Baire hands.

That the Baire category theorem can be used to construct nondifferentiable, continuous functions (see Example 5.4.6) is a discovery of Banach in 1931 [54].

Example 5.4.23 is from Knaster–Kuratowski [500]; see also [874] and Wikipedia[1]. Our analysis using the Baire category theorem comes from [500].

Theorem 5.4.24 seems to be a known folk theorem, although I haven't found it explicitly in the published literature. I consulted Henry Wilton

---

[1] http://en.wikipedia.org/wiki/Knaster-Kuratowski_fan

about a proof. Henry posted about it at the website mathoverflow.net and the proof I give was suggested by Bill Johnson[2]

Körner [**513**] has a proof of the existence of Besicovitch–Kakeya sets (i.e., sets of Lebesgue measure zero in $\mathbb{R}^\nu$ which contain a unit line segment in every direction) using the Baire category theorem; see Stein–Shakarchi [**876**] for a textbook version of his argument.

Problems

1. Prove that any subset of $\mathbb{Q}$ is a countable intersection of dense open subsets of $\mathbb{Q}$ and thereby conclude that Theorem 5.4.1 requires completeness.

2. Let A be a dense G_δ in a complete metric space with no isolated points. For every ball, $B_r(x)$, $r > 0$, prove that $A \cap B_r(x)$ is uncountable. In particular, prove that any perfect set in $\mathbb{R}$ is uncountable.

3. (a) In any metric space, X, for any function $f\colon X \to [a,b]$, define
$$(Vf)(x) = \lim_{n\to\infty} \Big[\sup_{\rho(y,x)<1/n} f(y) - \inf_{\rho(y,x)<1/n} f(y)\Big] \qquad (5.4.41)$$

Show that f is continuous at x_0 if and only if $(VF)(x_0) = 0$.

(b) Prove that $\{x \mid (VF)(x) \geq 1/m\}$ is closed, and conclude $C_f \equiv \{x \mid f$ is continuous at $x\}$ is a G_δ. Let $D_f = X \setminus C_f$, the points of discontinuity of f.

(c) If f is continuous on a dense set, prove that D_f is a first category set.

(d) We saw there is $f\colon [0,1] \to [0,1]$, so $D_f \equiv \mathbb{Q} \cap [0,1]$, the rationals in $[0,1]$. Is there an f with $D_f = [0,1] \setminus \mathbb{Q}$, the irrationals?

(e) If X is a complete metric space, prove there are not $f,g\colon X \to [a,b]$, each continuous on dense sets, so that $D_f \cup D_g = X$.

Remark. Baire found the Baire category theorem in studying what sets of points could be sets of discontinuity. He did this because of his interest in Rieman integrability.

4. (a) Let
$$E_\beta(C) = \Big\{ \alpha \in [0,1] \ \Big| \ \forall p,q \in \mathbb{Z}, \ \Big| \alpha - \frac{p}{q}\Big| \geq \frac{C}{q^\beta}\Big\}$$

Prove that $\|[0,1] \setminus E_\beta(C)\| \leq C(2 + \sum_{q=2}^\infty q^{-(\beta-1)})$

(b) If $\beta > 2$, prove $\|[0,1] \setminus D_\beta\| = 0$, where D_β is given by (5.4.7).

5. (a) Prove that the set L_C of (5.4.9) is a dense G_δ.

(b) If (5.4.10) holds, prove that $|L_C| = 0$.

---

[2]http://mathoverflow.net/questions/16578/

6. This problem will prove that if α is an irrational algebraic number of degree n (i.e., $P(\alpha) = 0$ for a polynomial of degree n with integral coefficients and for no smaller polynomial), then there is a C so that

$$\left| \frac{p}{q} - \alpha \right| \geq \frac{C}{q^n} \tag{5.4.42}$$

for all p, q with q sufficiently large.

(a) Prove there are $\delta, C > 0$ so that for all $x \in (\alpha - \delta, \alpha + \delta)$, $|P(x)| \leq C^{-1}|x - \alpha|$, and if $x \neq \alpha$ and in this interval, then $P(x) \neq 0$.

(b) Prove that if p/q is in this interval, then $q^n |P(p/q)| \geq 1$, and deduce that (5.4.42) holds for all large q.

(c) Prove that $\sum_{j=1}^{\infty} 10^{-j!}$ is transcendental.

Remark. This argument is due to Liouville; the real number in (c) is sometimes called Liouville's number.

7. Let $B_n \subset C([0, 1])$ be given by

$$B_n = \left\{ f \,\Big|\, \left| f\left(\frac{j}{2^n}\right) - f\left(\frac{j+1}{2^n}\right) \right| > \frac{1}{2^{n/2}} \text{ for } j = 0, \ldots, 2^n - 1 \right\}$$

Prove that if $f \in \bigcap_{n=1}^{\infty} (\bigcup_{m=n}^{\infty} B_m) \equiv Q$, then f is not differentiable at any point in $[0, 1]$. Then prove that Q is nonempty, and so conclude (nonconstructively) that there exist nowhere differentiable functions.

8. This problem will prove $\{\mu \in \mathcal{M}_{+,1}([0, 1]) \mid \mu$ is purely singular continuous$\}$ is a dense G_δ in $\mathcal{M}_{+,1}([0, 1])$ (in the topology of vague convergence; see Problem 4 in Section 4.5).

(a) Let $\mu_m \to \mu$ vaguely. Suppose there is $c > 0$ and $x_m \in [0, 1]$ so that $c_m \equiv \mu_m(\{x_m\}) \geq c$. Prove μ has a pure point x with $\mu(\{x\}) \geq c$. (*Hint:* Find a subsequence $c_{m_j} \to c_\infty$ and $x_{m_j} \to x_\infty$ and $\mu_{m_j} - c_{m_j}\delta_{x_j} \to \tilde{\mu}$.) Conclude that $S_\ell \equiv \{\mu \mid \mu$ has a pure point with weight at least $1/\ell\}$ is a closed set.

(b) Prove $\{\mu \in \mathcal{M}_{+,1}([0, 1]) \mid \mu$ has no pure points$\}$ is a G_δ.

(c) Prove that any measure is a vague limit of purely a.c. measures, and so conclude $\{\mu \in \mathcal{M}_{+,1}([0, 1]) \mid \mu$ has no pure points$\}$ is a dense G_δ. (*Hint:* Shrink the support of μ and convolute with an approximate identity.)

(d) Let $\mu_m \to \mu$ vaguely. Suppose that for some $c > 0$ and $Q < \infty$, there exist nonnegative $f_m \in L^2([0, 1], dx)$ with $\int f_m \, dx \geq c$, $\|f_m\|_{L^2} \leq Q$, and $d\mu_m \geq f_m \, dx$. Prove there exist $f \in L^2$ with $\|f\|_{L^2} \leq Q$ and $\int f \, dx \geq c$ so $d\mu \geq f \, dx$. (*Hint:* Use the strategy of (a) and compactness of $L^2([0, 1], dx)$ in the weak topology.) Conclude that $T_{\ell,Q} = \{\mu \mid d\mu \geq f \, dx$ for some f with $\|f\|_{L^2} \leq Q$ and $\int f \, dx \geq 1/\ell\}$ is closed.

(e) Show $\{\mu \mid \mu$ is singular wrt $dx\} = \mathcal{M}_{+,1} \setminus \bigcup_{\ell,Q} T_{\ell,Q}$ and conclude this set of measures is a G_δ.

(f) Prove that any measure is a limit of pure point measures and conclude that $\{\mu \mid \mu$ is singular wrt $dx\}$ is a dense G_δ. (*Hint*: Recall the definition of Riemann–Stieltjes integration.)

(g) Prove that $\{\mu \in \mathcal{M}_{+,1}([0,1]) \mid \mu$ is purely singular continuous$\}$ is a dense G_δ.

Remark. The result proven here is from Zamfirescu [**1016**]. The proof sketched is from Lenz–Stollmann [**569**]. See Simon [**850**] for another approach.

9. Prove that in $\mathcal{M}_{+,1}([0,1])$, $\{\mu \mid \mathrm{supp}(\mu) = [0,1]\}$ is a dense G_δ. (*Hint*: For each closed set, $K \subset [0,1]$, prove that $\{\mu \mid \mathrm{supp}(\mu) \subset K\}$ is closed.)

10. (a) Let $T\colon C(X) \to C(X)$ for X a compact Hausdorff space be given by

$$(Tf)(x) = \int t(x,y)f(y)\,d\mu(y) \tag{5.4.43}$$

where $\mu \in \mathcal{M}_+(X)$ and $t \in C(X \times X)$. Prove that

$$\|T\| = \sup_x \int |t(x,y)|\,d\mu(y) \tag{5.4.44}$$

(b) In particular, prove that if S_N is given by (3.5.6), then (D_N given by (3.5.15))

$$L_N = \|S_N\| = \int_0^{2\pi} |D_N(\theta)|\,\frac{d\theta}{2\pi} \tag{5.4.45}$$

L_N are called the *Lebesgue numbers*.

(c) Prove that $L_N \to \infty$ as $N \to \infty$ (as $\log(N)$).

(d) Prove that for some $f \in C(\partial\mathbb{D})$, we have

$$\sup_N \|S_N f\|_\infty = \infty \tag{5.4.46}$$

and, in particular, $S_N f$ does not converge uniformly.

(e) For the f in (d), prove that $\sum_{n=-\infty}^\infty |f_n^\sharp| = \infty$.

(f) For $g \in L^1(\partial\mathbb{D}, \frac{d\theta}{2\pi})$, prove

$$\|g\|_1 = \sup_{\substack{f \in C(\partial\mathbb{D}) \\ \|f\|_\infty = 1}} \left| \int_0^{2\pi} g(\theta)f(\theta)\,\frac{d\theta}{2\pi} \right| \tag{5.4.47}$$

(g) Prove that L_N is the norm of S_N is a map of L^1 to L^1 and that there is $f \in L^1$ so that $\sup_N \|S_N f\|_1 = \infty$.

Remark. More precisely than (c), it is known (see Problem 11) that $L_N = 4\pi^{-2} \log N + O(1)$. Indeed, Watson [**977**] proved that $\lim_{N \to \infty} L_N - 4\pi^{-2} \log N$ exists and is approximately 1.27.

11. This will show the constant L_N of (5.4.45) is $4\pi^{-2} \log N + O(1)$.

(a) Show that if $\widetilde{D}_N(\theta)$ is $D_N(\theta)$, with $\sin(\frac{\theta}{2})$ in the denominator replaced by $\frac{\theta}{2}$, then $\int_0^{2\pi} |D_n(\theta) - \widetilde{D}_N(\theta)| \frac{d\theta}{2\pi} = O(1)$.

(b) If in each interval between zeros of $\sin((n+\frac{1}{2})\theta)$, $\theta/2$ is replaced by $\theta_j/2$, where θ_j is the midpoint of the interval, then the error is $O(1)$.

(c) Prove $\int_0^{2\pi} |\sin \theta|\, d\theta = 2$ and deduce that

$$L_N = \frac{4}{\pi^2} \sum_{j=0}^{N-1} \frac{1}{j + \frac{1}{2}} + O(1)$$

(d) Show $L_N = 4\pi^{-2} \log N + O(1)$.

12. (a) Under the hypothesis of Problem 10(a), prove that

$$\sup_{f;\, \|f\|_\infty = 1} |(Tf)(x)| = \int |t(x,y)|\, d\mu(y) \qquad (5.4.48)$$

(b) Define $\ell_N^{(\theta)}(f) = (S_N f)(e^{i\theta})$ and prove that $\sup_N \|\ell_N^{(\theta)}\| = \infty$ for each θ.

(c) Conclude that for each fixed θ, $\sup_N |(S_N f)(e^{i\theta})| = \infty$ for a dense G_δ of f's.

13. (a) Let g_N be a family of real-valued continuous functions on a topological space. Prove that $\{x \mid \sup_N |\varphi_N(x)| = \infty\}$ is a G_δ.

(b) Using Problem 12, show that for a Baire generic continuous function on $\partial \mathbb{D}$, $\{\theta \mid \sup_N |(S_N f)(e^{i\theta})| = \infty\}$ is a dense G_δ in $\partial \mathbb{D}$.

14. (a) Let $B \colon X \times X \to \mathbb{C}$ be bilinear. Suppose that for each x, $B(x, \cdot) \in X^*$ and $B(\cdot, x) \in X^*$. Prove that B is jointly continuous, that is, if $x_n \to x$, $y_n \to y$, then $B(x_n, y_n) \to B(x,y)$.

(b) Let $f \colon \mathbb{R}^2 \to \mathbb{R}$ by

$$f(x,y) = \begin{cases} \frac{xy}{x^2+y^2}, & (x,y) \neq (0,0) \\ 0, & (x,y) = 0 \end{cases}$$

Prove that $f(x, \cdot)$ and $f(\cdot, y)$ are continuous but that f is not continuous as a function on $\mathbb{R}^2$.

15. (Hellinger–Toeplitz [**411**]) Let $\{a_{k\ell}\}_{k,\ell=0}^{\infty}$ be a matrix of complex numbers. Suppose for each $x, y \in \ell^2(\mathbb{Z}_+)$, we have

$$\sup_{n,m} \left| \sum_{k=1}^{n} \sum_{\ell=1}^{m} a_{k\ell} x_k y_\ell \right| < \infty$$

For each $x \in \ell^2(\mathbb{Z}_+)$ and each $k = 1, 2, \ldots$, prove that $\sum_{\ell=1}^{\infty} a_{k\ell} x_\ell$ converges and $x \mapsto \sum_{\ell=1}^{\infty} a_{k\ell} x_\ell$ is a bounded linear map of $\ell^2(\mathbb{Z}_+)$ to itself.

16. Suppose that A, B are two linear maps (not a priori bounded) of $\mathcal{H}$ to $\mathcal{H}$, where $\mathcal{H}$ is a infinite-dimensional Hilbert space, and that for all $\varphi, \psi \in \mathcal{H}$, we have $\langle \varphi, A\psi \rangle = \langle B\varphi, \psi \rangle$. Prove that A and B are both bounded.

17. This problem will prove a theorem of Grothendieck [**374**] that if $\mu(X) = 1$ and $E \subset L^\infty(X, d\mu)$ is a closed subspace of $L^p(X, d\mu)$ for some $1 \le p < \infty$, then E is finite-dimensional. The proof uses the closed graph theorem and the fact in Theorem 5.2.6 that if $\mu(X) = 1$ and $q \le p$, then $L^p \subset L^q$ and $\|f\|_q \le \|f\|_p$.

(a) Prove that if $q \le p$ and $f_n \to f$ in L^p and $f_n \to g$ in L^q for any $q \le p$, then $f = g$. (*Hint:* $\|f_n - f\|_q \to 0$.)

(b) Prove that the graph of $I \colon E \subset L^p \to L^\infty$ by $I(f) = f$ is closed and conclude that for some A_1, $\|f\|_\infty \le A_1 \|f\|_p$ for all $f \in E$.

(c) Prove that for a constant A_2, $\|f\|_\infty \le A_2 \|f\|_2$ (*Hint:* If $p < 2 < \infty$, use $\|f\|_p \le \|f\|_2$ and if $2 < p < \infty$, use $\|f\|_p^p \le \|f\|_2^2 \|f\|_\infty^{p-2}$.)

(d) Let $f_1, \ldots, f_\ell$ be an orthonormal family in E. Prove for a.e. $X \in X$ and all $(\alpha_1, \ldots, \alpha_\ell) \in \mathbb{C}^\ell$

$$\left| \sum_{j=1}^{\ell} \alpha_j \, f_j(x) \right| \le A_2 \left(\sum_{j=1}^{\ell} |\alpha_j|^2 \right)^{1/2} \tag{5.4.49}$$

(e) Conclude that $\sum_{j=1}^{\ell} |f_j(x)|^2 \le A_2^2$ and then that $\ell \le A_2^2$ so $\dim(E) \le A_2^2$.

18. This problem will lead the reader through a proof of the uniform boundedness principle using the *gliding hump method* that goes back to Lebesgue. ($T_n x_n$ below is the hump that glides as n increases.)

(a) Suppose $c(x) = \sup_{T \in \mathcal{F}} \|Tx\|_Y < \infty$ for all x, but that $\sup_{T \in \mathcal{F}} \|T\|_{\mathcal{L}(X,Y)} = \infty$. Prove that you can pick $T_1, x_1, T_2, x_2, \ldots$ inductively with $T_j \in \mathcal{F}$ so that

$$\|T_n\| \ge 4 \, 3^n \left(\sum_{k<n} c(x_k) + n \right) \tag{5.4.50}$$

$$\|x_n\| \le 3^{-n}, \qquad \|T_n x_n\| \ge \tfrac{3}{4} 3^{-n} \|T_n\| \tag{5.4.51}$$

(b) Prove that

$$\left\| \sum_{k<n} T_n x_k \right\| \le \sum_{k<n} c(x_k) \tag{5.4.52}$$

$$\left\| \sum_{k>n} T_n x_k \right\| \le \tfrac{1}{2} 3^{-n} \|T_n\| \tag{5.4.53}$$

(c) Show $x = \sum_{k=1}^{\infty} x_k$ exists in X and that $\|T_n x\| \ge n$. Thus, deduce there is a contradiction and so conclude $\sup_{T \in \mathcal{F}} \|T\| < \infty$.

19. Fix $p, q \in (1, \infty)$ with $p^{-1} + q^{-1} = 1$. Let $\{a_n\}_{n=1}^{\infty}$ be a sequence of complex numbers so that for all $\{b_n\}_{n=1}^{\infty} \in \ell^q$, we have $\sup_N |\sum_{n=1}^N a_n b_n| < \infty$. Prove that $\{a_n\}_{n=1}^{\infty} \in \ell^p$. This is a theorem of Landau.

20. Prove Theorem 5.4.18 using the principle of uniform boundedness.

21. Assuming Theorem 5.4.11, prove Theorem 5.4.9, and then using that, prove Theorem 5.4.1.

22. Let X be a locally compact Hausdorff space. This problem will prove that a countable intersection of dense open sets is dense, so X is a Baire space.

(a) Prove that the result for compact spaces implies the result for locally compact spaces. (*Hint*: One point compactification.) So henceforth, suppose X is compact.

(b) If A is a dense open set and U is a nonempty open set, prove that there are V open and nonempty and C closed, so that $V \subset C \subset U \cap A$. (*Hint*: First show that there is $x \in U \cap A$ and then pick a continuous f with $f = 0$ on $X \setminus (U \cap A)$ and $f(x) = 1$.)

(c) If U is a nonempty open set and $\{A_j\}_{j=1}^{\infty}$ are dense open sets, show that you can define $C_1, U_1, C_2, U_2, \ldots$ inductively, all nonempty, so that $C_1 \subset A_1 \cap U$, $U_j \subset C_j$, and $C_{j+1} \subset A_{j+1} \cap U_j$.

(d) Prove $Q \equiv \bigcap_j C_j \ne \emptyset$ and $C \subset U \cap (\bigcap_{j=1}^{\infty} A_j)$.

(e) Conclude that $\bigcap_{j=1}^{\infty} A_j$ is dense.

5.5. The Hahn–Banach Theorem

Our main goal in this section is to prove the following (and an analog with $\mathbb{C}$ in place of $\mathbb{R}$):

Theorem 5.5.1 (Hahn–Banach Theorem). *Let X be a real vector space and p a convex function from X to $\mathbb{R}$. Let $Y \subset X$ be a subspace and*

$\ell \colon Y \to \mathbb{R}$ *a linear functional obeying*

$$\ell(y) \leq p(y) \tag{5.5.1}$$

for all $y \in Y$. Then there exists a linear functional $L \colon X \to \mathbb{R}$ so that for all $x \in X$,

$$L(x) \leq p(x) \tag{5.5.2}$$

and $L \upharpoonright Y = \ell$.

The most important case will be where X is an NLS and $p(y) = \|y\|$. The Hahn–Banach theorem will imply that there are lots of continuous linear functions on an NLS, X, enough so that for any $x \in X$, there is an ℓ with $\ell(x) \neq 0$. Lest this seem like something that must be obvious, in the next section we'll discuss $L^p([0,1], dx) = \{\text{Baire } f \mid \int_0^1 |f(x)|^p \, dx < \infty\}$, where $0 < p < 1$.

$$\rho_p(f, g) = \int |f(x) - g(x)|^p \, dx \tag{5.5.3}$$

(no p-th root) will define a metric and thereby a topology on L^p, in which addition and scalar multiplication are continuous. We'll show L^p, $0 < p < 1$, has no nonzero continuous linear functionals (see Proposition 5.7.4).

If $L(x) \leq c\|x\|$, then since $\|-x\| = \|x\|$, we get $\pm L(x) \leq c\|x\|$ so $|L(x)| \leq c\|x\|$, i.e.,

$$L(x) \leq c\|x\| \Leftrightarrow |L(x)| \leq c\|x\| \tag{5.5.4}$$

Thus Theorem 5.5.1 implies

Corollary 5.5.2. *Let X be a real normed linear space and $Y \subset X$. Then, given any $\ell \in Y^*$, there is $L \in X^*$ with $L \upharpoonright Y = \ell$ and $\|L\| = \|\ell\|$.*

Once we have linear functionals, since we've defined X^* as a Banach space (see Problem 1 of Section 3.1), then we'll have $X^{**} = (X^*)^*$ and the notion of reflexive space. In particular, we'll see that while $(L^1)^* = L^\infty$, $(L^\infty)^*$ is strictly larger than L^1. Similarly, $C(X)^{**}$ is larger than $C(X)$.

The key to the proof of Theorem 5.5.1 will be to add a single vector $x \notin Y$ to the domain of L and then use "induction." To do this, we need the following lemma. Lest it seem from left field, we'll find both upper and lower bounds that have to hold on $\lambda = L(x)$. The lemma says that every required lower bound is smaller than every required upper bound, which will be necessary and sufficient to find a suitable λ.

Lemma 5.5.3. *Let X, Y, ℓ, p be as in Theorem 5.5.1. Then for every $y_1, y_2 \in Y$, $x \in X \setminus Y$, and $\alpha, \beta \in (0, \infty)$, we have*

$$\frac{-p(y_1 - \beta x) + \ell(y_1)}{\beta} \leq \frac{p(y_2 + \alpha x) - \ell(y_2)}{\alpha} \tag{5.5.5}$$

Proof. Let $\theta = \beta/(\alpha + \beta)$. Then

$$\ell((1-\theta)y_1 + \theta y_2) \leq p((1-\theta)(y_1 - \beta x) + \theta(y_2 + \alpha x)) \qquad (5.5.6)$$

$$\leq (1-\theta)p(y_1 - \beta x) + \theta p(y_2 + \alpha x) \qquad (5.5.7)$$

where (5.5.6) comes from $(1-\theta)\beta = \theta\alpha$ and (5.5.1), and (5.5.7) comes from convexity of p.

Multiplying (5.5.7) by $(\alpha + \beta)$ yields

$$\alpha\ell(y_1) + \beta\ell(y_2) \leq \alpha p(y_1 - \beta x) + \beta p(y_2 + \alpha x) \qquad (5.5.8)$$

or

$$\alpha(\ell(y_1) - p(y_1 - \beta x)) \leq \beta(p(y_2 + \alpha x) - \ell(y_2)) \qquad (5.5.9)$$

which is (5.5.5). $\qquad\qquad\square$

Proposition 5.5.4. *Given X, Y, ℓ, p as in Theorem 5.5.1 and $x \in X \setminus Y$, there exists $\widetilde{L} \colon \widetilde{Y} \equiv Y + \{\alpha x \mid \alpha \in \mathbb{R}\} \to \mathbb{R}$ so that*

$$\widetilde{L}(z) \leq p(z) \qquad (5.5.10)$$

for all $z \in \widetilde{Y}$ and $\widetilde{L} \restriction Y = \ell$.

Proof. Suppose that we set $\widetilde{L}(x) = \lambda$. Then, since every $\tilde{y} \in \widetilde{Y}$ has the form $y + \alpha x$, $\alpha \in \mathbb{R}$, (5.5.10) is equivalent to

$$\ell(y_1) + \alpha\lambda \leq p(y_1 + \alpha x) \qquad (5.5.11)$$

$$\ell(y_2) - \beta\lambda \leq p(y_2 - \beta x) \qquad (5.5.12)$$

for all $y_1, y_2 \in X$, $\alpha, \beta \in (0, \infty)$. This is equivalent to

$$\frac{-p(y_2 - \beta x) + \ell(y_2)}{\beta} \leq \lambda \leq \frac{p(y_1 + \alpha x) - \ell(y_1)}{\alpha} \qquad (5.5.13)$$

If we take

$$\lambda = \inf_{\substack{\alpha \in (0,\infty) \\ y_1 \in Y}} \frac{p(y_1 + \alpha x) - \ell(y_1)}{\alpha} \qquad (5.5.14)$$

then, by Lemma 5.5.3, λ is finite and (5.5.13) holds. $\qquad\qquad\square$

Proof of Theorem 5.5.1. This is a simple Zornification. Let $\mathcal{L}$ be the set of pairs, $\widetilde{Y}$, so that $Y \subset \widetilde{Y} \subset X$, and linear $\widetilde{L} \colon \widetilde{Y} \to \mathbb{R}$ obeying (5.5.10) for all $z \in \widetilde{Y}$, with $\widetilde{L} \restriction Y = \ell$. Say $(Y_1, L_1) \rhd (Y_2, L_2)$ if and only if $Y_2 \subset Y_1$ and $L_1 \restriction Y_2 = L_2$.

This makes $\mathcal{L}$ into a partially ordered set. $\mathcal{L}$ is nonempty since $(Y, \ell) \in \mathcal{L}$. If $\{(Y_\alpha, L_\alpha)\}_{\alpha \in I}$ is a chain in $\mathcal{L}$ and $\widetilde{Y} = \bigcup_\alpha Y_\alpha$, $\widetilde{L}(y) = L_\alpha(y)$ if $y \in Y_\alpha$, then $(\widetilde{Y}, \widetilde{L})$ is an upper bound. Thus, by Zorn's lemma, $\mathcal{L}$ has maximal elements (Y_∞, L_∞). If $Y_\infty \neq X$, by Proposition 5.5.4, we can find $x \in X \setminus Y_\infty$ and an $\widetilde{L}$ on $\widetilde{Y}_\infty \equiv Y_\infty + \{\alpha x \mid \alpha \in \mathbb{R}\}$ so that $\widetilde{L} \restriction Y_\infty = L_\infty$. Thus, (Y_∞, L_∞)

is not maximal. We conclude that $Y_\infty = X$ and $L = L_\infty$ obeys (5.5.2) with $L \restriction Y = \ell$. $\qquad\square$

Remark. If X is a separable space and $p(x) = \|x\|$, one can avoid Zorn's lemma. Pick a countable dense $\{x_n\}_{n=1}^\infty$ and define Y_j inductively by $Y_0 = Y$, $Y_{n+1} = Y_n + \{\alpha x_n \mid \alpha \in \mathbb{R}\}$ so $Y_{n+1} = Y_n$ or Proposition 5.5.4 is applicable. In this way, one extends ℓ to $\widetilde{L}$ on $\widetilde{Y} = \bigcup_{n=0}^\infty Y_n$ by $\widetilde{L} \restriction Y_n = L_n$, the extension at step n. $\widetilde{Y}$ is dense in X and $\widetilde{L}(x) \leq \|x\|$ for $\pm x$ implies $|\widetilde{L}(x)| \leq \|x\|$, meaning $\widetilde{L}$ can be extended to all of X. Thus, in the separable case with p the norm on an NLS, we can use ordinary induction in place of Zorn's lemma.

Next, we turn to the complex case.

Definition. Let X be a complex vector space. A function $p\colon X \to \mathbb{R}$ is called *symmetric* if for all $x \in X$, $\alpha \in \partial\mathbb{D}$,

$$p(\alpha x) = p(x) \qquad (5.5.15)$$

In particular, the norm on a complex NLS is convex and symmetric.

Theorem 5.5.5 (Complex Hahn–Banach Theorem). *Let X be a complex vector space, p a symmetric convex function on X, $Y \subset X$ a complex subspace, and ℓ a complex linear map of Y to $\mathbb{C}$ obeying*

$$|\ell(y)| \leq p(y) \qquad (5.5.16)$$

for all $y \in Y$. Then there exists a complex linear $L\colon X \to \mathbb{C}$ so that for all $x \in X$,

$$|L(x)| \leq p(x) \qquad (5.5.17)$$

and $L \restriction Y = \ell$.

Proof. Let $\lambda = \operatorname{Re} \ell$. Thus, $\operatorname{Im} \ell(x) = \operatorname{Re}(-i\ell(x)) = \lambda(-ix)$, and we see that

$$\ell(x) = \lambda(x) + i\lambda(-ix) \qquad (5.5.18)$$

Clearly, by (5.5.16), $\lambda(x) \leq p(x)$, so by the (real) Hahn–Banach theorem, there is Λ, a real linear function from $X \to \mathbb{R}$, so

$$\Lambda(x) \leq p(x) \qquad (5.5.19)$$

and $\Lambda \restriction Y = \lambda$.

Since $p(-x) = p(x)$ (by the symmetry hypothesis), (5.5.19) implies

$$|\Lambda(x)| \leq p(x) \qquad (5.5.20)$$

Define

$$L(x) = \Lambda(x) + i\Lambda(-ix) \qquad (5.5.21)$$

Then $L(ix) = \Lambda(ix) + i\Lambda(x) = i(\Lambda(x) + i\Lambda(-ix))$ (since $\Lambda(ix) = -\Lambda(-ix)$), so L is complex linear, and by (5.5.18), $L \upharpoonright Y = \ell$. Thus, we need only prove (5.5.17).

Given x, pick θ so $L(x) = e^{i\theta}|L(x)|$. Then

$$|L(x)| = L(e^{-i\theta}x) = \Lambda(e^{-i\theta}x) \le p(e^{-i\theta}x) = p(x) \qquad (5.5.22)$$

by (5.5.20). We used $\Lambda = \operatorname{Re} L$ and the reality of $|L(x)|$ to get (5.5.22). $\quad\square$

By this Theorem, Corollary 5.5.2 extends to the complex case.

We've seen in Chapter 4 that positive functionals are often important, so an extension theorem for such functionals is also useful.

Definition. A *proper generating convex cone* (*positive cone* for short) is a subset, V_+, of a real vector space, X, that obeys (where $V_- = \{-x \mid x \in V_+\}$)

(i) $\lambda \ge 0,\ x \in V_+ \Rightarrow \lambda x \in V_+$ $\hfill (5.5.23)$

(ii) $V_+ + V_+ \subset V_+$ $\hfill (5.5.24)$

(iii) $V_+ + V_- = X$ $\hfill (5.5.25)$

(iv) $V_+ \cap V_- = \{0\}$ $\hfill (5.5.26)$

An *ordered vector space* is a real vector space, X, with positive cone, V_+. We put a partial order (see Problem 2) on X by

$$x \le y \Leftrightarrow y - x \in V_+ \qquad (5.5.27)$$

A *positive functional* is a linear map $\varphi \colon X \to \mathbb{R}$ so that $x \in V_+ \Rightarrow \varphi(x) \ge 0$.

Remarks. 1. When (i) holds, (5.5.24) is equivalent to convexity of V_+.

2. We do not require that X be a vector lattice in the order generated by V_+. For example, in $\mathbb{R}^3$, the standard cone, $\{(x, y, z) \mid z \ge 0,\ x^2 + y^2 \le z^2\}$ is a positive cone, but the ordered space is not a lattice.

3. We have $x \ge y \Rightarrow \forall z,\ x + z \ge y + z$ and $\lambda x \ge \lambda y$ for all $\lambda \ge 0$ (see Problem 2).

Definition. Let (X, V_+) be an ordered vector space. A subspace, $Y \subset X$, is called *dominating* if and only if

$$\forall x \in V_+,\ \exists y \in V_+ \cap Y \text{ so that } x \le y$$

Proposition 5.5.6. *Let Y be a dominating subspace of an ordered vector space, X. Then $V_+ \cap Y$ is a positive cone in Y. Moreover, if $Y \subset Y_1$, Y_1 is also a dominating subspace.*

Remarks. 1. If $V_+ = \{(x, y) \mid x \ge 0,\ y \ge 0\}$ in $\mathbb{R}^2$ and $Y = \{(x, -x) \mid x \in \mathbb{R}\}$, then $Y \cap V_+ = \{(0, 0)\}$ is not a generating cone in Y, so an extra condition like domination is needed.

2. The order on Y given by $V_+ \cap Y$ is called the *induced order*.

Proof. Let $W_+ = V_+ \cap Y$. (i), (ii), and (iv) are immediate. For (iii), suppose $x \in Y$. Then $x = x_+ - x_-$ with $x_\pm \in V_+$ so there is $y \in W_+$ so $x_+ \leq y$. Thus, $y \geq x_+ = x + x_- \geq x$. Therefore, $y - x \in W_+$, so $x = y - (y - x) \in W_+ - W_+$.

Clearly, if $x \in V_+$ and $y \in V_+ \cap Y$ with $x \leq y$, y is also in $V_+ \cap Y_1$, and so, dominating. $\square$

Notice if Y is dominating and $x \in X$, we can write $x = x_+ - x_-$, with $x_\pm \in V_+$, and then find $y_\pm \in V_+ \cap Y$ so that $x_\pm \leq y_\pm$. Thus, if $y = y_+ + y_-$, then

$$y + x = y_+ + x_+ + (y_- - x_-) \geq 0 \tag{5.5.28}$$

$$y - x = (y_+ - x_+) + y_- + x_- \geq 0 \tag{5.5.29}$$

that is,

Proposition 5.5.7. *If Y is a dominating subspace of an ordered vector space, (X, V_+), then for all $x \in X$, there is $y \in V_+ \cap Y$ so that*

$$-y \leq x \leq y \tag{5.5.30}$$

Theorem 5.5.8 (M. Riesz Extension Theorem). *Let Y be a dominating subspace of an ordered vector space, (X, V_+). Suppose $\ell\colon Y \to \mathbb{R}$ is a positive functional in the induced order. Then there exists $L\colon X \to \mathbb{R}$, a positive functional, so that $L \restriction Y = \ell$.*

Remarks. 1. Problem 3 gives an example in $\mathbb{R}^2$ of a V_+, a one-dimensional subspace, Y, so $Y \cap V_+$ is a positive cone, and a positive $\ell\colon Y \to \mathbb{R}$, but so ℓ has no positive extension to $\mathbb{R}^2$. Clearly, Y is not a dominating subspace—this example shows the dominating subspace condition is critical.

2. That Y is dominating enters in the proof to assure that the sets S_+ and S_- below are not empty. Otherwise, it could happen, for example, that $S_+ = \emptyset$ and $s_- = \infty$.

3. A different extension theorem for positive linear functionals exists requiring that X be a NLS and V_+ be open.

Proof. Pick $x \notin Y$ and let Y_1 be $Y + \{\lambda x \mid \lambda \in \mathbb{R}\}$. We want to find a value, α, for $\ell_1(x)$ that will let us define ℓ_1 on Y_1 by

$$\ell_1(y + \lambda x) = \ell(y) + \lambda \alpha \tag{5.5.31}$$

Define

$$S_+ = \{y_+ \in Y \mid y_+ \geq x\}, \quad S_- = \{y_- \in Y \mid y_- \leq x\} \tag{5.5.32}$$

By Proposition 5.5.7, S_+ and S_- are nonempty. If $y_\pm \in S_\pm$, then $y_- \leq x \leq y_+$, so $y_- \leq y_+$, so $y_+ - y_- \in V_+ \cap Y$, so $\ell(y_+ - y_-) \geq 0$, so $\ell(y_-) \leq \ell(y_+)$.

Thus,

$$s_- \equiv \sup_{y_- \in S_-} \ell(y_-) \leq s_+ \equiv \inf_{y_+ \in S_+} \ell(y_+) \tag{5.5.33}$$

are each finite, so we can pick α with

$$s_- \leq \alpha \leq s_+ \tag{5.5.34}$$

and then define ℓ_1 by (5.5.31).

We claim ℓ_1 is positive (note Y_1 is dominating, so $V_+ \cap Y_1$ is a positive cone in Y_1). For if $\lambda > 0$,

$$y + \lambda x \geq 0 \Rightarrow x \geq -\lambda^{-1}y \Rightarrow \alpha \geq \ell(-\lambda^{-1}y) = -\lambda^{-1}\ell(y)$$
$$\Rightarrow \lambda\alpha + \ell(y) = \ell_1(y + \lambda x) \geq 0$$

and similarly, if $\lambda < 0$,

$$y + \lambda x \geq 0 \Rightarrow x \leq -\lambda^{-1}y \Rightarrow \alpha \leq \ell(-\lambda^{-1}y) = -\lambda^{-1}\ell(y)$$
$$\Rightarrow \lambda\alpha + \ell(y) = \ell_1(y + \lambda x) \geq 0$$

Now we use the same Zornification we used for the proof of Theorem 5.5.1. We need the fact that if $Y \subset \widetilde{Y}$, then $\widetilde{Y}$ is dominating, so if $\widetilde{Y} \neq X$, we can, as above, extend by one more dimension. $\qquad\square$

The Hahn–Banach theorems have two important consequences for NLS.

Theorem 5.5.9. *Let X be an NLS over $\mathbb{K} = \mathbb{R}$ or $\mathbb{C}$ and X^* its dual. For any $x_0 \in X$, there exists $\ell \in X^*$ so that*

$$\ell(x_0) = \|x_0\|, \qquad \|\ell\| = 1 \tag{5.5.35}$$

In particular, if $x_0 \neq 0$, there exists $\ell \in X^*$ so $\ell(x_0) \neq 0$.

Remark. In particular, since for any $\lambda \in X^*$, $|\lambda(x_0)| \leq \|\lambda\|\|x_0\|$, we see that

$$\|x_0\| = \sup_{\substack{\|\lambda\| \leq 1 \\ \lambda \in X^*}} |\lambda(x_0)| \tag{5.5.36}$$

Proof. We'll suppose $x_0 \neq 0$, leaving the case $x_0 = 0$ to the reader. Let $Y = \{\alpha x_0 \mid \alpha \in \mathbb{K}\}$ and $\lambda \colon Y \to \mathbb{K}$ by

$$\lambda(\alpha x_0) = \alpha\|x_0\| \tag{5.5.37}$$

Then, for all $y \in Y$,

$$|\lambda(y)| \leq \|y\| \tag{5.5.38}$$

so by the Hahn–Banach theorems, there exists ℓ a $\mathbb{K}$-linear function with $\ell \restriction Y = \lambda$, so $\ell(x_0) = \|x_0\|$ and

$$|\ell(x)| \leq \|x\| \tag{5.5.39}$$

Since $x_0 \neq 0$ and $\ell(x_0) = \|x_0\|$, we see $\|\ell\| \geq 1$. By (5.5.39), $\|\ell\| \leq 1$. $\qquad\square$

Theorem 5.5.10. *Let X be an NLS, $Y \subset X$ and closed subspace, and $x_0 \in X \setminus Y$. Then there exists $\ell \in X^*$ so that*

$$\ell \upharpoonright Y = 0, \qquad \ell(x_0) \neq 0 \tag{5.5.40}$$

Proof. We claim that there exists a constant $c > 0$ so that

$$\|y + \alpha x_0\| \geq c|\alpha| \tag{5.5.41}$$

for all $\alpha \in \mathbb{C}$ and $y \in Y$. For if (5.5.41) fails, we can find $\tilde{y}_n \in Y$, $\tilde{\alpha}_n$ so $\|\tilde{y}_n + \tilde{\alpha}_n x_0\| \leq \frac{1}{n}|\tilde{\alpha}_n|$. Clearly, $\tilde{\alpha}_n \neq 0$, so taking $y_n = -\tilde{\alpha}_n^{-1}\tilde{y}_n$, we find $y_n \in Y$ so $\|y_n - x_0\| \leq \frac{1}{n}$, that is, $y_n \to x_0$, so $x_0 \in \bar{X} = X$, contrary to hypothesis. Thus, (5.5.41) holds for some $c > 0$.

Define λ on $\{y + \alpha x_0 \mid y \in Y, \alpha \in \mathbb{C}\}$ by

$$\lambda(y + \alpha x_0) = c\alpha \tag{5.5.42}$$

By (5.5.41), $|\lambda(y + \alpha x_0)| \leq \|y + \alpha x_0\|$, so by the Hahn–Banach theorem, there is $\ell \colon X \to \mathbb{K}$ so $\|\ell\| \leq 1$ and $\ell(x_0) = c \neq 0$. $\quad\square$

Recall that the annihilator of a subspace Y in X, an NLS, is given by (5.1.14).

Corollary 5.5.11. *Let X be an NLS and $Y \subset X$ a (not necessarily) closed subspace. Then*

$$(Y^\perp)^\perp = \overline{Y} \tag{5.5.43}$$

Remarks. 1. This is an abuse of notation! Most naturally, $(Y^\perp)^\perp \subset (X^*)^*$. In terms of the map ι of (5.5.47), $(Y^\perp)^\perp \cap \iota(X) = \iota(\overline{Y})$.

2. As a subset of X^{**}, $(Y^\perp)^\perp$ is the weak-* (i.e., $\sigma(X^{**}, X^*)$ in the notation of Section 5.7) closure of $\iota(Y)$.

3. In the dual pair language of Section 5.7, the generalization of this result is that if X, Z are a dual pair and $Y \subset X$ a subspace, then $(Y^\perp)^\perp$ is the $\sigma(X, Z)$-closure of Y. In place of Theorem 5.5.10, one uses separating hyperplane theorems to prove this. Those theorems imply that the weak (i.e., $\sigma(X, X^*)$) closure of a subspace, Y, of X is the norm closure.

Proof. $(Y^\perp)^\perp = \bigcap_{\ell \in Y^\perp} \mathrm{Ker}(\ell)$ is norm closed, so since trivially $Y \subset (Y^\perp)^\perp$, we see that $\overline{Y} \subset (Y^\perp)^\perp$.

On the other hand, the theorem says that if $x_0 \notin \overline{Y}$, there is $\ell \in \overline{Y}^\perp = Y^\perp$ with $\ell(x_0) \neq 0$, i.e., $x_0 \notin (Y^\perp)^\perp$. $\quad\square$

Definition. Let X be a Banach space and Y a closed subspace. We say $w_1, \ldots, w_n$ are *independent over* Y if and only if $\sum_{j=1}^m \lambda_j w_j \in Y$ for $(\lambda_1, \ldots, \lambda_m) \in \mathbb{K}^m$ implies all $\lambda_j = 0$.

Definition. The *codimension* of Y, $\mathrm{codim}(Y)$, is the $\sup\{m \mid w_1, \ldots, w_m$ independent over $Y\}$.

Independence over Y is equivalent to independence of $\{[w_j]\}_{j=1}^m$ in X/Y. The codimension of Y is therefore the dimension of X/Y.

Theorem 5.5.12. *Let X be a Banach space and Y a closed subspace. Then* $\dim\{\ell \in X^* \mid \ell \restriction Y = 0\} = \mathrm{codim}(Y)$.

Proof. Let $\{w_j\}_{j=1}^m$ be independent over Y. As in the proof of Theorem 5.5.10, if we define ℓ_k on $\{Y + \sum_{j=1}^m \lambda_j w_j\}$ by

$$\ell_k\left(y + \sum_{j=1}^m \lambda_j w_j\right) = \lambda_k \tag{5.5.44}$$

then ℓ_k is continuous. So, by the Hahn–Banach theorem, they can be extended to X and are linearly independent. $\square$

Duality lets us define a natural map of $\mathcal{L}(X, Y)$ to $\mathcal{L}(Y^*, X^*)$:

Definition. Let $A\colon X \to Y$ be a continuous linear map between TVS. The *dual*, $A^t\colon Y^* \to X^*$, is defined by

$$(A^t \ell)(x) = \ell(Ax) \tag{5.5.45}$$

A is always continuous where the weak topology is put on both spaces ($\sigma(Y^*, Y)$ and $\sigma(X^*, X)$ in the language of the next section). If X and Y are NLS, then A^t is bounded from Y^* to X^* and, by the Hahn–Banach theorem,

$$\|A^t\| = \|A\| \tag{5.5.46}$$

Remark. We use A^t rather than A^* to distinguish from the Hilbert space case. A^* is close to A^t but since $\mathcal{H}^*$ is conjugate isomorphic to $\mathcal{H}$, $A \mapsto A^*$ is antilinear, while $A \to A^t$ is linear.

One important consequence of the existence of a large X^* is a large $(X^*)^*$ and a property of a natural map of $\iota\colon X \to X^{**}$, defined by

$$\iota(x)(\ell) = \ell(x) \tag{5.5.47}$$

for $\ell \in X^*$, $x \in X$.

Theorem 5.5.13. ι *is an isometry. In particular, ι is one-one and, if X is complete, $\mathrm{Ran}(\iota)$ is a closed subspace of X^{**}.*

Proof. Clearly, by (5.5.47),

$$|\iota(x)(\ell)| \le \|\ell\|\,\|x\| \tag{5.5.48}$$

so
$$\|\iota(x)\| \leq \|x\| \tag{5.5.49}$$

On the other hand, given $x_0 \in X$, let ℓ_0 be the map given by (5.5.35). Then
$$\|\ell_0\| \, \|x_0\| = |\iota(x_0)(\ell_0)| \tag{5.5.50}$$

so
$$\|\iota(x_0)\| \geq \|x_0\| \tag{5.5.51}$$

proving that
$$\|\iota(x_0)\| = \|x_0\| \tag{5.5.52}$$

$\square$

Definition. A Banach space, X, is called *reflexive* if and only if $\mathrm{Ran}(\iota)$ is all of X^{**}.

If $1 < p < \infty$ and $q = p/(p-1)$, then $(L^p)^* = L^q$ and $(L^q)^* = L^p$, so tracking these isomorphisms shows that for $1 < p < \infty$, L^p is reflexive. Later (Theorem 5.7.12) we'll prove that any uniformly convex space is reflexive, providing another proof of this L^p reflexivity.

In Problem 5, the reader will show that X is reflexive if and only if X^* is, and that if X is not reflexive, $X, X^{**}, X^{****}, \dots$ are all distinct. We end this section by showing ℓ^1 and $C(X)$ are not reflexive; we'll treat general $L^1(X, d\mu)$ in Problem 6. We'll return to these nonreflexivities in Section 5.11.

Example 5.5.14 (ℓ^1 is not reflexive). In ℓ^∞, let $(\ell^\infty)_0$ be $\{\{a_n\}_{n=1}^\infty$ so that $\lim_{n \to \infty} a_n = 0\}$. It is easy to see this is closed in $\|\cdot\|_\infty$. Clearly, $(1, 1, 1, \dots) \notin (\ell^\infty)_0$, so by Theorem 5.5.10, there is $y \in (\ell^\infty)^*$ so $y \upharpoonright (\ell^\infty)_0 = 0$ and $y(1, 1, \dots, 1, \dots) = 1$. (Indeed, one can show that y can be picked with $\|y\|_{(\ell^\infty)^*} = 1$ (Problem 7).) If $x \in \ell^1$, $\iota(x)(\delta_k) = x_k$, where δ_k is the element of ℓ^∞ with $(\delta_k)_n = \delta_{kn}$. Thus, if $i(x) \upharpoonright (\ell^\infty)_0 \equiv 0$, then, since $\delta_k \in (\ell^\infty)_0$, $x_k = 0$, that is, $x = 0$. It follows if $\iota(x) \upharpoonright (\ell^\infty)_0 \equiv 0$, then $\iota(x) = 0$, so the y constructed above is not in $\mathrm{Ran}(\iota)$. Thus, ℓ^1 is *not* reflexive. $\square$

Example 5.5.15 (L^1 is not reflexive). Let X be a compact metric space and μ a measure so there exists $x_0 \in X$ with $\mu(\{x_0\}) = 0$ and $\mu(A) \neq 0$ for every open neighborhood, A, of x_0. Let $\ell \colon C(X) \to \mathbb{C}$ by $\ell(f) = f(x_0)$. Then $C(X) \subset L^\infty(X, d\mu)$ and so, by the Hahn–Banach theorem, there is $L \colon L^\infty(X, d\mu) \to \mathbb{C}$ so $L \upharpoonright C(X) = \ell$. If $f_n \in C(X)$, $0 \leq f_n(x) \leq 1$, $f_n(x_0) = 1$, $\mathrm{supp}(f_n) \subset \{x \mid \rho(x, x_0) < \frac{1}{n}\}$, then $L(f_n) \equiv 1$ but $\int g(x) f_n(x) \, d\mu \to 0$ for all $g \in L^1$. Thus, $L \notin \iota[L^1]$. There is a much larger set of elements of $(L^\infty)^* \setminus \iota[L^1]$. For if Y is any compactification of $X \setminus \{x_0\}$ (we'll say a lot about compactifications in Section 6.5 of Part 4) and μ a measure on

$Y \setminus (X \setminus \{x_0\})$, then $C(Y) \subset L^\infty$ and $f \mapsto \int f \, d\mu$ for $f \in C(Y)$ has an extension to L^∞ which cannot come from a $g \in L^1(X, d\mu)$. $\square$

Example 5.5.16 ($C(X)$, X a compact metric space, is not reflexive). Let X be a compact metric space with an infinite number of points. Thus, every $\{x\}$ is closed and not all $\{x\}$ are open (since if they were, $\{\{x\}\}_{x \in X}$ would not have a finite cover). Pick an x_0 so $\{x_0\}$ is not open.

If μ is a signed measure in $C(X)^*$, $L(\mu) = \mu(\{x_0\})$ is a continuous functional on $C(X)^*$, and it is easy to see (Problem 9) that it is not an $\iota(f)$ for $f \in C(X)$. Thus, $C(X)$ is not reflexive. $\square$

Notes and Historical Remarks. The Hahn–Banach theorem is named after work of Hahn in 1927 [**384**] and Banach in 1929 [**51, 52**]. Earlier, in 1922, M. Riesz [**789**] proved Theorem 5.5.8, which is related (because Marcel Riesz's brother, Frigyes Riesz, did so much, there is a tendency to mention Marcel's name explicitly for his work). Riesz did this work in connection with his solution of the moment problem discussed in the next section. Indeed, he didn't prove a general abstract theorem at all, but only the special case needed for the moment problem. That said, his proof is exactly the one we give for the abstract theorem. The case where $X = C([a,b])$, including the critical Lemma 5.5.3, appeared fifteen years earlier in 1912 in Helly [**412**]; it is unfortunate that Helly often isn't given credit for this result. This paper of Helly is remarkable—not only did it have this special case of the Hahn–Banach theorem, but he also found that $C([a,b])^*$ is a space of measures independently of Riesz and had the Banach–Alaoglu theorem for $C([a,b])$ (known in this case as the *Helly selection theorem*) and the uniform boundedness principle for $C([a,b])$, long before the general theorems were found.

So why isn't Eduard Helly (1884–1943) better known? He is a paradigm for the Chinese proverb that "may you live in interesting times" is a curse. Born into a Jewish family in Vienna, he got his degree there and then spent time in Göttingen on a fellowship arranged by his advisor, Wirtinger. He returned to Vienna in 1908 but was unable to get a university post, instead working as a high school teacher and making money writing solution manuals for college texts. During this period, he wrote the great paper [**412**].

When war broke out in 1914, Helly enlisted, serving as a lieutenant. In 1915, he was shot in a lung and was captured by the Russians. He spent the next few years in a hospital and prison in Siberia. He suffered from the lung injury and strain on his heart for the rest of his life. Even after Russian involvement in the World War ended, he was not repatriated because the civil war in Russia made travel difficult. He only returned to Vienna in 1920. While he was able to get a habilitation, he couldn't get a paid academic position—his wife believed this was because he was Jewish and because Hahn favored someone younger than a person fifteen years past doctorate. (Yes, that Hahn. There is no indication that Hahn knew of Helly's work when he later proved his version of the Hahn–Banach theorem. Banach did quote Helly's paper elsewhere, but may not have realized the connection with extension of functionals.)

Helly found a position in a bank which failed in 1929, but eventually found work as an actuary. After the Nazi occupation of Austria in 1938, Helly and his wife fled to the U.S. There things improved somewhat—with Einstein's aid, he obtained a teaching position in a community college and then a position writing mathematical training manuals for the Signal Corps at the start of America's involvement in World War II. Finally, he was offered a mathematics professorship at Illinois Institute of Technology but died of a heart attack shortly thereafter.

Helly only dealt with the Hahn–Banach theorem in $C([a, b])$ which is separable. Both Hahn and Banach used transfinite induction to do the general case. Helly and Hahn both looked at a functional bounded by a multiple of a norm. The more general version we have with a convex function is Banach's in [52].

The key formula, (5.5.18), needed to go from the real to complex Hahn–Banach theorem appeared in Löwig [607]. The formal complex Hahn–Banach theorem is usually attributed to Murray [671], Bohnenblust–Sobczyk [107], and Soukhomlinoff [870].

The first nonreflexive Banach space (see Problem 10) was found by Helly in 1921 [413]. The name "reflexive" is from Lorch [603]. True understanding of reflexivity only came with the Banach–Alaoglu theorem, see Theorem 5.8.2. Even simpler than Example 5.5.14 is to see directly that $[(\ell^\infty)_0]^* = \ell^1$ and $(\ell^1)^* = \ell^\infty \neq (\ell^\infty)_0$ (Problem 8).

There is an algebraic Hahn–Banach theorem, that is, a version on linear spaces without topology (see Problem 11). In particular, every infinite-dimensional Banach space has discontinuous linear functionals, so codimension 1, not closed subspaces.

Problems

1. Let $p\colon X \to \mathbb{R}$ be convex on a complex vector space X. Prove that p is symmetric if and only if
$$\forall \alpha, \beta \in \mathbb{C},\ \forall x, y \in X,\ |\alpha| + |\beta| = 1 \Rightarrow p(\alpha x + \beta y) \leq |\alpha| p(x) + |\beta| p(y)$$

2. Prove that (5.5.27) defines a partial order (see Section 1.4) with $x \leq y \Rightarrow \forall z,\ x + z \leq y + z$ and $\lambda \geq 0$ and $x \leq y \Rightarrow \lambda x \leq \lambda y$.

3. (a) In $\mathbb{R}^2$, let

$$V_+ = \{(x, y) \mid y > 0\} \cup \{(x, 0) \mid x \geq 0\}$$

Let $Y = \{(x, 0) \mid x \in \mathbb{R}\}$ and let $\ell((x, 0)) = x$ as a map of $Y \to \mathbb{R}$. Prove that $V_+ \cap Y$ is a positive cone and ℓ a positive functional.

(b) If $L((x, y)) = x + \alpha y$, prove that $L((-\alpha - 1, 1)) = -1$ so that L is not positive. Thus, ℓ has no positive extension to $\mathbb{R}^2$.

(c) Is Y a dominating subspace?

4. Prove the nonlinear Hahn–Banach theorem: If X is an NLS and $Y \subset X$ is a subspace and if $f : Y \to \mathbb{R}$ is a (possibly nonlinear) function obeying $|f(y_1) - f(y_2)| \leq \|y_1 - y_2\|$ for all $y_1, y_2 \in Y$, then there is $F : X \to \mathbb{R}$ with $F \restriction Y = f$ and $|F(x_1) - F(x_2)| \leq \|x_1 - x_2\|$ for all $x_1, x_2 \in X$.

5. (a) Let X be an NLS. Let $\tilde{\iota} : X^* \to X^{***}$ be the ι associated to X^*. For $\ell \in X^*$ and $x \in X$, prove that $\tilde{\iota}(\ell)[\iota(x)] = \ell(x)$.

(b) If $\tilde{\iota}(\ell) \restriction \iota(X) = 0$, prove that $\tilde{\iota}(\ell) \equiv 0$.

(c) If X is not reflexive, prove that X^* is not reflexive.

(d) Prove that X is reflexive if and only if X^* is reflexive.

6. Let X be a compact metric space and μ a measure so that ℓ_μ is strictly positive.

(a) If X is not finite, prove that $C(X)$ is a proper subspace of $L^\infty(X, d\mu)$.

(b) Prove that there exists $L \in (L^\infty)^*$, so $L \restriction C(X) \equiv 0$ but $L \neq 0$.

(c) Prove that $L^1(X, d\mu)$ is not reflexive.

7. Let $c = \{a \in \ell^\infty \mid \lim_{n \to \infty} a_n \text{ exists}\}$. Let $\ell : c \to \mathbb{C}$ by $\ell(a) = \lim_{n \to \infty} a_n$. Prove $\|\ell\| = 1$. Prove that the y of Example 5.5.14 can be chosen with $\|y\| = 1$.

8. Prove that $((\ell^\infty)_0)^* = \ell^1$. Conclude that $(\ell^\infty)_0$ is not reflexive, and then that ℓ^1 is not reflexive.

9. Let $x_0 \in X$, a compact Hausdorff space, be such that $\{x_0\}$ is not open. Let $L(\mu) = \mu(\{x_0\})$ for $\mu \in C(X)^*$. If $L = \iota(f)$, for $f \in C(X)$, prove $f(x) = 0$ for $x \neq x_0$, and then that $f \equiv 0$. Conclude that $L \notin \iota(C(X))$.

10. This problem will analyze Helly's initial example of a nonreflexive Banach space [**413**].

(a) Let H be the space of sequences $\{a_n\}_{n=1}^\infty$ for which $\lim_{N \to \infty} \sum_{n=1}^N a_n$ exists (in $\mathbb{C}$). Put a norm on H by $\|\{a_n\}_{n=1}^\infty\| = \sup_{M=1,2,\dots} \|\sum_{n=M}^\infty a_n\|$. Show H is a Banach space.

(b) Let B be the set of sequences $\{b_n\}_{n=1}^\infty$ for which $\|b\| = |b_1| + \sum_{n=1}^\infty |b_{n+1} - b_n|$ is finite (sequences of bounded variation). Prove B is a Banach space.

(c) If $b \in B$, $a \in H$, prove $\ell_b(a) = \sum_{n=1}^\infty b_n a_n$ exists. (*Hint*: $\sum_{n=1}^\infty b_n a_n = b_1 \sum_{n=1}^\infty a_n + \sum_{k=1}^\infty (b_{k+1} - b_k) \sum_{n=k+1}^\infty a_k$.)

(d) Prove $b \mapsto \ell_b$ sets up an isometry of B and H^*.

(e) Prove that $L(b) = \lim_{n\to\infty} b_n$ exists for any $b \in B$ and defines an element of B^*, and that $L \notin \iota(H)$. Thus, H is not reflexive.

(f) Let $T(a)_m = \sum_{n=m}^\infty a_n$ for $a \in H$. Prove that T is an isometry of B and $(\ell^\infty)_0$, showing in another way that B is not reflexive (see Problem 8).

11. (a) Let X be a vector space over $\mathbb{K} = \mathbb{R}$ or $\mathbb{C}$, $Y \subset X$ a subspace, and $\ell: Y \to \mathbb{K}$ a linear functional. If $x_0 \in X \setminus Y$, prove ℓ can be extended to a functional on $Y \dotplus \{\lambda x_0 \mid \lambda \in \mathbb{K}\}$.

(b) Using Zorn's lemma, prove in the context of part (a) that there is a linear map, $L: X \to \mathbb{K}$, so that $L \restriction Y = \ell$.

(c) Let X be an infinite-dimensional Banach space. Show there exists $\{x_n\}_{n=1}^\infty$ with $\|x_n\| = 1$ and the x's linear independent (i.e., $\sum_{n=1}^N \alpha_n x_n = 0 \Rightarrow \alpha_1 = \alpha_2 = \cdots = \alpha_N = 0$).

(d) Let Y be the set of finite linear combinations of the $\{x_j\}_{j=1}^\infty$. Let $\ell: Y \to \mathbb{K}$ by $\ell(\sum_{n=1}^N \alpha_n x_n) = \sum_{n=1}^N n\alpha_n$. Show there is $L: X \to \mathbb{K}$ so that $L(x_n) = n$ and thus, L is not in X^*.

(e) Prove that X has subspaces Z so Z is dense in X and $\mathrm{codim}(X) = 1$.

12. This problem will use the Hahn–Banach theorem to prove that ℓ^∞ is a kind of universal recipient in that any separable Banach space, X, is isometrically isomorphic to a closed subspace of ℓ^∞.

(a) Pick $\{x_n\}_{n=1}^\infty$ a dense subset of X with each $x_j \neq 0$. For each j, pick $\ell_j \in X^*$ with $\|\ell_j\| = 1$ and $\ell_j(x_j) = 1$. Prove that for all $x \in X$

$$\|x\| = \sup_j |\ell_j(x)| \tag{5.5.53}$$

(b) Prove that $T : X \to \ell^\infty$ by $T(x)_j = \ell_j(x)$ is a isometric isomophism of X to a closed subset of ℓ^∞.

(c) For which measure spaces (Y, Σ, μ) can ℓ^∞ be replaced by $L^\infty(Y, \Sigma, \mu)$.

13. This problem will use the Hahn–Banach theorem to prove that ℓ^1 is a kind of universal donor in that for any separable Banach space, X, there is a closed subspace, $Y \subset \ell^1$, so X is isometrically isomorphic to the quotient space ℓ^1/Y.

(a) If $\{x_j, \ell_j\}_{j=1}^\infty$ are as in Problem 12, prove that

$$T(\{a_j\}_{j=1}^\infty) = \sum a_j \left(x_j / \|x_j\|\right) \tag{5.5.54}$$

defines a bounded map of ℓ^1 to X with norm 1.

(b) Prove that for finite sequences, $\{a_j\}_{j=1}^N$,

$$\inf_{b \in \ell_1} \{b \mid T(b) = \sum_{j=1}^N a_j x_j\} = \|\sum_{j=1}^N a_j x_j\|_X$$

and conclude that $\widetilde{T} : \ell^1 / \mathrm{Ker}(T) \to X$ is an isometric isomorphism.

14. This problem will prove the Banach–Mazur theorem, Theorem 5.0.1. The reader will need the Banach–Alaoglu theorem (see Section 5.9) and the Alexandroff–Hausdorff theorem of Problem 5 of Section 4.2.

(a) Let X_1^* be the unit ball of X^* in the weak-* topology. If X is separable, prove that X_1^* is a compact metric space.

(b) Let $L \colon X \to C(X_1^*)$ by $L(x)(\ell) = \ell(x)$. Prove that L is a linear isometry of X onto a closed subspace of $C(X_1^*)$.

(c) Let B, D be two compact Hausdorff spaces and $F \colon B \to D$ a continuous surjection. Define $F^* \colon C(D) \to C(B)$ by $F^*(f)(b) = f(F(b))$. Prove that F^* is a linear isometry of $C(D)$ onto a subspace of $C(B)$.

(d) Using the Alexandroff–Hausdorff theorem construct a linear isometry of X onto a closed subspace of $C([0,1])$.

Remark. The results of the last two problems go back to Banach and Mazur.

5.6. Bonus Section: The Hamburger Moment Problem

In this section, we'll prove the main existence theorems for the Stieltjes and Hamburger moment problems. The reader should review the discussion in Section 4.17 through Theorem 4.17.3 and, in particular, Hankel matrices and determinants. Our two main results here are:

Theorem 5.6.1 (Hamburger Moment Theorem). *Let $c_0 = 1$ and $\{c_n\}_{n=0}^\infty$ be a sequence of real numbers. Then there exists a nontrivial measure, μ, on $\mathbb{R}$ obeying (4.17.1) if and only if (4.17.9) holds.*

Theorem 5.6.2 (Stieltjes Moment Theorem). *Let $c_0 = 1$ and $\{c_n\}_{n=0}^\infty$ be a sequence of real numbers. Then there exists a nontrivial measure, μ, on $[0, \infty)$ obeying (4.17.1) if and only if (4.17.9) and (4.17.10) hold.*

We have already proven the "only if" parts (in Theorem 4.17.3), so we'll only need to prove the "if" part, that is, (4.17.9) (respectively, (4.17.9) and

(4.17.10)) implies the existence of a μ on $\mathbb{R}$ (respectively, $[0, \infty)$). This we'll show using the M. Riesz extension theorem (Theorem 5.5.8). We'll then say a little bit about the uniqueness question.

We let $\mathcal{P}$ denote the set of real polynomials on $\mathbb{R}$ and $\mathcal{G}$ the set of real-valued continuous functions, f, on $\mathbb{R}$ so that for some m and C,

$$|f(x)| \leq C(1 + |x|)^m \tag{5.6.1}$$

$\mathcal{P}_+^{\mathbb{R}}$ and $\mathcal{G}_+^{\mathbb{R}}$ are the elements of $\mathcal{P}$ and $\mathcal{G}$, nonnegative on $\mathbb{R}$, and $\mathcal{P}_+^{[0,\infty)}$ and $\mathcal{G}_+^{[0,\infty)}$ those nonnegative on $[0, \infty)$

Lemma 5.6.3. *Suppose $\ell \colon \mathcal{G} \to \mathbb{R}$ is a linear function where*

$$\ell(f) \geq 0 \tag{5.6.2}$$

for all f in $\mathcal{G}_+^{\mathbb{R}}$ (respectively, $\mathcal{G}_+^{[0,\infty)}$). Then there is a measure, μ, on $\mathbb{R}$ (respectively, $[0, \infty)$) so that

$$\ell(x^n) = \int x^n \, d\mu(x) \tag{5.6.3}$$

for all $n = 0, 1, 2 \ldots$.

Proof. Since $C(\mathbb{R}_\infty)$, the continuous functions on $\mathbb{R}_\infty \equiv \mathbb{R} \cup \{\infty\}$ or equivalently $f \in C(\mathbb{R})$ for which $\lim_{|x| \to \infty} f(x)$ exists, lies in $\mathcal{G}$ (and $\mathcal{G}_+^{[0,\infty)} \subset \mathcal{G}_+^{\mathbb{R}}$), $\ell \upharpoonright C(\mathbb{R}_\infty)$ is a positive functional on $C(\mathbb{R}_\infty)$ and so defines a positive measure, μ, on $\mathbb{R} \cup \{\infty\}$ of total mass $\ell(\mathbb{1})$.

For each $n = 1, 2, \ldots$ and $R > 0$, define $f_{n,R}(x)$ by

$$f_{n,R}(x) = \begin{cases} (-1)^n R^n & \text{if } x \leq -R \\ x^n & \text{if } |x| \leq R \\ R^n & \text{if } x \geq R \end{cases} \tag{5.6.4}$$

Then $x^{2n} - f_{2n,R}(x) \geq 0$, so since $f_{2n,R} \in C(\mathbb{R}_\infty)$,

$$\int f_{2n,R}(x) \, d\mu(x) \leq \ell(x^{2n}) \tag{5.6.5}$$

Since $f_{2n,R} \geq R^{2n}$ on $\mathbb{R} \cup \{\infty\} \setminus [-R, R]$, we conclude

$$R^{2n}\mu(\{\infty\}) + R^{2n}\mu(\{x \in \mathbb{R} \mid |x| \geq R\}) \leq \ell(x^{2n}) \tag{5.6.6}$$

We conclude, by taking $R \to \infty$, that

$$\mu(\{\infty\}) = 0 \tag{5.6.7}$$

and, for all x,

$$\int x^{2n-2} \, d\mu(x) < \infty \tag{5.6.8}$$

In particular, μ has finite moments and, by the dominated convergence theorem, for any n,

$$\lim_{R\to\infty} \ell(f_{n,R}) = \int x^n \, d\mu(x) \tag{5.6.9}$$

On the other hand, since $\ell \geq 0$,

$$|\ell(f)| \leq \ell(|f|) \tag{5.6.10}$$

and

$$|f_{n,R}(x) - x^n| \leq \begin{cases} 0, & |x| \leq R \\ |x|^n, & |x| \geq R \end{cases} \tag{5.6.11}$$

for any even $m > n$,

$$|f_{n,R} - x^n| \leq R^{-(m-n)} x^m \tag{5.6.12}$$

(5.6.10) and (5.6.12) imply

$$|\ell(f_{n,R}) - \ell(x^n)| \leq R^{-(m-n)} \ell(x^m) \tag{5.6.13}$$

so that

$$\lim_{R\to\infty} \ell(f_{n,R}) = \ell(x^n) \tag{5.6.14}$$

that is, by (5.6.9) and (5.6.14), we have proven (5.6.3).

All that remains is to show if $\ell \geq 0$ on $\mathcal{G}_+^{[0,\infty)}$, then μ is supported on $[0,\infty)$. Given $b < 0$, let

$$g_b(x) = \begin{cases} -1, & x \leq b \\ x/(-b), & b \leq x \leq 0 \\ 0, & x \geq 0 \end{cases} \tag{5.6.15}$$

Then $\ell(g_b) \geq 0$ since $g \in \mathcal{G}_+^{[0,\infty)}$, but

$$\ell(g_b) = \int g_b(x) \, d\mu(x) \leq -\mu((-\infty, b]) \tag{5.6.16}$$

It follows that $\mu((-\infty, b]) = 0$ for all $b < 0$, so $\mu((-\infty, 0)) = 0$. $\quad\square$

Lemma 5.6.4. *For any* $P \in \mathcal{P}_+^{\mathbb{R}}$, *there exist* $Q_j \in \mathcal{P}$, $j = 1, \ldots, J$ *so that* $P = \sum_{j=1}^J Q_j^2$. *For any* $P \in \mathcal{P}_+^{[0,\infty)}$, *there exists* $Q_j \in \mathcal{P}$, $j = 1, \ldots, J$, *and* $R_\ell \in \mathcal{P}$, $\ell = 1, \ldots, L$, *so that*

$$P = \sum_{j=1}^J Q_j^2 + x \sum_{\ell=1}^L R_\ell^2 \tag{5.6.17}$$

Proof. Let $P \in \mathcal{P}_+^{\mathbb{R}}$. The zeros of any $P \in \mathcal{P}$ lie in $\mathbb{R}$ or complex conjugate pairs. Since $P \geq 0$ on $\mathbb{R}$, the zeros on $\mathbb{R}$ must be of even order or else P will change sign on $\mathbb{R}$. Thus,

$$P(x) = \prod_{s=1}^{S}[(x-a_s)^2 + b_s^2]\prod_{t=1}^{T}(\lambda - c_t)^{2m_t} \tag{5.6.18}$$

is a sum of Q_j^2.

If $P \in \mathcal{P}_+^{[0,\infty)}$, the zeros on $(-\infty, 0]$ can be of odd order, so (5.6.18) has to be written to include $\prod_{u=1}^{U}(x + b_u)$ with $b_u \geq 0$. Such a product is a sum of Q_j^2 and xR_ℓ^L. $\square$

Proof of Theorem 5.6.1. Given $\{c_n\}_{n=0}^{\infty}$, define φ on $\mathcal{P}$ by

$$\varphi\left(\sum_{k=0}^{n}\alpha_k x^k\right) = \sum_{k=0}^{n}\alpha_k c_k \tag{5.6.19}$$

By (4.17.8) and Lemma 4.17.2, for all $Q \in \mathcal{P}$, $\varphi(Q^2) \geq 0$. Thus, by Lemma 5.6.4, $\varphi \geq 0$ on $\mathcal{P}_+^{\mathbb{R}}$.

If $g \in \mathcal{G}_+^{\mathbb{R}}$, then $|g(x)| \leq C(1 + |x|)^m$, and thus,

$$0 < g(x) < 2^m C(1 + x^{2m}) \tag{5.6.20}$$

Therefore, in the language of Theorem 5.5.8, $\mathcal{P}$ is a dominant subspace for $\mathcal{G}$. By that theorem, φ has a positive extension to $\mathcal{G}$. By Lemma 5.6.3, there is a measure, μ, solving (4.17.1).

We claim μ is nontrivial. If not, μ is supported on $\{x_\ell\}_{\ell=1}^{L}$ and $\int [\prod_{\ell=1}^{L}(x - x_\ell)]^2 \, d\mu(x) = 0$, contrary to the strict positivity of the Hankel matrices. $\square$

Proof of Theorem 5.6.2. The proof parallels that of Theorem 5.6.1. By (4.17.11) and (4.17.12), φ obeys $\varphi(Q^2) \geq 0$ and $\varphi(xR^2) \geq 0$. So, by Lemma 5.6.4, $\varphi \upharpoonright \mathcal{P}_+^{[0,\infty)} \geq 0$. We now put an order on $\mathcal{G}$, that $g \geq 0 \Leftrightarrow g \upharpoonright [0,\infty) \geq 0$ as a function. In this, the positive cone in $\mathcal{P}$ is $\mathcal{P}_+^{[0,\infty)}$ which dominates $\mathcal{G}$. $\square$

That completes our discussion of the existence question where the necessary and sufficient conditions are definitive. We turn now to say a little about uniqueness where there are no necessary and sufficient conditions in terms of the c_n's.

Example 5.6.5 (Log-normal distribution). We claim (Problem 1) for $k = 0, 1, 2, \dots$,

$$\frac{1}{\sqrt{\pi}}\int_0^\infty u^k u^{-\log u}\, d\mu = \exp(\tfrac{1}{4}(k+1)^2) \tag{5.6.21}$$

$$\frac{1}{\sqrt{\pi}} \int_0^\infty u^k u^{-\log u} \sin(2\pi \log u)\, d\mu = 0 \qquad (5.6.22)$$

Thus, for $\theta \in [-1, 1]$,

$$d\nu_\theta(u) = u^{-\log u}(1 + \theta \sin(2\pi \log u))\, du \qquad (5.6.23)$$

has

$$\int u^k\, d\nu_\theta(u) = \exp(\tfrac{1}{4}(k+1)^2) \qquad (5.6.24)$$

so the moment problem associated to $c_n = \exp(\tfrac{1}{4}(n+1)^2)$ is indeterminate. In fact (see the Notes), the set of ν's with those moments is a lot more than one-dimensional—it is always infinite-dimensional in the indeterminate case. Since $u^{-\log u} = \exp(-(\log u)^2)\, d\nu_{\theta=0}$ is sometimes called the *log-normal distribution*. $\qquad\qquad\square$

In the other direction, we have

Theorem 5.6.6. *Let $\{c_n\}_{n=0}^\infty$ be the moments of a probability measure, μ, on $\mathbb{R}$ and suppose that for some $A > 0$,*

$$|c_n| \le A^n n! \qquad (5.6.25)$$

Then the moment problem is determinate.

Remarks. 1. We'll use some simple results from complex analysis in the proof.

2. By a general result relating when the Hamburger problem is determinate and when the Stieltjes problem is, one can see (Problem 2) that if μ is supported on $[0, \infty)$ and

$$|c_n| \le A^n (2n)! \qquad (5.6.26)$$

then the Stieltjes problem is determinate.

Proof. Let ν also solve the moment problem. Pick $b > 0$ so $bA < 1$. Then

$$\sup_N \sum_{n=0}^N \frac{b^{2n} c_{2n}}{(2n)!} < \infty \qquad (5.6.27)$$

so, by the monotone convergence theorem, $\cosh(bx)$ (= monotone limit of $\sum_{n=0}^N x^{2n} b^{2n}/(2n)!$) is in $L^1(\mathbb{R}, d\mu)$ and $L^1(\mathbb{R}, d\nu)$.

It follows (e.g., by Theorem 3.1.6 of Part 2A) that

$$F_\mu(z) = \int e^{izx}\, d\mu(x), \qquad F_\nu(z) = \int e^{izx}\, d\nu(x) \qquad (5.6.28)$$

are analytic in $\{z \mid |\mathrm{Im}\, z| < b\}$. Since the Taylor coefficients at $z = 0$ are moments, $F_\mu(z) = F_\nu(z)$ for $|z|$ small and so, by analyticity, in the strip, and so for $z \in \mathbb{R}$.

By Fubini's theorem and $\int_0^\infty e^{iayx}e^{-y}\,dy = (1-iax)^{-1}$ (for a and x real), we see that for a real,

$$\int (1-iax)^{-1}\,d\mu(x) = \int (1-iax)^{-1}\,d\nu(x) \qquad (5.6.29)$$

Again, by Theorem 3.1.6 of Part 2A, we have analyticity and so, equality of derivatives, that is,

$$\int (1\pm ix)^{-n}\,d\mu(x) = \int (1\pm ix)^{-n}\,d\nu(x) \qquad (5.6.30)$$

By repeated use of

$$(1+ix)^{-1}(1-ix)^{-1} = \tfrac{1}{2}\left[(1+ix)^{-1}+(1-ix)^{-1}\right] \qquad (5.6.31)$$

we get that for all n,m,

$$\int (1+ix)^{-n}(1-ix)^{-m}\,d\mu(x) = \int (1+ix)^{-n}(1+ix)^{-m}\,d\nu(x)$$

By the Stone–Weierstrass theorem, polynomials in $(1\pm ix)^{-1}$ are dense in $C(\mathbb{R}_\infty)$, so $\mu = \nu$. □

Example 5.6.7. We saw (see Theorem 4.11.11) that Gauss measure (with $a=1$) given by (4.11.25) has $c_{2n+1}=0$ and

$$c_{2n} = 2^{-n}\frac{(2n)!}{n!} \qquad (5.6.32)$$

certainly obeys (5.6.25) and so is the unique measure with those moments. The Notes discuss $c_\beta \exp(-|x|^\beta)$. □

Notes and Historical Remarks. In their work on the central limit theorem (see Section 7.3 and its Notes), Chebyshev and his student, Markov, considered moments (this work is discussed in Krein [**525**]) of measures of the form $f(x)\,dx$ and, in particular, asked if the Gaussian distribution was determined by its moments. In this work, Markov developed the continued fraction method extended so successfully by others.

The central paper in the development of the moment problem is Stieltjes' great 1894 paper [**881**] (see the Notes to Section 4.1 for a capsule biography). He defined general Riemann–Stieltjes integrals (so one could formulate the problem!), found the remarkable Example 5.6.5 and, most importantly, proved Theorem 5.6.2 using continued fractions (see below).

In the early 1920s, there was an explosion of interest in the subject, starting with Hamburger's 1920–21 paper [**389**] which stated and proved Theorem 5.6.1. In short order, Carleman [**161**], Hellinger [**410**], Nevanlinna [**684**], and M. Riesz [**784**] produced new results, insights, and proofs. Riesz used the linear functional extension approach we present, and Nevanlinna, and then Riesz developed a remarkable parametrization of the solutions we discuss later.

Important later work includes that of Stone (discussed soon), relating the moment problem to the question of self-adjoint extensions, and papers by Akhiezer and Krein. Two classic books are those of Akhiezer [**4**] and Shohat–Tamarkin [**844**]. Simon has a long review article [**851**] on the operator theory approach and Simon [**855**] has a section on a simple approach using finite approximation. We return to this in Section 7.7 of Part 4.

Formally, if μ solves (4.17.1), we have

$$\int \frac{d\mu(x)}{x-z} = -\int \left(\sum_{n=0}^{\infty} x^n z^{-n-1} \right) d\mu(x) = -\sum_{n=0}^{\infty} c_n z^{-n-1} \qquad (5.6.33)$$

While the power series will have zero radius of convergence if supp(μ) is unbounded, one can instead try a Hermite–Padé approximation, that is, $-Q_n(x)/P_n(x)$ where P_n is a polynomial of degree n and $Q_n(x)$ of degree $n-1$ so that the first $(2n-2)$ terms of the Laurent series for $-Q_n/P_n$ near ∞ agrees with $-\sum_{j=0}^{2n-3} c_j z^{-j-1}$. The P_n are orthogonal polynomials for $d\mu$ and Q_n related polynomials. Because a truncated continued fraction expansion simplifies to $-Q_n/P_n$, this is called the continued fraction expansion. What Stieltjes showed is that in the half-line case, $-Q_n/P_n$ has a limit for $z \in \mathbb{C} \setminus [0, \infty)$ and that limit is $\int \frac{d\mu(x)}{x-z}$ for a measure solving (4.17.1). Wall's book [**975**] has an exposition of this result.

Simon [**855**] has a simple direct proof of Theorem 5.6.1. Using orthogonal polynomials, he shows $M_n \equiv \{\mu \mid \int x^k \, dx = c_k, \, k = 0, \dots, 2n-1, \int x^{2n} \, dx \leq c_{2n}\}$ is nonempty. It is compact, so by the finite intersection problem, $\bigcap M_n \neq \emptyset$.

Nevanlinna found a remarkable parametrization of the solutions in the indeterminate case which is always an infinite-dimensional manifold parametrized by $\mathcal{H}$, the Herglotz functions, that is, analytic functions $\Phi \colon \mathbb{C}_+ \to \overline{\mathbb{C}}_+$ (either $\Phi(z) = s$, a real constant, or its values lies in $\mathbb{C}_+$). Nevanlinna built four entire analytic functions, $A(z), B(z), C(z), D(z)$, from the $P_n(z)$ and $Q_n(z)$. The solution, μ_Φ, of (4.17.1) associated to $\Phi \in \mathcal{H}$ is given by (for $z \in \mathbb{C}_+$)

$$\int \frac{d\mu_\Phi(x)}{x-z} = -\frac{C(z)\Phi(z) + A(z)}{D(z)\Phi(z) + B(z)} \qquad (5.6.34)$$

In particular, one can show that in the indeterminate case, there are always μ_Φ which are discrete pure point, but also purely singular continuous, and also purely absolutely continuous μ_Φ's. In terms of the language of Section 5.11, the set of measures solving (4.17.1) is a compact, convex set with the remarkable property that its extreme points are dense! For an exposition of this theory, see Akhiezer [**4**] or Simon [**851**] and Section 7.7 of Part 4.

Stone [**884**] found a deep connection between moment problems and the question of self-adjoint extensions of Hilbert space operators. When the Hankel determinants are all strictly positive, one can use the moments to define an inner product on the polynomials, $\mathcal{P}$ (or $\mathcal{P} + i\mathcal{P}$ in our notation in this section). $\mathcal{H}$ is the abstract completion and, in the notation of Section 7.1 of Part 4, $P(x) \to xP(x)$ defines a symmetric operator. This operator has deficiency indices $(0,0)$ in case the problem is determinate and $(1,1)$ if indeterminate. Simon [**851**] and Section 7.7 of Part 4 discuss this point of view.

Krein [**523**] proved a remarkable theorem implying certain problems are indeterminate:

Theorem 5.6.8 ([**523**]). *Let μ be a probability measure on $\mathbb{R}$ with Lebesgue decomposition*

$$d\mu(x) = F(x)\,dx + d\mu_s(x) \tag{5.6.35}$$

If μ has finite moments and

$$\int \frac{\log(F(x))}{1 + x^2}\,dx > -\infty \tag{5.6.36}$$

then the moment problem for the moments of μ is indeterminate.

For a monograph proof, see Simon [**855**, Sect. 3.9]. As an example for $\beta > 0$, define

$$d\mu_\beta(x) = c_\beta \exp(-|x|^\beta)\,dx \tag{5.6.37}$$

where c_β is picked to make this a probability measure. Krein's theorem shows the Hamburger problem for these sets of moments is indeterminate if $0 < \beta < 1$. By explicitly computing the moments in terms of gamma functions and getting their asymptotics from Stirling's formula, one finds that if $1 \leq \beta$, then (5.6.25) holds, and so the problem is determinate. For details, see Simon [**855**, Sects. 3.8/3.9].

Closely related to the moment problem on $\mathbb{R}$ is the *trigonometric moment problem*, that is, which $\{c_n\}_{n=-\infty}^{\infty}$ obey

$$c_n = \int e^{in\theta}\,d\mu(\theta) \tag{5.6.38}$$

for a measure on $\partial\mathbb{D}$. We will study this in Section 5.5 of Part 4.

Problems

1. Verify (5.6.21) and (5.6.22). (*Hint*: Let $x = (\log u) - \frac{1}{2}(k+1)$.)

2. Let μ be a measure on $[0, \infty)$ and let

$$d\rho(x) = \tfrac{1}{2} \left[\chi_{[0,\infty)}(x)\, d\mu(x^2) + \chi_{(-\infty,0]}(x)\, d\mu(x^2) \right] \qquad (5.6.39)$$

as a measure on $\mathbb{R}$.

(a) Let c_n be the moments of μ and Γ_n of ρ. Prove that

$$\Gamma_{2n+1} = 0, \qquad \Gamma_{2n} = c_n \qquad (5.6.40)$$

(b) Suppose c_n is a set of moments of a measure on $[0, \infty)$ and c_n obeys (5.6.26). Prove that the Stieltjes moment problem for $\{c_n\}_{n=0}^{\infty}$ is determinate.

Remark. There are moments, $\{c_n\}_{n=0}^{\infty}$, which are determinate for the Stieltjes problem but indeterminate for the Hamburger problem; see Simon [**851**] or Section 7.7 of Part 4.

3. This problem will show that the moments of the probability measure

$$d\mu_0(x) = \frac{1}{24}\, \exp(-x^{1/4})\, dx \qquad (5.6.41)$$

have multiple solutions for the moment problem.

(a) Prove that $\int x^n\, d\mu_0(x) = \tfrac{1}{6}\Gamma\!\left(\tfrac{n}{4}+4\right)$.

(b) For any complex α with $\operatorname{Re}\alpha > 0$, prove that

$$\int_0^\infty y^n\, e^{-\alpha y}\, dy = \alpha^{-n-1}\, n! \qquad (5.6.42)$$

(c) Pick $\alpha = 1 + i$, prove that for $m = 0, 1, 2, \dots$

$$\int_0^\infty y^{4m+3} \operatorname{Im}\!\left(e^{-(1+i)y}\right) dy = 0 \qquad (5.6.43)$$

(d) Prove that

$$\int x^n\, \sin(x^{1/4})\, d\mu_0(x) = 0 \qquad (5.6.44)$$

(e) If $d\mu_w = \left(1 + w\, \sin(x^{1/4})\right) d\mu_0$, for $-1 \le w \le 1$, prove that $d\mu_w \ge 0$ and $\int x^n\, d\mu_w(x) = \int x^n\, d\mu_0(x)$.

5.7. Weak Topologies and Locally Convex Spaces

Given an NLS, X, the weak topology is the weakest in which $x \mapsto \ell(x)$ is continuous for each $\ell \in X^*$. We already studied this in the Hilbert space case in Section 3.6. Among the main results there were:

(a) The weakly continuous linear functionals are exactly X^* (Corollary 3.6.7).

(b) The weak topology is not metrizable if X has infinite dimension (Theorem 3.6.8).

(c) The unit ball is compact in the weak topology.

Our goal in this section will be to extend (a) and (b) to the case of general Banach space. We'll eventually see (Theorem 5.8.2) that (c) holds for a Banach space, X, if and only if X is reflexive. Instead, we'll get (c) in the next section for X^* in the weak-$*$ topology; a second goal of this section will be to define this topology and prove several of its properties, leading to a proof that uniformly convex spaces are reflexive. A third goal will be to look at which TVS have large dual spaces. We'll discuss L^p for $0 < p < 1$, prove it has a natural metric (but not norm) topology in which it is complete and a TVS but with no continuous linear functionals! This will lead us to single out a class of TVS that includes NLS in the norm and in the weak topology: the locally convex spaces.

Given the need to define weak topologies on X^* based on the functionals in X^{**} and also in X, it is natural to set up a general framework.

Definition. A *dual pair* is a vector space, X, over $\mathbb{K}$ and a vector space, Y, of linear functionals on X with the property that for each $x \neq 0$, there is $\ell \in Y$ with $\ell(x) \neq 0$.

This definition looks asymmetric in X and Y but it isn't, for to say Y is a set of linear functionals means if $\ell \neq 0$, there is $x \in X$ with $\ell(x) \neq 0$. We will emphasize this duality by writing $\langle y, x \rangle$ rather than $y(x)$ for $x \in X$, $y \in Y$. Equivalently, we see a dual pair is a pair of vector spaces, X and Y, over $\mathbb{K}$ and a bilinear map $x, y \mapsto \langle y, x \rangle$ of $X \times Y \to \mathbb{K}$, which is nondegenerate in the sense that $\forall x, \exists y \langle y, x \rangle \neq 0$ and $\forall y, \exists x \langle y, x \rangle \neq 0$.

Definition. Given a dual pair, (X, Y), the *Y-weak topology* on X, denoted $\sigma(X, Y)$, is the weakest topology on X in which the maps $x \mapsto \langle y, x \rangle$ of X to $\mathbb{K}$ are continuous for all $y \in Y$.

Because of the nondegeneracy condition, σ is a Hausdorff topology. If X is a Banach space, the $\sigma(X, X^*)$-topology on X is the weak topology and the $\sigma(X^*, X)$-topology on X^* is called the *weak-$*$ topology*.

For any $y_1, \ldots, y_\ell \in Y$ and $\varepsilon > 0$, define

$$N(y_1, \ldots, y_\ell; \varepsilon) = \{x \mid |\langle y_j, x \rangle| < \varepsilon \text{ for } j = 1, \ldots, \ell\} \qquad (5.7.1)$$

These sets, as $y_1, \ldots, y_\ell$ run through all of Y, $\ell = 1, 2, \ldots$ and $\varepsilon > 0$, are a neighborhood basis for $\sigma(X, Y)$.

Lemma 3.6.5 and Proposition 3.6.6 are vector-space results and so apply to a dual pair. Theorem 3.6.3 depends only on the norm density and separability. We conclude that Theorem 3.6.3, Corollary 3.6.7, and Theorem 3.6.8 extend.

Theorem 5.7.1. *The $\sigma(X, Y)$ continuous linear functionals on X is precisely Y.*

Theorem 5.7.2. *The $\sigma(X, Y)$-topology is metrizable if and only if Y has countable algebraic dimension. In particular, if X is a Banach space which is not finite-dimensional, the $\sigma(X, X^*)$- and $\sigma(X^*, X)$-topologies are not metrizable.*

In addition, if X^* (respectively, X) are separable, the $\sigma(X, X^*)$ (respectively, $\sigma(X^*, X)$) topology restricted to the unit ball in X (respectively, X^*) is metrizable.

The "in particular" relies on Theorem 5.4.20.

Example 5.7.3 (Weak sequential convergence in ℓ^1)**.** We want to note the remarkable fact that if $x_n \to 0$ in the $\sigma(\ell^1, \ell^\infty)$-topology, then $\|x_n\| \to 0$. By the uniform boundedness principle (Theorem 5.4.9), $\sup_n \|x_n\| < \infty$, so if $\|x_n\|$ does not go to zero, by passing to a subsequence, we can find $x_n \xrightarrow{w} 0$ with $0 < \alpha \leq \|x_n\| \leq \beta < \infty$ for all n. We'll find $L \in \ell^\infty$, so $L(x_n)$ does not go to zero.

Pick $n(j)$, $m(j)$, and $\ell(j)$ inductively as follows. Pick $n(1) = 1$ and $m(1)$ so (with $x_{n,k}$ the coordinates of the vector $x_n \in \ell^1$)

$$\sum_{k=1}^{m(1)} |x_{n(1),k}| \geq \frac{\alpha}{2} \tag{5.7.2}$$

Now pick $\ell(1) > m(1)$ so that

$$\sum_{k=\ell(1)}^{\infty} |x_{n(1),k}| \leq \frac{\alpha}{8} \tag{5.7.3}$$

Having picked $n(1) \leq \cdots \leq n(j)$, $m(1) < \ell(1) < m(2) < \cdots < \ell(j)$, pick $n(j+1)$, $m(j+1)$, and $\ell(j+1)$ as follows. Since $x_{n,k} \to 0$ for each fixed k, $\sum_{k=1}^{\ell(j)} |x_{n,k}| \to 0$, so pick $n(j+1) \geq n(j)$ so that

$$n \geq n(j+1) \Rightarrow \sum_{k=1}^{\ell(j)} |x_{n,k}| \leq \frac{\alpha}{8} \tag{5.7.4}$$

Since $\|x_{n(j+1)}\| \geq \alpha$, pick $m(j+1) > \ell(j)$ so

$$\sum_{k=\ell(j)}^{m(j+1)} |x_{n(j+1),k}| \geq \frac{\alpha}{2} \tag{5.7.5}$$

and then $\ell(j+1) > m(j+1)$ so

$$\sum_{k=\ell(j+1)}^{\infty} |x_{n(j+1),k}| \leq \frac{\alpha}{8} \tag{5.7.6}$$

Now pick the components of $L \in \ell^{\infty}$ as follows. Each $|L_k|$ is 0 or 1. It is 1 precisely in the intervals $k \in [1, m(1)] \cup [\ell(1), m(2)] \cup \cdots \cup [\ell(j), m(j+1)] \cup \ldots$, chosen so that for $k \in [\ell(j), m(j+1)]$,

$$L_k(x_{n(j+1),k}) = |x_{n(j+1),k}| \tag{5.7.7}$$

Then $L \in \ell^{\infty}$ and

$$L(x_{n(j+1)}) \geq \sum_{k=\ell(j)}^{m(j+1)} |x_{n(j+1),k}| - \sum_{k=1}^{\ell(j)} |x_{n(j+1),k}| - \sum_{\ell(j+1)}^{\infty} |x_{n(j+1),k}| \tag{5.7.8}$$

$$\geq \frac{\alpha}{2} - 2\frac{\alpha}{8} \geq \frac{\alpha}{4}$$

which implies that $L(x_n)$ does not go to zero.

This does not imply that the $\sigma(\ell^1, \ell^{\infty})$- and $\|\cdot\|$-topologies are equal! For there exist nets $x_{\alpha} \in \ell^1$ so $x_n \to 0$ in $\sigma(\ell^1, \ell^{\infty})$ but $\|x_{\alpha}\| = 1$ for all α (Problem 8). $\qquad \square$

Next, we consider an example that shows TVS, unlike NLS, need not have continuous linear functionals. Let $0 < p < 1$. $L^p(0,1)$ is the set of complex-valued Borel functions, f, on $[0,1]$ with

$$\rho(f) \equiv \int_0^1 |f(x)|^p \, dx < \infty \tag{5.7.9}$$

Note there is no p-th root for ρ as there is for $\|\cdot\|_p$ if $1 \leq p < \infty$. Since $|y+z|^p \leq 2^p \max(|y|^p, |z|^p) \leq 2^p(|y|^p + |z|^p)$, we see $L^p(0,1)$ is a vector space, so we define

$$\rho(f,g) = \rho(f-g) \tag{5.7.10}$$

on L^p. Here are the main properties of L^p, $0 < p < 1$:

Proposition 5.7.4. *Let $0 < p < 1$.*

(a) *ρ is a metric on $L^p(0,1)$.*
(b) *In the metric topology, L^p is a TVS and is complete.*
(c) *The only nonempty, open convex set in L^p is all of L^p.*
(d) *The only continuous linear functional on L^p is the 0 functional.*

Proof. (a) Let $q = 1/p$. Minkowski's inequality on $\mathbb{R}^2$ says $\|(a,0) + (0,b)\|_q \leq \|(a,0)\|_q + \|(0,b)\|_q$ or

$$(|a|^q + |b|^q)^{1/q} \leq |a| + |b| \tag{5.7.11}$$

so if $\alpha = |a|^q$, $\beta = |b|^q$, we see

$$|\alpha + \beta|^p \le |\alpha|^p + |\beta|^p \qquad (5.7.12)$$

leading directly to

$$\rho(f + g) \le \rho(f) + \rho(g)$$

which gives the triangle inequality. Thus, ρ is a metric.

(b)   It is easy to see that in any metric with $\rho(f, g) = \rho(f - g, 0)$, addition is continuous (Problem 1(a)), and that in such a metric with $\sup_{f \neq 0} \rho(\alpha f)/\rho(f) \to 0$ as $|\alpha| \to 0$, scalar multiplication is continuous (Problem 1(b)). Thus, L^p is a TVS. A modification of the Riesz–Fischer argument (Problem 2) shows that L^p is complete.

(c)   Let $A \subset L^p$ be an open convex set which is nonempty. Let $x_0 \in A$. To show $A = L^p$, it suffices to show $A - x_0 = L^p$ so, without loss, we can suppose $0 \in A$. Since A is open, there exists r_0 so $\rho(f) < r_0 \Rightarrow f \in A$. Given $g \in L^p$, $g \neq 0$, define $x_j^{(n)}$, $j = 1, \ldots, n - 1$, by requiring

$$\int_0^{x_j^{(n)}} |g(y)|^p \, dy = \frac{\rho(g)j}{n}$$

By continuity of $x \mapsto \int_0^x |g(y)|^p \, dy$, this is possible.

   Let $g_j^{(n)}$ be defined by

$$g_j^{(n)}(y) = \begin{cases} 0, & y \le x_{j-1}^{(n)} \text{ or } y > x_j^{(n)} \\ ng(y), & x_{j-1}^{(n)} < y \le x_j^{(n)} \end{cases} \qquad (5.7.13)$$

Then

$$\rho(g_j^{(n)}) = n^{p-1}\rho(g), \qquad g = \sum_{j=1}^{n} \frac{1}{n} g_j^{(n)} \qquad (5.7.14)$$

Pick n so large that $n^{p-1}\rho(g) < r_0$. Then each $g_j^{(n)} \in A$, and thus, by convexity and (5.7.14), $g \in A$. Therefore, $A = L^p$.

(d)   Let $L \colon L^p \to \mathbb{C}$ be continuous. Let $A = \{g \mid |L(g)| \le 1\}$. Then A is open and convex and $0 \in A$, so $A = L^p$, that is, $|L(\alpha g)| < 1$ for all $\alpha \in (0, \infty)$, and $g \in L^p$, that is, $L(g) = 0$ for all g, so $L = 0$. $\square$

This example suggests that there might be a class of TVS larger than NLS that at least includes spaces with a $\sigma(X, Y)$-topology so that these spaces have lots of continuous linear functionals. The above suggests open convex sets might be the key. So we define:

Definition. A *locally convex space* (LCS) is a vector space, X, over $\mathbb{K}$ with a topology, τ, in which it is a TVS so that 0 has a τ-neighborhood base, $\mathcal{B}$, of open, convex, balanced sets.

It is enough for there to be a neighborhood base of open convex sets—that implies there is a base of open, convex, balanced sets (Problem 3). Recall that any open set containing zero is absorbing (since it is pseudo-open). Thus, the gauge of the sets in $\mathcal{B}$ are a family of seminorms $\{\rho_\beta\}_{\beta \in \mathcal{B}}$. The sets of the form

$$N(\beta_1, \ldots, \beta_\ell; \varepsilon) = \{x \mid \rho_{\beta_j}(x) < \varepsilon, \ j = 1, \ldots, \ell\} \tag{5.7.15}$$

are a basis for τ, which shows that τ is a weak topology defined by $\{\rho_\beta\}_{\beta \in \mathcal{B}}$, and a net $\{x_\alpha\}_{\alpha \in I}$ converges to x in τ if and only if for all $\beta \in \mathcal{B}$, $\rho_\beta(x_\alpha - x) \to 0$. Conversely, if $\{\rho_\beta\}_{\beta \in \mathcal{B}}$ is a family of seminorms, then each set N is an open, convex, balanced set. So long as $\{\rho_\beta\}_{\beta \in \mathcal{B}}$ obeys the nondegeneracy condition

$$\forall \beta \in \mathcal{B}, \ \rho_\beta(x) = 0 \Rightarrow x = 0 \tag{5.7.16}$$

the topology is Hausdorff and so makes X into a TVS. We have thus proven that:

Theorem 5.7.5. *Any LCS has the weak topology defined by a family of seminorms obeying* (5.7.16). *Conversely, the weak topology defined by a family of seminorms obeying* (5.7.16) *defines an LCS.*

Corollary 5.7.6. *Let $\mathcal{U}$ be a family of absorbing, balanced, convex subsets of a vector space, X. Suppose that*

$$\bigcap_{U \in \mathcal{U}} U = \{0\} \tag{5.7.17}$$

Then there is a unique topology on X making it into a locally convex space so that the set of intersections of sets in $\{\lambda U \mid \lambda \in (0, \infty), U \in \mathcal{U}\}$ is a neighborhood base at zero.

Proof. Let ρ_U be the gauge of U. By the theorem, $\{\rho_U \mid U \in \mathcal{U}\}$ defines a locally convex topology since (5.7.17) implies (5.7.16). Clearly, each λU is a neighborhood of 0. Any ball about zero in ρ_U contains a λU, so the finite intersections are a neighborhood base. $\qquad\square$

Definition. Two families, $\{\rho_\beta\}_{\beta \in \mathcal{B}}$ and $\{\sigma_\gamma\}_{\gamma \in \mathcal{C}}$, of seminorms are called *equivalent* if and only if $\forall \beta \in \mathcal{B}$, $\exists \gamma_1, \ldots, \gamma_n \in \mathcal{C}$ and $C > 0$ so that

$$\rho_\beta \leq C(\sigma_{\gamma_1} + \cdots + \sigma_{\gamma_n}) \tag{5.7.18}$$

and $\forall \gamma \in \mathcal{C}$, $\exists \beta_1, \ldots, \beta_\ell \in \mathcal{B}$ and $D > 0$ so that

$$\sigma_\gamma \leq D(\rho_{\beta_1} + \cdots + \rho_{\beta_\ell}) \tag{5.7.19}$$

By comparing neighborhood bases, we conclude:

Theorem 5.7.7. *The topologies defined by two families of seminorms obeying* (5.7.16) *are the same if and only if the families are equivalent.*

Clearly, an NLS is an LCS. Since $x \mapsto |\ell(x)|$ is a seminorm for any linear functional on X, any $\sigma(X, Y)$-topology defines an LCS. A key fact is:

Theorem 5.7.8. *Let X be a locally convex space. Then for any $x \neq 0$, there is an element $\ell \in X^*$, the continuous linear functionals on X, with $\ell(x) = 1$.*

Proof. This is essentially the standard Hahn–Banach argument. We'll do the case $\mathbb{K} = \mathbb{R}$. Find A, an open, convex, balanced set containing 0 and not x. If ρ_A is the gauge of A, then $x \notin A \Rightarrow \rho_A(x) \geq 1$. Thus, if $\ell_0 \colon Y \equiv \{\lambda x \mid \lambda \in \mathbb{R}\} \to \mathbb{R}$ by $\ell_0(\lambda x) = \lambda$, then $\ell_0(y) \leq \rho_A(y)$ for all $y \in Y$, so we can find $\ell \colon X \to \mathbb{K}$ with $\ell(y) \leq \rho_A(y)$ for all $y \in X$. By $\rho_A(\pm y) = \rho_A(y)$, we find $|\ell(y)| \leq \rho_A(y)$. If $y_\alpha \to y$, then $\rho_A(y_\alpha - y) \to 0$, so $|\ell(y - y_\alpha)| \to 0$, that is, ℓ is continuous. $\qquad\square$

A similar proof (Problem 4) shows that

Theorem 5.7.9. *Let X be an LCS and Y a closed subspace. If $x \notin Y$, there exists $\ell \in X^*$ so $\ell \restriction Y = 0$ and $\ell(x) = 1$. More generally, given any continuous functional $\tilde{\ell}$ on Y and any $\alpha \in \mathbb{K}$, there is a continuous $\widetilde{L}$ from X to $\mathbb{K}$ so $\widetilde{L}(x) = \alpha$ and $\widetilde{L} \restriction Y = \tilde{\ell}$.*

In Section 5.10, we extend this to a more geometric form. As a final topic, we want to discuss the connection between weak topologies and reflexive Banach spaces. The following shows a connection:

Theorem 5.7.10. *Let X be a Banach space. Then $\iota[X]$ is $\sigma(X^{**}, X^*)$-dense in X^{**}.*

Remark. In distinction, $\iota[X]$ is $\|\cdot\|$-closed, so if X is not reflexive, $\iota[X]$ is not $\|\cdot\|$-dense in X^{**}.

Proof. If not, there is $x_0 \in \overline{\iota[X]}$, the $\sigma(X^{**}, X^*)$-closure of $\iota[X]$. By Theorem 5.7.9, find ℓ, a $\sigma(X^{**}, X^*)$ continuous functional with $\ell \restriction \iota[X] = 0$ but $\ell(x_0) \neq 0$. By Theorem 5.7.1, $\ell \in X^*$ so $\ell \restriction \iota[X] = 0$ means $\ell(x) = 0$ for all $x \in X$, that is, ℓ is 0 as an element of X^*, so $\ell(x_0) = 0$. This contradiction proves the result. $\qquad\square$

In Section 5.10, we'll prove a stronger result:

Theorem 5.7.11 (Goldstine's Lemma). *Let Y_1 denote the closed unit ball $(\{y \mid \|y\| \leq 1\})$ of a Banach space, Y. For any Banach space, X, the $\sigma(X^{**}, X^*)$-closure of $\iota[X_1]$ is $(X^{**})_1$.*

Recall that in the Notes to Section 5.4 we informally defined uniformly convex spaces, which we now make formal.

Definition. A Banach space is called *uniformly convex* if and only if

$$\forall \varepsilon > 0, \ \exists \delta \ \forall x, y \colon \|x\| \leq 1, \ \|y\| \leq 1, \ \|\tfrac{1}{2}(x+y)\| > 1 - \delta \Rightarrow \|x - y\| < \varepsilon \tag{5.7.20}$$

This is a strong form of strict convexity of unit ball (i.e., x and y linearly independent, $\theta \in (0,1) \Rightarrow \|(1-\theta)x + \theta y\| < (1-\theta)\|x\| + \theta\|y\|$ with strict inequality). An important property is:

Theorem 5.7.12 (Milman–Pettis Theorem). *Every uniformly convex Banach space is reflexive.*

Proof. It suffices to show if $\eta \in X^{**}$ with $\|\eta\| = 1$, then $\eta \in \iota[X_1]$. By Theorem 5.7.11, pick a net $\{x_\alpha\}_{\alpha \in I}$ in X_1 with $\iota(x_\alpha) \to \eta$ in the $\sigma(X^{**}, X^*)$-topology.

Given ε, let δ be given by (5.7.20). Since $\|\eta\| = 1$, we can find $\ell \in X^*$, so

$$\|\ell\| = 1, \qquad \eta(\ell) > 1 - \delta \tag{5.7.21}$$

Let

$$N = \{\kappa \in X^{**} \mid \|\kappa\| \leq 1, \ \kappa(\ell) > 1 - \delta\} \tag{5.7.22}$$

We claim

$$x, y \in X_1, \quad \iota(x), \iota(y) \in N \Rightarrow \|x - y\| < \varepsilon \tag{5.7.23}$$

For rhs of (5.7.23) $\Rightarrow \ell(\tfrac{1}{2}x + \tfrac{1}{2}y) > 1 - \delta \Rightarrow \|\tfrac{1}{2}(x+y)\| > 1 - \delta \Rightarrow \|x-y\| < \varepsilon$.

By the choice of x_α, we have $\iota(x_\alpha)(\ell) \to \eta(\ell)$, so for some α_0, we have that $\alpha > \alpha_0 \Rightarrow \iota(x_\alpha) \in N$. But then $\alpha, \beta > \alpha_0 \Rightarrow \|x_\alpha - x_\beta\| < \varepsilon$. Thus, x_α is $\|\cdot\|$-Cauchy, so converges to some $x_\infty \in X_1$. But then $\iota(x_\alpha) \to \iota(x_\infty)$ in norm, and so in the weak-$*$ topology. We have thus proven $\eta = \iota(x_\infty)$. $\square$

Notes and Historical Remarks. Dual pairs were defined by Dieudonné [241] and Mackey [619]. Theorem 5.7.1 is from Phillips [721]. We have only scratched the surface. Much more can be found in Bourbaki [121], Köthe [518], and Simon [856]. The deepest theorem is the Arens–Mackey theorem [32, 620] which describes all TVS topologies on X in which Y is the dual space.

von Neumann [966] first introduced TVS with a base of neighborhoods which were convex and introduced the seminorms that topologize it. Tychonoff [941] coined the term *locally convex space*. Books on the theory of locally convex spaces include [19, 121, 436, 461, 518, 519, 677, 693, 712, 726].

The proof in Example 5.7.3 is a typical case of the gliding hump method mentioned in the Notes to Section 5.4. Its use in this context and the first realization that weak convergence of a sequence in ℓ^1 implies norm convergence is from Schur [**827**].

That $L^p(0, 1; dx)$ for $0 < p < 1$ has no continuous linear functionals is a result of Day [**217**]. Goldstine's lemma is from Goldstine [**354**].

As noted earlier, uniformly convex spaces were defined by Clarkson [**200**]. Going back to Carlson, there is a weaker notion of spaces for which $x \neq y$ and $\|x\| = \|y\| = 1 \Rightarrow \|\theta x + (1 - \theta)y\| < 1$ for all $\theta \in (0, 1)$. Connections of this to reflexivity are in Akhiezer–Krein [**5**] and Day in a series of papers beginning with [**218**] and summarized in his book [**221**]. In the book, he dubbed this property *rotund*. Some authors use *uniformly rotund* for uniformly convex. See Megginson [**648**] for more on this subject.

For books that include a lot on the geometry of Banach spaces, see Albiac–Kalton [**9**], Beauzamy [**65**], Fabian et al. [**292**], Lindenstrauss–Tzafriri [**594**, **595**], and Megginson [**648**]. The Milman–Pettis theorem is named after [**656**, **716**]. Neither their proofs nor the one of Kakutani [**467**], which appeared shortly thereafter, is that complicated, but they are certainly more involved than the half-page proof we give, which is due to Ringrose [**792**]. The essence of the proof is that in a uniformly convex space, weak convergence plus convergence of norms implies norm convergence (see Problem 5).

Problems

1. (a) If τ is a metric topology on a vector space, X, with

$$\rho(x + z, y + z) = \rho(x, y) \tag{5.7.24}$$

for all x, y, z, prove that addition is continuous as a map of $X \times Y \to X$.

(b) If τ is a metric topology on a vector space in which (5.7.24) holds, and moreover, $\rho(\alpha x, 0) \leq f(|\alpha|)\rho(x, 0)$, where $f(\zeta) \to 0$ as $\zeta \downarrow 0$, prove that vector multiplication is continuous.

2. By mimicking the Riesz–Fischer proof, show that L^p for $0 < p < 1$ is complete.

3. This problem will prove that if X is a TVS and 0 has a neighborhood base of open convex sets, then it has a neighborhood base of open, convex, balanced sets.

(a) In a TVS, prove the convex hull (*not* closed convex hull) of an open set is open.

(b) If N is an open neighborhood of 0, prove there is $\varepsilon > 0$ and V an open neighborhood of 0 so $|\alpha| < \varepsilon$ and $x \in V$ implies $\alpha x \in N$. (*Hint*: Multiplication is continuous.)

(c) Prove that any open convex neighborhood of 0 contains an open, convex, balanced neighborhood of 0. (*Hint*: If V is given in (b), consider the convex hull of $\bigcup_{|\alpha|<\varepsilon} \alpha V$.)

4. (a) Let Y be a closed subspace of an LCS, X, with $x_0 \notin Y$. Show that there is a continuous seminorm so that for all $y \in Y$, $\rho_A(x_0 + y) \geq 1$ and that also for all $\lambda \in \mathbb{K}$, $\rho_A(\lambda x_0 + y) \geq |\lambda|$.

    (b) Prove Theorem 5.7.9.

5. Let X be a uniformly convex Banach space. Suppose $x_\alpha \to x$ in $\sigma(X, X^*)$-topology and $\|x_\alpha\| \to \|x\|$. Prove that $\|x_\alpha - x\| \to 0$. (*Hint*: Show it suffices to consider the case $\|x_\alpha\| = \|x\| = 1$ and then use the argument in the proof of Theorem 5.7.12.)

6. Find $f_n \in L^1([0,1]; dx)$ so that $f_n \xrightarrow{w} f$, $\|f_n\|_1 \to \|f\|_1$ but $\|f_n - f\|_1 \nrightarrow 0$. (*Hint*: $\sin(2\pi n x) \xrightarrow{w} 0$.)

7. (a) In $C([0,1])$, find $g_n \to 0$ pointwise, $g_n \equiv 0$ on $[\frac{1}{2}, 1]$, $\|g_n\| = 1$.

    (b) Let $h(x) = 0$ (respectively, $x - \frac{1}{2}$) if $x \leq \frac{1}{2}$ (respectively, $x \geq \frac{1}{2}$). Show that $f_n \equiv g_n + h \xrightarrow{w} h$, $\|f_n\|_\infty = \|h\|_\infty$ but $\|h - f_n\|_\infty \nrightarrow 0$.

8. (a) Use the construction in Example 3.6.9 to find in any infinite-dimensional Banach space, X, a net $\{x_\alpha\}_{\alpha \in I}$ so $x_\alpha \to 0$ in $\sigma(X, X^*)$ by $\|x_\alpha\| \to \infty$.

    (b) Do the same but with $\|x_\alpha\| \equiv 1$ rather than $\|x_\alpha\| \to \infty$.

9. This problem will show there exists a closed subspace $X \subset \ell^1$ so that there is no closed subspace Y with $Y \cap X = \{0\}$ and $X + Y = \ell^1$ (if such a Y exists, it is called a (*closed*) *complement* to X; see Corollary 5.4.16). This shows there are closed subspaces without complements. Once we have the language of projections (see Section 2.1 of Part 4), this will imply there is no bounded projection P on ℓ^1 with $\text{Ran}(P) = X$.

    (a) Let Z be a separable Banach space and $\{z_n\}_{n=1}^\infty$ a dense subset of the unit ball of Z. Let $T: \ell^1 \to Z$ by

$$T(\{\alpha_n\}_{n=1}^\infty) = \sum_{n=1}^\infty \alpha_n z_n$$

Prove that $\|T\| = 1$ and $\text{Ran}(T) = Z$. (*Hint*: Given $z \in Z$ with $\|z\| = 1$, find $\{z_{n(j)}\}_{j=1}^\infty$ inductively so $\|z - z_{n(j)}\| \leq \frac{1}{2}, \ldots, \|z - z_{n(1)} - \frac{1}{2} z_{n(2)} - \frac{1}{4} z_{n(3)} \cdots, -\frac{1}{2^j} z_{n(j)}\| \leq \frac{1}{2^{j+1}}$.)

    (b) Let $X = \text{Ker}(T)$. If Y is a complement of X, prove that $T \upharpoonright Y$ is a homeomorphism of Y and Z.

(c) If $X = \text{Ker}(T)$ has a complement, prove that any weakly convergent sequence in Z is norm convergent.

(d) Prove there is $X \subset \ell^1$ without a complement. (*Hint:* Take $Z = \ell^2$.)

5.8. The Banach–Alaoglu Theorem

In this section, we'll prove the following:

Theorem 5.8.1 (Banach–Alaoglu Theorem). *Let X be a Banach space. Then its unit ball, X_1^*, $(= \{\ell \in X^* \mid \|\ell\| \le 1\})$ is compact in the weak-$*$ (i.e., $\sigma(X^*, X)$) topology.*

This is, of course, to be distinguished from the $\|\cdot\|$-topology where we saw in Theorem 5.1.7 that X_1^* is never compact if X is infinite-dimensional. Notice, since open sets in the weak topology are unbounded, X^* is not locally compact in either the norm or weak-$*$ topology; see Theorem 5.1.9. One consequence of Theorem 5.8.1 is existence of minimizers for some nonlinear functions (see Section 5.9). Another is

Theorem 5.8.2. *Let X be a Banach space. Then the unit ball, X_1, $(= \{x \in X \mid \|x\| \le 1\})$ is compact in the weak (i.e., $\sigma(X, X^*)$) topology if and only if X is reflexive.*

Proof. If X is reflexive, then $\iota[X_1]$ in the $\sigma(X, X^*)$-topology is all of $(X^{**})_1$ in the $\sigma(X^{**}, X^*)$-topology. Since ι is then a bicontinuous bijection and X_1^{**} is compact by Theorem 5.8.1, X_1 is compact.

Conversely, suppose X_1 is compact in the $\sigma(X, X^*)$-topology. Then $\iota[X_1]$ is compact, hence closed, in the $\sigma(X^{**}, X^*)$-topology. By Theorem 5.7.11, $\iota[X_1]$ is $\sigma(X^{**}, X^*)$-dense in $(X^{**})_1$. So, since $\iota[X_1]$ is $\sigma(X^{**}, X^*)$-closed, it is all of $(X^{**})_1$. Thus, any $f \ne 0 \in X^{**}$ has $f/\|f\| \in i[X]$, so $\iota[X] = X^{**}$. □

Another consequence is:

Theorem 5.8.3. *Any Banach space, Y, is isometrically isomorphic to a closed subspace of some $C(X)$ with X a compact Hausdorff space.*

Remarks. 1. To appreciate that this is interesting, note not every Banach space is isomorphic to a subspace of an L^2 space.

2. If Y is separable, one can take $X = [0, 1]$, see Theorem 5.0.1.

3. See also Problem 14 of Section 5.5.

Proof. Let $X = (Y^*)_1$, the unit ball of Y^* in the weak-$*$ topology. We have just seen that X is a compact Hausdorff space. Let $j: Y \to C(X)$ by $j(y)(\ell) = \ell(y)$. Then $\|j(y)\|_\infty = \sup_{\|\ell\| \le 1} |\ell(y)| = \|y\|$, so j is isometric and, clearly, an isomorphism of Y and $\text{Ran}(j)$. □

Proof of Theorem 5.8.1. For $x \in X$, let

$$\mathbb{D}_x = \{\lambda \in \mathbb{K} \mid |\lambda| \leq \|x\|\} \qquad (5.8.1)$$

and let

$$\Omega = \underset{x \in X}{\times} \mathbb{D}_x \qquad (5.8.2)$$

which is compact by Tychonoff's theorem. Let $\Upsilon(\ell)_x = \ell(x)$ as a map of $(X^*)_1 \to \Omega$. Since $|\ell(x)| \leq \|x\|$, the map Υ is into Ω. Since $\ell_1 \neq \ell_2$ means $\exists x$ so $\ell_1(x) = \ell_2(x)$, Υ is one-one. Since $\ell_\alpha \to \ell$ in $\sigma(X^*, X)$ if and only if $\Upsilon(\ell_\alpha) \to \Upsilon(\ell)$ in the Ω-topology, Υ is a homeomorphism. If we show $\mathrm{Ran}(\Upsilon)$ is closed, it is compact, so since Υ is a homeomorphism, X_1^* is compact.

Let ℓ_α be a net with $\Upsilon(\ell_\alpha) \to \omega$. Thus, $\ell_\alpha(x) \to \omega_x$ for each x. Since $\ell_\alpha(x+y) = \ell_\alpha(x) + \ell_\alpha(y)$, we have $\omega_{x+y} = \omega_x + \omega_y$, and similarly, $\omega_{\lambda x} = \lambda \omega_x$. Thus, $x \mapsto \omega_x$ is a linear functional. Since $|\omega_x| \leq \|x\|$, there is a bounded linear functional, that is, $\ell \in X^*$ with

$$|\ell(x)| \leq \|x\| \qquad (5.8.3)$$

Thus, $\ell \in (X^*)_1$ and $\omega = \Upsilon(\ell)$. Thus, $\mathrm{Ran}(\Upsilon)$ is closed. $\qquad \square$

As proven, we used the full Tychonoff theorem. If X is separable and $\{x_n\}_{n=1}^\infty$ is dense, we can use $\widetilde{\Omega} = \times_{n=1}^\infty \mathbb{D}_{x_n}$ and $\widetilde{\Upsilon}$ by $\widetilde{\Upsilon}(\ell)_n = \ell(x_n)$ in place of Ω and Υ, and so only use the countable Tychonoff theorem.

Notes and Historical Remarks.

> To be historically complete, one should speak of the Ascoli–Hilbert–Fréchet–Riesz–Helly–Banach–Tychonoff–Alaoglu–Cartan–Bourbaki–Shmulyan–Kakutani Theorem.   —*A. Pietsch* [**727**]

Weak-$*$ compactness had many special cases before the general one we prove. The earliest was Hilbert [**426**] for ℓ^2 (Ascoli is on Pietsch's list for the first compactness result in function space, although it is in the norm topology), Riesz [**780**] for L^p and ℓ^p, $1 < p < \infty$, Helly [**412**] for $C^*[a, b]$, and Banach [**52**] for the general separable Banach space. The general case proven via Tychonoff's theorem was obtained about the same time, independently by Alaoglu [**6, 7**], Bourbaki [**119**], Shmulyan [**843**], and Kakutani [**468**]. Alaoglu's name has stuck.

5.9. Bonus Section: Minimizers in Potential Theory

Many problems in physics, engineering, and economics (as well as some in pure mathematics) involve variational principles, that is, with a class of objects (paths or measures or economic output), one determines the one of interest because there is a function, f, on the set, Q, of objects and the special object, x_∞, is determined by

$$f(x_\infty) = \inf_{x \in Q} f(x) \tag{5.9.1}$$

Typically, X is a subset of an infinite-dimensional space, so the existence of a minimum, that is, a point x_∞ where the inf is taken, can be tricky.

In this section, we'll illustrate one common idea. It places a topology on Q where it is compact and uses the Banach–Alaoglu theorem to get the compactness. Thus, we need to use the weak-$*$ topology, and here, the second piece of the strategy enters.

Theorem 5.9.1. (a) *In any infinite-dimensional Banach space, X, there is a net $\{x_\alpha\}_{\alpha \in I}$ with $\|x_\alpha\| \equiv 1$ so that $x_\alpha \to 0$ in the $\sigma(X, X^*)$-topology.*
(b) *$\{x \mid \|x\| = 1\}$ is $\sigma(X, X^*)$-dense in $\{x \mid \|x\| \le 1\}$.*
(c) *$x \mapsto \|x\|$ is not $\sigma(X, X^*)$-continuous.*
(d) *$x \mapsto \|x\|$ is lower semicontinuous in the $\sigma(X, X^*)$-topology.*

Proof. (a) Let I be the set of finite subsets $\alpha = \{\ell_1, \ldots, \ell_n\}$ of X^* made into a directed set by $\alpha \triangleright \beta$ if and only if $\beta \subset \alpha$. For each α, $Y_\alpha = \{x \mid \ell_j(x) = 0$ for $j = 1, \ldots, n$ if $\alpha = \{\ell_1, \ldots, \ell_j\}\}$ is a nonzero subspace since $\dim(X) = \infty$. Pick $z_\alpha \in Y_\alpha$ with $z_\alpha \ne 0$ and $x_\alpha = z_\alpha / \|z_\alpha\|$. Then $x_\alpha \to 0$ in $\sigma(X, X^*)$ since $\alpha \triangleright \{\ell\} \Rightarrow \ell(x_\alpha) = 0$.

(b) If $\|x\| < 1$ and x_α is the net of (a), there is $\lambda_\alpha \in (0, 2)$ so $y_\alpha = x + \lambda_\alpha x_\alpha$ has $\|y_\alpha\| = 1$ (since $\|x + 0 x_\alpha\| < 1$ and $\|x + 2 x_\alpha\| \ge 2 - \|x\| > 1$ and $\lambda \mapsto \|x + \lambda x_\alpha\|$ is continuous). Since λ_α is bounded, $y_\alpha \to x$ in $\sigma(X, X^*)$.

(c) If it were, $\{x \mid \|x\| = 1\}$ would be closed, but we have seen it is not.

(d) We need to show that $\{x \mid \|x\| > a\}$ is σ-open or that $B_a \equiv \{x \mid \|x\| \le a\}$ is σ-closed. If $\ell \in X^*$ with $\|\ell\| \le 1$ and $x \in B_a$, then $|\ell(x)| \le a$. On the other hand, by the Hahn–Banach theorem (Theorem 5.5.9), if $x \notin B_a$, there is such an ℓ with $\ell(x) = \|x\| > a$. Thus,

$$B_a = \bigcap_{\substack{\ell \in X^* \\ \|\ell\| = 1}} \{x \mid |\ell(x)| \le a\} \tag{5.9.2}$$

is an intersection of σ-closed sets, and so σ-closed. $\square$

Thus, we have to expect that many interesting functions will only be lsc in the weak-$*$ topology. But while full continuity is needed for existence of min and max, lsc is enough for existence of min (by Theorem 2.3.13). So the strategy for proving existence of an x_∞ obeying (5.9.1) is:

(1) Find a weak topology in which Q is compact.
(2) Prove f is lsc.
(3) Apply Theorem 2.3.13.

We'll illustrate this in two problems. The first involves the existence of potential theoretic equilibrium measures on an arbitrary compact subset of $\mathbb{R}^\nu$, $\nu \geq 2$. Let μ be a measure of compact support on $\mathbb{R}^\nu$. Define its *Coulomb energy* (*energy* for short) by

$$\mathcal{E}(\mu) = \int |x-y|^{-(\nu-2)} \, d\mu(x) d\mu(y), \qquad \nu \geq 3 \qquad (5.9.3)$$

$$= -\int \log|x-y| \, d\mu(x) d\mu(y), \qquad \nu = 2 \qquad (5.9.4)$$

Since $|x-y|^{-(\nu-2)}$ is positive and for bounded x, y, $-\log|x-y|$ is bounded below, these integrals converge or are $+\infty$ (so we allow $\mathcal{E}(\mu) = \infty$). The correct physical energy (see Section 6.8) has a constant out front: $\frac{1}{2}[(\nu - 2)\sigma_\nu]^{-1}$ (σ_ν = area of unit sphere) times some physical parameters, but the constant doesn't affect the minimum problem—so we'll ignore it for now.

Given compact $K \subset \mathbb{R}^\nu$, $\mathcal{M}_{+,1}(K)$ denotes the probability measures on K. For some K (e.g., a single point), $\mathcal{E}(\mu) = \infty$ for all $\mu \in \mathcal{M}_{+,1}(K)$. If that happens, we say $C(K)$, the *capacity* of K, is 0. Otherwise, we say $C(K) > 0$. Indeed, we define $C(K)$ by

$$C(K) = \begin{cases} (\min_{\mu \in \mathcal{M}_{+,1}(K)} \mathcal{E}(\mu))^{-1/(\nu-2)}, & \nu \geq 3 \\ \exp(-\min_{\mu \in \mathcal{M}_{+,1}(K)} \mathcal{E}(\mu)), & \nu = 2 \end{cases} \qquad (5.9.5)$$

The $(\nu - 2)$-th root and exp are inverse to $|\cdot|^{-(\nu-2)}$ and $-\log|\cdot|$. Thus, if one looks instead at total mass $\mu(K) = Q$, the minimum energy is Q^2/C when $\nu = 3$, a familiar formula from high school physics.

Lemma 5.9.2. *The map $\mu \mapsto \mathcal{E}(\mu)$ from $\mathcal{M}_{+,1}(K) \to (-\infty, \infty]$ is lower semicontinuous in the $\sigma(\mathcal{M}(K), C(K))$-topology.*

Remark. If $\nu \geq 3$, $[0, \infty)$ can be used.

Proof. Let $f \in C(K \times K)$ and define

$$\mathcal{E}_f(\mu) = \int f(x,y) \, d\mu(x) d\mu(y) \qquad (5.9.6)$$

If

$$f(x,y) = \sum_{i=1}^{m} h_i(x) g_i(y) \qquad (5.9.7)$$

then

$$\mathcal{E}_f(\mu) = \sum_{i=1}^{m} \mu(h_i) \mu(g_i) \qquad (5.9.8)$$

is σ-continuous, since $\mu \mapsto \mu(h)$ is.

By Lemma 4.11.3, the f's of the form (5.9.7) are $\|\cdot\|_\infty$-dense in $C(K \times K)$, so since, for $\mu \in \mathcal{M}_{+,1}(K)$,

$$|\mathcal{E}_f(\mu) - \mathcal{E}_g(\mu)| \le \|f - g\|_\infty$$

we conclude any $\mathcal{E}_f$ is a uniform limit on $\mathcal{M}_{+,1}(K)$ of $\mathcal{E}_f$'s for f of the form (5.9.7), and so every $\mathcal{E}_f$ is continuous.

Let

$$f_n(x, y) = \min(|x - y|^{-1}, n) \tag{5.9.9}$$

Then each $\mathcal{E}_{f_n}$ is continuous and

$$\mathcal{E}(\mu) = \sup_n \mathcal{E}_{f_n}(\mu) \tag{5.9.10}$$

By Proposition 2.1.9, $\mathcal{E}$ is lsc. $\qquad\square$

Theorem 5.9.3. *For any compact $K \subset \mathbb{R}^\nu$, $\nu \ge 3$, there exists $\mu \in \mathcal{M}_{+,1}(K)$ so that*

$$\mathcal{E}(\mu) = \inf_{\nu \in \mathcal{M}_{+,1}(K)} \mathcal{E}(\nu) \tag{5.9.11}$$

Remarks. 1. This illustrates the use of the Banach–Alaoglu theorem to obtain minimizers.

2. μ is called the (potential theoretic) *equilibrium measure for K*. We say "the" because we'll eventually prove that the μ is unique.

3. Some physicists might say this theorem (and uniqueness) are physically obvious—just put a unit charge on K and wait until it reaches equilibrium and that is the unique minimizer! One should not totally dismiss this attitude—it does suggest that there should be such a theorem. The point of the mathematics is many: First, intellectual coherence of the theory. Second, maybe there is only apparent equilibrium, but at some microscopic level, there isn't. Third, while the physicists can hope to do the experiment on, say, an ellipsoid, it is clear how to build the one-dimensional Cantor set as a subset in $\mathbb{R}^3$.

Proof. By the Banach–Alaoglu theorem (Theorem 5.8.1), the unit ball in $\mathcal{M}(K)$ is compact in the $\sigma(\mathcal{M}, C)$-topology. $\mathcal{M}_{+,1}(K)$ is closed in the unit ball, so it too is compact. By Lemma 5.9.2, $\mathcal{E}$ is lower semicontinuous, so by Theorem 2.3.13, $\mathcal{E}$ takes its minimum value. $\qquad\square$

This is the only first step in potential theory and we will see other aspects later:

(1) The minimizer is unique. This will be proven in Section 6.8.
(2) If ν is a signed measure on K with $\nu(K) = 1$, then $\mathcal{E}(\nu) \ge \mathcal{E}(\mu)$, where μ is the equilibrium measure, and there is equality only if $\nu = \mu$. This will also be proven in Section 6.8.

(3) The potential, $\phi_\mu(x)$, of μ is defined for $x \in \mathbb{R}^\nu$ by

$$\phi_\mu(x) = \begin{cases} \int |x - y|^{-(\nu-2)} \, d\mu(y), & \nu \geq 3 \\ -\int \log|x - y| \, d\mu(y), & \nu = 2 \end{cases} \qquad (5.9.12)$$

The Euler–Lagrange equation of μ, that is, the formal result from Lagrange multipliers that $\delta\mathcal{E}/\delta\mu$ is constant says that $\phi_\mu(x)$ is constant on K. Since

$$\mathcal{E}(\mu) = \int \phi_\mu(x) \, d\mu(x) \qquad (5.9.13)$$

the constant must be $\mathcal{E}(\mu)$. A more careful analysis shows $\phi_\mu(x)$ is only constant on most of K (there can be an exceptional set of zero capacity) and that if K has some regularity, then it holds for all $x \in K$. These issues will be discussed further in Section 3.6 of Part 3.
(4) There are important connections between potential theory and complex analysis discussed in Section 3.8 of Part 3.
(5) Formally,

$$-\Delta\phi = c_\nu \mu \qquad (5.9.14)$$

where c_ν is a ν-dependent constant; this is discussed further in Section 6.8.
(6) Again formally, by (5.9.13) and an integration by parts, we have

$$\mathcal{E}(\mu) = c_\nu^{-1} \int |\nabla \phi_\mu(x)|^2 \, dx \qquad (5.9.15)$$

which leads to a different minimization formula for the capacity. This is discussed further in Lieb–Loss [**587**, Ch. 11]. This is connected to the Dirichlet principle (see the Notes).

We end this section by describing one other example, without a formal theorem.

Example 5.9.4 (Thomas–Fermi (TF) Equation). In $\mathbb{R}^3$, let $Z_1, \ldots Z_k$ be nonnegative, $R_1, \ldots, R_K$ fixed in $\mathbb{R}^3$, and

$$V(x) = \sum_{j=1}^{K} Z_j |x - R_j|^{-1} \qquad (5.9.16)$$

the Coulomb potential of nuclei of charge Z_j at points R_j. For a nonnegative measurable function, $\rho(x)$, on $\mathbb{R}^3$, the TF energy is given by

$$\mathcal{E}_{\mathrm{TF}}(\rho) = \tfrac{3}{5} \int \rho(x)^{5/3} \, d^3x - \int V(x)\rho(x) \, d^3x + \tfrac{1}{2} \iint \frac{\rho(x)\rho(y)}{|x - y|} \, d^3x d^3y \qquad (5.9.17)$$

The first term is a quasiclassical approximation to the kinetic energy; see the end of Section 7.5 of Part 4.

The proper test function space is

$$\mathcal{T} = \{\rho \in L^1(\mathbb{R}^3) \cap L^{5/3}(\mathbb{R}^3) \mid \rho \geq 0\} \tag{5.9.18}$$

It is not hard to see (Problem 1) that $\mathcal{E}_{\mathrm{TF}}(\rho)$ is well-defined on $\mathcal{T}$ and that in a suitable weak topology, $\mathcal{E}_{\mathrm{TF}}$ is lsc.

Let

$$\mathcal{T}_N = \left\{\rho \in \mathcal{T} \,\Big|\, \int \rho(x)\, d^3x \leq N\right\} \tag{5.9.19}$$

One shows

$$E(N) = \inf_{\rho \in \mathcal{T}_N} \mathcal{E}_{\mathrm{TF}}(\rho) > -\infty \tag{5.9.20}$$

and that $\|\rho\|_{5/3}$ is also bounded on

$$\{\rho \mid \rho \in \mathcal{T}_N;\, \mathcal{E}_{\mathrm{TF}}(\rho) \leq E(N) + 1\} \tag{5.9.21}$$

so that, by a Banach–Alaoglu-type argument, this set is compact. Thus, there exists a minimizer, ρ_N, by the strategy of this section.

Further analysis shows that $\int \rho_N(x)\, d^3x = N$ if and only if $N \leq \sum_{j=1}^{k} Z_j \equiv Z$ and that if $N > Z$, $\rho_N = \rho_Z$, so that ρ_Z is an absolute minimizer which solves the TF equation

$$\rho(x)^{3/2} = V(x) - \int |x - y|^{-1}\rho(y)\, d^3y \tag{5.9.22}$$

See the Notes for references on the details and applications. $\square$

Notes and Historical Remarks. The definition of functions via a variational principle—typically, a minimum, but sometimes a maximum or even saddle point—is known as the *calculus of variations*. The idea of determining a minimum via a lower semicontinuity argument is called the *direct method* of the calculus of variations.

While the language of function spaces and functions on them ("functionals") was not available, the idea on an informal level goes back to the discovery of calculus and its aftermaths (one can even say the isoperimetric problem, which goes back to the Greeks, is part of the calculus of variations). A famous eighteenth-century problem was the catenary, that is, the shape a uniformly weighted hanging string takes, was solved by Johann Bernoulli (see the Notes to Section 9.7 of Part 2A for capsule biographies of the Bernoullis). High points of the pre-twentieth–century developments are the Euler–Lagrange equations, the least action formalism of classical mechanics, and the reformulations of various problems in electrostatics and continuum mechanics as problems in the calculus of variations. An important impetus for further work was the Dirichlet principle: that to solve $\Delta u = 0$ in a connected open region, Ω, of $\mathbb{R}^\nu$ with $u \restriction \partial\Omega$ a given function, f, is to minimize $\int_\Omega (\nabla u)^2\, d^\nu x$ over all continuous u on $\bar{\Omega}$ with $u \restriction \partial\Omega = f$. The realization that it was not trivial to know there was a minimum spurred late nineteenth-century developments.

The key figure in the initiation of the direct method was the Italian mathematician, Leonida Tonelli (1885–1946), a student of Arzelà. Starting in 1911, Tonelli focused on the calculus of variations (he took time off as an artillery soldier in World War I), with work culminating with a 1920 article [**926**] and 1921 book [**927**]. He realized that the notion of lsc that Baire introduced for real-valued functions on $\mathbb{R}$ was a key idea in infinite dimensions. In his early work, the compactness he exploited came from an Arzelà–Ascoli-type theorem, not the use of a weak topology.

One of Tonelli's key insights is that convex functions tend to be lsc. In modern language, suppose $f \colon X \to \mathbb{R}$ is norm-continuous on a Banach space, X, and is convex so

$$U_a = \{x \mid f(x) \le a\}$$

is norm-closed and convex. By the separating hyperplane theorem of the next section, this implies U_a is also weakly closed (see Corollary 5.10.7). Thus, f is lsc in the weak topology.

There is a huge literature on the calculus of variations since it is central to many applications in engineering, economics, and physics. Among textbooks, many of which focus on the direct method, we mention [**140, 211, 226, 291, 458, 945**].

The idea of $\int |x - y|^{-1}\, d\mu(y) = \varphi_\mu(x)$ as the gravitational potential of a mass distribution, μ, goes back to Newton who, in particular, computed this for uniform distribution on a sphere and on a ball. With the realization that Coulomb's law applies also to electric charges (indeed, Coulomb discovered it for electric charges! Newton did it for gravity) and the understanding that charges in a perfect conductor redistributed themselves to minimize the electric energy, $\frac{1}{2} \int d\mu(x)\, \varphi_\mu(x)$, the equilibrium measure became a natural object. $\log |x - y|^{-1}$ arose from consideration of infinite cylinders in three-space. Thus, potential theory for $\nu = 2$ and $\nu = 3$ was a major concern of mathematicians and physicists, starting in the nineteenth century, with important developments in the twentieth. We'll say more about potential theory and its history in Section 3.6 of Part 3, but we note here that it was Robin [**795**] who first considered the minimization problem for $\mathcal{E}(\mu)$. The minimum is called Robin's constant. Among books and review articles on potential theory are [**28, 414, 544, 639, 758, 807, 854, 872, 937**].

The Thomas–Fermi equation was introduced by them [**303, 915**] in 1926–27 as a semiclassical approximation to the quantum theory of large atoms (they considered the case $K = 1$). The $\rho(x)^{5/3}$ term in (5.9.17) is the semiclassical kinetic energy. For the $K = 1$ case, (5.9.22) can be reduced, assuming ρ is spherically symmetric, to an ODE and one can see solutions exist that way. The analysis we give, using the direct method of the calculus of variations, is due to Lieb–Simon [**588**] in 1973–77. They also proved uniqueness of solutions. Lieb [**585**] reviews this work and discusses extensions and applications, including the use by Lieb and Thirring of TF theory in the so-called "stability of matter" problem.

Problem

1. This requires Young's inequality proven in Theorem 6.6.3. If $\rho \in \mathcal{T}$, given by (5.9.18), prove that each integral in (5.9.17) is convergent.

5.10. Separating Hyperplane Theorems

In this section, we'll see a geometric side of the Hahn–Banach theorem that will be useful in the next section and will allow us to prove Theorem 5.7.11.

Definition. A *closed, affine hyperplane* (*hyperplane* for short) of a real TVS, X, is $\{x \mid \ell(x) = \alpha\}$ for some continuous, nonzero linear functional, ℓ, on X and some $\alpha \in \mathbb{R}$. (We can drop the complex structure if X is a complex vector space.)

Recall that we proved in Theorem 3.3.2 that $\{x \mid \ell(x) = \alpha\}$ is closed if and only if ℓ is continuous. It is easy to see that $\{x \mid \ell(x) = 0\}$ is a hyperplane, that is, has codimension 1 (see Theorem 5.5.12). "Affine" comes from the fact that if $\ell(x_0) = \alpha$, then $\{x \mid \ell(x) = \alpha\} = x_0 + \mathrm{Ker}(\ell)$ is a translate of a hyperplane.

Definition. Let X be a real TVS, A and B disjoint sets in X. We say A and B are *separated* if there is a continuous linear functional, ℓ, and $\alpha \in \mathbb{R}$ so that

$$A \subset \{x \mid \ell(x) \leq \alpha\}, \qquad B \subset \{x \mid \ell(x) \geq \alpha\} \qquad (5.10.1)$$

If $\leq \alpha$, $\geq \alpha$ can be replaced by $< \alpha$, $> \alpha$, we say they are *strictly separated*. If there is $\beta < \alpha < \gamma$ so

$$A \subset \{x \mid \ell(x) \leq \beta\}, \qquad B \subset \{x \mid \ell(x) \geq \gamma\} \qquad (5.10.2)$$

we say they are *strongly separated*.

The main results of this section are (throughout, without explicit comment, we suppose A and B are nonempty):

(1) If A is an open convex set and B a disjoint convex set, they can be separated.

(2) If A and B are disjoint, open convex sets, they can be strictly separated.

(3) If A is a compact convex set and B a closed convex set, and if X is an LCS, they can be strongly separated.

(1) will come from a simple variant of the argument showing X^* separates points in an LCS, X. (2) and (3) will then follow from some simple geometric considerations. We start with a special case of (1) where $0 \in A$ and B has a single point.

Lemma 5.10.1. *Let A be an open convex set in a TVS, X, with $0 \in A$, and let $x_0 \notin A$. Then there exists $\ell \in X^*$ so*

$$\ell(x_0) = 1, \qquad y \in A \Rightarrow \ell(y) < 1 \tag{5.10.3}$$

Proof. Since $0 \in A$ and A is open, it is absorbing and convex, and so there is, by Theorem 5.3.10, a convex function p given by (5.3.34) with

$$A = \{x \mid p(x) < 1\} \tag{5.10.4}$$

Let $Y = \{\lambda x_0 \mid \lambda \in \mathbb{R}\}$ and $\ell_0 \colon Y \to \mathbb{R}$ by

$$\ell_0(\lambda x_0) = \lambda \tag{5.10.5}$$

By (5.10.4) and $x_0 \notin A$, $p(x_0) \geq 1$ and, by (5.3.36), for $\lambda \geq 0$,

$$p(\lambda x_0) \geq \lambda = \ell_0(\lambda x_0) \tag{5.10.6}$$

For $\lambda < 0$, $\ell_0(\lambda x_0) < 0 \leq p(\lambda x_0)$, so on Y, $\ell_0(y) \leq p(y)$.

Thus, by the Hahn–Banach theorem (Theorem 5.5.1), there is $\ell \colon X \to \mathbb{R}$ so for all $x \in X$,

$$\ell(x) \leq p(x) \tag{5.10.7}$$

and $\ell \upharpoonright Y = \ell_0$. We claim that ℓ is continuous. For $x \in A \Rightarrow \ell(x) < 1$ and $x \in (-A) \Rightarrow \ell(-x) < 1 \Rightarrow \ell(x) > -1$, that is,

$$\ell^{-1}((-1,1)) \supset A \cap (-A) \tag{5.10.8}$$

which is a neighborhood of 0 (since A is open). It follows (by Problem 1) that ℓ is continuous.

Since $x \in A \Rightarrow p(x) < 1$, $A \subset \{x \mid \ell(x) < 1\}$, while $\ell(x_0) = \ell_0(x_0) = 1$. Thus, (5.10.3) holds. $\qquad\square$

Theorem 5.10.2. *Let A be an open convex set in a TVS, X, and B a convex set with $A \cap B = \emptyset$. Then A and B are separated.*

Proof. $A - B$ is an open convex set and $A \cap B = \emptyset \Rightarrow 0 \notin A - B$. Pick $x_0 \in -(A - B)$ and let

$$\widetilde{A} = A - B + x_0 \tag{5.10.9}$$

Then $x_0 \notin \widetilde{A}$ and $0 \in \widetilde{A}$ which is open and convex. By the lemma, there is $\ell \in X^*$ so $\ell(x_0) = 1$ and $\ell \upharpoonright \widetilde{A} \subset (-\infty, 1)$.

Let $a \in A$, $b \in B$, so $a - b + x_0 \in \widetilde{A}$. Thus,

$$\ell(a) - \ell(b) + \ell(x_0) < 1 = \ell(x_0)$$

or
$$\forall a \in A,\, b \in B, \qquad \ell(a) < \ell(b)$$
If $\alpha = \sup_{a \in A} \ell(a)$, then $\alpha \le \inf_{b \in B} \ell(b)$, that is, (5.10.1) holds. $\qquad \square$

Lemma 5.10.3. *Let ℓ be a nonzero continuous linear functional on a TVS, X, and $A \subset X$ open. Then $\ell[A]$ is open in $\mathbb{R}$.*

Proof. Pick $y_0 \in X$ so $\ell(y_0) = 1$. Given $x_0 \in A$, let $f\colon \mathbb{R} \to X$ by $f(\lambda) = \ell(x_0 + \lambda y) - \ell(x_0)$. Then f is continuous, so $f^{-1}[A]$ is open. Since $0 \in f^{-1}[A]$, for some $\varepsilon > 0$, $(-\varepsilon, \varepsilon) \subset f^{-1}[A]$, so $\ell[A] \supset (\ell(x_0) - \varepsilon, \ell(x_0) + \varepsilon) \Rightarrow \ell[A]$ is open. $\qquad \square$

Theorem 5.10.4. *Let A, B be disjoint, open convex subsets of a TVS, X. Then A and B are strictly separated.*

Proof. By Theorem 5.10.2, there are ℓ continuous and nonzero and α so that (5.10.1) holds. Since $\ell[A]$ and $\ell[B]$ are open, they must lie in $(-\infty, \alpha)$ and (α, ∞), respectively. $\qquad \square$

Lemma 5.10.5. *If A is a compact convex set in an LCS, X, and B a closed convex set disjoint from A, there is an open convex set, C, with $A \subset C$ and $B \cap C = \emptyset$.*

Proof. Since $X \setminus B$ is open and X is an LCS, for each $x \in A$, there is U_x, a convex neighborhood of 0, so that $(x + U_x) \cap B = \emptyset$. Since $A \subset \bigcup_{x \in A}(x + \frac{1}{2}U_x)$, we can find, by compactness, $x_1, \dots, x_n \in A$ so that
$$A \subset \bigcup_{j=1}^{n}(x_j + \tfrac{1}{2}U_{x_j}) \tag{5.10.10}$$

Let $V = \bigcap_{j=1}^{n} U_{x_j}$, which is an open convex neighborhood of 0. Clearly, $x_j + \frac{1}{2}U_{x_j} + \frac{1}{2}V \subset x_j + U_{x_j}$ is disjoint from B, so $C = A + \frac{1}{2}V$ is open, convex, and disjoint from B, and we have $A \subset C$. $\qquad \square$

Theorem 5.10.6. *Let A be a compact convex set in an LCS, X, and B a closed convex set disjoint from A. Then A and B are strongly separated.*

Remark. It is not enough that A and B be closed and convex (one must be compact). In $\mathbb{R}^2$, if $A = \{(x,y) \mid x \le 0\}$ and $B = \{(x,y) \mid xy \ge 1,\, x \ge 0\}$, the sets are separated, but not strictly separated; see Figure 5.10.1.

Proof. By Lemma 5.10.5, find an open convex set, C, disjoint from B and containing A. By Theorem 5.10.2 and Lemma 5.10.3, find a nonzero, continuous ℓ some γ
$$B \subset \{x \mid \ell(x) \ge \gamma\}, \qquad C \subset \{x \mid \ell(x) < \gamma\} \tag{5.10.11}$$

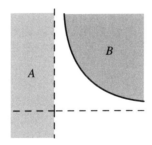

Figure 5.10.1. Closed convex sets not strictly separated.

Since A is compact, $\beta = \sup\{\ell(x) \mid x \in A\}$ is taken by some $x \in A$. Thus, $\beta < \gamma$.   □

Corollary 5.10.7. *Let C be a closed convex set of an LCS, X. Then C is weakly closed (i.e., closed in the $\sigma(X, X^*)$ topology).*

Proof. For each $x \notin C$, $\{x\}$ is a compact set disjoint from C, so by Theorem 5.10.6, there is $\gamma_x \in \mathbb{R}$, and a continuous real linear function, ℓ_x, so that $\ell_x(y) < \gamma_x$ for all $y \in C$ and $\ell_x(y) > \gamma_x$. Let $D_x = \{y \mid \ell_x(y) \leq \gamma_x\}$. D_x is weakly closed and by construction

$$C = \bigcap_{x \notin C} D_x \qquad (5.10.12)$$

so C is weakly closed.   □

As another application, we'll prove Goldstine's lemma.

Theorem 5.10.8 (Goldstine's Lemma ≡ Theorem 5.7.11). *Let Y_1 denote the closed unit ball ($\{y \mid \|y\| \leq 1\}$) of a Banach space, Y. For any Banach space, X, the $\sigma(X^{**}, X^*)$-closure of $\iota[X_1]$ is $(X^{**})_1$.*

Proof. Let $B = \overline{\iota(X_1)}^\sigma$, the closure in the $\sigma(X^{**}, X^*)$-topology and $A = \{z_0\}$ for some $z_0 \notin B$. X^{**} in the σ-topology is an LCS, so by Theorem 5.10.6 (perhaps flipping the sign of ℓ), there is $\ell \in (X^{**})^{*\sigma}$, the σ-dual, and γ and β with $\gamma < \beta$, so that

$$\gamma = \sup_{z \in B} \ell(z) < \beta = \ell(z_0) \qquad (5.10.13)$$

Since $0 \in B$, $\gamma \geq 0$, and then, by scaling, we can suppose $\beta = 1$.

By Theorem 5.7.1, there is $\lambda \in X^*$, so $\ell(z) = z(\lambda)$. Moreover, by continuity of ℓ, the sup over B is the sup over $\iota(X_1)$. Since $i(x)(\lambda) = \lambda(x)$, we conclude

$$\gamma = \sup_{x \in X_1} |\lambda(x)| < 1 = z_0(\lambda) \leq \|z_0\| \|\lambda\| \qquad (5.10.14)$$

Here we used the fact that $x \in X_1 \Rightarrow -x \in X_1$ and $|\ell(x)| = \max(\ell(x), \ell(-x))$. By (5.10.14), $\|\lambda\| = \gamma < 1$ and so $\|z_0\| \geq \gamma^{-1} > 1$, that is, $z_0 \notin (X^{**})_1$. We have thus proven $\overline{\iota(X_1)}^\sigma \supset (X^{**})_1$ and $\overline{\iota(X_1)}^\sigma \subset (X^{**})_1$ is trivial. $\qquad\square$

Notes and Historical Remarks. The geometric interpretation of Hahn–Banach theorems as separation theorems is due to Ascoli [**40**], who considered separable Banach spaces, and Mazur [**642**], who considered general Banach spaces. Both these authors considered separating a point from a convex set with nonempty interior (i.e., Lemma 5.10.1). The general result, Theorem 5.10.2, is due to Dieudonné [**240**]. Theorem 5.10.6 is from Klee [**493**] and Tukey [**939**]. An extensive study of separation theorems is due to Klee [**494, 495, 496, 497, 498, 499**].

Problems

1. This problem will prove that if $\ell\colon X \to \mathbb{R}$ is a linear functional on a TVS and $\ell^{-1}((-1,1))$ is a neighborhood of 0, then ℓ is continuous.

   (a) For any ε, prove that $\ell^{-1}((-\varepsilon,\varepsilon)) \equiv A_\varepsilon$ is a neighborhood of 0.

   (b) If $x_\alpha \to x$, prove that eventually $x_\alpha - x \in A_\varepsilon$.

   (c) Prove that eventually $|\ell(x_\alpha) - \ell(x)| < \varepsilon$.

   (d) Conclude that ℓ is continuous.

5.11. The Krein–Milman Theorem

In this section, we'll discuss the structure of compact convex subsets of a locally convex space (ccslcs) and see that many classical integral representation theorems can be seen as examples of the main theorem (the Krein–Milman theorem) and that the theorem also implies that some Banach spaces are not reflexive.

Definition. Let $A \subset X$, a TVS. The *closed convex hull* of A, cch(A), is the smallest closed convex set containing A.

Since an arbitrary intersection of closed convex sets is a closed convex set, there is such a smallest set. In fact, it can be constructed (recall the simplex, S_{n-1}, is given by (5.3.6))

$$\mathrm{ch}(A) = \left\{ \sum_{j=1}^n \theta_j x_j \ \bigg|\ \{x_j\}_{j=1}^n \in A,\ \{\theta_j\}_{j=1}^n \in S_{n-1},\ n=1,2,\dots \right\} \quad (5.11.1)$$

is easily seen to be the convex hull of A, that is, the smallest convex set containing A. And we have

$$\mathrm{cch}(A) = \overline{\mathrm{ch}(A)} \quad (5.11.2)$$

Definition. Let A be a convex set. An *extreme point* of A is a point $x \in A$ which is not an interior point of any nontrivial line segment in A, that is, $x = \theta y + (1 - \theta)z$ with $\theta \in (0,1)$ and $y, z \in A \Rightarrow y = z = x$. $\mathcal{E}(A)$ will denote the set of the extreme points of A.

For a closed strictly convex polygon in $\mathbb{R}^2$, the extreme points are its vertices (e.g., the corners of a triangle or rectangle), and for a closed disk, all the boundary points are extreme points. An unbounded closed convex set (e.g., a half-plane) may have no extreme points. In finite dimensions, there is a beautiful theorem of Carathéodory–Minkowski, discussed in the Notes, that if A is a compact convex subset of $\mathbb{R}^n$, any $x \in A$ is a convex combination of $n + 1$ points of $\mathcal{E}(A)$. The main result of this section is the following infinite-dimensional analog.

Theorem 5.11.1 (Krein–Milman Theorem). *If A is a ccslcs, then*

$$A = \text{cch}(\mathcal{E}(A)) \tag{5.11.3}$$

Example 5.11.2 ($L^1(X, d\mu)$). Let (X, Σ, μ) be a nonatomic measure space (see the Notes to Section 4.7 for the definition) and let $A = [L^1(X, d\mu)]_1$, the unit ball in L^1. Given $f \in A$, if $\alpha = \|f\|_1 < 1$, the line from 0 to f (any line if $f = 0$) hits ∂A in two points which are multiples of f (but not f) and f is an interior point of the line segment between them. If $\|f\|_1 = 1$, since X is nonatomic, we can find $B \subset X$ with $g = f\chi_B$ and $h = f\chi_{X \setminus B}$ both nonzero. Then $\|g\|_1 + \|h\|_1 = 1$ and if $\theta = \|h\|_1 = 1 - \|g\|_1$, then $f = \theta(h/\|h\|_1) + (1 - \theta)(g/\|g\|_1)$, which means f is not an extreme point, that is, $\mathcal{E}(A) = \emptyset$. Thus, by Theorem 5.11.1, there is no locally convex topology in which A is compact! In particular, L^1 cannot be reflexive, since if it were, the Banach–Alaoglu theorem would imply A was compact in the $\sigma(L^1, (L^1)^*)$-topology. Indeed, we see that L^1 cannot be the dual of any space! $\qquad\square$

Example 5.11.3 (ℓ^1). This side example will show the fact that L^1 is not a dual space depends on the measure being nonatomic. Let $c_0 = \{a \in \ell^\infty(\mathbb{Z}^+) \mid \lim_{n \to \infty} a_n = \infty\}$. Then (Problem 9) $c_0^* = \ell^1$, $\ell_1^* = \ell^\infty$, so ℓ^1 is a dual space. It is not hard to see (Problem 10) that $\mathcal{E}((\ell^1)_1) = \{\pm\delta_n\}$ where $(\delta_n)_m = \delta_{nm}$ in the real case. The reader can check that in the weak-* topology, $\text{cch}(\mathcal{E}((\ell^1)_1)) = (\ell^1)_1$. $\qquad\square$

Example 5.11.4 ($C_{\mathbb{R}}(X)$). Let X be a connected compact Hausdorff space. Then it is easy to see (Problem 1) that the only extreme points in $A = C_{\mathbb{R}}(X)_1$, the unit ball in $\mathbb{C}_R(X)$, are $\pm\mathbb{1}$. Thus, $\text{cch}(\mathcal{E}(A)) = \{\lambda\mathbb{1} \mid -1 \leq \lambda \leq 1\}$ is not A if X has more than one point. As in the penultimate example, this shows $C_{\mathbb{R}}(X)$ is not a dual space and, in particular, not reflexive. Problems 11 and 12 illuminate this example. $\qquad\square$

The key to proving the Krein–Milman theorem will be to prove that $\mathcal{E}(X)$ is not empty. Once we do that, the full proof will be easy. We'll use the notion of face:

Definition. Let A be a ccslcs. A subset $B \subset A$ is called a *face* if B is a nonempty closed convex set and

$$\theta x + (1 - \theta)y \in B, \; x, y \in A, \; \theta \in (0,1) \Rightarrow x, y \in B \qquad (5.11.4)$$

That is, if a line segment in A has an interior point in B, then the entire segment lies in B. A *proper face* is one with $B \neq A$.

Proposition 5.11.5. *Let A be a ccslcs.*

(a) $x \in A$ *is an extreme point if and only if* $\{x\}$ *is a face.*
(b) *If ℓ is a continuous linear functional on X which is not constant on A, then $\{x \in A \mid \ell(x) = \sup_{y \in A} \ell(y)\}$ is a proper face of A.*
(c) *A face of a face is a face, that is, if $C \subset B \subset A$ and B is a face of A and C is a face of B, then C is a face of A. In particular, if B is a face of A, then*

$$\mathcal{E}(B) \subset \mathcal{E}(A) \qquad (5.11.5)$$

Proof. (a) is immediate from the definition. (b) and (c) are easy and left to the reader (Problem 2). ∎

Proposition 5.11.6. *Let A be a ccslcs. Then $\mathcal{E}(A) \neq \emptyset$.*

Proof. Suppose A is not a single point (since if it is, $\mathcal{E}(A) = A \neq \emptyset$). Let $\mathcal{F}$ be the set of proper faces of A. Since X^* (X is the underlying LCS) separates points, $\mathcal{F}$ is nonempty by (b) of the last proposition. Order $\mathcal{F}$ by $B \triangleright C$ if $B \subset C$. $\mathcal{F}$ has the chain property since if $\{B_\alpha\}_{\alpha \in I}$ is a chain, $B = \cap_{\alpha \in I} B_\alpha$ is nonempty by the f.i.p. criteria for compactness (see Theorem 2.3.1), is easily seen to be a face (Problem 3), and is an upper bound for $\{B_\alpha\}_{\alpha \in I}$ in the order.

Thus, by Zorn's lemma, $\mathcal{F}$ has maximal elements. Let F be such a maximal face. If F has more than one point, it has a proper face by the first argument in this theorem. But if $F_1 \subset F$, $F_1 \triangleright F$, violating maximality. Thus, $F = \{x\}$, that is, $x \in \mathcal{E}(A)$. ∎

Proof of Theorem 5.11.1. Let $B = \mathrm{cch}(\mathcal{E}(A))$. If $B \neq A$, pick $x_0 \in A \backslash B$. Since $\{x_0\}$ and B are both compact convex sets, by Theorem 5.10.6, there exist $\ell \in X^*$ with

$$\sup_{y \in B} \ell(y) < \ell(x_0) \qquad (5.11.6)$$

By Proposition 5.11.5(b),

$$F = \left\{ z \in A \mid \ell(z) = \sup_{y \in A} \ell(y) \right\}$$

is a face of A. By (5.11.6), $F \cap B = \emptyset$. By Proposition 5.11.5, $\mathcal{E}(F) \neq \emptyset$, and by (5.11.5), $\mathcal{E}(F) \subset \mathcal{E}(A) \subset B$, so $F \cap B \supset \mathcal{E}(F) \neq \emptyset$. This contradiction proves that $B = A$. $\qquad\square$

Example 5.11.7 ($\mathcal{M}_{+,1}(X)$). Let $A = \mathcal{M}_{+,1}(X)$, the probability measures on a compact Hausdorff space, X. $A \subset [C(X)^*]_1$ and is weakly (i.e., in $\sigma(C(X)^*, C(X))$-topology) closed, and so compact since $[C(X)^*]_1$ is, by the Banach–Alaoglu theorem. It can be seen (Problem 4) that $\mathcal{E}(A) = \{\delta_x\}_{x \in X}$, the set of point measures. $\qquad\square$

Thus, by the Krein–Milman theorem, we have that

Theorem 5.11.8. *Let X be a compact Hausdorff space. For any measure $\mu \in \mathcal{M}_{+,1}(X)$, there exists a net $\mu^{(\alpha)}$ converging to μ so that each $\mu^{(\alpha)}$ is a finite convex combination of point masses.*

An attractive idea is that points in $\mathrm{cch}(\mathcal{E}(A))$ should be some kind of average of points in $\mathcal{E}(A)$. The following captures the notion of average:

Theorem 5.11.9. *Let A be a ccslcs, X. Then for each $\mu \in \mathcal{M}_{+,1}(A)$, there is a unique point, $B(\mu) \in A$, so that for all $\ell \in X^*$, we have*

$$\ell(B(\mu)) = \int_A \ell(x) \, d\mu(x) \tag{5.11.7}$$

Moreover,

(a) $\mu \mapsto B(\mu)$ *is a continuous map if $\mathcal{M}_{+,1}(A)$ is given its weak (i.e., $\sigma(\mathcal{M}_{+,1}(A), C(X))$-topology) and A is given its weak topology (i.e., $\sigma(X, X^*)$)*

(b) $\mu \mapsto B(\mu)$ *is onto A*

(c) B *is affine, that is, if $\mu_1, \mu_2 \in \mathcal{M}_{+,1}(A)$, $\theta \in [0,1]$, then*

$$B(\theta\mu_1 + (1-\theta)\mu_2) = \theta B(\mu_1) + (1-\theta)B(\mu_2) \tag{5.11.8}$$

More generally, if $C \subset A$ is closed, there is a map $\mu \mapsto B(\mu)$ from $\mathcal{M}_{+,1}(C)$ to A so that (5.11.7) and properties (a) and (c) hold.

Remarks. 1. $B(\mu)$ is called the *barycenter* of μ.

2. If C is a G_δ, we can get the result for $\mathcal{M}_{+,1}(C)$ just by viewing $\mathcal{M}_{+,1}(C)$ as a subset of $\mathcal{M}_{+,1}(A)$ via $\mu(B) = \mu(B \cap C)$ if B is a Baire set of A.

Proof. Since X^* separates point of A, there is at most one point, $B(\mu)$, for which (5.11.7) holds. If

$$\mu = \sum_{j=1}^n \theta_j \delta_{x_j} \tag{5.11.9}$$

where $\{\theta_j\}_{j=1}^n \in S_{n-1}$ and $\{x_j\}_{j=1}^n \subset A$, we let

$$B(\mu) = \sum_{j=1}^n \theta_j x_j \qquad\qquad (5.11.10)$$

and (5.11.7) is trivial. For arbitrary μ, let μ_α be a net of measures in $\mathcal{M}_{+,1}(A)$, each of the form (5.11.9) (variable n). Since A is compact, there is a point x_∞ which is a limit of a subnet, $B(\mu_{\alpha(\beta)})$, of $B(\mu_n)$. Taking limits in (5.11.7), we see x_∞ can be taken for $B(\mu)$.

Given (5.11.7), continuity is trivial, and clearly, $B(\delta_y) = y$, so B is onto. That B is affine is immediate from uniqueness.

The result for C has the same proof as for A. $\square$

This allows a rephrasing of the Krein–Milman theorem:

Theorem 5.11.10. *Let A be a ccslcs, X. Then for any $x \in A$, there is a measure μ on $\overline{\mathcal{E}(A)}$ whose barycenter is X.*

Remark. We need to use $\overline{\mathcal{E}(A)}$ rather than $\mathcal{E}(A)$ because we've only developed barycenters for closed sets. For general A, $\mathcal{E}(A)$ need not even be a Borel set in A (but see the Notes).

Proof. By the Krein–Milman theorem, we can find μ_α of the form (5.11.9) with $x_j \in \overline{\mathcal{E}(A)}$ so $B(\mu_\alpha) \to x$. Since $\mathcal{M}_{+,1}(\overline{\mathcal{E}(A)})$ is compact, we can find a limit, μ, of a subnet $\mu_{\alpha(\beta)}$. Then $B(\mu) = \lim B(\mu_{\alpha(\beta)}) = x$. $\square$

This result or its specialization to the case where $\mathcal{E}(A)$ is closed is sometimes called the strong Krein–Milman theorem. As we'll discuss in the Notes, many integral representation theorems can be viewed as special cases of the strong Krein–Milman theorem.

Barycenters are also key to the following which is clearly related to Theorem 5.3.17, Mazur's theorem.

Theorem 5.11.11 (Krein–Šmulian Theorem). *Let X be a separable Banach space. Let K be a subset of X which is compact in the weak (i.e., $\sigma(X, X^*)$) topology. Then $\mathrm{cch}(K)$ (taken in the $\sigma(X, X^*)$ topology) is compact in the $\sigma(X, X^*)$ topology.*

Remarks. 1. This result is also true for arbitrary Banach spaces. The extension from this case is obtained from some structure theorems on Banach spaces.

2. There is a different theorem from the same paper which is also (and more often) called the Krein–Šmulian theorem, namely a convex subset, K, of X is weakly closed if and only if $K \cap \overline{B_r(0)}$ is weakly closed for each $r < \infty$. In

cases where X^* is separable and the weak-topology is metrizable on $\overline{B_r(0)}$ this is useful; indeed it can be used to prove Lemma 5.11.12 below.

3. It is easy to extend the proof to the circled closed convex hull of K.

Our construction of barycenters in Theorem 5.11.9 used that fact that the convex combinations of points A was compact, but since what we want to prove is that $\mathrm{cch}(K)$ is compact, we can't use that! Instead, we'll construct the barycenter as a point in X^{**} so the following is critical:

Lemma 5.11.12. *Let X be a separable Banach space and $\alpha \in X^{**}$. Suppose α is weak-* sequentially continuous, i.e., $\ell_n \to \ell_\infty$ (for $\ell_n \in X^*$) in the $\sigma(X^*, X)$ topology $\Rightarrow \alpha(\ell_n) \to \alpha(\ell_\infty)$. Then for some $x_0 \in X$,*

$$\alpha = \iota(x_0) \tag{5.11.11}$$

equivalently, α is $\sigma(X^*, X)$ continuous.

Proof. By Theorem 5.5.13, $\iota(X) \equiv \widetilde{X}$ is closed in X^{**} so if $\alpha \notin \widetilde{X}$, we can, by the Hahn–Banach theorem, find $L \in X^{***}$ so that $\|L\| = 1$, $L \restriction \widetilde{X} \equiv 0$ and $L(\alpha) \equiv d > 0$.

Let $\{x_n\}_{n=1}^{\infty}$ be a dense subset of X. By Goldstine's lemma (Theorem 5.10.8) applied to X^*, for each N there is $\ell_N \in X^*$ so that

$$\|\ell_N\| = 1; \quad |\ell_N(x_j)| < \frac{d}{2}, \text{ for } j = 1, \dots, N; \quad \alpha(\ell_N) > \frac{d}{2} \tag{5.11.12}$$

(i.e., $\iota_{X^*}(\ell_N)$ is in a weak neighborhood of L).

For any $x \in X$ and any ε, there is N_0 so $\|\varepsilon^{-1}x - x_{N_0}\| \le 1$. It follows that for $N \ge N_0$, $|\ell_N(\varepsilon^{-1}x) - \ell_N(x_{N_0})| \le 1$, i.e.,

$$|\ell_N(x)| \le \varepsilon(\frac{d}{2} + 1) \tag{5.11.13}$$

Since ε and x are arbitrary, we conclude that

$$\ell_N \to 0 \text{ in } \sigma(X^*, X) \text{ topology} \tag{5.11.14}$$

By the hypothesis of the lemma, $\alpha(\ell_N) \to 0$ contradicting $\alpha(\ell_N) > \frac{d}{2}$. Thus $\alpha \in \widetilde{X}$, i.e., (5.11.11) holds for some x_0. $\qquad\square$

Proof of Theorem 5.11.11. For any positive Baire measure, μ, on K, define $\alpha_\mu \colon X^* \to \mathbb{C}$ by

$$\alpha_\mu(\ell) = \int \ell(x) \, d\mu(x) \tag{5.11.15}$$

Clearly

$$|\alpha_\mu(\ell)| \le \|\ell\| \int \|x\| \, d\mu(x) \tag{5.11.16}$$

so $\alpha_\mu \in X^{**}$. Moreover, if $\ell_n \to \ell_\infty$ in the $\sigma(X^*, X)$ topology, $\ell_n(x) \to \ell_\infty(x)$ pointwise and (by the uniform boundedness principle), $\sup_{n, x \in K} |\ell_n(x)| < \infty$

so, by the dominated convergence theorem, $\alpha_\mu(\ell_n) \to \alpha_\mu(\ell)$. Therefore, by the lemma, there is $B(\mu) \in X$ so

$$\alpha_\mu(\ell) = \ell\big(B(\mu)\big) \qquad (5.11.17)$$

for all $\ell \in X^*$ (i.e., we can specify a point in X so (5.11.7) holds).

The $\sigma\big(\mathcal{M}(K), C(K)\big)$ is a topology in which $\mu \mapsto \int f(x)\, d\mu(x)$ is continuous for each continuous f. Since $x \mapsto \ell(x)$ is continuous (in the weak topology), we see that B is a continuous map of $\mathcal{M}(K)$ in the $\sigma\big(\mathcal{M}(K), C(K)\big)$ topology to X in the $\sigma(X, X^*)$-topology. In particular, since B is affine and $\mathcal{M}_{+,1}(K)$ is compact, its image is compact and convex. Since $B(\delta_x) = x$, $K \subset B[\mathcal{M}_{+,1}(K)]$ so K is contained in a compact convex set and, therefore, $\mathrm{cch}(K)$ is compact. $\qquad\square$

Remarks. 1. To apply both uniform boundedness and dominated convergence to get $\alpha_\mu(\ell_n) \to \alpha_\mu(\ell)$, we need to use sequences, not nets. That's why the lemma was needed.

2. It is easy to see (because convex combinations of point mass are dense in $\mathcal{M}_{+,1}(K)$) that $B[\mathcal{M}_{+,1}(K)]$ is equal to $\mathrm{cch}(K)$.

Notes and Historical Remarks. The Krein–Milman theorem was proven by them in 1940 [**528**]. The proof via minimal faces (i.e., maximal in the inverse order we use) is due to Kelley [**483**].

Minkowski [**659**] proved the analog of the Krein–Milman theorem for compact convex subsets of $\mathbb{R}^\nu$ and Carathéodory [**157**] proved the refinement that one only needs $\nu + 1$ points in the convex combination. Simon [**856**] has the following geometric proof of this result: First, one shows that any compact convex $A \subset \mathbb{R}^\nu$ lies in a plane, P, so that if viewed as a subset of the plane, A has nonempty interior. So, without loss, suppose $A^{\mathrm{int}} \neq \emptyset$. In that case, one proves ∂A is the union of all proper faces of A and that each face lies in an affine subspace of $\mathbb{R}^\nu$ of lower dimension. Given $x_1 \in \mathcal{E}(A)$ and $x_0 \in A$, the line segment from x_1 through x_0 leaves A at a point $\tilde{x} \in \partial A$. $\tilde{x}$ lies in a face, F, of lower dimension so, by induction, is a convex combination of at most ν extreme points of F which are extreme points of A. Thus, x_0 is a convex combination of at most $\nu + 1$ points.

What we call the strong Krein–Milman theorem is the starting point for what has come to be called *Choquet theory* after [**188, 189, 187, 190**] published in 1956–60. Choquet proved that if A is separable, then $\mathcal{E}(A)$ is a G_δ and there is, for any $x \in A$, a probability measure μ with $B(\mu) = x$, so that $\mu(\mathcal{E}(A)) = 1$. There exist nonseparable A's where $\mathcal{E}(A)$ is not a Baire set. The theory then defines an order on measures so that larger measures are more diffuse, proves that in the separable case, μ's are maximal in this order if and only if $\mu(\mathcal{E}(A)) = 1$, and shows in all cases, there is for any x

a maximal μ with $B(\mu) = x$. There is also a study of when the maximal measures are unique for each x (called Choquet simplexes) due to Choquet [187] and Choquet–Meyer [192]. For monographs on Choquet theory, see Alfsen [18], Choquet [191], Phelps [719], and Simon [856, Ch. 8–11].

Among the integral representation theorems that can be realized as special cases of the strong Krein–Milman theorem are Bernstein's theorem on completely positive functions, Bochner's theorem on positive definite functions (see Theorem 6.6.6), Löwner's theorem on matrix monotone functions, the Herglotz representation theorem (see Theorem 5.4.1 of Part 3), and the Lévy–Khinchin formula (see (7.3.36)). The books of Choquet [191] and Simon [856] have details.

Theorem 5.11.11 is from Krein–Šmulian [527]. Our proof of Lemma 5.11.12 is from Whitley [988]. It is notable that the Krein–Šmulian paper was published in English in an American journal not long after contact with foreigners could get one in trouble in the Soviet Union and that without the terminology of dual topologies and separating hyperplanes, its language seems quaint.

Problems

1. Let X be a connected compact Hausdorff space. If $f \in [C_{\mathbb{R}}(X)]_1 \equiv A$ and $f(x_0) \in (-1, 1)$, prove that f is an interior point of a line segment in A.

2. Complete the proof of Proposition 5.11.5.

3. (a) Let $B \subset A$ be a face. Let $C \subset B$ and suppose $[xy]$ for $x, y \in A$ has an interior point in C. Prove $x, y \in B$.

   (b) Prove that an arbitrary nonempty intersection of faces is a face.

4. Let X be a compact Hausdorff space. This problem will first show that there is a Baire measure, δ_x, associated to each $x \in X$ and then prove that $\mathcal{E}(\mathcal{M}_{+,1}(X)) = \{\delta_x\}_{x \in X}$. You will need the notion of $\mathrm{supp}(\mu)$ and that $\mathrm{supp}(\mu) \neq \emptyset$ (Proposition 4.4.14).

   (a) For each $x \in X$, show the linear functional $f \mapsto f(x)$ defines a (positive) Baire measure, δ_x, on X with $\delta_x(X)$ and prove that if $x \neq y$, $\delta_x \neq \delta_y$.

   (b) Prove that each δ_x is an extreme point of $\mathcal{M}_{+,1}(X)$. (*Hint*: First prove that if $\mu = \theta\nu + (1 - \theta)\kappa$ with $\theta \in (0, 1)$, then ν and κ are a.c. wrt μ.)

   (c) Let μ be a Baire measure and $A \subset X$ be a Baire set with $0 < \mu(A) < 1$. Define $\theta = \mu(A)$, $\mu_A(Y) = \mu(A)^{-1}\mu(Y \cap A)$. Prove μ_A is a Baire measure in $\mathcal{M}_{+,1}(X)$ and that

$$\mu = \theta\mu_A + (1-\theta)\mu_{X\setminus A} \tag{5.11.18}$$

(d) If μ is an extreme point of $\mathcal{M}_{+,1}(X)$, prove for all $f \in C(X)$ and open F_σ's, A, with $\mu(A) > 0$, one has

$$\int f(x)\,d\mu(x) = \mu(A)^{-1}\int_A f(x)\,d\mu(x) \tag{5.11.19}$$

(e) If μ is an extreme point and $x_0 \in \mathrm{supp}(d\mu)$, prove that

$$\int f(x)\,d\mu(x) = f(x_0) \tag{5.11.20}$$

so $\mu = \delta_{x_0}$.

5. (a) By mimicking the proof in Problem 4, prove that if $C(X)$ are the complex-valued functions on a compact Hausdorff space, X, then the extreme points of the unit ball, $\mathcal{M}_1(X)$, of $C(X)^*$ (i.e., complex Baire measures, μ, with $|\mu|(X) \le 1$) are precisely of the form $\alpha\delta_x$ for some $\alpha \in \partial\mathbb{D}$ and $x \in X$.

(b) If X and Y are two compact Hausdorff spaces and $T\colon C(X) \to C(Y)$ is a linear isometric bijection, prove that there is a homeomorphism, $\tau\colon Y \to X$ and continuous function $\alpha\colon Y \to \partial\mathbb{D}$ so that

$$(Tf)(y) = \alpha(y)f\big(\tau(y)\big) \tag{5.11.21}$$

In particular, X and Y are homeomorphic.

(c) If T is either positivity-preserving or $T(fg) = (Tf)(Tg)$, prove that $\alpha(x) \equiv 1$.

Note. That $C(X)$ and $C(Y)$ linearly isometric and isomorphic implies X and Y are homeomorphic is known as the *Banach–Stone theorem* after Banach [**55**] and Stone [**885**].

6. This problem will lead the reader through a proof, due to de Branges [**223**], of the Stone–Weierstrass theorem using the Krein–Milman theorem. You will need some facts about supports of measures proven in Problem 4. So let X be a compact Hausdorff space and let $A \subset C_{\mathbb{R}}(X)$ be an algebra with the property that for any $x \ne y$ in X and any $\alpha, \beta \in \mathbb{R}$, there is $f \in A$ with $f(x) = \alpha$, $f(y) = \beta$. Define

$$\mathcal{L} = \{\mu \in C(X)^* \mid \|\mu\| \le 1,\ \mu(f) = 0 \text{ for all } f \in A\} \tag{5.11.22}$$

where $\|\cdot\|$ is the norm as a dual space to $C(X)$ with $\|\cdot\|_\infty$.

(a) If $\mathcal{L} = \{0\}$, prove that A is dense. (*Hint*: Hahn–Banach.)

(b) If $\mathcal{L} \ne \{0\}$, prove that $\mathcal{L}$ has nonzero extreme points. (*Hint*: Krein–Milman.)

(c) If $\mu \in \mathcal{L}$ and $g \in \mathcal{A}$ with $0 \leq g(x) \leq 1$ for all x, prove that $g\mu \in \mathcal{L}$.

(d) If $\mu \in \mathcal{E}(\mathcal{L})$ and $0 \leq g(x) \leq 1$ for all x, prove that g must be constant on supp($d\mu$). (*Hint:* Prove first that $\|g\mu\| + \|(1-g)\mu\| = \|\mu\|$ and then write

$$\mu = \|g\mu\| \frac{g\mu}{\|g\mu\|} + \|(1-g)\mu\| \frac{(1-g)\mu}{\|(1-g)\mu\|}$$

to see $g\mu$ must be a multiple of μ.)

(e) If $x_0 \neq y_0$ in X, prove that there is $g \in \mathcal{A}$ with $g(x_0) \neq g(y_0)$ and $0 \leq g(x) \leq 1$ for all x.

(f) If $\mu \in \mathcal{E}(\mathcal{L})$, $\mu \neq 0$, prove that supp(μ) has a single point. Then prove that $\mathcal{L}$ doesn't have such elements, and so conclude that $\mathcal{L} = \{0\}$.

7. Let $A = \mathcal{H}_1$, the unit ball in a Hilbert space. What is $\mathcal{E}(\mathcal{H}_1)$?

8. Let $1 < p < \infty$. Prove that every $f \in L^p(X, d\mu)$, with $\|f\|_p = 1$, is an extreme point of $(L^p)_1$. (*Hint:* Find $L \in (L^p)^*$ so $L(f) = 1$ and $L(g) < 1$ if $g \in (L^p)_1$ with $g \neq f$.)

9. Verify that $c_0^* = \ell^1$ (that $(\ell^1)^* = \ell^\infty$ is, of course, general).

10. (a) Prove that any extreme point, x, in $(\ell^1)_1$, the unit ball of ℓ^1, has $x_n \neq 0$ for a single n and so find $\mathcal{E}((\ell^1)_1)$.

(b) Check that cch($\mathcal{E}((\ell^1)_1)) = (\ell^1)_1$ in the $\sigma(\ell^1, c_0)$-topology.

11. Let X be a compact Hausdorff space. This problem will prove that the closed (in the $\| \cdot \|_\infty$-topology) convex hull of the extreme points of the unit ball, U, of $C_\mathbb{R}(X)$ is all of U if and only if X is totally disconnected.

(a) Prove that f is an extreme point of U if and only if there is an open and closed set, Y, of X so that if g is the characteristic function of Y, then $f = 1 - 2g$.

(b) If $x \neq y$ (i.e., in the same connected subset of X) prove that $f(x) = f(y)$ for all extreme points and conclude that if cch$(\mathcal{E}(U)) = U$, then X is totally disconnected.

(c) If X is totally disconnected, prove that cch$(\mathcal{E}(U)) = U$.

12. Let X be a compact Hausdorff space. This problem will prove that if V is the unit ball of $C(X)$, the *complex-valued* continuous function, then in the $\| \cdot \|$-topology, cch$(\mathcal{E}(V)) = V$.

(a) If the conclusion is false, prove there is $L \in C(X)^*$ with $\|L\| = 1$ and $\alpha < 1$ so that for all extreme points, f,

$$\text{Re}(L(f)) \leq \alpha \tag{5.11.23}$$

(*Hint:* Separating hyperplane theory.)

(b) Prove that $f \in C(X)$ is an extreme point of V if and only if for all x, $|f(x)| = 1$.

(c) If $\|L\| = 1$ and (5.11.23) holds, prove that there is a probability measure, μ, and a Baire measurable function, g, so that

$$L(f) = \int g(x)\, f(x)\, d\mu(x) \tag{5.11.24}$$

and $|g(x)| = 1$ for a.e. μ. (*Hint*: Problem 4 in Section 4.8.)

(d) Show that $g(x) = e^{i\varphi(x)}$ where $|\varphi(x)| \le \pi$ and φ is Baire measurable. Then show, for each ε, there is ψ continuous on X and $\mu(\{x \mid \varphi(x) \ne \psi(x)\}) \le \varepsilon$. (*Hint*: Lusin's theorem plus the Tietze extension theorem.)

(e) Show that, if $f(x) = e^{-i\psi(x)}$,

$$\operatorname{Re} L(f) \ge 1 - 2\varepsilon \tag{5.11.25}$$

(f) Conclude (5.11.23) can't hold for any $\alpha < 1$ and so the claimed result, $\operatorname{cch}(\mathcal{E}(V)) = V$.

Remark. This result and proof are due to Phelps [**718**].

5.12. Bonus Section: Fixed Point Theorems and Applications

An important part of analysis is the study of existence of solutions of certain equations. In Section 5.9, we discussed the direct method of the calculus of variations which had one method of sometimes accomplishing that. This section will focus on a different class of techniques. Namely, one has $K \subset X$, a TVS, and $F\colon K \to K$ (continuous but not necessarily linear) and one can rewrite the relevant equation as

$$F(x) = x \tag{5.12.1}$$

so existence is equivalent to showing that F has a fixed point. We begin with two examples that show it is far from automatic that F has any fixed points.

Example 5.12.1. Let $X = \mathbb{R}$, $K = (-1, 1)$, $F(x) = \frac{1}{2}(1 + x)$. For $x \in K$, $F(x) > x$, so F has no fixed point in K. All our fixed point theorems will involve a closed K. □

Example 5.12.2. Let $X = \ell^2$, $K = \{x \mid \|x\|_2 \le 1\}$,

$$F((x_1, x_2, \dots)) = \left(\sqrt{1 - \|x\|^2}, x_1, x_2, \dots\right) \tag{5.12.2}$$

Then F has no fixed point: if $F(x) = x$, then $(x_1, x_2, \dots) = (x_2, x_3, \dots)$, so $x_1 = x_2 = x_3 = \dots$. If $x \in \ell^2$, that implies $x = 0$ but $f((0,0,\dots)) = (1,0,\dots) \ne (0,0,\dots)$. We'll see that compactness of K is often important.

It is not hard to see that F is continuous in the norm topology but K is not compact in that topology. In the weak topology, K is compact, but if δ_j has $(\delta_j)_k = \delta_{jk}$, then $\frac{3}{5}\delta_j \to 0$ weakly as $j \to \infty$, while $F(\frac{3}{5}\delta_j) \to (\frac{4}{5}, 0, \dots) \neq F(0)$, so F is not continuous in that topology. $\qquad\square$

Our last example shows that some equations that don't appear in the form (5.12.1) can be rewritten in that form.

Example 5.12.3 (Existence for ODEs). Let $G\colon [0,T]\times Y \to Y$ for a Banach space, Y (even $Y = \mathbb{R}$ is interesting). We seek C^1 solutions of

$$\frac{df(t)}{dt} = G(t, f(t)) \tag{5.12.3}$$

for $f\colon [0,T] \to Y$ with initial condition

$$f(0) = y_0 \tag{5.12.4}$$

This doesn't appear to have the form (5.12.1). Suppose that G is jointly continuous when Y is given the norm topology and bounded on sets where $\|y\|$ is bounded. Let $X = C([0,T]; Y)$, the continuous Y-valued functions on $[0,T]$. Then (5.12.3)/(5.12.4) is easily seen to be equivalent to

$$F(x) = x, \qquad F(x)(t) \equiv y_0 + \int_0^t G(s, x(s))\, ds \tag{5.12.5}$$

for if $x \in X$, then $F(x)$ given by (5.12.5) is C^1 (and so in X) with $F(x)(0) = y_0$ and

$$\frac{dF(x(t))}{dt} = G(t, x(t)) \tag{5.12.6}$$

We'll continue this analysis soon. $\qquad\square$

Having illustrated the usefulness in principle of fixed point results, we can summarize the rest of this section. First, we study the contraction mapping theorem and two of its applications: to existence and uniqueness of ODEs and to the implicit/inverse function theorems. Then we discuss the Markov–Kakutani theorem on existence of fixed points for commuting families of affine maps of a compact convex subset of an LCS. Next, the Schauder–Tychonoff theorem on fixed points of any map of a compact convex subset of an LCS and apply it to existence of solutions of ODEs. Finally, we'll use the Schauder–Tychonoff theorem to prove that compact operators on Banach spaces have nontrivial invariant subspaces.

The most frequently used and simplest to prove (but still powerful) fixed point theorem is the *contraction mapping theorem*, also known as the *Banach fixed point theorem*:

Theorem 5.12.4 (Contraction Mapping Theorem). *Let (K, ρ) be a complete metric space and $T\colon K \to K$ a map so that for some $C < 1$ and all $x, y \in K$,*

$$\rho(Tx, Ty) \le C\rho(x, y) \tag{5.12.7}$$

Then there exists a unique $x_\infty \in K$ with

$$T(x_\infty) = x_\infty \tag{5.12.8}$$

Remark. The proof is constructive in that, as we'll see, $x_\infty = \lim_{n\to\infty} T^n x_0$ for any x_0.

Proof. If $T(x_\infty) = x_\infty$ and $T(y_\infty) = y_\infty$, then by (5.12.7), $\rho(x_\infty, y_\infty) \le C\rho(x_\infty, y_\infty)$. So, since $C < 1$, we must have $\rho(x_\infty, y_\infty) \le 0 \Rightarrow x_\infty = y_\infty$. Thus, there is uniqueness.

Pick x_0 and let $x_n = T^n x$. Then, by (5.12.7) and induction,

$$\rho(x_{n+1}, x_n) \le C\rho(x_n, x_{n-1}) \le \cdots \le C^n \rho(x_1, x_0) \tag{5.12.9}$$

Thus, by the triangle inequality if $m > n$,

$$\rho(x_m, x_n) \le \sum_{j=1}^{m-n} \rho(x_{n+j}, x_{n+j-1}) \le \left[\sum_{j=1}^{m-n} C^{n+j-1}\right] \rho(x_1, x_1)$$
$$\le C^n (1-C)^{-1} \rho(x_1, x_0) \tag{5.12.10}$$

since $C < 1$ and we can sum the geometric series.

(5.12.10) implies that $\{x_n\}_{n=1}^\infty$ is Cauchy, so it has a limit, x_∞, since K is complete. Writing $x_{n+1} = T(x_n)$ and taking limits in (5.12.9), we get $\rho(T(x_\infty), x_\infty) = 0$, so (5.12.8) holds. $\qquad\square$

Example 5.12.3 (continued). Let G be defined and continuous on $[0, t_0] \times Y$. For each R, suppose we have C_1, C_2 so that

$$0 \le s \le t_0; \|y\| \le R \Rightarrow \|G(s, y)\| \le C_1 \tag{5.12.11}$$
$$0 \le s \le t_0; \|y_1\|, \|y_2\| \le R \Rightarrow \|G(s, y_1) - G(s, y_2)\| \le C_2\|y_1 - y_2\| \tag{5.12.12}$$

Given $y_0 \in Y$, let $R = 2\|y_0\|$ and C_1, C_2 given by (5.12.11) and (5.12.12). Let $t_1 = R/2C_1$. Let T be given by the map F of (5.12.5). Let X be the Banach space $C([0, t]; Y)$ with norm

$$\|x\|_\infty = \sup_{0 \le s \le t} \|x(s)\| \tag{5.12.13}$$

Here t is a number with $0 < t \le \min(t_0, t_1)$ to be determined later. Let

$$K = \left\{x \in X \;\middle|\; \|x\|_\infty \le R\right\} \tag{5.12.14}$$

If $x \in X$ and $0 \le u \le t$, by (5.12.11),

$$\left\| \int_0^u G(s, x(s))\, ds \right\| \le u C_1 \le t_1 C_1 = \frac{R}{2} = \|y_0\| \qquad (5.12.15)$$

so T maps K to itself.

Let $x_1, x_2 \in K$. By (5.12.12) for any $0 \le u \le t$,

$$\|T(x_1)(u) - T(x_2)(u)\| \le \int_0^u C_2 \|x_1 - x_2\|_\infty\, du \le (C_2 t)\|x_1 - x_2\|_\infty \quad (5.12.16)$$

Pick t by

$$t = \min\left(t_0, t_1, \frac{1}{2C_2}\right) \qquad (5.12.17)$$

By (5.12.16), for the resulting K, we have

$$\|T(x_1) - T(x_0)\|_\infty \le \tfrac{1}{2}\|x_1 - x_2\|_\infty \qquad (5.12.18)$$

Thus, T is a strict contraction, meaning $T(x_\infty) = x_\infty$ has a unique solution in K. It is not hard to see (Problem 2) that there will be a unique solution in X. We summarize in the theorem below. □

Theorem 5.12.5 (Picard Iteration). *If G obeys (5.12.11) and (5.12.12), then for any R_1, there is a t so that if y_0 has $\|y_0\| \le R_1$, then (5.12.3)/(5.12.4) has a unique solution.*

Example 5.12.6. Let $Y = \mathbb{R}$ and ($\sqrt{\cdot} = $ positive square root)

$$G(t, y) = 2\sqrt{|y|} \qquad (5.12.19)$$

Fix $t_0 > 0$ and let

$$f(t) = \begin{cases} 0, & 0 \le t \le t_0 \\ (t - t_0)^2, & \text{otherwise} \end{cases} \qquad (5.12.20)$$

Then (5.12.3)/(5.12.4) with $y_0 = 0$ is solved on $[0, \infty)$ by (5.12.20) for any t_0. So continuity of G is not sufficient for uniqueness of solutions (combined with uniform boundedness, it is sufficient for existence; see Theorem 5.12.24 below). Of course, (5.12.19) does not obey (5.12.12). □

Example 5.12.7. Let $Y = \mathbb{R}$ and

$$G(t, y) = y^2 \qquad (5.12.21)$$

Fix $t_0 > 0$ and let

$$f(t) = (t_0 - t)^{-1}, \qquad 0 \le t < t_0 \qquad (5.12.22)$$

This solves (5.12.3)/(5.12.4) with $y_0 = t_0^{-1}$ on $(0, t_0)$. This shows that, under the hypotheses of Theorem 5.12.5, (5.12.3)/(5.12.4) has local solutions but may not have global solutions. In Problem 3, the reader will prove the result in the next theorem that provides a proof of global solvability under an additional assumption. □

Theorem 5.12.8 (Gronwall's Method). *Let G be defined and continuous on $[0, \infty) \times Y$. Suppose in addition to (5.12.3)/(5.12.4) for each t_0, (C_j may depend on t_0), we have for each t_0 a C_3 so that for*

$$0 \le s \le t_0 \Rightarrow \|G(s, y)\| \le C_3(\|y\| + 1) \qquad (5.12.23)$$

Then for any y_0, (5.12.3)/(5.12.4) has a solution for all $t \in [0, \infty)$.

The other classical application of the contraction mapping theorem is to the inverse mapping and implicit function theorems.

Recall that $F \colon U \to Y$ with $U \subset X$, where X and Y are Banach spaces, is Fréchet differentiable at x_0 in U if (5.1.24) holds. We say F is C^1 on U if $x \mapsto Df_x$ as a map of U to $\mathcal{L}(X, Y)$ is continuous (when $\mathcal{L}(X, Y)$ is given the norm topology).

Theorem 5.12.9 (Inverse Mapping Theorem). *Let X be a Banach space, $U \subset X$, and f a C^1 function from U to X. For some $x_0 \in U$, suppose that Df_{x_0} has a bounded inverse in $\mathcal{L}(X, X)$. Let $y_0 = f(x_0)$. Then there exist ε and δ so for $\|y - y_0\| < \varepsilon$, there exists a unique x with $\|x - x_0\| < \delta$ so that*

$$f(x) = y \qquad (5.12.24)$$

Moreover, if we use $g(y)$ for this unique solution, then g is C^1 on $\{y \mid \|y - y_0\| < \varepsilon\}$ with

$$Dg_{y_0} = (Df_{x_0})^{-1} \qquad (5.12.25)$$

Remark. This is often stated in $X = \mathbb{R}^n$, in which case invertibility of Df_{x_0} is stated as

$$\det\left(\frac{\partial f_i}{\partial x_j}\right) \ne 0 \qquad (5.12.26)$$

Proof. Let $\widetilde{f}$ be defined on $U - x_0$ by

$$\widetilde{f}(x) = (Df_{x_0})^{-1}[f(x + x_0) - y_0] \qquad (5.12.27)$$

Then $f(x) = y \Leftrightarrow \widetilde{f}(x) = (Df_{x_0})^{-1}(y - y_0)$. Thus, the result for $\widetilde{f}$ implies it for f, that is, without loss of generality, we can and will suppose that

$$x_0 = y_0 = 0, \qquad Df_{x_0} \equiv \mathbb{1} \qquad (5.12.28)$$

Let

$$q(x) = x - f(x) \qquad (5.12.29)$$

Then q is C^1 and $Dq_{x=0} = 0$, so we can find δ so that

$$\|x\| \le \delta \Rightarrow \|Dq_x\| \le \tfrac{1}{2} \qquad (5.12.30)$$

By the fundamental theorem of calculus,

$$q(x_1) - q(x_2) = \int_0^1 \left[\frac{d}{d\theta} q(\theta x_1 + (1 - \theta)x_2)\right] d\theta$$

$$= \int_0^1 Dq_{\theta x_1 + (1-\theta)x_2}(x_1 - x_2)\, d\theta \qquad (5.12.31)$$

so by (5.12.30),

$$\|x_1\|, \|x_2\| \le \delta \Rightarrow \|q(x_1) - q(x_2)\| \le \tfrac{1}{2}\|x_1 - x_2\| \qquad (5.12.32)$$

Fix y with $\|y\| \le \delta/2$ and for $\|x\| \le \delta$, let

$$h^{(y)}(x) = y + q(x) \qquad (5.12.33)$$

For such x,

$$\|h^{(y)}(x)\| \le \frac{\delta}{2} + q(x)$$
$$\le \frac{\delta}{2} + \frac{1}{2}\|x\| \qquad \text{(by (5.12.32))}$$
$$\le \delta \qquad (5.12.34)$$

Thus, if $K = \{x \mid \|x\| \le \delta\}$, then (5.12.34) says $h^{(y)}$ maps K to itself.

By (5.12.32), on K,

$$\|h_y(x_1) - h_y(x_2)\| \le \tfrac{1}{2}\|x_1 - x_2\| \qquad (5.12.35)$$

so, by the contraction mapping theorem, there is a unique solution of $x = h_y(x) = y + x - f(x)$, that is, if $f(x) = y$. Thus, with $\varepsilon = \delta/2$, we have the claimed unique solution $x = g(y)$ of (5.12.24).

$h^{(y)}(x)$ is trivially jointly continuous in x and y, so $h_n^{(y)}(x) = h^{(y)} \circ \cdots \circ h^{(y)}(x)$ (n times) is jointly continuous. By the proof of the contraction mapping theorem and (5.12.35), $h_n^{(y)}(0) \to g(y)$ uniformly in y, so $g(y)$ is continuous.

We claim that g is Fréchet differentiable at $y = 0$ with derivative $Dg_{y=0} = \mathbb{1}$. For let

$$\kappa(R) = \max_{\|x\| \le R} \|Dq_x\| = o(R) \qquad (5.12.36)$$

at $R = 0$, by continuity. The above proof shows that $g(y)$ is contained in $K_{\|y\|} = \{x \mid \|x\| \le 2\|y\|\}$ and on that set,

$$\|h^{(y)}(x_1) - h^{(y)}(x_2)\| \le \kappa(2\|y\|)\|x_1 - x_2\| \qquad (5.12.37)$$

Define y_n inductively by

$$y_0 = 0, \qquad y_{n+1} = h^{(y)}(y_n) \qquad (5.12.38)$$

By (5.12.37),

$$\|y_{n+1} - y_n\| \le \kappa(2\|y\|)\|y_n - y_{n-1}\| \le \kappa(2\|y\|)^n\|y\| \qquad (5.12.39)$$

since $y_1 = h^{(y)}(0) = y$. Since $y_n \to g(y)$, we conclude that

$$\|g(y) - y\| \leq \left[\sum_{j=1}^{\infty} \kappa(2\|y\|)^j \right] \|y\| = o(1)\|y\| \tag{5.12.40}$$

proving the claimed differentiability and derivative at $y = 0$.

Returning to general f's, we see if g is the inverse, then $Dg_y = (Df_{g(y)})^{-1}$ is continuous in y (given the continuity of $A \to A^{-1}$ on $\mathcal{L}(X)$; see Problem 4). $\square$

The implicit function theorem concerns Banach spaces, X and Y, and open sets, $U \subset X$ and $V \subset Y$, and

$$G: U \times V \mapsto Y \tag{5.12.41}$$

Given $x_0, y_0 \in U \times V$ and $z_0 \equiv G(x_0, y_0)$, we seek for x near x_0 a solution $y(x)$ near y_0 of

$$G(x, y) = z_0 \tag{5.12.42}$$

Define

$$H: U \times V \to X \times Y \tag{5.12.43}$$

by

$$H(x, y) = (x, G(x, y)) \tag{5.12.44}$$

Suppose H is C^1 near x_0, y_0 and $DH_{(x_0, y_0)}$ is invertible. Then $H(\tilde{x}, \tilde{y}) = (x_1, z_1)$ has a unique solution $(\tilde{x}, \tilde{y}) \equiv W(x, y)$ (near (x_0, y_0)) for (x, y) near $H(x_0, y_0)$. In particular,

$$\tilde{x} = x_1, \qquad G(\tilde{x}, \tilde{y}) = z_1 \tag{5.12.45}$$

We can take $z_1 = z_0$ and $x_1 = x$ near x_0. Then $y = W(x, z_0)$ solves (5.12.42) (by (5.12.44)).

In Problem 5, the reader will prove that $DH_{(x_0, y_0)}$ is invertible if and only if $D^{(2)}G_{(x_0, y_0)}$ (as a map of Y to Y) is invertible. (Recall that $DG = (D^{(1)}G, D^{(2)}G)$, where $D^{(1)}G$ maps X to Y and $D^{(2)}G$ maps Y to Y). Thus, we have

Theorem 5.12.10 (Implicit Function Theorem). *Let X and Y be Banach spaces, $U \subset X$, $V \subset Y$ open sets, and $G: U \times V \to Y$ a C^1 function on $U \times V$. Let*

$$z_0 = G(x_0, y_0) \tag{5.12.46}$$

Suppose $D^{(2)}G_{(x_0, y_0)}$ is invertible as an element of $\mathcal{L}(Y)$. Then there exist δ and ε so that for all x with $\|x - x_0\| < \delta$, there is a unique $y(x)$ with $\|y - y_0\| < \varepsilon$ so that

$$z_0 = G(x, y(x)) \tag{5.12.47}$$

for all x with $\|x - x_0\| < \delta$. Moreover, y is a C^1 function and

$$D_{x_0} y = [D^{(2)} G_{(x_0, y_0)}]^{-1} D^{(1)} G_{(x_0, y_0)} \tag{5.12.48}$$

Remarks. 1. Typically, z_0 is 0.

2. This is often stated with $X = \mathbb{R}^k$, $Y = \mathbb{R}^n$, and the invertibility is stated as

$$\det \left(\frac{\partial G_j(x_0, y_0)}{\partial y_i} \right) = 0 \tag{5.12.49}$$

for the $n \times n$ determinant.

3. In Problem 6, the reader will verify (5.12.48).

Example 5.12.11. $G(x_1, \ldots, x_n) = x_1^2 + \cdots + x_n^2 - 1$. Think of $(x_1, \ldots, x_{n-1})$ as x and $G = 0$ as defining x_n implicitly as a function of x. Clearly, $x_n = \pm \sqrt{1 - x_1^2 + \cdots + x_{n-1}^2}$. We have that $\partial G / \partial x_n = 2 x_n$, so $x_n = 0$ are singular points. We can define x_n implicitly away from $x_1^2 + \cdots + x_{n-1}^2 = 1$. This shows that this theorem is local and not global. □

$$* \qquad * \qquad * \qquad * \qquad *$$

Next, we turn to the Markov–Kakutani theorem on families of commuting affine maps of K to itself, where K is a compact convex subset of an lcs. We start with a single affine map.

Lemma 5.12.12. *Let $K \subset X$, an lcs, be a nonempty compact convex set and let $T \colon K \to K$ be continuous and affine. Then there exists $x \in K$ with*

$$Tx = x \tag{5.12.50}$$

Proof. Pick any $x_1 \in K$ and let

$$x_n = \frac{1}{n} \sum_{j=1}^{n} T^{j-1} x_1 \tag{5.12.51}$$

If $\ell \in X^*$, we have

$$|\ell(T x_n - x_n)| = \left| \ell \left(\frac{1}{n} (T^n x_1 - x_1) \right) \right| \le \frac{2}{n} \sup_{y \in K} |\ell(y)| \tag{5.12.52}$$

Since K is compact, x_n has a limit point, x_∞, with a subnet $x_{n(\alpha)} \to x_\infty$. By continuity and (5.12.52),

$$\ell(T x_\infty) = \ell(x_\infty) \tag{5.12.53}$$

By the Hahn–Banach theorem (Theorem 5.7.8), $T x_\infty = x_\infty$. □

Theorem 5.12.13 (Markov–Kakutani Theorem). *Let $\mathcal{T}$ be a family of continuous affine maps of K to itself, where $K \subset X$, an lcs, is a nonempty compact convex set. Suppose for all $T_1, T_2 \in \mathcal{T}$, we have that*

$$T_1 T_2 = T_2 T_1 \tag{5.12.54}$$

Then there is $x \in K$ with

$$Tx = x \tag{5.12.55}$$

for all $T \in \mathcal{T}$.

Remark. (5.12.54) can be replaced by requiring $\mathcal{T}$ to be a soluble group instead of a commutative group (Problem 9).

Proof. Given $T_1, \ldots, T_n \in \mathcal{T}$, let

$$K(T_1, \ldots, T_n) = \{x \in K \mid T_j x = x \text{ for } j = 1, \ldots, n\} \tag{5.12.56}$$

Then $K(T_1, \ldots, T_n)$ is closed, so compact and convex.

By (5.12.55), if $T \in \mathcal{T}$ and $x \in K(T_1, \ldots, T_n)$, then $T_j(Tx) = T(T_j x) = Tx$, so $Tx \in K(T_1, \ldots, T_n)$ also. Thus, by the lemma, if $K(T_1, \ldots, T_n)$ is nonempty, so is $K(T_1, \ldots, T_n, T)$. By induction, each $K(T_1, \ldots, T_n)$ is nonempty.

Since

$$K(T_1) \cap \cdots \cap K(T_n) = K(T_1, \ldots, T_n)$$

$\{K(T)\}_{T \in \mathcal{T}}$ has the f.i.p. property and each $K(T)$ is closed. So, by Theorem 2.3.1, there is $x \in \bigcap_{T \in \mathcal{T}} K(T)$, that is, so (5.12.55) holds for all $T \in \mathcal{T}$. □

Example 5.12.14 (Haar measure for compact abelian groups). Let G be a compact abelian group. On $\mathcal{M}_{+,1}(G)$, define for each $x \in G$, $T_x = \tau_x^*$, where $\tau_x \colon C(G) \to C(G)$ by $(\tau_x f)(y) = f(x+y)$. Since $\tau_x \tau_y = \tau_y \tau_x$, we have $T_x T_y = T_y T_x$. Thus, there is an invariant measure by Theorem 5.12.13. Of course, we have already constructed Haar measure in much greater generality (see Section 4.19), but the next two examples extend this idea much further. □

Example 5.12.15 (Finitely additive set functions on S^1). Let X be the set of finite-valued real functions on $S^1 = \{e^{i\theta} \mid 0 \le \theta < 2\pi\}$ (with no measurability condition). Let X^* be its algebraic dual and $K \subset X^*$ the set of $\ell \colon X \to \mathbb{R}$ with $\ell(\mathbb{1}) = 1$ and $\ell(f) \ge 0$ if $f \ge 0$. By Tychonoff's theorem, K is compact in the $\sigma(X^*, X)$-topology.

If χ_A is the characteristic function of $A \subset S^1$, then $\mu(A) = \ell(\chi_A)$ is a finitely additive set function. Rotations act as a commutative group on X and so, by duality on X^*, are a commutative group of continuous maps on K. Thus, by Theorem 5.12.13, S^1 supports a rotation invariant, finitely additive set function. That S^2 does not have such a set function is connected to the nature of the rotation group, $\mathbb{SO}(3)$ (see the discussion in the Notes to Section 4.3). □

Example 5.12.16 (Banach limit). This example follows the theme in the last two—from measurable functions on compact abelian groups and, in the last example, to general functions on such groups, to, in this example, non-compact groups (or rather, semigroups since $\mathbb{Z}_+$ has no additive inverses). We'll have only a single map, and so Lemma 5.12.12 suffices, but the idea works on more general abelian groups. Moreover, for this case, one can use the Hahn–Banach theorem (see Problem 10), as was done originally.

As usual, let ℓ^∞ be bounded sequences, $\{a_j\}_{j=1}^\infty$. Let T be given by

$$T(a)_j = a_{j+1} \qquad (5.12.57)$$

A *Banach limit* is a map $L \in (\ell^\infty)^*$ with

(i) $a_j \geq 0$ for all $j \Rightarrow L(a) \geq 0$
(ii) $L(Ta) = L(a)$
(iii) $L((1, 1, \dots, 1, \dots)) = 1$

As usual, (i) and (iii) (and, for a real-valued $\|a\|(1, 1, \dots) \pm a \geq 0$) imply that

$$\|L(a)\| \leq \|a\|_\infty \qquad (5.12.58)$$

By the Banach–Alaoglu theorem, $\{L$ obeying (i) plus (iii)$\}$ is compact in the $\sigma((\ell^\infty)^*, \ell^\infty)$-topology. If $T^*(L) = L \circ T$, T^* is affine, so by Lemma 5.12.12, there is fixed point, that is, there exist Banach limits. The name comes from the easy fact (Problem 11) that if $\lim a_n = \alpha$, then $L(A) = \alpha$. So this extends the notion of limits (see also Problems 12 and 13). □

$$* \qquad * \qquad * \qquad * \qquad *$$

The final fixed point theorem we want to discuss is the Schauder–Tychonoff theorem. A topological space, X, is said to have the *fixed point property* if and only if any continuous map $T\colon X \to X$ has a fixed point. The most basic and most famous result asserting the fixed point property is:

Theorem 5.12.17 (Brouwer Fixed Point Theorem). *Let $\overline{B^n}$ be the closed unit ball in $\mathbb{R}^n$, that is,*

$$\overline{B^n} = \{x \in \mathbb{R} \mid x_1^2 + \cdots + x_n^2 \leq 1\} \qquad (5.12.59)$$

Then $\overline{B^n}$ has the fixed point property.

After using this to prove the infinite-dimensional analog, we'll prove the Brouwer theorem but using some calculus on manifolds (for this, we assume the reader knows that from elsewhere; a summary of calculus on manifolds can be found in Section 1.5 of Part 2A).

Theorem 5.12.18 (Schauder–Tychonoff Fixed Point Theorem). *Any compact convex subset, K, of a locally convex vector space, X, has the fixed point property.*

We won't prove the theorem in this generality but under an additional assumption. The full result is in Problem 14. We say K has *countable coordinates* if there exists $\{\ell_n\}_{n=1}^\infty$ in X^*, so for any $x \neq y$ both in K, there is n with $\ell_n(x) \neq \ell_n(y)$. We'll prove Theorem 5.12.18 when K has countable coordinates.

Proposition 5.12.19. (a) *If X is a Banach space and K is norm compact, then K has countable coordinates.*

(b) *If X^* is separable in the $\sigma(X^*, X)$-topology, then any $K \subset X^*$ has countable coordinates.*

Proof. (a) The topology is given by a metric. By Theorem 2.3.6 and Proposition 2.3.5, K is separable. Pick $\{z_n\}_{n=1}^\infty$ a dense set and $\{(x_n, y_n)\}_{n=1}^\infty$ so as n goes from 1 to ∞, (x_n, y_n) runs through all pairs of distinct points among the z's, each ordered pair once. By the Hahn–Banach theorem, pick $\ell_n \in X^*$ so

$$\|\ell_n\| = 1, \qquad \ell_n(x_n - y_n) = \|x_n - y_n\| \qquad (5.12.60)$$

Given $x, y \in K$, we can find $n(j)$, so $x_{n(j)} \to x$ and $y_{n(j)} \to y$. Then by (5.12.60),

$$\begin{aligned}\ell_{n(j)}(x - y) &= \ell_{n(j)}(x_{n(j)} - y_{n(j)}) - \ell_{n(j)}(x - y - (x_{n(j)} - y_{n(j)})) \\ &\geq \|x_{n(j)} - y_{n(j)}\| - \|x - y - (x_{n(j)} - y_{n(j)})\| \qquad (5.12.61) \\ &\to \|x - y\|\end{aligned}$$

It follows for j large that $\ell_{n(j)}(x - y) \neq 0$, so $\{\ell_n\}_{n=1}^\infty$ are countable coordinates.

(b) Let $\{\ell_n\}_{n=1}^\infty$ be a $\sigma(X^*, X)$-dense subset of X^*. If $x \neq y$ are in K, pick $\ell \in X^*$ so $\ell(x - y) \neq 0$ and a subnet, $n(\alpha)$, so $\ell_{n(\alpha)} \to \ell$ weakly. Then $\ell_{n(\alpha)}(x - y) \to \ell(x - y) \neq 0$, so for some n, $\ell_n(x - y) \neq 0$. Thus, $\{\ell_n\}_{n=1}^\infty$ are countable coordinates. $\square$

Recall the Hilbert cube, H, of Example 2.2.11, that is, $[0, 1]^{\mathbb{Z}_+}$ with the metric (2.2.18). An equivalent metric is

$$\tilde{\rho}(x, y) = \left(\sum_{n=1}^\infty [2^{-n}(x_n - y_n)]^2 \right)^{1/2} \qquad (5.12.62)$$

so we can view H as a compact subset of the Hilbert space $\widetilde{\ell^2}$ with the metric (5.12.62). Using the Brouwer theorem, we'll first prove that H has the fixed point property, then that a compact convex subset of H does, and finally, that if K has countable coordinates, then K is homeomorphic to a compact convex subset of H.

Proposition 5.12.20. *The Hilbert cube has the fixed point property.*

Proof. Let $T\colon H \to H$ be continuous. Define $\pi_n\colon H \to [0,1]^n$ by $\pi_n(x)_j = x_j$ for $j = 1, \ldots, n$ and then $T_n = \pi_n T \pi_n \upharpoonright [0,1]^n$. Since $[0,1]^n$ is homeomorphic to $\overline{B_n}$, there is $x^{(n)} \in [0,1]^n$ with $T_n(x^{(n)}) = x^{(n)}$. If $x^{(n)}$ is used for the point in H with $(x^{(n)})_j = x_j^{(n)}$ (respectively, 0) if $j \leq n$ (respectively, $j \geq n$), then

$$T(x^{(n)})_j = x_j^{(n)} \qquad \text{for } j \leq n \qquad (5.12.63)$$

Since H is compact, $\{x^{(n)}\}$ has a limit point $x^{(\infty)}$. Since T is continuous, (5.12.63) implies $T(x^{(\infty)}) = x^{(\infty)}$. $\qquad\square$

Definition. If K is a topological space and $Q \subset K$, we say Q is a *retract* of K if there exists $f\colon K \to Q$ so $f(x) = x$ for all $x \in Q$. f is called the *retraction*.

Example 5.12.21. If $j < n$, $\overline{B^j} \subset \overline{B^n}$ via adding 0's for components $j+1, \ldots, n$. Then $\pi_{j,n}(x)$ which drops components $j+1, \ldots, n$ is a retraction. $\qquad\square$

Proposition 5.12.22. *If Q is a retract of K and K has the fixed point property, so does Q.*

Proof. Let $f\colon K \to Q$ be the retraction. If $T\colon Q \to Q$, then $\widetilde{T} = T \circ f$ maps K to K, so there is $x \in K$ with $\widetilde{T}(x) = x$. Since $\operatorname{Ran}(\widetilde{T}) \subset Q$, we have $x \in Q$, so $f(x) = x$ and $Tx = \widetilde{T}x = x$. $\qquad\square$

Proposition 5.12.23. *Any compact convex subset, Q, of the Hilbert cube, H, is a retract of H and, in particular, it has the fixed point property.*

Proof. As noted above, H is a subset of $\widetilde{\ell^2}$ in the Hilbert space norm $\tilde{\rho}$ of (5.12.62). By Theorem 3.2.1, for any $x \in \widetilde{\ell^2}$, there is $f(x) \in Q$ minimizing $\tilde{\rho}(x,y)$ among $y \in Q$. It is easy to see (Problem 15) that f is continuous. $f \upharpoonright H$ is a retraction of K to Q. $\qquad\square$

Proof of Theorem 5.12.18 if K has countable coordinates. Let $\{\ell_n\}_{n=1}^{\infty}$ be a sequence of coordinates and drop any ℓ_n which is identically 0. Define $f\colon K \to H$ by

$$f(x)_n = \tfrac{1}{2}\left(1 + \|\ell_n\|_{\infty}^{-1} \ell_n(x)\right) \qquad (5.12.64)$$

where $\|\ell_n\|_\infty = \sup_{y \in K} |\ell_n(y)| < \infty$. Since $x \neq y$ in K implies $\ell_n(x) \neq \ell_n(y)$ for some n, f is an affine one-one map that is obviously continuous. Thus, by Theorem 2.3.11, f is a homeomorphism from K to $\mathrm{Ran}(f)$ and K is homeomorphic to a compact convex subset of H. It follows that K has the fixed point property. $\qquad\square$

Example 5.12.3 (continued). Suppose the G in (5.12.3) is continuous and obeys (5.12.11), but not necessarily (5.12.12). The argument from (5.12.15) shows the set K of (5.12.14) is mapped to itself by K and that $K_0 = \mathrm{cvh}(T[K]) \subset K$. By a simple estimate, the elements of K_0 are uniformly bounded and uniformly equicontinuous. So by Theorem 2.3.14, K_0 is compact and convex in the Banach space norm $\|\cdot\|_\infty$. Thus, T, which maps K_0 to K_0, has a fixed point. We summarize in the theorem below. $\qquad\square$

Theorem 5.12.24 (Peano's Theorem). *If G obeys (5.12.11), then for any R_1, there is a t so that if y_0 has $\|y_0\| \leq R_1$, then (5.12.3)/(5.12.4) has a solution.*

Remark. As Example 5.12.6 shows, the solution may not be unique.

Finally, assuming familiarity with calculus on manifolds, we turn to a proof of the Brouwer fixed point theorem.

Proposition 5.12.25. (a) *If $T \colon \overline{B^n} \to \overline{B^n}$ has no fixed point and $S^{n-1} = \partial \overline{B^n} = \{x \mid \|x\| = 1\}$, then S^{n-1} is a retract of $\overline{B^n}$ to S^{n-1}.*

(b) *If there is a retraction, f, of $\overline{B^n}$ to S^{n-1}, then there exists $\widetilde{f} \colon \mathbb{R}^n \to S^{n-1}$, which is C^∞, and $\widetilde{f}(x) = x/\|x\|$ if $\|x\| \geq 1$ (so, in particular, $\widetilde{f}$ is a smooth retraction).*

Proof. (a) If $T(x) \neq x$, there is a unique half-line that starts at $T(x)$ and runs to ∞ going through x. Let $f(x)$ be the intersection of this half-line and S^{n-1}. Clearly, $f \upharpoonright S^{n-1}$ is the identity, and an easy argument (Problem 16) shows that f is continuous, so a retraction.

(b) Extend f to $\mathbb{R}^n$ by setting $f(x) = x$ if $\|x\| \geq 1$. Then if $f^\sharp(x) = \frac{1}{2}f(2x)$, we have $f^\sharp(x) = x$ if $\|x\| \geq \frac{1}{2}$. Let j_δ be a spherically symmetric, C^∞ approximate identity with support in $\{x \mid \|x\| \leq \delta\}$. If $\delta < \frac{1}{2}$, it is easy to see that $\tilde{g} = j_\delta * f^\sharp$ is smooth and, by symmetry, if $\|x\| > \frac{1}{2} + \delta$, then $\tilde{g}(x)$ is a multiple of x. By taking δ small, we can be sure for some $\varepsilon > 0$, if $\|x\| \geq 1 - \varepsilon$, then $\tilde{g}(x)$ is a nonzero multiple of x, say $\|\tilde{g}(x)\| \geq \alpha > 0$ for all x with $\|x\| \geq 1 - \varepsilon$. Let $h \colon (-1, \infty) \to (0, \infty)$ be smooth with $h(y) = y$ if $y \geq \alpha$. Then $\widetilde{f}(x) = \tilde{g}(x)/h(\tilde{g}(x))$ is the required map. $\qquad\square$

Proof of Theorem 5.12.17. If the theorem is false, by the last proposition, there exists a map $f \colon \overline{B^n} \to S^{n-1}$ which is smooth including up to the boundary (indeed, extends to a smooth map on $\mathbb{R}^n$) with $f \equiv 1$ on $S^{n-1} \subset \overline{B^n}$. Let ω be the standard volume form on S^{n-1} (induced by the usual Riemann metric). Then

$$0 < \int_{S^{n-1}} \omega = \int_{f[S^{n-1}]} \omega \tag{5.12.65}$$

$$= \int_{\partial \overline{B^n}} f^*(\omega) \tag{5.12.66}$$

$$= \int_{\overline{B^n}} d(f^*(\omega)) \tag{5.12.67}$$

$$= \int_{\overline{B^n}} f^*(d\omega) \tag{5.12.68}$$

$$= 0 \tag{5.12.69}$$

and the contradiction proves such a smooth retraction cannot exist.

(5.12.65) comes from $f \equiv 1$ on S^{n-1}, (5.12.66) from (1.5.13) of Part 2A, (5.12.67) from Stokes' theorem (Theorem 1.5.2 of Part 2A), (5.12.68) from (1.5.12) of Part 2A, and (5.12.69) from $d\omega = 0$ since ω is an $n - 1$-form and there are no n-forms on S^{n-1}. $\qquad \square$

Remark. In the above, we showed $\sim$ Brouwer $\Rightarrow S^{n-1}$ is a retract of $\overline{B^n}$, but the converse is also true. For if S^{n-1} is a retract of $\overline{B^n}$ and the Brouwer theorem holds, then by Proposition 5.12.22, S^{n-1} would have the fixed point property. But the antipodal map $x \mapsto -x$ has no fixed point on S^{n-1}.

As a final application of the Schauder–Tychoff theorem, we will prove Lomonosov's strengthening of the Aronszajn–Smith theorem that compact operators on an arbitrary Banach space have nontrivial invariant subspaces. We clearly need to explain first what compact operators are and what an invariant subspace is. An operator $A \in \mathcal{L}(X)$ where X is a Banach space is called a *compact operator* if

$$A\big[\{x \mid \|x\| \leq 1\}\big] \tag{5.12.70}$$

has compact closure. Since balls in infinite-dimensional Banach spaces are not compact (see Theorem 5.1.7), this is a much stronger condition than just that A is bounded. Chapter 3 of Part 4 will have an extensive discussion of compact operators, especially on a Hilbert space. In particular, if X is reflexive and X^* separable, the set in (5.12.70) is already closed when A is compact. We won't need anything about compact operators except their basic definition and the easy fact that if A is compact and B is bounded, AB and BA are also compact.

Definition. Let $A \in \mathcal{L}(X)$, the bounded operators on a Banach space, X. A closed subspace $Y \subset X$ is called an *invariant subspace for A (invariant* for short) if and only if $A[Y] \subset Y$, i.e., $Ay \in Y$ for all $y \in Y$. Y is called *hyperinvariant* for A if for all $B \in \mathcal{L}(X)$ with $BA = AB$, Y is invariant for B. If $Y \neq \{0\}, X$, we say it is a *nontrivial* invariant or hyperinvariant space. Since $AA = AA$, any hyperinvariant space for A is an invariant subspace of A.

For finite matrices, A, which can be diagonalized, it is easy to see that Y is invariant for A if and only if Y has a basis of eigenvectors for A. It is hyperinvariant if and only if it is a sum of some number of complete eigenspaces, i.e., subspaces of the form $\{x \mid Ax = \lambda x\}$ for some X. Thus, invariant subspaces are a first step in structure theory for A.

For a long time, it was a famous open question if every operator on any Banach space had invariant subspaces. It is now known (see the Notes) that some quite reasonable Banach spaces can have operators with no nontrivial invariant subspaces but the problem is still open for a Hilbert space.

Our goal below will be to prove that compact operators have nontrivial hyperinvariant subspaces. The proof will be by contradiction so we begin by focusing on algebras with no nontrivial invariant subspaces. An *algebra*, $\mathcal{A}$, of operators on X is a subspace of $\mathcal{L}(X)$ with $\mathbb{1} \in \mathcal{A}$ and $A, B \in \mathcal{A} \Rightarrow AB \in \mathcal{A}$. $Y \subset X$ is invariant for $\mathcal{A}$ if and only if it is invariant for each $A \in \mathcal{A}$. For any A, $\{A\}' = \{B \mid BA = AB\}$ (called the *commutant* of A) is an algebra and Y is hyperinvariant for A if and only if it is invariant for $\{A\}'$.

Definition. An algebra, $\mathcal{A}$, in $\mathcal{L}(X)$ is called *transitive* if and only if it has no nontrivial invariant subspaces.

The name comes from

Proposition 5.12.26. *$\mathcal{A}$, an algebra in $\mathcal{L}(X)$, is transitive if and only if for all $x \neq 0$, $x \in X$, $\{Ax \mid A \in \mathcal{A}\}$ is dense in X.*

Proof. Suppose that $\mathcal{A}$ is transitive. Since $\mathbb{1} \in \mathcal{A}$ and $x \neq 0$, $Y = \overline{\{Ax \mid A \in \mathcal{A}\}}$ is a closed subspace and not $\{0\}$. Since $B(Ax) = (BA)x$, Y is invariant so if $\mathcal{A}$ has no nontrivial invariant subspace, we must have $Y = X$.

Conversely, if $\mathcal{A}$ is not transitive, let Y be a nontrivial invariant subspace for $\mathcal{A}$ and $y \neq 0$ in Y. Then $\{Ay \mid A \in \mathcal{A}\} \subset Y$ and is clearly not dense in X since $Y \neq X$. $\square$

Theorem 5.12.27 (Lomonosov's Lemma). *Let $\mathcal{A}$ be a transitive subalgebra of $\mathcal{L}(X)$ and $K \in \mathcal{L}(X)$ a nonzero compact operator. Then there exist $C \in \mathcal{A}$ so that CK has eigenvalue 1, i.e., there is $x_1 \in X$, $x_1 \neq 0$, so that*

$$CKx_1 = x_1 \tag{5.12.71}$$

Proof. The idea of the proof will be to find a ball $\overline{B_1(x_0)}$ in $X \setminus \{0\}$, using transitivity and a function $x \mapsto C(x) \in \mathcal{A}$ for $x \in B_1(x_0)$, so that $\Phi(x) = C(x)Kx$ maps $\overline{B_1(x_0)}$ into a precompact subset of $\overline{B_1(x_0)}$. By Mazur's theorem, $Q = \mathrm{cch}\big(\Phi\big[\overline{B_1(x_0)}\big]\big)$ is compact and in $\overline{B_1(x_0)}$ so Φ is a continuous map of Q to itself. Since Q is a compact, convex set, we can apply the Schauder–Tychonoff theorem to find $x_1 \in Q$ with $\Phi(x_1) = x_1$, i.e., $\big[C(x_1)K\big]x_1 = x_1$ which is what is desired.

Without loss we can suppose that $\|K\| = 1$. We can pick $x_0 \in X$, so that

$$\|Kx_0\| > 1, \quad \|x_0\| > 1 \qquad (5.12.72)$$

(where $\|K\| = 1$ means the first fact implies the second). Let

$$L = \overline{K\big[B_1(x_0)\big]} = \overline{\{Kx \mid \|x - x_0\| \leq 1\}} \qquad (5.12.73)$$

Since $\|x_0\| > 1$, $0 \notin \overline{B_1(x_0)}$ and since $x \in B_1(x_0) \Rightarrow \|Kx - Kx_0\| \leq 1$ and $\|Kx_0\| > 1$, $0 \notin L$. L is clearly convex and, because K is a compact operator, L is also compact.

Define for each $T \in \mathcal{A}$

$$U_T = \{y \in X \mid \|Ty - x_0\| < 1\} \qquad (5.12.74)$$

We claim that

$$\bigcup_{T \in \mathcal{A}} U_T = X \setminus \{0\} \qquad (5.12.75)$$

for $\|x_0\| > 1$ implies $0 \notin U_T$ for any T. Given any $y \neq 0$, by transitivity and the proposition, there is $T \in \mathcal{A}$ with $\|Ty - x_0\| < 1$.

Since L is compact and $L \subset X \setminus \{0\}$, by compactness we can find $T_1, \dots, T_n \in \mathcal{A}$ so that

$$L \subset \bigcup_{k=1}^{n} U_{T_k} \qquad (5.12.76)$$

By Theorem 2.3.16, find continuous functions, $\{j_k\}_{k=1}^{n}$, on X so that $\sum_{k=1}^{n} j_k = 1$ on L and supp $j_k \subset U_{T_k}$.

Define Ψ and Φ on X to be

$$\Psi(x) = \sum_{k=1}^{n} j_k(x)T_k x \qquad (5.12.77)$$

and

$$\Phi(x) = \Psi(Kx) \qquad (5.12.78)$$

For any $x \in \overline{B_1(x_0)}$, $Kx \in L$, so $\sum_{k=1}^{n} j_k(Kx) = 1$. We have that for such x that

$$x_0 = \sum_{k=1}^{n} j_k(Kx)x_0 \qquad (5.12.79)$$

and thus, since $\operatorname{supp}(j_k) \subset U_{T_k}$, we have that for $x \in \overline{B_1(x_0)}$ that $\Phi(x) \in \overline{B_1(x_0)}$.

For $x \in \overline{B_1(x_0)}$, $\Phi(x)$ is a convex combination of points in the compact set $\bigcup_{k=1}^n T_k \big[L \cap \overline{U_{T_k}}\big] \equiv Q_1 \subset \overline{B_1(x_0)}$. If $Q = \operatorname{cch}(Q_1)$, Q is compact by Mazur's theorem (Theorem 5.3.17). Since $\overline{B_1(x_0)}$ is convex, $Q \subset \overline{B_1(x)}$. Thus Φ maps Q to itself, so by the Schauder–Tychonoff theorem, there is $x_1 \in Q$ with $\Phi(x_1) = x_1$, i.e.,

$$\left(\sum_{k=1}^n j_k(x_1)T_k\right)Kx_1 = x_1 \tag{5.12.80}$$

Since $\mathcal{A}$ is an algebra, $C = \sum_{k=1}^n j_k(x_1)T_k \in \mathcal{A}$. $\qquad \square$

Remark. Actually, one doesn't need the full Mazur theorem. U_{T_k} is convex, so $T_k\big[L \cap U_{T_k}\big]$ is a compact convex set. Thus, we only need the fact that if $C_1, \ldots, C_n$ are compact convex sets

$$Q = \{\sum_{k=1}^n \theta_k x_k \mid x_k \in C_k (\theta_1, \ldots, \theta_n) \in S_n\}$$

is compact and this follows from the fact that it is the image of $C_1 \times \cdots \times C_n \times S_n$ under the continuous map $F(x_1, \ldots, x_n, \theta) = \sum_{k=1}^n \theta_k x_k$.

Theorem 5.12.28 (Lomonosov's Theorem). *Let $A \in \mathcal{L}(X)$ be an operator on a Banach space X which is not a multiple of the identity, and suppose that there is a nonzero compact operator, K, commuting with A. Then A has a nontrivial hyperinvariant subspace.*

Proof. Let $\mathcal{A} = \{A\}'$ be the commutant of A. If A doesn't have any nontrivial hyperinvariant subspaces, then $\mathcal{A}$ is transitive, so, by Lomonosov's lemma, there is C in $\mathcal{A}$, so that $CK \equiv K_1$ has eigenvalue one. Let

$$Y_1 = \{x \mid K_1 x = x\} \tag{5.12.81}$$

Clearly $Y_1 \cap \overline{B_1(0)} \subset K_1\big((\overline{B_1(0)})\big)$ is compact since K_1 is compact and $Y_1 \cap \overline{B_1(0)}$ is closed. By Theorem 5.1.7, Y_1 is finite-dimensional.

Since A commutes with C and K, it commutes with K_1 and thus $A[Y_1] \subset Y_1$. It follows that A has an eigenvector $y_1 \in Y_1$, i.e., $Ay_1 = \lambda y_1$. Let

$$Y = \{x \in X \mid Ax = \lambda x\} \tag{5.12.82}$$

By the construction $Y \neq \{0\}$ and clearly Y is invariant for any $C \in \mathcal{A}$. Thus $Y = X$ but that would mean $A = \lambda \mathbb{1}$ violating the hypothesis. This contradiction shows that $\mathcal{A}$ has a nontrivial invariant subspace. $\qquad \square$

Corollary 5.12.29 (Weak Lomonosov Theorem). *Any compact operator on a Banach space has a nontrivial hyperinvariant subspace.*

Remarks. 1. Just take $A = K$ in the last theorem.

2. We state this separately because Section 3.3 of Part 4 will have a proof of this result that does not use any fixed point theorems.

Corollary 5.12.30 (Aronszajn–Smith Theorem). *Any compact operator has a nontrivial invariant subspace.*

Remarks. 1. This is separated to acknowledge its inventors.

2. The proof shows that this and the former result only require $P(K)$ be compact for some polynomial.

3. It is not hard to show (see Section 3.3 of Part 4) that if $\lambda \neq 0$ lies in the spectrum of K compact, then λ is an eigenvalue and $\{x \mid Kx = \lambda x\}$ is finite-dimensional, so a nontrivial invariant subspace. Thus, this result is of interest for operators with spectrum $\{0\}$ which are the same as those obeying $\|K^n\|^{1/n} \to 0$.

Notes and Historical Remarks.

> Compared to Brouwer's revolutionary methods, those of Hadamard were very traditional, but Hadamard's participation in the birth of Brouwer's ideas resembles that of a midwife more than that of a mere spectator.
> —H. Freudenthal [**327**]

There is an enormous literature on fixed points theorems. Among the texts and monographs are [**3, 137, 210, 353, 360, 445, 491, 766, 861, 922**]. As early as 1928, von Neumann [**961, 969**] applied fixed point theorems to game theory and mathematical economics. For recent work on the subject, see [**109, 160**].

The earliest fixed point theorems occurred as special cases in specific problems—in particular, Poincaré, whose work we'll discuss when we talk about the Brouwer theorem, and Picard (see below) were pioneers.

In 1890 (with a longer 1893 article), Picard [**722, 724**], essentially iterating the integral equation (5.12.5), proved existence and uniqueness of solutions of ODEs with Lipschitz coefficients. This was refined by Lindelöf [**592**], so the method is called either *Picard iteration* or *Picard–Lindelöf iteration.*

In 1903, Goursat [**355**] proved a version of the implicit function theorem using what he called an analog of Picard's iteration method. It was Banach [**49**] who abstracted these ideas and stated and proved the general contraction mapping theorem.

Theorem 5.12.24 is due to Peano with a wrong proof in 1886 [**704**] and a correct one in 1890 [**707**].

Gronwall's method goes back to [**372**] in 1919. An integral version is due to Bellman [**67**], so this is sometimes called the *Gronwall–Bellman inequality*.

Example 5.12.2 with the explicit elegant example of a norm-continuous map on the unit ball of ℓ^2 with no fixed points is essentially due to Kakutani [**470**] (he used $\frac{1}{2}(1 - \|x\|)$ where we use $(1 - \|x\|^2)^{1/2}$).

The implicit function theorem has versions in different classes of functions. Our method easily extends to C^k functions, $k \geq 1$, that is, C^k functions have C^k inverses or implicit functions. There are also results for real analytic and complex analytic functions, and the earliest results are in this case.

In 1669, Newton [**683**] already considered

$$f_a(x, y) = y^3 + a^2 y - 2a^3 + axy - x^3$$

where a is a nonzero parameter. For $x = 0$, there is a root at $y = a$. Note that $\frac{\partial f_a}{\partial y}(x = 0, y = a) = 4a^2 \neq 0$. Newton showed and found the formal series for $y(x)$ valued near $x = 0$. In 1770, Lagrange [**540**] found a more general result in the analytic case. It was Cauchy [**172**] in 1831 who stated a general abstract theorem.

That the theorem was a real variable (i.e., C^1) result was realized by Dini in 1878 [**245**]. As we noted above, Goursat [**355**] noted the connection to Picard iteration. Krantz–Park [**520**] have an entire book on the subject, including history and a variety of extensions.

The Markov–Kakutani theorem was proven first by Markov [**634**] in 1936 using Tychonoff's theorem. The proof we use is due to Kakutani [**466**] two years later.

The Banach limit of Example 5.12.16 is from Banach [**55**] who used the Hahn–Banach theorem (see Problem 10). As Problem 9 shows, more general groups than abelian have an analogous invariant mean. The study of groups with such an analog was initiated by von Neumann [**963**] who realized the relation to the Banach–Tarski paradox. Day [**219, 220**] introduced the name "amenable group" for such groups as a pun (between a mean and the naive meaning as "being agreeable"). See [**367, 725, 806**] for more on amenable groups.

The Brouwer fixed point theorem is named after his fundamental 1912 paper [**132**] which was a key milestone in the development of algebraic topology. Poincaré, in trying to to use qualitative methods in the study of ODEs, initiated the subject, which he dubbed "analysis situs" in a fundamental 1895 paper [**734**]. Even earlier, in 1886, Poincaré [**732**] had proven a theorem that we now know is equivalent to the Brouwer theorem.

In 1904, Bohl [**105**] proved the Brouwer theorem for $n = 3$. The general n case is in Brouwer's 1912 paper. It is also in a 1910 paper of Hadamard [**379**], but this paper resulted from extensive correspondence between Brouwer and Hadamard. For more on the history, see [**243, 327, 695**].

Our proof of the Brouwer theorem seems to have first appeared explicitly in Kannai [**476**], although it is close in spirit to Hadamard's original argument. For two other analytic proofs of the Brouwer theorem, see Milnor [**657**] (also Rogers [**798**]) and Dunford–Schwartz [**262**]. We discuss the topological view below.

The extension of the theorem to compact subsets of Banach spaces is due to Schauder [**815**] in 1930 who conjectured it for weak topologies, and the general case to Tychonoff [**941**].

Underlying the Brouwer theorem is the fundamental topology of the sphere. As we've seen, the Brouwer theorem is equivalent to B^n not being a retract of the sphere, S^{n-1}. If such a retract, $f\colon B^n \to S^{n-1}$, exists, then $\gamma_r\colon S^{n-1} \to S^{n-1}$, defined for $0 \le r \le 1$ by $\gamma_r(w) = f(rw)$, is a homotopy of the identity map (for $r = 1$) and the trivial map. Such a homotopy would imply all the homology and homotopy groups of S^{n-1} are trivial, but $\pi_{n-1}(S^{n-1}) = H^{n-1}(S^{n-1}) = \mathbb{Z}$. In particular, the Brouwer theorem for $n = 2$ is a consequence of the covering space notions discussed in Section 1.7 of Part 2A; see Hatcher [**400**] for the basics of homology and homotopy.

The formal definition and the basic theory of retracts is due to Karol Borsuk (1905–82) in his 1930 thesis and 1931 paper [**116**]. The actual name was suggested by this thesis advisor, Stefan Mazurkiewicz (1888–1945).

A particular way of seeing the identity map of S^{n-1} to itself is nontrivial is via degree theory—any $g\colon S^{n-1} \to S^{n-1}$ has a degree in $\mathbb{Z}$, g is homotopy invariant, $\det(\mathrm{id}) = 1$, and $\deg(\text{trivial map}) = 0$. In some sense, the degree for the sphere was defined by Kronecker in 1869 [**529**] and is sometimes called the *Kronecker index*. Hadamard [**379**] refers to the Kronecker index in the title of his work.

Infinite-dimensional degree theory was developed in 1934 by Leray and Schauder [**572**] (see also Leray [**570, 571**]) and is called *Leray–Schauder degree theory* (see Cronin [**210**] for more on the theory).

That compact operators on Banach spaces have invariant subspaces is a 1954 result of Aronszajn–Smith [**36**] who remark that von Neumann informed them that he had a proof of the Hilbert space case of this since the 1930's but never published it. They conjectured that if $P(K)$ was compact for some polynomial, K, there is an invariant subspace and this was proven by Bernstein–Robinson [**80**].

The 1973 paper of Lomonosov [**601**] changed the landscape because it simply and elegantly obtained much stronger results. Because it was in Russian, the expository paper of Pearcy–Shields [**708**], which we follow, was widely used in the US.

The more general invariant subspace problem was open for many years until Enflo [**279**] found an example of an operator on a certain Banach space with no invariant subspaces. Read [**761, 762**] even found examples on ℓ^1. You may wonder why a 1987 paper of Enflo [**278**] is mentioned as having the first example when Read's paper is from 1985. In fact, Enflo announced and sketched his result in 1976 but there were some gaps which took over ten years to fill. Read used some of Enflo's ideas.

In Section 3.4 of Part 4, we use invariant subspaces in the study of compact operators.

Problems

1. Let G obey (5.12.11) and (5.12.12). For any R_0, prove there is a t_0 so if $s_0 \leq T - t_0$ and f, g solve (5.12.3) with $\|f(s)\| \leq R_0$, $\|g(s)\| \leq R_0$ for $s_0 \leq s \leq s_0 + t_0$ and $f(s_0) = g(s_0)$, then $f(s) = g(s)$ on $[s_0, s_0 + t_0]$.

2. Using Problem 1, prove that if (5.12.3)/(5.12.4) has a solution on $[0, T_0]$, then there is no other solution continuous on all of $[0, T_0]$. (*Hint*: Let $R_0 = \sup_{0 \leq s \leq T_0}(|f(s)| + |g(s)|)$ for the given solution and another putative solution.)

3. This will prove Theorem 5.12.8. X is a Banach space.

   (a) If f is a C^1 X-valued function, prove that for any $s > s_0$,

   $$\|f(s)\| \leq \|f(s_0)\| + \int_{s_0}^{s} \left\|\frac{df}{ds}\right\| ds \qquad (5.12.83)$$

   (b) If $\|\frac{df}{ds}(s)\| \leq C\|f(s)\|$, by iterating (5.12.83), prove that

   $$\|f(s)\| \leq \|f(s_0)\| \exp(C(s - s_0)) \qquad (5.12.84)$$

   (c) Using Problem 1, show that if $f(s)$ solves (5.12.3) on $(0, T_0)$ and $\sup_{0 \leq s \leq T_0}\|f(s)\| < \infty$, then f can be extended past T_0. So if $(0, T_0)$ is the maximal interval for a solution, we must have $\limsup_{s \uparrow T_0}\|f(s)\| = \infty$.

   (d) Prove Theorem 5.12.8.

4. Let X be a Banach space and $\mathbb{GL}(X) = \{A \in \mathcal{L}(X) \mid A \text{ is invertible}\}$. Prove that $\mathbb{GL}(X)$ is open (in the norm topology) and $A \mapsto A^{-1}$ is continuous. (*Hint*: Write $A + \delta A = A(1 + A^{-1}\delta A)^{-1}$ if $A \in \mathcal{L}(X)$ and use a geometric series for $(1 + B)^{-1}$.)

5. If $X = Y \oplus Z$, write $E = \left(\begin{smallmatrix} A & B \\ C & D \end{smallmatrix}\right)$ for $E \in \mathcal{L}(X)$, with $A \in \mathcal{L}(Y)$, $B \in$ BLT(Z,Y), etc. If $B \in \mathcal{L}(Z)$ is invertible, prove that for any A, $\left(\begin{smallmatrix} 1 & 0 \\ A & B \end{smallmatrix}\right)$ is invertible with $\left(\begin{smallmatrix} 1 & 0 \\ A & B \end{smallmatrix}\right)^{-1} = \left(\begin{smallmatrix} 1 & 0 \\ -AB^{-1} & B^{-1} \end{smallmatrix}\right)$.

6. Prove (5.12.48). (*Hint*: Use Problem 5.)

7. Prove that if one knows the implicit function theorem, one can deduce the inverse mapping theorem.

   Remark. We went the other way, which was harder.

8. Prove the implicit function theorem directly using the contraction mapping theorem.

9. (a) Let G be a group so that there is a normal subgroup N with N and G/N both abelian (a nonabelian example is the set of maps $\tau_{a,b}(x) = ax + b$, $a \in (0, \infty)$, $b \in \mathbb{R}$ of $\mathbb{R}$ to $\mathbb{R}$). Suppose that for each $g \in G$, there is a continuous affine map of K, a compact convex set of an lcs, to itself so that $\tau_{gh} = \tau_g \tau_h$. Prove there is $x \in K$ so $\tau_g(x) = x$ for all g. (*Hint*: Consider first $K_N = \{x \mid \tau_n(x) = x$ for all $n \in N\}$.)

   (b) A group is called *solvable* if there exist subgroups $G \supset N_1 \supset N_2 \supset \cdots \supset N_k = \{0\}$ so that N_1 is normal in G and N_{j+1} is normal in N_j and so that $G/N_1, N_1/N_2, \ldots, N_k$ are all abelian. Extend (a) to the case of solvable groups.

10. This problem will follow Banach [**55**] in proving the existence of a Banach limit (Example 5.12.16).

    (a) For $a \in \ell^\infty$, prove that $\|a\|_\infty \geq \liminf_{N \to \infty} \frac{1}{N} |\sum_{j=1}^N a_j|$.

    (b) Let $Y = \{a - T(a) + c(1, 1, \ldots) \mid T$ given by (5.12.57), $a \in \ell^\infty, c \in \mathbb{C}\}$. Prove that $\|a - T(a) - c(1, 1, \ldots)\|_\infty \geq |c|$. (*Hint*: Part (a).)

    (c) Define ℓ on Y by $\ell(a - T(a) - c(1, 1, \ldots)) = c$. Prove that ℓ has a continuous extension L to ℓ^∞ that obeys $L(Ta) = L(a)$ and $L((1, 1, \ldots)) = 1$ and $L(\bar{a}) = \overline{L(a)}$.

    Remark. The next problem shows $a_j \geq 0$ for all $j \Rightarrow L(a) \geq 0$.

11. Let $L \colon \ell^\infty \to \mathbb{C}$ obey $L(Ta) = a$ (T given by (5.12.57)), $L((1, 1, \ldots)) = 1$, $L(\bar{a}) = \overline{L(a)}$, and $\|L(a)\| \leq c\|a\|_\infty$.

    (a) Prove $L(\delta_j) = 0$ for any j where $(\delta_j)_k = \delta_{jk}$. (*Hint*: Look at $L(\frac{1}{n} \sum_{\ell=0}^{n-1} T^\ell \delta_j.)$

    (b) For a in ℓ^∞ is real, prove $\liminf a_n \leq \ell(a) \leq \limsup a_n$.

    (c) If $\lim a_n = \alpha$, prove that $\ell(a) = \alpha$.

    (d) Prove that $a \geq 0 \Rightarrow \ell(a) \geq 0$.

    (e) Prove that $|\ell(a)| \leq \|a\|_\infty$.

12. (a) Let $a_n = e^{ink}$ for some $k \notin \mathbb{Z}$. If L is a Banach limit, prove that $L(a) = 0$.

(b) If a_n is almost periodic, prove that $L(a) = \lim_{n\to\infty} \frac{1}{n} \sum_{j=1}^{n} a_j$.

Remark. See Section 6.6 of Part 4 for discussion of almost periodic functions.

13. Let $a \in \ell^\infty$. We say that a_n almost converges to α if uniformly in n, we have that $\lim_{p\to\infty} \frac{1}{p} \sum_{j=n}^{n+p-1} a_j = \alpha$. Prove that if L is a Banach limit and a_n almost converges to α, then $L(a) = \alpha$.

Remark. It is a theorem of Lorentz [**604**] (see also Bennet–Kalton [**69**]) that if $a \in \ell^\infty$ has $L(a) = \alpha$ for all Banach limits, then a almost converges to α.

14. This problem will prove that full Schauder–Tychonoff theorem (Theorem 5.12.18). K is a compact convex subset of an lcs, X. Let $T_\infty \colon K \to K$ be continuous.

(a) Let ℓ, $\{\ell_n\}_{n=1}^\infty$ be in X^*. We say $\{\ell_n\}_{n=1}^\infty$ T-determine ℓ on K if $x, y \in X \,\&\, \forall n\, \ell(x) = \ell_n(y) \Rightarrow \ell(Tx) = \ell(Ty)$. (*Hint:* $\ell(T\cdot)$ is uniformly continuous (see Problem 12 of Section 5.1) and neighborhoods are determined by finitely many ℓ_j's.)

(b) Given any ℓ, prove that there exists $\{\ell_n\}_{n=2}^\infty$ and $\ell_1 = \ell$ so that any $\{\ell_n\}_{n=1}^\infty$ T-determines ℓ_j on K for each j.

(c) Given a family $\{\ell_n\}_{n=1}^\infty$ as in (b), with all $\ell_j \neq 0$, define $\mathcal{L} \colon K \to H$, the Hilbert cube, by

$$\mathcal{L}(x) = \frac{1}{2}\left(1 + \frac{\ell_j(x)}{\sup_{y\in K}|\ell_j(y)|}\right)$$

Prove there is a continuous map $\mathcal{T} \colon H \to H$ as $\mathcal{L}(Tx) = \mathcal{T}(\mathcal{L}(x))$.

(d) Conclude $\{x \mid \mathcal{L}(Tx) = \mathcal{L}(x)\}$ is nonempty.

(e) Prove there is $x \in K$ with $Tx = x$. (*Hint:* Finite intersection property on $\{x \mid \ell_j(Tx) = \ell_j(x)$ for $\ell_1, \dots, \ell_n \in X^*\}$.)

15. Let Q be a closed convex subset of a Hilbert space, $\mathcal{H}$. Let $x, y \in \mathcal{H}$ and x_1, y_1 the points in Q closest to x and y, respectively.

(a) Prove that

$$\tfrac{1}{4}\|x_1 - y_1\|^2 \leq \tfrac{1}{2}\left(-\|x - y_1\|^2 + (\|y - y_1\| + \|x - y\|)^2\right)$$

(*Hint:* (3.2.3).)

(b) Prove that $\|y - y_1\| \leq \|x - x_1\| + \|x - y\|$.

(c) Prove that as $x \to y$, we have $x_1 \to y_1$, that is, the map f of Proposition 5.12.23 is continuous.

16. Show that the map, f, of the proof of Proposition 5.12.25(b) is continuous.

Chapter 6

Tempered Distributions and the Fourier Transform

Distribution theory was one of the two great revolutions in mathematical analysis in the 20th century. It can be thought of as the completion of differential calculus, just as the other great revolution, measure theory (or Lebesgue integration theory), can be thought of as the completion of integral calculus. There are many parallels between the two revolutions. Both were created by young, highly individualistic French mathematicians (Henri Lebesgue and Laurent Schwartz). Both were rapidly assimilated by the mathematical community, and opened up new worlds of mathematical development. Both forced a complete rethinking of all mathematical analysis that had come before, and basically altered the nature of the questions that mathematical analysts asked. (This is the reason I feel justified in using the word 'revolution' to describe them.)

—*R. S. Strichartz* [**889**]

Big Notions and Theorems: Countably Normed Space, Fréchet Space, Equivalent Norms, Induced metric, $C^\infty(\partial\mathbb{D})$, $\mathcal{S}(\mathbb{R}^\nu)$, Tempered Distributions, Operations on Distributions, Convolution, Periodic Distributions, Hermite Polynomials, Harmonic Oscillator Basis, Completeness of HO Basis, Schwartz Kernel Theorem, Fourier Transform, Inverse Fourier Transform, Fourier Inversion Theorem, Plancherel Theorem, Riemann–Lebesgue Lemma, Riesz–Thorin Theorem, Hausdorff–Young Inequality, Young's Inequality, Bochner's Theorem, Bochner–Schwartz Theorem, Positive Definite Function, Poisson Summation Formula, Fourier Transforms of Inverse Powers, Uniqueness of Equilibrium Measure, Hyperbolic PDE, Wave Equation, Parabolic PDE, Heat Equation, Elliptic PDE, Poisson Equation, Helmholtz Equation, Malgrange–Ehrenpreis Theorem

In this chapter, one of the two big themes will be the theory of tempered distributions. The paradigm is the *delta function* (aka *Dirac delta function*), $\delta(x)$, a "function" on $\mathbb{R}$ so that

$$\int_{-\infty}^{\infty} f(x)\delta(x)\,dx = f(0) \tag{6.0.1}$$

Clearly, there is no L^1 function obeying (6.0.1) since integrals of L^1 functions don't change if their values change at a single point. At some intuitive level, δ is a function which is zero at all $x \neq 0$ and really, really infinite at $x = 0$. In fact, $\delta(x)$ is, at best, poetry—but $\delta(x)\,dx$ is just a point measure, that is, the Baire measure μ on $\mathbb{R}$ which obeys

$$\mu(A) = \begin{cases} 1 & \text{if } 0 \in A \\ 0 & \text{if } 0 \neq A \end{cases} \tag{6.0.2}$$

has $\int f(x)\,d\mu(x) = f(0)$ for any $f \in C_\infty(\mathbb{R})$. Thus, the Dirac delta function is a measure, a subject we've already studied in Chapter 4. The main lesson that we take from that study is that we should think of distributions like $\delta(x)$ as continuous linear functionals on some TVS of functions.

The new twist in this setting is that we want to be able to take derivatives of distributions. $\delta(x)$ is already so singular, what could we mean by $\delta'(x)$? Integration by parts is nice, so we might hope $\int_{-\infty}^{\infty} f(x)\delta'(x)\,dx = -\int_{-\infty}^{\infty} f'(x)\delta(x)\,dx$. Thus, just as (6.0.1) *defines* δ, we define δ' by

$$\int_{-\infty}^{\infty} f(x)\delta'(x)\,dx = -f'(0) \tag{6.0.3}$$

So if we want to define δ' as a linear functional, we need the functions in our space to be C^1. To take arbitrarily many derivatives, we need C^∞ functions, and so an infinite number of seminorms $\{\|f^{(n)}\|_\infty\}_{n=0}^{\infty}$ which, in the case of functions on $\partial\mathbb{D}$, will be the right function space to take. Thus, we'll need to consider TVS whose topologies are given by a countable family of seminorms $\|\cdot\|_n$ with the condition

$$\|f\|_n = 0 \quad \text{for all } n \Rightarrow f = 0 \tag{6.0.4}$$

This condition is needed to make the topology a Hausdorff topology. The presentation of abstract countably normed spaces will be the subject of Section 6.1, where a main general result will be that such spaces are precisely the metrizable LCS.

When the underlying set on which the functions live is unbounded like $\mathbb{R}$, we'll need to consider what kind of behavior to allow at infinity. To understand the choice we'll make, we need to introduce the second main theme of this chapter: the Fourier transform given (in one dimension) by

$$\widehat{f}(k) = (2\pi)^{-1/2} \int_{-\infty}^{\infty} e^{-ikx} f(x) \, dx \qquad (6.0.5)$$

We suppose for now that all functions and derivatives go to zero so fast that there are no boundary terms at infinity when we integrate by parts. In particular, if we integrate by parts and use $-\frac{d}{dx}(e^{-ikx}) = ike^{-ikx}$, we see that

$$\widehat{f'}(k) = ik\widehat{f}(k) \qquad (6.0.6)$$

Thus, if f is C^∞ and all derivatives decay fast enough, then $|k|^n \widehat{f}(k)$ will be bounded for all n. If we hope for a class of functions left invariant by $\widehat{}$, we'll want the original functions to obey $|x|^n f(x)$ bounded. Since our class of functions needs to be invariant under derivative, we'll define $\mathcal{S}(\mathbb{R})$ to be those C^∞ functions on $\mathbb{R}$ with $\|x^n f^{(m)}\|_\infty < \infty$ for all $n, m = 0, 1, \ldots$. One might consider using $\|\cdot\|_1$ or $\|\cdot\|_2$ rather than $\|\cdot\|_\infty$, but we'll see (Theorem 6.1.6) that it doesn't matter—all choices lead to the same topology. In Section 6.9 of Part 4, we'll discuss the Fourier transform on a general locally compact abelian group and so present a third approach to the Fourier inversion and Plancherel theorems to the two we present here in Sections 6.2 and 6.5. This approach has Bochner's theorem, a result discussed in Section 6.6 as its central tool.

With this background, we can describe the chapter in detail. Section 6.1 will discuss abstract countably normed spaces using $C^\infty(\partial\mathbb{D})$ and $\mathcal{S}(\mathbb{R}^\nu)$ as examples. Section 6.2 will discuss $\mathcal{S}(\mathbb{R}^\nu)$, its dual space, $\mathcal{S}'(\mathbb{R}^\nu)$, and the general notion of extending operations from $\mathcal{S}$ to $\mathcal{S}'$. Section 6.3 will further illustrate the theory of duals by looking at the dual of $C^\infty(\partial\mathbb{D})$, which we'll see is associated to periodic distributions. As a preliminary to the study of Fourier transforms, Section 6.4 will discuss Hermite expansions in $\mathcal{S}$, and Section 6.5 will bear the fruit with proofs of the Fourier inversion and Plancherel theorems in a few lines. Section 6.6 and Bonus Section 6.7 will study the Fourier transform further, notably the Poisson summation formula in Section 6.6. As an application, in Section 6.8, we'll continue the study of potential theoretic equilibrium measures begun in Section 5.8 by proving they are unique. The chapter ends with a first glimpse of the relation of Fourier transforms and partial differential equations. Chapter 4 of Part 3 continues the study of Fourier transforms. It could be called "More Fourier Transforms" (but is called "Phase Space Analysis"). Included are pseudodifferential operators and an introduction to wavelets.

6.1. Countably Normed and Fréchet Spaces

Definition. A *countably normed space* (CNS) is a vector space, X, over $\mathbb{K}$ ($= \mathbb{R}$ or $\mathbb{C}$) together with a countable family $\{\rho_n\}_{n=1}^{\infty}$ of seminorms obeying

$$\rho_n(x) = 0 \qquad \text{for } n = 1, 2, \dots \quad \Rightarrow x = 0 \tag{6.1.1}$$

A more accurate name might be "nondegenerate countably seminormed space" but since (6.1.1) is "norm-like," we use this terminology. In most cases of interest, one can choose all the ρ_n's to be norms, but, for example, if $X = \ell^2$ and $\rho_n(x) = |x_n|$, one cannot choose equivalent norms—every continuous seminorm is only a seminorm. Our goal in this section is to first show the CNS are precisely the metrizable LCS, then define Fréchet spaces (CNS which are complete in the associated metric), and finally define the notion of equivalent seminorms and study some important examples.

As we saw in Section 5.7, a family of seminorms obeying (6.1.1) defines a topology in which the space is an LCS. In this case, it is given by a metric.

Definition. The *Fréchet metric* defined by a family of seminorms is given by

$$d(x, y) = \sum_{n=1}^{\infty} \min(2^{-n}, \rho_n(x - y)) \tag{6.1.2}$$

Remark. There are many equivalent metrics given by other formulae; see the Notes.

Notice that since the min in the sum is bounded by 2^{-n}, the sum is always convergent and $d(x, y) \leq 1$ for all x, y (showing d has no chance to be a norm).

Theorem 6.1.1. *d is a metric. Convergence in the metric is equivalent to convergence in the topology defined by $\{\rho_n\}_{n=1}^{\infty}$.*

Proof. (6.1.1) implies $d(x, y) = 0 \Leftrightarrow \forall n, \rho_n(x - y) = 0 \Leftrightarrow x - y = 0$, so d has a strong zero property. For $a, b, c \geq 0$,

$$\min(a, b + c) \leq \min(a, b) + \min(a, c)$$

which implies

$$\rho(x, y) \leq \rho(x, z) + p(z, y)$$

since $\rho_n(x - y) \leq \rho_n(x - z) + \rho_n(z - y)$.

It is easy to see that $d(x_m, x_\infty) \to 0 \Leftrightarrow \forall n, \rho_n(x_m, x_\infty) \to 0$. $\qquad\square$

The point is that there is a converse:

Theorem 6.1.2. *Let X be a metrizable LCS. Then there is a countable set of seminorms obeying (6.1.1) which generate the topology of X.*

Proof. By the construction in Theorem 5.7.5, if $\mathcal{B}$ is a neighborhood basis of 0 of open, convex, balanced sets, then the gauges $\{\rho_B\}_{B \in \mathcal{B}}$ are a family of seminorms generating the topology. So it suffices to show that there is such a neighborhood basis which is countable (since (6.1.1) then follows from the Hausdorff nature of the topology).

Let $\mathcal{B}_0$ be a neighborhood basis of 0 of open, convex, balanced sets. If d is a metric which generates the topology, let

$$\mathcal{B}_1 = \left\{ C_n \equiv \left\{ x \;\middle|\; \rho(x,0) < \frac{1}{n} \right\} \right\} \tag{6.1.3}$$

For each $C_n \in \mathcal{B}_1$, pick $B_n \in \mathcal{B}$, so $B_n \subset C_n$. Then $\{B_n\}$ is a countable neighborhood basis of 0 of X consisting of open, convex, balanced sets. $\quad\square$

We have thus proven that the CNS are precisely the metrizable LCS.

Definition. A *Fréchet space* is a CNS which is complete in the induced metric.

In (5.7.18)/(5.7.19), we defined the notion of equivalent sets of seminorms—and that notion extends to the CNS case. Recall that equivalent sets of seminorms generate the same topology. We close this section with three key examples (the first two are the subjects of Sections 6.2 and 6.3), present classes of equivalent seminorms, and prove they are Fréchet spaces. Later (in Sections 6.2, 6.3, and 6.4), we'll have even more equivalent seminorms.

Example 6.1.3 (Periodic C^∞ functions). Let C_{per}^∞ be the C^∞ functions on $\mathbb{R}$ which are 1-periodic, that is,

$$f(x + n) = f(x) \tag{6.1.4}$$

for all $n \in \mathbb{Z}$ and $x \in \mathbb{R}$. It then follows for each k that $\frac{d^k f}{dx^k}$ is periodic. If $g \in C^\infty(\partial\mathbb{D})$ and $f(x) = g(e^{2\pi i x})$, then $f \in C_{\mathrm{per}}^\infty$ and it is easy to see that this sets up a one-one correspondence between $C^\infty(\partial\mathbb{D})$ and C_{per}^∞.

If $1 \le p \le \infty$, $k = 0, 1, 2, \ldots$, and $f \in C_{\mathrm{per}}^\infty$, define

$$\|f\|_{k,p} = \left(\int_0^1 \left| \frac{d^k f}{dx^k} \right|^p dx \right)^{1/p} \tag{6.1.5}$$

(for $p = \infty$, we use $\sup_{0 \le x \le 1} \left| \frac{d^k f}{dx^k} \right|$ rather than (6.1.5)).

We claim for any two p's, $\{\|\cdot\|_{k,p}\}_{k=0}^\infty$ are equivalent families of seminorms. We use any of these families to make C_{per}^∞ into a CNS (since $\|f\|_{k=0,p} = 0 \Rightarrow f = 0$). We use $\|\cdot\|_p$ for $\|\cdot\|_{k=0,p}$.

To see the claim, note that for any g,

$$\|g\|_1 \le \|g\|_p \le \|g\|_\infty \tag{6.1.6}$$

If we prove

$$\|g\|_\infty \le \|g\|_1 + \|g'\|_1 \tag{6.1.7}$$

then it is easy to see that our claim of equivalent norms is true.

Suppose first $\int_0^1 g(x)\,dx = 0$. Then $g(y) = 0$ for some y, and thus, $|g(x)| \le \int_x^y |g'(z)|\,dz \le \|g'\|_1$. Since $g - \int_0^1 g(y)\,dy$ has zero integral and the same derivative as g, we conclude

$$\left\| g - \int_0^1 g(y)\,dy \right\|_\infty \le \|g'\|_1 \tag{6.1.8}$$

which implies (6.1.7).   □

We summarize and extend the example in

Theorem 6.1.4. *The families of seminorms $\{\|\ \|_{k,p}\}_{k=0}^\infty$ on C^∞_{per} are equivalent as p runs from 1 to ∞. They make C^∞_{per} into a Fréchet space. C^∞_{per} is not a Banach space, that is, its topology cannot be given by a single norm.*

Proof. We have shown equivalence above. If f_n is Cauchy in the metric d of (6.1.2) with $\rho_n = \|\cdot\|_{n,\infty}$, then $f_n^{(k)}$ is Cauchy in $\|\cdot\|_\infty$, so there exist continuous functions, g_k, so

$$\|f_n^{(k)} - g_k\|_\infty \to 0 \tag{6.1.9}$$

Taking limits in

$$f_n^{(k)}(y) - f_n^{(k)}(x) = \int_x^y f_n^{(k+1)}(z)\,dz \tag{6.1.10}$$

we see

$$g_k(x) - g_k(y) = \int_x^y g_{k+1}(z)\,dz \tag{6.1.11}$$

Since g_{k+1} is continuous, we conclude g_k is C^1 and $\frac{dg_k}{dx} = g_{k+1}$, so if set $f_\infty \equiv g_0$, we have that f_∞ is C^∞ and $g_k = \frac{d^k f_\infty}{dx_k}$. By (6.1.9), $f_n \to f_\infty$ in each $\|\ \|_{k,\infty}$ and so in d. Thus C^∞_{per} is complete.

Suppose that there is a single norm $\|\cdot\|$ equivalent to $\{\|\cdot\|_{k,\infty}\}_{k=0}^\infty$. Then for some C and L,

$$\|f\| \le C \sum_{\ell=0}^{L} \|f\|_{\ell,\infty} \tag{6.1.12}$$

Also, for some D,

$$\|f\|_{L+1,\infty} \le D\,\|f\| \tag{6.1.13}$$

so

$$\|f\|_{L+1,\infty} \le CD \sum_{\ell=0}^{L} \|f\|_{\ell,\infty} \tag{6.1.14}$$

Let
$$f_n(x) = \exp(2\pi i n x) \tag{6.1.15}$$

Then
$$\|f_n\|_{\ell,\infty} = (2\pi n)^\ell \tag{6.1.16}$$

so (6.1.15) implies for each $n = 1, 2, \ldots$,
$$(n)^{L+1} \le CDLn^L \tag{6.1.17}$$

which fails once $n > CDL$. Thus, C_{per}^∞ does not have a topology given by a single norm. □

Example 6.1.5 (Schwartz Space, $\mathcal{S}(\mathbb{R}^\nu)$). A *multi-index*, $\alpha \in \mathcal{I}_\nu$, is a ν-tuple $(\alpha_1, \ldots, \alpha_\nu)$ of nonnegative integers. $|\alpha| = \sum_{j=1}^\nu |\alpha_j|$. We set

$$x^\alpha = x_1^{\alpha_1} \ldots x_\nu^{\alpha_\nu} \tag{6.1.18}$$

$$D^\alpha = \frac{\partial^{|\alpha|}}{\partial x_1^{\alpha_1} \partial x_2^{\alpha_2} \ldots \partial x_\nu^{\alpha_\nu}} \tag{6.1.19}$$

Schwartz space is the set of C^∞ functions on $\mathbb{R}^\nu$ for which every derivative $D^\alpha f$ obeys

$$\lim_{|x| \to \infty} (1 + |x|)^\ell |D^\alpha f(x)| \to 0 \tag{6.1.20}$$

for each fixed $\ell = 0, 1, \ldots$. We define for $\alpha, \beta \in \mathcal{I}_\nu$, $p \in [1, \infty]$,

$$\|f\|_{\alpha,\beta,p} = \|x^\alpha D^\beta f\|_p \tag{6.1.21}$$

where $\|\cdot\|_p$ means $L^p(\mathbb{R}^\nu, d^\nu x)$ norm. Since (6.1.20) holds, it is easy to see if $f \in \mathcal{S}$, $x^\alpha D^\beta f \in L^p$ for all $p \in [1, \infty]$. Thus, the norms are finite. We also define

$$\|f\|_{t;\alpha,\beta,p} = \|D^\beta(x^\alpha f)\|_p \tag{6.1.22}$$
□

Theorem 6.1.6. $\{\|f\|_{\alpha,\beta,p}\}_{\alpha,\beta \in \mathcal{I}_\nu}$ *and* $\{\|f\|_{t;\alpha,\beta,p}\}_{\alpha,\beta \in \mathcal{I}_\nu}$ *are equivalent sets of norms as p runs from 1 to ∞ (any two p's and either t or no t for each). They make $\mathcal{S}$ into a Fréchet space. $\mathcal{S}$ is not a Banach space.*

Proof. Neither (6.1.6) nor (6.1.7) holds, but because
$$(1 + x^2)^{-\nu} \in L^1(\mathbb{R}^\nu, d^\nu x) \tag{6.1.23}$$

there are replacements.

By (6.1.23), one sees that for any $1 \le p \le q \le \infty$,
$$\|f\|_p \le C(p, q)\|(1 + x^2)^\nu f\|_q \tag{6.1.24}$$

Moreover, we have
$$|f(x_1, \ldots, x_\nu)| \le \int_{x_1}^\infty \left| \frac{\partial f}{\partial x_1}(y, x_2, \ldots) \right| dx_1 \tag{6.1.25}$$

so iterating,

$$\|f\|_\infty \le \|D^{(1,1,\dots,1)}f\|_1 \qquad (6.1.26)$$

With these two inequalities and repeated use of $[\frac{\partial}{\partial x_j}, x_i] = \delta_{ij}$, one sees that all the stated seminorms are equivalent.

If f_n is Cauchy in all $\|\cdot\|_{\alpha,\beta,\infty}$, it is immediate that $x^\alpha D^\beta f_n \to g_{\alpha,\beta}$ uniformly as $n \to \infty$ for some $g_{\alpha,\beta} \in C(\mathbb{R}^\nu)$. Thus, $x^\gamma g_{\alpha,\beta} = g_{\alpha+\gamma,\beta}$, so $(1+|x|)^\nu x^\alpha D^\beta f_n \to (1+|x|^\nu)g_{\alpha,\beta}$ in $\|\cdot\|_\infty$, from which it follows that one can take limits of ($\delta_\ell = (0,\dots,1,\dots,0)$ with 1 in the ℓ-th place)

$$(D^\beta f)(x) = \int_{-\infty}^0 (D^{\beta+\delta_\ell}f)(x+y\delta_\ell)\,dy$$

and so show that $g_{\alpha,\beta}$ is C^1 with derivative $g_{\alpha,\beta+\delta_\ell}$. Thus, $g_0 \equiv f_\infty$ is C^∞ and $x^\alpha D^\beta f_\infty \in L^\infty$, so $f_\infty \in \mathcal{S}$ and is the limit of f_n in $\mathcal{S}$. Thus, $\mathcal{S}$ is a Fréchet space.

The proof that $\mathcal{S}$ is not a Banach space is similar to the case for C^∞_{per}. □

Example 6.1.7 ($\mathfrak{A}(\Omega)$). This uses notions and results from Part 2A. Let Ω be an open connected subset of $\mathbb{C}$ and $\mathfrak{A}(\Omega)$, the set of all functions analytic in Ω. Let $K_n \subset K_{n+1}^{\mathrm{int}} \subset \Omega$ with $\bigcup K_n = \Omega$, where K_n is compact and $\|f\|_{K_n} \equiv \sup_{z\in K_n}|f(z)|$. Different choices of K_n yield equivalent norms and, by the Weierstrass convergence theorem (Theorem 3.1.5 of Part 2A), $\mathfrak{A}(\Omega)$ is a Fréchet space; see Section 6.1 of Part 2A. □

Notes and Historical Remarks.

> The audacity deployed and the effort of abstraction accomplished by Fréchet is, it seems to me, without precedent in all that has been done since the work of Galois.
>
> —*Jacques Hadamard*[1]

The name Fréchet metric for (6.1.2) is based on the fact that already in his 1906 thesis [**315**], which introduced metric spaces, Fréchet discussed a metric on $\mathbb{R}^\infty$ (i.e., sequences of reals)

$$d(x,y) = \sum_{n=1}^\infty \frac{1}{n!}\frac{|x_n - y_n|}{1+|x_n - y_n|} \qquad (6.1.27)$$

This has the same form as (6.1.2), $\frac{1}{n!}\frac{c}{1+c}$ and $\min(2^{-n}, c)$ have the three basic properties that they go to zero as $c \to 0$, obey a triangle inequality, and they have summable sups. Any similar function, for example, $[\sum_{n=1}^\infty n^{-2}(\rho_n(x-y)/1+\rho_n(x-y))^2]^{1/2}$ will serve as a metric.

---

[1](Fréchet's teacher) in a letter, written in 1933 (almost thirty years after Fréchet's thesis), supporting Fréchet's election to the French Academy (Julia got the slot, caused by the death of Painlevé; in the end, Fréchet was only elected in 1956 at age 77), quoted (my translation to English) in Taylor [**908**].

In terms of the precise definition, the name Fréchet space for complete metrizable lcs is less justified. In 1926, Fréchet [**321**] did consider spaces which had a translation invariant metric, but he required neither completeness nor local convexity (the latter wasn't even defined until ten years later). Banach, in his book [**55**], added completeness but not local convexity, and called them (F) spaces. The notion we now call Fréchet space appeared first in 1948 in a paper of Mazur–Orlicz [**643**]. Only in their 1953 book on topological vector spaces [**121**] did Bourbaki call what we call Fréchet space by that name. As one of the founding members of Bourbaki explained:

> Fréchet was always striving for generality without caring for applications, and this was thoroughly repugnant to the Bourbaki spirit, where no notion could be accepted if we could not be convinced that it was useful in some classical problem (although many readers, for lack of background, did not realize it). Nevertheless, we thought that Fréchet's name deserved to be attached to those spaces, not so much for his 1926 paper, but because in his 1906 thesis.
>
> —*Dieudonné*, letter to Taylor quoted in [**910**]

Maurice Fréchet (1878–1973) was a French mathematician born in the provinces. After his family moved to Paris, he had the good fortune to attend a lycée where, at age 12, he had as a teacher Jacques Hadamard who had just completed his doctoral studies. Hadamard recognized Fréchet's talent and was a life-long mentor and supporter. After his 1906 thesis, Fréchet spent four years teaching in lycée, ten years at the University of Poitiers (during part of the time, he served in the army during the First World War as an interpreter and liaison to the British), and eight years in Strasbourg, after which he returned to Paris.

These days his best-known work is probably on derivatives in infinite-dimensional spaces (see Section 5.1) but, as we've seen, he is also a co-discoverer of the Riesz representation theorem on the dual of L^2 and the first person to consider measures on abstract spaces (i.e., beyond $\mathbb{R}^n$).

Most importantly, his foundational work on metric and topological spaces makes him a key figure in the development of modern analysis. Because these great accomplishments involved only concepts and definitions and neither major theorems nor solutions of major problems, it has been undervalued by some, most especially Bourbaki in the historical summary in their great book on topology [**120**], where they overemphasized the contributions of Hausdorff over those of Fréchet—their attitude is reflected in the Dieudonné quote above.

But there is a small group that feels Fréchet's contributions were vital (see the 200+ pages in Taylor's three papers [**908, 909, 910**]). For the last several generations of mathematicians brought up—if anything—with too much abstraction, the revolutionary nature of Fréchet's work is difficult to fathom. But prior to his work, almost all analysis was on $\mathbb{R}$, $\mathbb{C}$, or $\mathbb{R}^n$. Weierstrass, the Italian school (Volterra, Ascoli, and Arzelà), and Hadamard had considered explicit spaces of functions. Fréchet's idea of defining something like a metric on an abstract set of points was new and, in the end, fruitful. In a world that didn't yet talk standardly about open and closed sets, Fréchet's work on compactness in a general metric space was innovative.

We'll give the last word on Fréchet to Alexandroff, a key figure in point set topology from 1920 onwards. In a letter, written when he was 71, to the 89-year old Fréchet and addressed to "Cher Maître et ami," Alexandroff said:

> What is your place and role—it is a place among the greatest mathematicians of our time, it is the role of a true master.
>
> —*Alexandroff*, letter to Fréchet written in 1967[2]

There is another more spectacular way of seeing that the spaces $C^\infty_{\mathrm{per}}, \mathcal{S}(\mathbb{R}^\nu)$ and $\mathfrak{A}(\Omega)$ are not Banach spaces, that is, given by a single norm. A subset, S, in a TVS is called *bounded* if for every continuous seminorm, ρ_α, $\sup_{x \in S} \rho_\alpha(x) < \infty$. These spaces are all *Montel spaces*: spaces in which every closed bounded set is compact (to be a Montel space, they also have to be barreled—a technical condition that every convex, balanced, absorbing, closed set is a neighborhood of zero). For bounded subsets are uniformly bounded and uniformly equicontinuous in $\|\cdot\|_\infty$, so compact by the Ascoli–Arzelà theorem (for $C^\infty_{\mathrm{per}}, \mathcal{S}(\mathbb{R}^\nu)$, one does this also for derivatives). The name Montel comes from Montel's theorem (Theorem 6.2.1 of Part 2A) that bounded subsets of $\mathfrak{A}(\Omega)$ are precompact. Of course, in an infinite-dimensional Banach space, the unit ball is bounded and closed but not compact (see Theorem 5.1.9).

Problems

1. Prove that products, quotients, and closed subspaces of Fréchet spaces are Fréchet spaces.

6.2. Schwartz Space and Tempered Distributions

In Example 6.1.5, we defined $\mathcal{S}(\mathbb{R}^\nu)$, the Schwartz space of C^∞ functions on $\mathbb{R}^\nu$ of greater than polynomial decay. A *tempered distribution* is an element of $\mathcal{S}'(\mathbb{R}^\nu)$, the continuous linear functions from $\mathcal{S}(\mathbb{R}^\nu)$ to $\mathbb{C}$. Thus, $\tau \in \mathcal{S}'(\mathbb{R}^\nu)$ if and only if $f \mapsto \tau(f)$ is linear, and for some $N \in \mathbb{Z}^+$ and

---

[2]Quoted (my translation to English) in [**908**].

$C < \infty$,

$$|\tau(f)| \le C \left(\sum_{\substack{\alpha,\beta \\ |\alpha|,|\beta| \le N}} \|f\|_{\alpha,\beta;\infty} \right) \tag{6.2.1}$$

Remark. Below we'll usually drop "tempered," but in many cases, one wants to consider "ordinary distributions"—that is, functionals on the dual of $\mathbb{C}_0^\infty(\mathbb{R}^\nu)$, the C^∞ functions of compact support. The topology on $\mathbb{C}_0^\infty(\mathbb{R}^\nu)$ is not metrizable and requires some care to define. We'll discuss it in Chapter 9.

We'll normally put the $\sigma(\mathcal{S}', \mathcal{S})$-weak topology on $\mathcal{S}'$.

Example 6.2.1 (Polynomially Bounded Functions and $\mathcal{S}(\mathbb{R}^\nu)$). Let $F \colon \mathbb{R}^\nu \to \mathbb{C}$ be measurable and obey

$$|F(x)| \le C(1 + |x|^2)^N \tag{6.2.2}$$

Then $\jmath(F)$ is defined by

$$(\jmath(F))(f) = \int F(x) f(x) \, d^\nu x \tag{6.2.3}$$

Since

$$|\jmath(F)(f)| \le C \int (1 + |x|^2)^N |f(x)| \, d^\nu x$$

$$\le C \left(\int (1 + |x|^2)^{-\nu} \, d^\nu x \right) \sup_x |(1 + |x|^2)^{N+\nu} f(x)|$$

this lies in $\mathcal{S}'(\mathbb{R}^\nu)$.

In particular, if $f \in \mathcal{S}(\mathbb{R}^\nu)$, $\jmath(f) \in \mathcal{S}'(\mathbb{R}^\nu)$, so $\mathcal{S}$ is naturally embedded in $\mathcal{S}'$. $\square$

Notice that since

$$\jmath(f)(\bar{f}) = \int |f(x)|^2 \, d^\nu x \tag{6.2.4}$$

$\jmath$ restricted to $\mathcal{S}(\mathbb{R}^\nu)$ is injective.

Example 6.2.2 (Measures, δ-function). Let μ be a Baire measure on $\mathbb{R}^\nu$ with

$$\mu(\{x \mid |x| \le R\}) \le C(R + 1)^N \tag{6.2.5}$$

for some N. Then

$$\tau_\mu(f) = \int f(x) \, d\mu(x) \tag{6.2.6}$$

is easily seen to define a distribution (Problem 1). In particular,

$$\delta(f) = f(0) \tag{6.2.7}$$

is a distribution called the δ-*function* or *Dirac δ-function*. $\square$

Theorem 6.2.3 ($\equiv$ Corollary 6.4.6). $\mathcal{S}$ *is dense in* $\mathcal{S}'$; *more precisely,* $\jmath[\mathcal{S}(\mathbb{R}^\nu)]$ *is* $\sigma(\mathcal{S}', \mathcal{S})$-*dense in* $\mathcal{S}'(\mathbb{R}^\nu)$.

We'll provide three proofs of this, but none right now. In Section 6.4, this will follow from the Hermite expansion. Problem 2 has a really soft proof: in essence, $\jmath = \jmath^t$, so by general facts, that $\jmath = \jmath^t$ is injective implies $\jmath$ has dense range. And Problem 3 will use convolution and multiplication to make an explicit approximation.

Remark. Convolution and multiplication are operations on distributions; below we'll use Theorem 6.2.3 in proving uniqueness of certain definitions of operations. However, the argument is not circular—our definitions of convolution and multiplication make sense even if we don't have uniqueness a priori!

We turn now to operations on $\mathcal{S}'(\mathbb{R}^\nu)$, certain linear maps of $\mathcal{S}'$ to itself. These will all extend maps of $\mathcal{S}$ to $\mathcal{S}$. The point of Theorem 6.2.3 is that it implies uniqueness of such extensions.

Theorem 6.2.4. (a) *Let* $T\colon \mathcal{S}(\mathbb{R}^\nu) \to \mathcal{S}(\mathbb{R}^\nu)$ *be a continuous linear map. Then there is at most one extension* $T\colon \mathcal{S}'(\mathbb{R}^\nu) \to \mathcal{S}'(\mathbb{R}^\nu)$, *which is* $\sigma(\mathcal{S}', \mathcal{S})$-*continuous.*

(b) *Suppose* T *is given and there is another continuous linear map* $S\colon \mathcal{S}(\mathbb{R}^\nu) \to \mathcal{S}(\mathbb{R}^\nu)$ *so that for all* $f, g \in \mathcal{S}$,

$$\jmath(Tf)(g) = \jmath(f)(Sg) \tag{6.2.8}$$

Then the unique $\sigma(\mathcal{S}', \mathcal{S})$-*continuous extension of* T *to* $\mathcal{S}'$ *is given by*

$$(T\tau)(g) = \tau(Sg) \tag{6.2.9}$$

Remark. By extension, $\widetilde{T}$, we mean

$$\widetilde{T}(\jmath(f)) = \jmath(Tf) \tag{6.2.10}$$

and we drop the $\sim$.

Proof. (a) follows immediately from the density, since if $\jmath(f_n) \to \tau$, we must have $T(\tau) = \sigma\text{-}\lim \jmath(Tf_n)$. (b) is immediate since (6.2.9) defines a σ-continuous map obeying (6.2.10). $\qquad\square$

Example 6.2.5 (Translations and Convolutions). Define *translation* on $\mathcal{S}(\mathbb{R}^\nu)$ by

$$(T_xf)(y) = f(x+y) \tag{6.2.11}$$

Remark. $f(y-x)$ might be more natural since if f is peaked at 0, $f(\cdot-x)$ is peaked at x, but with (6.2.11) in one dimension, $f' = \lim_{x\to 0,\, x\neq 0}(T_xf-f)/x$.

Since

$$\int f(x+y)g(y)\,d^\nu y = \int f(y)g(y-x)\,d^\nu y \qquad (6.2.12)$$

we have

$$j(T_x f)(g) = j(f)(T_{-x}g) \qquad (6.2.13)$$

so we can extend T_x to $\mathcal{S}'$ by defining

$$(T_x\tau)(f) = \tau(T_{-x}g) \qquad (6.2.14)$$

If $f, g \in \mathcal{S}(\mathbb{R}^\nu)$, we define their *convolution* by

$$(f * g)(x) = \int f(x-y)g(y)\,d^\nu y \qquad (6.2.15)$$

It is easy to see (Problem 4(a)) that $f * g \in \mathcal{S}$, that (Problem 4(b)) $f * g = g * f$, and that (Problem 4(c)) $h * (g * f) = (h * g) * f$. Notice, too, that if

$$f^\flat(x) \equiv f(-x) \qquad (6.2.16)$$

then

$$\int f(x)h(y-x)g(y)\,d^\nu x d^\nu y = \int f(x)h^\flat(x-y)g(y)\,d^\nu x d^\nu y \qquad (6.2.17)$$

or

$$j(h * f)(g) = j(f)(h^\flat * g) \qquad (6.2.18)$$

so we can define convolution of $h \in \mathcal{S}(\mathbb{R}^\nu)$ and $\tau \in \mathcal{S}'(\mathbb{R}^\nu)$ by

$$(h * \tau)(g) = \tau(h^\flat * g) \qquad (6.2.19)$$

But as functions on $\mathcal{S}$,

$$h^\flat * g = \int g(y)h^\flat(\cdot - y)\,d^\nu y = \int g(y)(T_{-y}h^\flat)\,d^\nu y \qquad (6.2.20)$$

and thus,

$$(h * \tau)(g) = \int g(y)\tau(T_{-y}h^\flat)\,d^\nu y \qquad (6.2.21)$$

for the integral in (6.2.20) converges in $\mathcal{S}$. Note that

$$\delta * f = f \qquad (6.2.22)$$

Sometimes we can even define the convolution of two distributions. For example, we also have, for $f, g, h \in \mathcal{S}(\mathbb{R}^\nu)$,

$$\int (f * g)(x)h(x)\,d^\nu x = \int f(w)g(y)h(y+w)\,d^\nu w d^\nu y \qquad (6.2.23)$$

Thus, to define $\tau * \sigma$ for two distributions, we need to be able to apply the distribution $\tau \otimes \sigma$ defined via (for $f \in \mathcal{S}(\mathbb{R}^{2\nu})$)

$$(\tau \otimes \sigma)(f) = \tau_x(\sigma_y(f)) \qquad (6.2.24)$$

(i.e., $x \mapsto \sigma(f(x, \, \cdot \,))$ is in $\mathcal{S}(\mathbb{R}^\nu)$, so we can apply τ on the resulting function) to $h(y + w)$ which is not in $\mathcal{S}$. For example, if σ has compact support, $x \mapsto \sigma(f(x, \, \cdot \,))$ will lie in $\mathcal{S}$. As another example, if μ, ν are two probability measures on $\mathbb{R}^\nu$, we can define $\mu * \nu$ by

$$(\mu * \nu)(h) = \int h(x + y) \, d\mu(x) d\nu(y) \qquad (6.2.25)$$

If $h \in \mathcal{S}$, it is easy to see that $h(x + y) \in L^1(\mathbb{R}^\nu, d\mu(x) d\mu(y))$. $\mu * \nu$ defined this way is a positive linear functional and (6.2.25) is even valid for bounded continuous functions so $\mu * \nu$ is also a probability measure.

In particular, if $d\mu(x) = f(x) \, d^\nu x$, $d\nu(x) = g(x) \, d^\nu x$ with $f, g \in L^1(\mathbb{R}^\nu, d^\nu x)$, $d(\mu * \nu) = (f * g) \, d^\nu x$, where $f * g$ is defined by the integral (6.2.15) which converges for a.e. x and defines an L^1 function. $\qquad \square$

Theorem 6.2.6. (a) *If $h \in \mathcal{S}$ and $\tau \in \mathcal{S}'$, then*

$$y \mapsto \tau(T_y h) \qquad (6.2.26)$$

is a C^∞ polynomially bounded function of y (and all derivatives are polynomially bounded).

(b) *If $h \in \mathcal{S}$ and $\tau \in \mathcal{S}'$, $h * \tau$ is given by a C^∞ polynomially bounded function (more precisely, is equal to $\jmath(F)$ with F C^∞ and polynomially bounded).*

Proof. (a) For any norm, $\|\cdot\|_{\alpha, \beta; \infty}$, it is easy to see that $\|T_y h\|_{\alpha, \beta; \infty}$ is polynomially bounded. Since $D^\beta T_y h = T_y(D^\beta h)$, the same is true of derivatives.

(b) is immediate from (a) and (6.2.21). $\qquad \square$

Example 6.2.7 (Multiplication Operators). If F is a C^∞ function on $\mathbb{R}^\nu$, so that for any α, there are $C_\alpha > 0$ and N_α in $\mathbb{Z}_+$ with

$$|D^\alpha F(x)| \leq C_\alpha (1 + |x|^2)^{N_\alpha} \qquad (6.2.27)$$

then it is easy to see (Problem 5) that $f \mapsto Ff$ is a continuous linear map of $\mathcal{S}$ to $\mathcal{S}$. Clearly,

$$\jmath(Ff)(g) = \jmath(f)(Fg) \qquad (6.2.28)$$

so we can define for $\tau \in \mathcal{S}'(\mathbb{R}^\nu)$,

$$(F\tau)(g) = \tau(Fg) \qquad (6.2.29)$$

In particular, we can define $f\tau$ for $f \in \mathcal{S}(\mathbb{R}^\nu)$. $\qquad \square$

Example 6.2.8 (Derivatives). Integration by parts holds when $f, g \in \mathcal{S}(\mathbb{R}^\nu)$ with no boundary terms at infinity (because of the rapid decay of $D^\alpha f$ for all α), that is,

$$\int f(x)(D^\alpha g)(x) \, d^\nu x = (-1)^{|\alpha|} \int (D^\alpha f)(x) g(x) \, d^\nu x$$

Thus,

$$j(D^\alpha g)(f) = j(g)((-1)^{|\alpha|} D^\alpha f) \qquad (6.2.30)$$

so we'll define D^α on $\tau \in \mathcal{S}'(\mathbb{R}^\nu)$ by

$$(D^\alpha \tau)(f) = \tau((-1)^{|\alpha|} D^\alpha f) \qquad (6.2.31)$$

In particular, if P is a polynomial in ν-variables, we can define $P(D)$ by replacing X_j by $\frac{\partial}{\partial x_j}$ and define $P(D)\tau$.

It can be checked (Problem 6) that if δ_j is the ν-vector with components δ_{jk}, then

$$\frac{\partial \tau}{\partial x_j} = \lim_{\substack{\varepsilon \to 0 \\ \varepsilon \neq 0}} \frac{\tau_{\varepsilon \delta_j} - \tau}{\varepsilon} \qquad (6.2.32)$$

where the limit is in the $\sigma(\mathcal{S}', \mathcal{S})$-topology.

If $f, g \in \mathcal{S}(\mathbb{R}^\nu)$, it is immediate (by justifying interchange of derivative and integral) that

$$D^\alpha(f * g) = D^\alpha f * g = f * D^\alpha g \qquad (6.2.33)$$

Thus, by finding $g_n \to \tau$, we see

$$D^\alpha(f * \tau) = (f * D^\alpha \tau) = (D^\alpha f) * \tau \qquad (6.2.34)$$

Given a constant coefficient partial differential operator, $p(D)$, a distribution, τ, is called a *fundamental solution* if

$$p(D)\tau = \delta \qquad (6.2.35)$$

If one can find a fundamental solution, one can solve $p(D)u = f$ for any $f \in \mathcal{S}(\mathbb{R}^\nu)$, for if $u = \tau * f$, then by Theorem 6.2.6, u is a C^∞ function, and by (6.2.34) and (6.2.22),

$$p(D)u = p(D)\tau * f = \delta * f = f \qquad (6.2.36)$$

We'll say more about fundamental solutions in the Notes and in Section 6.9.
$\square$

We'll prove the following in Section 6.4 (and also in Problem 7):

Theorem 6.2.9 ($\equiv$ Theorem 6.4.9). *For every distribution, τ, there is a multi-index, α, and a polynomially bounded, continuous function, F, so that*

$$\tau = D^\alpha F \qquad (6.2.37)$$

Remarks. 1. More pedantically, $\tau = D^\alpha(j(F))$.

2. See Problem 8 for reductions to another version that is easier to prove.

Finally, we turn to the basics of Fourier transform, something we'll study further in Sections 6.5 and 6.6.

Definition. The *Fourier transform* of a function $f \in \mathcal{S}(\mathbb{R}^\nu)$ is given by

$$\widehat{f}(\mathbf{k}) = (2\pi)^{-\nu/2} \int \exp(-i\mathbf{k} \cdot \mathbf{x}) f(\mathbf{x}) \, d^\nu x \qquad (6.2.38)$$

and the *inverse Fourier transform* by

$$\check{f}(\mathbf{k}) = (2\pi)^{-\nu/2} \int \exp(+i\mathbf{k} \cdot \mathbf{x}) f(\mathbf{x}) \, d^\nu x \qquad (6.2.39)$$

Remarks. 1. Since $f \in \mathcal{S}$, the integrals converge absolutely.

2. See the start of Section 6.5 for a discussion of other conventions.

3. We'll eventually prove the inverse Fourier transform is the inverse of the Fourier transform. For now, it is just a name.

4. There are connections between $\widehat{}$, $\check{}$, and $^\flat$. Since $(-\mathbf{k}) \cdot (-\mathbf{x}) = \mathbf{k} \cdot \mathbf{x}$, we have

$$(\widehat{f})^\flat = (f^\flat)^\wedge \qquad (6.2.40)$$

Moreover,

$$\check{f} = (\widehat{f})^\flat \qquad (6.2.41)$$

Using these relations and $(f^\flat)^\flat = f$, we see that once we know $\widehat{\check{f}} = f$, we see $(\widehat{f})^\wedge = f^\flat$, so the fourth iteration of $\widehat{}$ is the identity, a fact which will be important in Section 6.5.

Fourier transform has a simple connection to derivatives and multiplication. Since $f \in \mathcal{S}$, one can get convergence of derivatives by the monotone convergence theorem and find

$$\left(\frac{d}{dk}\widehat{f}\right)(k) = \widehat{-ixf}(k), \qquad \left(\frac{d}{dk}\check{f}\right)(k) = \widetilde{ixf}(k) \qquad (6.2.42)$$

By integrating by parts, one gets

$$\widehat{\frac{df}{dx}}(k) = ik\widehat{f}(k), \qquad \widetilde{\frac{df}{dx}}(k) = -ik\check{f}(k) \qquad (6.2.43)$$

Here is the connection to convolution:

Theorem 6.2.10. *For $f, g \in \mathcal{S}(\mathbb{R}^\nu)$, we have*

$$\widehat{f * g} = (2\pi)^{\nu/2}\widehat{f}\,\widehat{g} \qquad (6.2.44)$$

Remarks. 1. The $(2\pi)^{\nu/2}$ is unnatural, which is one reason some use other conventions; see the start of Section 6.5.

2. Once we have $\widehat{f}$,

$$\widehat{fg} = (2\pi)^{-\nu/2}\widehat{f} * \widehat{g} \qquad (6.2.45)$$

3. We will see below (see (6.6.15)) that if μ is a probability measure, its Fourier transform defined via duality (viewing μ as a distribution) is the function given by

$$\widehat{\mu}(k) = (2\pi)^{-\nu/2} \int \exp(-ik \cdot x) \, d\mu(x) \qquad (6.2.46)$$

Given (6.2.25) and $\exp(-ik \cdot (x+y)) = \exp(-ik \cdot x) \exp(-ik \cdot y)$, we see that (6.2.44) extends to measures, that is,

$$\widehat{(\mu * \nu)}(k) = (2\pi)^{\nu/2} \, \widehat{\mu}(k) \widehat{\nu}(k) \qquad (6.2.47)$$

Proof.

$$\widehat{f * g}(\mathbf{k}) = (2\pi)^{-\nu/2} \int e^{-i\mathbf{k} \cdot \mathbf{x}} f(\mathbf{x} - \mathbf{y}) g(\mathbf{y}) \, d^{\nu}x d^{\nu}y$$

$$= (2\pi)^{-\nu/2} \int e^{-i\mathbf{k} \cdot (\mathbf{y} + \mathbf{w})} f(\mathbf{w}) g(\mathbf{y}) \, d^{\nu}x d^{\nu}y \qquad (6.2.48)$$

$$= (2\pi)^{\nu/2} \widehat{f}(\mathbf{k}) \widehat{g}(\mathbf{k})$$

In (6.2.48), we changed variables from x to $w = x - y$ using $x = w + y$. □

Example 6.2.11 (Fourier Transforms of Gaussians). Define for $a \in (0, \infty)$ and $\mathbf{x}$ in $\mathbb{R}^\nu$,

$$g_a(\mathbf{x}) = a^{-\nu/2} \exp\left(-\frac{\mathbf{x}^2}{2a}\right) \qquad (6.2.49)$$

Then (4.11.29) says that

$$\widehat{(g_a)} = a^{-\nu/2} g_{1/a} \qquad (6.2.50)$$

In particular, g_1 is its own Fourier transform!

For later purposes, we note that $(2\pi)^{-\nu/2} g_a$ is an approximate identity as $a \downarrow 0$, so as distributions in $\sigma(\mathcal{S}', \mathcal{S})$ we have that

$$g_a \to (2\pi)^{\nu/2} \delta \qquad (\text{as } a \downarrow 0) \qquad (6.2.51)$$

On the other hand, as $a \to \infty$, $a^{1/2} g_a(x)$ is monotone increasing to 1, so by the dominated convergence theorem, as distribution

$$a^{\nu/2} g_a \to 1 \qquad (\text{as } a \to \infty) \qquad (6.2.52)$$

(where $1(f) = \int f(\mathbf{x}) \, d^{\nu}x$). □

To extend to $\mathcal{S}'$ (and for other purposes), the following, which depends on the fact that $\exp(-i\mathbf{k} \cdot \mathbf{x})$ is symmetric in $\mathbf{k}$ and $\mathbf{x}$, is critical. For $f, g \in \mathcal{S}(\mathbb{R}^\nu)$,

$$\int \widehat{f}(\mathbf{k}) g(\mathbf{k}) \, d^{\nu}k = \int f(\mathbf{x}) \widehat{g}(\mathbf{x}) \, d^{\nu}x \qquad (6.2.53)$$

for both sides are

$$\int f(\mathbf{x}) g(\mathbf{k}) \exp(-i\mathbf{k} \cdot \mathbf{x}) \, d^{\nu}x d^{\nu}k \qquad (6.2.54)$$

(6.2.53) can be rewritten

$$j(\widehat{f})(g) = j(f)(\widehat{g}) \tag{6.2.55}$$

so $\widehat{}$ has a $\sigma(\mathcal{S}', \mathcal{S})$-continuous extension to $\mathcal{S}'(\mathbb{R}^\nu)$, that is,

$$\widehat{\tau}(f) = \tau(\widehat{f}) \tag{6.2.56}$$

Since $\widehat{}$ is continuous on $\mathcal{S}'$, (6.2.50), (6.2.51), and (6.2.52) imply

$$\widehat{1} = (2\pi)^{\nu/2}\delta, \qquad \widehat{\delta} = (2\pi)^{-\nu/2} \tag{6.2.57}$$

The second half is formally the pleasing formula

$$(2\pi)^{-\nu/2} \int \exp(-i\mathbf{k} \cdot \mathbf{x})\delta(\mathbf{x})\, d^\nu x = (2\pi)^{-\nu/2} \tag{6.2.58}$$

Formally, we just set $\mathbf{x} = 0$ but, of course, since the exponential is not in $\mathcal{S}$, we can't really evaluate that way.

The first half of (6.2.57) is essentially the Fourier inversion theorem!

Theorem 6.2.12 (Fourier Inversion Formula for $\mathcal{S}$). *For any $f \in \mathcal{S}$,*

$$\widecheck{\widehat{f}} = \widehat{\widecheck{f}} = f \tag{6.2.59}$$

Proof. Pick $\tau = 1$ in (6.2.56) and use (6.2.57):

$$(2\pi)^{\nu/2}f(\mathbf{0}) = \int \widehat{f}(\mathbf{k})\, d^\nu k \tag{6.2.60}$$

Next, note

$$\begin{aligned}
\widehat{T_{\mathbf{y}}f}(\mathbf{k}) &= \int e^{-i\mathbf{k}\cdot\mathbf{x}} f(\mathbf{x} + \mathbf{y})\, d^\nu y \\
&= \int e^{-i\mathbf{k}\cdot(\mathbf{w}-\mathbf{y})} f(\mathbf{w})\, d^\nu w \\
&= e^{i\mathbf{k}\cdot\mathbf{y}} \widehat{f}(\mathbf{k})
\end{aligned} \tag{6.2.61}$$

Plugging $T_{\mathbf{y}}f$ into (6.2.4) using $(T_{\mathbf{y}}f)(\mathbf{0}) = f(\mathbf{y})$ yields

$$(2\pi)^{1/2}f(\mathbf{y}) = \int \widehat{f}(\mathbf{k})e^{-i\mathbf{k}\cdot\mathbf{y}}\, d^\nu k \tag{6.2.62}$$

which is $\widecheck{\widehat{f}} = f$.

In (6.2.62), replace $\mathbf{k}$ by $-\mathbf{k}$ and use $\widehat{f}(-\mathbf{k}) = \widecheck{f}(\mathbf{k})$ to get $\widehat{\widecheck{f}} = f$. $\qquad\square$

By continuity and density of $\mathcal{S}$ in $\mathcal{S}'$, we extend immediately to $\mathcal{S}'$:

Theorem 6.2.13 (Fourier Inversion Formula for $\mathcal{S}'$). *For any $\tau \in \mathcal{S}'$, we have*

$$\widecheck{\widehat{\tau}} = \widehat{\widecheck{\tau}} = \tau \tag{6.2.63}$$

The Fourier inversion formula plus convolution immediately yields the Plancherel theorem.

Theorem 6.2.14 (Plancherel Theorem). *For any $f \in \mathcal{S}(\mathbb{R}^\nu)$, we have*

$$\int |\widehat{f}(k)|^2 \, d^\nu k = \int |f(x)|^2 \, d^\nu x \qquad (6.2.64)$$

Proof. Note first that

$$(\overline{f^\flat} * f)(0) = \int |f(x)|^2 \, d^\nu x \qquad (6.2.65)$$

Next, compute

$$\widehat{\overline{f^\flat}}(k) = (2\pi)^{-\nu/2} \int e^{-ik \cdot x} \, \overline{f(-x)} \, d^\nu x$$

$$= (2\pi)^{-\nu/2} \int e^{ik \cdot x} \, \overline{f(x)} \, d^\nu x \qquad (6.2.66)$$

$$= (2\pi)^{-\nu} \overline{\int e^{-ik \cdot x} f(x) \, d^\nu x}$$

$$= \overline{\widehat{f}(k)} \qquad (6.2.67)$$

where (6.2.66) comes from changing x to $-x$.

Therefore, by (6.2.44),

$$\widehat{\overline{f^\flat} * f}(k) = (2\pi)^{\nu/2} |\widehat{f}(k)|^2 \qquad (6.2.68)$$

(6.2.60) for the function $\overline{f^\flat} * f$ is exactly (6.2.64) on account of (6.2.65) and (6.2.68). $\qquad\qquad\square$

Notes and Historical Remarks.

> In 1948 Laurent Schwartz visited Sweden to present his distributions to the local mathematicians. He had the opportunity of conversing with Marcel Riesz. Having written on the blackboard the integration-by-parts formula to explain the idea of a weak derivative, he was interrupted by Riesz saying, 'I hope you have found something else in your life.' Later Schwartz told Riesz of his hopes that the following theorem would eventually be proved: every linear partial differential equation with constant coefficients has a fundamental solution (a concept made precise and general by distribution theory). 'Madness!' exclaimed Riesz. 'This is a project for the twenty first century!' The general theorem was proved by Ehrenpreis and Malgrange in 1952.
>
> —F. Trèves [**934**][3]

---

[3]Adding to the irony, Riesz's students, Gårding and Hörmander used distribution theory as a central element of their work—Gårding in axiomatic quantum field theory and Hörmander to revolutionize the theory of PDEs.

The notion of "generalized functions," that is, function-like objects that can be manipulated like functions, has roots over fifty years older than Schwartz's formal definition of distributions in the late 1940s. The earliest work came from electrical engineering and physics—most notably, Heaviside's 1893 "operational calculus" [**407**] and Dirac's heavy use of his delta function as part of his general formulation of quantum mechanics [**248**]. Oliver Heaviside (1850–1925) discussed the formal derivative of the step function (so he had a delta function), manipulating his objects in terms of Laplace transforms. P. A. M. Dirac (1902–84) not only used higher-dimensional $\delta(x)$ but even objects like $\delta(x_4^2 - x_1^2 - x_1^2 - x_3^2)$, a delta function of a light cone, something we'll turn to later in the Notes. Both Heaviside and Dirac found much opposition to these formalisms not only from mathematicians but within their own discipline, but in time, given the usefulness of their formalisms and the fact that pitfalls did not arise, these ideas became common among electrical engineers and physicists.

Another input came from mathematicians attempting to deal with PDEs. Hadamard, in work of 1903 [**377**] codified in his 1923 book [**380**], attempted to define "finite parts" of integrals in order to define fundamental solutions of the wave equation. In modern distributional notation, the simplest such example is

$$\lim_{\varepsilon \downarrow 0} \frac{1}{x + i\varepsilon} = \mathcal{P}\left(\frac{1}{x}\right) - i\pi\delta(x) \qquad (6.2.69)$$

in terms of the principal part and δ-function distributions (see Problem 10).

(6.2.69) is called by mathematicians the Plemelj or Sokhotskii–Plemelj (or Sokchotsky–Plemelj) formula. Both these authors prove results for closed curves in $\mathbb{C}$—(6.2.69) is a special case (of a limit) when the curve is $\mathbb{R}$. Plemelj [**731**] found it in 1908—it was in Sokhotskii's Ph.D. thesis [**867**] already 35 years earlier. This formula is widely used by theoretical physicists but rarely with a name.

A different slice came from attempts in the 1930s by Friedrichs, Bochner, and Sobolev to define weak solutions of PDEs, what we would now call distributional solutions. In his 1932 book, Bochner [**101**] considered formal objects of the form

$$\sum_{n=0}^{N} \frac{d^n}{dx^n}\left(P_n(x)f_n(x)\right) \qquad (6.2.70)$$

where P_n are polynomials and $f_n \in L^2(\mathbb{R}^\nu, d^\nu x)$, but there were no test functions, dual spaces, derivatives taken, or even the idea that this included the δ-function. Sobolev, in two papers in the mid-30s [**865, 866**], came closest to distribution theory. For each finite m, he considered the dual space of $C_0^m(\mathbb{R}^\nu)$, the C^m function of compact support, but by not taking

C_0^∞, his spaces didn't support derivatives within the space, so he needed to define derivatives from $(C_0^m)^*$ to $(C_0^{m+1})^*$. There was no use of convolution or Fourier transform. Lützen has a book [609] on the "prehistory" of distribution theory.

With these forebears, Schwartz went much further. His use of C_0^∞ functions was regarded as radical. Indeed, Henri Cartan warned him that such functions were "trop monstrueuses" (very monstrous), according to Trèves's biographical note [934]. This was despite the fact that as early as 1926, Wiener [995] showed how to approximate C^k function by C^∞ function by convoluting with C_0^∞ functions. Moreover, by linking the theory to the recently developed theory of duality in locally convex spaces, he found a very general framework. In 1945–46, he presented the first steps of the theory of ordinary distributions [830] and, in 1948, to discuss Fourier transforms, he invented $\mathcal{S}(\mathbb{R}^\nu)$ and $\mathcal{S}'(\mathbb{R}^\nu)$ [831]. He codified the theory in his two-volume book [832].

Despite some resistance from the old guard, distribution theory made a sufficient splash that in 1950, the 35-year old Schwartz became the first (but certainly not the last!) French Fields' medal winner. The congress that year was in the U.S.A. and the organizers had trouble getting Schwartz, a former supporter of Trotsky, a visa for the U.S.A., but they succeeded in the end. During the 1950s, distribution theory changed the face of analysis—high points included applications to PDEs (notably the Malgrange–Ehrenpreis theorem discussed below and the work of Lars Hörmander (1931–2012), codified in his five books on linear PDEs [433, 434]), to quantum field theory (the Gårding–Wightman axioms [1000, 999, 888, 460]), to representation theory of Lie groups (the work of Bruhat [138] and Harish-Chandra [398]), and to structure of smooth manifolds (the work of de Rham [236] and Schwartz [834]). An important development of the 1950s was the series of books on "generalized functions" (the name for distributions used by the Russians going back to Sobolev) by Gel'fand and various coauthors [344].

Laurent Schwartz (1915–2002) was a French Jewish mathematician born in Paris to a family of famous physicians. Hadamard was his great uncle, but there is no indication that Hadamard had any influence on Schwartz, other than the story that Hadamard was dismayed that the budding 16-year-old mathematician didn't know what the Riemann zeta function was. Schwartz was an undergraduate student at the prestigious École Normale Supérieure, in the same class as Choquet and Marie-Hélène Lévy (the daughter of Paul Lévy), who became Schwartz's wife. After college, he served in the Army.

During the early part of the Second World War, he and his wife were in Clermont-Ferrand in Vichy France, where many professors from Strasbourg, including Dieudonné, Ehresmann, Lichnerowicz, and Valiron (who was his formal Ph.D. mentor), were refugees. After the Germans occupied the south of France, the Schwartzes were in danger as Jews and leftists and were saved by using assumed names (Laurent-Marie Sélimartin and Marie-Hélène Lengé). Schwartz did his fundamental work on distributions initially in Grenoble and then in Nancy. He moved to Paris in 1952, initially to the Sorbonne and from 1959 onwards at École Polytechnique. Schwartz was often controversial politically—for a while, because of his protests over the war in Algeria, he was barred from teaching by the military administration at École Polytechnique. His students included Boutet de Monvel, Grothendieck, Jacques-Louis Lions, Malgrange, Maurey, Nachbin, Pisier, and Trèves.

Our proof of the Fourier inversion formula may seem to be "magic by distributions," but the distributions are really secondary: the key formula (6.2.60) is obtained by taking $g = a^{1/2}g_a$ in (6.2.53) and taking $a \to \infty$. One doesn't need distributions to understand the limit.

If F defines a bounded hypersurface in $\mathbb{R}^\nu$, that is, $F(x_1, \ldots, x_\nu)$ is C^∞, and ∇F is nonvanishing on the set $\{\mathbf{x} \mid F(\mathbf{x}) = 0\}$ which is assumed bounded, then one can define $\delta(F(x))$ by locally changing coordinates. If $\frac{\partial F}{\partial x_\nu} \neq 0$ in a neighborhood, we use $dx_1 \ldots dx_{\nu-1}/|\frac{\partial F}{\partial x_\nu}|$ in that neighborhood to define a measure on the hypersurface. If F is well-behaved at infinity (e.g., $F(x) = x_4^2 - x_1^2 - x_2^2 - x_3^2 - 1$), one can even define a tempered distribution for unbounded manifolds and one can handle some singular points (e.g., $F(x) = x_4^2 - x_1^2 - x_2^2 - x_3^2$).

The fact that any constant coefficient PDE has a fundamental solution is known as the Malgrange–Ehrenpreis theorem. We will discuss the history and provide a proof in Section 6.9.

The development of the theory of integral equations in the ten years following 1900 led to the increasing use of what we now call convolutions, which, without a name, go back at least to Laplace's work on the central limit theorem (see the Notes to Section 7.3). For a long time the German term "Faltung" introduced by Hilbert was in common use, with an occasional utilization of its literal translation "folding." Wintner, in a series of papers starting in 1935 [**1006**], began using an unusual cognate of "folding," namely, "convolution"—and the name stuck.

Problems

1. (a) If μ is a measure on $\mathbb{R}^\nu$ with $\mu(\{x \mid |x| \leq R\}) \leq C(R+1)^N$, prove that for all $\varepsilon > 0$,

$$\int (1 + |x|)^{-N-\varepsilon} \, d\mu(x) < \infty \qquad (6.2.71)$$

(*Hint*: Integrate by parts.)

(b) Prove that (6.2.6) defines a tempered distribution.

2. (a) If $K \subset \mathcal{S}'(\mathbb{R}^\nu)$ is a $\sigma(\mathcal{S}', \mathcal{S})$-closed subspace and $\tau \notin K$, prove there is $f \in \mathcal{S}$ so $\tau(f) \neq 0$ and $\sigma(f) = 0$ for all $\sigma \in K$.

   (b) For any $f \in \mathcal{S}$, $f \neq 0$, prove that $\jmath(\bar{f})(f) \neq 0$.

   (c) Prove that $\jmath[\mathcal{S}]$ is $\sigma(\mathcal{S}', \mathcal{S})$-dense in $\mathcal{S}'$.

3. (a) If $f, g \in \mathcal{S}(\mathbb{R}^\nu)$ and $\tau \in \mathcal{S}'(\mathbb{R}^\nu)$, prove that $f(g * \tau)$ is in $\mathcal{S}(\mathbb{R}^\nu)$.

   (b) Prove that $\jmath[\mathcal{S}]$ is $\sigma(\mathcal{S}', \mathcal{S})$-dense in $\mathcal{S}'$.

4. (a) If $f, g \in \mathcal{S}$, prove that $f * g$ defined by (6.2.15) is in $\mathcal{S}$.

   (b) Prove that $f * g = g * f$.

   (c) Prove that $h * (g * f) = (h * g) * f$.

5. If F is a C^∞ function obeying (6.2.27), prove that $f \mapsto Ff$ is a continuous map of $\mathcal{S}$ to $\mathcal{S}$.

6. If $\frac{\partial}{\partial x_j}$ on distributions is defined by (6.2.31), prove that (6.2.32) holds.

7. (a) Fix ν and M. Let ℓ be a linear function on $Q_M \equiv \{f \in C_\infty(\mathbb{R}^\nu) \mid \sup_{x \in \mathbb{R}^\nu} (1 + |x|)^M |f(\alpha)| < \infty\}$ that obeys

$$|\ell(f)| \leq C_1 \sup_{x \in \mathbb{R}^\nu} (1 + |x|)^M |f(x)| \qquad (6.2.72)$$

   Prove there is a measure μ on $\mathbb{R}^\nu$ which obeys

$$\mu(\{x \mid |x| \leq R\}) \leq C_2 (1 + R)^M \qquad (6.2.73)$$

   so that

$$\ell(f) = \int f(x) \, d\mu(x) \qquad (6.2.74)$$

   (b) Suppose $\tau \in \mathcal{S}'(\mathbb{R}^\nu)$ obeys

$$|\tau(f)| \leq C \sum_{|\alpha|, |\beta| \leq M} \|x^\alpha D^\beta f\|_\infty \qquad (6.2.75)$$

   Let $\#(M) = \#\{\beta \mid |\beta| \leq M\}$. Let Y be the set of $\#(M)$-tuples $\{g_\beta\}_{|\beta| \leq M}$ of functions in Q_M. Let $\kappa \colon \mathcal{S}(\mathbb{R}^\nu) \to Y$ by

$$\kappa(f) = \{D^\beta f\}_{|\beta| \leq M} \qquad (6.2.76)$$

   Use the Hahn–Banach theorem to prove there is $L \in Y^*$ so that

$$\tau(f) = L(\kappa(f)) \qquad (6.2.77)$$

   (c) Use the Riesz–Markov theorem to show there are measures $\{\mu_\beta\}_{|\beta| \leq M}$ obeying (6.2.75) so that

$$\tau(f) = \sum_{|\beta| \leq M} \int (D^\beta f) \, d\mu_\beta \qquad (6.2.78)$$

and that

$$\tau = \sum_{|\beta|\leq M} (-1)^{|\beta|} D^\beta \mu_\beta \qquad (6.2.79)$$

(d) Let μ be a measure obeying (6.2.73). Let

$$F(x_1,\ldots,x_\nu) = \mu(\chi_{(x_1,\ldots,x_\nu)}) \qquad (6.2.80)$$

where $\chi(y)$ is $(-1)^k$ if k of the x_j's are less than 0 and y_j lies between 0 and x_j. Prove that F is a polynomially bounded measurable (but not necessarily continuous) function, so in terms of distributional derivatives,

$$\frac{\partial^\nu F}{\partial x_1 \ldots \partial x_\nu} = \mu \qquad (6.2.81)$$

(e) Let G be defined by

$$G(x_1,\ldots,x_\nu) = \int_0^{x_1} dy_1 \int_0^{x_2} dy_2 \ldots \int_0^{x_\nu} dy_\nu\, F(y_1,\ldots,y_\nu)$$

Prove that G is a polynomially bounded continuous function and

$$\frac{\partial^{2\nu} G}{\partial x_1^2 \ldots \partial x_\nu^2} = \mu \qquad (6.2.82)$$

(f) Conclude that τ has the form

$$\tau = \sum_{|\beta|\leq M+2} D^\beta G_\beta \qquad (6.2.83)$$

for suitable polynomially bounded functions, G_β. Given Problem 8, conclude Theorem 6.2.9 holds.

8. (a) If F is a polynomially bounded continuous function and $G(x_1,x_2,\ldots,x_\nu) = \int_0^{x_1} F(y_1,x_2,\ldots,x_\nu)\,dy_1$, then $F = \frac{\partial G}{\partial x_1}$ as distributions.

(b) If F, G are polynomially bounded functions and β, γ are multi-indexes, prove there is a polynomially bounded function, H, so that in terms of distributional derivatives,

$$D^\beta F + D^\gamma G = D^{\beta+\gamma} H \qquad (6.2.84)$$

9. Prove (6.2.45) given (6.2.44) and the Fourier inversion formula.

10. (a) Let $f \in \mathcal{S}(\mathbb{R})$. Prove that

$$\lim_{\varepsilon\downarrow 0} \int_{|x|>\varepsilon} \frac{f(x)}{x}\,dx \equiv \mathcal{P}\left(\frac{1}{x}\right)(f) \qquad (6.2.85)$$

exists and obeys

$$\left| \mathcal{P}\left(\frac{1}{x}\right)(f) \right| \le C(\|f'\|_\infty + \|xf\|_\infty) \tag{6.2.86}$$

and so defines a tempered distribution. It is called the *principal value* distribution.

(b) Prove that in the $\sigma(\mathcal{S}', \mathcal{S})$-topology, $\jmath(x(x^2 + \varepsilon^2)^{-1}) \to \mathcal{P}(\frac{1}{x})$ as $\varepsilon \downarrow 0$.

(c) Prove (6.2.69).

11. This will provide an alternate proof of the Fourier inversion and Plancherel formulae for $\mathcal{S}(\mathbb{R}^\nu)$.

(a) Let $f \in C_0^\infty(\mathbb{R}^\nu)$ with

$$\operatorname{supp}(f) \subset \{x \mid |x_j| < R \text{ for } j = 1, 2, \dots, \nu\} \tag{6.2.87}$$

Fix any $L > R$. Using Fourier series on $[-L, L]^\nu$, show that for $|x_j| \le L$,

$$f(\mathbf{x}) = (2\pi)^{-\nu/2} \sum_{\mathbf{n} \in \mathbb{Z}^\nu} \left(\frac{\pi}{L}\right)^\nu \hat{f}\left(\frac{\pi \mathbf{n}}{L}\right) \exp\left(\frac{\pi i \mathbf{n} \cdot \mathbf{x}}{L}\right) \tag{6.2.88}$$

and

$$\int |f(\mathbf{x})|^2 \, d^\nu x = \sum_{\mathbf{n}} \left(\frac{\pi}{L}\right)^\nu \left| \hat{f}\left(\frac{\mathbf{n}}{L}\right) \right|^2 \tag{6.2.89}$$

(b) By taking $L \to \infty$, prove that for such f,

$$f(\mathbf{x}) = (2\pi)^{-\nu/2} \int \hat{f}(\mathbf{k}) e^{i\mathbf{k} \cdot \mathbf{x}} \, d^\nu k \tag{6.2.90}$$

and

$$\int |f(\mathbf{x})|^2 \, d^\nu x = \int |\hat{f}(\mathbf{k})|^2 \, d^\nu k \tag{6.2.91}$$

(c) Prove (6.2.90) and (6.2.91) from (b) for all $f \in \mathcal{S}(\mathbb{R}^\nu)$.

(d) In the text, we used the value of the Gaussian integral, (4.11.21), to determine the normalization (i.e., $(2\pi)^{-\nu/2}$) needed for the Plancherel formula to hold, but we proved (6.2.91) above directly from Fourier series, suggesting we can go backwards to now deduce (4.11.21). That is what this subproblem will do. First show that if $\int_{-\infty}^\infty e^{-x^2/2} \, dx = c^{1/2}$, then all the conclusions of Theorem 4.11.11 hold with 2π in (4.11.24) and (4.11.25) replaced by $c^{1/2}$, so that if $f(x) = e^{-x^2/2}$, then $\hat{f}(k) = df(x)$ for some $d > 0$. Then use (6.2.91) to see $d = 1$ and then (6.2.109) for $x = 0$ to obtain (4.11.21)

12. This will prove the Fourier inversion formula on $\mathcal{S}(\mathbb{R})$ up to a constant.

(a) Prove that $[\varphi(0) = 0 \Rightarrow \int \hat{\varphi}(k) \, dk = 0]$ implies $\int \hat{\varphi}(k) \, dx = C\varphi(0)$ and this implies $\int e^{ik \cdot x} \hat{\varphi}(k) \, dx = C\varphi(x)$.

(b) If $\varphi(0) = 0$ and $\varphi \in \mathcal{S}(\mathbb{R})$, prove there is $\psi \in \mathcal{S}(\mathbb{R})$ with $\varphi(x) = x\psi(x)$ and $\widehat{\varphi}(k) = i\frac{d}{dk}\widehat{\psi}(k)$.

(c) Conclude $\varphi(0) = 0 \Rightarrow \int \widehat{\varphi}(k)\, dk = 0$.

Remark. This argument is due to Richards [**771**].

13. This problem will use the Zak transform to provide yet another proof of the Plancherel and Fourier inversion theorems. Let $f \in L^2(\mathbb{R})$. The *Zak transform* is defined as a function on $\mathbb{R}^2$ by

$$(Zf)(x,k) = \sum_{j \in \mathbb{Z}} f(x+j)e^{-2\pi ijk} \tag{6.2.92}$$

(a) Prove that for a.e. $x \in \mathbb{R}$, that $\sum_{j \in \mathbb{Z}} |f(x+j)|^2 < \infty$ so the sum in (6.2.92) can be interpreted for a.e. x as an $L^2([0,1], dk)$ convergent sum. Thereby define Zf as an a.e. defined measurable function of (x,k).

(b) Prove that

$$\int_0^1 dx \int_0^1 dk\, |(ZF)(x,k)|^2 = \int_{-\infty}^{\infty} |f(x)|^2 dx \tag{6.2.93}$$

(c) Prove that (6.2.92) defines Zf on all of $\mathbb{R} \times \mathbb{R}$ and that Zf obeys for all $l \in \mathbb{Z}$ and a.e. (x,k)

$$(Zf)(x+l,k) = e^{2\pi ilk}(Zf)(x,k) \tag{6.2.94}$$
$$(Zf)(x,k+l) = (Zf)(x,k) \tag{6.2.95}$$

(d) Let $\mathcal{Z}$ be the set of measurable functions φ on $\mathbb{R}^2$ obeying, for all $l \in \mathbb{Z}$ and a.e. (x,k)

$$\varphi(x+l,k) = e^{2\pi ilk}\varphi(x,k); \quad \varphi(x,k+l) = \varphi(x,k) \tag{6.2.96}$$

with

$$\|\varphi\|_{\mathcal{Z}}^2 = \int_0^1 dx \int_0^1 dk\, |\varphi(x,k)|^2 < \infty \tag{6.2.97}$$

Prove that Z is an isometry of $L^2(\mathbb{R}, dx)$ onto $\mathcal{Z}$.

(e) Let $\widetilde{\mathcal{Z}}$ be the set of functions on $\mathbb{R}^2$ obeying

$$\widetilde{\varphi}(x+l,k) = \widetilde{\varphi}(x,l); \quad \widetilde{\varphi}(x,k+l) = e^{-2\pi ilk}\widetilde{\varphi}(x,l) \tag{6.2.98}$$

with norm the same as (6.2.91). Prove that

$$(U\varphi)(x,k) = e^{-2\pi ixk}\varphi(x,k) \tag{6.2.99}$$

is a unitary map of $\mathcal{Z}$ to $\widetilde{\mathcal{Z}}$.

(f) Define the *modified Zak transform* by

$$(\widetilde{Z}f)(x,k) = \sum_{j \in \mathbb{Z}} f(k+j)e^{2\pi ijx} \tag{6.2.100}$$

and prove that $\widetilde{Z}$ is a unitary map of $L^2(\mathbb{R})$ to $\widetilde{\mathcal{Z}}$.

(g) Prove that if $f \in \mathcal{S}(\mathbb{R})$ then

$$\left[(\tilde{Z}^{-1}UZ)f\right](k) = \int e^{-2\pi ikx} f(k)dx \equiv (\mathcal{F}f)(k) \qquad (6.2.101)$$

and that

$$\left[(Z^{-1}U^{-1}\tilde{Z})f\right](x) = \int e^{2\pi ikx} f(k)dk \equiv (\mathcal{F}^{\sharp}f)(x) \qquad (6.2.102)$$

(h) Conclude for $f \in \mathcal{S}$,

$$\|\mathcal{F}f\|_2 = \|f\|_2, \quad \mathcal{F}^{\sharp}\mathcal{F}f = \mathcal{F}\mathcal{F}^{\sharp}f = f \qquad (6.2.103)$$

(i) Conclude for $\hat{}$ and $\check{}$ given by (6.2.38)/(6.2.39) that the Plancherel and Fourier inversion formulae hold:

$$\|\hat{f}\|_2 = \|f\|; \quad (\check{\hat{f}}) = (\hat{\check{f}}) = f \qquad (6.2.104)$$

(j) For $f \in \mathcal{S}(\mathbb{R})$, prove that the a.e. formula (6.2.101)

$$(UZf)(x,k) = (Z\mathcal{F}f)(x,k) \qquad (6.2.105)$$

holds pointwise and that by evaluation at $x = k = 0$ that

$$\sum_{j \in \mathbb{Z}} f(j) = \sum_{j \in \mathbb{Z}} (\mathcal{F}f)(j) \qquad (6.2.106)$$

This is the Poisson summation formula, see (6.6.100).

Remarks. 1. The normalization $\mathcal{F}f$ for the Fourier transform is discussed in Section 6.5 and 6.6.

2. The approach to the basic Fourier transform theorems in this problem is due to Hernández et al. [**422**].

3. We'll say a lot more about the Zak transform, its use and history in Section 4.5 of Part 3.

14. (a) Let $f, g \in \mathcal{S}(\mathbb{R})$. Prove that

$$f - g = h' \quad \text{for some } h \in \mathcal{S}(\mathbb{R}) \qquad (6.2.107)$$

if and only if

$$\int_{-\infty}^{\infty} f(x)\,dx = \int_{-\infty}^{\infty} g(x)\,dx \qquad (6.2.108)$$

(b) If $T \in \mathcal{S}'(\mathbb{R})$ and $T' = 0$, prove there is a constant c so that $T = c$.

(c) If $T \in \mathcal{S}'(\mathbb{R})$ and $T^{(n)} = 0$, prove that T is a polynomial of degree at most $n-1$. (*Hint*: If $T^{(n-1)} = c$, then $(T - [(n-1)!]^{-1}cx^{n-1})^{(n-1)} = 0$.)

(d) If $T \in \mathcal{S}'(\mathbb{R}^\nu)$ and $\partial_j T = 0$ for $j = 1, 2, \ldots, \nu$, prove that T is constant.

15. The *support*, supp(T), of a distribution T in $\mathcal{S}'(\mathbb{R}^\nu)$ is the complement of the union over all open sets $U \subset \mathbb{R}^\nu$ with $T(f) = 0$ for all $f \in \mathcal{S}(\mathbb{R}^\nu)$ with supp$(f) \subset U$.

    (a) If $T \in \mathcal{S}'(\mathbb{R})$ has support $\{0\}$ and for some K, N,

$$|T(f)| \leq C \sum_{k=0}^{K} \|(1+x^2)^N f^{(k)}(a)\|_\infty \qquad (6.2.109)$$

    Prove that $T(f) = 0$ if $f \in \mathcal{S}$ and $f(0) = f'(0) = \cdots = f^{(K)}(0) = 0$.

    (b) If T has support $\{0\}$ and (6.2.109) holds, prove that $x^{K+1}T = 0$.

    (c) If $T \in \mathcal{S}'(\mathbb{R})$ has support $\{0\}$, prove that T is a finite sum of derivatives of delta functions. (*Hint*: Use Problem 14 on $\widehat{T}$.)

    (d) Prove an analog of (c) for $\mathbb{R}^\nu$.

16. (a) If $f \in L^1(\mathbb{R}^\nu)$, prove that the distributional Fourier transform is given by (6.2.38) as a convergent integral with f a continuous function.

    (b) For $f \in L^2(\mathbb{R}^\nu)$, prove that $\widehat{f}$ is the L^2-limit of the convergent integrals

$$(2\pi)^{-\nu/2} \int_{|x| \leq R} e^{-i\mathbf{kx}} f(x) d^\nu x$$

    ($L^2 \in k$; limit as $R \to \infty$). This is sometimes written as l.i.m. for *limit in mean*.

6.3. Periodic Distributions

$C^\infty(\partial\mathbb{D})$ is discussed in Example 6.1.3. It is the same as periodic C^∞ functions on $\mathbb{R}$. We'll consider here its dual space, $C^\infty(\partial\mathbb{D})'$. In Problem 1, the reader will show there is a natural bijection of this space and $\{\tau \in \mathcal{S}'(\mathbb{R}) \mid T_{2\pi}\tau = \tau\}$. The main point of this section is that Fourier series which map $C^\infty(\partial\mathbb{D})$ and $C^\infty(\partial\mathbb{D})'$ into sequence spaces makes certain aspects of $C^\infty(\partial\mathbb{D})$ transparent.

Proposition 6.3.1. $f \to f^\sharp$ *given by*

$$f_n^\sharp = \int_0^{2\pi} e^{-in\theta} f(e^{i\theta}) \frac{d\theta}{2\pi} \qquad (6.3.1)$$

is a bijection of $C^\infty(\partial\mathbb{D})$ and $\mathfrak{s} = \{(a_n)_{n=-\infty}^\infty \mid$ for all ℓ, $(1+|n|)^\ell a_n \to 0$ as $|n| \to \infty\}$. If $\mathfrak{s}$ is given the norms

$$\|a\|_\ell = \sup_n (1+|n|)^\ell |a_n| \qquad (6.3.2)$$

then this map is a bicontinuous map.

Moreover, in $C^\infty(\partial\mathbb{D})$,

$$\sum_{|n|\le N} f_n^\sharp e^{in\theta} \to f(\theta) \tag{6.3.3}$$

Proof. Let $\|a\|_{\ell;2}$ be given by

$$\|a_\ell\|_{\ell;2} = \left(\sum_{n=-\infty}^{\infty} |n|^{2\ell} |a_n|^2 \right)^{1/2} \tag{6.3.4}$$

As in the discussion in Section 6.1 (see Problem 2), $\{\|\cdot\|_{\ell;2}\}_{\ell=0}^{\infty}$ and $\{\|\cdot\|_\ell\}_{\ell=0}^{\infty}$ are equivalent norms on $\mathcal{S}$.

If $f \in C^\infty(\partial\mathbb{D})$,

$$\left(\frac{d^\ell f}{d\theta^\ell} \right)_n^\sharp = (-in)^\ell f_n^\sharp \tag{6.3.5}$$

by an integration by parts. Since $\frac{d^\ell f}{d\theta^\ell}$ is in L^2, we have $\|f^\sharp\|_{\ell;2} < \infty$ for all ℓ, and thus, $f^\sharp \in \mathcal{S}$.

If $\{a_n\} \in \mathcal{S}$, then

$$\sum_{|n|\le N} a_n e^{in\theta} \equiv f_N \tag{6.3.6}$$

converges uniformly in θ to a function f. Similarly, $\frac{d^\ell f_N}{d\theta^\ell}$ converges uniformly to a function g_ℓ. Since

$$\frac{d^\ell f_N}{d\theta_\ell}(\theta_1) - \frac{d^\ell f_N}{d\theta_\ell}(\theta_0) = \int_{\theta_0}^{\theta_1} \frac{d^{\ell+1} f_N}{d\theta^{\ell+1}}\, d\theta$$

we see g_ℓ is C^1 with derivative $g_{\ell+1}$, so inductively, f is C^∞. Moreover, $f_n^\sharp = a_n$. Thus, the map is onto.

Since

$$\|f\|_{L^2} = \sum_{n=-\infty}^{\infty} |f_n^\sharp|^2 \tag{6.3.7}$$

the map is injective.

In the L^2 norms of $\frac{d^\ell f}{d\theta^\ell}$, the map is isometric in all seminorms, so bicontinuous. $\qquad\square$

This lets us identify $C^\infty(\partial\mathbb{D})'$:

Theorem 6.3.2. *Let $\tau \in C^\infty(\partial\mathbb{D})'$. Let $\varphi_n \in C^\infty$ be the function*

$$\varphi_n(e^{i\theta}) = e^{in\theta} \tag{6.3.8}$$

Define

$$\tau_n^\sharp = \tau(\varphi_{-n}) \tag{6.3.9}$$

Then for some L and C,

$$|\tau_n^\sharp| \le C(1 + |n|)^L \tag{6.3.10}$$

For any $f \in C^\infty(\partial\mathbb{D})$ (with an absolutely convergent sum),

$$\tau(f) = \sum_{n=-\infty}^{\infty} \tau_{-n}^\sharp f_n^\sharp \tag{6.3.11}$$

Moreover, for any sequence $\tau_n^\sharp$ obeying (6.3.10), $\tau(\cdot)$ given by (6.3.11) defines an element of $C^\infty(\partial\mathbb{D})'$ whose $^\sharp$ is the given sequence. Thus, (6.3.9) sets up a bijection between $C^\infty(\partial\mathbb{D})'$ and $\mathfrak{s}'$, the set of all sequences obeying (6.3.10).

Proof. Straightforward, given the proposition (Problem 3). □

Corollary 6.3.3. *$\jmath[C^\infty(\partial\mathbb{D})]$ is $\sigma((C^\infty)', C^\infty)$-dense in $C^\infty(\partial\mathbb{D})'$.*

Proof. Let $\tau \in C^\infty(\partial\mathbb{D})'$. Then

$$\sum_{|n| \le N} \tau_{-n}^\sharp e^{in\theta} \equiv f_n(\theta) \tag{6.3.12}$$

lies in $C^\infty(\partial\mathbb{D})$. Indeed, it is analytic. By (6.3.11), $\jmath(f_n) \to \tau$. □

From the theorem, we also immediately get

Theorem 6.3.4. *For any $\tau \in C^\infty(\partial\mathbb{D})'$, there is K and $f \in C(\partial\mathbb{D})$ so that*

$$\tau = \left(1 - \frac{d^2}{d\theta^2}\right)^K f \tag{6.3.13}$$

Proof. (6.3.10) holds for some L and some C. Pick K so

$$2K > L + 1 \tag{6.3.14}$$

Let

$$f(\theta) = \sum_{n=-\infty}^{\infty} (1 + n^2)^{-K} \tau_n^\sharp e^{in\theta} \tag{6.3.15}$$

By (6.3.10) and (6.3.14), for $\varepsilon = 2K - L - 1 > 0$,

$$|(1 + n^2)^{-K} \tau_n^\sharp| \le C 2^K (1 + |n|)^{-1-\varepsilon} \tag{6.3.16}$$

(since $(1 + |n|)^2 \leq 2(1 + |n|^2)$), which implies that the sum in (6.3.15) converges uniformly. Thus, $f \in C(\partial\mathbb{D})$. Since

$$\left[\left(1 - \frac{d^2}{d\theta^2}\right)\sigma\right](g) = \sigma\left(\left(1 - \frac{d}{d\theta^2}\right)g\right) \tag{6.3.17}$$

we see

$$\left[\left(1 - \frac{d^2}{d\theta^2}\right)^K f\right]_n^\sharp = (1 + n^2)^K f_n^\sharp = \tau_n^\sharp$$

proving (6.3.13). $\square$

Problems

1. (a) Let $\sigma \in C^\infty(\partial\mathbb{D})'$. For $f \in \mathcal{S}(\mathbb{R})$, define

$$W(f)(x) = \sum_{n=-\infty}^{\infty} f(x + 2\pi n) \tag{6.3.18}$$

and prove there is $\widetilde{W}(f) \in C^\infty(\partial\mathbb{D})$ so that

$$\widetilde{W}(f)(e^{i\theta}) = W(f)(\theta) \tag{6.3.19}$$

(b) Let $\tau \in \mathcal{S}'(\mathbb{R})$ be given by $\tau = \widetilde{W}^t(\sigma)$, that is,

$$\tau(f) = \sigma(\widetilde{W}(f)) \tag{6.3.20}$$

Prove that τ obeys $T_{2\pi}\tau = \tau$.

(c) Prove that $\widetilde{W}^t$ is a continuous bijection of $C^\infty(\partial\mathbb{D})'$ and $\{\tau \in \mathcal{S}'(\mathbb{R}) \mid T_{2\pi}\tau = \tau\}$ (continuous with the $\sigma((C^\infty)', C^\infty)$-topology on $(C^\infty)'$ and $\sigma(\mathcal{S}', \mathcal{S})$-topology on $\mathcal{S}'$).

2. Prove the seminorms $\{\|\cdot\|_{\ell;2}\}_{\ell=0}^{\infty}$ of (6.3.4) and $\{\|\cdot\|_\ell\}_{\ell=0}^{\infty}$ of (6.3.2) are equivalent.

3. Provide the details of the proof of Theorem 6.3.2.

6.4. Hermite Expansions

In the last section, we saw the map $f \mapsto f^\sharp$ from $C^\infty(\partial\mathbb{D})$ to a sequence space was useful—it turned a C^∞ condition to something simple (namely, decay) and made $C^\infty(\partial\mathbb{D})'$ into a sequence space also. The analog of Theorem 6.2.9 was easy in terms of $(-\frac{d^2}{d\theta^2} + 1)$.

In this section, we find something similar for $\mathcal{S}(\mathbb{R}^\nu)$. At first sight, one might imagine the analog of Fourier series should be Fourier transform, but the range is not a sequence space and instead of the complicated combination of C^∞ and polynomial decay, we get polynomial decay and C^∞—that is, no change! In place of $-\frac{d^2}{d\theta^2}$, we'll deal (when $\nu = 1$) with $-\frac{d^2}{dx^2} + x^2$, or more precisely,

$$H_0 = \frac{1}{2}\left(-\frac{d^2}{dx^2} + x^2 - 1\right) \tag{6.4.1}$$

which is clearly a continuous operator of $\mathcal{S}$ to $\mathcal{S}$. It will turn out that H_0 has a complete L^2-basis of eigenvectors in $\mathcal{S}(\mathbb{R})$, $\{\varphi_n(x)\}_{n=0}^\infty$ and the Fourier coefficients in this basis will be the analog of $f \mapsto f^\sharp$. We'll do $\mathbb{R}$ first and then $\mathbb{R}^\nu$ will be easy.

In this section, we'll prove structural results for $\mathcal{S}$ and $\mathcal{S}'$, for example, a form of Theorem 6.2.9 that any $\tau \in \mathcal{S}'(\mathbb{R}^\nu)$ can be written

$$\tau = (H_0 + 1)^L F \tag{6.4.2}$$

for some L and some $F \in C(\mathbb{R}^\nu)$ (i.e., bounded continuous functions on $\mathbb{R}^\nu$). In the next section, we'll see that this basis provides new insights and simple proofs for the basics of Fourier transform. In this section, we'll also use the Hermite expansion to study the Segal–Bargmann transform, a map of $\mathcal{S}'(\mathbb{R}^\nu)$ to a space of analytic functions on $\mathbb{C}^\nu$.

(6.4.1) is the quantum mechanical harmonic oscillator Hamiltonian, so we call the φ_n the *harmonic oscillator* or H.O. *basis*. Since the φ_n's will essentially be Hermite polynomials times a Gaussian, the expansion $f = \sum_{n=0}^\infty f_n^\sharp \varphi_n$ we'll call the Hermite expansion. As noted, we start with $\mathbb{R}$, that is, $\nu = 1$. As a preliminary (from which we'll get completeness of the φ_n's as an orthonormal basis):

Theorem 6.4.1. *Let*

$$\varphi_0(x) = \pi^{-1/4} \exp(-\tfrac{1}{2}x^2) \tag{6.4.3}$$

so that

$$\int |\varphi_0(x)|^2 \, dx = 1 \tag{6.4.4}$$

Then $\{p(x)\varphi_0(x) \mid p \text{ a polynomial}\} \equiv \mathcal{R}$ is dense in $L^2(\mathbb{R}, dx)$ in $\|\cdot\|_2$.

Remark. If you read Section 5.6, you'll note some connections between our proof there of uniqueness of the moment problem and the argument here. Indeed, it is known (see Section 7.7 of Part 4) that if the moment problem for $d\mu$ is determinate, then the polynomials are dense in $L^2(\mathbb{R}, d\mu)$.

Proof. Define

$$d\mu_0(x) = \pi^{-1/2} \exp(-x^2) \, dx \tag{6.4.5}$$

By (4.11.24), $d\mu_0$ is a probability measure proving (6.4.4). The map $f \mapsto f\varphi_0$ is a unitary map of $L^2(\mathbb{R}, d\mu_0)$ to $L^2(\mathbb{R}, dx)$, so the claim is equivalent to saying $\mathcal{R}_0 = \{p \mid \text{polynomials}\}$ is dense in $L^2(\mathbb{R}, d\mu_0)$.

For any $z \in \mathbb{C}$, for all $x \in \mathbb{R}$,

$$f_{N,z}(x) = \sum_{n=0}^{N} \frac{z^n x^n}{n!} \to e^{zx} \tag{6.4.6}$$

Moreover,

$$|f_{N,z}(x)| \le \exp(|xz|) \le \exp(|z|x) + \exp(-|z|x)$$

so, by the dominated convergence theorem, $f_{N,z}(x) \to e^{zx}$ in $L^2(\mathbb{R}, d\mu)$, so $e^{iax} \in \overline{\mathcal{R}}_0$ for all $a \in \mathbb{R}$.

For $b > 0$,

$$\int_0^\infty e^{\pm iax} e^{-ab} \, da = (b \mp ix)^{-1} \tag{6.4.7}$$

converges in $L^2(\mathbb{R}, d\mu)$, so $(x \pm ic)^{-1} \in \overline{\mathcal{R}}_0$ for all $c > 0$. Taking repeated derivatives which also converge in $L^2(\mathbb{R}, d\mu)$, we see for all $N = 0, 1, 2, \ldots$ that

$$(x \pm i)^{-N} \in \overline{\mathcal{R}}_0 \tag{6.4.8}$$

By repeated use of

$$(x + i)^{-1}(x - i)^{-1} = \tfrac{1}{2} i[(x + i)^{-1} - (x - i)^{-1}] \tag{6.4.9}$$

we see $(x + i)^{-N}(x - i)^{-M}$ can be written as a sum of $(x \pm i)^{-L}$, so $\overline{\mathcal{R}}_0$ contains all finite linear combinations of $(x+i)^{-N}(x-i)^{-M}$. Such sums are an algebra, closed under complex conjugation, and which separates points. So, by the Stone–Weierstrass theorem, $C(\mathbb{R}_\infty)$, the continuous functions with a limit at ∞, are in the uniform closure, and so L^2-closure of $\mathcal{R}_0$. But $C(\mathbb{R}_\infty)$ is dense in L^2, so $\overline{\mathcal{R}}_0 = L^2(\mathbb{R}, d\mu_0)$. $\square$

Now we use some algebra of "creation and annihilation operators" that the reader may have seen in quantum mechanics courses. As maps of $\mathcal{S}(\mathbb{R})$ to $\mathcal{S}(\mathbb{R})$, we define

$$A = \frac{1}{\sqrt{2}}\left(x + \frac{d}{dx}\right), \qquad A^\dagger = \frac{1}{\sqrt{2}}\left(x - \frac{d}{dx}\right) \tag{6.4.10}$$

where "x" is shorthand for the map $f(x) \to xf(x)$. Here are the simplest properties ($\langle \cdot, \cdot \rangle$ is shorthand for $L^2(\mathbb{R}, dx)$ inner product and $[B, C] = BC - CB$):

Theorem 6.4.2. (a) *For $f, g \in \mathcal{S}(\mathbb{R})$,*

$$\langle f, Ag \rangle = \langle A^\dagger f, g \rangle \tag{6.4.11}$$

(b) *If φ_0 is given by (6.4.3), then*

$$A\varphi_0 = 0 \tag{6.4.12}$$

(c) *We have*

$$\left[\frac{d}{dx}, x\right] = 1, \quad [A, A^\dagger] = 1, \quad [A^\dagger, H_0] = -A^\dagger \tag{6.4.13}$$

(d) *If H_0 is given by* (6.4.1), *then*

$$H_0 = A^\dagger A \tag{6.4.14}$$

(e) *If F is a polynomially bounded C^∞ function (with all derivatives polynomially bounded), then*

$$A^\dagger(F\varphi_0) = \frac{1}{\sqrt{2}}\,(2xF - F')\varphi_0 \tag{6.4.15}$$

Remark. The use of $1/\sqrt{2}$ in (6.4.10) is so that $[A, A^\dagger]$ will be 1.

Proof. (a) is a simple integration by parts.

(b) Immediate from $\frac{d}{dx}\varphi_0 = -x\varphi_0$.

(c) An easy computation, given $[\frac{d}{dx}, x] = 1$ (see below).

(d) $[\frac{d}{dx}, x] = 1$ is just Liebnitz's rule; $[A, A^\dagger] = 1$ follows from that. Finally,

$$[A^\dagger, H_0] = [A^\dagger, A^\dagger A] = A^\dagger[A^\dagger, A] = -A^\dagger \tag{6.4.16}$$

(e) $\frac{d}{dx}(F\varphi_0) = F'\varphi_0 + F\varphi_0' = F'\varphi_0 - xF\varphi_0$. $\qquad\qquad\square$

Theorem 6.4.3 (H.O. Basis). (a) *We have that*

$$\|\varphi_n\| = 1, \qquad H_0\varphi_n = n\varphi_n \Rightarrow \|A^\dagger\varphi_n\|^2 = (n+1) \tag{6.4.17}$$

and

$$H_0(A^\dagger\varphi_n) = (n+1)A^\dagger\varphi_n \tag{6.4.18}$$

(b) *If we define φ_n by*

$$\varphi_n = \frac{1}{\sqrt{n!}}\,(A^\dagger)^n\varphi_0 \tag{6.4.19}$$

then

$$\|\varphi_n\| = 1, \quad H_0\varphi_n = n\varphi_n, \quad \langle\varphi_n, \varphi_m\rangle = 0 \text{ if } n \neq m \tag{6.4.20}$$

and

$$A\varphi_n = \sqrt{n}\,\varphi_{n-1}, \quad A^\dagger\varphi_n = \sqrt{n+1}\,\varphi_{n+1}, \quad \varphi_n(-x) = (-1)^n\varphi_n(x) \tag{6.4.21}$$

(c) *$\{\varphi_n\}_{n=0}^\infty$ is an orthonormal basis for $L^2(\mathbb{R}, dx)$.*

(d) *For $\ell = 0, 1, 2, \ldots$ and $m = 0, 1, 2, \ldots$, there are constants $C_{\ell,m} > 0$ so that*

$$\left\|x^m \frac{d^\ell\varphi_n}{dx^\ell}\right\|_\infty \leq C_{\ell,m}(1 + |n|)^{\frac{1}{2}\ell + \frac{1}{2}m + 1} \tag{6.4.22}$$

Remarks. 1. There is an alternate proof of $\langle \varphi_n, \varphi_m \rangle = 0$ if $n \neq m$ using (6.4.21); see Problem 1.

2. We'll prove
$$\varphi_n(x) = p_n(x)\varphi_0 \tag{6.4.23}$$
where p_n is a polynomial of degree n. It is related to the Hermite polynomials discussed in Section 14.4 of Part 2B. Indeed, if $H_n(x)$ is the n-th Hermite polynomial, we have
$$\varphi_n(x) = (2^n n!)^{-1/2} H_n(x) \varphi_0(x) \tag{6.4.24}$$

3. (6.4.22) is not optimal; for example, it is known that $\|\varphi_n\|_\infty$ is bounded.

Proof. (a) We have
$$\begin{aligned}
\|A^\dagger \varphi_n\|^2 &= \langle A^\dagger \varphi_n, A^\dagger \varphi \rangle \\
&= \langle \varphi_n, (AA^\dagger)\varphi_n \rangle \qquad \text{(by (6.4.11))} \\
&= \langle \varphi_n, (H_0 + 1)\varphi_n \rangle \qquad \text{(by (6.4.13) and (6.4.14))} \\
&= (n+1)
\end{aligned}$$

By (6.4.13),
$$H_0(A^\dagger \varphi_n) = A^\dagger(H_0 \varphi_n) - [A^\dagger, H_0]\varphi_n = (n+1)A^\dagger \varphi_n \tag{6.4.25}$$

(b) By induction and (6.4.18), $H_0 \varphi_n = n\varphi_n$. By induction and (6.4.17), $\|\varphi_n\| = 1$. We have
$$(n-m)\langle \varphi_n, \varphi_m \rangle = \langle H_0 \varphi_n, \varphi_m \rangle - \langle \varphi_n, H_0 \varphi_m \rangle = 0 \tag{6.4.26}$$
Since $n - m \neq 0$, $\langle \varphi_n, \varphi_m \rangle = 0$.

The second formula in (6.4.21) is immediate from (6.4.19). The first formula follows from $AA^\dagger = A^\dagger A + 1 = (H_0 + 1)$ and $\varphi_n = n^{-1/2}A^\dagger \varphi_{n-1}$. The final formula is immediate from
$$A^\dagger(f^\flat) = -(A^\dagger f)^\flat, \qquad \varphi_0^\flat = \varphi_0 \tag{6.4.27}$$

(c) By induction and (6.4.15), it follows that (6.4.23) holds, where p_n is a polynomial of degree precisely n. It follows that $\{p_n\}_{n=0}^\infty$ is an algebraic basis for all polynomials, so by Theorem 6.4.1, the span of $\{\varphi_n\}_{n=0}^\infty$ is dense in L^2. Since $\langle \varphi_n, \varphi_m \rangle = \delta_{nm}$, we have an orthonormal basis.

(d) We first note that since $(1 + x^2)^{-1/2} \in L^2(\mathbb{R}, dx)$,
$$|f(x)| = \left| \int_{-\infty}^\infty (1 + x^2)^{-1/2}(1 + x^2)^{1/2} \frac{df}{dx} \right| \tag{6.4.28}$$
$$\leq C \left\| (1 + x^2)^{1/2} \frac{df}{dx} \right\|_2 \tag{6.4.29}$$

so that

$$\left\| x^m \frac{d^\ell f}{dx^\ell} \right\|_\infty^2 \leq C^2 \left(\left\| \frac{d}{dx} \left(x^m \frac{d^\ell}{dx^\ell} \right) f \right\|_2^2 + \left\| x \frac{d}{dx} \left(x^m \frac{d^\ell}{dx^\ell} \right) f \right\|_2^2 \right) \qquad (6.4.30)$$

Since $\frac{d}{dx} = \frac{1}{\sqrt{2}}(A - A^\dagger)$, $x = \frac{1}{\sqrt{2}}(A + A^\dagger)$, we see that $\| x^m \frac{d^\ell f}{dx^\ell} \|_\infty$ is bounded by a constant times a finite sum of $\| A_1^\sharp \dots A_{m+\ell+1}^\sharp f \|_2$ terms and $\| A_1^\sharp \dots A_{m+\ell+2}^\sharp f \|_2$ terms, where each $A_j^\sharp$ is an A or $A^\dagger$. By (6.4.21),

$$\| A_1^\sharp \dots A_k^\sharp \varphi_n \| \leq C_k (n+1)^k \qquad (6.4.31)$$

(6.4.30) and (6.4.31) imply (6.4.22).   □

For $f \in \mathcal{S}(\mathbb{R})$, define its *Hermite coefficients*

$$f_n^\sharp = \langle \varphi_n, f \rangle \qquad (6.4.32)$$

Let $\mathfrak{s}_1 = \{ \{a_n\}_{n=0}^\infty \mid \sup_n |n^\ell a_n| < \infty \text{ for all } \ell \}$ with the seminorms

$$\|a\|_{\ell;2} = \left(\sum_{n=0}^\infty |(n+1)^\ell a_n|^2 \right)^{1/2} \qquad (6.4.33)$$

This is close to, but because sequences are one-sided, distinct from $\mathfrak{s}$.

Theorem 6.4.4 (Hermite Expansion for $\mathcal{S}(\mathbb{R})$ and $\mathcal{S}'(\mathbb{R})$). (a) $\sharp$ *is a bijection of $\mathcal{S}(\mathbb{R})$ to $\mathfrak{s}_1$ and a homeomorphism of the topology on $\mathcal{S}$ and the one on $\mathfrak{s}_1$ generated by $\{\|\cdot\|_{\ell;2}\}_{\ell=0}^\infty$. Moreover,*

$$\sum_{n=0}^N f_n^\sharp \varphi_n(x) \to f(x) \qquad (6.4.34)$$

as $N \to \infty$ in the topology of $\mathcal{S}$.

(b) *For $\tau \in \mathcal{S}'(\mathbb{R})$, define for $n = 0, 1, \dots$, its Hermite coefficients*

$$\tau_n^\sharp = \tau(\varphi_n) \qquad (6.4.35)$$

Then for some C and L,

$$|\tau_n^\sharp| \leq C(1 + |n|)^L \qquad (6.4.36)$$

For any $f \in \mathcal{S}$,

$$\tau(f) = \lim_{N \to \infty} \sum_{n=0}^N \tau_n^\sharp f_n^\sharp \qquad (6.4.37)$$

(c) *If $\tau_n^\sharp$ is a sequence obeying (6.4.36), then (6.4.37) defines a distribution whose Hermite coefficients are the given $\tau_n^\sharp$. Thus, $\sharp$ sets up a bijection of $\mathcal{S}'(\mathbb{R})$ and sequences obeying (6.4.36).*

Proof. (a) If $f \in \mathcal{S}$,

$$[(H_0 + 1)^\ell f]_n^\sharp = (n+1)^\ell f_n^\sharp \tag{6.4.38}$$

since $\langle \varphi_n, H_0 f \rangle = \langle H_0 \varphi_n, f \rangle = n \langle \varphi_n, f \rangle$. Since $(H_0 + 1)$ maps $\mathcal{S}$ to $\mathcal{S}$, $(H_0 + 1)^\ell f \in \mathcal{S} \subset L^2$ for all ℓ, so $f_n^\sharp \in \mathfrak{s}_1$ and

$$\|f^\sharp\|_{\ell;2} = \|(H_0 + 1)^\ell f\|_{L^2} \tag{6.4.39}$$

Thus, the $\|f^\sharp\|_{\ell;2}$ norms are bounded by finite sums of $\|x^k \frac{d^\ell}{dx} f\|_2$, proving $^\sharp$ is continuous from $\mathcal{S}$ into $\mathfrak{s}_1$.

If $a_n \in \mathfrak{s}_1$, by (6.4.22), $\sum_{n=0}^{\infty} a_n x^m \frac{d^\ell \varphi_n}{dx^\ell}$ converges in $\|\cdot\|_\infty$ for each ℓ to a function $g_{\ell,m}$. Clearly, $x^m g_{\ell,0} = g_{\ell,m}$ and, as usual,

$$g_{0,0}(x) - g_{0,0}(0) = \int_0^x g_{1,0}(y)\, dy \tag{6.4.40}$$

so $g_{\ell,0} = \frac{d^\ell}{dx^\ell} g_{0,0}$. Thus, $g_{0,0}$ is in $\mathcal{S}$ and $(g_{0,0})_n^\sharp = a_n$. Thus, $^\sharp$ is a bijection.

From

$$\left\| x^m \frac{d^\ell}{dx^\ell} f \right\|_2^2 = \sum_{n=0}^{\infty} \left| \left\langle \frac{d^\ell}{dx^\ell} x^m \varphi_n, f \right\rangle \right|^2 \tag{6.4.41}$$

we see, using the same $A_1^\sharp \dots A_k^\sharp$ argument that we used to prove Theorem 6.4.3(d), that $\|x^m \frac{d^\ell}{dx^\ell} f\|_2$ is bounded by an $\|f^\sharp\|_{L;2}$, proving equivalence of the norms.

If $a_n \in \mathfrak{s}$, $(a_0, \dots, a_N, 0, 0, \dots) \to a$ in $\mathfrak{s}$, which implies (6.4.34).

(b), (c) As for $C^\infty(\partial\mathbb{D})'$, this is immediate given (a); see Problem 2. $\qquad\square$

Corollary 6.4.5. $\mathcal{S}(\mathbb{R})$ *is separable.*

Proof. $\{\sum_{n=0}^N a_n \varphi_n \mid a_n \in \mathbb{Q},\ N = 1, 2, \dots\}$ is dense in $\mathcal{S}$. $\qquad\square$

Corollary 6.4.6. $\jmath[\mathcal{S}]$ *is dense in* $\mathcal{S}'$. $\mathcal{S}'$ *is separable in the* $\sigma(\mathcal{S}', \mathcal{S})$-*topology.*

Proof. By (6.4.37), in the $\sigma(\mathcal{S}', \mathcal{S})$-topology,

$$\tau = \lim_{N \to \infty} \jmath \left(\sum_{n=0}^N \tau_n^\sharp \varphi_n \right) \tag{6.4.42}$$

$\qquad\square$

We now turn to $\mathbb{R}^\nu$. For any ν-tuple, $\boldsymbol{\alpha} = (\alpha_1, \dots, \alpha_\nu)$ of nonnegative integers; we define

$$\varphi_{\boldsymbol{\alpha}}(\mathbf{x}) = \prod_{j=1}^\nu \varphi_{\alpha_j}(x_j) \tag{6.4.43}$$

By Theorem 4.11.8, $\{\varphi_{\boldsymbol{\alpha}}\}_{\boldsymbol{\alpha}\in\mathcal{I}_\nu}$ is an orthonormal basis for $L^2(\mathbb{R}^\nu, d^\nu x)$. We let $\mathfrak{s}_\nu$ be the set of *multisequences*, $a_{\boldsymbol{\alpha}}$, indexed by $\boldsymbol{\alpha}\in\mathcal{I}_\nu$, that obey

$$\|a\|_\ell = \sup_{\boldsymbol{\alpha}}(1+|\boldsymbol{\alpha}|)^\ell|a_{\boldsymbol{\alpha}}| < \infty \tag{6.4.44}$$

and we define

$$\|a\|_{\ell;2} = \left(\sum_{\boldsymbol{\alpha}\in\mathcal{I}_\nu}(1+|\boldsymbol{\alpha}|^2)|a_{\boldsymbol{\alpha}}|^2\right)^{1/2} \tag{6.4.45}$$

For $f\in\mathcal{S}(\mathbb{R}^\nu)$, we define the multisequence of *Hermite coefficients*

$$f^\sharp_{\boldsymbol{\alpha}} = \langle\varphi_{\boldsymbol{\alpha}}, f\rangle \tag{6.4.46}$$

Theorem 6.4.7 (Hermite Expansion for $\mathcal{S}(\mathbb{R}^\nu)$ and $\mathcal{S}'(\mathbb{R}^\nu)$). (a) $^\sharp$ *is a bijection of $\mathcal{S}(\mathbb{R}^\nu)$ and $\mathfrak{s}_\nu$ and a homeomorphism of the topology on $\mathcal{S}$ and the one on $\mathfrak{s}_\nu$ generated by $\|\cdot\|_{\ell;2}$. Moreover,*

$$\sum_{|\boldsymbol{\alpha}|\le N} f^\sharp_{\boldsymbol{\alpha}}\varphi_{\boldsymbol{\alpha}}(\mathbf{x}) \to f(\mathbf{x}) \tag{6.4.47}$$

as $N\to\infty$ in the topology of $\mathcal{S}(\mathbb{R}^\nu)$.

(b) *For $\tau\in\mathcal{S}'(\mathbb{R}^\nu)$, define the multisequence*

$$\tau^\sharp_{\boldsymbol{\alpha}} = \tau(\varphi_{\boldsymbol{\alpha}}) \tag{6.4.48}$$

its Hermite coefficients. Then for some C and L,

$$|\tau^\sharp_{\boldsymbol{\alpha}}| \le C(1+|\boldsymbol{\alpha}|)^L \tag{6.4.49}$$

For any $f\in\mathcal{S}$,

$$\tau(f) = \lim_{N\to\infty}\sum_{|\boldsymbol{\alpha}|\le N}\tau^\sharp_{\boldsymbol{\alpha}}f^\sharp_{\boldsymbol{\alpha}} \tag{6.4.50}$$

(c) *If $\tau^\sharp_{\boldsymbol{\alpha}}$ is a multisequence obeying (6.4.49), then (6.4.50) defines a distribution whose Hermite coefficients are the given $\tau^\sharp_{\boldsymbol{\alpha}}$. Thus, $^\sharp$ sets up a bijection of $\mathcal{S}'(\mathbb{R}^\nu)$ and multisequences obeying (6.4.50).*

Proof. By the product nature of $\varphi_{\boldsymbol{\alpha}}$, we have

$$\|x^\gamma D^\beta\varphi_{\boldsymbol{\alpha}}\|_\infty \le C_{\boldsymbol{\alpha},\beta,\gamma}(1+|\boldsymbol{\alpha}|)^{\frac{1}{2}|\beta|+\frac{1}{2}|\gamma|+\nu} \tag{6.4.51}$$

Given this, the proofs are essentially unchanged from the one-dimensional case (Problem 3). ∎

Corollary 6.4.8. $\mathcal{S}(\mathbb{R}^\nu)$ *is separable in its metric topology.* $\jmath[\mathcal{S}(\mathbb{R}^\nu)]$ *is $\sigma(\mathcal{S}',\mathcal{S})$-dense in $\mathcal{S}'(\mathbb{R}^\nu)$.*

The Hermite expansion is useful because it replaces complicated conditions in both x and k by a single decay/growth. For example, the following is a variant of Theorem 6.2.9 (see Problem 4):

Theorem 6.4.9. *For any* $\tau \in \mathcal{S}'(\mathbb{R}^\nu)$, *there is* $M \in \mathbb{N}$ *and a bounded continuous function* F *so that*

$$\tau = (H_0 + 1)^M F \qquad (6.4.52)$$

Proof. Let τ obey (6.4.49). Pick $M = L + 2\nu + 1$ and

$$F(\mathbf{x}) = \sum_{\boldsymbol{\alpha} \in \mathcal{I}_\nu} (1 + |\boldsymbol{\alpha}|)^{-M} \tau_{\boldsymbol{\alpha}}^\sharp \varphi_{\boldsymbol{\alpha}}(\mathbf{x}) \qquad (6.4.53)$$

By (6.4.51),

$$\sum_{\boldsymbol{\alpha} \in \mathcal{I}_\nu} (1 + |\boldsymbol{\alpha}|)^{-M} |\tau_{\boldsymbol{\alpha}}^\sharp| \, \|\varphi_{\boldsymbol{\alpha}}\|_\infty < \infty \qquad (6.4.54)$$

so the sum in (6.4.53) converges to a bounded continuous function. Since $H_0 \varphi_{\boldsymbol{\alpha}} = (\alpha_1 + \cdots + \alpha_\nu)\varphi_n = |\boldsymbol{\alpha}|\varphi_{\boldsymbol{\alpha}}$, we have (6.4.52). $\qquad \square$

Another interesting application (Problem 5) is to prove that, as topological vector spaces, $\mathcal{S}(\mathbb{R}^{\nu_1})$ and $\mathcal{S}(\mathbb{R}^{\nu_2})$ are isomorphic for all ν_1, ν_2! An important application is

Theorem 6.4.10 (Schwartz Kernel Theorem). *Let* $T \colon \mathcal{S}(\mathbb{R}^{\nu_1}) \times \mathcal{S}(\mathbb{R}^{\nu_2}) \to \mathbb{C}$ *be a bilinear functional which is separately continuous. Then there is* $\tau \in \mathcal{S}'(\mathbb{R}^{\nu_1 + \nu_2})$ *so that with*

$$(f \otimes g)(x, y) = f(x)g(y) \qquad (6.4.55)$$

we have

$$T(f, g) = \tau(f \otimes g) \qquad (6.4.56)$$

Remark. This theorem made a big splash at the time it was found. A variety of operators from some L^p to L^q have the form

$$f \mapsto \int K(x, y) f(y) \, d\mu(y) \qquad (6.4.57)$$

for some measurable function K and were said to have an *integral kernel*; see Section 4.9. The identity operator on L^2 is a good example of an operator which doesn't have an integral kernel. But the above theorem says that formally, if $A \colon \mathcal{S}(\mathbb{R}^{\nu_1}) \to \mathcal{S}'(\mathbb{R}^{\nu_2})$, then formally,

$$(Af)(x) = \int \tau(x, y) g(y) \, d^\nu x \qquad (6.4.58)$$

so A *always* has an integral kernel! Of course, since $\mathcal{S}(\mathbb{R}^\nu) \subset L^p(\mathbb{R}^\nu, d^\nu x) \subset \mathcal{S}'(\mathbb{R}^\nu)$, any map $A \colon L^p(\mathbb{R}^{\nu_1}, d^{\nu_1} x) \to L^q(\mathbb{R}^{\nu_2}, d^{\nu_2} x)$ restricts to a map of $\mathcal{S}(\mathbb{R}^{\nu_1})$ to $\mathcal{S}'(\mathbb{R}^{\nu_2})$ and so has a *distributional* integral kernel. So the identity on L^2 has an "integral kernel" after all, namely, $\delta(x - y)$!

Proof. For Banach spaces, you showed in Problem 14 of Section 5.4 that separate continuity of bilinear forms implies joint continuity. The same is true for Fréchet spaces (Problem 6), that is, if T is separately continuous, it is jointly continuous; so there exist continuous seminorms, ρ_j, on $\mathcal{S}(\mathbb{R}^{\nu_j})$ so that

$$|T(f,g)| \leq \rho_1(f)\rho_2(g) \qquad (6.4.59)$$

Since $\|(H_0+1)^\ell f\|_2$ are increasing in ℓ, that means (Problem 7) there are C_1, ℓ_1, and ℓ_2 so that

$$|T(f,g)| \leq C\|(H_0+1)^{\ell_1}f\|_2 \, \|(H_0+1)^{\ell_2}g\| \qquad (6.4.60)$$

(where the H_0's are $\sum_{j=1}^{\nu_1} H_{0,j}$ and $\sum_{j=1}^{\nu_2} H_{0,j}$, respectively). If $\alpha \in \mathcal{I}_{\nu_1}$ and $\beta \in \mathcal{I}_{\nu_2}$, define

$$\tilde{\tau}_{(\alpha,\beta)} = T(\varphi_\alpha, \varphi_\beta) \qquad (6.4.61)$$

By (6.4.59),

$$\tilde{\tau}_{(\alpha,\beta)} \leq C(1+|\alpha|)^{\ell_1}(1+|\beta|)^{\ell_2} \leq C(1+|\alpha|+|\beta|)^{\ell_1+\ell_2} \qquad (6.4.62)$$

Thus, there is a distribution $\tau \in \mathcal{S}'(\mathbb{R}^{\nu_1+\nu_2})$ so that

$$\tau^\sharp_{(\alpha,\beta)} = \tilde{\tau}_{(\alpha,\beta)} \qquad (6.4.63)$$

By (6.4.47), we have

$$
\begin{aligned}
T(f,g) &= \lim_{N\to\infty} T\left(\sum_{|\alpha|\leq N} f^\sharp_\alpha \varphi_\alpha, \sum_{|\beta|\leq N} g^\sharp_\beta \varphi_\beta\right) \\
&= \lim_{N\to\infty} \sum_{\substack{|\alpha|\leq N \\ |\beta|\leq N}} f^\sharp_\alpha g^\sharp_\beta \tilde{\tau}_{(\alpha,\beta)} \\
&= \lim_{N\to\infty} \tau\left(\left(\sum_{|\alpha|\leq N} f^\sharp_\alpha \varphi_\alpha\right) \otimes \left(\sum_{|\beta|\leq N} g^\sharp_\beta \varphi_\beta\right)\right) \\
&= \tau(f \otimes g) \qquad (6.4.64)
\end{aligned}
$$

$\square$

As an aside and separate topic, we turn to a representation of $\mathcal{S}(\mathbb{R}^\nu)$ and $\mathcal{S}'(\mathbb{R}^\nu)$ as spaces of entire analytic functions—which can be a useful tool in the study of the Fourier transform since the Fourier transform will turn out to be change of variables from z to iz. Part of the motivation comes from $[A, A^\dagger] = 1$ (see (6.4.13)) which will be realized with

$$\widetilde{A}^\dagger = \text{multiplication by } z, \qquad \widetilde{A} = \frac{\partial}{\partial z} \qquad (6.4.65)$$

As for Hermite expansions, a central role is played by a Hilbert space and a distinguished orthonormal basis. We'll call this space Fock space and the map of $L^2(\mathbb{R}, d^\nu x)$, $\mathcal{S}(\mathbb{R}, d^\nu x)$, $\mathcal{S}'(\mathbb{R}^\nu, d^\nu x)$ to entire analytic functions, the Segal-Bargmann transform.

We'll suppose some elementary knowledge of analytic function theory, at the least Chapter 2 of Part 2A. In particular, we'll use the symbols $z = x + iy \in \mathbb{C}$, $\bar{z} = x - iy$, and $\partial, \bar{\partial}$ (Wirtinger calculus) defined by

$$\partial = \frac{1}{2}\left(\frac{\partial}{\partial x} - i\frac{\partial}{\partial y}\right), \ \bar{\partial} = \frac{1}{2}\left(\frac{\partial}{\partial x} + i\frac{\partial}{\partial y}\right) \qquad (6.4.66)$$

so $\partial, \bar{\partial}$ obey Leibniz's rule and

$$\partial z = 1, \ \bar{\partial}z = 0, \ \partial\bar{z} = 0, \ \bar{\partial}\bar{z} = 1 \qquad (6.4.67)$$

The Cauchy-Riemann equations say that a C^1 function of x and y is analytic if and only if

$$\bar{\partial}f = 0, \ \text{and then} \ f'(z) = (\partial f)(z) \qquad (6.4.68)$$

We'll need the measure on $\mathbb{C}^\nu$:

$$d\lambda(z) = \pi^{-\nu}\exp(-|z|^2)d^2z_1\ldots d^2z_\nu \qquad (6.4.69)$$

For now, we'll pick it out of a hat, but the calculation below that, for the case $\nu = 1$, the adjoint of $\frac{\partial}{\partial z}$ is z works only for multiples of $\exp(-|z|^2)d^2z$. *Fock space*, $\mathcal{F}_\nu$, is the set of all entire analytic functions, f, on $\mathbb{C}^\nu$ with

$$\int |f(z)|^2 d\lambda(z) < \infty \qquad (6.4.70)$$

The inner product is the one induced by viewing $\mathcal{F}_\nu$ as a subspace of $L^2(\mathbb{C}^\nu, d\lambda)$. Cauchy estimates imply that L^2 convergence of analytic functions implies local uniform convergence, so $\mathcal{F}_\nu$ is a closed subspace of $L^2(\mathbb{C}, d\lambda)$ and thus a Hilbert space. We'll use $\mathcal{P}_\nu \subset \mathcal{F}_\nu$ for the space of polynomials in $\{z_j\}_{j=1}^\nu$ which we'll soon see are dense in $\mathcal{F}_\nu$.

Theorem 6.4.11. (a) *Let $A_j^\dagger$ be multiplication by z_j and A_j be ∂_j defined on $\mathcal{P}_\nu$. Then $A_j^\dagger$ is the formal adjoint of A_j in the sense that for all $f, g \in \mathcal{P}$,*

$$< f, A_j g > = < A_j^\dagger f, g > \qquad (6.4.71)$$

(b) *For any multi-index $\alpha = (\alpha_1, \ldots, \alpha_j)$ define*

$$\widetilde{\varphi}_\alpha(z) = \prod_{j=1}^\nu (\alpha_j!)^{-1/2} z_j^{\alpha_j} \qquad (6.4.72)$$

Then the $\{\widetilde{\varphi}_a\}_{\alpha \in \mathcal{I}_\nu}$ are an orthonormal set.

(c) *The $\widetilde{\varphi}_\alpha$ are an orthonormal basis. Thus the Fourier expansion*

$$\sum_\alpha < \widetilde{\varphi}_\alpha, f > \widetilde{\varphi}_\alpha \qquad (6.4.73)$$

is the Taylor expansion of f.

(d) *An entire function*

$$f(z) = \sum_\alpha a_\alpha z^\alpha \tag{6.4.74}$$

lies in $\mathcal{F}_\nu$ if and only if

$$\sum_\alpha |a_\alpha|^2 \left(\prod_{j=1}^\nu \alpha_j!\right) < \infty \tag{6.4.75}$$

Remark. $\mathcal{F}_\nu$ is an L^2 reproducing kernel Hilbert space in the sense of Problem 6 of Section 3.3. In Problem 8 of this section, the reader will prove that the reproducing kernel is given by

$$K(z, w) = \exp\left(\sum_{j=1}^\nu z_j \bar{w}_j\right) \tag{6.4.76}$$

Proof. (a) Because of the decay of $\exp(-|z|^2)$, which is faster than any polynomial, we can integrate by parts. Because of the complex conjugate in the inner product, ∂_j turns as $\bar{\partial}_j$. If $W(z) = \exp(-|z|^2)$, we need to compute

$$\begin{aligned}
-\bar{\partial}_j[Wf] &= (-\bar{\partial}_j W)f \tag{6.4.77} \\
&= \bar{\partial}_j \left[|z|^2\right](Wf) \\
&= z_j W f \tag{6.4.78}
\end{aligned}$$

proving (6.4.71). To get (6.4.77), we use the Cauchy-Riemann equation $\bar{\partial}_j f = 0$ and to get (6.4.78) we use

$$\bar{\partial}_j |z_j|^2 = \bar{\partial}_j(z_j \bar{z}_j) = z_j \bar{\partial}_j \bar{z}_j = z_j \tag{6.4.79}$$

since $\partial_j z_j = 0$ (and for $k \neq j$, $\bar{\partial}_j z_k = \bar{\partial}_j \bar{z}_k = 0$)

(b) $[A_j, A_k^\dagger] = \delta_{jk} \mathbb{1}$ on polynomials, and $< \widetilde{\varphi}_0, \tilde{\varphi}_0 >= 1$, and $A_j \tilde{\varphi}_0 = 0$ so the algebra that proved the Hermite basis was orthonomal in $L^2(\mathbb{R}^\nu, d^\nu x)$ implies the $\widetilde{\varphi}_\alpha$'s are orthonormal.

(c), (d) By the Cauchy integral formula, if f is given by (6.4.74), then

$$\int f(R_1 e^{i\theta_1}, \dots, R_\nu e^{i\theta_\nu}) e^{-i\sum_{j=1}^\nu \alpha_j \theta_j} \frac{d\theta_1}{2\pi} \cdots \frac{d\theta_\nu}{2\pi} = a_\alpha \tag{6.4.80}$$

Then, changing in $d^2 z_j$ to polar coordinates shows

$$< \varphi_\alpha, f >= a_\alpha \prod_{j=1}^\nu (\alpha_j!)^{1/2} \tag{6.4.81}$$

Thus, if $f \in \mathcal{F}_\nu$ and is orthonormal to all φ_α, all of its Taylor coefficients are zero, so $f = 0$. This proves completeness, i.e., that $\{\varphi_\nu\}_{\alpha \in \mathcal{F}_\nu}$ is a basis.

(6.4.7) is the Parseval relation and that $f \in \mathcal{F}$ if and only if (6.4.7) holds is the description of a Hilbert space and the Fourier coefficients of a basis. $\qquad \square$

Given a distribution, $\tau \in \mathcal{S}'(\mathbb{R}^\nu)$, we define its *Segal-Bargmann transform* as a function of $\mathbb{C}^\nu$ by

$$(\mathbb{B}\tau)(z) = \pi^{-\nu/4} \int \exp\left(-\frac{1}{2}(z^2 + x^2) + \sqrt{2}zx\right)\tau(x)d^\nu x \qquad (6.4.82)$$

As usual, this is formal notation and the integral means applying τ to the function $\left(z \in \mathbb{C}^\nu, x \in \mathbb{R}^\nu, z^2 = \sum_{j=1}^\nu z_j^2, z \cdot x = \sum_{j=1}^\nu z_j x_j\right)$

$$A_z(x) = \exp\left(-\frac{1}{2}(z^2 + x^2) + \sqrt{2}z \cdot x\right) \qquad (6.4.83)$$

The reason for this choice and how it might be computed is found in Problems 9 and 11. Here are the basic properties of $\mathbb{B}$.

Theorem 6.4.12. (a) *Each $\mathbb{B}\tau$ defines an entire analytic function.*

(b) *For $f \in \mathcal{S}(\mathbb{R}^\nu)$, we have for $j = 1, \dots, \nu$*

$$\widetilde{A}_j(\mathbb{B}f) = \mathbb{B}(A_j f), \quad \widetilde{A_j^\dagger}(\mathbb{B}f) = \mathbb{B}(A_j^\dagger f) \qquad (6.4.84)$$

(c) $\mathbb{B}\varphi_\alpha = \tilde{\varphi}_\alpha$ $\qquad\qquad\qquad\qquad\qquad\qquad\qquad\qquad (6.4.85)$

for any multi-index α.

(d) $\mathbb{B}$ *is a unitary map of $L^2(\mathbb{R}^\nu, d^\nu x)$ onto $\mathcal{F}_\nu$.*

(e) *If $\mathbb{B}\tau = \mathbb{B}\sigma$, then $\tau = \sigma$.*

(f) $g = \mathbb{B}f$ *for some f in $\mathcal{S}(\mathbb{R}^\nu)$ if and only if*

$$g(z) = \sum_\alpha a_\alpha z^\alpha \qquad (6.4.86)$$

with

$$\sup\left[(1 + |\alpha|^2)^N |a_\alpha| \prod_{j=1}^\nu (\alpha_j!)^{1/2}\right] < \infty \qquad (6.4.87)$$

for all N.

(g) $g = \mathbb{B}\tau$ *for some τ in $\mathcal{S}'(\mathbb{R}^\nu)$ if and only if for some N and C and all α*

$$|a_\alpha| \prod_{j=1}^\nu (\alpha_j!)^{1/2} \leq C(1 + |\alpha|^2)^N \qquad (6.4.88)$$

(h) *For every $\tau \in \mathcal{S}'(\mathbb{R}^\nu)$, we have that*

$$|(\mathbb{B}\tau)(z)| \leq C_1 \exp(C_2 |z|^2) \qquad (6.4.89)$$

(i) *For any $\tau \in \mathcal{S}'(\mathbb{R}^\nu)$,*

$$(B\hat{\tau})(z) = (\mathbb{B}\tau)(-iz) \qquad (6.4.90)$$

Remarks. 1. Apriori, (6.4.84) is claimed for f with $\mathbb{B}f \in \mathcal{P}$, so $\widetilde{A}\mathbb{B}f$, $\widetilde{A}^{\dagger}\mathbb{B}f$ are defined, but we'll prove it for $f \in \mathcal{S}$!

2. The reader will prove (Problem 8 (e)) that (6.4.89) holds (with a prefactor of $(1 + |z|)^N$) for $C_2 = \frac{1}{2}$ which is best possible since $f(z) = e^{az^2} \in \mathcal{F}$, for any $a < \frac{1}{2}$.

3. From the point of view of this chapter, part (i) is the most significant since it shows that $\mathbb{B}\tau$ contains information about τ and $\hat{\tau}$. We'll use this in Theorems 4.1.7 and 4.5.1 of Part 3.

4. That $\mathbb{B}\tau$ is unitary implies an inverse formula for $f \in \mathcal{F}_\nu$:

$$(\mathbb{B}^{-1}f)(x) = \pi^{-5\nu/4} \int \overline{A_z(x)} f(z) d^2 z \qquad (6.4.91)$$

Indeed for any $f \in L^2(\mathbb{C}, d^\nu z)$, the right-hand side is $\mathbb{B}^{-1}Pf$ where P is the projection on $\mathcal{F}_\nu$.

Proof. (a) The function A_z is clearly in $\mathcal{S}(\mathbb{R}_\nu)$ and is differentiable in each z_j as an $\mathcal{S}$-valued function (in that the difference quotient converges in each $\mathcal{S}$-norm). Thus, $\tau(A_z)$ is an entire analytic function.

(b) (This is the key step!) We note that

$$\frac{\partial A_z}{\partial x_j} = (-x_j + \sqrt{2}z_j)A_z, \quad \frac{\partial A_z}{\partial z_j} = (-z_j + \sqrt{2}x_j)A_z \qquad (6.4.92)$$

The first equation and an integration by parts proves that for $f \in \mathcal{S}(\mathbb{R}^\nu)$, we have that

$$\mathbb{B}\left(\frac{\partial f}{\partial x_j}\right) = \mathbb{B}((x_j - \sqrt{2}z_j)f) \qquad (6.4.93)$$

so, by definition of $A_j^{\dagger}$, we see for all $f \in \mathcal{S}$,

$$\mathbb{B}(A_j^{\dagger}f) = z_j \mathbb{B}(f) \qquad (6.4.94)$$

proving the second equation in (6.4.84) for all f with $\mathbb{B}(f) \in \mathcal{P}$. It is then easy to extend it to all distributions so long as $\widetilde{A}_j^{\dagger}$ is still defined as multiplication by z_j.

The second equation in (6.4.92) shows that

$$
\begin{aligned}
\frac{\partial}{\partial z_j}\mathbb{B}(f) &= \mathbb{B}((\sqrt{2}x_j - z_j)f) \\
&= \mathbb{B}((\sqrt{2}x_j - A_j^{\dagger})f) \\
&= \mathbb{B}(A_j f) \qquad (6.4.95)
\end{aligned}
$$

since $A_j + A_j^{\dagger} = \sqrt{2}x_j$.

(c) Since

$$A_z(x)e^{-1/2x^2} = \exp\left(-(x - \frac{z}{\sqrt{2}})^2\right) \tag{6.4.96}$$

we see (doing the Gaussian integral when $z = 0$), that $\mathbb{B}\varphi_0$ is constant and that the constant is 1, i.e., (6.4.85) holds with $\alpha = 0$. The formula for $\varphi_\alpha, \widetilde{\varphi}_\alpha$ in terms of $A_j^\dagger, \widetilde{A}_j^\dagger$ and φ_0 and (6.4.84) imply (6.4.85) in general.

(d) Immediate since $\mathbb{B}$ maps an orthonormal basis to an orthonormal basis.

(e) If $\mathbb{B}\tau = \mathbb{B}\sigma$, then they have the same Taylor coefficients, so τ and σ have the same Hermite coefficients so by Theorem 6.4.7, $\tau = \sigma$.

(f), (g) The a_α's are up to a factor of $\prod_{j=1}^{\nu}(\alpha_j!)^{1/2}$, the Hermite coefficients of τ, so this is Theorem 6.4.7.

(h) follows from a simple Schwartz space norm estimate on the function $A_z(x)$ of (6.4.83).

(i) This requires the relation between the Fourier transform and Hermite expansions only proved in the next section. Since (see (6.5.15)) $(\hat{f})_\alpha^\sharp = (-i)^\alpha f_\alpha^\sharp$, we see that

$$\begin{aligned}
(\mathbb{B}\hat{\tau})(z) &= \sum_\alpha (\hat{\tau})_\alpha z^\alpha / \prod \sqrt{\alpha_j!} \\
&= \sum_\alpha (\tau)_\alpha(-iz)^\alpha / \prod \sqrt{\alpha_j!} \\
&= (\mathbb{B}\tau)(-iz) \tag{6.4.97}
\end{aligned}$$

$\square$

Notes and Historical Remarks. The use of Hermite expansions to study Fourier transform (as we do in the next section) goes back to Wiener [**996**, **998**] in the early 1930s. It is also used for this purpose in Dym–McKean [**268**]. Its use for structure theorems and especially for the kernel theorem for $\mathcal{S}$ is from Simon [**847**].

Charles Hermite (1822–1901) is best known for his polynomials (which others had earlier) and Hermitian matrices—an extremely useful idea—but he had much deeper mathematics. His first important contribution was suggesting to Liouville, one of his mentors, the use of complex integration methods in the study of elliptic functions. He first made a big splash with his method for solving quintic equations (which it was known couldn't be solved in terms of roots) using elliptic functions. In 1873, he proved that e was transcendental—his methods were used in 1882 by von Lindeman to prove that π is transcendental.

Hermite had difficulties with his education, in part because he was lame from his youth and students at the École Polytechnique were required to be army officers. But by 1862, he was established as faculty at École Polytechnique and afterwards at the Sorbonne. His formal students include Padé and Poincaré but he was a legendary teacher and both Hadamard and Picard regarded him as a mentor. He championed Stieltjes and had an extensive correspondence with him.

The name *creation* and *annihilation operators* comes from the analogs in quantum field theory. In quantum mechanics, they are also called *ladder operators*. They were used first by Dirac [**248**]—if $p = -i\frac{d}{dx}$, our A is $x + ip$. Dirac used $p - ix$.

Schwartz's kernel theorem appeared with an involved proof in his earliest papers. A simple proof of the version for $C_0^\infty(\mathbb{R}^\nu)$ (essentially using Fourier series in hypercubes) is due to Gel'fand–Vilenkin [**344**, Vol. 4].

What we call Fock space (also called Segal-Fock or Bargmann–Fock space) is named after a 1932 paper by the Russian theoretical physicist, Fock [**307**], who noted that ∂ and z obey the same commutation relations as A and $A^\dagger$. This paper also had a construction of a related object, also called Fock space, which in modern language (see e.g., Reed-Simon [**763**, **764**]) is described as follows. Given a Hilbert space $\mathcal{H}$, form $\oplus_{n=1}^\infty \mathcal{S}_n(\mathcal{H})$ (as defined in (3.8.26)). This is the *Fock space*, $\mathcal{F}(\mathcal{H})$, over $\mathcal{H}$. For each $f \in \mathcal{H}$, one can define operators $A^\dagger(f)$ (respectively, $A(f)$) from $\mathcal{S}_n$ to $\mathcal{S}_{n+1}$ (respectively, $\mathcal{S}_n$ to $\mathcal{S}_{n-1}$) so that $[A(f), A^\dagger(g)] = < f, g > \mathbb{1}$. Our $\mathcal{F}_\nu$ can be associated to $\mathcal{F}(\mathbb{C}^\nu)$ where $\mathcal{S}_n(\mathbb{C}^\nu)$ is realized as polynomials $z_1, \ldots, z_\nu$ of exact degree n and $A^\dagger(z_i) = \tilde{A}_i^\dagger$.

There are various books that explore analysis on the Fock space, $\mathcal{F}_\nu$—see Berezin [**72**], Folland [**308**], Neretin [**682**], or Zhu [**1020**].

The Segal-Bargmann transform (also called the Bargmann transform or Bargmann-Fock transform) is named after work of Bargmann [**59**, **60**] and Segal [**835**]. It was discovered independently in 1960–1961 by the two—Segal reported in lectures at a 1960 summer school (which appeared in [**836**]) and Bargmann in a paper submitted in March 1961. We follow standard terminology in the order of the names although there is no good reason, given the nearly simultaneous and independent discovery, to put Segal first. Indeed, Bargmann developed the idea further and only he had the explicit kernel (6.4.83) computed via the method in Problem 9.

The Segal–Bargmann transform is a special case of the *FBI transform*:

$$(\mathcal{F}_a f)(k, y) = (2\pi)^{-\nu/2} \int f(x) e^{-a|x-y|^2/2} e^{-ix \cdot k} d^\nu x \qquad (6.4.98)$$

short for Fourier-Bros-Iagolnitzer after Bros-Iagolnitzer [**131**] who used it to study real analyticity of solutions of PDEs, a theme heavily studied since, for example, by Córdoba–Fefferman [**205**], Delort [**231**], and Sjöstrand [**858**].

Problems

1. (a) Using (6.4.11), (6.4.12), and (6.4.19), prove that for all $n > 0$, $\langle \varphi_n, \varphi_0 \rangle = 0$.

   (b) Using (6.4.21), prove that if $m > n$, then $A^m \varphi_n = 0$.

   (c) For $m > n$, prove that $\langle \varphi_m, \varphi_n \rangle = 0$, so $\langle \varphi_m, \varphi_n \rangle = 0$ for all $m \neq n$.

2. Prove (b) and (c) of Theorem 6.4.4.

3. Provide the details of the proof of Theorem 6.4.7.

4. Using Theorem 6.4.9, prove that any τ in $\mathcal{S}'(\mathbb{R}^\nu)$ can be written as $\sum_{|\alpha|,|\beta| \leq n} D^\beta(x^\alpha g_\alpha)$ for bounded continuous functions g_α. Thus, given Problem 8 of Section 6.2, prove Theorem 6.2.10.

5. (a) Find a map, $q \colon \mathcal{I}_2 \to \mathcal{I}_1$, which is a bijection with $|q(\alpha)| \leq C(1+|\alpha|)^2$. (*Hint*: See Figure 1.6.1 from Chapter 1.)

   (b) If $\nu_1 \geq \nu_2$, find a map, $q_{\nu_1,\nu_2} \colon \mathcal{I}_{\nu_1} \to \mathcal{I}_{\nu_2}$, so that for some k, $|q_{\nu_1,\nu_2}(\alpha)| \leq C(1+|\alpha|)^k$.

   (c) Prove that as topological vector spaces, $\mathfrak{s}_{\nu_1}$ and $\mathfrak{s}_{\nu_2}$ are isomorphic.

   (d) Prove that as topological vector spaces, $\mathcal{S}(\mathbb{R}^{\nu_1})$ and $\mathcal{S}(\mathbb{R}^{\nu_2})$ are isomorphic.

6. If X and Y are Fréchet spaces, prove that a separately continuous bilinear map of $X \times Y$ to $\mathbb{K}$ is jointly continuous. (*Hint*: Baire category theorem.)

7. A family of norms, $\{\|\cdot\|_n\}_{n=1}^\infty$, on a Fréchet space is called increasing if $\|x\|_n \leq \|x\|_{n+1}$ for all n.

   (a) If X has a topology generated by an increasing family of norms $\{\|\cdot\|_n\}_{n=1}^\infty$ and $\ell \colon X \to \mathbb{C}$ is continuous, prove that $|\ell(x)| \leq C\|x\|_n$ for some C and n.

   (b) If Y also has such an increasing family, $\{\|\ \|_n^\sim\}_{n=1}^\infty$ and $T \colon X \times Y \to \mathbb{C}$ is a jointly continuous bilinear form, prove that for some C, n, and m, $|T(x,y)| \leq C\|x\|_n\|y\|_m^\sim$.

8. (a) Prove that the reproducing kernel for $\mathcal{F}_\nu$ is given by

$$K(z,w) = \exp(\sum_{j=1}^n z_j \bar{w}_j) \tag{6.4.99}$$

(*Hint*: See Problem 8 of Section 3.4.)

(b) If $\varphi_w(z) = K(z, w)$ prove that

$$||\varphi_w(z)||_{\mathcal{F}}^2 \le \exp\left(|w|^2\right) \tag{6.4.100}$$

(c) For $f \in \mathcal{F}_\nu$, prove that

$$|f(z)| \le ||f||_{\mathcal{F}_\nu} \exp\left(\tfrac{1}{2}|z|^2\right) \tag{6.4.101}$$

(d) Prove that for $\ell = 1, 2, \ldots$ there is C_ℓ so that

$$\left|\left|\frac{\partial^\ell}{\partial z_{i_1} \ldots \partial z_{i_\ell}} \varphi_w\right|\right| \le C_\ell(1 + |w|)^\ell \exp(\tfrac{1}{2}|w|)^\ell \tag{6.4.102}$$

and calculate a pointwise bound on derivatives in terms of $||f||$ if $f \in \mathcal{F}_\nu$.

(e) Using the relation between distributions and L^2 functions, prove that for any $\tau \in \mathcal{S}(\mathbb{R}^\nu)$, there is C and N so that

$$|(\mathbb{B}\tau)(z)| \le C(1 + |z|)^N \exp(\tfrac{1}{2}|z|^2) \tag{6.4.103}$$

9. Prove that up to a small constant, the kernel A_ν is determined by (6.4.92) and calculate that the kernel for the Segal-Bargmann kernel can be computed by the demand for (6.4.8).
10. Derive the form of the measure in $\mathcal{F}_\nu$, by the requirement that the adjoint of ∂_j be multiplication by z_j.
11. Prove that (6.4.85) determines the form of the kernel (6.4.83). (*Hint:* Look at $\sum_\alpha \tilde{\varphi}_\alpha(z)\varphi_\alpha(x)$.)

6.5. The Fourier Transform and Its Basic Properties

In this section, we restate the basic definitions of Fourier transform, discuss alternative conventions, and turn to its three most central theorems: Fourier inversion, Plancherel, and Riemann–Lebesgue. The first two we've already proven one way in Section 6.2—here we'll discuss them from the point of view of Hermite expansions and get new insight into why they are true. The Riemann–Lebesgue lemma asserts that if $f \in L^1(\mathbb{R}^\nu, d^\nu x)$, then $\hat{f} \in C_\infty(\mathbb{R}^\nu)$, the continuous functions vanishing at infinity. It will imply that if $1 \le p \le 2$ and $f \in L^p(\mathbb{R}^\nu, d^\nu x)$, then $\hat{f}$ is a function.

Recall (6.2.38)/(6.2.39),

$$\hat{f}(\mathbf{k}) = (2\pi)^{-\nu/2} \int \exp(-i\mathbf{k} \cdot \mathbf{x}) f(\mathbf{x}) \, d^\nu x \tag{6.5.1}$$

$$\check{f}(\mathbf{k}) = (2\pi)^{-\nu/2} \int \exp(+i\mathbf{k} \cdot x) f(\mathbf{x}) \, d^\nu x \tag{6.5.2}$$

One annoyance with this is the $(2\pi)^{\nu/2}$ in (6.2.44):

$$\widehat{f * g} = (2\pi)^{\nu/2} \hat{f} \hat{g} \tag{6.5.3}$$

Our convention is the most common in the physics literature (but see the Notes) and the older mathematical literature, but much of the more modern mathematical literature defines

$$(\mathcal{F}f)(\mathbf{k}) = \int e^{-2\pi i \mathbf{k} \cdot \mathbf{x}} f(\mathbf{x}) \, d^{\nu}\mathbf{x} \qquad (6.5.4)$$

With this convention,

$$\mathcal{F}(f * g) = (\mathcal{F}f)(\mathcal{F}g) \qquad (6.5.5)$$

and (in the Notes to Section 6.6) as we'll see, there are then fewer annoying 2π's in the Poisson summation formula.

There is another way of getting rid of the $(2\pi)^{-\nu/2}$ in $\widehat{}$—put 2π's into $d^{\nu}k$. Specifically, let

$$đ^{\nu}k = \frac{d^{\nu}k}{(2\pi)^{\nu}} \qquad (6.5.6)$$

Then define

$$\Phi(f)(\mathbf{k}) = \int e^{-i\mathbf{k} \cdot \mathbf{x}} f(\mathbf{x}) \, d^{\nu}x \qquad (6.5.7)$$

$$\Psi(f)(\mathbf{x}) = \int e^{i\mathbf{k} \cdot \mathbf{x}} f(\mathbf{k}) \, đ^{\nu}k \qquad (6.5.8)$$

The inversion formula is $\Psi \cdot \Phi = \Phi \cdot \Psi = \mathbb{1}$. We now have

$$\Phi(f * g) = \Phi(f)\Phi(g) \qquad (6.5.9)$$

We also have

$$\Phi(fg)(\mathbf{k}) = \int f(\mathbf{k} - \boldsymbol{\ell}) f(\boldsymbol{\ell}) đ^{\nu}\ell \qquad (6.5.10)$$

so convolution in "k-space" needs to use $đ^{\nu}\ell$, not $d^{\nu}\ell$. The Plancherel formula takes the form

$$\int |f(\mathbf{x})|^2 \, d^{\nu}x = \int |\Phi(f)(\mathbf{k})|^2 \, đ^{\nu}k \qquad (6.5.11)$$

From the point of view of general Fourier analysis on groups, this use of $đ^{\nu}k$ is quite natural; see the Notes. In spite of praising these alternate conventions, we doggedly follow (6.5.1)/(6.5.2).

*   *   *   *   *

Here is the remarkable relation between Fourier transform and Hermite expansion:

Theorem 6.5.1. (a) *For any* $f \in \mathcal{S}(\mathbb{R})$,

$$\widehat{Af} = iA\widehat{f} \qquad (6.5.12)$$

$$\widehat{A^{\dagger}f} = -iA^{\dagger}\widehat{f} \qquad (6.5.13)$$

(b) *For any $\boldsymbol{\alpha} \in \mathcal{I}_\nu$,*

$$\widehat{\varphi}_{\boldsymbol{\alpha}} = (-i)^{|\boldsymbol{\alpha}|}\varphi_{\boldsymbol{\alpha}} \tag{6.5.14}$$

(c) *For any $f \in \mathcal{S}(\mathbb{R}^\nu)$,*

$$(\widehat{f})^\sharp_{\boldsymbol{\alpha}} = (-i)^{|\boldsymbol{\alpha}|} f^\sharp_{\boldsymbol{\alpha}} \tag{6.5.15}$$

(d) $(\check{f})^\sharp_{\boldsymbol{\alpha}} = (i)^{|\boldsymbol{\alpha}|} f^\sharp_{\boldsymbol{\alpha}}$ $\qquad(6.5.16)$

Proof. (a) This is immediate from (6.4.10), (6.2.42), and (6.2.43).

(b) For any $n = 0, 1, 2, \ldots$, we have, by (6.4.13),

$$\widehat{\varphi}_n = \widehat{(A^\dagger)^n \varphi_0} = (-i)^n (A^\dagger)^n \widehat{\varphi}_0$$

$$= (-i)^n (A^\dagger)^n \varphi_0 = (-i)^n \varphi_n \tag{6.5.17}$$

where we used (6.2.50) for $a = 1$ to see $\widehat{\varphi}_0 = \varphi_0$. Since $\varphi_{\boldsymbol{\alpha}} = \prod_{j=1}^n \varphi_{a_j}$, (6.5.17) implies (6.5.14).

(c) We have

$$\widehat{f} = \sum_{\boldsymbol{\alpha}\in\mathcal{I}_\nu} \widehat{f^\sharp_{\boldsymbol{\alpha}} \varphi_{\boldsymbol{\alpha}}} = \sum_{\boldsymbol{\alpha}\in\mathcal{I}_\nu} f^\sharp_{\boldsymbol{\alpha}} \widehat{\varphi}_{\boldsymbol{\alpha}}$$

$$= \sum_{\boldsymbol{\alpha}\in\mathcal{I}_\nu} f^\sharp_{\boldsymbol{\alpha}} (-i)^{|\boldsymbol{\alpha}|} \varphi_{\boldsymbol{\alpha}} = \sum_{\boldsymbol{\alpha}\in\mathcal{I}_\nu} (\widehat{f})^\sharp_{\boldsymbol{\alpha}} \varphi_{\boldsymbol{\alpha}} \tag{6.5.18}$$

implying (6.5.15).

(d) is immediate from $\overline{\overline{\check{f}}} = \widehat{f}$. $\qquad\square$

Theorem 6.5.2. (a) (Fourier Inversion Theorem).

$$\check{\widehat{f}} = \widehat{\check{f}} = f \tag{6.5.19}$$

(b) (Plancherel Theorem). *For any $f \in \mathcal{S}(\mathbb{R}^\nu)$, we have that*

$$\int |f(\mathbf{x})|^2 \, d^\nu x = \int |\widehat{f}(\mathbf{k})|^2 \, d^\nu k \tag{6.5.20}$$

Proof. (a) is immediate from (6.5.15), (6.5.16), and

$$(-i)^{|\boldsymbol{\alpha}|}(i)^{|\boldsymbol{\alpha}|} = (i)^{|\boldsymbol{\alpha}|}(-i)^{|\boldsymbol{\alpha}|} = 1 \tag{6.5.21}$$

(b) is immediate from $|(-i)^{|\boldsymbol{\alpha}|}| = 1$ and

$$\|f\|^2_{L^2(\mathbb{R}^\nu)} = \sum_{\boldsymbol{\alpha}\in\mathcal{I}_\nu} |f^\sharp_{\boldsymbol{\alpha}}|^2 \tag{6.5.22}$$

$\qquad\square$

Basically, the point is that the φ_α are a complete set of simultaneous eigenvectors for $\hat{}$ and $\check{}$. That all eigenvalues (namely, $\pm 1, \pm i$) are in $\partial\mathbb{D}$ implies $\hat{}$ is unitary. That the eigenvalues are inverse implies the operators are inverse. In fact, all the eigenvalues are fourth roots of unity, so the fourth power of $\hat{}$ is the identity.

$$* \qquad * \qquad * \qquad * \qquad *$$

Next, we turn to the Fourier transform of L^1 functions. Any function in some $L^p(\mathbb{R}^\nu, d^\nu x)$ is a distribution, so it has a distributional Fourier transform. The following specifies what it is when $p = 1$:

Theorem 6.5.3 (Riemann–Lebesgue Lemma). *If $f \in L^1(\mathbb{R}^\nu, d^\nu x)$, then the distributional Fourier transform, $\widehat{f}$, is a $C_\infty(\mathbb{R}^\nu)$ function given pointwise by*

$$\widehat{f}(\mathbf{k}) = (2\pi)^{-\nu/2} \int f(\mathbf{x}) \exp(-i\mathbf{k}\cdot\mathbf{x})\, d^\nu x \tag{6.5.23}$$

where the integral is an absolutely convergent one. We have

$$\|\widehat{f}\|_\infty \leq (2\pi)^{-\nu/2}\|f\|_1 \tag{6.5.24}$$

Remarks. 1. However, not every $C_\infty(\mathbb{R}^\nu)$ is the Fourier transform of an L^1 function; see Section 6.7.

2. See Problem 1 for a direct proof that the integral is in $C_\infty(\mathbb{R}^\nu)$.

3. The analog for Fourier series is that if $f \in L^1(\partial\mathbb{D}, \frac{d\theta}{2\pi})$, then (with $f^\sharp$ given by (3.5.1)) $f_n^\sharp \to 0$ as $n \to \infty$.

Proof. The integral on the right side of (6.5.23) is absolutely convergent for any $f \in L^1$ and all $x \in \mathbb{R}^\nu$, so call if $\widetilde{f}(x)$. Clearly,

$$\|\widetilde{f}\|_\infty \leq (2\pi)^{-\nu/2}\|f\|_1 \tag{6.5.25}$$

Since $C_0^\infty(\mathbb{R}^\nu)$ is dense in L^1, pick $f_n \in C_0^\infty$ so $\|f - f_n\|_1 \to 0$. Thus, $\|\widetilde{f} - \widetilde{f_n}\|_\infty \to 0$. Since $\widetilde{g} = \widehat{g}$ for $g \in \mathcal{S}(\mathbb{R}^\nu)$, $\widetilde{f_n} \in \mathcal{S}(\mathbb{R}^\nu)$, and so in $C_\infty(\mathbb{R}^\nu)$. Since $C_\infty(\mathbb{R}^\nu)$ is closed in $\|\cdot\|_\infty$, we conclude that $\widetilde{f} \in C_\infty(\mathbb{R}^n)$.

Since $\widetilde{f_n} = \widehat{f_n}$ and $\|g - g_n\|_\infty \to 0 \Rightarrow \jmath(g) - \jmath(g_n) \to 0$ in $\sigma(\mathcal{S}', \mathcal{S})$, we see, in distribution sense,

$$\widetilde{f} = \lim \jmath(\widehat{f_n}) = \lim \widehat{\jmath(f_n)} = \widehat{f} \tag{6.5.26}$$

since $\|g - g_n\|_1 \to 0 \Rightarrow \jmath(g_n) \to \jmath(g)$. $\qquad\square$

In applications, one often uses the Fourier inversion form of this, i.e., $\widehat{f} \in L^1 \Rightarrow f \in C_\infty$. In this regard the following extension is often useful:

Theorem 6.5.4. *Let $\ell \in \mathbb{Z}_+$ and $f \in \mathcal{S}'(\mathbb{R}^\nu)$ so that*

$$\int (1 + |k|)^\ell |\hat{f}(k)| d^\nu k < \infty \qquad (6.5.27)$$

Then f is a C^ℓ function where $\widehat{D^\alpha f}(k) = (ik)^\alpha \hat{f}(k)$ for $|\alpha| \leq \ell$ and each such $D^\alpha f(k)$ goes to zero as $|k| \to \infty$.

Proof. Suppose first that $\ell = 1$. For $\mathbf{z} \in \mathbb{R}^\nu$

$$e^{i\mathbf{k}\cdot\mathbf{z}} - 1 - i\mathbf{k}\cdot\mathbf{z} = -i\mathbf{k}\cdot\mathbf{z} + \int_0^1 \frac{d}{d\lambda}(e^{i\lambda\mathbf{k}\cdot\mathbf{z}})d\lambda$$

$$= \int_0^1 (e^{i\lambda\mathbf{k}\cdot\mathbf{z}} - 1)(i\mathbf{k}\cdot\mathbf{z})d\lambda \qquad (6.5.28)$$

It follows that

$$|z|^{-1}|e^{i\mathbf{k}\cdot\mathbf{z}} - 1 - i\mathbf{k}\cdot\mathbf{z}| \leq 2|k| \qquad (6.5.29)$$

and goes to zero as $|z| \to 0$ (by the dominated convergence theorem).

By the Riemann-Lebesgue lemma, f can be defined by

$$f(x) = (2\pi)^{-\nu/2} \int \hat{f}(k)e^{ik\cdot x} d^\nu k \qquad (6.5.30)$$

and is in C_∞. Define

$$g_j(x) = (2\pi)^{-\nu/2} \int k_j \hat{f}(x)e^{ik\cdot x} d^\nu k \qquad (6.5.31)$$

so

$$f(x) - f(y) - (\mathbf{x}-\mathbf{y})\cdot\mathbf{g}(y) = (2\pi)^{-\nu} \int \left[e^{i\mathbf{k}\cdot(\mathbf{x}-\mathbf{y})} - 1 - \mathbf{k}\cdot(\mathbf{x}-\mathbf{y})\right]e^{ik\cdot y}\hat{f}(k)d^\nu k \qquad (6.5.32)$$

Since $|k|\hat{f}(k) \in L^1$, (6.5.29) and the dominated convergence theorem show that f is differentiable at y and $\frac{\partial f}{\partial x_j}(y) = g_j(y)$.

Thus $\frac{\partial f}{\partial x_j}$ is in C_∞ and $(1+|k|)^{\ell-1}\widehat{\frac{\partial f}{\partial x_j}} \in L^2$. By induction, f is C^ℓ. $\square$

Corollary 6.5.5. *Let $\ell \in \mathbb{Z}_+$ and $f \in \mathcal{S}'(\mathbb{R}^\nu)$. If $(1 + |k|)^{\ell+\nu/2+\varepsilon}\hat{f}(k) \in L^2(\mathbb{R}^\nu)$ for some $\varepsilon > 0$, then f is C^ℓ.*

Proof. $(1+|k|)^{-\nu/2-\varepsilon} \in L^2(\mathbb{R}^\nu)$, so this follows from the Schwarz inequality. $\square$

While there isn't a convergent integral formula for $\hat{f}$ when $f \in L^2$, the Plancherel theorem lets us see that $\hat{f}$ is a distribution given by a measurable function.

Theorem 6.5.6 (L^2 Fourier Transform). *Let $f \in L^2(\mathbb{R}^\nu, d^\nu x)$. Then the distributional Fourier transform, $\widehat{f}$, is given by an L^2-function. Moreover,*

$$\|\widehat{f}\|_{L^2(\mathbb{R}^\nu, d^\nu x)} = \|f\|_{L^2(\mathbb{R}^\nu, d^\nu x)} \tag{6.5.33}$$

and $\widehat{f}$ is the L^2-limit of the $C_\infty(\mathbb{R})$ functions

$$\int_{|x| \leq R} e^{-ik \cdot x} f(x)\, d^\nu x \tag{6.5.34}$$

as $R \to \infty$.

Proof. Let $f \in L^2$. Pick $f_n \in \mathcal{S}$ converging in L^2 to f. Then

$$\|\widehat{f_n} - \widehat{f_m}\|_2 = \|f_n - f_m\|_2 \tag{6.5.35}$$

by the Plancherel theorem for $\mathcal{S}$. Thus, $\widehat{f_n}$ is Cauchy in L^2, so has an L^2-limit $\tilde{f}$ obeying $\|\tilde{f}\|_2 = \|f\|_2$. Since $\widehat{f_n} \to \widehat{f}$ in $\sigma(\mathcal{S}', \mathcal{S})$ and $\widehat{f_n} \to \tilde{f}$ in $\sigma(\mathcal{S}', \mathcal{S})$, we conclude $\tilde{f} = \widehat{f}$. Thus, $\widehat{f}$ is an L^2-function and (6.5.33) holds. If χ_R is the characteristic of $\{x \mid |x| < R\}$, then $\chi_R f \to f$ in L^2, so $\widehat{\chi_R f} \to \widehat{f}$ in L^2. Since $\chi_R f \in L^1$ (by the Schwarz inequality), $\widehat{\chi_R f}$ is given by the convergent integral (6.5.34). $\square$

Let $p \leq q$. $L^p + L^q$ is the set of functions h so $h = f + g$ with $f \in L^p$, $g \in L^q$. We norm $L^p + L^q$ by

$$\|h\|_{L^p + L^q} = \inf\{\|f\|_p + \|g\|_q \mid h = f + g,\ f \in L^p,\ g \in L^q\} \tag{6.5.36}$$

We have $\bigcup_{p \leq r \leq q} L^r \subset L^p + L^q$. As an immediate corollary of the last two theorems, we have

Theorem 6.5.7. *For each $p \in [1,2]$ and $f \in L^p(\mathbb{R}^\nu, d^\nu x)$, the $\widehat{f}$, distributional Fourier transform, is a function in $L^\infty + L^2$ and*

$$\|\widehat{f}\|_{L^\infty + L^2} \leq \|f\|_{L^1 + L^2} \tag{6.5.37}$$

Moreover, $\widehat{f}$ is the limit in $L^\infty + L^2$ of (6.5.34).

Remarks. 1. We'll see in the next section (see Theorem 6.6.2) that $L^2 + L^\infty$ for $f \in L^p$ can be replaced by L^q, where $q = p/(p-1)$ is the dual index to p.

2. For any $p > 2$, there exist $f \in L^p$ so $\widehat{f}$ is not given by a function; see Section 6.7.

3. In Section 2.11 of Part 3, we'll prove that if $f \in L^p$ with $1 \leq p < 2$, then the convergence of (6.5.34) to $\widehat{f}(k)$ holds for a.e. k. This is also true for $p = 2$, but is more subtle; see the Notes to that section.

Notes and Historical Remarks. The Fourier inversion theorem goes back to Fourier's work on Fourier integrals [**311**] published in 1822 (see the Notes to Section 3.5 for more on Fourier). The Plancherel formula is named after a 1910 paper of Michel Plancherel [**730**] which had one of the earliest proofs.

The Riemann–Lebesgue lemma was found for Riemann integrable functions for Fourier series by Riemann [**774**]. Of course, he didn't discuss distributional Fourier series, but defined $f^\sharp$ by (3.5.1) (when $\nu = 1$) and proved that $f_n^\sharp$ vanished at infinity. Lebesgue's name was added because of his extension to Lebesgue integrable functions.

To understand the issue of conventions, it helps to put the Fourier transform on $\mathbb{R}$ into the context of general locally compact abelian (LCA) groups, a subject we'll study in detail in Section 6.9 of Part 4. An LCA group is a topological space, G, which is locally compact and Hausdroff, and which is also an abelian group in such a way to $x \to -x$ and $(x, y) \mapsto (x + y)$ are continuous functions. We also suppose that G is σ-compact. As we've seen in Section 4.19, G has a unique (up to normalization) Haar measure, μ_G, in which $\int f(x + y)\, d\mu_G(x) = \int f(x)\, d\mu_G(x)$ for any $y \in G$.

A *character* on G is a continuous map $\chi \colon G \to \partial\mathbb{D}$ so that $\chi(x + y) = \chi(x)\chi(y)$ (and then $\chi(e) = 1$ and $\chi(-x) = \overline{\chi(x)}$). The set of all characters, $\widehat{G}$, is a group under $(\chi_1\chi_2)(y) = \chi_1(y)\chi_2(y)$ with $\chi_1^{-1} = \bar\chi_1$. It can be shown that $\widehat{G}$ is also an LCA if $\widehat{G}$ is viewed as a subset of $L^\infty(G, d\mu_G) = L^1(G, d\mu_G)^*$ and given the $\sigma(L^\infty, L^1)$-topology. Moreover, given a normalized $d\mu_G$, there is a natural normalization, $d\mu_{\widehat{G}}$, for the Haar measure on $\widehat{G}$ (for which the Fourier inversion formula holds). Moreover, if G is compact, $\widehat{G}$ is discrete and vice-versa, and if μ_G is normalized in that compact case by $\mu_G(G) = 1$, then $\mu_{\widehat{G}}$ is normalized by $\mu_{\widehat{G}}(\{y\}) = 1$ (and vice-versa).

Let $C_0(G)$ be the continuous functions of compact support on G. For $f \in C_0(G)$, define $\widehat{f}$ on $\widehat{G}$ by

$$\widehat{f}(\chi) = \int \overline{\chi(y)}\, f(y)\, d\mu_G(y) \tag{6.5.38}$$

and for $f, g \in C_0(G)$, $f * g$ by

$$(f * g)(x) = \int f(x - y)g(y)\, d\mu_G(y) \tag{6.5.39}$$

Then

$$\widehat{f * g} = \widehat{f}\,\widehat{g} \tag{6.5.40}$$

In this generality, the Fourier inversion formula says

$$f(y) = \text{``}\int\text{''} \chi(y)\widehat{f}(\chi)\, d\mu_{\widehat{G}}(\chi) \tag{6.5.41}$$

where $\int$ is in " " since the integral may not converge and we may need some kind of limiting process, for example, taking $\lim_{n\to\infty}$ of the integral over K_n, where K_n is compact and $K_n \subset K_{n+1}^{\mathrm{int}}$, $\bigcup_n K_n = \widehat{G}$, and taking a limit in $L^2(G, d\mu_G)$. The Plancherel theorem says

$$\int |\widehat{f}(\chi)|^2 \, d\mu_{\widehat{G}}(\chi) = \int |f(y)|^2 \, d\mu_G(y) \tag{6.5.42}$$

From this point of view, we can understand the various conventions discussed. It happens that $\widehat{\mathbb{R}^\nu} \cong \mathbb{R}^\nu$, but the isomorphism is not unique. The convention (6.5.4) is associated to defining

$$\chi_{\mathbf{k}}(\mathbf{x}) = e^{2\pi i \mathbf{k} \cdot \mathbf{x}} \tag{6.5.43}$$

If $d\mu_G(x) = d^\nu x$, then $d\mu_{\widehat{G}}(y) = d^\nu k$.

The convention (6.5.7)/(6.5.8) is also clear. Now,

$$\chi_{\mathbf{k}}(\mathbf{x}) = e^{i \mathbf{k} \cdot \mathbf{x}} \tag{6.5.44}$$

If one takes $d\mu_G = d^\nu x$, then $d\mu_{\widehat{G}} = d^\nu k = \frac{d^\nu k}{(2\pi)^\nu}$. Just because $\widehat{\mathbb{R}^\nu}$ is isomorphic to $\mathbb{R}^\nu$ doesn't mean the dual measure must be the same as the original measure, only up to a constant. In fact, if one takes (6.5.44), one could get our formula for $\widehat{f}$ if we took $d\mu_G = \frac{d^\nu x}{(2\pi)^{\nu/2}}$. Then $d\mu_{\widehat{G}} = \frac{d^\nu k}{(2\pi)^{\nu/2}}$. The Plancherel theorem has $(2\pi)^{-\nu/2}$ on both sides compared to the usual one, but that is harmless. The change is that since $f * g$ has $d\mu_G$, the convolution would then take the form $(f*g)(x) = \int f(x-y)g(y) \frac{d^\nu y}{(2\pi)^{\nu/2}}$. But putting $(2\pi)^{\nu/2}$ into $*$, we get rid of it in (6.5.3)! Of course, we don't make that choice. Our conventions just don't respect the general LCA theory!

To say our convention is the one used by physicists is only part of the truth. Their complete convention is

$$\chi_p(x) = \exp\left(\frac{ip \cdot x}{\hbar}\right) \tag{6.5.45}$$

and

$$\widehat{f}(p) = (2\pi\hbar)^{-\nu/2} \int \exp\left(-\frac{ip \cdot x}{\hbar}\right) f(x) \, d^\nu x \tag{6.5.46}$$

Most often, $\hbar$ is taken to be 1, which is the convention we use. But recall $\hbar = h/2\pi$, so if h is 1, then we have exactly (6.5.4)! Of course, then the free energy of quantum mechanics isn't $-(2m)^{-1}\Delta$ on $L^2(\mathbb{R}^3)$, but $-(8\pi^2 m)^{-1}\Delta$.

Problems

1. (a) If $f \in L^1$, use the dominated convergence theorem to show that $\widetilde{f}$, the integral on the right of (6.5.33) is continuous.

   (b) If $f \in L^1$ and $f_a(x) = f(x-a)$, prove that $\lim_{a\to 0}\|f_a - f\|_1 = 0$.

(c) If $|\mathbf{k}| \neq 0$, prove that

$$\widehat{f_{\pi\mathbf{k}/|\mathbf{k}|^2}}(\mathbf{k}) = -\widehat{f}(\mathbf{k}) \tag{6.5.47}$$

and conclude that

$$\sup_{|\mathbf{k}| \geq R} |\widehat{f}(\mathbf{k})| \leq \tfrac{1}{2} (2\pi)^{-\nu/2} \sup_{|a| \leq R^{-1}} \|f_a - f\|_1 \tag{6.5.48}$$

and then that $\widehat{f}(\mathbf{k}) \to 0$ as $\mathbf{k} \to \infty$.

2. Let $f \in L^1(\mathbb{R}^\nu, d^\nu x)$. For each $\omega \in S^{\nu-1}$ and $a \in \mathbb{R}$, we define the *Radon transform* by

$$(\mathcal{R}f)(\omega, a) = \int_{x \cdot \omega = a} f(x) \, d^{\nu-1}x \tag{6.5.49}$$

where $d^{\nu-1}x$ is the induced measure on the hyperplane $x \cdot \omega = a$.

(a) If $(\mathcal{R}f)(\omega, a) = (\mathcal{R}g)(\omega, a)$ for $f, g \in L^1$, prove $f = g$ for a.e. x.

(b) If $f \in \mathcal{S}(\mathbb{R}^\nu)$, prove the inversion formula

$$f = \check{g}; \ g(k\omega) = (2\pi)^{-\nu/2} \int (\mathcal{R}f)(\omega, a)e^{-ika} \, da, \ k \in [0, \infty), \ \omega \in S^{\nu-1}$$

Remark. The Radon transform goes back to Radon [**754**]. It a critical element in interpreting CAT scans. For more on Radon transforms, see [**222**, **409**], [**344**, Vol. 5].

3. Let $f \in C_{00}^\infty(\mathbb{R}^\nu)$, the C^∞ functions of compact support lying in $\mathbb{R}^\nu \setminus \{0\}$. Define the *Mellin transform* for $k \in \mathbb{R}$, $\omega \in S^{\nu-1}$, by

$$(\mathcal{M}f)(k, \omega) = \int_0^\infty r^{-ik-1} f(r\omega) \, dr \tag{6.5.50}$$

(where $r^\beta = \exp(\beta(\log r))$.) Find an inversion formula for recovering f from $\mathcal{M}f$. (*Hint*: $y = \log r$ in (6.5.50).)

Remark. Mellin transforms are named after the Finnish mathematician H. Mellin (1854–1933) but appear in Laplace's writing. In the language of Section 6.9 of Part 4, Mellin transforms are just Fourier transforms on the group $\mathbb{R}^+$ with multiplication.

6.6. More Properties of Fourier Transform

This section will discuss further important, general properties of the Fourier transform—specifically four:

(1) The Hausdorff–Young inequality: The promised result that for $1 \leq p \leq 2$, $\widehat{}$ is bounded from L^p to L^q with $q = p/(p-1)$, the dual index to L^p. We will do this via a general interpolation theorem, which will also give us some L^p inequalities on convolution. Specifically, if $p^{-1} + q^{-1} \geq 1$

and if $f \in L^p$, $g \in L^q$, then $f * g \in L^r$ where $r^{-1} = p^{-1} + q^{-1} - 1$—this is Young's inequality.

(2) Bochner's theorem: We'll describe precisely the Fourier transforms of finite (positive) measures.

(3) Wiener's theorem: If μ is a finite measure on $\mathbb{R}^\nu$, this computes $\sum_x |\mu(\{x\})|^2$ in terms of $\widehat{\mu}$.

(4) The Poisson summation formula: In its simplest form, it says that if $\tau \in \mathcal{S}'(\mathbb{R})$ is given by

$$\tau = \sum_{n=-\infty}^{\infty} \delta\big(n\sqrt{2\pi}\,\big) \tag{6.6.1}$$

(i.e., $\tau(f) = \sum_{n=-\infty}^{\infty} f(n\sqrt{2\pi}))$, then

$$\widehat{\tau} = \tau \tag{6.6.2}$$

The general form (6.6.50) below is obtained from (6.6.2) by scaling and translation.

First, we discuss the Hausdorff–Young inequality. We know $\widehat{\ } : L^2 \to L^2$ and $L^1 \to L^\infty$. The following general result interpolates between L^p spaces:

Theorem 6.6.1 (The Riesz–Thorin Theorem). *Let (Ω, μ) be a measure space. Let $p_0, p_1, q_0, q_1 \in [1, \infty]$ and define, for $t \in (0,1)$,*

$$p_t^{-1} = (1-t)p_0^{-1} + tp_1^{-1} \qquad q_t^{-1} = (1-t)q_0^{-1} + tq_1^{-1} \tag{6.6.3}$$

Let T be a linear transformation from $L^{p_0} \cap L^{p_1}$ to $L^{q_0} \cap L^{q_1}$ with

$$\|Tf\|_{q_j} \leq C_j \|f\|_{p_j} \tag{6.6.4}$$

for $j = 0, 1$ and all $f \in L^{p_0} \cap L^{p_1}$. Then for all $t \in (0,1)$ and $f \in L^{p_0} \cap L^{p_1}$,

$$\|Tf\|_{q_t} \leq C_t \|f\|_{p_t} \tag{6.6.5}$$

where

$$C_t = C_0^{1-t} C_1^t \tag{6.6.6}$$

Remark. Since $L^{p_0} \cap L^{p_1}$ is dense in each L^{p_t}, T extends to a bounded map of L^{p_t} to L^{q_t}.

This is actually a result in complex analysis. We'll prove it as Theorem 5.2.2 in Part 2A. We also note there are other interpolation theorems which will be discussed in Section 6.1 of Part 3. We can apply the Riesz–Thorin theorem as follows:

Theorem 6.6.2 (Hausdorff–Young Inequality). *Let $f \in L^p(\mathbb{R}^\nu)$, $1 \leq p \leq 2$. Then $\widehat{f} \in L^q(\mathbb{R}^\nu)$, where $q = p/(p-1)$ and*

$$\|\widehat{f}\|_q \leq (2\pi)^{-\nu(\frac{1}{p} - \frac{1}{2})} \|f\|_p \tag{6.6.7}$$

Remark. In Problem 5, the reader will use scaling to show that if an estimate like (6.6.7) holds, then p and q are dual indices. Problem 7 of Section 7.2 will show that an estimate like (6.6.7) cannot hold if $p > 2$.

Proof. By hypothesis, $\hat{}$ from $L^1 \cap L^2$ is bounded to $L^\infty \cap L^2$ with norms obeying (6.6.7) for $\frac{1}{q} = \frac{1}{2}$, 0. For $\log\|\cdot\|_{L^p \to L^q}$ to be convex in $1/p$ implies (6.6.7) for all $p \in [1, 2]$ and $f \in L^1 \cap L^2$. Since $L^1 \cap L^2$ is dense in L^p, $1 \le p \le 2$, we get the general result. □

Here is another application of the Riesz–Thorin theorem:

Theorem 6.6.3 (Young's Inequality). *Let p, q be such that*

$$p^{-1} + q^{-1} \ge 1, \qquad 1 \le p, q \le \infty \tag{6.6.8}$$

Let

$$r^{-1} = p^{-1} + q^{-1} - 1 \tag{6.6.9}$$

Then $f \in L^p(\mathbb{R}^\nu)$, $g \in L^q(\mathbb{R}^\nu)$ implies $f * g \in L^r(\mathbb{R}^\nu)$ and

$$\|f * g\|_r \le \|f\|_p \|g\|_q \tag{6.6.10}$$

Remarks. 1. Problem 1 has a proof of this using just Hölder's inequality and not interpolation.

2. See the Notes for a discussion of extensions and optimal constants.

3. There is a more symmetric form of (6.6.10), namely if

$$1 \le p, q, s \le \infty, \qquad p^{-1} + q^{-1} + s^{-1} = 2 \tag{6.6.11}$$

then, for $f \in L^p(\mathbb{R}^\nu)$, $g \in L^q(\mathbb{R}^\nu)$, $h \in L^s(\mathbb{R}^\nu)$, we have that

$$\left| \int f(x) g(x - y) h(y) d^\nu x \, d^\nu y \right| \le \|f\|_p \|g\|_q \|h\|_s \tag{6.6.12}$$

Proof. The set of p, q obeying (6.6.8) is a triangle in (p^{-1}, q^{-1}) (see Figure 6.6.1). If $p^{-1} + q^{-1} = 1$, then $r = \infty$, for indeed,

$$\left\| \int f(x - y) g(y) \, d^\nu y \right\|_\infty \le \|f\|_p \|g\|_q \tag{6.6.13}$$

is just Hölder's inequality.

If $p = q = 1$, then by a change of variables from x, y to $x - y, y$,

$$\left\| \int f(\cdot - y) g(y) \, d^\nu y \right\|_1 \le \int |f(x - y)| |g(y)| \, d^\nu x \, d^\nu y = \|f\|_1 \|g\|_1 \tag{6.6.14}$$

Thus, (6.6.10) holds at the hypotenuse and opposite vertex of the triangle. The convex hull of these points is the whole triangle, so (6.6.10) in these special cases and the Riesz–Thorin theorem implies the full remark. □

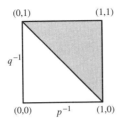

Figure 6.6.1. Region of validity of Young's inequality.

There is one significant complement of Young's inequality to note:

Theorem 6.6.4. *If p and q are dual indices, i.e.,*

$$p^{-1} + q^{-1} = 1, \quad 1 < p, q < \infty$$

and $f \in L^p(\mathbb{R}^\nu)$, $g \in L^q(\mathbb{R}^\nu)$, then $f * g \in C_\infty(\mathbb{R}^\nu)$, the continuous functions vanishing at infinity.

Proof. If $f, g \in C_0^\infty(\mathbb{R}^\nu)$, it is easy to see that $f * g$ is also in $C_0^\infty(\mathbb{R}^\nu)$. Now use that C_0^∞ is dense in L^p and L^q. Since $\|f * g\|_\infty \leq \|f\|_p \|g\|_q$, if $f_n \to f$ in L^p and $g_n \to g$ in L^q, with $f_n, g_n \in C_0^\infty$, then

$$\|f_n * g_n - f * g\|_\infty \to 0$$

so $f * g$ is a uniform limit of $C_\infty(\mathbb{R}^\nu)$ functions, so is $C_\infty(\mathbb{R}^\nu)$. $\qquad\square$

$$* \qquad * \qquad * \qquad * \qquad *$$

Next, we turn to the question of describing the Fourier transforms of finite measures. If μ is a finite measure on $\mathbb{R}^\nu$,

$$\widehat{\mu}(\mathbf{x}) = (2\pi)^{-\nu/2} \int \exp(-i\mathbf{k} \cdot \mathbf{x}) \, d\mu(\mathbf{k}) \qquad (6.6.15)$$

The integral is finite, so this defines $\widehat{\mu}$ as a function, and a simple use of Fubini's theorem proves that $\widehat{\mu}(\mathbf{x})$ is the distributional Fourier transform (pedantically, $\jmath(\widehat{\mu})$). Here is the key property of $\widehat{\mu}$ that we'll eventually prove characterizes Fourier transforms of measures:

Theorem 6.6.5. $\widehat{\mu}(\mathbf{x})$ *is a bounded continuous function of $\mathbf{x}$ with the following property:*

$$\forall n = 1, 2, \dots \quad \forall \{\mathbf{x}_j\}_{j=1}^n \subset \mathbb{R}^\nu \quad \forall \{\zeta_j\}_{j=1}^n \subset \mathbb{C}$$

$$\sum_{j,\ell=1}^n \bar{\zeta}_j \zeta_\ell \widehat{\mu}(\mathbf{x}_j - \mathbf{x}_\ell) \geq 0 \qquad (6.6.16)$$

Proof. Continuity is immediate from the dominated convergence theorem and boundedness from

$$|\widehat{\mu}(\mathbf{x})| \leq (2\pi)^{-\nu/2}\mu(\mathbb{R}) = \widehat{\mu}(\mathbf{0}) \tag{6.6.17}$$

We get (6.6.16) by noting

$$\sum_{j,\ell=1}^{n} \zeta_j \zeta_\ell \widehat{\mu}(\mathbf{x}_j - \mathbf{x}_\ell) = \int \sum_{j,\ell=1}^{n} \bar{\zeta}_j \zeta_\ell e^{-i\mathbf{k}(\mathbf{x}_j - \mathbf{x}_\ell)} \, d\mu(\mathbf{k}) \tag{6.6.18}$$

$$= \int \left| \sum_{\ell=1}^{n} \zeta_\ell e^{i\mathbf{k}\cdot\mathbf{x}_\ell} \right|^2 d\mu(\mathbf{k}) \tag{6.6.19}$$

$$\geq 0$$

We get (6.6.19) from (6.6.18) by expanding the square. □

Definition. A complex-valued function f on $\mathbb{R}^\nu$ is called *positive definite* if and only if

(i) f is continuous.

(ii) For any $\{x_j\}_{j=1}^n$, the $n \times n$ matrix

$$C_{k\ell} = f(x_k - x_\ell) \tag{6.6.20}$$

is a positive matrix.

Remarks. 1. We don't suppose f is bounded. We'll prove it is.

2. By positive matrix, we mean for all $\zeta_j \in \mathbb{C}^n$, we have $\sum \bar{\zeta}_k C_{k\ell} \zeta_\ell \geq 0$. (*Note*: We do not require strict positivity.)

We'll prove the following:

Theorem 6.6.6 (Bochner's Theorem). *A distribution, τ, is the Fourier transform of a finite measure if and only if τ is a positive definite function.*

Remark. More pedantically, $\tau = \jmath(f)$ for f positive definite.

We are heading towards a proof of this.

Lemma 6.6.7. *Let $\{a_{ij}\}_{1\leq i,j\leq n}$ and $\{b_{ij}\}_{1\leq i,j\leq n}$ be positive matrices. Define*

$$c_{ij} = a_{ij}b_{ij} \tag{6.6.21}$$

Then $\{c_{ij}\}_{1\leq i,j\leq n}$ is a positive matrix.

Remark. C is called the *Schur product* of A and B.

Proof. If A is the operator associated to a positive matrix, there is an orthonormal basis of eigenvectors, $\{\varphi^{(\ell)}\}_{1 \le \ell \le n}$, with

$$A\varphi^{(\ell)} = \mu^{(\ell)}\varphi^{(\ell)} \qquad (6.6.22)$$

and $\mu^{(\ell)} \ge 0$; see Theorem 1.7.9.

Since

$$\langle \psi, A\eta \rangle = \sum_{\ell=1}^{n} \mu^{(\ell)} \langle \psi, \varphi^{(\ell)} \rangle \langle \varphi^{(\ell)}, \eta \rangle \qquad (6.6.23)$$

we conclude that

$$a_{ij} = \sum_{\ell=1}^{n} \mu^{(\ell)} \varphi_i^{(\ell)} \bar{\varphi}_j^{(\ell)} \qquad (6.6.24)$$

Similarly,

$$b_{ij} = \sum_{k=1}^{n} \lambda^{(k)} \psi_i^{(k)} \bar{\psi}_j^{(k)} \qquad (6.6.25)$$

Thus,

$$c_{ij} = \sum_{\ell,k=1}^{n} \mu^{(\ell)} \lambda^{(k)} \psi_i^{(k)} \varphi_i^{(\ell)} \bar{\psi}_j^{(k)} \bar{\varphi}_j^{(\ell)} \qquad (6.6.26)$$

Each term in the sum defines a positive matrix, so c is positive. $\square$

Proposition 6.6.8. *Let f be a positive definite function on $\mathbb{R}^\nu$. Then*

(a) $|f(x)| \le f(0), \qquad f(-x) = \overline{f(x)}$ *for all x* $\qquad (6.6.27)$

(b) *If g is also positive definite, so is fg.*

(c) *For every $h \in \mathcal{S}(\mathbb{R}^\nu)$,*

$$\int \overline{h(x)}\, f(x-y)h(y)\, d^\nu x d^\nu y \ge 0 \qquad (6.6.28)$$

(d) *For any $\alpha > 0$,*

$$g(x) = e^{-\alpha|x|^2} \qquad (6.6.29)$$

is positive definite.

Remarks. 1. Conversely (Problem 3), if (6.6.28) holds for all $h \in \mathcal{S}(\mathbb{R}^\nu)$, then f is positive definite.

2. If f is only assumed in $L^\infty(\mathbb{R}^\nu)$, a function obeying (6.6.28) is called *weakly positive definite*. It is known that such a function is equal a.e. to a positive definite function. (See the discussion in the Notes and Problem 6.)

Proof. (a) If $x_1 = 0$, $x_2 = x$, the 2×2 matrix is

$$\begin{pmatrix} f(0) & f(x) \\ f(-x) & f(0) \end{pmatrix} \qquad (6.6.30)$$

If this is positive, it is Hermitian, so $f(-x) = \overline{f(x)}$ and its trace and determinant are nonnegative, that is, $f(0) \geq 0$ and $f(0)^2 - |f(x)|^2 \geq 0$.

(b) This is immediate from Lemma 6.6.7.

(c) Since $\overline{h(x)}f(x-y)h(y)$ is continuous with rapid decay, it is the limit as $n \to \infty$ of

$$\sum_{\substack{\ell,j\in\mathbb{Z}^\nu \\ |\ell_k|,|j_k|\leq 2^{2n}}} \overline{h\left(\frac{j}{2^n}\right)} f\left(\frac{j-\ell}{2^n}\right) h\left(\frac{\ell}{2^n}\right) \frac{1}{2^{2n}} \tag{6.6.31}$$

which is nonnegative by the positive definiteness of f.

(d) g is the Fourier transform of $(2\alpha)^{-\nu/2}\exp(-k^2/4\alpha)\,d^\nu k$, and thus, g is positive definite by Theorem 6.6.5. $\qquad\square$

Proof of Theorem 6.6.6. Suppose first that f is positive definite and L^1. If f and h are in L^1, we have

$$\widetilde{f * h} = (2\pi)^{\nu/2}\check{f}\check{h} \tag{6.6.32}$$

Thus, since $\check{}$ is L^2 inner product-preserving,

$$\text{LHS of (6.6.28)} = \langle h, f * h \rangle$$
$$= (2\pi)^{\nu/2}\langle \check{h}, \check{f}\check{h}\rangle \tag{6.6.33}$$
$$= (2\pi)^{\nu/2}\int |\check{h}(k)|^2 \check{f}(k)\,d^\nu k \tag{6.6.34}$$
$$\geq 0 \tag{6.6.35}$$

by (6.6.28).

Given a positive definite function, F, let $f_\alpha(x) = F(x)e^{-\alpha|x|^2}$. By Proposition 6.6.8(b), f_α is positive definite. Since F is bounded by $F(0)$, $f_\alpha \in L^1$, so by (6.6.35), for any $h \in \mathcal{S}$,

$$\int |\check{h}(k)|^2 \check{f}_\alpha(k)\,d^\nu k \geq 0 \tag{6.6.36}$$

For any $k_0 \in \mathbb{R}^\nu$, we can pick h so $|\check{h}(k)|^2 = (2\pi\beta)^{-1/2}\exp(-(k-k_0)^2/2\beta)$. Taking $\beta \downarrow 0$ and using the continuity of $\check{f}_\alpha$, we conclude, by (6.6.36), that for all $k_0 \in \mathbb{R}^\nu$, $\alpha > 0$,

$$\check{f}_\alpha(k_0) \geq 0 \tag{6.6.37}$$

If we take $h(x) = (2\pi\beta)^{-1/2}\exp(-|x|^2/2\beta)$ and take $\beta \downarrow 0$, given the continuity of $f_\alpha(x)$, we see the left side of (6.6.28) $\to f_\alpha(0) = F(0)$ and (6.6.34) converges to $(2\pi)^{-\nu/2}f\int \check{f}_\alpha(k)\,d^\nu k$ monotonically, that is, for each α,

$$(2\pi)^{-\nu/2}\int \check{f}_\alpha(k)\,d^\nu k = F(0) \tag{6.6.38}$$

so

$$d\mu_\alpha(k) = \check{f}_\alpha(k)\, d^\nu k \tag{6.6.39}$$

is a family of finite measures with

$$\widehat{\mu}_\alpha(x) = F(x)e^{-\alpha|x|^2} \tag{6.6.40}$$

As $\alpha \downarrow 0$, $f_\alpha \to F$ weakly as distributions. Thus, $\check{F}$ is a distributional limit of measures of size $(2\pi)^{\nu/2}F(0)$. Since the measure of size $(2\pi)^{\nu/2}F(0)$ are compact in the $\mathcal{M}(\mathbb{R}^\nu \cup \{\infty\})$, $\check{F}$ is a measure μ, that is, we have proven

$$F(x) = \widehat{\mu}(x) \tag{6.6.41}$$

for a finite measure μ. $\qquad\square$

Remark. We can see $\mu(\mathbb{R}^\nu) = F(0)$, so the weak limit in $\mathbb{R}^\nu \cup \{\infty\}$ has $\mu(\{\infty\}) = 0$.

$$* \qquad * \qquad * \qquad * \qquad *$$

The following relates $\widehat{\mu}$ to the issue of where μ has pure points:

Theorem 6.6.9 (Wiener's Theorem). *Let μ be a finite measure on $\mathbb{R}^\nu$ and $\widehat{\mu}$ its distributional Fourier transform. Then*

$$\lim_{R\to\infty}\left(\frac{\pi}{R}\right)^\nu \int_{\substack{|k_j|\le R \\ j=1,\dots,\nu}} |\widehat{\mu}(k)|^2\, d^\nu k = \sum_{x\in\mathbb{R}^\nu} |\mu(\{x\})|^2 \tag{6.6.42}$$

Remark. The sum in (6.6.42) is countable and convergent since $\sum_{x\in\mathbb{R}^\nu}\mu(\{x\}) \le \mu(\mathbb{R}^\nu)$.

Proof. Let $F(R)$ be the quantity within the limit on the left side of (6.6.42). Since

$$|\widehat{\mu}(k)|^2 = (2\pi)^{-\nu}\left(\int e^{ik\cdot x}\, d\mu(x)\right)\left(\int e^{-ik\cdot y}\, d\mu(y)\right) \tag{6.6.43}$$

and

$$(2R)^{-1}\int_{-R}^{R} e^{-ik(u-v)}\, dk = \frac{\sin(R(u-v))}{R(u-v)} \tag{6.6.44}$$

we have that

$$F(R) = \iint \prod_{j=1}^{\nu} \frac{\sin(R(x_j - y_j))}{R(x_j - y_j)}\, d\mu(x)d\mu(y) \tag{6.6.45}$$

$|\sin\eta/\eta| \le 1$ for all η and goes to zero as $|\eta| \to \infty$. Thus, the integrand in (6.6.45) is bounded by 1 and goes pointwise to 1 if $x = y$ and 0 if $x \ne y$.

It follows from the dominated convergence theorem for $d\mu \otimes d\mu$ that with $\Delta = \{(x,x) \mid x \in \mathbb{R}^\nu\}$,

$$\lim_{R\to\infty} F(R) = (\mu \otimes \mu)(\Delta) \tag{6.6.46}$$

$$= \int \mu(\{x\})\, d\mu(x) \tag{6.6.47}$$

$$= \sum_{x\in\mathbb{R}^\nu} |\mu(\{x\})|^2 \tag{6.6.48}$$

$\square$

*   *   *   *   *

Finally, we turn to the Poisson summation formula and applications.

Theorem 6.6.10. *Let f be a continuous function on $\mathbb{R}$ obeying*

$$|f(x)| \le C(1+|x|)^{-1-\varepsilon}, \quad |f(x)-f(y)| \le C|x-y|^h(1+|x|)^{-1-\varepsilon} \tag{6.6.49}$$

for some $\varepsilon > 0$, $h > 0$, and $C < \infty$ and all $x,y \in \mathbb{R}$ with $|x-y| < 1$. Then for any $x \in \mathbb{R}$ and $\alpha > 0$, we have that

$$\sum_{n=-\infty}^{\infty} f(x+2\pi\alpha n) = \lim_{N\to\infty} \sum_{m=-N}^{N} \frac{1}{\alpha\sqrt{2\pi}} \widehat{f}\left(\frac{m}{\alpha}\right) e^{imx/\alpha} \tag{6.6.50}$$

Remarks. 1. In many applications, one has $f \in C^2$ (even $f \in \mathcal{S}$) with

$$|f(x)| + |f'(x)| + |f''(x)| \le D(1+|x|)^{-1-\varepsilon} \tag{6.6.51}$$

in which case, $|\widehat{f}(k)| \le \widetilde{D}(1+|k|)^{-2}$, and so the sum on the right side of (6.6.50) is absolutely convergent and we can write it as $\sum_{m=-\infty}^{\infty}$. The proof can then use the elementary argument in Problem 10 of Section 3.5 rather than the somewhat more subtle Dini test.

2. By using Problem 9 of Section 3.5, one sees that the convergence on the right is uniform in x.

3. The most common form is $\alpha = 1$, $x = 0$ in a case where the sum is absolutely convergent so that (6.6.50) becomes

$$\sum_{n=-\infty}^{\infty} f(2\pi n) = (2\pi)^{-1/2} \sum_{m=-\infty}^{\infty} \widehat{f}(m) \tag{6.6.52}$$

This is sometimes called the *Poisson summation formula*, although the more general (6.6.50) has that name also. Actually, (6.6.50) follows from (6.6.52) for the function $g(y) = f(x+\alpha y)$ by the relations for $\widehat{f}$ under translation and scaling.

4. There is a version for $f \in L^1(\mathbb{R})$ with a Cesàro sum on the right-hand side; see Problem 9.

5. There is an $\mathbb{R}^\nu$ version of this; see Problem 10.

6. The $\mathcal{F}f$ convention for Fourier transform leads to a cleaner version of this; see the Notes.

7. If $q \in \mathbb{R}$ and $e^{-iqx}f(x) = g(x)$, then g obeys (6.6.49) if f does. Moreover,

$$\widehat{g}(k) = \widehat{f}(k+q) \tag{6.6.53}$$

(6.6.50) for g leads to a more symmetric looking expression for f (stated, for simplicity, for $\alpha = 1$):

$$e^{-iqx} \sum_{n=-\infty}^{\infty} e^{-2\pi i n q} f(x + 2\pi n) = \lim_{N\to\infty} \sum_{m=-N}^{N} \frac{1}{\sqrt{2\pi}} \widehat{f}(q+m) e^{imx} \tag{6.6.54}$$

This is also called the *Poisson summation formula*. We'll say more about this in the remark below.

Proof. Define a function g on $\partial\mathbb{D}$ by

$$g(e^{i\theta}) = \sum_{n=-\infty}^{\infty} f(\theta\alpha + 2\pi\alpha n) \tag{6.6.55}$$

By (6.6.49), this sum converges absolutely, and the resulting function obeys the condition of Dini's test (Theorem 3.5.4) at all θ, so we have, by that theorem,

$$g(e^{i\theta}) = \lim_{N\to\infty} \sum_{m=-N}^{N} g_k^\sharp(e^{ik\theta}) \tag{6.6.56}$$

Here $g_k^\sharp$, given by (3.5.1), is

$$g_k^\sharp = \int_0^{2\pi} e^{-ik\theta} \sum_{n=-\infty}^{\infty} f(\theta\alpha + 2\pi\alpha n) \frac{d\theta}{2\pi} \tag{6.6.57}$$

By (6.6.49), we can interchange the sum and integral since the sum converges uniformly. Replacing θ by x/α, we find

$$g_k^\sharp = \frac{1}{\alpha\sqrt{2\pi}} \widehat{f}\left(\frac{k}{\alpha}\right) \tag{6.6.58}$$

so (6.6.56) implies (6.6.50). $\qquad\square$

Remark. In Theorem 2.4.9 of Part 3, we'll show that if $f \in L^1(\partial\mathbb{D}, \frac{d\theta}{2\pi})$, then the Cesàro average of the Fourier series for f converges to $f(e^{i\theta})$ for a.e. θ. If $f \in L^1(\mathbb{R}, dx)$, then by Fubini's theorem the sum on the left-hand side of (6.6.54) converges for a.e. x and defines an $L^2(\partial\mathbb{D}, \frac{d\theta}{2\pi})$ function. We conclude that for such f, for every q, (6.6.54) holds for a.e. x if the limit on the right-hand side is replaced by a Cesàro average (since $f \in L^1, \widehat{f}$ is continuous and so defined for all k and not just a.e. k).

Example 6.6.11 (Functional equation for the Jacobi theta function). The Jacobi theta function (one of many functions with the name—the others have different normalization or are translates; they are discussed in Section 10.5 of Part 2A) is defined, for $x > 0$, by

$$\theta_0(x) = \sum_{n=-\infty}^{\infty} e^{-\pi n^2 x} \tag{6.6.59}$$

Recall that (see (6.2.50)), if $h_a(y) = e^{-ay^2/2}$, then $\widehat{h}_a(k) = a^{-1/2}h_{1/a}(k)$. Notice that

$$\theta_0(x) = \sum_{n=-\infty}^{\infty} h_{x/2\pi}(2\pi n)$$

and that, by the above, $(2\pi)^{-1/2}\widehat{h}_{x/2\pi}(n) = x^{-1/2}e^{-\pi n^2/x}$. Thus, (6.6.52) yields the *functional equation for the Jacobi theta function*:

$$\theta_0\left(\frac{1}{x}\right) = \sqrt{x}\,\theta_0(x) \tag{6.6.60}$$

This formula is famous in part because Riemann used it in his proof of the functional equation for his zeta function (see Problem 5 of Section 13.3 of Part 2B). We will see another way of understanding it in the Notes to Section 10.5 of Part 2A. More generally, (6.6.50) implies that if, for $x > 0$, $w \in \mathbb{C}$, we define

$$\theta_0(w \mid x) = \sum_{n=-\infty}^{\infty} e^{-\pi n^2 x}e^{2\pi i w n} \tag{6.6.61}$$

Then for $w \in \mathbb{R}$ (Problem 13),

$$\theta_0\left(w \,\middle|\, \frac{1}{x}\right) = \sqrt{x}\,e^{-\pi w^2 x}\theta_0(iwx \mid x) \tag{6.6.62}$$

$$= \sqrt{x}\sum_{n=-\infty}^{\infty} e^{-\pi(n+w)^2 x} \tag{6.6.63}$$

$\square$

Example 6.6.12 (The Basel Sum). Fix $\beta > 0$. Let $h_\beta(x) = e^{-\beta|x|}$. Then a simple calculation (Problem 14) shows that

$$h_\beta(x) = e^{-\beta|x|} \Rightarrow \widehat{h}_\beta(k) = \frac{2\beta}{\sqrt{2\pi}}\frac{1}{k^2 + \beta^2} \tag{6.6.64}$$

Since

$$\sum_{n=-\infty}^{\infty} e^{-2\pi\beta|n|} = 2(1 - e^{-2\pi\beta})^{-1} - 1 = \coth(\pi\beta) \tag{6.6.65}$$

(6.6.52) becomes

$$\sum_{m=-\infty}^{\infty} \frac{1}{m^2 + \beta^2} = \frac{\pi}{\beta} \coth(\pi\beta) \qquad (6.6.66)$$

which leads to (Problem 15)

$$\sum_{m=1}^{\infty} \frac{1}{m^2} = \frac{\pi^2}{6} \qquad (6.6.67)$$

a formula of Euler proven in Problem 21 of Section 3.5 and several times in Part 2A (see the discussion in the Notes to Section 5.7 of Part 2A). □

Example 6.6.13. Fix $\beta > 0$ and let $g_\beta(x) = \text{sgn}(x)e^{-\beta|x|}$ which, up to a factor of β, is the (distributional) derivative of the function $h_\beta(x)$ of the last example, so

$$g_\beta(x) = \text{sgn}(x)e^{-\beta|x|} \Rightarrow \widehat{g}_\beta(k) = \frac{(2\pi)^{-1/2}(ik)}{k^2 + \beta^2} \qquad (6.6.68)$$

If, for now, we ignore the fact that the hypotheses of Theorem 6.6.10 don't hold, (6.6.50) for $\alpha = 1$ and $x = \pi/2$, so $e^{imx} = (i)^m$, implies that

$$\lim_{N \to \infty} \frac{1}{2\pi} \sum_{m=-N}^{N} (i)^{m+1} \frac{m}{m^2 + \beta^2} = \sum_{n=-\infty}^{\infty} g_\beta(2\pi(n + \tfrac{1}{4})) \qquad (6.6.69)$$

The left side is the conditionally convergent sum $\frac{1}{2\pi}\sum_{n=0}^{\infty}(-1)^n \frac{2n+1}{(2n+1)^2+\beta^2}$ and, by summing a geometric series and doing some algebra, the right side is (Problem 16) $1/2\cosh(\pi\beta/2)$. Thus, we have

$$\sum_{m=\infty}^{\infty} (-1)^n \frac{2n+1}{(2n+1)^2 + \beta^2} = \frac{\pi}{\cosh(\pi\beta/2)} \qquad (6.6.70)$$

Even though g_β isn't continuous at $x = 0$, so the sum in (6.6.55) with $f = g_\beta$ isn't continuous at $e^{i\theta} = 1$, it is smooth away from there and, in particular, at $e^{i\theta} = i$. Dini's test is local, so the proof of Theorem 6.6.10 proves (6.6.50) for $\alpha = 1$, $f = g_\beta$, and $x \in (0, 2\pi)$ and, in particular, at $x = \pi/2$. Thus, (6.6.70) is proven. □

Remark. Problems 19 and 22 of Section 5.7 of Part 2A will have a contour integral proof of (6.6.70).

Example 6.6.14. Let $f(x) = (\cosh x)^{-1}$. Then (Problem 17)

$$\widehat{f}(k) = (2\pi)^{-1/2} \sum_{n=0}^{\infty} (-1)^n \frac{2n+1}{(2n+1)^2 + k^2} \qquad (6.6.71)$$

so, by (6.6.70), we see that

$$f_\gamma(x) = [\cosh(\gamma x)]^{-1}, \qquad \widehat{f}_\gamma(k) = \frac{\pi}{\gamma}(2\pi)^{-1/2} f_{\pi/2\gamma}(k) \qquad (6.6.72)$$

and the Poisson summation formula implies that

$$\sum_{n=-\infty}^{\infty} \frac{e^{2\pi i x n}}{\cosh(\pi n/\gamma)} = \gamma \sum_{n=-\infty}^{\infty} \frac{1}{\cosh(\pi(n+x)\gamma)} \tag{6.6.73}$$

$\square$

Remark. Problem 1 of Section 13.1 of Part 2B will have a contour integral proof of (6.6.72). That section has an application of (6.6.73) to number theory.

An application of the Poisson summation formula, which is important in many applied fields, is

Theorem 6.6.15 (Nyquist–Shannon Sampling Theorem; First Form). *Let* $g \in L^1(\mathbb{R})$ *have* $\operatorname{supp}(\widehat{g}) \subset [-\pi B, \pi B]$. *Then* g *is determined by its values at* $\{\frac{m}{B}\}_{m=-\infty}^{\infty}$, *that is, if two such* g's *agree at those points, they agree at all points.*

Remarks. 1. This is sometimes phrased as "if g is band-limited to frequencies at most $\frac{1}{2}B$, it need only be sampled at times $1/B$ apart."

2. The support hypothesis implies g is C^∞ (Problem 18), so $g(\frac{m}{B})$ is well-defined.

3. As we'll see below, the result is true for $L^2(\mathbb{R})$ (and, by Problem 18, for band-limited functions $f \in L^1$ implies $f \in L^2$).

4. There is a generalization (Problem 19): if g is C^ℓ (always true if g is band-limited and in L^1), $\{g^{(j)}(\frac{m\ell}{B})\}_{j=1,\ldots,\ell; m \in \mathbb{Z}}$ determine g.

Proof. In (6.6.50) (in the improved form (6.6.126)), let $f = \widehat{g}$ and $\alpha = B$. By that formula, $\{g(\frac{m}{B})\}_{m=\infty}^{\infty}$ determines the sum on the left for a.e. "x" which, by hypothesis, has a single term. Thus, $f = \widehat{g}$ is determined, and so g is determined by the Fourier inversion formula. $\square$

Remarkably, there is a simple explicit formula for g in terms of the sampling values. It involves the function, $\operatorname{sinc}(x)$, called the *sinc kernel*, defined by

$$\operatorname{sinc}(x) = \begin{cases} \sin(\pi x)/\pi x, & x \neq 0 \\ 1, & x = 0 \end{cases} \tag{6.6.74}$$

Theorem 6.6.16 (Nyquist–Shannon Sampling Theorem; Second Form). *Let* $g \in L^2(\mathbb{R})$ *have* $\operatorname{supp}(\widehat{g}) \subset [-\pi B, \pi B]$. *Then* g *is continuous, we have*

$$\sum_{m=-\infty}^{\infty} \left| g\left(\frac{m}{B}\right) \right|^2 < \infty \tag{6.6.75}$$

and for any $x \in \mathbb{R}$,

$$g(x) = \sum_{m=-\infty}^{\infty} g\left(\frac{m}{B}\right) \operatorname{sinc}(Bx - m) \tag{6.6.76}$$

Remarks. 1. The series (6.6.76) is called the *cardinal series*. It has an involved history of rediscovery. As we'll explain, our approach in the second proof below is due to Hardy. We note this second proof does not depend on the Poisson summation formula.

2. Since $\sum_{m \neq 0} \frac{1}{m^2} < \infty$, we see that the series in (6.6.76) converges uniformly on compacts in x.

3. We call this the second form of the Nyquist–Shannon theorem since the explicit formula clearly implies the uniqueness, and modulo some technicalities, uniqueness implies (6.6.76), as we'll see in the first proof below.

4. $\{g \in L^2(\mathbb{R}) \mid \operatorname{supp}(g) \subset [-\pi, \pi]\}$ is a reproducing Hilbert space in the sense of Problem 6 of Section 3.3. The reproducing kernel (see Problem 20) is $\operatorname{sinc}(x - y)$, that is, in addition to (6.6.76), one has

$$g(x) = \int_{-\infty}^{\infty} g(y)\operatorname{sinc}(x - y) \, dy \tag{6.6.77}$$

5. If $\widehat{g} \in L^1$, there are simple explicit error estimates about how far the two sides of (6.6.76) differ if $\widehat{g}$ is not supported in $[-2\pi B, 2\pi B]$, namely, (see Problem 21)

$$\left| g(x) - c\text{-}\sum_{m=-\infty}^{\infty} g\left(\frac{m}{B}\right) \operatorname{sinc}(Bx - m) \right| \leq \sqrt{\frac{2}{\pi}} \int_{|k| > \pi B} |\widehat{g}(k)| \, dk \tag{6.6.78}$$

where $c\text{-}\sum_{m=-\infty}^{\infty}$ is the Cesàro sum

$$c\text{-}\sum_{m=-\infty}^{\infty} a_m = \lim_{M \to \infty} \frac{1}{M+1} \sum_{N=0}^{M} \left(\sum_{j=-N}^{N} a_j \right) \tag{6.6.79}$$

In particular,

$$\widehat{g} \in L^1 \Rightarrow \lim_{B \to \infty} c\text{-}\sum_{m=-\infty}^{\infty} g\left(\frac{m}{B}\right) \operatorname{sinc}(Bx - m) = g(x) \tag{6.6.80}$$

First (Partial) Proof. We'll provide a proof assuming one knows $\sum_{m=-\infty}^{\infty}(m+1)^{-1}|g(\frac{m}{B})| < \infty$ and not worrying about the L^1 condition in Theorem 6.6.15. By this hypothesis, the sum in (6.6.76) is uniformly convergent. Moreover, since for $\ell \in \mathbb{Z}$,

$$\operatorname{sinc}(\ell) = \delta_{\ell 0} \tag{6.6.81}$$

the right side evaluated at $x = \frac{\ell}{B}$ is $g(\frac{\ell}{B})$. Thus, by the uniqueness in Theorem 6.6.15, the two sides agree for all x.   □

Second Proof. By scaling, we'll suppose $B = 1$. Define the *Paley–Wiener space* $\mathrm{PW}_\pi \subset L^2(\mathbb{R}, dx)$ to be the subset of f with $\mathrm{supp}(\widehat{f}) \subset [-\pi, \pi]$. Then $\widehat{\ }: \mathrm{PW}_\pi \to L^2([-\pi, \pi], dk)$ is a unitary map showing PW_π is complete, and that if $\varphi_n \in \mathrm{PW}_\pi$ is defined by

$$\widehat{\varphi}_n(k) = \chi_{[-\pi, \pi]}(k) e^{-ink} / \sqrt{2\pi} \qquad (6.6.82)$$

then $\{\varphi_n\}_{n=-\infty}^\infty$ is an orthonormal basis in PW_π. By the Fourier inversion formula,

$$\varphi_0(x) = \frac{1}{2\pi} \int_{-\pi}^{\pi} e^{-ikx}\, dk = \mathrm{sinc}(x) \qquad (6.6.83)$$

by an elementary integration, and similarly,

$$\varphi_n(x) = \mathrm{sinc}(x - n) \qquad (6.6.84)$$

Let $g \in \mathrm{PW}_\pi$. Then the Fourier expansion in the basis $\{\varphi_n\}_{n=-\infty}^\infty$ says

$$g(x) = \sum_{n=-\infty}^{\infty} a_n(g)\mathrm{sinc}(x - n) \qquad (6.6.85)$$

converging in L^2. By the Parseval relation,

$$\sum_{n=-\infty}^{\infty} |a_n(g)|^2 < \infty \qquad (6.6.86)$$

This fact and $|\mathrm{sinc}(x)| \leq \min(1, \frac{1}{|x|})$ implies the series in (6.6.85) converges uniformly on compacts in x to a continuous function $\widetilde{g}(x)$. Since a subsequence of partial sums converges to $g(x)$ for a.e. x, we conclude $g = \widetilde{g}$.

By (6.6.85) and (6.6.81), $a_n(g) = g(n)$, proving (6.6.76). (6.6.75) is just (6.6.86).   □

Notes and Historical Remarks.

> Bochner's conversation gives me the impression of genuine devotion to his science. He says he is interested in the whole field of analysis. Personally I have heard nothing much of Bochner in Vienna, Budapest, Szeged, Göttingen, or Berlin, which seems to indicate that he is not the man of outstanding promise. It is easy to understand that Carathéodory's recommendations are slightly tinged by his personal relations to B., and also perhaps, by a feeling (not rare here) that any second-rate European youngster is good enough for us.
>
> —*George Birkhoff*, letter to Collidge, Kellogg and Graustein, his colleagues at Harvard, July 7, 1928 quoted in [**846**][4]

---

[4]Birkhoff went on to mention von Neumann (only positively) but then settled on Van der Waerden. There are many who think Birkhoff's documented anti-Semitism (see the references in the Notes to Section 2.7 of Part 3) was a factor in this acid opinion although Birkhoff's defenders [**621**] say it was a desire to give preference to young Americans.

The Riesz–Thorin theorem was proven by Thorin in 1938 [**916, 917**], with initial results by his advisor, Marcel Riesz, in 1927 [**790, 791**]. For the context of their work, extensions to an abstract setting, and the proof, see Section 5.2 of Part 2A and its Notes.

The Hausdorff–Young inequality was proven for Fourier series (see Problem 4(a)) in 1913 by Young [**1010**] (who had some values of q) and for general q in 1923 by Hausdorff [**404**] and for Fourier integrals by Titchmarsh in 1924 [**920**].

The constant in (6.6.7) is not optimal. The optimal constant in the Hausdorff–Young inequality is

$$\|\widehat{f}\|_q \leq (2\pi)^{-\nu(\frac{1}{p}-\frac{1}{2})}[q^{-1/2q}p^{1/2p}]^\nu \|f\|_p \tag{6.6.87}$$

For $1 < p < 2$, this is a strictly smaller number than (6.6.7). Babenko [**44**] found the optimal constant when $q = 4, 6, 8, \ldots$; the general version is due to Beckner [**66**]. The optimal constant is realized in three cases: if $p = 2$, we, of course, have equality for all f, and when $p = 1$, for many f's (e.g., any $f \geq 0$), and for $1 < p < 2$, only for suitable translated Gaussians. This last is a result of Lieb [**586**], who also found a simpler proof of (6.6.87). Kunze [**532**] and Fournier [**312**] have versions of the Hausdorff–Young inequality for some more general, even nonabelian, groups, G (rather than $\mathbb{R}^\nu$).

The Young inequality for convolutions on $\partial\mathbb{D}$ is due to Young [**1011**]. As with the Hausdorff–Young inequality, the naive constant (1 in (6.6.10)) is not optimal. The best constant is

$$\|f * g\|_r \leq (C_p C_q C_{r'})^\nu \|f\|_p \|g\|_q \tag{6.6.88}$$

where

$$C_p = p^{1/2p}(p')^{-1/2p'} \tag{6.6.89}$$

where $p' = p/(p-1)$ is the dual index to p. This result is due to Beckner [**66**] and Brascamp–Lieb [**125**]. The latter prove that equality holds only for suitable translated Gaussians. For nonabelian groups, there are surprising twists in Young-type inequalities. For example, Kunze–Stein [**533**] prove that if G is the group of 2×2 unimodular matrices ($\mathbb{SL}(2, \mathbb{R})$) and $1 \leq p < 2$, then $\|f * g\|_2 \leq A_p \|f\|_2 \|g\|_p$! This has been extended by Cowling [**207**].

(6.6.88) is sometimes written in the symmetric form (the r below is the dual of the r in (6.6.88)),

$$\frac{1}{p} + \frac{1}{q} + \frac{1}{r} = 2 \Rightarrow \int |h(x)f(x-y)g(y)| \, d^\nu x d^\nu y \leq (C_p C_q C_r)^\nu \|f\|_p \|g\|_q \|h\|_r \tag{6.6.90}$$

An extension of (6.6.90) (proven for $\nu = 1$ by Hardy–Littlewood) is the *Sobolev inequality*,

$$\int \frac{|h(x)||g(y)|}{|x-y|^\lambda} \, d^\nu x \, d^\nu y \le C_{\lambda,p,q}\|h\|_p\|g\|_q \tag{6.6.91}$$

if $0 < \lambda < \nu$ and $p^{-1} + q^{-1} + (\lambda/\nu) = 2$. $|x-y|^{-\lambda}$ is barely not in L^r— the L^r integral diverges only logarithmically both at $|x| = 0$ and $|x| = \infty$. Extensions of this type will be extensively discussed in Section 6.2 of Part 3;. (6.6.91) is important since it says something about derivatives ($|x-y|^{-\lambda}$ is a kind of inverse fractional derivative)—this is also something we'll explore in Part 3.

Bochner's theorem appeared first in his 1932 book on the Fourier transform [**101**]. He used it as a key result in his presentation and its extensions have been central in representation theory. Some have referred to the Herglotz–Bochner–Weil–Raikov theorem, putting it in the context of its precursors and successors.

The earliest versions were for $\mathbb{Z}$ rather than $\mathbb{R}$ and arose during the followup to Carathéodory's 1907 paper [**156**] on analytic functions on the disk with positive real part (see Simon [**852**, Sect. 1.3] on these Carathéodory functions and also Section 5.4 of Part 3). One result that can be viewed as the analog of Bochner's theorem for $\mathbb{Z}$ is the Carathéodory [**157**]–Toeplitz [**923**] theorem. Given a sequence $\{c_n\}_{n=-\infty}^\infty$ of complex numbers, the *Toeplitz matrix*, $T^{(n)}$, is the $n \times n$ matrix with $(T^{(n)})_{jk} = c_{j-k}$, $1 \le j, k \le n$, which depends on $\{c_j\}_{j=-n+1}^{n-1}$. Then

Theorem 6.6.17 (Carathéodory–Toeplitz Theorem). *There is a* (*positive*) *measure μ in $\partial\mathbb{D}$ with*

$$c_n = \int e^{-in\theta} \, d\mu(\theta) \tag{6.6.92}$$

for all n if and only if $T^{(n)}$ is positive definite for all n.

Remarks. 1. They stated it in terms of $\det(T^{(n)}) > 0$ for all n, but it is not hard to see that is equivalent to each $T^{(n)}$ positive definite (see Problem 2 of Section 4.17).

2. The condition that each $T^{(n)}$ is positive definite is equivalent to $\sum_{j,\ell=0}^N \bar\zeta_j \zeta_\ell c_{n_j - n_\ell} \ge 0$ for any distinct $n_1, \ldots, n_N$ (for just pick $n \ge 2\max|n_j|$). This is just Bochner's theorem for $\mathbb{Z}$.

3. As we discussed in the Notes to Section 5.6, this theorem is connected to the moment problem for $\partial\mathbb{D}$.

4. We will prove this theorem and the moment problem on $\partial\mathbb{D}$ in Section 5.5 of Part 4.

A different precursor is the Herglotz theorem due to Herglotz [**418**] and Riesz [**781**]. This says

Theorem 6.6.18 (Herglotz Representation Theorem). *Let F be analytic in $\mathbb{D}$ with $F(0) = 1$. Then $\mathrm{Re}\, F \geq 0$ on $\mathbb{D}$ if and only if there is a probability measure on $\partial\mathbb{D}$ with*

$$F(z) = \int \frac{e^{i\theta} + z}{e^{i\theta} - z}\, d\mu(\theta) \tag{6.6.93}$$

The positivity condition here is a little less clearly a version of positive definite functions and the relation of moments of $d\mu$ to $\mathrm{Re}\, f$ a little more obscure. But if $c_n = \int e^{-in\theta}\, d\mu(\theta)$, (6.6.93) says that $\mathrm{Re}\, F(re^{i\theta}) = \sum_{n=-\infty}^{\infty} c_n r^{-|n|} e^{in\theta}$, making the connection somewhat less obscure.

Bochner's theorem has been extended to general locally compact abelian groups independently by Povzner [**749**], Raikov [**756**], and Weil [**980**]. They use it as a fundamental tool in the theory of such groups (see Loomis [**602**] or Rudin [**805**]). Raikov and the two mentioned books use the theory of commutative Banach algebra (see also Section 6.9 of Part 4).

As the remark at the end of the discussion of Bochner's theorem mentions, some versions of Bochner's theorem have a third equivalence: $f \in L^\infty$ is called *weakly positive definite* if and only if it is equal a.e. to a positive definite function (see, e.g., the discussion in Simon [**856**] or Problem 6(e)).

Another extension we should mention is the Bochner–Schwartz theorem [**833**]. Notice that (6.6.28) can be rewritten

$$\int f(x)(h^\flat * \bar{h})(x)\, d^\nu x \geq 0 \tag{6.6.94}$$

where, as usual, $h^\flat(x) = h(-x)$. A tempered distribution, τ, in $\mathcal{S}'(\mathbb{R}^\nu)$ is called a *positive definite distribution* if and only if

$$\forall h \in \mathcal{S}(\mathbb{R}^\nu), \quad \tau(h^\flat * \bar{h}) \geq 0 \tag{6.6.95}$$

Theorem 6.6.19 (Bochner–Schwartz Theorem). *A distribution is positive definite if and only if it is the Fourier transform of a measure on $\mathbb{R}^\nu$ obeying*

$$\mu(\{x \mid |x| \leq R\}) \leq C(1 + R)^n \tag{6.6.96}$$

for some $C > 0$ and n.

The reader will prove this in Problem 6.

There are generalizations of Bochner's theorem to infinite-dimensional spaces due to Minlos [**660**]. For example, there is a notion of probability measures on $\mathcal{S}'(\mathbb{R}^\nu)$ (with the smallest Σ-field making $\tau \to \tau(f)$ measurable for each $f \in \mathcal{S}(\mathbb{R}^\nu)$) and one has

Theorem 6.6.20 (Minlos's Theorem). *Let* $\Phi\colon \mathcal{S}(\mathbb{R}^\nu) \to \mathbb{C}$ *obey* $\{\Phi(f_j - f_k)\}_{1\leq j,k\leq n}$ *is positive definite for every* $f_1, \ldots, f_k$ *in* $\mathcal{S}(\mathbb{R}^\nu)$ *and* $\Phi(0) = 1$. *Then there is a probability measure,* μ, *on* $\mathcal{S}'(\mathbb{R}^\nu)$ *so that*

$$\Phi(f) = \int \exp(i\tau(f))\, d\mu(\tau) \qquad (6.6.97)$$

For a proof, see Simon [**849**].

We should mention two other proofs of Bochner's theorem in part to put it in context. One proof uses the Krein–Milman theorem; this proves that the set of weakly positive functions with $\|f\|_\infty \leq 1$ is compact in the $\sigma(L^\infty, L^1)$-topology. Its extreme points are proven to be $\{e^{ik\cdot x}\}_{k\in\mathbb{R}^\nu}$ and 0. This set is closed, so as discussed in Section 5.11, there is a strong Krein–Milman theorem which implies Bochner's theorem. The details of this proof can be found in the books of Choquet [**191**] and Simon [**856**].

Reed–Simon [**764**] have a proof that goes from the spectral theorem plus Stone's theorem to Bochner's theorem, but the point here is that, in essence, one can go in the other direction. For if $t \mapsto U_t$ is a family of unitaries on a Hilbert space, $\mathcal{H}$, with $t \mapsto \langle \varphi, U_t\psi\rangle$ continuous for each $\varphi, \psi \in \mathcal{H}$ and with $U_t U_s = U_{t+s}$ and $U_0 = \mathbb{1}$, then for any φ, $f(t) = \langle \varphi, U_t\varphi\rangle$ is positive definite on $\mathbb{R}$ (Problem 7). Thus, there is a measure, $d\mu_\varphi(t)$, with

$$\langle \varphi, U_t\varphi\rangle = \int e^{i\lambda t}\, d\mu_\varphi(t) \qquad (6.6.98)$$

If A is a bounded self-adjoint operator, one can let $U_t = \sum_{n=0}^\infty (itA)^n/n!$ and prove $d\mu_\varphi(t)$ has finite support and $\int t^n\, d\mu_\varphi(t) = \langle \varphi, A^n\varphi\rangle$ and go from there to the spectral theorem for such operators (see Chapters 5 and 7 of Part 4). In the general case, one can construct in this way an unbounded A so that $U_t = e^{itA}$ and so get Stone's theorem.

Salomon Bochner (1899–1982) was born to a religious Jewish family near Krakow, then part of the Austro-Hungarian empire. In 1914, fearful of a Russian invasion, his family moved to Berlin, where he received a Ph.D. in 1921 supervised by Schmidt. In his dissertation, he introduced what has come to be called the Bergman kernel—a subject we discuss in Section 12.5 of Part 2B (Bergman's thesis was essentially simultaneous with Bochner). He then quit academia for an import-export business to try and aid his family during the hyperinflation. In 1924, he returned to mathematical research initially making a splash due to his work on almost periodic functions (which we discuss in Section 6.6 of Part 4).

From 1924 to 1933, Bochner lectured at the University of Munich but despite the support of Carathéodory and Perron, the mathematics professors there, the ministry refused to give him a regular appointment. The official reason was his Polish citizenship (Poland didn't exist until long after his family left!) but Carathéodory claimed it was due to antisemitism. As part of the campaign to get him an appointment in Munich, Carathéodory tried to arrange unsuccessfully an appointment as a visitor to Harvard which prompted the Birkhoff letter quoted at the start of the Notes. Instead, Bochner moved to Princeton in 1933 where he remained for 35 years.

Besides his theorem in this section which was the centerpiece in a 1932 book on the Fourier integral and the work on almost periodic functions and the Bochner integral of Section 4.18, he is known for foundational work in the theory of several complex variables, and also the connection of curvature and algebraic topology. His students include Askey, Calabi, Cheeger, Furstenberg, Gunning, Helgason, Karlin, Knapp, Loomis, and Washnitzer.

Wiener's theorem (Theorem 6.6.9) appeared in his 1933 book [**998**]. We'll use Wiener's theorem to prove the so-called RAGE Theorem in Section 5.5 of Part 4.

The Poisson summation formula was found by Poisson in 1827 [**741**]. Gauss had found (6.6.52) in a note written sometime between 1799 and 1813. This was only published a century later with his complete works [**342**]. No proof was given in this note.

The functional equation for theta (Example 6.6.11) appeared in a paper of Jacobi [**447**] who wrote out (6.6.60), saying it was a result of Poisson. The Basel sum of Example 6.6.12 is discussed in the Notes to Section 5.7 of Part 2A. As discussed there, this series has many proofs of it.

Using the Fourier transform normalized by

$$(\mathcal{F}f)(k) = \int_{-\infty}^{\infty} f(x)e^{-2\pi i k x}\,dx \tag{6.6.99}$$

the Poisson summation formula takes the simpler-looking form

$$\sum_{n=-\infty}^{\infty} f(x+n) = \sum_{m=-\infty}^{\infty} (\mathcal{F}f)(m)e^{2\pi i m x} \tag{6.6.100}$$

Part 2A has two alternate proofs of the Poisson summation formula in its Problems. Problem 29 of Section 5.7 has a proof using contour integrals and Problem 7 of Section 9.7 has a proof using the Euler–Maclaurin summation formula.

The Poisson summation formula on $\mathbb{R}^\nu$ has been applied to compute sums of dipole Coulomb energies for charges at each point in the lattice. The sums in Fourier space are more rapidly convergent. This is known as Ewald's method, after Ewald [**290**] who developed the idea in 1921.

The sampling theorem (Theorem 6.6.15) is named after work of Nyquist [**687**] and Shannon [**840**]. There is related work of Whittaker [**990**] and Kotelnikov [**516**], whose names are sometimes included with the theorem.

The ideas in the theorem are important in communications theory and information theory, so much so that there are entire books on effective sampling methods [**637**].

Before turning to the involved history of the sampling theorem (where Arnold's principle definitely applies), we note two mathematical aspects relevant to the history. One concerns polynomial interpolation called Newton–Gauss or Lagrange interpolation. If P is a polynomial vanishing simply and exactly at distinct points $x_1, \ldots, x_{n+1}$ and Q is a polynomial of degree n, then

$$Q(x) = P(x) \sum_{j=1}^{n+1} Q(x_j) \frac{1}{P'(x_j)(x - x_j)} \tag{6.6.101}$$

as follows from a partial faction expansion of Q/P. In particular, if $Q(x)$ has degree $2n$, we have, with $P_n(x) = x \prod_{j=1}^{n}(1 - \frac{x^2}{j^2})$,

$$Q(x) = x \prod_{j=1}^{n}\left(1 - \frac{x^2}{j^2}\right) \sum_{j=-n}^{n} Q(j) \frac{1}{P_n'(j)(x - j)} \tag{6.6.102}$$

Formally taking $n \to \infty$, $P_n(x) \to \sin(\pi x)/\pi$ by a famous formula of Euler (see Section 9.2 of Part 2A) and $P_n'(x) \to \cos(\pi x)$. Thus, formally, (6.6.102) becomes

$$f(x) = \frac{\sin(\pi x)}{\pi} \sum_{j=-\infty}^{\infty} f(j) \frac{(-1)^j}{x - j} \tag{6.6.103}$$

Noticing that $\sin(\pi(x - j)) = (-1)^j \sin(\pi x)$, we see that the cardinal series (6.6.76) is exactly (6.6.103).

Secondly, we note the Paley–Wiener theorem that appears as Theorem 11.1.2 of Section 11.1 of Part 2A. It says PW_π is precisely the restrictions to $\mathbb{R}$ of those entire analytic functions which are L^2 on $\mathbb{R}$ and obey a bound of the form $|g(z)| \leq C \exp(\pi|\mathrm{Im}\, z|)$. Some of the early work on sampling is expressed in terms of such analytic functions.

While there have been claims the cardinal series goes back to Cauchy and to Poisson, the comprehensive reviews of their history and theory by Higgins [**424**] says that seems to be unfounded (although both did not unrelated work). The first work related to the sampling theorems seems to be Borel [**111**] in 1897 who stated that if $f(x) = \int_{-\pi}^{\pi} \psi(k)e^{ikx}\, dk$, where ψ obeyed Dirichlet's condition for convergence of Fourier series, then f is determined by its values at $x \in \mathbb{Z}$ (i.e., he had a version of the first form of the sampling theorem). He never found the second form, although a year later [**113**], in a different context, he discussed series of the form $\frac{\sin \pi z}{z} \sum a_n(z - n)^{-1}$.

In 1915, E. T. Whittaker [**990**] picked out the cardinal series as an especially interesting function interpolating between values at $\{\frac{n}{B}\}_{n \in \mathbb{Z}}$ singling it out as being entire and free of "violent oscillations," but he had no uniqueness result. It was Whittaker who coined the phrase cardinal series. Interestingly enough, if you Google "cardinal series," the mathematical references are dwarfed by references to a set of custom bathroom showers, to sports teams named the Cardinals, to the Church's influence in medieval history, and to two sets of books with the main characters Laura Cardinal and John Cardinal.

The first rigorous proofs of cardinal series expansions for suitable classes of entire functions seem to be by the Japanese mathematician, Kinnosuke Ogura (1885–1962) [**689**], but his work was unknown in the West until many years later. Butzer et al. [**142**] discuss the work of Whittaker and Ogura. This paper also discusses the history of these ideas in the engineering literature, including work of Kostelnikov, Nyquist, and Shannon quoted above.

Before leaving the subject, we should mention Hardy's beautiful paper [**394**] which noted the reproducing kernel for PW_π and that the cardinal series is just Fourier series in the orthonormal basis $\{\mathrm{sinc}(\cdot - m)\}_{m=-\infty}^\infty$, and that Boas [**97**] seems to be the person, only in 1972, to explicitly note that sampling theorems follow from the Poisson summation formula.

Finally, we note an extensive series of papers by Butzer and collaborators [**141, 143, 144, 145, 146**]. Among the ideas this work contains is the connection to the Euler–Maclaurin expansions (Problem 7 of Section 9.7 of Part 2A has a proof of the Poisson summation formula from this expansion, the subject of the section) and the connection to the Cauchy integral formula (see Problem 29 of Section 5.7 of Part 2A).

While we stated the Poisson summation formula requiring (6.6.49), we note that it holds so long as

$$\sum_m \left| \widehat{f}\left(\frac{m}{\alpha}\right) \right| < \infty \tag{6.6.104}$$

and f is in L^1, continuous, and the sum $\sum_{n=-N}^N |f(x + 2\pi\alpha n)|$ converges uniformly in x. For, as noted in Problem 9, it holds for a.e. x with the right side in Cesàro sense, and if the left side is a continuous function of x, for all x. If (6.6.104) holds, the ordinary sum and Cesàro sum agree. In particular, (6.6.50) holds in $\mathbb{R}^\nu$

$$|f(x)| + |\widehat{f}(x)| \le C(1 + |x|)^{-\nu - \varepsilon} \tag{6.6.105}$$

a condition found in some presentations. We also note the result at some x as discussed in Example 6.6.13 that relies on the local nature of the Dini test.

One important topic missing from our discussion of the basics of Fourier transform is the relation of support of f or τ to the analyticity of $\widehat{f}$ or $\widehat{\tau}$

(Paley–Wiener theory). This involves analyticity and so belongs in Part 2. Section 11.1 of Part 2A discusses this subject.

Problems

1. This problem will prove Young's inequality just from Hölder's inequality. Let
$$p^{-1} + q^{-1} + r^{-1} = 2 \qquad (6.6.106)$$
(this r is the dual of the r in (6.6.9)).

(a) Prove that Young's inequality (6.6.10) is equivalent to
$$\int f(x)g(x-y)h(y)\, d^\nu x\, d^\nu y\, d^\nu z \le \|f\|_p \|g\|_q \|h\|_r \qquad (6.6.107)$$
for $f, g, h \ge 0$ and p, q, r obeying (6.6.106).

(b) Let $s' = (1 - s^{-1})^{-1}$. Prove (6.6.106) implies that
$$(p')^{-1} + (q')^{-1} + (r')^{-1} = 1 \qquad (6.6.108)$$
$$\frac{r}{p'} + \frac{r}{q'} = 1 \qquad (6.6.109)$$

(c) Let
$$A(x,y) = f(x)^{p/r'} g(x-y)^{q/r'}, \;\; B(x,y) = g(x-y)^{q/p'} h(y)^{r/p'},$$
$$C(x,y) = f(x)^{p/q'} h(y)^{r/q'} \qquad (6.6.110)$$
Prove that (6.6.107) is equivalent to $\int A(x,y)B(x,y)C(x,y)\, d^\nu x\, d^\nu y \le \|f\|_p \|g\|_q \|h\|_r$.

(d) Use Hölder's inequality to prove that
$$\int A(x,y)B(x,y)C(x,y)\, d^\nu x\, d^\nu y \le \|A\|_{r'} \|B\|_{p'} \|C\|_{q'} \qquad (6.6.111)$$

(e) Prove that
$$\|A\|_{r'} = \|f\|_p^{p/r'} \|g\|_q^{q/r'}, \quad \|B\|_{p'} = \|g\|_q^{q/p'} \|h\|_r^{r/p'},$$
$$\|C\|_{q'} = \|f\|_p^{p/q'} \|h\|_r^{r/q'} \qquad (6.6.112)$$

(f) Complete the proof of (6.6.107).

2. Prove Steinhaus' theorem [**877**] that if $E \subset \mathbb{R}^\nu$ has positive Lebesgue measure, then $E - E = \{x - y \mid x, y \in E\}$ contains a neighborhood of 0. (*Hint*: If E is bounded, prove that $(\chi_E * \chi_{-E})(0) \ne 0$ and use the continuity of $\chi_E * \chi_{-E}$.)

3. Prove that if f is bounded and continuous, then (6.6.28) for all $h \in \mathcal{S}(\mathbb{R}^\nu)$ implies that f is positive definite. (*Hint*: Pick $h(x) = \sum_{j=1}^n \zeta_j (2\pi\alpha)^{-\nu/2} \exp(-(x - x_j)^2/2\alpha)$ and let $\alpha \to 0$.)

4. (a) If $f_n^\sharp$ are the Fourier series coefficients of $f \in C(\partial \mathbb{D})$ (given by (3.5.1)), prove first that ($\|\cdot\|_p$ is ℓ^p norm)

$$\|f^\sharp\|_2 \le \|f\|_{L^2(\partial\mathbb{D},\frac{d\theta}{2\pi})}, \qquad \|f^\sharp\|_\infty \le \|f\|_{L^1(\partial\mathbb{D},\frac{d\theta}{2\pi})} \tag{6.6.113}$$

and then that for $1 \le p \le 2$ and $q = p/(p-1)$, we have

$$\|f^\sharp\|_q \le \|f\|_{L^p(\partial\mathbb{D},\frac{d\theta}{2\pi})} \tag{6.6.114}$$

(b) Prove first that

$$\|f\|_{L^2(\partial\mathbb{D},\frac{d\theta}{2\pi})} \le \|f^\sharp\|_2, \qquad \|f\|_{L^\infty(\partial\mathbb{D},\frac{d\theta}{2\pi})} \le (2\pi)^{-1}\|f^\sharp\|_1 \tag{6.6.115}$$

and then that for $1 \le p \le 2$ and $q = p/(p-1)$, we have

$$\|f\|_{L^q(\partial\mathbb{D},\frac{d\theta}{2\pi})} \le (2\pi)^{(1-2/p)}\|f^\sharp\|_p \tag{6.6.116}$$

5. This problem will use scaling to show that the exponents in Hölder's, Young's and the Hausdorff–Young inequalities are the right ones.

   (a) If $f \in \mathcal{S}(\mathbb{R}^\nu)$ and $f_\lambda(x) = f(\lambda x)$, prove that $\|f_\lambda\|_p = \lambda^{-\nu/p}\|f\|_p$.

   (b) If $\|fg\|_s \le C\|f\|_p\|g\|_q$ for some p, q, s and C and all $f, g \in \mathcal{S}(\mathbb{R}^\nu)$, prove that $s^{-1} = p^{-1} + q^{-1}$.

   (c) Prove that $(f * g)_\lambda = \lambda^\nu (f_\lambda * g_\lambda)$.

   (d) If $\|f * g\|_s \le C\|f\|_p\|g\|_q$ for some p, q, s and C and all $f, g \in \mathcal{S}(\mathbb{R}^\nu)$, prove that $p^{-1} + q^{-1} = 1 + s^{-1}$.

   (e) Prove that $(f_\lambda)^\wedge = \lambda^{-\nu}(\widehat{f})_{\lambda^{-1}}$.

   (f) If $\|\widehat{f}\|_s \le C\|f\|_p$ for some p, s and C and all $f \in \mathcal{S}(\mathbb{R}^\nu)$, prove that $p^{-1} + s^{-1} = 1$.

6. This problem will prove the Bochner–Schwartz theorem (Theorem 6.6.19) and that weakly positive definite functions are a.e. equal to positive definite functions.

   (a) If g_a is given by (6.2.59), prove that $g_a * g_a = (2\pi)^{\nu/2}g_{a/2}$, so that $(2\pi)^{-\nu}g_a * g_a \to \delta$ as $a \downarrow 0$.

   (b) Suppose τ is a positive definite distribution (i.e., (6.6.95) holds). Define

$$\tau_a = (2\pi)^{-\nu}(g_a * g_a) * \tau \tag{6.6.117}$$

Prove that for $h \in \mathcal{S}(\mathbb{R}^\nu)$,

$$\tau_a(h^\flat * \bar{h}) = (2\pi)^{-\nu}\tau\big((g_a * h)^\flat \, \overline{(g_a * h)}\big) \tag{6.6.118}$$

(c) Prove that τ_a is a positive definite continuous function and conclude that for a finite measure, $d\mu_a$, on $\mathbb{R}^\nu$,

$$\tau_a(x) = (2\pi)^{-\nu/2} \int e^{-ik\cdot x} \, d\mu_a(k) \tag{6.6.119}$$

(d) Prove that $\check{\tau}$ is a measure, μ, on $\mathbb{R}^\nu$ and that if

$$|\check{\tau}(f)| \leq C_1 \sum_{|\alpha|,|\beta| \leq n} \|x^\alpha D^\beta f\|_\infty \tag{6.6.120}$$

then

$$\mu(\{x \mid |x| < R\}) \leq C_2(1+R)^n \tag{6.6.121}$$

Thus, you've proven Theorem 6.6.19.

(e) If τ is $\jmath(f)$ with $f \in L^\infty$, prove that for all a,

$$\tau_a(0) \leq \|f\|_\infty \tag{6.6.122}$$

and conclude that the measure μ of (d) is a finite measure. Then conclude that f is a.e. equal to a continuous positive definite function.

7. If $t \to U_t$ is weakly continuous, unitary and $U_t U_s = U_{t+s}$, prove that $\sum_{j,k=1}^n \bar{\zeta}_j \zeta_k U_{t_j - t_k} = (\sum_{j=1}^n \zeta_j U_{-t_j})^* (\sum_{j=1}^n \zeta_j U_{-t_j})$ and conclude that (6.6.98) defines a positive definite function.

8. Prove a discrete analog of Wiener's theorem, explicitly if μ is a measure on $\partial\mathbb{D}$ and

$$\mu_n^\sharp = \int e^{-in\theta} \, d\mu(\theta) \tag{6.6.123}$$

then

$$\lim_{N\to\infty} \frac{1}{2N+1} \sum_{n=-N}^N |\mu_n^\sharp|^2 = \sum_{e^{i\theta} \in \partial\mathbb{D}} |\mu(\{e^{i\theta}\})|^2 \tag{6.6.124}$$

9. Let $\Sigma_n^{(\alpha)}(f;x)$ denote the sum on the right in (6.6.50) and

$$\Gamma_N^{(\alpha)}(f;x) = \frac{1}{N} \sum_{j=0}^{N-1} \Sigma_j^{(\alpha)}(f;x) \tag{6.6.125}$$

(a) If $f \in L^1(\mathbb{R}, dx)$, prove that the sum on the left side of (6.6.50) is absolutely convergent for a.e. x.

(b) Let $f \in L^1(\mathbb{R}, dx)$. For a.e. x, prove that

$$\sum_{n=-\infty}^\infty f(x + 2\pi\alpha n) = \lim_{N\to\infty} \Gamma_n^{(\alpha)}(f;x) \tag{6.6.126}$$

(c) If the left side of (6.6.126) is continuous in x, prove that (6.6.126) holds at every x and the convergence on the right is uniform. (*Hint for* (b) *and* (c): Fejér.)

10. (a) Let $\mathbb{Z}^\nu$ be the integer lattice in $\mathbb{R}^\nu$. Suppose $f \in \mathcal{S}(\mathbb{R}^\nu)$. For all $\alpha \in (0, \infty)$, $x \in \mathbb{R}^\nu$, prove that

$$\sum_{n \in \mathbb{Z}^\nu} f(x + 2\pi \alpha n) = \frac{1}{(\alpha \sqrt{2\pi})^\nu} \sum_{m \in \mathbb{Z}^\nu} \widehat{f}\left(\frac{m}{\alpha}\right) e^{im \cdot x\alpha} \tag{6.6.127}$$

(b) A *lattice* $\mathcal{L}$ in $\mathbb{R}^\nu$ is a set of the form $\{m_1 e_1 + \cdots + m_\nu e_\nu \mid m \in \mathbb{Z}^\nu\}$. Here $\{e_j\}_{j=1}^\nu$ is a basis for $\mathbb{R}^\nu$. The *dual lattice* is

$$\mathcal{L}' = \{y \in \mathbb{R}^\nu \mid \ell \cdot y \in \mathbb{Z} \text{ for all } \ell \in \mathcal{L}\} \tag{6.6.128}$$

The *unit cell*, C, for $\mathcal{L}$ is the subset of $\mathbb{R}^\nu$ of those x with $x = \sum_{j=1}^\nu b_j e_j$ and $\max|b_j| \leq \frac{1}{2}$. Prove that

$$|C| = \det(\langle e_j, e_k \rangle) \tag{6.6.129}$$

(c) For $f \in \mathcal{S}(\mathbb{R}^\nu)$ and any lattice, $\mathcal{L}$, prove that for all $x \in \mathbb{R}^\nu$,

$$\sum_{\ell \in \mathcal{L}} f(x + 2\pi \ell) = \sum_{y \in \mathcal{L}'} (2\pi)^{-\nu/2} |C|^{-1} \widehat{f}(y) e^{ix \cdot y} \tag{6.6.130}$$

Remark. We state this for $f \in \mathcal{S}$ for simplicity. All the one-dimensional refinements extend to $\mathbb{R}^\nu$.

11. In this problem the reader will use the Poisson summation formula to prove a theorem of Minkowski that if $K \subset \mathbb{R}^\nu$ is convex and balanced and if $\mathcal{L}$ is a lattice with unit cell C then (with $|\cdot| = $ volume)

$$|K| \geq 2^\nu \operatorname{vol} |C| \Rightarrow K \cap (\mathcal{L} \setminus \{0\}) \neq \emptyset \tag{6.6.131}$$

(a) Rewrite (6.6.130) as (for $f \in \mathcal{S}(\mathbb{R}^\nu)$)

$$\sum_{\ell \in \mathcal{L}} f(\ell) = |C|^{-1} \sum_{y \in \mathcal{L}'} (\mathcal{F}f)(g) \tag{6.6.132}$$

(where $\mathcal{F}f$ is given by (6.6.99))

(b) Prove that for $f \in \mathcal{S}(\mathbb{R}^\nu)$

$$\sum_{\ell \in \mathcal{L}} f(2\ell) = 2^{-\nu} |C|^{-1} \sum_{y \in \mathcal{L}'} (\mathcal{F}f)\left(\frac{y}{2}\right) \tag{6.6.133}$$

(c) Prove if χ is the characteristic function of K and $f = \chi * \chi$, that (6.6.133) is still valid and says that

$$\sum_{\ell \in \mathcal{L}} f(2\ell) = 2^{-\nu} |K| \sum_{y \in \mathcal{L}'} \left| \mathcal{F}\chi\left(\frac{y}{2}\right) \right|^2 \tag{6.6.134}$$

(d) Suppose that
$$K \cap (\mathcal{L} \setminus \{0\}) = \emptyset \qquad (6.6.135)$$
Prove that
$$f(2\ell) = \begin{cases} |K|, & \ell = 0 \\ 0, & \ell \neq 0 \end{cases} \qquad (6.6.136)$$

(e) Prove that $(\mathcal{F}\chi)(0) = |K|$.

(f) Prove that if g has $(\mathcal{F}g)(\frac{y}{2}) = 0$ for all $y \in \mathcal{L}' \setminus \{0\}$, then $h(x) = \sum_{\mathcal{L}} g(x + 2\ell)$ is constant. If $h(x) = \sum_{\mathcal{L}} \chi(x + 2\ell)$, prove that $h(0) = 1$ and $h(\ell) = 0$ if $\ell \in \mathcal{L} \setminus 2\mathcal{L}$ and consider that h is not constant. Conclude that $(\mathcal{F}\chi)(\frac{y}{2}) \neq 0$ for some $y \in \mathcal{L}' \setminus \{0\}$.

(g) Prove that
$$K \cap (\mathcal{L} \setminus \{0\}) \neq \emptyset \Rightarrow |K| > 2^{-\nu} |C|^{-1} |K|^2$$
and conclude (6.6.131)

(h) Show that the constant $2^{-\nu}$ cannot be improved (*Hint*: Take the cubic lattices and K a multiple of the unit cell.)

Remark. This result is from Minkowski [**658**]. This proof is basically due to Siegel [**845**] although we follow Rademacher's presentation [**752**]; see also Chandrasekharan [**180**] or Dym-McKean [**268**].

12. (a) Let $\Delta_\alpha(x) = \sum_{n \in \mathbb{Z}} \delta(x + 2\pi\alpha n)$. Prove that $\Delta_\alpha(x)$ defines a tempered distribution.

(b) Prove that the Poisson summation formula for $f \in \mathcal{S}$ is equivalent to
$$\widehat{\Delta}_\alpha = (\alpha\sqrt{2\pi})^{-1}\Delta_{1/\alpha} \qquad (6.6.137)$$

13. Verify that (6.6.62) and (6.6.63) result from the application of the Poisson summation formula.

14. Compute the Fourier transform of $h_\beta(x) = e^{-\beta|x|}$ as a function on $\mathbb{R}$.

15. (a) Prove that
$$\lim_{\beta \downarrow 0} \left[\frac{\pi}{\beta} \coth(\pi\beta) - \frac{1}{\beta^2} \right] = \frac{\pi^2}{3} \qquad (6.6.138)$$

(b) Deduce (6.6.67) from (6.6.66).

16. Let $g_\beta(x) = \text{sgn}(x)e^{-\beta|x|}$. Prove that
$$\sum_{n=-\infty}^{\infty} g_\beta(2\pi(n + \tfrac{1}{4})) = \frac{1}{2\cosh(\pi\beta/2)}$$

17. (a) Verify (6.6.71). (*Hint*: Expand in a geometric series.)

    (b) Verify (6.6.72).

    (c) Verify (6.6.73).

18. Suppose that $f \in \mathcal{S}'(\mathbb{R})$ has supp$(\widehat{f}) \subset K$ a compact subset of $\mathbb{R}$.

    (a) If $f \in L^p(\mathbb{R})$, $1 \leq p < 2$, prove that $f \in L^2$; indeed,

    $$\|f\|_2 \leq \left(\frac{|K|}{2\pi}\right)^{2p/(2-p)} \|f\|_p$$

    (b) If $f \in L^2(\mathbb{R})$, prove that f is an entire analytic function and

    $$|f(x) - f(y)| \leq (2\pi)^{-1/2}\left(\sup_{k \in K}|k|\right)|K|^{1/2}\|f\|_2|x - y| \qquad (6.6.139)$$

    $$\|f\|_\infty \leq (2\pi)^{-1/2}|K|^{1/2}\|f\|_2 \qquad (6.6.140)$$

19. Suppose that $f \in L^1$ and supp$(f) \subset [-\pi B, \pi B]$.

    (a) Prove that $\{f^{(j)}(\frac{m\ell}{B})\}_{m=-\infty}^{\infty}$ determine, for a.e. $k \in [-\pi B, -\pi B + \frac{2\pi B}{\ell}]$, $\sum_{q=0}^{\ell-1}(k + q\frac{2\pi B}{\ell})^j \, \widehat{f}(k + q\frac{2\pi B}{\ell})$.

    (b) Prove that $\{\{f^{(j)}(\frac{m\ell}{B})\}_{m=-\infty}^{\infty}\}_{j=0,\dots,\ell-1}$ determine $\widehat{f}(k)$ for a.e. k, and so f. (*Hint*: Vandermonde determinants.)

20. (a) In terms of the notions of Problem 6 of Section 3.3, prove that PW_π is a reproducing kernel Hilbert space. (*Hint*: (6.6.139) and (6.6.140).)

    (b) Find the reproducing kernel. (*Hint*: If $f \in \mathrm{PW}_\pi$, then $\widehat{f} = \chi_{[-\pi,\pi]}\widehat{f}$ and $\check{\chi}_{[-\pi,\pi]}$ and its translates lie in PW_π.)

21. Suppose $\widehat{f} \in L^1(\mathbb{R})$ so f is continuous.

    (a) Prove that, with $c\text{-}\sum_{m=-\infty}^{\infty} a_m$, the Cesàro sum (6.6.79), we have that

    $$c\text{-}\sum_{m=-\infty}^{\infty} g\left(\frac{m}{B}\right)\mathrm{sinc}(Bx - m)$$

    $$= \frac{1}{\sqrt{2\pi}} \sum_{k=-\infty}^{\infty} e^{2\pi ikBx} \int_{(2k-1)\pi B}^{(2k+1)\pi B} \widehat{f}(k)e^{-ikx}\, dk \qquad (6.6.141)$$

    (b) Prove (6.6.78).

Remark. This bound appeared in print first in a 1967 paper of J. L. Brown [**135**]. Earlier, in 1963. P. Weiss [**981**] gave a talk at an AMS meeting that included this in his abstract, but a paper never appeared. The proof sketched here is from Butzer–Stens [**145**].

22. (a) If $f \in \mathrm{PW}_\pi$, prove that

$$\sum_{n=-\infty}^{\infty} |f(n)|^2 = \int_{-\infty}^{\infty} |f(x)|^2 \, dx \qquad (6.6.142)$$

(b) For any $\alpha \in (0, \pi]$ and any θ, prove that

$$\sum \left| \frac{\sin(n\alpha + \theta)}{n\alpha + \theta} \right|^2 = \frac{\pi}{\alpha} \qquad (6.6.143)$$

(c) If $f \in \mathrm{PW}_\pi$ and $|f(x)| \le C(1 + |x|)^{-\beta}$ for some $\beta > 1$, prove that

$$\sum_{n=-\infty}^{\infty} f(n) = \int_{-\infty}^{\infty} f(x) \, dx \qquad (6.6.144)$$

23. Let $f_0(x) = e^{-\frac{1}{2}x^2}$ on $\mathbb{R}^\nu$. Prove that finite linear combinations of $\{f_0(\cdot - y) \mid y \in \mathbb{R}^1\}$ are dense in $\mathcal{S}(\mathbb{R}^\nu)$. (*Hint:* First show that one need only prove the same for $\{f_0(\cdot)e^{-iy\cdot} \mid y \in \mathbb{R}\}$ and then show one need only prove the same for $\{$polynomials in $x_1, \ldots, x_\nu f_0(x)\}$.)

24. Let f_0 be in $L^2(\mathbb{R}^\nu, d^\nu x)$ obey $\widehat{f_0}(k) \ne 0$ for $d^\nu k$-a.e. k. Prove that finite linear combinations of f_0 are dense in $L^2(\mathbb{R}^\nu, d^\nu x)$.

6.7. Bonus Section: Riesz Products

In this section, we will first construct some singular continuous measures, μ, on $\partial \mathbb{D}$ with $\sum_{n \in \mathbb{Z}} |\mu_n^\sharp|^p < \infty$ for all $2 < p < \infty$ and then use them to construct $f \in \cap_{2 < p \le \infty} L^p(\mathbb{R}, dx)$ so that $\widehat{f}$ is not a function. This implies first that for $1 < p < 2$, $\widehat{L^p(\mathbb{R}^\nu)}$ is not all of $L^q(\mathbb{R}^\nu)$ and that Hausdorff–Young does not extend beyond $1 \le p \le 2$. We'll also find $f \in C_\infty(\mathbb{R})$ so that $\widehat{f} \notin L^1$.

Formally, the measure μ above is given by

$$\prod_{n=1}^{\infty} (1 + (n+1)^{-1/2} \cos(3^n \theta)) \frac{d\theta}{2\pi} \qquad (6.7.1)$$

Here is the main theorem:

Theorem 6.7.1. *Let $a_j \in (-1, 1)$ for $j \in \{1, 2, \ldots\}$ and define*

$$d\mu_N(\theta) = \prod_{j=1}^{N} (1 + a_j \cos(3^j \theta)) \frac{d\theta}{2\pi} \qquad (6.7.2)$$

as measures on $\partial \mathbb{D}$. Then

(a) *As $N \to \infty$, $d\mu_N$ has a limit $d\mu_\infty$ in the weak (i.e., $\sigma(M(\partial \mathbb{D}), C(\partial \mathbb{D}))$)- topology.*

(b) *For any $p \in [1, \infty)$,*

$$\sum_{n \in \mathbb{Z}} |(\mu_\infty)_n^\sharp|^p < \infty \Leftrightarrow \sum_{j=1}^\infty |a_j|^p < \infty \tag{6.7.3}$$

(c) *$d\mu_\infty$ is a probability measure with no pure points.*
(d) *If $\sum_{j=1}^\infty |a_j|^2 < \infty$, $d\mu_\infty$ is a.c. wrt $\frac{d\theta}{2\pi}$.*
(e) *If $\sum_{j=1}^\infty |a_j|^2 = \infty$, $d\mu_\infty$ is singular wrt $\frac{d\theta}{2\pi}$.*

Remarks. 1.   The intuition behind (d) and (e) is that the variables $\{\cos(3^j\theta)\}_{j=1}^\infty$ are almost independent, so (6.7.3) is almost a product measure.   Thus, in line with Kakutani's dichotomy theorem (see Theorem 4.12.9), we care about $\prod_{j=1}^\infty \int \sqrt{f_j(\theta)} \frac{d\theta}{2\pi}$ with $f_j(\theta) = (1 + a_j \cos(3^j\theta))$ and that will look like $\prod_{j=1}^\infty (1 - |a_j|^2)$.

2. $d\mu_\infty$ is called a *Riesz product*.

We need two preliminary lemmas:

Lemma 6.7.2. *If $\{n_j\}_{j=0}^k$ is a set of integers, each among $0, \pm 1, \pm 2$ and $n_k \neq 0$, then*

$$\sum_{j=0}^k n_j 3^j \neq 0 \tag{6.7.4}$$

Proof. By flipping signs, we can suppose $n_k = 1$ or 2. Since

$$3^{-k} \sum_{j=0}^{k-1} |n_j 3^j| < 2 \sum_{j=-\infty}^{k-1} 3^{j-k} = 2\left(\frac{\frac{1}{3}}{1 - \frac{1}{3}}\right) = 1$$

we see that the terms with $j \leq k-1$ cannot cancel even 3^k, let alone $2 \cdot 3^k$. $\square$

Lemma 6.7.3. *For all $\beta \in (-1, 1)$, we have*

$$\sqrt{1 + \beta} \leq 1 + \tfrac{1}{2}\beta - \tfrac{1}{16}\beta^2 \tag{6.7.5}$$

Proof. Let $g(\beta) = (1+\beta)^{1/2}$, so $g^{(k)}(\beta) = (-1)^{k-1} c_k (1+\beta)^{\frac{1}{2}-k}$, where $c_1 = \frac{1}{2}$ and $c_{k+1} = (k - \frac{1}{2}) c_k$, so inductively, $c_k \geq 0$. In particular, $g^{(4)}(\beta) < 0$, so by Taylor's theorem with remainder (since $\frac{c_2}{2!} = \frac{1}{8}$, $\frac{c_3}{3!} = \frac{1}{16}$),

$$\sqrt{1 + \beta} \leq 1 + \tfrac{1}{2}\beta - \tfrac{1}{8}\beta^2 + \tfrac{1}{16}\beta^3 \leq 1 + \tfrac{1}{2}\beta - \tfrac{1}{16}\beta^2$$

since $\beta^2 - \beta^3 = \beta^2(1 - \beta) > 0$. $\square$

Remark. While the explicit $\frac{1}{16}$ is nice, the $c\beta^2$ bound on $(1 + \frac{1}{2}\beta - \sqrt{1 + \beta})$ is easy to see since the expression is nonnegative on $(-1, 1)$ and $O(\beta^2)$ at $\beta = 0$.

Proof of Theorem 6.7.1. (a) By Lemma 6.7.2, if m_j, ℓ_j are $0, \pm 1$ and $\sum_{j=0}^{k} m_j 3^j = \sum_{j=0}^{k} \ell_j 3^j$, then $m_j = \ell_j$. Thus, when we expand

$$f_N(\theta) = \prod_{j=1}^{N} \left(1 + \frac{a_j}{2} e^{3^j i\theta} + \frac{a_j}{2} e^{-3^j i\theta} \right) \tag{6.7.6}$$

each $e^{im\theta}$ occurs in only one term. This means that the Fourier coefficients $f_{N+1}(\theta)$ and $f_N(\theta)$ agree for all $|m| \leq 3^N$. Thus, $(\mu_N)_m^\sharp$ is constant for m fixed and all N with $|m| \leq 3^N$. Therefore, each $(\mu_N)_m^\sharp \to (\mu_\infty)_m^\sharp$, so $\int h(\theta) \, d\mu_N(\theta)$ has a limit for h, a finite linear combination of $e^{im\theta}$. Since these are $\|\cdot\|_\infty$-dense in $C(\partial\mathbb{D})$, we have weak convergence.

(b) By looking first at m having values $\pm 3^{j_1}$, then $\pm 3^{j_1} \pm 3^{j_2}$ ($j_1 \neq j_2$), we see

$$\sum_m |(\mu_\infty)_m^\sharp|^p = 1 + 2 \sum_{j_1} \left| \frac{a_j}{2} \right|^p + 4 \sum_{j_1 < j_2} \left| \frac{a_{j_1}}{2} \right|^p \left| \frac{a_{j_2}}{2} \right|^p + \dots \tag{6.7.7}$$

$$= \prod_{j=1}^{\infty} (1 + 2^{1-p} |a_j|^p) \tag{6.7.8}$$

is finite if and only if $\sum |a_j|^p < \infty$.

(c) The same argument that led to (6.7.8) shows

$$\sum_m |(\mu_N)_m^\sharp|^2 = \prod_{j=1}^{N} (1 + \tfrac{1}{2} |a_j|^2) \leq (\tfrac{3}{2})^N$$

As noted in the proof of (a), $(\mu_\infty)_m^\sharp = (\mu_N)_m^\sharp$ if $|m| \leq 3^N$, so

$$3^{-N} \sum_{|m| \leq 3^N} |(\mu_\infty)_m^\sharp|^2 \leq 2^{-N} \to 0 \tag{6.7.9}$$

as $N \to \infty$. By Wiener's theorem (Theorem 6.6.9), there are no pure points.

(d) In this case, since $\sum |\mu_\infty^\sharp|^2 < \infty$ (by (b)), $d\mu_\infty = F(\theta) \frac{d\theta}{2\pi}$ with $F \in L^2$, so $d\mu_\infty$ is a.e. wrt $\frac{d\theta}{2\pi}$.

(e) Our argument follows the proof of Kakutani's dichotomy theorem in Problem 1 of Section 4.12. Let

$$g_N(\theta) = \prod_{j=1}^{N} (1 + a_j \cos(3^j \theta))^{1/2} \tag{6.7.10}$$

Since $\cos^2(u) = \tfrac{1}{2} + \tfrac{1}{2} \cos(2u)$, (6.7.5) implies that

$$g_N(\theta) \leq \prod_{j=1}^{N} \left[1 - \frac{a_j^2}{32} + \frac{a_j}{2} \cos(3^j \theta) - \frac{a_j^2}{32} \cos(2 \cdot 3^j \theta) \right] \tag{6.7.11}$$

Using Lemma 6.7.2, only the constant terms survive under integration, that is,

$$\int g_N(\theta)\,d\theta \le \prod_{j=1}^{N}\left(1 - \frac{a_j^2}{32}\right) \tag{6.7.12}$$

On the other hand, since $g_N(\theta)^{-1}$ is continuous and

$$\int g_N(\theta)^{-1}\,d\mu_\infty(\theta) = \lim_{M\to\infty}\int g_N(\theta)^{-1}\prod_{n=1}^{M}[1 + a_j\cos(3^j\theta)] \tag{6.7.13}$$

$$= \lim_{M\to\infty}\int g_N(\theta)\prod_{n=N+1}^{M}[1 + a_j\cos(3^k\theta)] \tag{6.7.14}$$

$$\le \limsup_{M\to\infty}\int (\text{RHS of } (6.7.11))\prod_{n=N+1}^{M}[1 + a_j\cos(3^j\theta)] \tag{6.7.15}$$

$$= \prod_{j=1}^{N}\left(1 - \frac{a_j^2}{32}\right)$$

by Lemma 6.7.2 again.

Since $\sum \frac{a_j^2}{32} = \infty$, $\lim_{N\to\infty}\prod_{j=1}^{N}(1 - \frac{a_j^2}{32}) = 0$. By Proposition 4.7.1, $\mu_\infty \perp \frac{d\theta}{2\pi}$. $\qquad\square$

Example 6.7.4. Let

$$d\mu = \prod_{n=1}^{\infty}(1 + \tfrac{1}{2}\cos(3^n\theta))\frac{d\theta}{2\pi} \tag{6.7.16}$$

This is a singular continuous measure for which $\mu_n^\sharp \nrightarrow 0$ (since $\mu_{3^n}^\sharp = \frac{1}{4}$). Riesz invented Riesz products for a variant of this example (see the Notes). The classical Cantor measure has a similar property (see Problem 4 of Section 4.12). $\qquad\square$

Example 6.7.5. Let

$$d\mu = \prod_{n=1}^{\infty}(1 + n^{-1/2}\cos(3^n\theta))\frac{d\theta}{2\pi} \tag{6.7.17}$$

Since $\sum_{n=1}^{\infty}n^{-p/2} < \infty$ if and only if $p > 2$, μ is singular continuous with $\mu^\sharp \in \ell^p$ for all $p > 2$. This proves for the discrete case the Hausdorff–Young inequality holds for $1 \le p \le 2$ and not for $p > 2$. It will be the basis for our discussion of the continuous analog. $\qquad\square$

To go from $^\sharp$ on $C^\infty(\partial\mathbb{D})'$ to $\widehat{}$ on $\mathcal{S}'(\mathbb{R})$, we'll embed $C^\infty(\partial\mathbb{D})'$ in $\mathcal{S}'(\mathbb{R})$ so that $\widehat{}$ is related to $^\sharp$. Explicitly, let $\tau \in C^\infty(\partial\mathbb{D})'$ and $f \in \mathcal{S}(\mathbb{R})$. Define

$$\Phi_f(\tau)(x) = \sum_{n=-\infty}^{\infty} \tau_n^\sharp f(x+n) \tag{6.7.18}$$

It is easy to see (Problem 1) that if

$$|\tau_n^\sharp| \le C(1+|n|)^k \tag{6.7.19}$$

then

$$|\Phi_f(\tau)(x)| \le C_1(1+|x|)^k \tag{6.7.20}$$

so each $\Phi_f(\tau) \in \mathcal{S}'(\mathbb{R})$.

Recall that in Problem 1 of Section 6.3, we defined a map from $C^\infty(\partial\mathbb{D})'$ into periodic distributions on $\mathbb{R}$. We call this map Q. If $g \in C^\infty(\partial\mathbb{D})$, then (Problem 2)

$$(Qg)(x) = g(e^{ix}) \tag{6.7.21}$$

This plus the weak continuity of Q determines Q.

Theorem 6.7.6. *For all $f \in \mathcal{S}(\mathbb{R})$ and $\tau \in C^\infty(\partial\mathbb{D})'$, we have that*

$$\widehat{\Phi_f(\tau)}(k) = \hat{f}(k)(Q\tau)(k) \tag{6.7.22}$$

Remarks. 1. $Q\tau \in \mathcal{S}'$ and $\hat{f} \in \mathcal{S}$, so we can form the product.

2. Ignoring 2π's, $\Phi_f(\tau)$ is the convolution of f and $\sum_{n=-\infty}^{\infty} \tau_n^\sharp \delta_{-n}$ which, by the Poisson summation formula, is the Fourier transform of $Q\tau$. Thus, (6.7.22) is just the fact that the Fourier transform of a convolution is the product of Fourier transforms.

Proof. Since both sides of (6.7.22) are continuous in τ when given the weak topology, it suffices to prove it for the weakly dense set of τ's of the form

$$\tau(e^{i\theta}) = \sum_{|n| \le N} \tau_n^\sharp e^{in\theta} \tag{6.7.23}$$

In that case, we have that

$$f_n(x) \equiv f(x+n) \Rightarrow \hat{f}_n(k) = e^{ikn} \hat{f}(k) \tag{6.7.24}$$

since $\int e^{-ikx} f(x+n)\,dx = \int e^{-ik(x-n)} f(x)\,dx$. Thus,

$$\widehat{\Phi_f(\tau)}(k) = \hat{f}(k)\tau(e^{ik}) = \hat{f}(k)(Q\tau)(e^{ik}) \tag{6.7.25}$$

on account of (6.7.21). $\qquad\square$

Example 6.7.7. Let $g(x) \in \mathcal{S}(\mathbb{R}^\nu)$ be nonnegative and obey $g(-x) = g(x)$ and $\mathrm{supp}(g) \subset [-\frac{1}{4}, \frac{1}{4}]$ with

$$\int g(x)^2 \, dx = (2\pi)^{-1/2} \tag{6.7.26}$$

Let $f: g * g$ so $\widehat{f}(k) = (2\pi)^{1/2} |\widehat{g}(k)|^2 > 0$. Let μ be the measure on $\partial\mathbb{D}$ given by (6.7.17) and

$$H(x) = \Phi_f(\mu)(x) \tag{6.7.27}$$

Since $\mu^\sharp \in \ell^p$ for $p > 2$ and (since $\mathrm{supp}(f) \subset [-\frac{1}{2}, \frac{1}{2}]$)

$$\int_{-\infty}^{\infty} |H(x)|^p \, dx = \left(\sum_n |\mu_n^\sharp|^p \right) \int_{-1/2}^{1/2} |f(x)|^p \, dx \tag{6.7.28}$$

we see $H \in \bigcap_{p>2} L^p(\mathbb{R}, dx)$. Moreover, H is C^∞ (and all derivatives lie in $\bigcap_{p>2} L^p(\mathbb{R}, dx)$). By (6.7.22), $\widehat{H}(k)$ is a singular continuous measure of total mass 1. This shows, for $1 < q < 2$, $\widehat{L^q}$ is not all of L^p ($p = q/(q-1)$) and also that for $p > 2$, $\widehat{L^p}$ contains objects that are not functions. Notice $H \in C_\infty(\mathbb{R})$, the functions vanishing at infinity but $\widehat{H}$ is not in L^1. $\square$

Example 6.7.8. In Problem 10(e) of Section 5.4, we showed indirectly there exists $f \in C(\partial\mathbb{D})$ so that $f_n^\sharp \notin \ell^1$. There are also explicit examples. If $\alpha \in (0,1)$ and $c > 0$, the series

$$\sum_{n=1}^{N} \frac{e^{icn \log n} e^{in\theta}}{n^{\frac{1}{2}+\alpha}} \tag{6.7.29}$$

converges uniformly on $\partial\mathbb{D}$ to a continuous function, $g_{\alpha,c}(e^{i\theta})$, (see the Notes) while

$$(\widehat{g}_{\alpha,c})_n = e^{icn \log n} n^{-\frac{1}{2}-\alpha} \tag{6.7.30}$$

is not in ℓ^1 if $\alpha < \frac{1}{2}$. With the f of the last example,

$$H(x) = \Phi_f(g_{\alpha,c})(x) \tag{6.7.31}$$

is not in L^1 if $0 < \alpha < \frac{1}{2}$. Indeed, for $0 < C_2 < C_1 < \infty$,

$$C_2 x^{-\frac{1}{2}-\alpha} \leq \int_x^{x+1} |H(y)| \, dy \leq C_1 x^{-\frac{1}{2}-\alpha} \tag{6.7.32}$$

But $\widehat{H}(k)$ is a function in $C_\infty(\mathbb{R})$. Indeed, it decays to zero faster than any power. This also shows that while $\widehat{L^1} \subset C_\infty$, it is not all of C_∞. $\square$

Notes and Historical Remarks. In 1923, Riesz [**785**] introduced the product $\prod_{n=1}^{\infty}(1 + \cos(4^n\theta))\frac{d\theta}{2\pi}$ to present a singular continuous measure μ with $\widehat{\mu}_n \nrightarrow 0$. Actually (Problem 4 of Section 4.12), the classical Cantor measure has this property. It was Zygmund [**1023**] in 1932 who considered products of the form $\prod_{n=1}^{\infty}(1 + a_n \cos(N_n\theta))\frac{d\theta}{2\pi}$ and proved under suitable growth conditions on the N_n (see, e.g., Problem 3) that there is the dichotomy $\sum |a_n|^2 < \infty \Rightarrow d\mu_\infty$ is a.c. wrt $\frac{d\theta}{2\pi}$ and $\sum |a_n|^2 = \infty \Rightarrow d\mu_\infty$ is singular wrt $\frac{d\theta}{2\pi}$. For more on Riesz products, see [**134, 717**], [**1024**, Sect. I.V.7], and [**852**, Sect. 2.11].

There is a similarity between the dichotomy given in (d)/(e) of Theorem 6.7.1 and the dichotomy of the Kakutani theorem (Theorem 4.12.9) as seen in the proof. The reason is that while a Riesz product is not a product measure, it is close to one. The factors are almost independent random variables for large j and k.

The function (6.7.28) of Example 6.7.8 is due to Hardy–Littlewood [**396**]. Zygmund [**1024**, Sect. I.V.4] has extensive discussion of the example and detailed proof of the claimed uniform convergence. Zygmund [**1024**, Sect. I.V.5] shows that if $0 < \alpha < 1$ and $\beta > 1 - \frac{1}{2}\alpha$, then $\sum_{n=1}^{N} n^{-\beta}e^{in\alpha}e^{in\theta}$ converges uniformly on $\partial\mathbb{D}$. If $\beta < 1$ (e.g., $\alpha = \frac{2}{3}$, $\beta = \frac{5}{6}$), the limit f has $f^\sharp \notin \ell^1$.

Measures on $\partial\mathbb{D}$ like that in (6.7.18) where $\mu_n^\sharp \to 0$ are called Rajchman measures by Lyons [**617**], who characterized them in terms of sets that they give zero weight to. The name is after Rajchman [**757**] who realized the connection to sets on which Fourier series can fail to converge. Lyons [**618**] has an extensive review of the subject.

Problems

1. If Φ_f is given by (6.7.18) and τ obeys (6.7.19), prove that (6.7.20) holds.

2. Verify (6.7.21) if $g \in C^\infty(\partial\mathbb{D})$.

3. Suppose $\{N_j\}_{j=1}^{\infty}$ is a sequence of integers with

$$N_{j+1} > r(N_1 + \cdots + N_{j-1}) \qquad (6.7.33)$$

for some $r > 2$.

(a) For any $a_j \in (-1, 1)$, prove that $\prod_{j=1}^{M}(1 + a_j \cos(N_j\theta))\frac{d\theta}{2\pi}$ has a weak limit, $d\mu_\infty$, as $M \to \infty$.

(b) Prove that $d\mu_\infty$ has no pure points.

(c) Prove that $\sum_\ell |(\mu_\infty)_\ell^\sharp|^p < \infty \Leftrightarrow \sum_\ell |a_\ell|^p < \infty$ for all $p \geq 1$.

(d) Prove that $d\mu_\infty$ is $\frac{d\theta}{2\pi}$-a.c. if $\sum_\ell |a_\ell|^2 < \infty$.

(e) Prove that $d\mu_\infty$ is $\frac{d\theta}{2\pi}$-singular if $\sum_\ell |a_\ell|^2 = \infty$.

6.8. Fourier Transforms of Powers and Uniqueness of Minimizers in Potential Theory

> I worked on the theory of Fourier integrals under his guidance for a good many years before I discovered for myself that this theory has applications in applied mathematics, if the solution of certain differential equations can be called "applied." I never heard him refer to these applications.
>
> —*Titchmarsh in his obituary of Hardy* [**921**] [5]

Our main goal in this section will be to compute $\widehat{p}_\gamma$ where

$$p_\gamma(x) = |x|^{-\gamma} \qquad (6.8.1)$$

when

$$0 < \gamma < \nu \qquad (6.8.2)$$

so that p_γ is in $L^1 + L^\infty$ and thus a tempered distribution. We'll then use this to compute the solution of $\Delta u = \delta$ in dimension $\nu \geq 3$ and we'll prove uniqueness of the minimizers discussed in Section 5.9.

p_γ is uniquely determined up to an overall constant by the fact that it is invariant under rotations, and if $T_\lambda x = \lambda x$, then $p_\gamma \circ T_\lambda = \lambda^{-\gamma} p_\gamma$ for $\lambda > 0$. This in turn implies that

$$\widehat{p}_\gamma = c_{\nu,\gamma} p_{\nu-\gamma} \qquad (6.8.3)$$

so the issue is computing the constants. In fact, our calculation will verify (6.8.3) directly without the uniqueness under rotations and scalings.

The constant will be expressed in terms of the Euler gamma function

$$\Gamma(s) = \int_0^\infty x^{s-1} c^{-x} \, dx \qquad (6.8.4)$$

studied heavily in Sections 9.6 and 9.7 of Part 2A. For our purposes, we note that (changing y^2 to x)

$$\int_0^\infty y^t e^{-y^2} \, dy = \tfrac{1}{2} \Gamma(\tfrac{1}{2} t + \tfrac{1}{2}) \qquad (6.8.5)$$

which we saw in Problem 5 of Section 4.11 implies that σ_ν, the surface area of the unit ball in $\mathbb{R}^\nu$, is

$$\sigma_\nu = \frac{2\pi^{\nu/2}}{\Gamma(\nu/2)} \qquad (6.8.6)$$

Theorem 6.8.1. *For $0 < \gamma < \nu$ in $\mathbb{R}^\nu$, we have*

$$\widehat{p}_\gamma(k) = \frac{2^{-\gamma/2}}{\Gamma(\gamma/2)} \frac{\Gamma(\tfrac{1}{2}(\nu-\gamma))}{2^{-(\nu-\gamma)/2}} \, p_{\nu-\gamma}(k) \qquad (6.8.7)$$

---

[5]describing his student days and Hardy's attitude towards applications like PDEs.

Proof. Let

$$h_a(x) = e^{-a|x|^2/2} \tag{6.8.8}$$

Then for $\gamma > 0$,

$$p_\gamma = \frac{2^{-\gamma/2}}{\Gamma(\gamma/2)} \int_0^\infty a^{\gamma/2-1} h_a \, da \tag{6.8.9}$$

One checks this pointwise by $b = a|x|^2/2$ change of variables and then as distributions by using Fubini's theorem. By Example 6.2.11, we have

$$\widehat{h}_a = a^{-\nu/2} h_{1/a} \tag{6.8.10}$$

so (6.8.9) implies

$$\widehat{p}_\gamma(k) = \frac{2^{-\gamma/2}}{\Gamma(\gamma/2)} \int_0^\infty e^{-|k|^2/2a} a^{-\nu/2+\gamma/2-1} \, da \tag{6.8.11}$$

$$= \frac{2^{-\gamma/2}}{\Gamma(\gamma/2)} \int_0^\infty b^{[(\nu-\gamma)/2]-1} h_b(k) \, dk \tag{6.8.12}$$

by $b = a^{-1}$ change of variables. Thus, (6.8.9) implies (6.8.7). $\qquad\square$

The first application is to find the free Green's function for Laplacians, that is, the solution of $\Delta u = \delta$.

Theorem 6.8.2. *Let $\nu \geq 3$. Let σ_ν be the area of the unit sphere in $\mathbb{R}^\nu$. Let*

$$u(x) = -[(\nu-2)\sigma_\nu]^{-1}|x|^{-(\nu-2)} \tag{6.8.13}$$

Then, as distributions,

$$\Delta u = \delta \tag{6.8.14}$$

Remarks. 1. The function (no minus sign)

$$G_\nu(x) = [(\nu-2)\sigma_\nu]^{-1}|x|^{-(\nu-2)} \tag{6.8.15}$$

or

$$G_\nu(x,y) = [(\nu-2)\sigma_\nu]^{-1}|x-y|^{-(\nu-2)} \tag{6.8.16}$$

is called the *Green's function*, free Green's function, Green's function for $\mathbb{R}^\nu$, or potential theoretic Green's function.

2. For two dimensions, the correct analog, as we'll discuss in the next section, is

$$u(x) = -(2\pi)^{-1} \log(|x|) \tag{6.8.17}$$

which also obeys $\Delta u = \delta$ (see Theorem 6.9.2).

3. See Problem 1 for an alternate way of computing and understanding the constant $[(\nu-2)\sigma_\nu]^{-1}$.

Proof. We have that (using (6.8.9))

$$\widehat{\Delta(|x|^{-(\nu-2)})} = \frac{2^{-(\nu-2)/2}}{\Gamma(\frac{\nu-2}{2})} \frac{\Gamma(1)}{2^{-1}} \tag{6.8.18}$$

Using $\Gamma(1) = 1$, $\Gamma(\frac{\nu}{2}) = (\frac{\nu-2}{2})\Gamma(\frac{\nu-2}{2})$ (an integration by parts shows that $\Gamma(s+1) = s\Gamma(s)$) and $\hat{\delta}(k) = (2\pi)^{-\nu/2}$, we see that

$$\text{RHS of } (6.8.18) = \frac{4\pi^{\nu/2}}{\Gamma(\nu/2)} \frac{(\nu-2)}{2} \hat{\delta} \tag{6.8.19}$$

$$= [\sigma_\nu(\nu-2)]\hat{\delta}$$

proving (6.8.14).   □

We want to return to the potential theory problem discussed in Section 5.9 and show the minimizer proven to exist there is unique. We'll provide the details for $\nu \geq 3$ and, in Problem 6 of the next section, the reader will extend the ideas to $\nu = 2$.

The key will be to prove that with

$$\mathcal{E}(\mu) = [2(\nu-2)\sigma_\nu]^{-1} \int d\mu(x)d\mu(y)|x-y|^{-(\nu-2)} \tag{6.8.20}$$

(this is (5.9.3) with the proper mathematical constant added (taking some physical constants to be 1)) we have that

$$\mathcal{E}(\tfrac{1}{2}\mu_1 + \tfrac{1}{2}\mu_2) < \tfrac{1}{2}\mathcal{E}(\mu_1) + \tfrac{1}{2}\mathcal{E}(\mu_2) \tag{6.8.21}$$

if $\mu_1 \neq \mu_2$. Since the inequality is strict ($\mathcal{E}$ is then called *strictly convex*), if μ_1 and μ_2 are strict minimizers of $\mathcal{E}(\mu)$, then $\mu_1 \neq \mu_2$ is impossible since $\frac{1}{2}(\mu_1+\mu_2)$ could have a strictly smaller energy, that is, minimizers are unique. The key in turn to get (6.8.21) will be

Lemma 6.8.3. *Let $\nu \geq 3$. For any positive measure μ of compact support,*

$$\mathcal{E}(\mu) = \tfrac{1}{2} \int \frac{|\hat{\mu}(k)|^2}{k^2} d^\nu k \tag{6.8.22}$$

Remarks. 1. While we will not prove (6.8.21) in this manner, some proofs extend $\mathcal{E}(\mu)$ to signed measures by proving that if $\mathcal{E}(|\mu|) < \infty$, then the integral in (6.8.20) is defined, and so, $\mathcal{E}(\mu)$ is a linear function on $\{\mu \mid \mathcal{E}(|\mu|) < \infty\}$. One then proves (6.8.22) for such signed μ, and using $\frac{1}{2}\mathcal{E}(\mu_1)+\frac{1}{2}\mathcal{E}(\mu_2) - \mathcal{E}(\frac{1}{2}\mu_1 + \frac{1}{2}\mu_2) = \mathcal{E}(\frac{1}{2}\mu_1 - \frac{1}{2}\mu_2)$, one gets (6.8.21).

2. We'll use the following (Newton's lemma) if $r, \rho > 0$, $\hat{e} \in \mathbb{R}^\nu$ of norm 1, and $\hat{\omega} \in S^{\nu-1}$ with $d^{\nu-1}\omega$, the normalized spherical measure, then

$$\int |r\hat{e} - \rho\hat{\omega}|^{-(\nu-2)} d^{\nu-1}\omega = \max(r,\rho)^{-(\nu-2)} \tag{6.8.23}$$

This is proven using harmonic function theory (see Problem 2).

Proof. Suppose $d\mu(x) = h(x)\,d^\nu x$ with $h \in \mathcal{S}(\mathbb{R}^\nu)$. Then by (6.6.34), Theorem 6.8.2, and $\widehat{\delta} = (2\pi)^{-\nu-2}$, we get (6.8.22) for μ.

If μ has compact support, let $\mu_\alpha = \mu * g_\alpha$ with

$$g_\alpha(x) = (2\pi\alpha)^{-\nu/2}\exp\left(-\frac{x^2}{2\alpha}\right) \qquad (6.8.24)$$

Then μ_α is of the form $h_\alpha(x)\,d^\nu x$ with $h \in \mathcal{S}(\mathbb{R}^\nu)$, so

$$\mathcal{E}(\mu_\alpha) = \tfrac{1}{2}\int \frac{|\widehat{\mu}_\alpha(k)|^2}{k^2}\,d^\nu k \qquad (6.8.25)$$

Since $\widehat{\mu}_\alpha(k) = e^{-\alpha k^2/2}\widehat{\mu}(k)$, by the monotone convergence theorem,

$$\lim_{\alpha\downarrow 0}\text{RHS of (6.8.25)} = \tfrac{1}{2}\int \frac{|\widehat{\mu}(k)|^2}{k^2}\,d^\nu k \qquad (6.8.26)$$

On the other hand, by (6.8.24),

$$(|x|^{(\nu-2)} * g_{2\alpha})(x) = \int \max(|x|,|y|)^{-(\nu-2)}g_{2\alpha}(y)\,d^\nu y \qquad (6.8.27)$$

so

$$[|x|^{-(\nu-2)} * g_\alpha](x) \leq |x|^{(\nu-2)} \qquad (6.8.28)$$

and uniformly on each $|x| > R$, as $\alpha \downarrow 0$,

$$\text{LHS of (6.8.28)} \to |x|^{-(\nu-2)} \qquad (6.8.29)$$

Since (note $g_\alpha * g_\alpha = g_{2\alpha}$)

$$\mathcal{E}(\mu_\alpha) = \int d\mu(x)d\mu(y)\,(|x|^{-(\nu-2)} * g_{2\alpha})(x-y) \qquad (6.8.30)$$

if $\mathcal{E}(\mu) < \infty$, then by the dominated convergence theorem and (6.8.28)/(6.8.29),

$$\lim_{\alpha\downarrow 0}\mathcal{E}(\mu_\alpha) = \mathcal{E}(\mu) \qquad (6.8.31)$$

and if $\mathcal{E}(\mu)$ is infinite, for every $R > 0$,

$$\liminf \mathcal{E}(\mu_\alpha) \geq \liminf \int_{|x-y|\geq R} \text{integrand in (6.8.30)}$$

$$= \int_{|x-y|\geq R} d\mu(x)d\mu(y)\,|x-y|^{-(\nu-2)} \qquad (6.8.32)$$

by the above argument. Taking $R \downarrow 0$, we see $\lim \mathcal{E}(\mu_\alpha) = \infty$. We therefore have (6.8.22) in general. $\qquad\square$

Theorem 6.8.4. *If μ_1, μ_2 are two measures of compact support with $\mathcal{E}(\mu_1) < \infty$, $\mathcal{E}(\mu_2) < \infty$, then $\mathcal{E}(\tfrac{1}{2}(\mu_1 + \mu_2)) < \infty$ and (6.8.21) holds.*

Proof. Since $|a+b|^2 \le 2a^2 + 2b^2$,

$$|(\tfrac{1}{2}\mu_1 + \tfrac{1}{2}\mu_2)^\wedge(k)|^2 \le \tfrac{1}{2}\widehat{\mu}_1(k)^2 + \tfrac{1}{2}\widehat{\mu}_2(k)^2 \qquad (6.8.33)$$

we see $\mathcal{E}(\tfrac{1}{2}\mu_1 + \tfrac{1}{2}\mu_2) < \infty$. Moreover,

$$\tfrac{1}{2}\widehat{\mu}_1^2 + \tfrac{1}{2}\widehat{\mu}_2^2 - (\tfrac{1}{2}\widehat{\mu}_1 + \tfrac{1}{2}\widehat{\mu}_2)^2 = (\tfrac{1}{2}\widehat{\mu}_1 - \tfrac{1}{2}\widehat{\mu}_2)^2 \qquad (6.8.34)$$

(6.8.22) implies that

$$\tfrac{1}{2}\mathcal{E}(\mu_1) + \tfrac{1}{2}\mathcal{E}(\mu_2) - \mathcal{E}(\tfrac{1}{2}\mu_1 + \tfrac{1}{2}\mu_2) = \int \frac{|\widehat{\mu}_1(k) - \widehat{\mu}_2(k)|^2}{k^2}\, d^\nu k \qquad (6.8.35)$$

If $\mu_1 \ne \mu_2$, $\widehat{\mu}_1 - \widehat{\mu}_2 \ne 0$ on some open set, so the right-hand side of (6.8.35) is strictly positive. $\qquad \square$

Corollary 6.8.5. *Let $K \subset \mathbb{R}^\nu$, $\nu \ge 3$, be compact so that there is some $\mu \in \mathcal{M}_{+,1}(K)$ with $\mathcal{E}(\mu) < \infty$, then there exists a unique $\mu \in \mathcal{M}_{+,1}(X)$ minimizing $\mathcal{E}(\mu)$.*

Proof. Existence of a minimizer is proven in Section 5.9. If c is the minimum and $\mathcal{E}(\mu_1) = \mathcal{E}(\mu_2) = c$, then

$$\mathcal{E}\left(\tfrac{1}{2}(\mu_1 + \mu_2)\right) \ge c = \tfrac{1}{2}\mathcal{E}(\mu_1) + \tfrac{1}{2}\mathcal{E}(\mu_2) \qquad (6.8.36)$$

By the theorem, this implies $\mu_1 = \mu_2$, that is, the minimizer is unique. $\quad \square$

Problems

1. Let $\nu \ge 3$. Let G_ν be given by (6.8.15).

   (a) For $\frac{\partial}{\partial n}$ the outward normal derivative. prove that for any sphere $\partial B_r = \{x \mid |x| = r\}$, $r > 0$, one has that (dS = unnormalized surface measure)

   $$\int_{\partial B_r} \frac{\partial G_\nu}{\partial n}\, dS = -1 \qquad (6.8.37)$$

   (b) Using the calculation in (a) and Green's theorem, verify (6.8.14) without using Fourier transform.

2. Let $\nu \ge 3$. For r and let $f(\rho\widehat{\omega})$ be the integral on the right of (6.8.23).

   (a) Prove that f is a function of ρ only and is continuous.

   (b) Prove that f is C^∞ on $\{x \mid |x| \ne r\}$ and $\Delta f = 0$ on $\{x \mid |x| \ne r\}$ and conclude that f is constant on $\{x \mid |x| < r\}$ and $d|x|^{-(\nu-2)}$ for some d on $\{x \mid |x| > r\}$.

   (c) Prove that $d = 1$ by considering asymptotics as $\rho \to \infty$.

   (d) Prove that for $|x| < r$, $f(x) = r^{-(\nu-2)}$. (*Hint:* Continuity.)

6.9. Constant Coefficient Partial Differential Equations

> The total amount of information which has been acquired about the
> physical world ...is enormous ...But it is ...possible for a physicist to
> retain a broad knowledge ...The reasons are threefold: ...Finally, there
> is the most remarkable coincidence: The equations for many different
> physical situations have exactly the same appearance.
>
> —*Richard Feynman* in a chapter on Laplace's equation entitled
> "Electrostatic Analogs" in [**304**].

One of the virtues of the Fourier transform is that it turns differentiation
into multiplication. It is thus ideal to study partial differential equations
(PDEs) with constant coefficients which are already a rich family of objects.
Our goal in this section is to use the Fourier transform and distribution
theory to explore four PDE's that arise in physics and then prove one general
theorem. The four equations are:

(1) *Poisson's equation.*

$$\Delta\varphi = \rho \qquad (6.9.1)$$

Given ρ, to find φ. This is the paradigmal *elliptic equation*. This
arises in physics as a model of gravitational or electrostatics where
ρ is a mass or charge density and φ = potential.

(2) The *heat equation.* This equation has the form for $(\mathbf{x}, t) \in \mathbb{R}^{\nu+1}$

$$\frac{\partial u}{\partial t} = \Delta u \qquad (6.9.2)$$

where Δ is in the $\mathbf{x}$-variables. We'll be interested in the *Cauchy
problem*, i.e., solving for u, given $u(x, t = 0)$. This is the paradigmal
parabolic equation. This arises in physics to describe heat flow—u
is a temperature profile—and also diffusion.

(3) The (free) *wave equation.* This equation has the form for $(\mathbf{x}, t) \in \mathbb{R}^{\nu+1}$

$$\frac{\partial^2 u}{\partial t^2} = \Delta u \qquad (6.9.3)$$

where Δ is in the $\mathbf{x}$-variables. We'll be interested in the *Cauchy
problem*, i.e., solving for u, given f, g on $\mathbb{R}^\nu$ so that

$$u(\mathbf{x}, t = 0) = f(\mathbf{x}), \quad \frac{\partial u}{\partial t}(\mathbf{x}, t = 0) = g(\mathbf{x}) \qquad (6.9.4)$$

This is the paradigmal *hyperbolic equation*. This arises in physics
for describing plucked strings, light and sound waves.

(4) The (free) *Schrödinger equation.* This equation has the form for
$(\mathbf{x}, t) \in \mathbb{R}^{\nu+1}$

$$i\frac{\partial u}{\partial t} = -\Delta u \qquad (6.9.5)$$

where Δ is in the **x**-variables. Again, we'll be interested in the Cauchy equation. This arises in physics to describe quantum waves for a noninteracting particle.

The one general result we'll discuss is the Malgrange–Ehrenpreis theorem, that for any polynomial P in ν-variables, if $P(D)$ is the operator

$$P(y_1, \ldots, y_\nu) = \sum_{j_1, \ldots, j_\nu} a_{j_1, \ldots, j_\nu} y_1^{j_1} \ldots y_\nu^{j_\nu} \Rightarrow$$

$$P(D) = \sum_{j_1, \ldots, j_\nu} a_{j_1, \ldots, j_\nu} \frac{\partial^{|j|}}{\partial y^{j_1} \ldots \partial y^{j_\nu}} \quad (6.9.6)$$

then there exits an ordinary distribution, τ, obeying

$$P(D)\tau = \delta \quad (6.9.7)$$

(a *fundamental solution* for $P(D)$), i.e., for all $\varphi \in C_0^\infty(\mathbb{R}^\nu)$

$$\tau(P(-D)\varphi) = \varphi(0) \quad (6.9.8)$$

where τ is a linear functional on $C_0^\infty(\mathbb{R}^\nu)$ with a continuity condition appropriate to ordinary distributions (we'll discuss this briefly below and more generally in Chapter 9).

Poisson's Equation. We begin with (6.9.1). It is formally solved by

$$\rho = (\Delta)^{-1}\varphi \quad (6.9.9)$$

The other explicit equations will also be formally solvable if we can make sense of $F(-\Delta)$ for suitable functions (or distributions), F. Formally, to define $F(-\Delta)$, i.e., to define, given F and f,

$$g = F(-\Delta)f \quad (6.9.10)$$

we take Fourier transforms and get

$$\widehat{g}(k) = F(k^2)\widehat{f}(k) \quad (6.9.11)$$

Thus, if multiplication by $F(k^2)$ is a distribution τ, then by (6.2.45)

$$g = (2\pi)^{-\nu/2} \check{\tau} * f \quad (6.9.12)$$

which we will usually write as

$$g = (2\pi)^{-\nu/2} \check{F} * f \quad (6.9.13)$$

This allows us to define (6.9.10) whenever $f \in \mathcal{S}(\mathbb{R}^\nu)$. In many cases, as we'll see, we can make sense of $\check{F} * f$ for f's not as regular as $\mathcal{S}(\mathbb{R}^\nu)$ functions.

For (6.9.9), we need $(k^2)^{-1}$ to be a distribution. If $\nu \geq 3$, it is locally L^1 and polynomially bounded near infinity (indeed, bounded there). Moreover, Theorem 6.8.1 computed the Fourier transform of k^{-2} in this case and Theorem 6.8.2 found $(2\pi)^{-\nu/2}(k^{-2})\check{}$, i.e., we have

Theorem 6.9.1. *Let $\nu \geq 3$ and $G_\nu(x)$ given by (6.8.15). For $f \in \mathcal{S}(\mathbb{R}^\nu)$*

$$g(x) = -\int G_\nu(x-y)f(y)d^\nu y \qquad (6.9.14)$$

is a C^∞ function and solves

$$\Delta g = f \qquad (6.9.15)$$

Remarks. 1. g is C^∞ since $D^\alpha g = G_\nu * D^\alpha f$ but g is not tempered; for example, if $\int f(y)d^\nu y \neq 0$, then $g(x) \sim c|x|^{-(\nu-2)}$ as $x \to \infty$ for $c \neq 0$, i.e., g doesn't decay faster than the inverse of any polynomial.

2. If $f \in L^1(\mathbb{R}^\nu) \cap L^\infty(\mathbb{R}^\nu)$, the integral in (6.9.14) converges and defines a bounded function which is a distributional solution of (6.9.15) (Problem 1). In many cases (e.g., f is Hölder continuous and say f has compact support), g is C^2 and (6.9.15) holds in the classical sense (see Problem 2).

3. $\Delta u = 0$ has many solutions (harmonic functions, studied in Chapter 3 of Part 3), e.g., $\text{Re}[(x_1 + ix_2)^n]$. Thus, the solution of (6.9.15) is not unique. However (Problem 3), for $f \in \mathcal{S}$, (6.9.14) is the unique solution that vanishes at infinity.

4. G_ν is called the Green's function.

What about $\nu = 2$. Since k^{-2} is not a well-defined distribution, you might think the situation is hopeless, but it isn't. We've already seen examples of regularization of non-L^1 functions. While $1/x$ is not in $L^1(\mathbb{R})$, in Problem 10 of Section 6.2, we defined a distribution $\mathcal{P}(1/x)$ with $\mathcal{P}(1/x)(f) = \int_{-\infty}^{\infty} x^{-1}f(x)dx$ if $f \in \mathcal{S}(\mathbb{R})$ with $f(0) = 0$. Abstractly, one can use the Hahn–Banach Theorem to prove such distributions exist. For $\nu = 1$, k^{-2} is also not L^1, but it is easy to see that the distribution, τ defined by the function $\frac{1}{2}|x|$ obeys $\frac{d^2}{dx^2}\tau = \delta(x)$.

Fix $\nu = 2$. By (6.8.7), with $\gamma = 2 - \varepsilon$, for $\varepsilon > 0$, $|k|^{-(2-\varepsilon)}$ has a Fourier transform $d_\varepsilon\Gamma(\frac{\varepsilon}{2})|x|^{-\varepsilon}$, where $\lim_{\varepsilon\downarrow 0} d_\varepsilon = 2$. Since $x\Gamma(x) = \Gamma(x+1)$, we see that

$$\lim_{\varepsilon\downarrow 0} \varepsilon\Gamma(\frac{\varepsilon}{2}) = \frac{1}{2} \qquad (6.9.16)$$

This confirms that if $g_\varepsilon(x)$ is $(2\pi)^{-1}$ times the Fourier transform of $k^{-(2-\varepsilon)}$, then $g_\varepsilon(x)$ diverges as $\varepsilon \downarrow 0$ as $(2\pi\varepsilon)^{-1}$ (since for $x \neq 0, |x|^{-\varepsilon} \to 1$). It suggests we subtract the constant $(2\pi\varepsilon)^{-1}$ and note that

$$(|x|^{-\varepsilon} - 1)\,\varepsilon^{-1} = \left[\exp(\varepsilon\log(|x|^{-1})) - 1\right]\varepsilon^{-1}$$
$$\to \log(|x|^{-1}) \qquad (6.9.17)$$

We have thus shown formally that

$$h_\varepsilon(x) \equiv g_\varepsilon(x) - (2\pi\varepsilon)^{-1} \to (2\pi)^{-1}\log(|x|^{-1}) \qquad (6.9.18)$$

It is not hard to show (Problem 4) that (6.9.18) holds in the sense of tempered distributions.

Since $\Delta(\text{constant}) = 0$, we see that

$$\widehat{\Delta h_\varepsilon} = \widehat{\Delta g_\varepsilon} = (2\pi)^{-1}|k|^2|k|^{-(2-\varepsilon)} \to (2\pi)^{-1} \qquad (6.9.19)$$

as distributions. Since $(2\pi)^{-1} = \hat{\delta}$, we have proven:

Theorem 6.9.2. *Let $G_2(x)$ be given by*

$$G_2(x) = (2\pi)^{-1}\log(|x|^{-1}) \qquad (6.9.20)$$

as a tempered distribution. Then

$$\Delta G_2 = -\delta \qquad (6.9.21)$$

Thus, for $f \in \mathcal{S}(\mathbb{R}^2)$, g given by (6.9.14) is a C^∞ function solving (6.9.15).

Remarks. 1. See Problem 5 for a "direct" proof of (6.9.21).

2. Unlike the case $\nu \geq 3$, the solution (6.9.14) for $\nu = 2$ may not obey $\lim_{|x|\to\infty} g(x) = 0$; indeed, if $A = \int f(x)d^2x \neq 0$, $g(x) = \frac{-A}{2\pi}\log|x|+O(|x|^{-1})$ as $|x| \to \infty$. In this case, there is no solution of (6.9.15) going to zero at infinity (for then, the difference with g would be a harmonic function which is $c(\log(|x|) + O(1)$ ($c \neq 0$) at infinity and such a function would have to be a polynomial). This means that for any constant, μ, $\mu + g(x)$ is a solution to (6.9.15), no more or less special then (6.9.14). Put differently, $G_2^{(\lambda)}(x) = (2\pi)^{-1}\log(\lambda|x|^{-1})$ solves (6.9.21). For $\nu \geq 3$, for $\lambda \in (0, \infty)$,

$$G_\nu(\lambda x) = \lambda^{2-\nu}G_\nu(x) \qquad (6.9.22)$$

If we set $G_1(x) = \frac{1}{2}|x|$, this also holds for $\nu = 1$. This scale covariance fails for $\nu = 2$, so two-dimensional Colomb gases have an intrinsic broken scaling symmetry which has important physical consequences (see the Notes).

3. Our construction of the Green's function, G_2, allows one to extend (6.8.21) to the two-dimensional case (Problem 6).

Before leaving the subject of Poisson's equation, we note three things:

(1) It is essentially the subject of Chapter 3 of Part 3.

(2) We also note from the point of view of equations, this would be a natural place to discuss the *Helmholtz equation* (κ is a positive parameter)

$$(\Delta - \kappa^2)\rho = \varphi \qquad (6.9.23)$$

but will defer this until the end of the discussion of the heat equation (for reasons that will become clear).

(3) We discussed the inhomogeneous problem $p(D)\rho = \varphi$ while for the three remaining equations, we'll discuss the Cauchy problem, i.e., "initial

value problem." The analog for Δ is the *Dirichlet problem*—i.e., we have a bounded $\Omega \in \mathbb{R}^1$ and a continuous f on $\partial\Omega$ and seek u continuous on $\bar{\Omega}$ and C^2 on Ω so $\Delta u = 0$ on Ω and $u \upharpoonright \partial\Omega = f$. This problem will be a major theme of Chapter 3 of Part 3. We'll prove uniqueness in Section 3.1 of Part 3 and existence under some conditions on Ω in Section 3.4. There is also a solution in terms of Brownian motion stopping times, see the discussion below and in the Notes.

The Heat Equation. We study (6.9.2) with initial condition

$$u(x_0, t = 0) = f(x) \tag{6.9.24}$$

Take the Fourier transform in the x but not t variables, using

$$\hat{u}(\mathbf{k}, t) = (2\pi)^{-\nu/2} \int e^{-i\mathbf{k}\mathbf{x}} u(\mathbf{x}, t) d^\nu x \tag{6.9.25}$$

Assuming u is nice enough to justify interchange of integral and derivatives, (6.9.2) becomes

$$\frac{\partial}{\partial t} \hat{u}(\mathbf{k}, t) = -k^2 \hat{u}(\mathbf{k}, t) \tag{6.9.26}$$

which is solved by

$$\hat{u}(\mathbf{k}, t) = e^{-tk^2} \hat{u}(\mathbf{k}, t = 0) \tag{6.9.27}$$

Thus, we want to use (6.9.13) with $F_t(\mathbf{k}) = e^{-tk^2}$. Of course, we've computed this Fourier transform (Example 6.2.11 with $a = 2t$), i.e., $\check{F}_t(\mathbf{x}) = (2t)^{-\nu/2} \exp(-x^2/4t)$.

Taking into account the $(2\pi)^{-\nu/2}$ in (6.9.13), we define the (ν-dimensional) *heat kernel* by

$$P_t(\mathbf{x}, \mathbf{y}) = (4\pi t)^{-\nu/2} \exp(-(\mathbf{x} - \mathbf{y})^2/4t) \tag{6.9.28}$$

No matter the formal steps that lead to (6.9.28), we guess the solution of (6.9.2) with initial value, f, is given by

$$u(\mathbf{x}, \mathbf{y}) = \int P_t(\mathbf{x}, \mathbf{y}) f(\mathbf{y}) d^\nu y \tag{6.9.29}$$

For $f \in \mathcal{S}(\mathbb{R}^\nu)$, one could justify (6.9.29) by taking Fourier transforms (and then, by duality, prove (6.9.29) when f is a tempered distribution; see Problem 7). However, using (6.9.29) directly, one can justify (6.9.29) for all continuous (rather than just smooth) f with not only bounded f allowed but even rather strong growth:

Theorem 6.9.3. *Let $f \in C(\mathbb{R}^\nu)$ with*

$$|f(\mathbf{x})| \leq C_a e^{ax^2} \tag{6.9.30}$$

for all a positive. Define $u(\mathbf{x}, t)$ *for* $t \geq 0$ *by* (6.9.29). *Then the integral converges for all* $\mathbf{x}, t > 0$ *and defines a* C^∞ *function on* $\mathbb{R}^\nu \times (0, \infty)$, *obeys* (6.9.2), *and* u *is continuous on* $\mathbb{R}^\nu \times [0, \infty)$ *if we define*

$$u(\mathbf{x}, t = 0) = f(x) \qquad (6.9.31)$$

Remark. Since P_t is an approximate identity, if $f \in L^p(\mathbb{R}^\nu)$, for some $p \in [1, \infty)$, (6.9.29) defines a function u with $\int |u(x, t) - f(x)|^p d^\nu x \to 0$ as $t \downarrow 0$ and by the argument below u is C^∞ on $\mathbb{R}^\nu \times (0, \infty)$ and obeys (6.9.2) there.

Proof. By the explicit form of P_t and the assumed bound (6.9.30), the integral converges for all t. An easy argument (Problem 8(a)) shows u is C^∞ on $\mathbb{R} \times (0, t)$ where all derivatives can be computed taking the derivatives inside the integral. Since $P_t(\mathbf{x}, \mathbf{y})$ obeys (6.9.2) for $(\mathbf{x}, t)$ in $\mathbb{R}^\nu \times (0, \infty)$ for each y, and we can take derivatives inside, we see that u solves (6.9.2) on $\mathbb{R}^\nu \times (0, \infty)$.

$P_t(\mathbf{x}) \equiv P_t(\mathbf{x}, \mathbf{0})$ is a strong approximate identity in the sense that

$$\int P_t(\mathbf{x}) d^\nu x = 1, \quad \lim_{t \downarrow 0} \int_{|x| > \varepsilon} e^{ax^2} P_t(\mathbf{x}) d^\nu x = 0 \text{ for all } \varepsilon_\nu, a > 0 \qquad (6.9.32)$$

and this implies (Problem 8(b)) that u extended to $\mathbb{R}^\nu \times [0, \infty)$ by (6.9.31) is continuous. $\qquad \square$

In Problem 9, the reader will prove the following uniqueness result: If u_1, u_2 are C^2 on $\mathbb{R}^\nu \times (0, \infty)$, both solve (6.9.2), if $u_1 - u_2$ extended to be zero if $t = 0$ is continuous on $\mathbb{R}^\nu \times [0, \infty)$ and if for some (not necessarily all) a,

$$|u_1(\mathbf{x}, t) - u_2(\mathbf{x}, t)| \leq C_a e^{ax^2} \qquad (6.9.33)$$

then $u_1 = u_2$. On the other hand, in Problem 10, the reader will construct solutions, $u(\mathbf{x}, t)$, which are C^∞ on $\mathbb{R}^\nu \times \mathbb{R}$, obey (6.9.2), $u(\mathbf{x} = 0, t) > 0$ for $t > 0$ but $u(\mathbf{x}, t) \equiv 0$ if $t \leq 0$. Thus, solutions are highly nonunique unless one adds the (mild) growth condition (6.9.33).

Before leaving the subject of the heat equation, we mention four items:

(1) The close connection of Brownian motion to the heat equation via (4.16.37). Indeed, because of the occurrence of Δ, it is also connected to Laplace's equation; for example, if $b(s)$ is a Brownian path in $\mathbb{R}^\nu$ and Ω an open set, for $x \in \Omega$, we define the *stopping time*, $\tau_{\Omega, x}(b)$ by $\tau_{\Omega, x}(b) = \inf_{s > 0}\{s \mid x + b(s) \notin \partial\Omega\}$. Thus, $x + b(\tau_{\Omega, x}(b)) \in \partial\Omega$. Given f, a continuous function on $\partial\Omega$, define a function u on Ω by

$$u(x) = \mathbb{E}(f(x + b(\tau_{\Omega, x}(b)))) \qquad (6.9.34)$$

Then u is harmonic (i.e., solves $\Delta u = 0$ on Ω) and if Ω is not too wild, $\lim_{x \to y \in \partial \Omega} u(x) = f(y)$, i.e., (6.9.34) solves the *Dirichlet problem*; see the Notes.

(2) We also mention some interesting results on periodic boundary conditions (Problem 11).

(3) $P_t(\mathbf{x}, \mathbf{y})$ is positive and has integral 1 for x finite. This, of course, is responsible for the connection to Brownian motion but also implies a maximum principle.

(4) The infinite speed of propagation. If f is nonnegative, even of compact support (and not identically zero), $u(\mathbf{x}, t) > 0$ for all $(\mathbf{x}, t) \in \mathbb{R}^\nu \times (0, \infty)$, i.e., instantaneously f spreads out to all of space.

Finally, we want to explain the relation of the heat equation to the solution of the Helmholtz equation, (6.9.23). Thus, we are interested in (6.9.10) where

$$F_\kappa(\mathbf{k}) = (k^2 + \kappa^2)^{-1} \tag{6.9.35}$$

We seek an "explicit" $Q_\kappa(x)$, given by (6.9.13), or at least a way to study its properties. We begin by noting by scaling (see the discussion at the start of Section 6.8),

$$Q_\kappa(x) = \kappa^{\nu-2} Q_1(\kappa x) \tag{6.9.36}$$

which explains why κ rather than κ^2 is a natural parameter. (6.9.36) is a priori true as distributions but we'll eventually see that $Q_1(x)$ is given by a function L^1 in $\{\mathbf{x} \mid |x| \leq 1\}$ and bounded on $\{\mathbf{x} \mid |x| \geq 1\}$ (and continuous on $\mathbb{R}^\nu \setminus \{0\}$).

For the explicit formula, we need the special function, $K_\alpha(z)$, called the MacDonald function or modified Bessel function of the second kind (I've also heard it jokingly called a Kessel function) defined in terms of Hankel functions in Section 14.5 of Part 2B. We'll need the integral formula that appears as (14.7.20) in Part 2B:

$$K_\alpha(z) = \int_0^\infty e^{-z \cosh(w)} \cosh(\alpha w) dw \tag{6.9.37}$$

We will also need some special facts that come from the detailed theory (see Section 14.5 of Part 2B).

Fact 1. When $\alpha \in \{\frac{1}{2}, \frac{3}{2}, \ldots\}$, $K_\alpha(z)$ is $z^{-1/2} e^{-z}$ times a polynomial of degree $\alpha - \frac{1}{2}$ in z^{-1}. In particular, $z^{1/2} K_\alpha(z)$ is analytic in $\mathbb{C} \setminus \{0\}$.

Fact 2. If $\alpha \in \{0, 1, 2, \ldots\}$, then $K_\alpha(z) = f_\alpha(z) + g_\alpha(z) \log(z)$ where f_α, g_α are analytic in $\mathbb{C} \setminus \{0\}$, indeed $g_\alpha(z)$ is entire and $z^\alpha f_\alpha(z)$ is entire.

The basic idea is that just as (6.8.9) led us to write $|x|^{-\gamma} \, (0 < \gamma < \nu)$ as an integral of Gaussians, we can write $(x^2+1)^{-1}$ as an integral of Gaussians:

$$(k^2 + 1)^{-1} = \int_0^\infty e^{-t} e^{-tk^2} dt \qquad (6.9.38)$$

Therefore,

$$Q_1(\mathbf{x}) = \int_0^\infty e^{-t} P_t(\mathbf{x}) dt \qquad (6.9.39)$$

$$= (4\pi)^{-\nu/2} \int_0^\infty e^{-t} \exp(-x^2/4t) t^{-\nu/2} dt$$

The successive change of variables

$$t = \frac{1}{2} s x^2, \quad u = |x| s, \quad u = e^w \qquad (6.9.40)$$

lead to three integral formulas, each of which is useful:

$$Q_1(\mathbf{x}) = \frac{1}{2} (2\pi)^{-\nu/2} |x|^{-(\nu-2)} \int_0^\infty \exp\left(-\frac{1}{2}[x^2 s + s^{-1}]\right) s^{-\nu/2} d\nu \qquad (6.9.41)$$

$$= \frac{1}{2} (2\pi)^{-\nu/2} |x|^{-(\nu-2)/2} \int_0^\infty \exp\left(-\frac{|x|}{2}[u + u^{-1}]\right) u^{-\nu/2} du \qquad (6.9.42)$$

$$= \frac{1}{2} (2\pi)^{-\nu/2} |x|^{-(\nu-2)/2} \int_{-\infty}^\infty \exp(-|x| \cosh(w)) e^{-(\nu-2)w/2} dw$$
$$\qquad (6.9.43)$$

This leads to

Theorem 6.9.4. *The kernel $Q_1(x)$ for $(-\Delta + 1)^{-1}$ on $\mathbb{R}^\nu$ obeys*

(a) *It is given by an L^1 function, indeed*

$$Q_1(x) = (2\pi)^{-\nu/2} |x|^{-(\nu-2)/2} K_{(\nu-2)/2}(x) \qquad (6.9.44)$$

(b) *If G_ν is given by (6.8.15)/(6.8.17) then*

$$\lim_{|x|\downarrow 0} Q_1(\mathbf{x})/G_\nu(\mathbf{x}) = 1 \qquad (6.9.45)$$

(c) $Q_1(\mathbf{x}) \sim 2^{-(\nu+1)/2} \pi^{-(\nu-1)/2} |x|^{-(\nu-1)/2} e^{-|x|}$ (6.9.46)
in the sense that the ratio goes to 1 as $|x| \to \infty$.

(d) $Q_1(\mathbf{x})$ *is real analytic in x in $\mathbb{R}^\nu \setminus \{0\}$.*

(e) Q_1 *can be analytically continued as a function of $z = |x|$ from $|x| \in (0, \infty)$ along any curve in $\mathbb{C} \setminus \{0\}$. If $\nu = 3, 5, 7, \ldots, |x|^{(\nu-2)} Q_1(x)$ is an entire function restricted to $(0, \infty)$. If $\nu = 2, 4, 6, \ldots$, there is a simple logarithmic branch point in that every time one circles once around 0 starting and ending at z_0, the function increases by the same z_0-dependent amount.*

(f) *As a function of $E = \kappa^2$, $Q_\kappa(x)$ for x fixed can be analytically continued along any curve in κ^2 avoiding $\kappa^2 = 0$. If $\nu = 3, 5, 7 \ldots$, the singularity at 0 is a square root branch point and if $\nu = 2, 4, 6, \ldots$, it is a logarithmic branch point.*

(g) $(-\Delta + E)^{-1}$ *as a bounded operator on L^2 has an analytic continuation from $[0, \infty)$ to $\mathbb{C} \setminus (-\infty, 0]$ with a kernel given by the analytic continuation of $Q_\kappa(x)$. For $f, g \in \mathcal{S}(\mathbb{R}^\nu)$, $\langle f, (-\Delta + E)^{-1} g \rangle$ has a continuous extension from both sides of $(-\infty, 0]$ (i.e., from $\mathbb{C}_+$ or $\mathbb{C}_-$) that are unequal.*

Remarks. 1. One can deduce (b)–(g) from known properties of K_ν, but we'll get (b), (c) with our "bare hands."

2. Putting κ back in, $Q_\kappa(x) \sim c_\kappa |x|^{-(\nu-1)/2} e^{-\kappa|x|}$ near ∞.

3. The most commonly used cases (given that

$$K_{\frac{1}{2}}(z) = \sqrt{\frac{\pi}{2z}} e^{-z} \tag{6.9.47}$$

(see after (14.5.38) in Part 2B)) are

$$Q_\kappa^{(\nu=2)}(x) = \frac{1}{2\pi} K_0(\kappa|x|), \quad Q_\kappa^{(\nu=3)}(x) = \frac{1}{4\pi|x|} e^{-\kappa|x|} \tag{6.9.48}$$

Proof. (a) follows from (6.9.43) if we note that $\cosh(-w) = \cosh(w)$ and $\frac{1}{2}[e^{-(\nu-2)w/2} + e^{(\nu-2)w/2}] = \cosh((\frac{\nu-2}{2})w)$.

(b) If $\nu \geq 3$, the integrand in (6.9.41) has an integrable limit and the integral can be done (Problem 12). The logarithmic result when $\nu = 2$ is slightly more subtle (Problem 13).

(c) The maximum of $u + u^{-1}$ occurs at $u = 1$ where $\frac{1}{2}(u + u^{-1})$ is 1 so this is "standard" use of Laplace's method (Section 15.2 of Part 2B); see Problem 14.

(d)–(g) follows from Fact 1 and Fact 2 above.   □

The Free Schrödinger Equation. Consider next (6.9.5). As with the heat equation, if $\hat{u}(\mathbf{k}, t)$ is given by (6.9.25), the formal solution (with $u(\mathbf{x}, t = 0) = f(\mathbf{x})$) is given by

$$\hat{u}(\mathbf{k}, t) = (2\pi)^{-\nu/2} e^{-ik^2 t} \hat{f}(\mathbf{k}) \tag{6.9.49}$$

Unlike the heat equation where $e^{-k^2 t}$ is L^1 in $\mathbf{k}$, $e^{-ik^2 t}$ is not. However, it is if $\text{Im}\, t > 0$, so we can define $e^{-ik^2 t}$ as the distributional limit as $\varepsilon \downarrow 0$ of $e^{-ik^2(t-i\varepsilon)}$, compute the Fourier transform and take the limit and prove the integral converges to see that:

Theorem 6.9.5. *For $t \neq 0$ and $f \in \mathcal{S}(\mathbb{R}^\nu)$,*

$$u(\mathbf{x}, t) = \int (4\pi i t)^{-\nu/2} \exp\left(\frac{i(\mathbf{x} - \mathbf{y})^2}{4t}\right) f(\mathbf{y}) d^\nu y; \; t \neq 0 \qquad (6.9.50)$$

defines a function in $\mathcal{S}(\mathbb{R}^\nu)$ for each t, which is C^∞ in (x, t) in $\mathbb{R}^{\nu+1}$, and which solves (6.9.5).

Proof. That the Fourier transform of $e^{-ik^2 t}\hat{f}(\mathbf{k})$ is given by (6.9.50) is sketched above. Since $g_t(\mathbf{k}) = e^{-ik^2 t}\hat{f}(\mathbf{k})$ is C^∞ in t as an $\mathcal{S}(\mathbb{R}^\nu)$-valued function is easy, taking Fourier transforms, we get the claimed C^∞. Clearly g_t, as an $\mathcal{S}$-valued function, obeys $i\frac{d}{dt}g_t = k^2 g_t$, so taking Fourier transforms, u obeys (6.9.5). $\qquad\square$

Remark. Multiplication by $e^{-ik^2 t}$ clearly preserves L^2 norms so by the Plancherel theorem

$$U_t f = (e^{-ik^2 t}\hat{f})^{\vee} \qquad (6.9.51)$$

defines a unitary map of L^2 to L^2 that agrees with (6.9.50) if $f \in \mathcal{S}$. As with the Fourier transform (see Problem 16 of Section 6.2) if $f \in L^1 \cap L^2$, (6.9.50) holds pointwise and, in general, (6.9.50) holds in a limit in mean sense (Problem 15).

Here is a lovely application of (6.9.50).

Theorem 6.9.6. *Let U_t be given by* (6.9.51) *and*

$$(V_t f)(x) = (2t)^{-\nu/2} e^{ix^2/4t}\hat{f}\left(\frac{x}{2t}\right) \qquad (6.9.52)$$

Then, for any $f \in L^2$,

$$\lim_{t \to \infty} \|U_t f - V_t f\|_{L^2(\mathbb{R}^\nu)} = 0 \qquad (6.9.53)$$

Proof. Notice first that V_t is unitary by a change of variables. Moreover,

$$(V_t f)(\mathbf{x}) = (4\pi t)^{-\nu/2} \int \exp\left(\frac{ix^2}{4t} - \frac{2i\mathbf{x} \cdot \mathbf{y}}{4t}\right) f(\mathbf{y}) d^\nu y \qquad (6.9.54)$$

Since

$$\exp\left(\frac{i|x - y|^2}{4t}\right) = \exp\left(\frac{ix^2}{4t} - \frac{2i\mathbf{x} \cdot \mathbf{y}}{4t}\right)\exp\left(\frac{iy^2}{4t}\right) \qquad (6.9.55)$$

we see that

$$U_t = V_t C_t, \; (C_t f)(x) = e^{ix^2/4t} f(x) \qquad (6.9.56)$$

Since V_t is unitary,

$$\|U_t f - V_t f\|^2 = \|(C_t - 1)f\|^2$$

$$= \int |e^{ix^2/4t} - 1|^2 |f(x)|^2 \qquad (6.9.57)$$

$$\to 0$$

by the dominated convergence theorem. □

Remarks. 1. If k is the classical mechanics momentum, then, since the energy is k^2, we have that $2m = 1$ so the velocity $v = \frac{k}{m} = 2k$. If the initial classical point in phase space is (x_0, k_0), the path is $x(t) = x_0 + 2k_0 t$ so as $t \to \infty$, $\frac{x(t)}{2t} \to k_0$. $|\widehat{f}(k)|^2$ is the quantum momentum distribution so

$$|(V_t f)(x)| = (2t)^{-\nu} \left| \hat{f}\left(\frac{x}{2t}\right) \right|^2 \qquad (6.9.58)$$

is describing a semiclassical asymptotic distribution (the $(2t)^{-\nu}$ is needed to preserve probabilities and is a natural spreading of a classical wave packet). Thus, Theorem 6.9.6 is a kind of semiclassical asymptotics.

2. If $\widehat{f}$ is supported in a compact set K with $0 \notin K$, this theorem says that most of $e^{-it\Delta}f$ (in L^2 sense) moves away from the origin at a linear rate. This can be useful in scattering theory. There are finer estimates that one can obtain using the method of stationary phase, see Theorem 15.3.2 of Part 2B. See also the discussion of Enss' theory in the Notes to that section.

The Wave Equation. We want to study the Cauchy problem for (6.9.3) with initial condition (6.9.4). We'll leave the uniqueness result (unlike the heat equation, there is no anomaly in this case) to Problem 17

As a warm-up, we start with the case $\nu = 1$ (which describes plucked strings as well as fictitious one-dimensional light; indeed much of the pre-1870 work on the wave equation was done in the study of sound, not light). It is a simple observation that $p(x \pm t)$ solves $\left(\frac{\partial^2}{\partial t^2} - \frac{\partial}{\partial x^2}\right)u = 0$ for any C^2 function p, so $p_1(x+t) + p_2(x-t)$ does also; indeed (Problem 18) these are the only solutions.

To get (6.9.4), we need

$$p_1(x) + p_2(x) = f(x), \quad p_1'(x) - p_2'(x) = g(x) \qquad (6.9.59)$$

so

$$p_1' = \tfrac{1}{2}(f' + g); \quad p_2' = \tfrac{1}{2}(f' - g) \qquad (6.9.60)$$

If g has compact support, we get

$$p_1(y) = \tfrac{1}{2}f(y) + \tfrac{1}{2}\int_{-\infty}^{y} g(z)dz; \quad p_2(y) = \tfrac{1}{2}f(y) - \tfrac{1}{2}\int_{-\infty}^{y} g(z)dz \qquad (6.9.61)$$

so, we have *d'Alembert's formula*

$$u(x,t) = \tfrac{1}{2}[f(x+t) + f(x-t)] + \tfrac{1}{2}\int_{x-t}^{x+t} g(y)dy \qquad (6.9.62)$$

and this solves (6.9.3)/(6.9.4) even if g does not have compact support.

Now we turn to the general case, first in k-space. If $\hat{u}(\mathbf{k},t)$ is given by (6.9.25), (6.9.3) becomes

$$\frac{\partial^2}{\partial t^2}\hat{u}(\mathbf{k},t) = -k^2\hat{u}(\mathbf{k},t) \qquad (6.9.63)$$

Thus, $\hat{u}(\mathbf{k},t)$ is a linear combination of e^{ikt} and e^{-ikt} or what is the same thing $\sin(|k|t)$ and $\cos(|k|t)$. Taking into account the initial condition (6.9.4), we conclude

$$\hat{u}(\mathbf{k},t) = \cos(|k|t)\widehat{f}(\mathbf{k}) + \frac{\sin(|k|t)}{|k|}\hat{g}(\mathbf{k}) \qquad (6.9.64)$$

With (6.9.13) in mind, we define the *Riemann function* (for the ν-dimensional wave equation) as that distribution $R(x,t)$ on $\mathbb{R}^{\nu+1}$ with (^ in x only!)

$$\widehat{R}(\mathbf{k},t) = (2\pi)^{-\nu/2}\sin(|k|t)/|k| \qquad (6.9.65)$$

Even though we use the word "function," it will be a fairly singular distribution once $\nu \geq 3$. Then, noting that $\cos(|k|t) = \frac{d}{dt}\sin(|k|t)/|k|$, we have by (6.9.13) that

$$u(x,t) = \int R(x-y,t)g(y)d^\nu y + \frac{d}{dt}\int R(x-y,t)f(y)d^\nu y \qquad (6.9.66)$$

This agrees with what we found in $\nu = 1$. For if χ_t is the characteristic function of $(-t,t)$, we have

$$\hat{\chi}_t(k,t) = (2\pi)^{-1/2}\int_{-t}^{t} e^{-iky}dy$$

$$= (2\pi)^{-1/2}[(e^{-ikt} - e^{ikt})/(-ik)]$$

$$= 2(2\pi)^{-1/2}\sin(|k|t)/|k| \qquad (6.9.67)$$

(since $\sin(kt)/k = \sin(|k|t)/|k|$ in one dimension). Thus,

$$R^{(\nu=1)}(x,t) = \tfrac{1}{2}\chi_t(x) \qquad (6.9.68)$$

so (6.9.66) is (6.9.61).

Looking ahead, we'll see shortly that in ($\nu = 3$) dimensions ($\delta(|x| - t)$ is shorthand for unnormalized measure on the sphere of radius t, i.e., $\int f(\mathbf{x})\delta(|x| - t)dx = 4\pi t^2 \int f(t\omega)d\omega$ where $d\omega$ is normalized measure on S^2)

$$\hat{\delta}(|x| - t)(k) = (2\pi)^{-3/2}(4\pi t)\sin(|k|t)/|k| \qquad (6.9.69)$$

so

$$R^{(\nu=3)}(\mathbf{x}, t) = \frac{1}{4\pi t}\hat{\delta}(|x| - t) \tag{6.9.70}$$

Thus, we find *Kirchoff's formula* (aka the *Kirchoff-Poisson formula*)

$$u(\mathbf{x}, t) = \int [f(\mathbf{x} + t\omega) + (t\omega \cdot \mathrm{grad} f)(\mathbf{x} + t\omega) - tg(\mathbf{x} + t\omega)]d\omega_j \tag{6.9.71}$$

The above suggests that it will be useful to compute the Fourier transform of $\delta(|x| - t)$ for $\mathbb{R}^\nu$. One often sees this calculation in terms of Bessel functions (and we will in Part 3—see Theorem 3.5.13 of that part) and one can obtain (6.9.79) below by manipulating Bessel functions, but we'll be able to use our bare hands (i.e., no special function theory): by rotation symmetry we need only compute $e^{ik|x_\nu}$, so the following lemma will be useful:

Lemma 6.9.7. *Let* $f \in C(\mathbb{R})$ *and* $B_R(0)$, *the ball of radius R in* $\mathbb{R}^\nu$, $\nu \geq 2$. *Then,*

(a) $$\int_{B_R(0)} f(x_\nu)d^\nu x = \frac{\sigma_{\nu-1}}{\nu - 1}\int_{-R}^{R}(R^2 - s^2)^{(\nu-1)/2}f(s)ds \tag{6.9.72}$$

(b) $$\int_{\partial B_R(0)} f(x_\nu)dS(x) = \sigma_{\nu-1}R\int_{-R}^{R}f(s)(R^2 - S^2)^{(\nu-3)/2}ds \tag{6.9.73}$$

where dS is unnormalized measure on the sphere, $\partial B_R(0)$ *of radius R, i.e.,* $R^{\nu-1}\sigma_\nu d\omega$.

Remarks. 1. As in Problem 5–6 of Section 4.11, σ_ν is the surface area of the unit ball and $\tau_\nu = \sigma_\nu \int_0^1 v^{\nu-1}dv = \sigma_\nu/\nu$ is the volume of the unit ball. σ_ν is given by (4.11.55).

2. Taking $\nu = 3$ and $f(s) = e^{-iks}$, (6.9.73) provides the promised proof of (6.9.69) since $2\sigma_2 = 4\pi$.

3. LHS of (6.9.73) is just $\int f(x_\nu)\delta(|x| - R)d^\nu x$.

Proof. The slice of the ball $B_R(0)$ with $x_\nu = s$ is a ball of radius $(R^2 - s^2)^{1/2}$ with volume $\tau_{\nu-1}(R^2 - s^2)^{(\nu-1)/2} = \sigma_{\nu-1}(\nu - 1)^{-1}(R^2 - s^2)^{(\nu-1)/2}$. Thus, (6.9.72) is immediate by first integrating out $x_1, \ldots, x_{\nu-1}$.

The left side of (6.9.73) is the d/dR-derivatives of the left side of (6.9.72). When we take derivatives of the right of (6.9.72), there is no end-point contribution since $(R^2 - s^2)^{(\nu-1)/2}|_{s=\pm R} = 0$. Thus (6.9.73) follows from

$$\frac{d}{dR}(R^2 - s^2)^{(\nu-1)/2} = 2R\frac{(\nu - 1)}{2}(R^2 - s^2)^{(\nu-3)/2} \tag{6.9.74}$$

$\square$

In the above proof, we showed that if $\alpha \geq 1$, then

$$\int_{-R}^{R} (R^2 - s^2)^{\alpha - 1} f(s) ds = 2\alpha \frac{1}{R} \frac{d}{dR} \int_{-R}^{R} (R^2 - s^2)^{\alpha} f(s) ds \qquad (6.9.75)$$

Thus, if $\nu = 2\ell + 3$, $\ell = 1, 2, \ldots$, we have that

$$\int_{-R}^{R} f(s) ds = c_{\nu}^{-1} \left(\frac{1}{R} \frac{d}{dR} \right)^{\ell} \int_{-R}^{R} (R^2 - s^2)^{(\nu-3)/2} f(s) ds \qquad (6.9.76)$$

where

$$c_{2\ell+3} = 2^{\ell} \ell!; \quad \ell = 0, 1, 2, \ldots \qquad (6.9.77)$$

Taking $f(x_{\nu}) = e^{i|k|x_{\nu}}$ and using (6.9.67), we find that

$$(2\pi)^{-\nu/2} \frac{\sin(|k|t)}{|k|} = \frac{1}{2 c_{\nu} \sigma_{\nu-1}} \left(\frac{1}{t} \frac{d}{dt} \right)^{\ell} \frac{1}{t} \widetilde{\delta(|x| - t)} (k) \qquad (6.9.78)$$

Thus, we have proven that

Theorem 6.9.8. *Let $\nu = 2\ell+3$, $\ell = 0, 1, 2, \ldots$. Then the Riemann function, $R^{(\nu)}$, for the wave equation is given by (c_{ν} given by (6.9.77))*

$$R^{(\nu)}(\mathbf{x}, t) = \frac{1}{2 c_{\nu} \sigma_{\nu-1}} \left(\frac{1}{t} \frac{d}{dt} \right)^{\ell} \frac{1}{t} \delta(|x| - t) \qquad (6.9.79)$$

Remark. If $g \in C_0^{\infty}(\mathbb{R}^{\nu})$, $(R^{(\nu)} * g)(x, t)$ (* in x variable only) must be $tg(x) = o(t)$ for t small. On the other hand, since the sphere of radius t has area $\sigma_{\nu} t^{\nu-1}$, the left side convoluted with g is, for t small, near

$$(2 c_{\nu} \sigma_{\nu-1})^{-1} \left(\frac{1}{t} \frac{d}{dt} \right)^{\ell} t^{\nu-2} g(x) \sigma_{\nu}$$

so we must have (c_{ν} given by (6.9.77))

$$2 c_{\nu} \sigma_{\nu-1} = (\nu - 2)(\nu - 4) \cdots (3)(1) \sigma_{\nu} \qquad (6.9.80)$$

It is interesting to check to confirm this (Problem 19).

Next, we turn to the case of even ν. A key will be what Hadamard called the *method of descent* which works more generally than the wave equation. Let g be a nice function on $\mathbb{R}^{\nu}$, so then $R^{(\nu)}(\cdot, t) * g = u^{(\nu)}$ solves $(\frac{\partial}{\partial t^2} - \Delta_{\nu}) u^{(\nu)} = 0$ with $u^{(\nu)}(t = 0) = 0$, $\frac{\partial}{\partial t} u^{(\nu)}(t = 0) = g$. Let $\widetilde{g}$ be the function on $\mathbb{R}^{\nu+1}$ given by

$$\widetilde{g}(x_1, \ldots, x_{\nu}, x_{\nu+1}) = g(x_1, \ldots, x_{\nu}) \qquad (6.9.81)$$

Then, $R^{(\nu+1)} * \widetilde{g}$ (which exists since for each t, $R^{(\nu+1)}(x, t)$ has compact support) is $x_{\nu+1}$ independent and so equals $\widetilde{u}^{(\nu+1)}$ for some $u^{(\nu+1)}$ on $\mathbb{R}^{\nu} \times [0, \infty)$. Since $\widetilde{u}$ is $x_{\nu+1}$ independent, the $\frac{\partial^2}{\partial x_{\nu+1}^2}$ derivative is zero, so $u^{(\nu+1)}$ obeys the same equation and same boundary conditions as $u^{(\nu)}$, i.e., $u^{(\nu+1)} =$

$u^{(\nu)}$. A little thought (and uniqueness (Problem 17)) shows that this is saying

$$R^{(\nu)}(\mathbf{x}, t) = \int_{-\infty}^{\infty} R^{(\nu+1)}((\mathbf{x}, x_{\nu+1}), t) dx_{\nu+1} \qquad (6.9.82)$$

as a distribution in $\mathbf{x}$. This formula is called the *method of descent*. Knowing $R^{(\nu)}$ for odd ν thus determines it for even ν! To make this explicit, we'll need the following analog of Lemma 6.9.7.

Lemma 6.9.9. *Let $f \in C(\mathbb{R}^\nu)$ and $B_R(0)$ the ball of radius R in $\mathbb{R}^{\nu+1}$ with $\nu \geq 1$. Then*

(a) $\int_{B_R(0)} f(x_1, \ldots, x_\nu) d^{\nu+1}x = 2 \int_{|x| \leq R} (R^2 - |x|^2)^{1/2} f(x) d^\nu x \qquad (6.9.83)$

(b) $\int_{\partial B_R(0)} f(x_1, \ldots, x_\nu) dS(x) = 2 \int_{|x| \leq R} R(R^2 - |x|^2)^{-1/2} f(x) d^\nu x$

$$(6.9.84)$$

Remark. Naively, one might think that $(R^2 - |x|^2)$ vanishes to second order at $|x| = R$ so $(R^2 - |x|^2)^{-1/2}$ causes a divergent integral. But $(R^2 - |x|^2) = (R - |x|)(R + |x|)$ has only a first-order zero and, so if f is bounded, the integral on the right side of (6.9.84) converges.

Proof. For $(x_1, \ldots, x_\nu)$ fixed, the set $\{y \in \mathbb{R} \mid |(x, y)| \leq R\}$ is an interval of length $2(R^2 - |x|^2)^{1/2}$ so (6.9.83) is immediate. The LHS of (6.9.84) is the $\frac{d}{dR}$-derivative of the LHS of (6.9.63). In the $\frac{d}{dR}$-derivatives of the RHS of (6.9.83), there is no boundary term since $(R^2 - |x|^2)^{1/2}$ vanishes on the boundary so (6.9.84) follows from $\frac{d}{dR}(R^2 - |x|^2)^{1/2} = R(R^2 - |x|)^{-1/2}$ $\qquad \square$

In (6.9.83) noting that the $x_{\nu+1}$ integral and time derivatives can be interchanged leads immediately to

Theorem 6.9.10. *Let $\nu = 2\ell + 2$, $\ell = 0, 1, \ldots$. Then the Riemann function, $R^{(\nu)}$, for the wave equation is given by*

$$R^{(\nu)}(\mathbf{x}, t) = \frac{1}{c_{\nu+1}\sigma_\nu} \left(\frac{1}{t}\frac{d}{dt}\right)^\ell \frac{1}{\sqrt{R^2 - |x|^2}} \chi_{|x| \leq t}(x) \qquad (6.9.85)$$

In particular,

$$R^{(2)}(x, t) = \frac{1}{2\pi} \frac{1}{\sqrt{t^2 - |x|^2}} \chi_{|x| \leq t}(x) \qquad (6.9.86)$$

Remark. It is an interesting exercise (Problem 20) to check that

$$\left[(t^{-1}R^{(2)}(\cdot, t)) * g\right](x) \to g(x) \qquad (6.9.87)$$

as it must!

With the fundamental Riemann function for the Cauchy problem in hand, we want to note the consequences of its properties.

Theorem 6.9.11 (Finite propagation speed). *In $\mathbb{R}^\nu \times [0, \infty)$, solutions of the Cauchy problem* (6.9.3)/(6.9.4) *have for t fixed (as sets of* **x***)*

$$\operatorname{supp} u(x,t) \subset \{y \mid \operatorname{dist}(\mathrm{y}, \operatorname{supp}(\mathrm{f}) \cup \operatorname{supp}(\mathrm{g})) \le \mathrm{t}\} \qquad (6.9.88)$$

Remark. So the waves described by the wave equation travel at speed at most 1. This is very different from the heat equation.

Proof. Immediate from $\operatorname{supp}(R(x,t)) \subset \{x \mid |x| \le t\}$. $\square$

Theorem 6.9.12 (Huygens' Principle). *For $\nu = 3, 5, 7, \ldots$ for the Cauchy problem* (6.9.3)/(6.9.4)

$$u(x,t) = 0 \text{ if } f(y) = g(y) = 0 \text{ for all } y \text{ with } |x - y| = t \qquad (6.9.89)$$

Remark. In other dimensions, $|x-y| = t$ has to be replaced by $|x-y| \le t$. It is remarkable that this physically significant fact is false in even dimensions but true in odd. A light "pulse" passes by in three dimensions but has a trailing $t^{-1/2}$ memory in two.

Proof. Immediate from $\operatorname{supp}(R(x,t)) \subset \{x \mid |x| = t\}$ $\square$

The Malgrange–Ehrenpreis Theorem. Finally, we will prove the following

Theorem 6.9.13 (Malgrange–Ehrenpreis Theorem). *Let P be a polynomial in ν variables (which is not the zero polynomial) and let $P(D)$ be given by* (6.9.49). *Fix $\varepsilon > 0$ and let $\langle x \rangle$ be the C^∞ function $\sqrt{|x|^2 + 1}$. Then there exists a linear functional, τ, on $C_0^\infty(\mathbb{R}^\nu)$ so that, for some K and C,*

$$|\tau(\varphi)| \le C \sum_{|\alpha| \le K} \|e^{-\varepsilon \langle x \rangle} D^\alpha \varphi\|_\infty \qquad (6.9.90)$$

and $P(D)\tau = \delta$ in the sense that for all $\varphi \in C_0^\infty(\mathbb{R}^\nu)$

$$\tau(P(-D)\varphi) = \varphi(0) \qquad (6.9.91)$$

Remarks. 1. This implies τ is an ordinary distribution in the sense defined in Chapter 9. Alternatively, one can define a function space of all C^∞ functions with the norms in (6.9.90) finite and develop distributions for it. For our needs below, the point is that if $|\boldsymbol{\eta}| < \varepsilon$, $\boldsymbol{\eta} \in \mathbb{R}^\nu$ and σ is a tempered distribution, then

$$\tau(\varphi) = \sigma(e^{\boldsymbol{\eta} \cdot \mathbf{x}} \varphi) \qquad (6.9.92)$$

defines a linear functional of C_0^∞ obeying (6.9.90). We'll denote it as $\tau = e^{\boldsymbol{\eta} \cdot \mathbf{x}} \sigma$.

2. It is known that one can find a tempered distribution but it appears that can't be proven by the method we use here.

3. Once one has τ, one can define $\tau * g$ for g in C_0^∞ (essentially by (6.2.19)), and show that $P(D)(\tau * g) = g$ (Problem 21); i.e., this theorem proves for any P and $g \in C_0^\infty$, there is a C^∞ function, f, with $P(D)f = g$. As we'll explain in the Notes, there are known to be simple nonconstant coefficient PDE's with no solutions.

We'll prove this theorem by an explicit formula! It will not be explicit in the sense that we've written down in x-space, the fundamental relation for the four central equations (plus the Helmholtz equation) of this section, but it will be a sum of explicit functions multiplying Fourier transforms of explicit distributions.

The naive way to find τ is to take the Fourier transform $1/P(i\mathbf{k})$. That's fine if $|P(i\mathbf{k})|$ is bounded away from 0 or at least if $1/|P(i\mathbf{k})| \in L^1_{\text{loc}}(\mathbb{R}^\nu)$ but not if it isn't. In looking for the fundamental solution for Δ in $(\nu = 2)$ dimensions, we found a way to solve this non-L^1 issue in that case and all proofs of the Malgrange-Ehrenpreis theorem have to cope with the zero set of $P(i\mathbf{k})$. Remarkably, all we'll need is that for each fixed $\eta \in R^\nu$, $P(\eta + i\mathbf{k})$ is nonvanishing for a.e. k (we'll prove this as Proposition 4.1.9 of Part 3). As a preliminary, we need an elementary piece of algebra:

Lemma 6.9.14. *If* $\lambda_0, \dots, \lambda_m \in \mathbb{C}$ *are distinct numbers and* $a_j = \prod_{k=0, k \neq j}^m (\lambda_j - \lambda_k)^{-1}$, *then*

$$\sum_{j=0}^n a_j \lambda_j^k = \begin{cases} 0 & \text{if } k = 0, \dots, m-1 \\ 1 & \text{if } k = m \end{cases} \tag{6.9.93}$$

Proof. Problem 22 has a proof using contour integration and Problem 23 using linear algebra. $\qquad\square$

Now suppose that

$$P(\mathbf{x}) = \sum_{|\alpha| \leq m} c_\alpha x^\alpha \tag{6.9.94}$$

where m is picked so that some c_α with $|\alpha| = m$ is nonzero. For $q = 0, 1, \dots, m$, let

$$P_q(\lambda) = \sum_{|\alpha| = q} c_\alpha x^\alpha \tag{6.9.95}$$

Since P_m is not identically zero, pick $\boldsymbol{\eta}$ with

$$P_m(\boldsymbol{\eta}) \neq 0, \quad |\boldsymbol{\eta}| < \varepsilon \tag{6.9.96}$$

Pick $\lambda_0, \dots, \lambda_m$ distinct in $\mathbb{R}$ with $\sup|\lambda_j| < 1$. Let

$$Q_j(\mathbf{k}) = P(i\mathbf{k} + \lambda_j \boldsymbol{\eta}) \tag{6.9.97}$$

If $\mathbf{k} = \alpha\boldsymbol{\eta}$ with $\alpha \in \mathbb{R}$, $P_m(i\mathbf{k} + \lambda_j\boldsymbol{\eta}_j) = (i\alpha + \lambda_j)^m P_m(\boldsymbol{\eta})$; so for large α, this dominates $P - P_m$, so $Q_j(\mathbf{k})$ is not the zero polynomial and thus, by Proposition 4.1.9 of Part 3, Q_j is a.e. nonzero and $\overline{Q_j(\mathbf{k})}/Q_j(\mathbf{k})$ is a well-defined L^∞ function and so a tempered distribution.

Proof of Theorem 6.9.13. Let $\boldsymbol{\eta}$, $\lambda_0, \ldots \lambda_m$, $Q_0, \ldots, Q_m$, $a_0, \ldots a_m$ be as above. We claim that

$$\tau = (2\pi)^{\nu/2} \left[\overline{P_m(2\boldsymbol{\eta})}\right]^{-1} \sum_{j=0}^{m} a_j e^{\lambda_j \boldsymbol{\eta} \cdot \mathbf{x}} \left(\frac{\overline{Q_j(\mathbf{k})}}{Q_j(\mathbf{k})}\right)^{\vee} \tag{6.9.98}$$

obeys (6.9.90) and obeys $P(D)\tau = \delta$. Since $|\lambda_j| < 1$, $e^{-\varepsilon\langle x\rangle} e^{\lambda_j \boldsymbol{\eta} \cdot \mathbf{x}}$ is bounded with all bounded derivatives, so (6.9.90) holds.

For any $y \in \mathbb{R}^\nu$ as operators on C_0^∞ functions,

$$P(D)(e^{\mathbf{y}\mathbf{x}} \cdot) = e^{\mathbf{y}\mathbf{x}} P(D + \mathbf{y})(\cdot) \tag{6.9.99}$$

so for any $\sigma \in \mathcal{S}'(\mathbb{R}^\nu)$ and any $\mathbf{y}$ with $|y| < \varepsilon$

$$\begin{aligned} P(D)(e^{\mathbf{y}\mathbf{x}}\breve{\sigma}) &= e^{\mathbf{y}\mathbf{x}} P(D + \mathbf{y})\breve{\sigma} \\ &= e^{\mathbf{y}\mathbf{x}}[P(i\mathbf{k} + \mathbf{y})\sigma]^{\vee} \end{aligned} \tag{6.9.100}$$

Moreover,

$$(2\pi)^{\nu/2} \left[\overline{P(i\mathbf{k} + \mathbf{y})}\right]^{\vee} = \overline{P}(-D + y)\delta \tag{6.9.101}$$

Thus, for any j, by (6.9.100)

$$(2\pi)^{\nu/2} P(D) \left[e^{\lambda_j \boldsymbol{\eta} \cdot \mathbf{x}} \left(\frac{\overline{Q_j(\mathbf{k})}}{Q_j(\mathbf{k})}\right)^{\vee}\right] = (2\pi)^{\nu/2} e^{\lambda_j \boldsymbol{\eta} \cdot \mathbf{x}} \left(\overline{Q_j(k)}\right)^{\vee}$$

$$= e^{\lambda_j \boldsymbol{\eta} \cdot \mathbf{x}} \overline{P}(-D + \lambda_j\boldsymbol{\eta})\delta \tag{6.9.102}$$

$$= \overline{P}(-D + 2\lambda_j\boldsymbol{\eta}) e^{\lambda_j \boldsymbol{\eta} \cdot x}\delta \tag{6.9.103}$$

$$= \overline{P}(-D + 2\lambda_j\boldsymbol{\eta})\delta \tag{6.9.104}$$

To get (6.9.102), we used (6.9.101). To get (6.9.103), we used (6.9.99), and to get (6.9.104), we used $e^{\lambda_j \boldsymbol{\eta} \cdot \mathbf{x}}\delta = \delta$.

$\overline{P}(-D + 2\lambda\boldsymbol{\eta})$ is clearly a polynomial in λ with coefficients which are differential operators. The only way to get λ^m is to have no D's, i.e.,

$$\overline{P}(-D + \lambda\boldsymbol{\eta}) = \lambda^m \overline{P_m(2\boldsymbol{\eta})} + \sum_{q=0}^{m-1} \lambda^q T_q \tag{6.9.105}$$

for suitable T_q. Therefore, by (6.9.93),

$$\sum_{j=0}^{m} a_j \overline{P}(-D + 2\lambda_j \boldsymbol{\eta})\delta = P_m(2\boldsymbol{\eta})\delta \qquad (6.9.106)$$

and (6.9.102) implies $P(D)\tau = \delta$.

$\square$

Notes and Historical Remarks.

> Thus the partial differential equation entered theoretical physics as a hand-maid, but has gradually become mistress.
> —Albert Einstein [275][6]

The five equations we discuss here are connected with an enormous amount of pure and applied mathematics—for example, one can make the case that a significant fraction of classical mathematical physics comes from understanding the solutions to these equations. That said, one cannot claim this section should be regarded as an introduction to or even a serious glimpse at the theory of partial differential equations (PDE). After all, there exist three multivolume expositions of PDE by Hörmander [**434**] and by Taylor [**912**] (and Hörmander only deals with the linear case). Our purpose here is solely to illustrate the usefulness of the combination of Fourier transform and distribution theory in the theory of PDE's. Among the hundreds (maybe even thousands if one counts books in engineering science) of PDE books let me mention [**206, 288, 310, 328, 349, 415, 434, 452, 459, 655, 768, 933, 912**] for those wishing to delve more deeply.

The earliest example of a fundamental solution for a PDE is d'Alembert's 1747 (published 1749) result [**212**] for the one-dimensional wave equation—he proved d'Alembert's formula, (6.9.62), for a vibrating string. In 1787, Laplace [**548**] noted that outside the support of a mass distribution, ρ, its gravitational potential $(4\pi)^{-1} \int |x - y|^{-1} \rho(y) dy$ obeyed Laplace's equation, $\Delta u = 0$ (named for this work) and his student, Poisson, [**736**], in 1813 noted that it solved Poisson's equation, $\Delta u = -\rho$ (named for this work). The name "Green's function" comes from Green's 1828 memoirs [**366**] where Green's formula appeared and was used to study what we now call the Poisson equation.

Remarkably, Poission is not only responsible for the Green's kernel for Lapalacians, but also the heat kernel and the solution of the wave equation in two and three dimensions. These appear in his 1818–19 papers [**737, 738**].

---

[6]The original had essays both on physics and philosophy. Most currently available versions, including the one available at `https://archive.org/details/AlbertEinsteinTheWorldAsISeeIt` are abridged and have dropped the physics essays including the one with this quote !

A lot about the heat equation appears also in Fourier's famous work [**311**]. The Helmholtz equation is named after the German physician, physicist, and philosopher, Herman von Helmholtz (1821–1894), who studied it in his book [**956**], but it was widely studied earlier than his work.

The Schrödinger equation appeared in his celebrated 1926 paper [**824**]. Theorem 6.9.6, its proof and application to scattering are due to Dollard [**252**].

Kirchoff's formula, (6.9.71), appeared first in the 1818 paper of Poisson [**737**] [**736**] mentioned above and written 65 years before Kirchoff's paper [**490**]. What Kirchoff had was a formula involving integration over other surfaces inside the cone but (6.9.71) is a special case of his results.

Poisson also had the wave equation Riemann function for $\nu = 2$ kernel which he got from what we call the method of descent; he referred to an earlier paper of Parseval [**701**] for the idea of this method.

The Riemann kernel for general ν is due to Tédone in 1898 [**914**]. It was rediscovered by Sobolev [**864**] 35 years later and is often known by his name in the Russian literature. Their proofs are by direct verification—the proof we give using Lemma 6.9.7 follows Torchinsky [**928**] except our proof of that key lemma avoids his use of multidimensional polar coordinates.

The Riemann function is named after an approach of Riemann [**773**] to certain hyperbolic systems. Riemann applied it to some first-order systems—Volterra [**953**, **954**] extended it to the wave equation. Hadamard [**380**] codified the method and also the method of descent which he named.

Huygens' principle appeared in his celebrated 1690 work [**443**] which championed the wave theory of light over Newton's corpuscular theory. Huygens didn't mention a wave equation but assumed each source of light generates a sharp spherical wave. We emphasize that if we lived in two dimensions, sound would be cacophonous. Open sets with the fundamental solution vanishing inside the edge of the support of that solution are called *lacunas*. They are unusual and unstable under small changes in the equation. For examples of other equations with such solutions, see [**880**, **947**] and for some general theory [**42**].

There are three approaches to proving the Malgrange–Ehrenpreis theorem. One defines the functional τ with $p(D)\tau = \delta$ on a set of functions where division by $p(k)$ is not a problem and uses the Hahn–Banach Theorem to extend it. This is the approach in the original papers of Malgrange [**622**] and Ehrenpreis [**273**]. In the modern guises, the key step is what is known as *Hörmander's inequality*: for every bounded open set, Ω, in $\mathbb{R}^\nu$, there is $C > 0$, so that for all $\varphi \in C_0^\infty(\Omega)$ we have that

$$\|p(D)\varphi\|_2 \geq C\|\varphi\|_2$$

A slick version of this approach is in Rosay [**803**].

The second approach defines divided polynomials in much the way a principal value is defined. The pioneer here is Hörmander [**432**]; see also Łojasiecwicz [**600**] and Bernstein [**81**].

The third approach, the one that we use, is "explicit" formulas. Again, the key first version is due to Hörmander, but in a different paper [**431**]. Following up on papers by König [**510**], Ortner–Wagner [**691**] had the idea to use $\bar{P}(k)/P(k)$. That paper has an integral of Fourier transforms. The sum via Vandemonde determinants was used in Wagner [**972**]. Ortner–Wagner [**692**] survey the explicit solution approach.

We proved here that every constant coefficient PDE has solutions. This may not be so for even some of the simplest nonconstant coefficients cases. In 1957, Lewy [**583**] proved that there are C^∞ functions $F(z,t)$ on $\mathbb{C} \times \mathbb{R}$ so that

$$\frac{\partial u}{\partial \bar{z}} - iz\frac{\partial u}{\partial t} = F(z,t) \tag{6.9.107}$$

has no solutions. Mizohata [**662**] proved the same for the even simpler equation on $\mathbb{R}^2$,

$$\frac{\partial u}{\partial x} + ix\frac{\partial u}{\partial y} = F(x,y) \tag{6.9.108}$$

The connection between solving the Dirichlet problem and Brownian motion stopping times is due to Kakutani [**471**] in 1944. Port–Stone [**748**] have a whole book on the subject.

For some discussion of the impact on physics of the long range Coulomb Green's function in two dimensions, see the papers of Fröhlich–Spencer [**332, 333**].

The example in Problem 10 showing nonuniqueness of the solution of the heat equation appears in the book of John [**452**]. It goes back at least to Tychonoff [**942**]. John also proves that if $u(x,t) \geq 0$ for all $(x,t) \in \mathbb{R}^\nu \times (0,\infty)$, then the solution is unique, a result due to Widder [**991**].

Rosenbloom–Widder [**804**] have several explicit solutions (given as integrals) of the heat equation with vanishing initial condition.

Problems

1. Verify that if $\nu \geq 3$ and $f \in L^1(\mathbb{R}^\nu) \cap L^\infty(\mathbb{R}^\nu)$, then g given by (6.9.14) is a bounded functon on $\mathbb{R}^\nu$ that obeys (6.9.15) in distributional sense. (*Hint*: Note that $\langle \varphi, G_\nu * f \rangle = \langle G_\nu * \varphi, f \rangle$ for $\varphi \in \mathcal{S}(\mathbb{R}^\nu)$.)

2. If f is Hölder continuous, prove the g in Problem 1 is C^2 and that (6.9.15) holds in the classical sense.

3. (a) Let $\nu \geq 3$. Prove that if $\Delta\varphi = 0$, then

$$\int_{S^{\nu-1}} \varphi(x + r\omega)d\omega = \varphi(x) \tag{6.9.109}$$

where $d\omega$ is a normalized rotation-invariant measure on $S^{\nu-1}$ (*Hint*: Show that the left side of (6.9.109) is a function of r, $A(r)$, so that $A(|x|)$ is harmonic on $\mathbb{R}^\nu$ and that this implies first that $A(r)$ obeys a differential equation on $(0, \infty)$, and then that $A(r) = c_1 + c_2 r^{-(\nu-2)}$. Then use $\lim_{r\downarrow 0} A(r) = \varphi(x)$ to conclude that (6.9.109) holds. See also Theorem 3.1.1 in Part 3.)

(b) If $\Delta\varphi = 0$ on $\mathbb{R}^\nu$ and $\varphi(x) \to 0$ as $x \to \infty$, prove that $\varphi \equiv 0$.

(c) If $g \in \mathcal{S}$ and $f_1, f_2 \in C^2_\infty(\mathbb{R})$, the C^2 functions vanishing at infinity, and obeys $\Delta f_j = g$, prove that $f_1 = f_2$.

4. Verify (6.9.18), i.e., that the limit holds if both sides are multiplied by $f \in \mathcal{S}(\mathbb{R}^2)$ and integrated.

5. Let $f \in \mathcal{S}(\mathbb{R}^2)$. Verify (6.9.21) by showing

$$\int (\Delta f)(x)G_2(x) = -f(0) \tag{6.9.110}$$

as follows.

(a) Prove first that

$$\lim_{r\downarrow 0} \lim_{R\to\infty} \int_{r<|x|<R} (\Delta f)(x)G_2(x) = \text{ LHS of } (6.9.110) \tag{6.9.111}$$

(b) Prove that $\Delta G_2 = 0$ on $\mathbb{R}^\nu \setminus \{0\}$ and use that to prove that LHS of (6.9.111) is a sum of boundary terms $B_r^{(1)}$ and $B_R^{(2)}$ over $|x| = r$ and $|x| = R$.

(c) Using the explicit form of G_2 and ∇G_2, prove that $\lim_{R\to\infty} B_R^{(2)} = 0$ and $\lim_{r\downarrow 0} B_r^{(1)} = -f(0)$ and so verify (6.9.110).

6. Define, for a probability measure, μ, of compact support on $\mathbb{R}^2$

$$\mathcal{E}(\mu) = -\frac{1}{4\pi}\int d\mu(x)d\mu(y)\log|x-y| \tag{6.9.112}$$

(a) Prove that the integral is either convergent or else is $+\infty$.

(b) Suppose that $\mathcal{E}(\mu_j) < \infty$ for μ_1 and μ_2. Prove that $\mathcal{E}(\frac{1}{2}(\mu_1+\mu_2)) < \infty$ and that

$$\frac{1}{2}\mathcal{E}(\mu_1) + \frac{1}{2}\mathcal{E}(\mu_2) - \mathcal{E}(\frac{1}{2}(\mu_1 + \mu_2))$$
$$= \frac{1}{4}\mathcal{E}((\mu_1 - \mu_2)) \tag{6.9.113}$$

where $\mathcal{E}((\mu_1 - \mu_2))$ is interpreted as the RHS of (6.9.112) with μ replaced by $\mu_1 - \mu_2$ (prove the corresponding integrals all converge).

(c) Prove that $\hat{\mu}_1(0) = \hat{\mu}_2(0)$ so that $[\hat{\mu}_1(k) - \hat{\mu}_2(k)]/|k|$ is given by a bounded continuous function $O(|k|^{-m})$ at ∞ for all m.

(d) Prove that

$$\mathcal{E}((\mu_1 - \mu_2)) = \frac{1}{2} \int \frac{|\hat{\mu}_1(k) - \hat{\mu}_2(k)|^2}{|k|^2} d^\nu k$$

and conclude (6.8.21) holds in two dimensions.

(e) Prove uniqueness of the potential theory minimum in ($\nu = 2$) dimensions.

7. For $f \in \mathcal{S}(\mathbb{R}^\nu)$, verify that (6.9.29) solves the heat equation with boundary condition f by taking Fourier transforms. Then, verify (6.9.29) for f in $\mathcal{S}'(\mathbb{R}^\nu)$ by duality (i.e., show it obeys the heat equation first in distributional sense and then in classical sense and then prove distributional convergence, i.e., $\sigma(\mathcal{S}', \mathcal{S})$ as $t \downarrow 0$.)

8. (a) Prove that if f obeys (6.9.30) for all $a > 0$, then the integral in (6.9.29) converges for all $y \in \mathbb{R}^\nu, t \in (0, \infty)$ and defines a function which is C^∞ and whose derivatives can be computed by taking them inside the integral. (*Hint*: Prove the differentiability inductively in the order by proving convergence of the integral with derivative inside and that the integral of the putative derivatives gives function differences.)

(b) Prove (6.9.32) and show that this implies continuity of $u(x, t)$ defined on $\mathbb{R}^\nu \times [0, \infty)$ by (6.9.29) (for $t > 0$) and (6.9.31) (for $t = 0$).

9. This problem will prove a uniqueness theorem for solutions of the heat equation under a weak growth hypothesis on the solutions.

(a) Let u be real-valued and continuous on $\Omega \equiv \{(\mathbf{x}, t) \in \mathbb{R}^{\nu+1} \mid 0 \le t \le T, |x| \le R\}$, C^2 on Ω_T^{int} and obey

$$\frac{\partial u}{\partial t} < \Delta u \tag{6.9.114}$$

there. Prove that for each $S < T$

$$\sup_{|x| \le R, 0 \le t < S} u(\mathbf{x}, t) \le \sup_{(x,t) \in \tilde{\partial}\Omega_S} u(\mathbf{x}, t) \tag{6.9.115}$$

where

$$\tilde{\partial}\Omega_S = \{(\mathbf{x}, 0) \mid |x| \le R\} \cup \{(\mathbf{x}, t) \mid |x| = R, 0 \le t \le S\} \tag{6.9.116}$$

(this is the boundary of the cylinder without the top). (*Hint*: If $u(x, t)$ takes its maximum value at some point in $\Omega_S \setminus \tilde{\partial}\Omega_S$, prove that $\frac{\partial u}{\partial t} \ge 0$ ($= 0$ unless $t = S$) and that $\Delta u \le 0$ and note this violates (6.9.114).)

(b) Extend the result of (a) to only require $\frac{\partial u}{\partial t} \leq \Delta u$. (*Hint:* If $v_\varepsilon = u - \varepsilon t$, then v_ε obeys (6.9.114).)

(c) If u obeys (6.9.30) for some $a > 0$ and all $(x,t) \in \mathbb{R}^\nu \times (0,T)$, obeys (6.9.2) and is continuous on $\mathbb{R}^\nu \times [0,T)$ if $u(x, t = 0) = 0$, prove that $u \equiv 0$. (*Hint:* Suppose first that $4aT < 1$, pick $\varepsilon \geq 0$ so that $4a(T + \varepsilon) < 1$ and note that for each $\delta > 0$, $\pm u(x,t) - \delta P_{t+\varepsilon}(x,0)$ is negative on $\{(x,t) \mid |x| = R, 0 < t < T\}$ when R is large (depending on δ). Conclude $\pm u \leq 0$ and so 0. Then use a finite number of time intervals with $4aT > 1$.)

10. This problem will construct solutions of the heat equation on $\mathbb{R} \times \mathbb{R}$ with $u(x,t) \equiv 0$ for all $t \leq 0$ and $u(\cdot, t) \not\equiv 0$ for $t > 0$. (Once one has this, by taking $u_\nu(x_1, \ldots, x_\nu, t) = u(x_1, t)$, one gets such solutions on $\mathbb{R}^\nu \times \mathbb{R}$.)

(a) Suppose that

$$u(x,t) = \sum_{j=0}^{\infty} g_j(t) x^j \tag{6.9.117}$$

converges uniformly for (x,t) in compact sets of $\mathbb{R}^2$. Show that $u_t = u_{xx}$ is equivalent to

$$g_1 = 0, \quad g_j' = (j+2)(j+1)g_{j+2}, \ j = 0,1,2,\ldots$$

so writing $g_1 \equiv g$, conclude that if one can just interchange differentiation and the sum, then

$$u(x,t) = \sum_{k=0}^{\infty} \frac{g^{(k)}(t)}{(2k)!} x^{2k} \tag{6.9.118}$$

solves the heat equation.

(b) For $\alpha > 1$, define

$$g(t) = \begin{cases} \exp(-t^{-\alpha}), & t > 0 \\ 0, & t \leq 0 \end{cases} \tag{6.9.119}$$

Prove that for each $\alpha > 1$, there is θ so that

$$|g^{(k)}(t)| \leq \frac{k!}{(\theta t)^k} \exp(-\tfrac{1}{2}t^{-\alpha}) \tag{6.9.120}$$

(c) Use the estimate on this g to prove that (6.9.118) is a solution of $\frac{\partial u}{\partial t} = \frac{\partial^2 u}{\partial x^2}$ and $u(x,t) = 0$ for $t \leq 0$ and $u(0,t) > 0$ for $t > 0$.

11. This problem will lead the reader through a "heat-kernel" proof of the functional equation (6.6.57) for the Jacobi theta function (it was proven earlier using the Poisson summation formula).

(a) Consider solving $\frac{\partial u}{\partial t} = \frac{\partial^2 u}{\partial x^2}$ on $\mathbb{R} \times (0, t)$ with initial condition f obeying $f(x+1) = f(x)$. Prove the solution is

$$u(x,t) = \int_0^1 P_t^{(\text{per})}(x,y,t) f(y) \, dy \tag{6.9.121}$$

$$P_t^{(\text{per})}(x,y,t) = (4\pi t)^{-1/2} \sum_{n=-\infty}^{\infty} e^{-(x-y-n^2)/4t} \tag{6.9.122}$$

(b) $-\frac{d^2}{dx^2}$ on $C_{\text{per}}^{\infty}(0,1)$, the C^{∞} function with periodic boundary conditions $(u^{(j)}(0) = u^{(j)}(1))$ has $\{e^{2\pi i n x}\}_{n=-\infty}^{\infty}$ as eigenfunctions with eigenvalues $4\pi^2 n^2$. Argue (a real proof requires a little unbounded operator theory) that

$$P_t^{(\text{per})}(x,y,t) = \sum_{n=-\infty}^{\infty} e^{2\pi i n(x-y)} e^{-4\pi^2 n^2 t} \tag{6.9.123}$$

(c) Taking $x = y = \frac{1}{2}$, $4t = \sigma^{-1}\pi^{-1}$, deduce (6.6.70), the functional equation for the Jacobi theta function.

12. Let $\nu \geq 3$. Use the dominated convergence theorem in (6.9.41) to prove that $|x|^{(\nu-2)}Q_1(x)$ has a limit as $x \to 0$ and compute the limit. Therefore, conclude (6.9.45).

13. Verify (6.9.45) when $\nu = 2$.

14. Using (6.9.42) and Laplace's method (see Section 15.2 of Part 2B), prove (6.9.46).

15. For $f \in L^2$, prove that $(e^{-ik^2 t}\hat{f})^{\vee}$ is the L^2 limit (limit in $L^2(\mathbb{R}^\nu, dx)$ as $R \to \infty$) of the convergent integrals

$$(4\pi i t)^{-\nu/2} \int_{|y| \leq R} \exp \frac{i(\mathbf{x}-\mathbf{y})^2}{4t} f(\mathbf{y}) \, d^\nu y \tag{6.9.124}$$

16. If $|V(x)| \leq C(1+|x|)^{-\alpha}$, $\alpha > 1$, prove that

$$\int_1^{\infty} \|V(x)(V_t f)(\cdot)\|_2 \, dt < \infty$$

for any $f \in \mathcal{S}(\mathbb{R}^\nu)$ with $\hat{f}(k) = 0$ for all $|k|$ small.

Remark. This is useful in scattering theory; see Section 15.3 of Part 2B.

17. This problem will show uniqueness of the solution of the Cauchy problem for the wave equation (without the need for the kind of growth hypothesis required for the heat equation). So suppose $u(\mathbf{x}, t)$ is C^2 on $\mathbb{R}^\nu \times (0, \infty)$

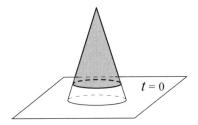

Figure 6.9.1. A backward light cone.

and $u, \partial u/\partial t$ and ∇u are continuous on $\mathbb{R}^\nu \times [0, \infty)$. Fix $(\mathbf{x}_0, t) \in \mathbb{R}^\nu \times (0, \infty)$ and define for $t \in [0, t_0)$

$$e(t) = \frac{1}{2} \int_{|x-x_0| \le (t_0 - t)} \left[\left(\frac{\partial u}{\partial t} \right)^2 + |\nabla u|^2 \right] d^\nu x \qquad (6.9.125)$$

(this is a time slice of the backward light cone with vertex at (x_0, t)—see Figure 6.9.1).

(a) Prove that

$$\frac{de}{dt} = \int_{|x-x_0| \le (t_0 - t)} \left[\left(\frac{\partial u}{\partial t} \right) \left(\frac{\partial^2 u}{\partial t^2} \right) + (\nabla u) \cdot \left(\nabla \frac{\partial u}{\partial t} \right) \right] d^\nu x$$
$$- \frac{1}{2} \int_{|x-x_0| = (t_0 - t)} \left[\left(\frac{\partial u}{\partial t} \right)^2 + (\nabla u)^2 \right] dS \qquad (6.9.126)$$

(b) Using $\frac{\partial^2 u}{\partial t^2} - \Delta^2 u = 0$ and Green's theorem, prove that ($\frac{\partial}{\partial n}$ = normal derivative)

$$\frac{de}{dt} = \int_{|x-x_0| = (t_0 - t)} \left[\left(\frac{\partial u}{\partial t} \right) \left(\frac{\partial u}{\partial n} \right) - \frac{1}{2} \left(\frac{\partial u}{\partial t} \right)^2 - \tfrac{1}{2} |\nabla u|^2 \right] dS \qquad (6.9.127)$$

(c) Conclude that $\frac{de}{dt} \le 0$ so $e(t) \le e(0)$.

(d) If $u(\cdot, t = 0)$ and $\frac{\partial u}{\partial t}(\cdot, t = 0)$ vanish on $|x - x_0| = t_0$, conclude that $e = 0$ and so u vanishes on $\{(x_0, t) \mid |x - x_0| < t_0 - t\}$.

(e) Conclude that if u and $\frac{\partial u}{\partial t}$ vanish at $t = 0$, they vanish for all t, i.e., solutions are unique.

18. (a) If u is C^∞ on $\mathbb{R}^2$ and $\frac{\partial^2 u}{\partial x \partial y} = 0$, prove that $u(x, y) = f_1(x) + f_2(y)$ for some C_1^∞ functions, f_1 and f_2.

(b) If $\eta = x + t$, $\lambda = x - t$ is a coordinate change, prove that if u is C^∞, then

$$\left(\frac{\partial^2}{\partial t^2} - \frac{\partial^2}{\partial x^2} \right) u = 0 \Leftrightarrow \frac{\partial^2}{\partial \eta \partial \lambda} u = 0 \qquad (6.9.128)$$

(c) Prove that any C^∞ solution of $\left(\frac{\partial^2}{\partial t^2} - \frac{\partial^2}{\partial x^2}\right)u = 0$ is of the form $f_1(x+t) + f_2(x-t)$ for f_j C^∞ functions.

19. Use (4.11.58) and (4.11.60) to verify (6.9.80) (where c_ν is given by (6.9.77)).

20. Check (6.9.87) by direct calculation.

21. Let τ obey (6.9.19) as a functional on C^∞. If $g \in C_0^\infty(\mathbb{R}^\nu)$, prove that $\tau * g$, (defined by (6.2.19)) is a C^∞ function of x, that $D^\alpha(\tau * f) = (D^\alpha \tau) * g$ and then that $p(D)(\tau * g) = (p(D)\tau) * g = g$ if $p(D)\tau = \delta$.

22. Let $f(z) = \prod_{j=0}^{m}(z - \lambda_j)$. Prove that for R large that $(2\pi)^{-1}$ $\int_{|z|=R} z^k(f(z))^{-1}dz = \delta_{km}$ (for $k = 0, 1, \ldots, m$) and use that to prove (6.9.93). (*Note*: This problem requires contour integration.)

23. (a) Prove that if $\lambda_0, \lambda_1, \ldots, \lambda_m$ are given and distinct, then the $(m+1) \times (m+1)$ (Vandemonde) determinant of the matrix $\{\lambda_i^j\}_{0 \leq i,j \leq m}$ is $\prod_{0 \leq i < j \leq m}(\lambda_i - \lambda_j)$. (*Hint*: Use induction on m proving first that for $\lambda_0, \ldots, \lambda_{m-1}$ fixed, the determinant is a degree m polynomial with roots $\lambda_0, \ldots, \lambda_{m-1}$.)

(b) Use (a) and Cramer's rule to solve for a_j in (6.9.93) as a ratio of Vandermonde determinants and so deduce (6.9.93) holds with a_j given by $a_j = \prod_{k=0,k\neq j}^{m}(\lambda_j - \lambda_k)^{-1}$.

Chapter 7

Bonus Chapter: Probability Basics

Progress in mathematical analysis, and in probability theory, was handicapped for many years by the failure of analysts to learn what probabilists were doing, and conversely.

—*D. J. H. Garling* [**339**]

Big Notions and Theorems: Probability Measure Space, Event, Expectation, Variance, Covariance, Standard Deviation, Distribution Function, Probability Density, Random Variable, Cumulative Distribution Function, Bernoulli Distribution, Binomial Distribution, Geometric Distribution, Poisson Distribution, Normal Distribution, Cauchy Distribution, Uniform Distribution, Tracy–Widom Distribution, Independence, Characteristic Function, Convergence in Distribution, Convergence in Probability, Almost Sure Convergence, $X_n \xrightarrow{\text{a.s.}} X_\infty \Rightarrow X_n \xrightarrow{\text{p}} X_\infty \Rightarrow X_n \xrightarrow{\text{d}} X_\infty$, Prokhorov's Theorem, Weak Law of Large Numbers, Strong Law of Large Numbers, Borel–Cantelli Lemmas, Khinchin's Inequality, deMoivre's Estimate, Lévy Reflection Principle, Law of the Iterated Logarithm, Lévy Convergence Theorem, Central Limit Theorem, Lyapunov's Method, Lindberg's Method, Poisson Limit, Poisson Process, Markov Chain, Convergence Theorem for Finite Markov Chains, Perron–Frobenius Theorem

Probability theory is an important discipline in its own right, but from a technical point of view, as we'll see, it can be regarded as a branch of measure theory, and so, firmly within the scope of this book. What can be disconcerting the first time you are exposed is that probabilists have their own names for familiar objects (the first few set-out definitions in Section 7.1

have a kind of glossary for some of the names). There is a point though—
the new language has a different focus and provides new insights and tools.
This chapter provides an introduction to the language, a few basic tools,
and some of the most important initial results. As an introduction, our
goal is to keep things simple, which we accomplish with two restrictions:
we will mainly consider sequences of random variables rather than processes
indexed by $t \in \mathbb{R}$ or $[0, \infty)$ (although Brownian motion, constructed in Section 4.16, is the paradigmal continuous process and Section 7.4 will discuss
a continuous process), and we will often settle for results with less than optimal hypotheses—for example, in this chapter, we'll only prove the strong
law of large numbers for independent, identically distributed random variables (iidrv) with $\mathbb{E}(X^2) < \infty$, although the result is true (and proven in
Problem 1 of Section 2.7 and in Problem 16 of Section 2.10 of Part 3) for
$\mathbb{E}(|X|) < \infty$.

Section 7.1 has the basic language and introduces the three basic notions
of convergence, each successively stronger, for random variables $\{X_n\}_{n=1}^{\infty}$
to X_∞: convergence in distribution ($X_n \xrightarrow{\mathrm{d}} X_\infty$) when $\mathbb{E}(f(X_n)) \to$
$\mathbb{E}(f(X_\infty))$ for all continuous functions of compact support, convergence in
probability ($X_n \xrightarrow{\mathrm{P}} X_\infty$) when $\mathbb{P}(|X_n - X_\infty| > \varepsilon) \to 0$ for all $\varepsilon > 0$, and
almost sure convergence ($X_n \xrightarrow{\mathrm{a.s.}} X_\infty$) where $X_n(\omega) \to X_\infty(\omega)$ for a.e. ω.

Chapter 2 of Part 3 discusses pointwise convergence in analysis generally
and two results—the Birkhoff ergodic theorem and the martingale convergence theorem—that are relevant to a.s. convergence in probability. In that
chapter, we will revisit some of the questions discussed in this chapter.

Sections 7.2 and 7.3 focus on two important methods tailor-made for
the most celebrated results in probability, both dealing with $S_n = \sum_{j=1}^{n} X_j$,
where X_j are iidrv. The law of large numbers says $\frac{1}{n} S_n$ converges to $\mathbb{E}(X_1)$.
The weak law, which we'll prove using Chebyshev's inequality, asserts con-
vergence in probability and the strong law asserts a.s. convergence. We
introduce a tool, called the Borel–Cantelli lemma, to prove this. Section 7.2
also uses that tool to prove the law of the iterated logarithm for the simplest
model iidrv, with $X_j = \pm 1$, each with probability $\frac{1}{2}$, that a.s. one has that
$\limsup[S_n / n^{1/2} \log(\log n)] = \sqrt{2}$.

Section 7.3 introduces the method of characteristic functions (aka
Fourier transforms of densities) and uses it to prove the central limit the-
orem: that if the X_j are iidrv with $\mathbb{E}(X_j) = \mu$, $\mathbb{E}(X_j^2) = \sigma^2$, then
$(S_n - \mu n)/\sigma\sqrt{n}$ converges in distribution to the standard normal distribution
$(2\pi)^{-1/2} \exp(-\frac{1}{2} x^2) \, dx$.

Sections 7.4 and 7.5 are introductions to two other ubiquitous probabilistic models: Section 7.4 discusses sums of Bernoulli random variables, not as

just $n \to \infty$ but with variable p_n as np_n goes to a finite limit; Section 7.5 defines and proves the first basic results for discrete Markov processes. One important topic missing in depth is conditional expectation. We discuss it in Sections 2.6 and 2.10 of Part 3, but not from an explicitly probabilistic point of view.

Notes and Historical Remarks.

> Perhaps more significant is the absence here of Fourier methods. I choose to omit them for two reasons. ... The second is that, when it applies, Fourier analysis often works so well that it can mask probabilistic insight.
>
> —*Dan Stroock* [**896**][1]

Among the numerous texts on mathematical probability, we mention [**127, 193, 195, 259, 265, 302, 329, 368, 474, 489, 511, 598, 842, 883, 895, 896, 1005**]. My personal favorite is Durrett [**265**], Chung's book [**195**] is lively reading, and Stroock [**895**] is aimed to analysts. Just as one can view continuous probabilities as a subset of analysis, or more profitably, use probabilistic intuition and tools in analysis, one can view discrete (countable or finite) probability as a subset of combinatorics or, more profitably, use probabilistic intuition and tools in combinatorics. For a book on this point of view, see Alon–Spencer [**22**].

7.1. The Language of Probability

> I had a not atypical functional analyst's suspicion of probability theory as nothing more than a subset of functional analysis with strange names whose purpose is to confuse those who have not bothered to join the club. There is a sense in which this attitude is correct: any statement in probability theory has a translation into functional analysis. But this somehow misses the point. Like any other foreign language, probability theory is structured around its own natural thought patterns and is critical to a mode of thinking; put more prosaically, certain exceedingly natural constructions of probability theory look ad hoc and unnatural when viewed as functional analytic constructions.
>
> —*Barry Simon* [**848**]

In this section, we'll discuss the basic definitions which are, in many ways, renaming of notions from measure theory. We'll also discuss the three fundamental notions of convergence and their relations. We start with many definitions:

Definition. A *probability measure space* is a triple (Ω, Σ, μ), where Ω is a set, Σ is a sigma-algebra of subsets of Ω, and μ is a probability measure, that is, $\mu \colon \Sigma \to [0, 1]$ with $\mu(\Omega) = 1$ and μ countably additive. Ω is called the *sample space*, an equivalence class $[A]$ of sets in Σ (with A equivalent

---

[1]We will not follow Stroock's advice but will use characteristic functions in Section 5.3; the proof of the CLT there is so simple, it is almost magical.

to B if and only if $\mu(A\triangle B) = 0$) is called an *event*. We write $\mu(A)$ as $\mathbb{P}(A)$, the *probability* of the event, A. If $X(\omega)$ is an integrable function, we say $\int X(\omega)\,d\mu(\omega)$ is its *mean* or *expectation*, written $\mathbb{E}(X)$. For positive measurable functions, we write $\mathbb{E}(X)$ which may be infinite. The *variance* of X, defined if $\mathbb{E}(X^2) < \infty$, is the quantity

$$\mathbb{V}\mathrm{ar}(X) = \mathbb{E}((X - \mathbb{E}(X))^2) = \mathbb{E}(X^2) - \mathbb{E}(X)^2 \qquad (7.1.1)$$

The *standard deviation*, denoted σ_X, is

$$\sigma_X = (\mathbb{V}\mathrm{ar}(X))^{1/2} \qquad (7.1.2)$$

If X, Y are two integrable functions with $\mathbb{E}(X^2) + \mathbb{E}(Y^2) < \infty$, their *covariance* is given by

$$\mathrm{Cov}(X,Y) = \mathbb{E}((X - \mathbb{E}(X))(Y - \mathbb{E}(Y))) = \mathbb{E}(XY) - \mathbb{E}(X)\mathbb{E}(Y) \qquad (7.1.3)$$

The Schwarz inequality implies that

$$|\mathrm{Cov}(X,Y)| \le \sigma_X \sigma_Y \qquad (7.1.4)$$

Definition. A *distribution function* is a monotone function, F, on $\mathbb{R}$ obeying

(i) F is right continuous, that is, for any x,

$$F(x) = \lim_{\varepsilon \downarrow 0} F(x + \varepsilon) \qquad (7.1.5)$$

(ii) $\lim_{x \downarrow -\infty} F(x) = 0, \quad \lim_{x \uparrow \infty} F(x) = 1 \qquad (7.1.6)$

The associated *probability density* is the Lebesgue–Stieltjes measure, that is, $dF((a, b]) = F(b) - F(a)$ and $F(x) = dF((-\infty, x])$.

Definition. A *random variable* on a probability measure space, (Ω, Σ, μ), is a measurable real-valued function $X \colon \Omega \to \mathbb{R}$. Its *cumulative distribution function* (cdf), F, is given by

$$F(x) = \mathbb{P}(X \le x) \qquad (7.1.7)$$

that is, $\mu(\{\omega \mid X(\omega) \le x\})$. Its *probability density* is the associated Stieltjes measure, μ_X. Often this is only used if $d\mu_X(X) = f(x)\,dx$, and then f is called the *density*.

We have violated our intention in this chapter to try to use only standard probability terminology. What we call the probability density is usually called the probability distribution, so "distribution" and "distribution function" are distinct notions (the second is the integral of the first)! Probability density is then reserved for the Radon–Nikodym derivative in the a.c. case. Some books studiously avoid this terminology problem by not giving $d\mu_X$ a name, but since we want to relate convergence in distribution to weak convergence of measures, we do need a name.

Example 7.1.1. This example will present some standard models; first of discrete random variables, that is, X's where $d\mu_X$ is a point measure at discrete points.

(1) (Bernoulli distribution). X takes two values, typically 0 and 1 (or -1 and 1) with $\mathbb{P}(X = 1) = p$, $\mathbb{P}(X = 0) = q \equiv 1 - p$, where $0 \leq p \leq 1$,

$$\mathbb{E}(X) = p, \qquad \mathrm{Var}(X) = p(1 - p) \tag{7.1.8}$$

(2) (Binomial distribution). We'll soon see this results from adding n independent Bernoulli random variables. This has two parameters: $n \in \mathbb{Z}_+$ and $p \in [0, 1]$. X takes the values $k = 0, \ldots, n$ with (Problem 1(a))

$$\mathbb{P}(X = k) = \binom{n}{k} p^k (1 - p)^{n-k}, \tag{7.1.9}$$

$$\mathbb{E}(X) = np, \quad \mathrm{Var}(X) = np(1 - p)$$

There is a variant from adding ± 1 variables rather than $\{0, 1\}$ variables, where the values are $-n, -n + 2, \ldots, n - 2, n$ with $\mathbb{P}_{\mathrm{RW}}(X = k) = \mathbb{P}_{\mathrm{BD}}(X = \frac{1}{2}(k + n))$. This variant when $p = \frac{1}{2}$ is called *simple random walk*. Figure 2.4.1 shows plots of some Bernoulli weights.

(3) (Geometric distribution). This has a single parameter, $p \in (0, 1]$, with values $k \in \mathbb{N}$ and (Problem 1(b))

$$\mathbb{P}(X = k) = p(1 - p)^k, \quad \mathbb{E}(X) = p^{-1}, \quad \mathrm{Var}(X) = (1 - p)p^{-2} \tag{7.1.10}$$

This distribution represents the probability that an infinite sequence of Bernoulli trials has its first value 1 after k zeros.

(4) (Poisson distribution). This has a single parameter, $\lambda \in (0, \infty)$, with values $k \in \mathbb{N}$ and (Problem 1(c))

$$\mathbb{P}(X = k) = \frac{\lambda^k e^{-\lambda}}{k!}, \quad \mathbb{E}(X) = \lambda, \quad \mathrm{Var}(X) = \lambda \tag{7.1.11}$$

This model and its generalizations are the subject of Section 7.4.

Next, some continuous, indeed, absolutely continuous distributions.

(5) (Normal distribution). Denoted $N(\mu, \sigma)$, called the *normal distribution of mean μ and standard deviation σ*, this is the most celebrated distribution in probability and statistics. It has values in $\mathbb{R}$ with (Problem 1(d))

$$d\mu_X(x) = (2\pi\sigma^2)^{-1} \exp\left(\frac{-(x - \mu)^2}{2\sigma^2}\right) dx, \tag{7.1.12}$$

$$\mathbb{E}(X) = \mu, \quad \mathrm{Var}(X) = \sigma^2$$

$N(0, 1)$ is called the *standard normal distribution*. The normal distribution is often called the *Gaussian distribution*, especially by its users outside of the professional probability and statistics community. Mainly probabilists, who have no problem using "Markov inequality," are insistent that this goes back to de Moivre and Laplace and so, Gaussian is inappropriate.

(6) (Exponential distribution). Defined on $[0, \infty)$ with a single parameter, $\lambda > 0$. It has (Problem 1(e))

$$
d\mu_X(x) = \lambda \chi_{[0,\infty)}(x) e^{-\lambda x} \, dx,
$$
$$
\mathbb{E}(X) = \lambda^{-1}, \quad \mathbb{V}\mathrm{ar}(X) = \lambda^{-2}
$$

(7.1.13)

(7) (Chi-squared distribution). This is the distribution of $\sum_{j=1}^{k} X_j^2$ for k-independent standard normal X's, $k = 1, 2, \ldots$. It is called $\chi(k)$ or χ_k. It has (Problem 1(f))

$$
d\mu_X(x) = \chi_{[0,\infty)}(x) 2^{-k/2} \Gamma\left(\frac{k}{2}\right)^{-1} x^{k/2-1} e^{-x/2},
$$
$$
\mathbb{E}(X) = k, \quad \mathbb{V}\mathrm{ar}(X) = 2k
$$

(7.1.14)

(8) (Cauchy distribution). This is the continuous density

$$
d\mu_X(x) = \frac{a}{\pi} \frac{1}{x^2 + a^2} \, dx
$$

(7.1.15)

It is interesting in part because $\mathbb{E}(|X|) = \infty$.

(9) (Tracy–Widom distribution). This has a cdf

$$
F_2(s) = \exp\left(-\int_s^\infty |x - s| q^2(x) \, dx\right)
$$

(7.1.16)

where $q(x)$ solves the Painlevé II equation $q'' = xq + 2q^3$ and is the solution asymptotic to the Airy function, $Ai(x)$, as $x \to \infty$. Its mean is about -1.77 and variance about 1.61. Any function with the right properties is a cdf, so the reader may wonder why we picked this of all the weird-looking examples. In fact, this distribution, only first written down in 1993, is ubiquitous in certain probability models; see the discussion in the Notes.

We have included so many examples (and there are many others!) because probability theory is marked by its myriad significant models. $\square$

Next, we turn to the critical notion of independence and sums of independent random variables.

Definition. Two events, A, B, are called *independent* if

$$
\mathbb{P}(A \cap B) = \mathbb{P}(A)\mathbb{P}(B)
$$

(7.1.17)

k-events, $A_1, \ldots, A_k$, are called *mutually independent* if for all $\{j_1, \ldots, j_\ell\} \subset \{1, \ldots, k\}$ with j_q distinct,

$$\mathbb{P}(A_{j_1} \cap \cdots \cap A_{j_\ell}) = \prod_{q=1}^{\ell} \mathbb{P}(A_{j_q}) \qquad (7.1.18)$$

Two random variables, X and Y, are called *independent* if for all A, B Borel sets in $\mathbb{R}$, $\{\omega \mid X(\omega) \in A\}$ and $\{\omega \mid Y(\omega) \in B\}$ are independent events. $X_1, \ldots, X_k$ are called *independent* if for all $A_1, \ldots, A_k$ Borel sets in $\mathbb{R}$, $\{\omega \mid X_1(\omega) \in A_1\}, \ldots, \{\omega \mid X_k(\omega) \in A_k\}$ are mutually independent. If also the $d\mu_{X_j}$ are equal, we say they are *independent, identically distributed random variables* (iidrv).

Definition. If $X_1, \ldots, X_k$ are k random variables, their *joint probabililty* is the unique measure $d\mu_{X_1, \ldots, X_k}(X_1, \ldots, X_k)$ on $\mathbb{R}^k$ with

$$\mathbb{E}(f_1(X_1) \ldots f_k(X_k)) = \int f_1(x_1) \ldots f_k(x_k) \, d\mu_{X_1, \ldots, X_k}(x_1 \ldots x_k) \quad (7.1.19)$$

for all bounded measurable functions $f_1, \ldots, f_k$.

Problem 2 will check that there is such a unique measure. We will use the name *indicator function* for an event A, for what elsewhere we've called the characteristic function, that is,

$$\chi_A(\omega) = \begin{cases} 1, & \omega \in A \\ 0, & \omega \notin A \end{cases} \qquad (7.1.20)$$

We need to do this because, shortly, we will define "characteristic function" in a very different way! It is easy to see (Problem 3(a)) that two (or even k) events are independent if and only if their indicator functions are independent random variables. Moreover (Problem 3(b)), $X_1, \ldots, X_k$ are independent if and only if the joint probability is a product

$$d\mu_{X_1, \ldots, X_k}(x_1, \ldots, x_k) = d\mu_{X_1}(x_1) \ldots d\mu_{X_k}(x_k) \qquad (7.1.21)$$

This leads the way, given a random variable, X, on (Ω, Σ, μ), to constructing a model which has $X_1, \ldots, X_k$ or even an infinite sequence $X_1, \ldots, X_k, \ldots$ of iidrv. Just form $(\Omega_1 \times \cdots \times \Omega_k, \Sigma, d\mu_1 \otimes \cdots \otimes d\mu_k)$, where Ω_j is a copy of Ω, μ_j of μ, and we use the finite or infinite product measure constructed in Sections 4.11 and 4.12. Thus, in future, we'll just say $X_1, \ldots, X_k, \ldots$ are an iidrv without specifying an explicit construction (see the discussion later of model independence).

Fourier transforms are useful in probability theory (as we'll see especially in Section 5.3), but they have their own name and normalization.

Definition. Let X be a random variable. Its *characteristic function*, $\varphi_X(t)$, is given by

$$\varphi_X(t) = \mathbb{E}(e^{itX}) \tag{7.1.22}$$

It is unfortunate that analysts use characteristic function for the function which is 1 on a set and 0 on its complement (probabilists use *indicator functions*), a notion very different from (7.1.22)!

The Fourier inversion formula implies that if $\widehat{f} \in L^1$, then

$$\mathbb{E}(f(X)) = (2\pi)^{-1/2} \int \widehat{f}(t)\varphi_X(t)\,dt \tag{7.1.23}$$

This immediately implies (since the f's with $\widehat{f} \in L^1$ are uniformly dense in the continuous functions of compact support) that if $\varphi_X = \varphi_Y$, then X and Y have the same probability distributions.

The dominated convergence theorem and $|e^{ix} - e^{iy}| = |\int_x^y e^{itx}\,dt| \leq |x-y|$ immediately implies that

Proposition 7.1.2. *If* $\mathbb{E}(|X|) < \infty$, *then* $\varphi_X(t)$ *is a* C^1 *function and*

$$\left.\frac{d}{dt}\varphi_X(t)\right|_{t=0} = i\mathbb{E}(X) \tag{7.1.24}$$

More generally, if $\mathbb{E}(|X|^k) < \infty$, $\varphi_X(t)$ *is* C^k *and for* $\ell = 1, \ldots, k$,

$$\frac{d^\ell}{dt^\ell}\varphi_X(t) = i^\ell \mathbb{E}(X^\ell e^{itX}) \tag{7.1.25}$$

In particular, if $\mathbb{E}(X^2) < \infty$, *near* $t = 0$,

$$\varphi_X(t) = 1 + it\mathbb{E}(X) - \frac{t^2}{2}\left(\mathbb{V}\mathrm{ar}(X) + \mathbb{E}(X)^2\right) + o(t)^2 \tag{7.1.26}$$

Characteristic functions are especially useful for independent X, Y because

$$X, Y \text{ independent} \Rightarrow \varphi_{X+Y}(t) = \varphi_X(t)\varphi_Y(t) \tag{7.1.27}$$

Example 7.1.3 (Example 7.1.1 revisited).

(1) (Bernoulli). If X has values ± 1 with probability $\frac{1}{2}$,

$$\varphi_X(t) = \cos t \tag{7.1.28}$$

(2) (Binomial). By (7.1.27), if $X_1, \ldots, X_n$ are iidrv with $\mathbb{P}(X_1 = \pm 1) = \frac{1}{2}$, we have

$$\varphi_X(t) = \cos^n t \tag{7.1.29}$$

More generally, if X is given by (7.1.9),

$$F_X(t) = (1 - p + pe^{it})^n \tag{7.1.30}$$

(3) (Geometric). If X obeys (7.1.10), then

$$\varphi_X(t) = p(1 - (1-p)e^{it})^{-1} \tag{7.1.31}$$

(4) (Poisson). If X obeys (7.1.11), then

$$\varphi_X(t) = \exp(-\lambda + \lambda e^{it}) \tag{7.1.32}$$

(5) (Normal). If X obeys (7.1.12), then

$$\varphi_X(t) = e^{i\mu t - \sigma^2 t/2} \tag{7.1.33}$$

(6) (Exponential). If X obeys (7.1.13), then

$$\varphi_X(t) = \lambda(\lambda - it)^{-1} \tag{7.1.34}$$

(7) (Cauchy). If X obeys (7.1.15), then (Problem 4(c))

$$\varphi_X(t) = e^{-a|t|} \tag{7.1.35}$$

$\square$

Recall that in Example 6.2.5, we defined the convolution of two distributions, and so of two measures on $\mathbb{R}$.

Proposition 7.1.4. *If X and Y are independent, then $X + Y$ has a probability density $d\mu_X * d\mu_Y$.*

Proof. We have noted that

$$\varphi_{X+Y}(t) = \mathbb{E}(e^{it(X+Y)}) = \mathbb{E}(e^{itX})\mathbb{E}(e^{itY}) = \varphi_X(t)\varphi_Y(t) \tag{7.1.36}$$

The result follows from (6.2.47). $\square$

Example 7.1.5 (Example 7.1.1 revisited again).

(1) (Bernoulli). If $X = X_1 + \cdots + X_n$, then X can equal $k \in \{0, 1, 2, \ldots, n\}$ in $\binom{n}{k}$ ways with equal probabilities $p^k(1-p)^{n-k}$. So X has the Bernoulli distribution.

(4) (Poisson). Let X and Y be independent, where X is Poisson distributed with parameter μ and Y with parameter λ. Then (Problem 4(a)), $X+Y$ is also Poisson distributed, but with parameter $\mu + \lambda$.

(5) (Normal). If X and Y are independent with $N(\mu_1, \sigma_1)$ and $N(\mu_2, \sigma_2)$ distributions, respectively, then (Problem 4(b)) $X + Y$ is $N(\mu_1 + \mu_2, (\sigma_1^2 + \sigma_2^2)^{1/2})$ distributed.

(8) (Cauchy). If Y_a is a Cauchy distribution with parameter a, then (Problem 4(c)) $\mathbb{E}(e^{itY_a}) = e^{-a|t|}$. Thus, independent Y_a and Y_b have distribution Y_{a+b}. If $X_1, \ldots, X_n, \ldots$ are iidrv, then $S_n = \frac{1}{n}(X_1 + \cdots + X_n)$ has $\mathbb{E}(e^{itS_n/n}) = (e^{-a|t/n|})^n = e^{-a|t|}$. So, first $2X_1$ and $X_1 + X_2$ have the same distribution—a very unintuitive result! More shocking, the

limiting distribution of S_n is that of X_1, that is, the central limit theorem fails. This illustrates the limitation of that theorem and hints at a wider phenomenon (see the Notes to Section 7.3). $\square$

Finally, we turn to modes of convergence.

Definition. Let $\{X_n\}_{n=1}^{\infty}$ and X_{∞} be random variables. We say

(a) X_n *converges to X_{∞} in distribution,* written $X_n \xrightarrow{\text{d}} X_{\infty}$ if and only if for any continuous function, f, of compact support, we have

$$\mathbb{E}(f(X_n)) \to \mathbb{E}(f(X_{\infty})) \qquad (7.1.37)$$

(b) X_n *converges to X_{∞} in probability,* written $X_n \xrightarrow{\text{p}} X_{\infty}$ if and only if for any $\varepsilon > 0$,

$$\mathbb{P}(|X_n - X_{\infty}| > \varepsilon) \to 0 \qquad (7.1.38)$$

(c) X_n *converges to X_{∞} almost surely,* written $X_n \xrightarrow{\text{a.s.}} X_{\infty}$ if and only if for a.e. ω, $X_n(\omega) - X_{\infty}(\omega) \to 0$.

For $X_n \xrightarrow{\text{d}} X_{\infty}$, it is not necessary for X_{∞} to even be defined on the same space as X_n. Indeed, the notion merely says that $d\mu_{X_n} \to d\mu_{X_{\infty}}$ in the weak-$*$ topology on $\mathbb{R}_{\infty}$, the one-point compactification of $\mathbb{R}$, for $\mathbb{E}(\mathbb{1}) = 1$ and the functions of the form $\alpha\mathbb{1} + f$, f of compact support are $\|\cdot\|_{\infty}$-dense in $C(\mathbb{R}_{\infty})$.

Theorem 7.1.6. (a) $X_n \xrightarrow{\text{p}} X_{\infty} \Rightarrow X_n \xrightarrow{\text{d}} X_{\infty}$

(b) $X_n \xrightarrow{\text{a.s.}} X_{\infty} \Rightarrow X_n \xrightarrow{\text{d}} X_{\infty}$

(c) *If X_{∞} is a.s. constant, then* $X_n \xrightarrow{\text{d}} X_{\infty} \Rightarrow X_n \xrightarrow{\text{p}} X_{\infty}$.

Remark. (c) holds only for the case X_{∞} constant.

Proof. (a) Given f and ε, by the uniform continuity of f, find δ so $|x-y| < \delta \Rightarrow |f(x) - f(y)| < \varepsilon$. Thus,

$$|\mathbb{E}(f(X_n)) - \mathbb{E}(f(X_{\infty}))| \leq \mathbb{E}(|f(X_n) - f(X_{\infty})|) \leq \varepsilon + \mathbb{P}(|X_n - X_{\infty}| > \delta)$$
$$(7.1.39)$$

Since $X_n \xrightarrow{\text{p}} X_{\infty}$, we have

$$\limsup|\mathbb{E}(f(X_n)) - \mathbb{E}(f(X_{\infty}))| \leq \varepsilon \qquad (7.1.40)$$

Since f and ε are arbitrary, $X_n \xrightarrow{\text{d}} X_{\infty}$.

(b) Fix $\varepsilon > 0$. Let χ_n be an indicator function of the event $|X_n - X_{\infty}| > \varepsilon$. By hypothesis, $\chi_n(\omega) \to 0$ a.e., so by the dominated convergence theorem, $\mathbb{E}(\chi_n) = \mathbb{P}(|X_n - X_{\infty}| > \varepsilon) \to 0$.

(c) Let c be the a.s. value of X_∞. Fix $\varepsilon > 0$. Let f be the function which is 1 at c, 0 on $\mathbb{R} \setminus (c - \varepsilon, c + \varepsilon)$, and linear on $(c - \varepsilon, c)$ and $(c, c + \varepsilon)$. Then

$$\mathbb{E}(f(X_\infty) - f(X_n)) \geq \mathbb{P}(|X_n - c| > \varepsilon)$$

so $\mathbb{E}(f(X_n)) - \mathbb{E}(f(X_\infty)) \to 0 \Rightarrow \mathbb{P}(|X_n - c| > \varepsilon) \to 0$. □

Theorem 7.1.7. (a) $X_n \xrightarrow{\mathrm{d}} X_\infty$ *is given by a metric topology on the μ_X's.*

(b) $X_n \xrightarrow{\mathrm{P}} X_\infty$ *is given by a metric topology on the X_n's.*

Proof. (a) $C_\infty(\mathbb{R})$ is a separable space, so the weak-$*$ topology on the unit ball of its dual is given by a metric (see Theorem 5.7.2). While $\{\mu \in \mathcal{M}_{+,1}(\mathbb{R} \cup \{\infty\}) \mid \mu(\{\infty\}) = 0\}$ is not weak-$*$ closed, the topology is still given by a metric.

(b) If

$$\rho(X, Y) = \mathbb{E}(\min(|X - Y|, 1)) \qquad (7.1.41)$$

then (Problem 8) $X_n \xrightarrow{\mathrm{P}} X_\infty \Leftrightarrow \rho(X_n, X) \to 0$. □

Remark. Not only is $X_n \xrightarrow{\mathrm{a.s.}} X_\infty$ not given by a metric, it is not given by convergence in any topology! See Problem 9.

We will further analyze $X_n \xrightarrow{\mathrm{d}} X_\infty$, the convergence type most unfamiliar to analysts. A key aspect, namely, the connection to characteristic functions will be postponed to Section 7.3.

Definition. A family of random variables $\{X_\alpha\}_{\alpha \in I}$ will be called *tight* if and only if $\forall \varepsilon > 0$, there exists R so that for all X_α,

$$\mathbb{P}(|X_\alpha| > R) < \varepsilon \qquad (7.1.42)$$

Theorem 7.1.8 (Prokhorov's Theorem). *A family of probability densities, $\{d\mu_{X_\alpha}\}_{\alpha \in I}$ has compact closure in $\mathcal{M}_{+,1}(\mathbb{R})$ if and only if $\{X_\alpha\}_{\alpha \in I}$ is tight. In particular, if $X_n \xrightarrow{\mathrm{d}} X_\infty$, $\{X_n\}_{n=1}^\infty$ is tight.*

Remark. This result is a pale reflection to the full Prokhorov theorem for Polish spaces, which we proved as Theorem 4.14.11. Since the special case for $X = \mathbb{R}$, which we need in this chapter, is easy without the full machinery of Section 4.14, we present it here.

Proof. We'll prove that tightness implies precompactness. The easier converse is in Problem 6. It suffices to show that any sequence in $\{X_\alpha\}_{\alpha \in I}$ has a convergent subsequence. By the Banach–Alaoglu theorem, this is so if we view the $d\mu_{X_\alpha}$ as measures on $\mathbb{R}_\infty$, that is, $d\mu_{X_{n_j}} \to d\mu_\infty$. We need only show that $\mu_\infty(\{\infty\}) = 0$.

Given ε, find R so (7.1.42) holds. Pick a continuous f so $0 \leq f \leq 1$, $f(x) \equiv 1$ if $|x| \leq R$, and $f(x) \equiv 0$ if $|x| \geq R + 1$. By (7.1.42), $\mathbb{E}(f(X_n)) \geq$

$1 - \varepsilon$. Thus, $\int f(\omega)\, d\mu_\infty(\omega) \geq 1 - \varepsilon$, so $\mu_\infty(\{\infty\}) \leq \varepsilon$. Since ε is arbitrary, the limit is a probability measure on $\mathbb{R}$. $\qquad\square$

Remark. If the measures are not tight, it is easy (Problem 6) to find a sequence $d\mu_n$ so its limit has $d\mu_\infty(\{\infty\}) \neq 0$, and so no limit point in the probability measures on $\mathbb{R}$.

The following is an easy consequence of this result (Problem 7):

Proposition 7.1.9. *Let $\{X_n\}_{n=1}^\infty$ be a sequence of random variables. Then there is an X_∞ with $X_n \xrightarrow{d} X_\infty$ if and only if*

(i) *$\{X_n\}_{n=1}^\infty$ is tight.*
(ii) *For all $\ell = 1, 2, \ldots$, $\mathbb{E}((1 + X_n^2)^{-\ell})$ and $\mathbb{E}(X_n(1 + X_n^2)^{-\ell})$ converge.*

The following relates our definition of convergence in distribution to the more usual one:

Theorem 7.1.10. (a) *Let $X_n \xrightarrow{d} X_\infty$. If $\mathbb{P}(X_\infty = a) = 0$, then*

$$F_{X_n}(a) \to F_{X_\infty}(a) \qquad (7.1.43)$$

(b) *Conversely, if $\{X_n\}_{n=1}^\infty$ are random variables and X_∞ another one so that (7.1.43) holds for all a's at which F_{X_∞} is continuous, then $X_n \xrightarrow{d} X_\infty$. It suffices that (7.1.43) holds for all but a set of a's of Lebesgue measure zero.*

Proof. (a) As a preliminary, we prove for any f continuous on $\mathbb{R}$ with $f(x) = 0$ for $x > R_0$ and $\lim_{x \to -\infty} f(x)$ exists, we have

$$\mathbb{E}(f(X_n)) \to \mathbb{E}(f(X_\infty)) \qquad (7.1.44)$$

For define

$$f_R(x) = \begin{cases} f(x), & x \geq -R \\ \theta f(-R), & x = -\theta R + (1-\theta)(-R-1), \theta \in [0,1] \\ 0, & x \leq -R - 1 \end{cases}$$

For any Y and all R,

$$\mathbb{E}(|f(Y) - f_R(Y)|) \leq 2\|f\|_\infty \mathbb{P}(|Y| > R)$$

Thus, by tightness, $\lim_{R \to \infty} \mathbb{E}(f_R(X_n)) = \mathbb{E}(f(X_n))$ uniformly in n. (7.1.44) then follows from $\mathbb{E}(f_R(X_n)) \to \mathbb{E}(f_R(X_\infty))$ for each R.

Now, given a, define $f_\varepsilon^\pm$ to be continuous, linear on the interval between a and $a \pm \varepsilon$, and 1 below that interval and 0 above. Then, for any $\varepsilon > 0$,

$$\mathbb{E}(f_\varepsilon^-(X_n)) \leq F_{X_n}(a) \leq \mathbb{E}(f_\varepsilon^+(X_n)) \qquad (7.1.45)$$

so, by $X_n \xrightarrow{d} X_\infty$, for any $\varepsilon > 0$,

$$\mathbb{E}(f_\varepsilon^-(X_\infty)) \leq \liminf F_{X_n}(a) \leq \limsup F_{X_n}(a) \leq \mathbb{E}(f_\varepsilon^+(X_\infty)) \qquad (7.1.46)$$

Since $F_\infty(x)$ is continuous at a, the two extreme numbers in (7.1.46) both converge to $F_{X_\infty}(a)$ as $\varepsilon \downarrow 0$.

(b) Let f be a C^∞ function of compact support. Then

$$\mathbb{E}(f(X)) = -\int f'(x) F_X(x)\, dx \qquad (7.1.47)$$

by any integration by parts in a Stieltjes integral (see Problem 3 in Section 4.15). Thus, by the dominated convergence theorem and (7.1.23), convergence of $F_{X_n}(x) \to F_{X_\infty}(x)$ for all x implies convergence of $\mathbb{E}(f(X_n))$ to $\mathbb{E}(f(X_\infty))$ for $f \in C_0^\infty(\mathbb{R})$, and so, by a limiting argument, for all continuous f. $\qquad\square$

Remark. The proof shows we only need $\int_a^b |F_{X_N}(x) - F_{X_\infty}(x)|\, dx \to 0$ for all $a, b \in \mathbb{R}$.

Corollary 7.1.11. *For X_n to have a limit in distribution, it is necessary and sufficient to show that $\{X_n\}_{n=1}^\infty$ are tight, and for Lebesgue a.e. a, $F_{X_n}(a)$ has a limit.*

Before leaving the presentation of the framework, we should emphasize that one thing that makes probability have such a different flavor is that *in probability, points don't matter, only events and random variables do.* In particular, all statements that are truly probabilistic cannot involve points or, at least, have to have an expression that makes no mention of points.

It may appear that a.s. convergence violates this dictum, but note that

$$\{\omega \mid \limsup X_n(\omega) > \alpha\} = \bigcup_{k=1}^\infty \bigcap_{m=1}^\infty \bigcup_{n=m}^\infty \left\{\omega \,\middle|\, X_n(\omega) > \alpha + \frac{1}{k}\right\}$$

so statements about $\limsup$, $\liminf$, and their equality are really statements about events.

For a probabilist, there is no difference between $\times_{n=1}^\infty \{0, 1, \ldots, 9\}$ with normalized counting measure on each factor and $X_1, X_2, \ldots$ as the n-th coordinate function in the product and $[0, 1]$ with Lebesgue measure and X_n is the n-th decimal coordinate.

Put differently, given random variables, $\{X_j\}_{j=1}^\infty$, what really matters is their joint probability distributions and not the underlying Ω or Σ.

Notes and Historical Remarks.

> The theory of probability as mathematical discipline can and should be developed from axioms in exactly the same way as Geometry and Algebra.
>
> —*Kolmogorov* [**507**]

These Notes will focus on the invention of the modern framework discussed in this section, the general prehistory, and some of the explicit distributions presented here. The later sections will have more details on the prehistory relevant to the particular topics we present in those sections.

More than most mathematical disciplines, even more than analysis, probability and its brother subject of statistics has its roots in applications. Before 1850, three areas of application dominated: gambling, financial mathematics (especially actuarial science), and the analysis of experimental data. Some of the earliest work was correspondence between Blaise Pascal (1623–62) and Pierre de Fermat (1601–65) about games of chance, starting in 1654 and including Pascal's work on the binomial theorem and Pascal's triangle. An early monograph on games of chance which had considerable impact is by Huygens in 1657 (the English translation of the Latin title is *The Value of Chance in Games of Fortune*) [442]. Bernoulli's book, discussed below, had Huygens' pamphlet as its first part.

Jakob Bernoulli (1654–1705), whose posthumous 1713 *Ars Conjectandi* [79] had the Bernoulli and binomial distributions (Section 9.7 of Part 2A has a capsule biography of several of the Bernoullis) and Abraham de Moivre (1667–1754), who made his living as a financial and insurance advisor, were motivated, in their first work on the law of large numbers and central limit theorem, respectively, by problems in investing. Pierre-Simon Laplace (1749–1827) and Carl Friedrich Gauss (1777–1855) (capsule biographies in Sections 15.2 and 14.4, respectively, of Part 2B) were analyzing astronomical data concerning comets and asteroids in their work on the central limit theorem. Two books on the pre-1800 development of probability theory are Daston [215] and Hacking [376].

From 1850–1940, the main center of innovation in probability theory was Russia (the major exception is the work of Borel and Lévy in France). As we'll discuss in the Notes to the next two sections, the first attempts at careful proofs in probability were by Pafnuty Chebyshev (1821–94) and his students Andrei Andreyevich Markov (1856–1922) and Aleksander Lyapunov (1857–1918) (see Sections 7.2, 7.5, and 7.3 for capsule biographies). And, as we'll see shortly, it was Kolmogorov and Khinchin in the 15 years following 1920 who revolutionized the way mathematicians think about probability.

The period since 1860 also saw the successive introduction of three other applications impacting probability. A wide variety of problems in physics, starting with probabilistic elements of thermal physics, especially statistical mechanics, but also the understanding of entropy depend on notions of probability theory. It is well known that among Hilbert's problems are the axiomatization of physics and also the axiomatization of probability—but they are part of the same problem—the sixth. Ergodic theory arose out of statistical mechanics and has an important impact on probability. And Brownian motion started as a physical phenomenon. In the twentieth century, quantum mechanics, quantum field theory, and random matrix theory all were fruitful sources of probabilistic models and notions.

Starting about 1905, probabilistic ideas in number theory became significant. As we'll see in the next section, both the strong law of large numbers and the law of the iterated logarithm began life as statements about typical real numbers. And most recently, information science, especially via algorithms and Shannon entropy, has produced interesting probability.

In 1923, Steinhaus [878] first formalized the notion of independent functions (in connection with convergence of random series, a subject later central to Kolmogorov's work) and in 1929, he defined [879] iidrv for his theorem that if $\sum_{n=0}^{\infty} c_n z^n$ is a power series with finite radius of convergence, r, and if $\{\omega_n\}_{n=0}^{\infty}$ are iidrv uniformly distributed on $\partial\mathbb{D}$, then for a.e. ω, $\sum_{n=0}^{\infty} c_n \omega_n z^n$ has $\partial\mathbb{D}_r(0)$ as a natural boundary (see the Notes to Section 2.3 of Part 2A).

Kolmogorov wrote fundamental papers on random series [502] and the strong law of large numbers [504] and in 1933 published the small sixty-page book [507] where the modern theory of probability measure spaces, random variables, consistent measures, etc., first appeared. There was at the time a competing theory of random sequences called collectives presented by von Mises in a 1919 paper [957] and later book [958]. It took until the 1950s for Kolmogorov's theory to totally win the battle.

Andrey Nikolaevich Kolmogorov (1903–87) was a major figure in Russian mathematics from his teen-age years onwards. His unwed mother died in childbirth and his last name was his maternal grandfather's, on whose estate he spent his early years.

In his undergraduate years, under the influence of V. V. Stepanov (1889–1950), he got interested in trigonometric series, finding first an L^1 function which had an a.e. divergent Fourier series and then everywhere divergent. He also found the first weak $(1,1)$ estimate for the conjugate harmonic function.

He then turned, as we have noted, to probability, an area to which he often returned. Besides the work on probability we discuss here, he made major contributions to topology (independently of Alexander, he introduced the cohomology algebra), Markov processes (Chapman–Kolmogorov equations), dynamical systems, (K systems, KAM theory, Kolmogorov–Sinai entropy), the theory of turbulence, and computer science (Kolmogorov complexity theory).

Kolmogorov's students include V. Arnol'd, R. Dobrushin, E. Dynkin, S. Fomin, I. Gel'fand, R. Minlos, A. Prokhorov, Ya. Sinai, and A. Yaglom.

As noted above, the Bernoulli and binomial distributions go back to Bernoulli and the normal distribution to de Moivre and Laplace (see the Notes to Section 7.3). The use of the Cauchy distribution in probability as a counterexample to the central limit theorem goes back to Poisson [**740**] in 1824. Almost thirty years later, Cauchy [**173**] used it in the same context in a dispute with Bienaymé and his name stuck to the distribution. Stigler [**882**] discusses the history, including the fact that as an interesting curve, it was used even earlier than Poisson and often called "the witch of Agnesi," a name he explains. In the physics literature, it is often called the Lorentz distribution after the physicist Hendrik Lorentz (1853–1928), who found it as line shape in his theory of radiation (ironically, Lorentz was born in the year of Cauchy's paper).

The Tracy–Widom distribution was found by them [**929**] to describe fluctuations of the largest eigenvalue of large random matrices in the limit as their dimension $N \to \infty$. They found this for the Gaussian case—that it holds more generally (universality) is a result of Deift et al. [**227**]. Baik et al. [**45**] found the distribution also occurs in the theory of large random permutations. Tracy–Widom [**930**] have a summary of some of the applications. More recently, Baik–Suidan [**46**] and Bodineau–Martin [**103**] have found the distribution occurs in some functions of arrays of sums of iidrv.

Oberhettinger [**688**] has a 200+-page table of Fourier transforms, including many characteristic functions.

Metrizability of convergence in probability is due to Fréchet [**320**]. Probabilists often use the metric due to his student, Ky Fan [**294**],

$$\rho_F(X,Y) = \inf\{\varepsilon > 0 \mid \mathbb{P}(|X-Y| > \varepsilon) \le \varepsilon\}$$

Prokhorov's theorem is discussed in the Notes to Section 4.14. Almost sure convergence in the form $\lim_{n\to\infty} \mathbb{P}(\cap_{k=1}^{\infty}\{|X_{n+k} - X| \le \varepsilon\}) = 1$ was introduced by Cantelli [**148**].

Problems

1. (*Hint*: For the discrete models, look at the proof of (a) and (b) in Lemma 2.4.6.)

   (a) Check $\sum_k \mathbb{P}(X = k) = 1$ given by (7.1.9) is a probability and verify the formulae for its mean and variance.

   (b) Check $\mathbb{P}(X = k)$ given by (7.1.10) is a probability and verify the formulae for its mean and variance.

   (c) Check $\mathbb{P}(X = k)$ given by (7.1.11) is a probability and verify the formulae for its mean and variance.

   (d) Check the $d\mu_X$ given by (7.1.12) is a probability measure and verify the formulae for its mean and variance.

(e) Check the $d\mu_X$ given by (7.1.13) is a probability measure and verify the formulae for its mean and variance.

(f) Check the $d\mu_X$ given by (7.1.14) is a probability measure and verify the formulae for its mean and variance.

(g) Check the $d\mu_X$ given by (7.1.15) is a probability.

2. Given random variables, $X_1, \ldots, X_k$, prove that there is a measure obeying (7.1.19) and that it is the unique such measure. (*Hint*: Consider $\mathbb{E}(F(X_1, \ldots, X_k))$ for $F \in C_\infty(\mathbb{R}^k)$ to get existence and use Stone–Weierstrass on $f_1 f_2 \ldots f_k \in C_\infty(\mathbb{R}^k)$ to get uniqueness.)

3. (a) If (7.1.18) holds for all $\{j_1, \ldots, j_\ell\} \subset \{1, \ldots, k\}$, prove that $\chi_{A_1}, \ldots, \chi_{A_k}$ are mutually independent. (*Hint*: If $B_j = \Omega \setminus A_j$, show one has the analog of (7.1.18) for one B and $\ell - 1$ A's, then two B's, etc.)

(b) Prove (7.1.21) for independent random variables. (*Hint*: See (7.1.19).)

4. (a) If X and Y are independent Poisson distributed with parameters μ and λ, respectively, show $X + Y$ is Poisson with parameter $\mu + \lambda$. Do this directly and also using characteristic functions.

(b) Prove that X and Y are independent with $N(\mu_1, \sigma_1)$ and $N(\mu_2, \sigma_2)$ distributions, respectively, then $X + Y$ has $N(\mu_1 + \mu_2, (\sigma_1^2 + \sigma_2^2)^{1/2})$ distribution. Do this directly and also using characteristic functions.

(c) Verify that the characteristic function of a Cauchy distribution with parameter a is $e^{-a|t|}$.

5. Fix $\alpha > 0$. Let $0 < p < 1$ and for $k = 0, 1, 2, \ldots$

$$\mathbb{P}(x = k) = \binom{k + \alpha - 1}{k} p^k (1 - p)^\alpha$$

where $\binom{y}{k} = \frac{y(y-1)\cdots(y-k+1)}{k!}$. This is the *negative binomial distribution*.

(a) Prove that $\mathbb{P}(x = k) > 0$ and $\sum_{k=0}^\infty \mathbb{P}(x = k) = 1$. (*Hint*: Binomial expansion for $(1 - p)^{-\alpha}$.)

(b) Compute $\mathbb{E}(X)$ and $\mathbb{V}(X)$.

(c) Compute the characteristic function $\varphi_X(t)$.

6. Let $d\mu_n$ be a family of probability measures on $\mathbb{R}$ so that as measures on $\mathbb{R}_\infty$, $\mu_n \to \mu_\infty$ weakly. Suppose $\mu_n(\mathbb{R} \setminus [-n, n]) \geq \varepsilon > 0$. Prove that $\mu_\infty(\{\infty\}) \geq \varepsilon$. Conclude if a family of probability measures on $\mathbb{R}$ is not tight, then it does not have compact closure in the weak topology in the set of probability measures on $\mathbb{R}$.

7. (a) Prove Proposition 7.1.9.

   (b) Prove Corollary 7.1.11.

8. Prove that metric (7.1.41) has convergence identical to convergence in probability.

9. This problem will show that in general $X_n \xrightarrow{\text{a.s.}} X$ does not come from an underlying topology.

   (a) Let X be a topological space. If $\{x_n\}_{n=1}^\infty$ is a sequence and $x_\infty \in X$ so that it is not true that $x_n \to x_\infty$, prove that there is a subsequence $x_{n(j)}$ with no subsubsequence converging to x_∞.

   (b) Prove that if $\{x_n\}_{n=1}^\infty$ is a sequence and $x_\infty \in X$ is such that any subsequence has a subsequence converging to x_∞, then $x_n \to x_\infty$.

   (c) If $\{f_n\}_{n=1}^\infty \in L^1(X, d\mu)$ for a Baire measure on a compact Hausdorff space, X, and $\|f_n\|_1 \to 0$, prove that every subsequence has a subsubsequence converging a.e. to 0. (*Hint*: Riesz–Fischer theorem.)

   (d) Find $f_n \in C([0,1])$ with $0 \le f_n \le 1$ and $\int |f_n(x)|\, dx \to 0$ so that for no x does $f_n(x)$ converge to 0. (*Hint*: Let f_n be supported on intervals of size at most $3/m$, identically 1 on $[\frac{j}{m}, \frac{j+1}{m}]$ as j runs from $0,1,2,\dots,m-1$ and $m = 2,3,\dots$.)

   (e) Conclude that a.s. convergence is not convergence in any topology.

7.2. Borel–Cantelli Lemmas and the Laws of Large Numbers and of the Iterated Logarithm

Let $\{X_n\}_{n=1}^\infty$ be iidrv and

$$S_n = X_1 + \cdots + X_n \tag{7.2.1}$$

The law of large numbers asserts that under suitable hypotheses S_n/n converges to the constant $X_\infty \equiv \mathbb{E}(X_1)$. The *weak law of large numbers* says that $S_n/n \xrightarrow{\text{p}} \mathbb{E}(X_1)$ and the *strong law of large numbers* that $S_n/n \xrightarrow{\text{a.s.}} \mathbb{E}(X_1)$.

We'll see that the weak law follows from Chebyshev's inequality (at least if $\mathbb{E}(X_1^2) < \infty$) but the strong law requires a new tool, the main one of this section. To describe that tool, we make a definition:

Definition. If $\{A_n\}_{n=1}^\infty$ is a family of events, then A_n-io, pronounced "A_n occurs infinitely often," is the set $\{\omega \mid \#(j \mid \omega \in A_j) = \infty\}$.

In line with the idea that points don't matter, this has a set definition (Problem 1)

$$A_n\text{-io} = \bigcap_{n=1}^\infty \left(\bigcup_{m=n}^\infty A_m \right) \tag{7.2.2}$$

The keys tools are:

Theorem 7.2.1 (First Borel–Cantelli Lemma). *If $\{A_n\}_{n=1}^{\infty}$ is an arbitrary set of events with*

$$\sum_{n=1}^{\infty} \mathbb{P}(A_n) < \infty \tag{7.2.3}$$

then

$$\mathbb{P}(A_n\text{-io}) = 0 \tag{7.2.4}$$

Theorem 7.2.2 (Second Borel–Cantelli Lemma). *If $\{A_n\}_{n=1}^{\infty}$ is a set of mutually independent events and*

$$\sum_{n=1}^{\infty} \mathbb{P}(A_n) = \infty \tag{7.2.5}$$

then

$$\mathbb{P}(A_n\text{-io}) = 1 \tag{7.2.6}$$

Remarks. 1. In particular, if the A_n are mutually independent, we have a 0-1 *law*, the probability of A_n-io is either 0 or 1; see the Notes on the Kolmogorov 0-1 law.

2. While Theorem 7.2.1 needs no hypothesis other than (7.2.3), the conclusion of Theorem 7.2.2 needs more than (7.2.5). If $\Omega = [0,1]$ with $d\mu = dx$ and $A_n = [0, a_n]$, A_n-io $= \emptyset$ if $a_n \to 0$ but (7.2.5) holds if $\sum_{n=1}^{\infty} a_n = \infty$; for example, if $a_n = n^{-1}$, (7.2.5) holds but (7.2.4), rather than (7.2.6), holds.

3. Independence is a strong hypothesis. There are variants of Theorem 7.2.2 which require less—for example, only (Problem 2) pairwise independence or (Problem 3) some kind of asymptotic independence.

The strong law will only need the first Borel–Cantelli lemma. To illustrate the use of the second Borel–Cantelli lemma, we'll prove the law of the iterated logarithm, that if $\mathbb{E}(X_1) = 0$ and other conditions hold, then

$$\limsup_{n \to \infty} \frac{S_n}{\sqrt{2\sigma^2 n \log(\log n)}} = 1 \tag{7.2.7}$$

a.s. By replacing X_j by $-X_j$, we see that a.s.

$$\liminf \frac{S_n}{\sqrt{2\sigma^2 n (\log n)}} = -1 \tag{7.2.8}$$

This has a much more subtle proof, and we'll settle for doing it where $X_n = \pm 1$ with $\mathbb{P}(X_n = \pm 1) = \frac{1}{2}$, that is, S_n is simple random walk.

We begin with the weak law of large numbers when $\mathbb{E}(X_1^2) < \infty$.

Theorem 7.2.3 (Weak Law of Large Numbers). *Let $\{X_n\}_{n=1}^\infty$ be iidrv with $\mathbb{E}(X_1^2) < \infty$. Let S_n be given by (7.2.1). Then*

$$n^{-1}S_n \xrightarrow{\text{P}} \mathbb{E}(X_1) \tag{7.2.9}$$

Proof. By replacing X_j by $X_j - \mathbb{E}(X_j)$, we can suppose $\mathbb{E}(X_j) = 0$. In that case, by independence, if $i \neq j$, $\mathbb{E}(X_i X_j) = \mathbb{E}(X_i)\mathbb{E}(X_j) = 0$, so

$$\mathbb{E}(S_n^2) = n\mathbb{E}(X_1^2) \tag{7.2.10}$$

Thus, Chebyshev's inequality (4.4.70) applied to $n^{-1}S_n$ says

$$\mathbb{P}(|n^{-1}S_n| \geq \varepsilon) \leq \varepsilon^{-2}\mathbb{E}((n^{-1}S_n)^2) = \varepsilon^{-2}n^{-1}\mathbb{E}(X_1^2) \tag{7.2.11}$$

goes to zero. $\qquad\square$

Remarks. 1. In this case, we've actually proven more than $n^{-1}(S_n - n\mathbb{E}(X_1)) \xrightarrow{\text{P}} 0$. We've proven that for any $\alpha > \frac{1}{2}$, $n^{-\alpha}(S_n - n\mathbb{E}(X_1)) \xrightarrow{\text{P}} 0$.

2. In Section 7.3, we'll prove this result if only $\mathbb{E}(|X_1|) < \infty$. And, as the discussion later of the strong law shows, if $\mathbb{E}(|X_1|) = \infty$, the weak law fails.

Considering how powerful the Borel–Cantelli lemmas are, it is remarkable how simple their proofs are.

Proof of Theorem 7.2.1. Let χ_n be the indicator function of A_n. (7.2.3) and the monotone convergence theorem say

$$\mathbb{E}\left(\sum_{n=1}^\infty \chi_n\right) = \sum_{n=1}^\infty \mathbb{E}(\chi_n) = \sum_{n=1}^\infty \mathbb{P}(A_n) < \infty$$

Thus, $\sum_{n=1}^\infty \chi_n(\omega) < \infty$ a.s. But that sum is finite if and only if ω is not in A_n-io, so $1 - \mathbb{P}_n(A_n\text{-io}) = 1$. $\qquad\square$

Proof of Theorem 7.2.2. Let B_n be the complement of A_n. Then (7.2.2) and Boolean algebra imply that

$$(A_n\text{-io})^c = \bigcup_{n=1}^\infty \bigcap_{m=n}^\infty B_m \tag{7.2.12}$$

By independence,

$$\mathbb{P}\left(\bigcap_{m=n}^\infty B_m\right) = \prod_{m=n}^\infty P(B_m) = \prod_{m=n}^\infty (1 - P(A_m)) = 0$$

since $\sum_{m=n}^\infty P(A_m) = \infty$. By (7.2.12), $\mathbb{P}((A_n\text{-io})^c) = 0$, so (7.2.6) holds. $\qquad\square$

Before turning to the strong law, we want to note that the loss of powers of n in (7.2.10) is true for successively higher powers (see also Problem 4).

Proposition 7.2.4. *If $\{X_n\}_{n=1}^{\infty}$ are iidrv with $\mathbb{E}(X_1) = 0$ and $\mathbb{E}(X_1^4) < \infty$, then*

$$\mathbb{E}(S_n^4) = n\mathbb{E}(X_1^4) + 3n(n-1)\mathbb{E}(X_1^2)^2 \tag{7.2.13}$$

Proof. In order for $\mathbb{E}(X_{i_1}X_{i_2}X_{i_3}X_{i_4}) \neq 0$, we must have either $i_1 = i_2 = i_3 = i_4$ or $i_1 = i_2 \neq i_3 = i_4$ or $i_1 = i_3 \neq i_2 = i_4$ or $i_1 = i_4 \neq i_2 = i_3$. These are exclusive possibilities with n possibilities in the first case and $n(n-1)$ in the last three. $\qquad\square$

Theorem 7.2.5 (Strong Law of Large Numbers). *Let $\{X_n\}_{n=1}^{\infty}$ be iidrv with $\mathbb{E}(X_1^2) < \infty$. Let S_n be given by (7.2.1). Then*

$$\frac{1}{n} S_n \xrightarrow{\text{a.s.}} \mathbb{E}(X_1) \tag{7.2.14}$$

Proof. As a warm-up, we suppose $\mathbb{E}(X_1^4) < \infty$, in which case the proof will be especially simple. The $\mathbb{E}(X_1^2) < \infty$ case will require an extra trick. As in the weak law proof, we can suppose $\mathbb{E}(X_1) = 0$ by replacing X_j by $X_j - \mathbb{E}(X_j)$. By (7.2.13) and Markov's inequality (Theorem 4.6.10),

$$\mathbb{P}(|S_n| > n\varepsilon) \leq \frac{\mathbb{E}(S_n^4)}{(n\varepsilon)^4} \leq C\varepsilon^{-4} n^{-2} \tag{7.2.15}$$

Thus,

$$\sum_{n=1}^{\infty} \mathbb{P}(|S_n| > n\varepsilon) < \infty \tag{7.2.16}$$

so, by the first Borel–Cantelli lemma (Theorem 7.2.1), for a.e. ω, eventually $|S_n(\omega)| \leq n\varepsilon$, that is,

$$\limsup_{n\to\infty} \frac{1}{n}|S_n(\omega)| \leq \varepsilon \tag{7.2.17}$$

for a.e. ω. Picking $\varepsilon = 1, \frac{1}{2}, \frac{1}{3}$, we see a.s. the $\limsup$ is 0, that is, (7.2.14) holds.

We now turn to the case where we only have $\mathbb{E}(X_1^2) < \infty$. Thus, we only have available (7.2.10) and (7.2.3) is replaced by

$$\mathbb{P}(|S_n| > n\varepsilon) \leq \frac{\|S_n\|^2}{(n\varepsilon)^2} = \frac{\mathbb{E}(X_1^2)}{n\varepsilon^2}$$

so we cannot conclude (7.2.16). But we can control the subsequence S_j for $j = n^2$, and so get an analog of (7.2.17) for $\limsup \frac{1}{n^2}|S_{n^2}(\omega)|$. That is, $\sum_{n=1}^{\infty}\mathbb{P}(|S_{n^2}| \geq n^2\varepsilon) < \infty$, so as above,

$$\lim_{n\to\infty} \frac{|S_{n^2}|}{n^2} = 0 \tag{7.2.18}$$

The idea will be to separately control fluctuations between n^2 and $(n+1)^2$. So define

$$D_n = \max_{n^2 \leq k < (n+1)^2} |S_k - S_{n^2}| \qquad (7.2.19)$$

Clearly,

$$D_n^2 \leq \sum_{k=n^2}^{(n+1)^2-1} (S_k - S_{n^2})^2 \qquad (7.2.20)$$

Since $S_k - S_{n^2} = \sum_{j=1}^{k-n^2} X_{n^2+j}$, as in (7.2.10), we have

$$\mathbb{E}((S_k - S_{n^2})^2) = \mathbb{E}(X_1^2)(k - n^2) \qquad (7.2.21)$$

so

$$\mathbb{E}(D_n^2) \leq \mathbb{E}(X_1^2) \sum_{k=n^2}^{n^2+2n} (k - n^2) = \mathbb{E}(X_1^2)n(2n+1)$$

By Markov's inequality,

$$\mathbb{P}(D_n > n^2\varepsilon) \leq \frac{\mathbb{E}(X_1^2)n(2n+1)}{n^4\varepsilon^2} \qquad (7.2.22)$$

so

$$\sum_{n=1}^{\infty} \mathbb{P}(D_n > n^2\varepsilon) < \infty \Rightarrow \limsup_{n\to\infty} \frac{D_n}{n^2} = 0$$

Since $k \geq n^2 \Rightarrow k^{-1} \leq n^{-2}$, it follows that a.s.

$$\sup_{k \geq n^2} \left|\frac{S_k}{k}\right| \leq \sup_{m \geq n} \frac{|S_{m^2}| + D_m}{m^2} \to 0 \qquad (7.2.23)$$

that is, (7.2.14) holds. $\qquad\qquad\qquad\qquad\qquad\qquad\qquad\qquad\qquad\square$

As a warm-up to our last topic, the law of the iterated logarithm for simple random walk, we compute $\limsup X_n/\sigma_n^2$, where X_n is $N(0, \sigma_n)$ and the X_n are independent. Since the S_n are asymptotically Gaussian (although not independent), this will give us some hints and show the use of both Borel–Cantelli lemmas.

Lemma 7.2.6. *Let*

$$G(x) = \int_x^\infty (2\pi)^{-1/2} \exp(-\tfrac{1}{2}y^2)\, dy \qquad (7.2.24)$$

Then there are constants C_1, C_2 in $(0, \infty)$, so for all $x \geq 1$,

$$C_1 x^{-1} \exp(-\tfrac{1}{2}x^2) \leq G(x) \leq C_2 x^{-1} \exp(-\tfrac{1}{2}x^2) \qquad (7.2.25)$$

In particular, for any $\varepsilon > 0$,

$$\lim_{x\to\infty} \frac{G(x+\varepsilon)}{G(x)} = 0 \qquad (7.2.26)$$

Proof. We have

$$G(x) = (2\pi)^{-1/2} \int_0^\infty \exp(-xy - \tfrac{1}{2}\,x^2 - \tfrac{1}{2}\,y^2)\,dy \qquad (7.2.27)$$

$$\leq (2\pi)^{-1/2} \exp(-\tfrac{1}{2}\,x^2) \int_0^\infty \exp(-xy)\,dy$$

$$= x^{-1}(2\pi)^{-1/2} \exp(-\tfrac{1}{2}\,x^2)$$

On the other hand, by (7.2.27) and $y^2 \leq 2xy$, if $x \geq 1$ and $y \leq 2$, we have

$$G(x) \geq (2\pi)^{-1/2} \exp(-\tfrac{1}{2}\,x^2) \int_0^2 \exp(-2xy)\,dy$$

$$= (2\pi)^{-1/2}(2x)^{-1} \exp(-\tfrac{1}{2}\,x^2)[1 - \exp(-4x)]$$

$$\geq (2\pi)\,\tfrac{1}{4}\,x^{-1} \exp(-\tfrac{1}{2}\,x^2)$$

if $x \geq 1$.

Clearly, (7.2.25) $\Rightarrow$ (7.2.26). $\qquad\square$

Theorem 7.2.7. *Let $\{X_n\}_{n=1}^\infty$ be independent with X_n, $N(0, \sigma_n)$ distributed. Then a.s.*

$$\limsup_{n\to\infty} \frac{X_n}{\sigma_n \sqrt{2\log n}} = 1 \qquad (7.2.28)$$

$$\liminf_{n\to\infty} \frac{X_n}{\sigma_n \sqrt{2\log n}} = -1 \qquad (7.2.29)$$

Proof. By symmetry, we only need (7.2.28) and, by replacing X_n by X_n/σ_n, we can suppose $\sigma_n \equiv 1$. By (7.2.25), for any $\varepsilon > 0$, for n large enough,

$$\mathbb{P}\big(X_n \geq (1+\varepsilon)\sqrt{2\log n}\,\big) \leq C_2 n^{-1-\varepsilon} \qquad (7.2.30)$$

$$\mathbb{P}\big(X_n \geq (1-\varepsilon)\sqrt{2\log n}\,\big) \geq C_\varepsilon n^{-1+\varepsilon/2} \qquad (7.2.31)$$

so for any such ε,

$$\sum_{n=1}^\infty \mathbb{P}\big(X_n \geq (1+\varepsilon)\sqrt{2\log n}\,\big) < \infty \qquad (7.2.32)$$

$$\sum_{n=1}^\infty \mathbb{P}\big(X_n \geq (1-\varepsilon)\sqrt{2\log n}\,\big) = \infty \qquad (7.2.33)$$

By the Borel–Cantelli lemmas, a.s. eventually, $X_n \leq (1+\varepsilon)\sqrt{2\log n}$ while i.o. $X_n \geq (1-\varepsilon)\sqrt{2\log n}$, that is, a.s.

$$1 - \varepsilon \leq \limsup \frac{X_n}{\sqrt{2\log n}} \leq 1 + \varepsilon \qquad (7.2.34)$$

$\qquad\square$

There are three apparent problems in this result supporting (7.2.7):

(1) The S_n in the random walk case are not independent.
(2) $\log n$ appears, not $\log(\log n)$.
(3) The S_n are not Gaussian, and while the central limit theorem says that $S_n/\sqrt{n} \to N(0,1)$, that is, in the region $|S_n/\sqrt{n}| \leq C$ for each C and we are interested in the tail region.

The third difficulty will be resolved by an analysis specific to random walk that shows the Gaussian approximation remains valid in regions where $|S_n/\sqrt{n}| \leq o(n^{1/6})$, including, of course, $|S_n/\sqrt{n}| = O(\log\log n)$. The first two difficulties will, in some sense, cancel out. The S_n are not independent, but for any γ and large n, the S_{γ^n} are "almost independent" and, of course, if $m = \gamma^n$, then $\log n \sim \log(\log m)$. We are thus heading towards a proof of

Theorem 7.2.8 (Law of the Iterated Logarithm). *Let S_n be simple random walk. Then (7.2.7)/ (7.2.8) hold a.s.*

Figure 7.2.1 has a graph (courtesy of Wikipedia) of a typical path of S_n/n on a log-log plot for huge values of n.

As explained, we are going to control asymptotics of S_{γ^n}. We control S_j for $\gamma^n \leq j \leq \gamma^{n+1}$ using a remarkable and elegant inequality of Lévy.

Theorem 7.2.9 (Lévy's Inequality). *Let $\{X_n\}_{n=1}^{N}$ be independent random variables so that each X_j has an even distribution (i.e., invariant under*

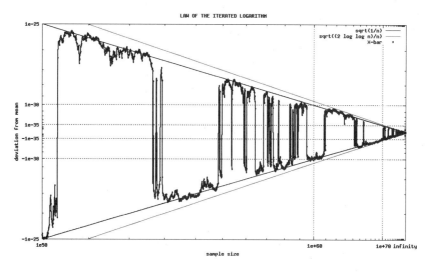

Figure 7.2.1. Law of the iterated logarithm (reproduced under GNU Free Documentation License from `http://en.wikipedia.org/wiki/File:Law_of_large_numbers_(blow_up).gif`).

$X_j \to -X_j$). Let $S_j = \sum_{k=1}^{j} X_k$ for $j = 1, \ldots, N$. Then

$$\mathbb{P}\big(\max_{j=1,\ldots,N} |S_j| > \alpha\big) \leq 2\mathbb{P}(|S_N| > \alpha) \qquad (7.2.35)$$

Proof. For each j, define an event, A_j, and random variable, T_j, by

$$A_j = \{|S_1|, \ldots, |S_{j-1}| \leq \alpha, |S_j| > \alpha\} \qquad (7.2.36)$$
$$T_j = S_j - X_{j+1} - \cdots - X_N \qquad (7.2.37)$$

Then

$$\{\max_{j=1,\ldots,N} |S_j| > \alpha\} = A_1 \cup \cdots \cup A_N \qquad (7.2.38)$$

and since $S_j = \frac{1}{2}(T_j + S_N)$,

$$A_j = (A_j \cap \{|T_j| > \alpha\}) \cup (A_j \cap \{|S_N| > \alpha\}) \qquad (7.2.39)$$

It follows that

$$\mathbb{P}\big(\max_{j=1,\ldots,N} |S_j| > \alpha\big) \leq \sum_{j=1}^{N} \mathbb{P}(A_j \cap \{|T_j| > \alpha\}) + \mathbb{P}(A_j \cap \{|S_N| > \alpha\}) \quad (7.2.40)$$

By the independence, the measure-preserving map $X_{j+1} \to -X_{j+1}, \ldots, X_N \to -X_N$ leaves A_j fixed and maps $\{|T_j| > \alpha\}$ to $\{|S_N| > \alpha\}$, so

$$\text{RHS of } (7.2.40) = 2 \sum_{j=1}^{N} \mathbb{P}(A_j \cap (|S_N| > \alpha)) \leq 2\mathbb{P}(|S_N| > \alpha) \qquad (7.2.41)$$

since the A_j's are disjoint. $\qquad\qquad\qquad\qquad\qquad\qquad\qquad\qquad\qquad\qquad\square$

We also need a bound on the tails of each S_N.

Theorem 7.2.10 (Khinchin's Inequality). *Let $\{X_j\}_{j=1}^{N}$ be iidrv with $\mathbb{P}(X_1 = \pm 1) = \frac{1}{2}$ and let $S_N = X_1 + \cdots + X_N$. Then*

(a) $\mathbb{E}(e^{\alpha S_N}) \leq e^{\alpha^2 N/2}$, *all $\alpha \in \mathbb{R}$, all N* $\qquad\qquad\qquad\qquad$ (7.2.42)

(b) $\mathbb{P}(|S_N| > \beta) \leq 2e^{-\beta^2/2N}$, *all $\beta \in (0, \infty)$, all N* $\qquad\qquad$ (7.2.43)

Remark. See Problem 6 for a strengthened form of this theorem, also called Khinchin's inequality.

Proof. (a) We begin by noting

$$\frac{(2m)!}{2^m m!} = \frac{(2m)(2m-1)\ldots(m+1)}{2^m} \geq 1$$

since it is a product of m factors each bigger than 1. Thus,

$$\mathbb{E}(e^{\alpha X_1}) = \sum_{m=0}^{\infty} \frac{\alpha^{2m}}{2m!} \leq \sum_{m=0}^{\infty} \frac{\alpha^{2m}}{2^m m!} = \exp(\tfrac{1}{2}\alpha^2) \qquad (7.2.44)$$

Note that $\mathbb{E}(e^{\alpha S_N}) = \mathbb{E}(e^{\alpha X_1})^N$ since the X_j are iidrv; this implies (7.2.42).

(b) By symmetry and then Markov's inequality,

$$\mathbb{P}(|S_N| > \beta) = 2\mathbb{P}(S_N > \beta) \le 2e^{-\beta\alpha}\mathbb{E}(e^{\alpha S_N}) \le 2e^{\alpha^2 N/2}e^{-\beta\alpha} \qquad (7.2.45)$$

by (7.2.42). Pick (the optimal value) $\alpha = \beta N^{-1}$ to get (7.2.43). $\qquad\square$

Proposition 7.2.11. *Let $\{X_j\}_{j=1}^\infty$ be iidrv with $\mathbb{P}(X_1 = \pm 1) = \frac{1}{2}$ and let $S_n = \sum_{j=1}^n X_j$. Then a.s.*

$$\limsup_{n\to\infty} \frac{|S_n|}{n^{1/2}\sqrt{2\log(\log n)}} \le 1 \qquad (7.2.46)$$

Proof. Pick $\varepsilon > 0$ and $\gamma > 1$. Let $m_\gamma(n) = [\gamma^n]$, the integral part of $[\gamma^n]$. Then for n so large that $[\gamma^n] \ge \frac{1}{2}\gamma^n$,

$$\mathbb{P}\left(\max_{1\le j\le m_\gamma(n)} |S_j| \ge (1+\varepsilon)m_\gamma(n)^{1/2}\sqrt{2\log(\log m_\gamma(n))}\right)$$

$$\le 2\mathbb{P}\left(|S_{m_\gamma(n)}| \ge (1+\varepsilon)m_\gamma(n)^{1/2}\sqrt{2\log(\log m_\gamma(n))}\right) \qquad (7.2.47)$$

$$\le 4\exp(-(1+\varepsilon)^2\log(n\log\gamma + \log(\tfrac{1}{2}))) \qquad (7.2.48)$$

$$\le 4(n\log\gamma - \log 2)^{-(1+\varepsilon)^2} \qquad (7.2.49)$$

is summable. Here (7.2.47) comes from (7.2.35) and (7.2.49) from (7.2.43).

Thus, for $n \ge N_0(\omega)$,

$$\max_{m_\gamma(n-1)\le j\le m_\gamma(n)} |S_j| \le (1+\varepsilon)m_\gamma(n)^{1/2}\sqrt{2\log(\log m_\gamma(n))} \qquad (7.2.50)$$

We have that

$$\frac{m_\gamma(n)^{1/2}\sqrt{2\log(\log m_\gamma(n))}}{m_\gamma(n-1)^{1/2}\sqrt{2\log(\log m_\gamma(n-1))}} \to \gamma^{1/2} \qquad (7.2.51)$$

so for a.e. ω,

$$\limsup \frac{|S_j|}{j^{1/2}\sqrt{2\log(\log j)}} \le (1+\varepsilon)\gamma^{1/2} \qquad (7.2.52)$$

Since ε can be taken to 0 and γ to 1 through countable sets, we have (7.2.46). $\qquad\square$

To get the lower bound needed to apply the second Borel–Cantelli lemma, we need what we'll call an *intermediate deviation estimate*. To explain, define

$$F(a,b) = (2\pi)^{-1/2}\int_a^b \exp(-\tfrac{1}{2}x^2)\,dx \qquad (7.2.53)$$

the probability an $N(0,1)$ variable lies in (a,b). The central limit theorem says that

$$\frac{\mathbb{P}(S_N/\sqrt{N} \in [a_N, b_N])}{F(a_N, b_N)} \to 1 \qquad (7.2.54)$$

for a_N, b_N *fixed*. Large deviation estimates involve asymptotics for $\mathbb{P}(S_n > \alpha N)$ typically $O(\exp(-g(\alpha)N))$ for suitable g, for example, (7.2.43) gets the upper bound $2\exp(-\alpha^2 N/2)$. Of course, if $\alpha > 1$, the probability is 0, so this is just a bound. We will want estimates of the form (7.2.54) where a, b are N-dependent and growing like $c_a \log(\log N)$ and $c_b \log(\log N)$.

The proof we give of the central limit theorem in the next section does not yield this kind of estimate, although it applies to very general sums of iidrv. So we'll use de Moivre's original 1730's proof of the central limit theorem for the special case of random walk. The key to this proof is Stirling's formula for $n!$ for large n, which says

$$\frac{n!}{n^{n+1/2}e^{-n}\sqrt{2\pi}} = 1 + O\!\left(\frac{1}{n}\right) \qquad (7.2.55)$$

In Part 2, we'll give two proofs of this: one relating $\sum_{j=1}^{n} \log j$ to $\int_1^n \log x\, dx$ (Section 9.7 of Part 2A) and the other based on asymptotics for $\int_0^\infty x^n e^{-x}\, dx = n!$ (Section 15.2 of Part 2B). Both proofs go back to work on the central limit theorem!

Theorem 7.2.12 (de Moivre's Limit Estimate). (a) *Let*

$$G(n, \alpha) = \frac{2}{\sqrt{2\pi n}} \exp(-2n\alpha^2) \qquad (7.2.56)$$

Then as $n \to \infty$ with α allowed to be n-dependent (with $(\frac{1}{2} + \alpha)n =$ integral),

$$G(n, \alpha)^{-1} 2^{-n} \binom{n}{(\frac{1}{2} + \alpha)n} = 1 + O(n\alpha^3) + O\!\left(\frac{1}{n}\right) + O(\alpha^2) \qquad (7.2.57)$$

uniformly in any region where $n\alpha^3 \to 0$, $n \to \infty$, $\alpha \to 0$.

(b) *For simple random walk, (7.2.54) holds for a_N, b_N N-dependent, so long as $0 \le a_N \le b_N$ are both $o(N^{1/6})$ and $b_N \ge a_N + c$ for some $c > 0$.*

Remark. Taking a_N, b_N fixed, this provides a proof of the central limit theorem for this case.

Proof. (a) If $|\alpha| \leq d < \frac{1}{2}$, we can use Stirling's formula (Theorem 9.7.1 of Part 2A) on $n!$, and $[(\frac{1}{2} \pm \alpha)n]!$ as $n \to \infty$ and get (Problem 5(a))

$$\log\left(2^{-n}\binom{n}{(\frac{1}{2}+\alpha)n}\bigg/\frac{2}{\sqrt{2\pi n}}\right) =$$

$$-[(\tfrac{1}{2}+\alpha)n + \tfrac{1}{2}]\log(1+2\alpha) - [(\tfrac{1}{2}-\alpha)n + \tfrac{1}{2}]\log(1-2\alpha) + O\left(\frac{1}{n}\right) \tag{7.2.58}$$

if $|\alpha| \leq d < \frac{1}{2}$.

If $\alpha \to 0$, $\frac{1}{2}\log(1+2\alpha) + \frac{1}{2}\log(1-2\alpha) = O(\alpha^2)$, and by $\log(1+x) = x - \frac{x^2}{2} + O(x^3)$, one obtains (Problem 5(b))

$$(\tfrac{1}{2}+\alpha)\log(1+2\alpha) + (\tfrac{1}{2}-\alpha)\log(1-2\alpha) = 2\alpha^2 + O(\alpha^3) \tag{7.2.59}$$

which implies (7.2.57) with an error of the form $Cn\alpha^3$ so long as $\alpha \to 0$.

(b) In Problem 5(c), the reader will prove that if h is nonnegative and monotone decreasing, then for any δ,

$$\left|\int_0^{m\delta} h(y)\,dy - \sum_{j=0}^{m-1} \delta h(j\delta)\right| \leq \delta h(0) \tag{7.2.60}$$

Note that for $S_N = j$, we need k, $+1$'s, and $N-k$, -1's where $k-(N-k) = j$, that is, $k = \frac{1}{2}N + \frac{1}{2}j$, so in the binomial coefficient, $\alpha_{j,N} = \frac{1}{2}j/N$. Thus, pick $\delta = 1/\sqrt{N}$, $\alpha_N^- = \frac{1}{2}a_N/\sqrt{N}$, $\alpha_N^+ = \frac{1}{2}b_N/\sqrt{N}$ (adjusted to $\frac{1}{2}N + \alpha_N^\pm \in \mathbb{Z}$) and find, using (7.2.57) and (7.2.24), that

$$\left|\mathbb{P}\left(\frac{S_N}{\sqrt{N}} \in [a_N, b_N]\right) - F(a_N, b_N)\right| \leq \frac{C}{\sqrt{N}}\exp\left(-\frac{a_N^2}{2}\right) \tag{7.2.61}$$

Thus, to get (7.2.54), we need as $N \to \infty$ that

$$\frac{N^{-1/2}\exp(-\frac{a_N^2}{2})}{F(a_N, b_N)} \to 0 \tag{7.2.62}$$

If a_N is bounded and $a_N - b_N \geq c$, $F(a_N, b_N)$ is bounded away from 0, so (7.2.58) holds since $N^{-1/2} \to 0$. If $a_N \to \infty$, by Lemma 7.2.6, we have

$$\text{LHS of } (7.2.62) \leq \frac{a_N}{N^{1/2}} \to 0 \tag{7.2.63}$$

since $a_N = o(N^{1/6})$. $\qquad\qquad\qquad\qquad\qquad\qquad\qquad\qquad\qquad\qquad\square$

Proof of Theorem 7.2.8. To use the second Borel–Cantelli lemma, we need independence. So we'll fix $\gamma \in \mathbb{Z}_+$ and look at

$$T_n^{(\gamma)} = S_{\gamma^n} - S_{\gamma^{n-1}} \tag{7.2.64}$$

which are independent. As in the proof of Theorem 7.2.7, we'll prove that a.s.

$$\limsup_{n \to \infty} \frac{T_n^{(\gamma)}}{\sqrt{2(\gamma^n - \gamma^{n-1}) \log n}} \geq 1 \tag{7.2.65}$$

We'll then use the upper bound we have on $S_{\gamma^{n-1}}$ to show

$$\limsup_{n \to \infty} \frac{S_{\gamma^n}}{\sqrt{2(\gamma^n - \gamma^{n-1}) \log n}} \geq (1 - \gamma^{-1/2}) \tag{7.2.66}$$

which will imply

$$\limsup_{n \to \infty} \frac{S_n}{\sqrt{2n \log(\log n)}} \geq (1 - \gamma^{-1})^{1/2} - \gamma^{-1/2} \tag{7.2.67}$$

Since γ can be taken to infinity, this will complete the proof. Here are the details.

Fix $\varepsilon > 0$ and let

$$a_n^{(\gamma)} = (1 - \varepsilon)\sqrt{2 \log(\log(\gamma^n - \gamma^{n-1}))} \tag{7.2.68}$$

Theorem 7.2.12(b) implies that

$$\mathbb{P}\left(a_n^{(\gamma)} \leq \frac{T_n^{(\gamma)}}{\sqrt{\gamma^n - \gamma^{n-1}}} \leq 2a_n^{(\gamma)}\right) \geq Cn^{-(1-\frac{\varepsilon}{2})} \tag{7.2.69}$$

because $a_n^{(\gamma)}$ are certainly $o((\gamma^n - \gamma^{n-1})^{1/6})$. Since then $\{T_n^{(\gamma)}\}_{n=1}^{\infty}$ are independent and the sum of the probabilities diverges, $T_n^{(\gamma)}/\sqrt{\gamma^n - \gamma^{n-1}} \geq a_n^{(\gamma)}$ i.o., that is, knowing that we can take $\varepsilon = 1, \frac{1}{2}, \frac{1}{3}, \ldots$, we see that

$$\limsup_{n \to \infty} \frac{T_n^{(\gamma)}}{\sqrt{2\gamma^n \log(\log \gamma^n)}} \geq (1 - \gamma^{-1})^{1/2} \tag{7.2.70}$$

where we used $\log(\log(\gamma^n - \gamma^{n-1}))/\log(\log \gamma^n) \to 1$ as $n \to \infty$ and $\sqrt{\gamma^n - \gamma^{n-1}} = \sqrt{\gamma^n}\sqrt{1 - \gamma^{-1}}$.

On the other hand,

$$S_{n^\gamma} \geq T_n^{(\gamma)} - |S_{n^{\gamma-1}}| \tag{7.2.71}$$

so

$$\limsup S_{\gamma^n} \geq \limsup T_n^{(\gamma)} - \limsup|S_{\gamma^{n-1}}| \tag{7.2.72}$$

By Proposition 7.2.11 and $\gamma^{n-1} \log(\log \gamma^{n-1})/\gamma^n \log(\log(\gamma^n)) \to \gamma^{-1}$,

$$\limsup \frac{|S_{n^{\gamma-1}}|}{\sqrt{2\gamma^n \log(\log \gamma^n)}} \leq \gamma^{-1/2} \tag{7.2.73}$$

(7.2.70), (7.2.73), and the fact that lower bounds on $\liminf$ can be taken through any sequence implies (7.2.67). Since γ can be taken to infinity, the left side of $(7.2.67) \geq 1$. Combining this with (7.2.46) yields (7.2.7). $X_n \to -X_n$ symmetry yields (7.2.9). $\qquad \square$

Notes and Historical Remarks. The Borel–Cantelli lemma is named after their papers [**114, 149**] in 1909 and 1917, respectively. Borel's paper was a landmark—not only the first proof of the strong law of large numbers but in the context of looking at random behaviors of decimal expansion, so starting the field of probabilistic number theory. He had the first Borel–Cantelli lemma under the assumption of independence; his proof has been criticized as not being quite correct. Cantelli, at the time an actuary, not an academic mathematician, noted the first lemma held without independence and proved the second.

It is striking that if the A_n are independent, A_n-io always has measure 0 or 1. This is a special case of a general 0-1 *law*, in this case the *Kolmogorov 0-1 law*. If $\{X_n\}_{n=1}^\infty$ are independent random variables, let $\widetilde{\Sigma}_n$ be the σ-algebra generated by $\{X_j\}_{j=n}^\infty$ and $\widetilde{\Sigma}_\infty = \bigcap_n \widetilde{\Sigma}_n$ the *tail σ-algebra*. (The reader may think $\widetilde{\Sigma}_\infty$ has to be empty but $\{\omega \mid \limsup n^{-1} \sum_{j=1}^n X_j = c\}$, for example, is in $\widetilde{\Sigma}_\infty$.) The Kolmogorov 0-1 law says that if μ is a product measure, then $\widetilde{\mu}(B)$ is 0 or 1 for any $B \in \widetilde{\Sigma}_\infty$. We prove it is in Section 2.10 of Part 3.

The weak law of large numbers goes back to Jakob Bernoulli [**79**], who proved the result for what are now called Bernoulli random variables. The proof appeared in his posthumous 1713 book. It took eight years after his death for the book to appear because of squabbling among his son, nephew, and brother! In 1835–36, Poisson [**743, 744**] invented the term "law of large numbers" and asserted the general result, but without a precise proof. In 1846, Chebyshev [**182**] found a general proof, and later, in 1867, the proof from his inequality [**183**] that we give.

Pafnuty Lvovich Chebyshev (1821–94) is regarded as the father of Russian mathematics. He was the son of a Russian nobleman who didn't follow the family tradition of a military career because he had a limp. He was educated in Moscow but spent most of his career in St. Petersburg, then the capital of the Russian empire. His initial work on the weak law was his master's thesis, although as we noted above, his proof using Chebyshev's inequality came later.

He developed results on the moment problem (later perfected by his student Markov and by Stieltjes; see Section 5.6) in connection with his work on the central limit theorem. His work on Chebyshev polynomials came out of his work in statistics—polynomial fitting of data. The one piece of mathematics not connected to probability for which he is known is his work on the distribution of primes (see Proposition 13.5.3 of Part 2B).

For ± 1 Bernoulli random variables with $p = \frac{1}{2}$, Borel proved the strong law in 1909 [**114**]. Cantelli [**147**] found the general result when $\mathbb{E}(X_1^4) < \infty$

along the lines of the proof we give in that case. Khinchin [**487**] extended the result and invented the "weak law"/"strong law" terminology. The optimal result in the independent case, that is, that the strong law holds if $\mathbb{E}(|X_1|) < \infty$, is due to Kolmogorov [**507**]; its proof will be sketched in Problems 15 and 16 of Section 2.10 of Part 3 (see also the remark after Theorem 2.7.2 of Part 3). We prove the weak law under that hypothesis in Theorem 7.3.3 below.

The law of the iterated logarithm was originally studied precisely in the random walk situation we consider and was the culmination of several attempts following Borel's 1909 paper [**114**] to get upper bounds on the deviation from the mean for distribution of digits of a typical real number's decimal expansion. Borel claimed a $\sqrt{n} \log n$ upper bound but his proof was murky, so much so that many regard the first true upper bound as the $n^{\frac{1}{2}+\varepsilon}$ bound that Hausdorff included in his set theory book of 1914 [**402**]. Hardy–Littlewood [**395**] proved $\sqrt{n \log n}$ also in 1914. The ultimate result in this case was proved in 1924 by Khinchin [**486**], who proved our Theorem 7.2.8. Kolmogorov [**503**] extended that to bounded iidrv and to certain independent but not identically distributed random variables. In 1941, Hartman–Wintner [**399**] proved the ultimate iidrv result: (7.2.7)/(7.2.8) hold for arbitrary sums of iidrv with $\mathbb{E}(X_1) = 0$, $\mathbb{E}(X_1^2) = \sigma^2$. For more recent refinements, including nonindependent cases and alternates to the Kolmogorov–Hartman–Wintner proofs, see [**887, 92**].

The history of Stirling's formula is given in the Notes to Section 9.7 of Part 2A. It was found by de Moivre (who had the $Cn^{n+1/2}e^{-n}$ behavior but not the C) and Stirling (who found the C) and should probably be called the de Moivre–Stirling formula. It was found precisely because of de Moivre's work on the central limit theorem.

Problems

1. Verify (7.2.2) given A_n-io in terms of Boolean operations on the A_n.

2. This problem will provide the conclusion of the second Borel–Cantelli lemma under the hypothesis that events A_n are pairwise independent (i.e., $\mathbb{P}(A_n \cap A_m) = \mathbb{P}(A_n)\mathbb{P}(A_m)$ rather than requiring full independence). Let X_n be the indicator function of A_n and $S_n = \sum_{j=1}^{n} X_j$, $S_\infty = \sum_{j=1}^{\infty} X_j$.

   (a) Prove that $\mathrm{Cov}(X_n, X_m) = \mathbb{P}(A_n \cap A_m) - \mathbb{P}(A_n)\mathbb{P}(A_m)$.

   (b) Prove that

$$\mathbb{V}\mathrm{ar}(S_n) = \sum_{j=1}^{n} \mathbb{P}(A_n) - \mathbb{P}(A_n)^2 \le \sum_{j=1}^{n} \mathbb{P}(A_n)$$

(c) Prove that

$$\mathbb{P}\left(S_n \leq \tfrac{1}{2}\sum_{j=1}^{n}\mathbb{P}(A_j)\right) \leq \frac{4}{\sum_{j=1}^{n}\mathbb{P}(A_j)}$$

(d) Prove that

$$\mathbb{P}\left(S_\infty \leq \tfrac{1}{2}\sum_{j=1}^{n}\mathbb{P}(A_j)\right) \leq \frac{4}{\sum_{j=1}^{n}\mathbb{P}(A_j)}$$

(e) Prove that if $\sum_{j=1}^{\infty}\mathbb{P}(A_j) = \infty$, then $\mathbb{P}(S_\infty < \infty) = 0$ and conclude that $\mathbb{P}(A_n\text{-io}) = 1$.

Remark. This result is due to Erdős–Rényi [**281**].

3. Suppose $\{A_n\}_{n=1}^{\infty}$ is a family of events which is "asymptotically" independent in the sense that

$$|\mathbb{P}(A_n \cap A_m) - \mathbb{P}(A_n)\mathbb{P}(A_m)| \leq \alpha_{nm}\mathbb{P}(A_n)^{1/2}\mathbb{P}(A_m)^{1/2}$$

with α_{nm} the matrix of a bounded operator on ℓ^2 (e.g., $\alpha_{nm} = e^{-\beta|n-m|}$). Suppose that $\sum_{n=1}^{\infty}\mathbb{P}(A_n) = \infty$. Prove that $\mathbb{P}(A_n\text{-io}) = 1$. (*Hint*: Look at Problem 2.)

4. Fix k. Let $\{X_n\}_{n=1}^{\infty}$ be iidrv with $\mathbb{E}(X_j^{2k}) < \infty$. Let $S_n = \sum_{j=1}^{n}X_j$. Prove that for some c, $\mathbb{E}(S_n^{2k}) \leq cn^k$.

5. (a) Using Stirling's formula, prove (7.2.58).

   (b) Using the Taylor expansion for $\log(1+x)$, verify (7.2.59).

   (c) If h is monotone decreasing, prove (7.2.64).
      (*Hint*: $h(a) \geq (b-a)^{-1}\int_a^b h(y)\,dy \geq h(b)$.)

6. This problem will extend Khinchin's inequality (Theorem 7.2.10) to allow weights. The result is also sometimes called Khinchin's inequality.

   (a) Let $\{X\}_{j=1}^{N}$ be iidrv with $\mathbb{P}(X_1 = \pm 1) = \tfrac{1}{2}$. Let $\{a_j\}_{j=1}^{N}$ be real. Prove that

$$\mathbb{E}\left(e^{\alpha\sum_{j=1}^{N}a_jX_j}\right) \leq e^{\frac{1}{2}\alpha^2\sum_{j=1}^{N}a_j^2} \qquad (7.2.74)$$

   (b) Prove that

$$\mathbb{P}\left(\left|\sum_{j=1}^{n}a_jX_j\right| > \lambda\right) \leq 2e^{-\frac{1}{2}\lambda^2(\sum_{j=1}^{N}a_j^2)^{-1}} \qquad (7.2.75)$$

   (c) Prove for any $1 \leq p < \infty$, we have a universal constant C_p with

$$\mathbb{E}\left(\left|\sum_{j=1}^{N}a_jX_j\right|^p\right)^{\frac{1}{p}} \leq C_p\left(\sum_{j=1}^{N}a_j^2\right)^{\frac{1}{2}} \qquad (7.2.76)$$

(d) For $p = 2$, prove that

$$\mathbb{E}\Big(|\sum_{j=1}^{N} a_j X_j|^2\Big)^{\frac{1}{2}} = \Big(\sum_{j=1}^{N} a_j^2\Big)^{\frac{1}{2}} \tag{7.2.77}$$

(e) If p' is the dual index for p, prove that for $1 < p < \infty$

$$\mathbb{E}\Big(|\sum_{j=1}^{N} a_j X_j|^p\Big)^{\frac{1}{p}} \geq (C_{p'})^{-1} \Big(\sum_{j=1}^{N} a_j^2\Big)^{\frac{1}{2}} \tag{7.2.78}$$

Hint: If Y is a real random variable, prove that

$$\mathbb{E}(Y^2) \leq \mathbb{E}(|Y|^p)^{\frac{1}{p}} \mathbb{E}(|Y|^{p'})^{\frac{1}{p'}}$$

(f) Now let (M, Σ, μ) be a measure space and the X_j random variables, as above, independent of M. For $f_1, \dots f_N$ measurable functions on M, prove that for $1 \leq p < \infty$,

$$\mathbb{E}\Big(\big|\big|\sum_{j=1}^{N} X_j f_j\big|\big|_{L^p(M, d\mu)}^p\Big) \leq C_p^p \big|\big|\Big(\sum_{j=1}^{N} |f_j|^2\Big)^{\frac{1}{2}}\big|\big|_{L^p(M, d\mu)}^p \tag{7.2.79}$$

and that for $1 < p < \infty$,

$$\mathbb{E}\Big(\big|\big|\sum_{j=1}^{N} X_j f_j\big|\big|_{L^p(M, d\mu)}^p\Big) \geq C_{p'}^{-p} \big|\big|\Big(\sum_{j=1}^{N} |f_j|^2\Big)^{\frac{1}{2}}\big|\big|_{L^p(M, d\mu)}^p \tag{7.2.80}$$

7. If p' is the dual index of p, we showed in Theorem 6.6.2 that for $1 \leq p \leq 2$, we have

$$\|\widehat{f}\|_{p'} \leq C_{p,\nu} \|f\|_p \tag{7.2.81}$$

where $\widehat{}$ is the Fourier transform on $\mathcal{S}(\mathbb{R}^\nu)$. This problem will use the improved Khinchin equality of Problem 6 to show (7.2.81) cannot hold if $p > 2$.

(a) If $\{X_j\}_{j=1}^{N}$ are the random variables of Problem 6 and $f_1, \dots, f_N$ lie in $\mathcal{S}(\mathbb{R}^\nu)$, prove that (7.2.81) implies that

$$\mathbb{E}\Big(\big|\big|\sum_{j=1}^{N} X_j \widehat{f}_j\big|\big|_{p'}^{p'}\Big) \leq C_{p,\nu}^{p'} \mathbb{E}\Big(\big|\big|\sum_{j=1}^{N} X_j f_j\big|\big|_p^{p'}\Big) \tag{7.2.82}$$

(b) Fix $g \in C_0^\infty$ and let $f_j(x) = g(x - b_j)$ where the b's are chosen so that the f_j's have disjoint support. Prove that for all N,

$$\text{RHS of } (7.2.82) = d \, N^{p'/p} \tag{7.2.83}$$

(c) Prove that

$$\|(\sum_{j=1}^{N}|\widehat{f_j}|^2)^{\frac{1}{2}}\|_{p'}^{p'} = e\,N^{p'/2} \tag{7.2.84}$$

(d) Use (7.2.80) and (7.2.82) to show that if $1 < p < \infty$ and (7.2.81) holds, then $\frac{1}{p} \geq \frac{1}{2}$, i.e., $p \leq 2$.

(e) Prove (7.2.81) also fails if $p = \infty$. (*Hint*: Interpolation.)

7.3. Characteristic Functions and the Central Limit Theorem

> It is difficult to understand why statisticians commonly limit their inquiries to Averages, and do not revel in more comprehensive views. Their souls seem as dull to the charm of variety as that of the native of one of our flat English counties, whose retrospect of Switzerland was that, if its mountains could be thrown into its lakes, two nuisances would be got rid of at once. An Average is but a solitary fact, whereas if a single other fact be added to it, an entire Normal Scheme, which nearly corresponds to the observed one, starts potentially into existence. Some people hate the very name of statistics, but I find them full of beauty and interest. Whenever they are not brutalised, but delicately handled by the higher methods, and are warily interpreted, their power of dealing with complicated phenomena is extraordinary.
> —*Sir Frances Galton* [**337**]

The main result in this section is the Central Limit Theorem (CLT) that if $\{X_n\}_{n=1}^{\infty}$ are iidrv with $\mathbb{E}(X_1) = \mu$, $\mathbb{V}\mathrm{ar}(X_1^2) = \sigma^2 < \infty$ and $S_n = \sum_{j=1}^{n} X_j$, then $(S_n - n\mu)/\sqrt{n} \xrightarrow{\mathrm{d}} N(0, \sigma)$. The main tool will be a simple convergence theorem for characteristic functions. After stating the variant of that result that we need, we'll use it first to get a very general weak law of large numbers and then the CLT, both for iidrv. We close with some results on sums of independent but not identically distributed random variables and the more general form of the convergence theorem for characteristic functions. As a preliminary, we note the following:

Theorem 7.3.1. *Let $\{X_\alpha\}_{\alpha \in I}$ be a family of random variables which is tight. Then $\{\varphi_{X_\alpha}(t)\}_{\alpha \in I}$ is a uniformly equicontinuous and uniformly bounded family of functions in $C(\mathbb{R})$.*

Remarks. 1. Recall $\varphi_X(t) = \mathbb{E}(e^{itX})$ is its characteristic function.

2. This relates Prokhorov's theorem (Theorem 7.1.8) to the Arzelà–Ascoli theorem (Theorem 2.3.14). It doesn't quite imply Prokhorov's theorem until we know (as we'll see below) that uniform limits of characteristic functions are characteristic functions (we'll prove that using Prokhorov's theorem in any event).

Proof. Given ε, pick R so for all $\alpha \in I$,

$$\mathbb{P}(|X_\alpha| > R) \leq \frac{\varepsilon}{3} \tag{7.3.1}$$

Let $|t - s| < \varepsilon/3R$. Let A_α be the indicator function of $\{|X_\alpha| > R\}$. Then

$$|\varphi_{X_\alpha}(t) - \varphi_{X_\alpha}(s)|$$
$$\leq \mathbb{E}(|e^{itX_\alpha} - e^{isX_\alpha}|A_\alpha) + \mathbb{E}(|e^{itX_\alpha} - e^{isX_\alpha}|(1 - A_\alpha)) \tag{7.3.2}$$
$$\leq 2\mathbb{P}(|X_\alpha| > R) + R|t - s| \tag{7.3.3}$$
$$< \frac{2\varepsilon}{3} + \frac{\varepsilon}{3} = \varepsilon$$

where we use $|e^{itX_\alpha} - e^{isX_\alpha}| \leq |t - s|\,|X_\alpha|$, since $e^{iu} - e^{iv} = \int_u^v ie^{is}\,ds$.

Thus, $\{\varphi_{X_\alpha}\}$ is uniformly equicontinuous. $\|\varphi_{X_\alpha}\|_\infty = 1$, so uniform boundedness is obvious. $\qquad\square$

Here is the main tool of this section:

Theorem 7.3.2 (Lévy Convergence Theorem–First Form). *Let $\{Y_n\}_{n=1}^\infty$ and Y_∞ be a sequence of random variables and $\varphi_n(t) = \mathbb{E}(e^{itY_n})$ (and φ_∞) their characteristic functions. Then the following are equivalent:*

(1) $Y_n \xrightarrow{\text{d}} Y_\infty$
(2) $\varphi_n(t) \to \varphi_\infty(t)$ *for each $t \in \mathbb{R}$*
(3) $\varphi_n(t) \to \varphi_\infty(t)$ *uniformly on each bounded interval of $\mathbb{R}$.*

Proof. $\underline{(1) \Rightarrow (2)}$. Fix $t \in \mathbb{R}$. By Prokhorov's theorem, the Y_n are tight, so pick R so that (7.3.1) holds for all Y_n and for Y_∞. Let f be the continuous function which is e^{itx} on $[-R, R]$, 0 on $\mathbb{R} \setminus [-R - 1, R + 1]$, and linear on $\pm[R, R + 1]$. Then $\lim_{n\to\infty} \mathbb{E}(f(Y_n)) = \mathbb{E}(f(Y_\infty))$, and for any X, $|\mathbb{E}(e^{itX} - f(X))| \leq 2\mathbb{P}(|X| > R)$. Thus,

$$\limsup|\varphi_n(t) - \varphi_\infty(t)| \leq 2\sup_n \mathbb{P}(|Y_n| > R) + 2\mathbb{P}(|Y_\infty| > R) \leq \frac{4\varepsilon}{3}$$

Since ε is arbitrary, $\varphi_n(t) \to \varphi_\infty(t)$.

$\underline{(2) \Rightarrow (1)}$. By (7.1.23), hypothesis (2), and the dominated convergence theorem, $(|\varphi_n(t)| \leq 1)$, if $\widehat{f} \in L^1$, then $\mathbb{E}(f(Y_n)) \to \mathbb{E}(f(Y_\infty))$. Any continuous f of compact support is a uniform limit of C^∞ functions of compact support (convolute with an approximate identity), so we get $Y_n \xrightarrow{\text{d}} Y_\infty$.

$\underline{(2) \Rightarrow (3)}$. Since $(2) \Rightarrow (1)$, we have uniform equicontinuity by Theorem 7.3.1. Thus, pointwise convergence implies uniform convergence on compact subsets of $\mathbb{R}$ (see Problem 1 of Section 2.3).

$\underline{(3) \Rightarrow (2)}$ is obvious. $\qquad\square$

With this weapon in our hands, optimal forms of the weak law of large numbers and CLT for iidrv are really simple!

Theorem 7.3.3 (Weak Law of Large Numbers for iidrv). *Let $\{X_n\}_{n=1}^{\infty}$ be iidrv with $\mathbb{E}(|X_1|) < \infty$. Then*

$$S_n \equiv \frac{1}{n} \sum_{j=1}^{n} X_j \xrightarrow{\mathrm{d}} \mathbb{E}(X_1) \tag{7.3.4}$$

Proof. By (7.1.24), if $\varphi(t) = \mathbb{E}(e^{itX_1})$, then φ is C^1 and $\varphi'(0) = i\mathbb{E}(X_1)$. By Taylor's theorem with remainder, (Theorem 1.8.2), $\varphi(t) - \varphi(0) = t\varphi'(s(t))$, where $|s(t)| \le |t|$. Thus,

$$\varphi(t) = 1 + it\mathbb{E}(X_1) + o(t) \tag{7.3.5}$$

Thus, for t small, $\operatorname{Re}\varphi(t) > 0$, so we can take the branch of $\log(\cdot)$ on $\mathbb{H}_+$ with $\log 1 = 0$. It follows that for every t,

$$\lim_{n\to\infty} n \log \varphi\left(\frac{t}{n}\right) = \lim_{n\to\infty} n \left[\frac{it}{n}\mathbb{E}(X_1) + o\left(\frac{t}{n}\right) + O\left(\frac{t}{n}\right)^2\right] = it\mathbb{E}(X_1) \tag{7.3.6}$$

Therefore, for any t,

$$\mathbb{E}(e^{itS_n}) = \varphi\left(\frac{t}{n}\right)^n \to e^{it\mathbb{E}(X_1)} \tag{7.3.7}$$

(7.3.4) follows by the Lévy convergence theorem. $\qquad\square$

Theorem 7.3.4 (CLT for iidrv). *Let $\{X_n\}_{n=1}^{\infty}$ be iidrv with $\sigma^2 = \mathbb{E}(X_1^2) < \infty$ and let $\mu = \mathbb{E}(X_1)$. Let Y_∞ be an $N(0,1)$ normal random variable. Then*

$$\frac{\sum_{j=1}^{n} X_j - \mu n}{\sigma\sqrt{n}} \xrightarrow{\mathrm{d}} Y_\infty \tag{7.3.8}$$

Proof. This is similar to the last proof. Replacing X_j by $X_j - \mu$, we can suppose $\mu = 0$. As in the last proof, $\varphi(t) \equiv \mathbb{E}(e^{itX_1})$ is C^2 and $\varphi(t) = 1 - \frac{t^2}{2}\sigma^2 + o(t^2)$, so

$$\mathbb{E}\left(\exp\left(\frac{it\sum_{j=1}^{n}X_j}{\sigma\sqrt{n}}\right)\right) = \mathbb{E}\left(\exp\left(\frac{itX_1}{\sigma\sqrt{n}}\right)\right)^n = \left(1 - \frac{t^2}{2n} + o\left(\frac{t^2}{n}\right)\right)^n$$

$$\to \exp\left(-\frac{t^2}{2}\right) = \mathbb{E}(e^{itY_\infty}) \tag{7.3.9}$$

The Lévy convergence theorem concludes the proof. $\qquad\square$

Having completed the main result, we want to say a little about two subjects: sums of not identically distributed random variables and the second form of the Lévy convergence theorem. With regard to the first, it is useful to allow the X_j's in $\sum_{j=1}^{n} X_j$ to be n-dependent, that is, consider triangular arrays: $\{X_{j,n}\}_{j=1,\ldots,n;\, n=1,2,\ldots}$. By replacing $X_{j,n}$ by $X_{j,n} - \mathbb{E}(X_{j,n})$, we'll discuss the case where $\mathbb{E}(X_{j,n}) = 0$.

Theorem 7.3.5 (Lindeberg–Feller CLT). *Let $\{X_{j,n}\}_{j=1,\ldots,n;\, n=1,2,\ldots}$ be a triangular array of random variables so that for each n, $\{X_{j,n}\}_{j=1}^{n}$ are independent and so that $\mathbb{E}(X_{j,n}) = 0$ and $\sigma_n^2 = \sum_{j=1}^{n} \mathbb{E}(X_{j,n}^2) < \infty$. Suppose for each ε, we have that (the Lindeberg condition)*

$$\lim_{n\to\infty} \left[\sum_{j=1}^{n} \sigma_n^{-2}\mathbb{E}(X_{j,n}^2 \chi_{(|X_{j,n}| \geq \varepsilon\sigma_n)}) \right] = 0 \qquad (7.3.10)$$

Then, with Y_∞ an $N(0,1)$ random variable,

$$\frac{\sum_{j=1}^{n} X_{j,n}}{\sigma_n} \xrightarrow{\ \mathrm{d}\ } Y_\infty \qquad (7.3.11)$$

Remarks. 1. If $\{X_j\}_{j=1}^{\infty}$ are iidrv with $\mathbb{E}(X_1) = 0$ and $X_{j,n} \equiv X_j/\sqrt{n}$, then $\sigma_n = \sigma_1$ and (7.3.10) is

$$n\mathbb{E}(n^{-1}X_1^2 \chi_{(|X_1| \geq \varepsilon\sqrt{n}\sigma_1)}) \to 0$$

by $\mathbb{E}(X_1^2) < \infty$. Thus, this result implies Theorem 7.3.4.

2. If $\{X_j\}_{j=1}^{\infty}$ are independent, $X_{j,n} = X_j$, and for some $\delta > 0$,

$$\sigma_n^{-2-\delta} \sum_{j=1}^{n} \mathbb{E}(|X_j|^{2+\delta}) \to 0 \qquad (7.3.12)$$

then (7.3.10), and so (7.3.11), holds (Problem 2). (7.3.12) is called the *Lyapunov condition*.

Proof. By replacing $X_{j,n}$ by $X_{j,n}/\sigma_n$, we can suppose

$$\sigma_n \equiv 1 \qquad (7.3.13)$$

Define

$$\sigma_{j,n} \equiv \mathbb{E}(X_{j,n}^2)^{1/2}, \qquad \sigma_{j,n}^{(\varepsilon)} = \mathbb{E}(X_{j,n}^2 \chi_{\{|X_{j,n}| \geq \varepsilon\}})^{1/2} \qquad (7.3.14)$$

Notice that

$$\sigma_{j,n}^2 \leq \varepsilon^2 + (\sigma_{j,n}^{(\varepsilon)})^2 \qquad (7.3.15)$$

and that (7.3.10) implies that

$$\max_{j=1,\ldots,n} \sigma_{j,n}^{(\varepsilon)} \leq \left(\sum_{j=1}^{n} (\sigma_{j,n}^{(\varepsilon)})^2 \right)^{1/2} \to 0 \qquad (7.3.16)$$

It follows that as $n \to \infty$,

$$\max_{j=1,\ldots,n} \sigma_{j,n}^2 \to 0 \qquad (7.3.17)$$

By Taylor's theorem with remainder and the fact that if $g(u) = e^{-u}$, $h(y) = e^{-iy}$, then on $[0, \infty)$, $|g''(u)| < 1$, and on $\mathbb{R}$, $|h''(y)| \leq 1$, $|h'''(y)| \leq 1$, we have that ($u \geq 0$, $y \in \mathbb{R}$)

$$|e^{iy} - (1 + iy)| \leq \tfrac{1}{2} y^2, \qquad |e^{-u} - (1 - u)| \leq \tfrac{1}{2} u^2 \tag{7.3.18}$$

$$\left| e^{iy} - \left(1 + iy - \frac{y^2}{2} \right) \right| \leq \tfrac{1}{6} |y|^3 \tag{7.3.19}$$

The first half of (7.3.18) implies

$$\left| e^{iy} - \left(1 + iy - \frac{y^2}{2} \right) \right| \leq y^2 \tag{7.3.20}$$

Thus, using (7.3.19) if $|X_{j,n}| \leq \varepsilon$, in which case $|X_{j,n}|^3 \leq \varepsilon X_{j,n}^2$, and (7.3.20) if $|X_{j,n}| \geq \varepsilon$, we see

$$\left| \mathbb{E}(e^{itX_{j,n}}) - \left(1 - \frac{t^2}{2} \sigma_{j,n}^2 \right) \right| \leq \tfrac{1}{6} \varepsilon t^3 \sigma_{j,n}^2 + (\sigma_{j,n}^{(\varepsilon)})^2 \tag{7.3.21}$$

The second half of (7.3.18) implies

$$\left| e^{-\sigma_{j,n}^2 t^2 / 2} - \left(1 - \frac{t^2}{2} \sigma_{j,n}^2 \right) \right| \leq \frac{t^4}{8} \sigma_{j,n}^2 \left(\max_{j=1,\ldots,n} \sigma_{j,n}^2 \right) \tag{7.3.22}$$

Thus,

$$|\mathbb{E}(e^{itX_{j,n}}) - e^{-\sigma_{j,n}^2 t^2 / 2}| \leq \sigma_{j,n}^2 \left[\tfrac{1}{6} \varepsilon t^3 + \tfrac{1}{8} \max_{j=1,\ldots,n} \sigma_{j,n}^2 \right] + (\sigma_{j,n}^{(\varepsilon)})^2 \tag{7.3.23}$$

If $a_1, \ldots, a_n, b_1, \ldots, b_n$ lie in $\overline{\mathbb{D}}$,

$$|a_n \ldots a_n - b_1 \ldots b_n| = \sum_{j=1}^{n} |a_1 \ldots a_{j-1}(a_j - b_j) b_{j+1} \ldots b_n|$$

$$\leq \sum_{j=1}^{n} |a_j - b_j| \tag{7.3.24}$$

Therefore, if $S_n = \sum_{j=1}^{n} X_{j,n}$, independent, (7.3.13) and (7.3.23) imply that

$$|\mathbb{E}(e^{itS_n}) - e^{-t^2/2}| \leq \tfrac{1}{6} \varepsilon t^3 + \tfrac{1}{8} \max_{j=1,\ldots,n} \sigma_{j,n}^2 + \sum_{j=1}^{n} (\sigma_{j,n}^{(\varepsilon)})^2 \tag{7.3.25}$$

Using (7.3.10) and (7.3.17), we see

$$\limsup_{n \to \infty} |\mathbb{E}(e^{itS_n}) - e^{-t^2/2}| \leq \tfrac{1}{6} \varepsilon t^3 \tag{7.3.26}$$

Since ε is arbitrary, we get (7.3.11). $\square$

Finally, we turn to the second form of Lévy's convergence theorem:

Theorem 7.3.6 (Lévy Convergence Theorem–Second Form). *Let* $\{Y_n\}_{n=1}^{\infty}$ *be a sequence of random variables and* $\varphi_n(t) = \mathbb{E}(e^{itY_n})$ *their characteristic function. Suppose that for each* $t \in \mathbb{R}$, $\varphi_\infty(t) \equiv \lim_{n\to\infty} \varphi_n(t)$ *exists and* $\varphi_\infty(t)$ *is continuous at* $t = 0$. *Then there is a random variable,* Y_∞, *so that* $\varphi_\infty(t) = \mathbb{E}(e^{itY_\infty})$ *and* $Y_n \xrightarrow{\text{d}} Y_\infty$. *Conversely, if* $Y_n \xrightarrow{\text{d}} Y_\infty$, *then* $\varphi_\infty(t) \equiv \lim_{n\to\infty} \varphi_n(t)$ *exists uniformly on each bounded interval and* $\varphi_\infty(t)$ *is continuous on* $\mathbb{R}$.

Proof. The converse was proven in Theorem 7.3.2. So suppose $\varphi_n(t)$ has a limit continuous at 0. We'll first prove that the $\{Y_n\}_{n=1}^{\infty}$ are tight. Begin by noting that

$$\frac{1}{2\delta}\int_{-\delta}^{\delta} e^{itx}\, dt = \frac{\sin(x\delta)}{x\delta} \tag{7.3.27}$$

and that if $|x| > 2\delta^{-1}$, $|\sin(x\delta)/|x\delta|| < \frac{1}{2}$. Thus, for any random variable, X,

$$\frac{1}{2\delta}\int_{-\delta}^{\delta}(\varphi_X(0) - \varphi_X(t))\, dt = \mathbb{E}\left(\left[1 - \frac{\sin(\delta X)}{\delta X}\right]\right) \tag{7.3.28}$$

$$\geq \mathbb{E}\left(\chi_{\{X\geq 2\delta^{-1}\}}\left[1 - \frac{\sin(\delta X)}{\delta X}\right]\right) \tag{7.3.29}$$

$$\geq \tfrac{1}{2}\,\mathbb{P}(|X| \geq 2\delta^{-1}) \tag{7.3.30}$$

To get (7.3.29), we used the fact that, by (7.3.27), $|\sin u/u| \leq 1$.

Given ε, pick δ so $|t| \leq \delta \Rightarrow |\varphi_\infty(t) - \varphi_\infty(1)| < \varepsilon/2$. Thus,

$$\frac{1}{2\delta}\int_{-\delta}^{\delta}|\varphi_\infty(0) - \varphi_\infty(t)|\, dt < \frac{\varepsilon}{2} \tag{7.3.31}$$

By $\varphi_n(t) \to \varphi_\infty(t)$ and dominated convergence, we conclude that for some N and all $n \geq N$,

$$\frac{1}{2\delta}\int_{-\delta}^{\delta}|\varphi_n(0) - \varphi_n(t)|\, dt < \frac{\varepsilon}{2} \tag{7.3.32}$$

so by (7.3.30) for $n > N$, $\mathbb{P}(|X_n| \geq 2\delta^{-1}) < \varepsilon$, that is, the Y_n are tight.

Any limit point Y_∞ for Y_{n_j} has $\varphi_{Y_\infty}(t) = \varphi(t)$, so all limit points are equal, that is, $Y_n \to Y_\infty$. □

Notes and Historical Remarks.

In the beginning there was de Moivre, Laplace, and many Bernoullis, and they begat limit theorems, and the wise men saw that it was good and they called it by the name of Gauss. Then there were new generations and they said that it had experimental vigor but lacked in rigor. Then came Chebyshev, Lyapunov, and Markov and they begat a proof and Pólya saw that it was momentous and he said that its name shall be called the Central Limit Theorem.

> Then came Lindeberg and he said that it was elementary, for Taylor
> had expanded that which needed expansion and he said it twice, but Lévy
> had seen that Fourier transforms are characteristic functions and he said
> "let them multiply and bring forth limit theorems and stable laws." And
> it was good, stable, and sufficient, but they asked "Is it necessary"? Lévy
> answered, "I shall say verily unto you say that it is not necessary, but the
> time shall come when Gauss will have no parts except that they be in the
> image of Gauss himself, and then it will be necessary." It was a prophecy,
> and then Cramér announced that the time had come, and there was much
> rejoicing and Lévy said that it must be recorded in the bibles and he did
> record it, and it came to pass that there were many limit theorems and
> many were central and they overflowed the chronicles and this was the
> history of the central limit theorem.
>
> —L. Le Cam [**566**]

The term "central limit theorem" comes from a 1920 paper of Pólya
[**746**], who even used the term "zentral Grenzwertsatz" in the title of the
paper. Pólya intended "central" in the sense of important and basic—not,
as some think, because the Gaussian is centered about the mean. The
case can be made that this is the most important theorem for applications
of mathematics. The fundamental theorem of calculus, Cauchy integral
formula, or curvature are important in theoretical physics and some parts
of engineering, but most of science and parts of the social sciences (think
political polling) are data driven, and the CLT is basic to all data analysis.

Because of its importance and the richness of its history, the history of
the CLT has developed a huge literature, including two books: Adams [**2**]
and Fischer [**306**]. In particular, Adams includes the Le Cam article quoted
at the start and several comments on that article.

Le Cam's summary, with which these Notes began, is perhaps overblown,
but it is an accurate summary of most of the history of the CLT. We focused
here on the "global" CLT (which we call just CLT); there is also a local CLT
where one controls asymptotics of individual probabilities in the discrete case
or limits of densities in the continuous case. The first CLT was de Moivre's
local CLT for Bernoulli random variables discussed in the last section. He
originally presented it in 1733 in a private pamphlet [**233**] and then in the
1738 edition of his book, *The Doctrine of Chances* [**234**].

Laplace is credited for realizing the universal nature of the CLT and
for introducing characteristic functions for their proof. He first approached
the issue in an early work on comets in 1776 [**546**] and in his first book on
probability [**547**]. His first variant using characteristic functions was in 1810
[**549**]. He expounded this in his masterpiece on probability theory [**550**] that
had considerable impact during the nineteenth century. His proof involved
the Fourier inversion formula and formal use of what we would now call
stationary phase methods. It was far from what we call a rigorous proof,

although it did use the key fact that $\mathbb{E}(e^{itS_n}) = \mathbb{E}(e^{itX_1})^n$ for iidrv. Despite the name Gaussian, Gauss had little to do with the CLT per se.

In the later half of the nineteenth century, Chebyshev and his student Markov attempted the first detailed, careful proof. Chebyshev's idea in his 1887 paper [**184**] was to prove convergence of moments and appeal to uniqueness of the moment problem for the Gaussian measure. Markov criticized the details and provided his own version in 1898 [**630**], expanded upon in his book on probability [**633**]. This proof would seem to require that the X_i have moments of all orders, but Markov, in his book, found a truncation procedure, since (in variant forms) a common tool in probability theory (see Problem 16 of Section 2.10 of Part 3).

Shortly after Markov's paper, Lyapunov, also a student of Chebyshev, published two remarkable papers [**615, 616**] (Adams [**2**] includes English translations of these papers and two related announcements) with a very general CLT for iidrv and even a result for independent but not identically distributed random variables. Lyapunov had his condition in the second of these papers. Except that he needed some efforts going to and from Fourier transform, Lyapunov's proof is close to the one give here.

In this regard, it should be mentioned that many historians think that the first rigorous proof of the CLT (under more restrictive conditions than Lyapunov but with explicit error estimates) was sketched by Cauchy in 1853 [**174**] also using characteristic functions. This sketch was fleshed out by Sleshinskii in 1892 [**860**]. Lyapunov even mentions Sleshinskii's work, but until historians championed this work around 1970, it was effectively lost. So it was Lyapunov who truly impacted the developments.

Aleksandr Mikhailovich Lyapunov (1857–1918) was the son of an astronomer, close friend of Markov (from their gymnasium days in Nizhny Novgorod), and student of Chebyshev. After getting his master's degree in 1884, he moved to Kharkov where he stayed on the faculty until 1902 when he moved to St. Petersburg to take up the position vacated by the death of Chebyshev. In 1886, he married his cousin Natalia Sechenov whom he had met as a teenager when being tutored by her father. In 1917, Lyapunov took up a position in Odessa where the family moved because of his wife's tuberculosis. Her condition deteriorated and she died on October 31, 1918. Later that day, Lyapunov shot himself, dying of the wounds three days later.

Lyapunov is best known for his work on stability of differential equations—the rate of exponential growth or decay is called the Lyapunov exponent (see Section 2.9 of Part 3). His students included Steklov.

The Lévy convergence theorem (in what we call the first form) is from a 1922 paper [**576**] of Lévy, expanded in his first probability theory book [**578**]. As Loève tells the story in his biographical obituary of Lévy [**599**], in 1919 at age 33, Lévy was asked to give three lectures on the "Calculus of Probability," an area in which he had not worked (he was what we'd now call a functional analyst). He learned the subject from the books of Bétrand, Borel, and Poincaré and was shocked by their lack of precision and rigor. Poincaré had formally used the generating function $\mathbb{E}(e^{\alpha X})$ for α real; Lévy had the idea of using α pure imaginary instead. Because the texts he read did not mention the Russian work of Lyapunov and Markov nor even the earlier work of Laplace and Cauchy, Lévy developed the theory of characteristic functions from scratch to the point where we use it here.

The extra element of the second form of the Lévy convergence theorem, namely, that continuity of F at $t = 0$ suffices for a limit to be a characteristic function, is intimately connected to Bochner's theorem (see Theorem 6.6.6 and the Notes to Section 6.6), so some mathematicians regard the second form as due to Bochner. The result within the context of characteristic functions is due to Cramér [209].

Harald Cramér (1893–1965) is one of many pivotal figures in probability and statistics drawn to the field initially by the job market and especially by opportunities in insurance and finance. de Moivre, a Huguenot refugee in London, is possibly the earliest example, and we've seen Cantelli was an actuary. Cramér could not make ends meet on an assistant professor's salary in Stockholm, so he started working also for an insurance company. Because he wouldn't sign a Nazi loyalty oath, William Feller (1906–70) took a position with Cramér's group that led him to probability theory. Joseph Doob (1910–2004), having trouble with obtaining a postdoc position in the Depression, took up statistics to get a job.

A different approach to the CLT, using a Taylor expansion of $f(S_n)$ for smooth instead of characteristic functions, is due to Lindeberg [591] in 1922, slightly before Lévy (see Problem 3). A pedagogic version of the argument can be found in Trotter [936]. Lindeberg allowed nonidentically distributed, independent random variables and introduced a cutoff condition equivalent to what is called the Lindeberg condition. The more standard version of what is called the Lindeberg condition is due to Lévy [577] in his paper that includes a discussion of Lindeberg's results.

One can ask about the rate of convergence of the distribution function of S_n to that of $N(0, \sigma)$. In the iidrv case, if $\mathbb{E}(X_1) = 0$, $\mathbb{E}(X_1^2) = \sigma^2 < \infty$, and $\mathbb{E}(|X_1|^3) = \rho$, and if φ_n is the distribution function of S_n and Φ of $N(0, \sigma)$, then for a constant C (now known to be less than 0.5, almost 8 in the original paper), one has

$$\|\varphi_n - \Phi\|_\infty \leq \frac{C\rho}{\sigma^3 \sqrt{n}} \tag{7.3.33}$$

This is called the *Berry–Esseen bound* after their discovery in [83, 283].

In the mid-1930s, Feller [**301**] and Lévy [**579**] found necessary and suffi-cient conditions for suitably normalized sums of independent (but not nec-essarily identically distributed) random variables to converge in distribution to $N(0, 1)$. They allow normalizations different from $(\sqrt{n})^{-1}$ but obtain similar conditions close to the Lindeberg condition. Le Cam [**566**] discusses the details and priority issues.

The study of some of the limiting distributions of iidrv and triangular arrays, with each row iidrv, goes beyond the normal case. There are two classes of limit distributions: stable and infinitely divisible. A distribution is called *stable* if for any $\alpha_1, \alpha_2 > 0$, there are α and β so that if X, X_1, X_2 have the given distribution and X_1 and X_2 are independent, then $\alpha_1 X_1 + \alpha_2 X_2$ has the same distribution as $\alpha X + \beta$. In terms of the characteristic function $\varphi_X(t)$, one has

$$\varphi(\alpha_1 t)\varphi(\alpha_2 t) = \varphi(\alpha t)e^{i\beta t} \qquad (7.3.34)$$

At a heuristic level, if $\{X_j\}_{j=1}^{\infty}$ are iidrv and there exist X and a_n, b_n so $a_n S_n + b_n \xrightarrow{\text{d}} X$ (where $S_n = \sum_{j=1}^{n} X_j$), then X should be stable (for if $\alpha_1 = p/q$ and $\alpha_2 = 1 - p/q$, then one takes limits of $S_{p\ell}, S_{(q-p)\ell}$ to see that X should be stable). Conversely, by taking X_j to be stable, it is easy to see that one can pick a_n, b_n so $a_n S_n + b_n \xrightarrow{\text{d}} X$.

In 1922, Levy [**575**] noted $\exp(-|t|^a)$ for $0 < a \le 2$ is a characteristic function and a solution of (7.3.34) and used this to provide counterexamples to the CLT. (We've already seen the Cauchy distribution does that—it is just $a = 1$.) In his 1925 book [**578**], Lévy found (almost) all stable distribu-tions and proved various limit theorems. (A paper of Pólya [**747**] resulting from correspondence between Lévy and him was a part of this history.) He expanded his discussion in his second book [**581**].

The characteristic functions of stable distributions have four parameters:

$$\varphi_{a,b,c,d}(t) = \exp\left[-d|t|^a\left(1 + ib\,\mathrm{sgn}(t)\tan\left(\frac{\pi a}{2}\right)\right) + ict\right] \qquad (7.3.35)$$

d and c correspond to scaling and translation of X, and so are often taken to be $c = 0$, $d = 1$. When $a = 1$, $\tan(\pi a/2) = \infty$ and one replaces the tan by $(2/\pi)\log t$. When $a = 2$, $\tan(\pi a/2) = 0$, so b drops out. The X's whose characteristic functions are given by $\varphi_{a,b,c,d}$ are called *Lévy laws*.

Notice that if $0 < a \le 1$, $\varphi_{a,b,c,d}$ is not C^1 at $t = 0$ and if $1 < a < 2$, not C^2, so except for the Gaussian case, Lévy laws never have finite variance, and if $0 < a \le 1$, they do not have finite expectation. Indeed, the laws have a.c. density which is asymptotic to $|x|^{-1-a}$ if $a < 2$.

One might think these laws with infinite variance are pathological and of no interest, but that is false! Distributions with power tails are common.

That this is so in economics was noted already by Pareto [**699**] in 1897! The famous 80-20 rule (that 80% of a country's wealth is held by the top 20%) is an impact of long tails. Stock price fluctuations are believed to be better fit by a non-Gaussian Lévy law. For further discussion, see Voit [**951**].

Outside of economics, this is often called Bradford's law after his 1934 paper [**124**] on distribution of papers in scientific journals. Other places where tailed distributions arise are internet file transfer sizes, supercomputer job sizes, solar flare statistics, and Brownian motion hitting times.

Among the Lévy laws (normalized by $c = 0$, $d = 1$), there are three that have explicit formulae for the density: the Cauchy, the normal, and φ for $a = \frac{1}{2}$, $b = 1$, where $\varphi(t) = \exp(-\sqrt{2it})$ and the distribution is $\chi_{[0,\infty)}(2\pi)^{-1/2}x^{-3/2}\exp(-1/2x)$. It is sometimes called the Lévy distribution.

The second class of alternate limits are the infinitely divisible distributions. A probability distribution is called *infinitely divisible* if and only if for every n, there is $\{X_j^{(n)}\}_{j=1}^n$ so that $\sum_{j=1}^n X_j^{(n)}$ has the given distribution. Equivalently, if for every n, there is a characteristic function $\varphi^{(n)}$ so $(\varphi^{(n)}(t))^n = \varphi_X(t)$, where X has the given distribution. Clearly, if φ is infinitely divisible, there is a triangular array so $\sum_{j=1}^n X_j^{(n)} \xrightarrow{d} X$ (since there is one where S_n equals X for all n!). And it is to be expected (and can be proven) that if a triangular array with iidrv row has a limit, that limit is infinitely divisible.

While nonnormal stationary distributions must be absolutely continuous and have long tails, this is not true in the infinitely divisible case; for example, the Poisson distribution is infinitely divisible, has moments of all orders, and is discrete. In 1932, Kolmogorov [**506**] found all infinitely divisible distributions with finite variance and then, in 1936–37, Lévy [**580**] and Khinchin [**488**] found the general infinitely divisible distribution given by the *Lévy–Khinchin* formula

$$\varphi_X(t) = \exp(g(t))$$
$$g(t) = ibt - at^2 - \int \left[e^{itx} - 1 - \frac{itx}{1+x^2}\right]\left(\frac{1+x^2}{x^2}\right)d\nu(x) \qquad (7.3.36)$$

where $b \in \mathbb{R}$, $a > 0$, and ν is a finite measure on $\mathbb{R}$ with $\nu(\{0\}) = 0$.

Important refinements of the limit theorems in the nonnormal case are due to Gnedenko [**351**], Doeblin [**251**], and the influential book of Gnedenko–Kolmogorov [**352**].

Brownian motion can be viewed as a result of paths with independent, stationary Gaussian increments. If Gaussian is dropped (but a technical continuity in measure condition added), one gets a wider class of processes studied first by Lévy in the 1930s, especially in his second probability theory book [**581**]. The Poisson process of the next section is an example of a Lévy process. For five books on Lévy process, including one on option pricing (!), see [**30, 61, 84, 584, 823**]. Applebaum [**31**] is a review article on the subject.

Paul Pierre Lévy (1886–1971) was a French mathematician who spent most of his student and professional career at École Polytechnique and École des Mines. He was a student of Hadamard and, in turn, Benoît Mandelbrojt was his student. Loève has a superb mathematical obituary [**599**]. While Lévy is now regarded with Kolmogorov as the founders of modern probability theory, he had trouble getting recognition. Both Borel and Fréchet dismissed much of his work in his early years as a probabilist, and Lévy felt keenly that, at least through the 1950s, Feller got credit for their independent work on necessary conditions for the CLT (e.g., in [**352**]). But as the dominance of his work in the Notes to this section shows, he was the critical figure in all the elements of sums of iidrv.

Problems

1. While we exploited characteristic functions, we haven't really seen any general sets of functions $f(x)$ which are the (unnormalized) Fourier transforms of probability measures. In this problem, the reader will prove that f is a characteristic function if (but certainly *not* only if) it has the following properties.

   (1) $f(0) = 1$ and f is continuous,
   (2) $f(x) = f(-x)$,
   (3) f is convex on $(0, \infty)$.

   (a) Prove that such an f is monotone decreasing, and so has a limit, $f(\infty)$, as $t \to \infty$.

   (b) Prove that $f(\infty) \geq 0$ and conclude (since the unnormalized Fourier transform of a point mass at 0 is 1) that one need only prove the result when $f(\infty) = 0$.

   (c) Prove that the second distributional derivatives of f restricted to $(0, \infty)$ is a measure. (*Hint*: Theorem 5.3.12.)

   (d) Prove that there is a probability measure ν on $(0, \infty)$ so that

   $$f(x) = \int_0^\infty \left(1 - a\,|x|\right)_+ d\nu(a) \qquad (7.3.37)$$

   and conclude it suffices to prove that $\left(1 - |x|\right)_+$ is a characteristic function.

(e) Compute the Fourier transform of $(1-|x|)_+$ exactly and conclude that $(1-|x|)_+$ is a characteristic function.

(f) As an application, prove that $e^{-|x|^\alpha}$, $0 < \alpha \leq 1$ is a characteristic function.

2. Prove that Lyapunov's condition, (7.3.13), implies the Lindeberg condition, (7.3.10), if the $X_{j,n}$ all equal X_j.

3. This problem will lead you through Lindeberg's proof of the CLT when a third moment condition holds. Let $X_{j,n}$ be a triangular array with $\mathbb{E}(X_{j,n}) = 0$, $\mathbb{E}(X_{j,n}^2) = \sigma_{j,n}^2$, $\sum_{j=1}^n \sigma_{j,n}^2 = \sigma_n^2 = 1$ and so that

$$\sup_j \sigma_{j,n} \to 0 \tag{7.3.38}$$

$$\tau_{j,n} \equiv \mathbb{E}(|X_{j,n}|^3), \qquad \sum_{j=1}^n \tau_{j,n} \to 0 \quad \text{as } n \to \infty \tag{7.3.39}$$

Let Y_∞ be $N(0,1)$ and $Y_n = \sum_{j=1}^n X_{j,n}$.

(a) Prove that it suffices to show that $\mathbb{E}(f(Y_n)) \to \mathbb{E}(f(Y_\infty))$ for f any C_0^∞ function.

(b) Let $Z_{j,n}$ be independent $N(0,\sigma_{j,n})$ random variables. Prove that $\sum_{j=1}^n Z_{j,n} = Y_\infty$ and that $\sum_{j=1}^n \mathbb{E}(|Z_{j,n}|^3) \to 0$.

(c) For any random variable R and U, prove that

$$|\mathbb{E}(f(R+U) - f(R) - Uf'(R) - \tfrac{1}{2}U^2 f''(R))| \leq \frac{\|f'''\|_\infty}{6} \mathbb{E}(|U|^3)$$

(d) Let $R_{k,n} = \sum_{j<k} X_{j,n} + \sum_{j>k} Z_{j,n}$ for $j = 1, 2, \ldots, n$. Prove that

$$f(Y_n) - f(Y_\infty) = \sum_{k=1}^n [f(R_k + X_{k,n}) - f(R_k + Z_{k,n})]$$

(e) Prove that

$$|\mathbb{E}(f(Y_n) - f(Y_\infty))| \leq \frac{\|f'''\|_\infty}{6} \sum_{j=1}^n (\tau_{j,n} + \mathbb{E}(|Z_{j,n}|^3))$$

and that this goes to zero.

(f) Prove the CLT for iidrv if $\mathbb{E}(|X_1|^3) < \infty$.

7.4. Poisson Limits and Processes

> Politicians use statistics in the same way that a drunk uses lamp-posts—for support rather than illumination.
>
> —*attributed to Andrew Lang* (1844-1912), 1910 speech

We start by considering Geiger-counter clicks from a chunk of radioactive matter. The physical model imagines each individual nucleus in the chunk has a probability, p, to decay in the next second and that the decays are uncorrelated, aka independent. If we label the atoms $1, 2, \ldots, N$, let X_j be 1 if atom j decays in the next second and 0 otherwise. Then the total number of counts observed is $C = \sum_{j=1}^{N} X_j$.

"Oh great!" you think. N is huge—even for specks well over 10^{20} and we know all about limits of sums of iidrv. But not so quick. Half-lives can also be huge, that is, p small. Suppose that we only expect, say, 10 counts typically. Then C is probably somewhere among $0, \ldots, 20$ (even less than 20, if we want to capture the number with, say, 95% probability; see Problem 1).

There is no way that a discrete probability distribution at a few values is well-approximated by a normal distribution. The point is that we not only need N to be large, but also pN, the expected number of counts. When it is, the distribution is still discrete, but $O(\sqrt{Np(1-p)})$ values are involved, so their discrete distribution is close to a normal one after rescaling.

To capture this example, we'll want a limit as $N \to \infty$, not with p fixed but with pN fixed. We'll see the proper limit is the Poisson distribution of (7.1.11) which depends on a parameter, λ. Recall that this random variable, which we call $P^{(\lambda)}$ in this section, has values in $\{0, 1, 2, \ldots\}$ with

$$\mathbb{P}(P^{(\lambda)} = n) = (n!)^{-1} \lambda^n e^{-\lambda}, \qquad \mathbb{E}(P^{(\lambda)}) = \lambda, \qquad \mathbb{V}\mathrm{ar}(P^{(\lambda)}) = \lambda \quad (7.4.1)$$

and characteristic function $\varphi_\lambda(t) \equiv \mathbb{E}(e^{itP^{(\lambda)}})$ given by

$$\varphi_\lambda(t) = \exp(-\lambda + \lambda e^{it}) \qquad (7.4.2)$$

Notice that

$$\varphi_\lambda(t)\varphi_\mu(t) = \varphi_{\mu+\lambda}(t) \qquad (7.4.3)$$

which, by Proposition 7.1.4 and (7.1.36), implies that if $P^{(\lambda)}$ and $\widetilde{P}^{(\mu)}$ are independent, then $P^{(\lambda)} + \widetilde{P}^{(\mu)}$ has the $P^{(\lambda+\mu)}$ distribution which we write

$$P^{(\lambda)} \oplus P^{(\mu)} = P^{(\lambda+\mu)} \qquad (7.4.4)$$

After proving the simple limit theorem, we'll discuss the Poisson process which essentially presents the Geiger-counter model as a function of time. We'll be able to characterize Poisson processes and also show that the time between Poisson events is given by an exponential distribution.

We will let $B^{(n,p)}$ be the binomial distribution of (7.1.9) with values in $\{0, \ldots, n\}$ with

$$\mathbb{P}(B^{(n,p)} = j) = \binom{n}{j} p^j (1-p)^{n-j}, \qquad \varphi_{n,p}^B = (1 - p + pe^{it})^n \qquad (7.4.5)$$

The motivational result of this section is:

Theorem 7.4.1 (Poisson Limit Theorem). *Fix $\lambda > 0$. Then, as $n \to \infty$,*

$$np_n \to \lambda \Rightarrow B^{(n,p_n)} \xrightarrow{d} P^{(\lambda)} \tag{7.4.6}$$

Remark. Problem 3 proves this by looking at probabilities.

Proof. For each $t \in \mathbb{R}$,

$$\varphi^B_{n,p_n}(t) = \left(1 - \frac{np_n}{n}\left(1 - e^{it}\right)\right)^n \to \varphi_\lambda(t) \tag{7.4.7}$$

by the compound interest formula (Problem 4). (7.4.6) follows from the Lévy convergence theorem (Theorem 7.3.2). $\qquad\square$

Example 7.4.2 (Uniform distribution in the thermodynamic limit). Imagine looking at a large box Λ in $\mathbb{R}^\nu$ and a fixed open set $\Omega \subset \Lambda$. Fix Ω and take Λ to $\mathbb{R}^\nu$. Consider putting particles in Λ at random at a fixed density ρ. Thus, if $|\Lambda|$ is the volume of Λ, we put $N = [\rho|\Lambda|]$ particles in Λ, each one uniformly random and independent of one another. (Problem 5 considers nonuniform density.) The probability, p, of any given particle winding up in Ω is

$$p = \frac{|\Omega|}{|\Lambda|} \tag{7.4.8}$$

Notice $pN \to \rho|\Omega|$, the expected number of particles in $|\Omega|$, and since there are independent trials, Theorem 7.4.1 applies, so $n(\Omega)$, the number of particles in Ω in the limit, is a Poisson random variable. Physicists call this $\Lambda \to \mathbb{R}^\nu$ limit the *thermodynamic limit*.

But more is going on here. We have random variables, $N(\Omega)$, for each open Ω. Indeed, we'll see that $N(\Omega)$ can be naturally defined for every Borel Ω, and $\Omega \mapsto N(\Omega)$ will define a random point measure. We thus also want to know about point distributions of the $N(\Omega)$.

Here is a formal argument that if Ω_1 and Ω_2 are disjoint, then $N(\Omega_1)$ and $N(\Omega_2)$ are independent. For any large Λ, we can get $\mathbb{P}(N(\Omega_1) = j, N(\Omega_2) = k)$ by asking for $N(\Omega_1 \cup \Omega_2) = j + k = n$. These n particles are Bernoulli distributed with probability $p = |\Omega_1|/(|\Omega_1| + |\Omega_2|)$ to get in Ω_1. Thus, in the limit,

$$\mathbb{P}(N(\Omega_1) = j, N(\Omega_2) = k)$$
$$= \frac{(j+k)!}{j!k!} \frac{|\Omega_1|^j|\Omega_2|^k}{|\Omega_1 + \Omega_2|^{j+k}} \frac{[\rho(|\Omega_1| + |\Omega_2|)]^{j+k}}{(j+k)!} e^{-\rho(|\Omega_1|+|\Omega_2|)} \tag{7.4.9}$$
$$= \mathbb{P}(N(\Omega_1) = j)\mathbb{P}(N(\Omega_2) = k) \tag{7.4.10}$$

Therefore, $N(\Omega_1)$ and $N(\Omega_2)$ are independent for disjoint sets.

The same argument shows that if $\{\Omega_j\}_{j=1}^m$ are disjoint, then $\{N(\Omega_j)\}_{j=1}^m$ are mutually independent. If we do the same for arbitrary Borel sets and use $N(\Omega_1) = N(\Omega_1 \cap \Omega_2) + N(\Omega_1 \setminus \Omega_2)$, $N(\Omega_2) = N(\Omega_1 \cap \Omega_2) + N(\Omega_2 \setminus \Omega_1)$, we determine the joint distribution in general. □

If $\nu = 1$, things are notationally simpler since we can look at $N(t) \equiv N([0,t))$ (essentially, we use the fact that measures on $\mathbb{R}$ are Stieltjes measures), so we begin with that case and then leave the details for $\nu > 1$ to the reader.

Theorem 7.4.3. *Fix $\rho > 0$. There exists a probability measure space (X, Σ, μ) with $L^2(X, d\mu)$ separable and with random variables $\{N(t)\}_{t \in \mathbb{R}}$ so that*

(a) *Each $(\operatorname{sgn}(t))N(t)$ is a Poisson random variable with*

$$\mathbb{E}(N(t)) = \rho t \tag{7.4.11}$$

(b) *If $t_0 < t_1 < \cdots < t_n$, then $\{N(t_j) - N(t_{j-1})\}_{j=1}^n$ are mutually independent Poisson random variables.*

These conditions essentially determine the probability measure space.

Remarks. 1. To avoid negative random variables, it is common to restrict to $t \geq 0$ and/or to look at

$$N([a, b]) = N(b) - N(a) \tag{7.4.12}$$

which are all positive.

2. By essentially unique, we mean if (X, Σ, μ) and $(\widetilde{X}, \widetilde{\Sigma}, \tilde{\mu})$ are two such spaces for which polynomials in $\{N(t)\}_{t \in \mathbb{R}}$ are dense in L^2, there is a unitary map between the L^2 spaces with $UNU^{-1} = \widetilde{N}$.

Proof. For each $K = 1, 2, \ldots$, we consider the $q_K \equiv 2\, 4^K + 1$ numbers $\{\frac{j}{2^K}, j = -4^K, \ldots, 4^K\}$. We can define a measure on $\mathbb{Z}^{q_K}$ by requiring $N(0) = 0$ and $N(\frac{j+1}{2^K}) - N(\frac{j}{2^K})$, $j = -4^K, \ldots, 4^K - 1$ be independent Poissons of expectation $\rho/2^K$. It is easy to see $\{\mu_K\}_{K=1}^\infty$ on $\mathbb{R}^{q_K}$ are consistent, so by the Kolmogorov consistency theorem (Theorem 4.12.6), there is a measure on $(\mathbb{R} \cup \{\infty\})^\infty$ so $N(t)$ is defined for all dyadic rational t obeying (a) and (b).

For a Poisson random variable,

$$\mathbb{E}([P^{(\mu)}]^2) = \mu^2 + \mu \tag{7.4.13}$$

so for dyadic rationals, t and s,

$$\mathbb{E}((N(t) - N(s))^2) = \rho^2 |t - s|^2 + \rho|t - s| \tag{7.4.14}$$

This implies, as L^2 functions, $N(t)$ has a unique extension from dyadic rationals to all reals. By continuity, this obeys (a) and (b). Uniqueness is left to the reader (Problem 6). □

As with the discussion of Brownian motion in Section 4.16, pointwise estimates for *all* t are not measurable but depend on a realization. Since $t > s \Rightarrow N(t) \geq N(s)$ as functions a.e., we have $N(t)(\omega) \geq N(s)(\omega)$ for all dyadic t's and a.e. ω. Since $\|N(t) - N(s)\| \to 0$ as $t \downarrow s$, by the monotone convergence theorem, for each dyadic s, we can arrange that $N(t)(\omega)$ is continuous (among dyadic t's) from above (indeed, we can arrange continuity at dyadic rationals for a.e. ω despite jumps!). One can then define $N(t)(\omega)$ as $\lim_{t_m \downarrow t} N(t)(\omega)$ as t_m approaches t through dyadic rationals. By monotonicity, the limit exists. We summarize in:

Theorem 7.4.4. *There is a realization of $N(t)(\omega)$ so for a.e. ω, $N(t)(\omega)$ is monotone and continuous from the right.*

Thus, for a.e. ω, we have a monotone function and so an associated Stieltjes measure. Since $N(t)(\omega)$ is integer-valued, the measure is a pure point measure with integer weights. It is not hard to see (Problem 7) that for a.e. ω, the weights are all 1 and $\mu_\omega([-R, R])$ is polynomial-bounded. Thus, the Poisson process an be thought of as random collections of points!

Next, we want to turn to characterizations of the Poisson process that don't explicitly mention the Poisson distributions. A first guess might be that, passing to $N([a, b]) = N(b) - N(a)$, the N's are integer-valued, independent for disjoint intervals, and $N([a, b]) + N([b, c]) = N([a, c])$, and that this characterizes N.

But this is wrong! $2N$ has all these properties. What is different about $2N$ and N? For N, $\mathbb{P}(N([a, a + \frac{1}{m}]) = 2)$ is $O(\frac{1}{m^2})$, but it is $O(\frac{1}{m})$ for $2N$. That is, we need a condition that guarantees we aren't describing multiple particles on top of one another.

Theorem 7.4.5. *Let $N([a, b])$ be a family of random variables defined for all dyadic rationals $a < b$ with values in $\{0, 1, 2, \dots\}$. Suppose that*

  (i) *N is stationary, that is, $\{N([a_i, b_i])\}_{i=1}^m$ and $\{N([a_i + c, b_i + c])\}_{j=1}^m$ are identically distributed for all c and all $a_i < b_i$, $m = 1, 2, \dots$.*

  (ii) *N is additive, that is,*

$$N([a, b]) + N([b, c]) = N([a, c]) \tag{7.4.15}$$

  (iii) *N has independent increments, that is, if $\{[a_j, b_j]\}_{j=1}^m$ intersect at most in single points, then $\{N([a_j, b_j])\}_{j=1}^m$ are mutually independent.*

  (iv) *We have*

$$\mathbb{P}(N([0, a]) \geq 2) = o(a) \tag{7.4.16}$$

  as $a \downarrow 0$.

Then $N([a, b])$ is the Poisson process.

Proof. Let

$$\rho = \mathbb{E}(N([0,1])) \qquad (7.4.17)$$

Then by stationarity, $\mathbb{E}(N([\frac{j}{2^m}, \frac{j+1}{2^m}])) = \mathbb{E}(N([0, \frac{1}{2^m}]))$. So by additivity,

$$\mathbb{E}\left(N\left(\left[0, \frac{1}{2^m}\right]\right)\right) = \frac{\rho}{2^m} \qquad (7.4.18)$$

By additivity again for any dyadic rational $a < b$,

$$\mathbb{E}(N([a,b])) = \rho(b-a) \qquad (7.4.19)$$

Let $\varphi_s(t)$ be the characteristic function of $N([0,s])$. By (7.4.16) and (7.4.18),

$$\varphi_{1/2^m}(t) = 1 - \frac{\rho}{2^m} + \frac{\rho e^{it}}{2^m} + o(2^{-m}) \qquad (7.4.20)$$

Thus, by the compound interest formula,

$$\lim_{m\to\infty} [\varphi_{1/2^m}(t)]^{2^m} = \exp(-\rho + \rho e^{it}) \qquad (7.4.21)$$

By stationarity, independence, and additivity for each m (no limit!),

$$[\varphi_{1/2^m}(t)]^{2^m} = \varphi_1(t) \qquad (7.4.22)$$

Thus, $N([0,1])$ is a Poisson random variable and a similar argument applies to each $N([a,b])$. By (7.4.19) and independence, $N([a,b])$ is the Poisson process. $\qquad\square$

Consider now the Poisson process in one dimension. Think of a point, ω, as a point measure on $\mathbb{R}$. Let its pure points be $\ldots < \lambda_{-n} < \cdots < \lambda_{-1} \leq 0 < \lambda_1 < \ldots$. Then

Theorem 7.4.6. *For the Poisson process with density parameter, ρ, the probability distribution for λ_1 is the exponential distribution, (7.1.13), with parameter $\lambda = \rho$.*

Proof. For λ_1 to be greater than t, it is necessary and sufficient that $N([0,t]) = 0$. Thus,

$$\mathbb{P}(\lambda_1 > t) = e^{-\rho t} \qquad (7.4.23)$$

This is the commutative distribution function of a random variable with probability density on $[0,\infty)$ of

$$-\frac{d}{dt}\left(e^{-\rho t}\right) = \rho e^{-\rho t} \qquad (7.4.24)$$

$\qquad\square$

Further consideration shows $\{\lambda_{j+1} - \lambda_j\}_{j=1}^\infty$ are iidrv with the same distribution (Problem 8). The reader should consider why this is clearly to be expected.

Finally, we state the extension to $\mathbb{R}^\nu$, leaving the proof to the reader (Problem 2).

Theorem 7.4.7. *Fix $\rho > 0$. There exists a probability measure on the polynomially bounded pure point measures, μ_ω, on $\mathbb{R}^\nu$ so that if $N_\omega(\Omega)$ is the measure $\mu_\omega(\Omega)$, then*

(a) *$N_\omega(\Omega)$ and $N_\omega(\Omega')$ are independent if $\Omega \cap \Omega' = \emptyset$.*
(b) *$N_\omega(\Omega)$ is a Poisson random variable of expectation $\rho|\Omega|$ (where $|\cdot|$ is $\mathbb{R}^\nu$ Lebesgue measure).*

Moreover, this process is unique.

Notes and Historical Remarks. Poisson introduced his density precisely as the limit of binomial distributions in the low probability regime and applied the idea to several practical problems. He did this in two publications in the 1830s [**742, 745**].

Poisson mentioned this in passing and it was ignored until the first decade of the twentieth century when it reappeared in two ways. One involved queueing theory, the modeling of waiting lines. A. K. Erlang (1878–1929) [**282**], the father of the subject, essentially used a Poisson process to simulate new people joining the queue. His paper was in Danish and it is probably not a coincidence that he was working in the technical group at the Danish telephone company, a group headed by Johan Jensen (the Jensen of Jensen's inequality and Jensen's formula).

The other starts with a work of William Sealy Gosset (1876-1937) who wrote papers under the pen name "Student" (he is responsible for Student's t-distribution) [**897**] and rediscovered the Poisson distribution. By the follow-up papers of Whitaker [**987**] and Soper [**869**], the connection to Poisson was understood.

In 1937, Raikov [**755**] proved that if X and Y are independent random variables and $X + Y$ has a Poisson distribution, then X and Y are Poisson. *Raikov's theorem* provides a universal aspect of the Poisson process. A similar theorem, known as *Cramer's theorem* [**208**], says the same thing for the normal distribution.

Problems

1. Use a computer algebra system like Mathematica or Maple to study the cumulative distribution function for a Poisson random variable, X, of mean 10. Prove that $\mathbb{P}(X \le 20) \ge .99$ and $\mathbb{P}(X \le 15) \ge .95$.

Remark. The cdf of a Poisson variable will be a primitive function in these systems.

2. Provide the details of the proof of Theorem 7.4.7.

3. Verify (7.4.6) by using the formula for $\mathbb{P}(B^{(n,p_n)} = j)$ directly.

4. Let $z_n \to z$ in $\mathbb{C}$. Prove that

$$\lim_{n \to \infty} \left(1 - \frac{z_n}{n} \right)^n = e^{-z} \tag{7.4.25}$$

(*Hint*: Look at logs.)

5. Let $\rho \colon \mathbb{R}^\nu \to (0, \infty)$ be a continuous function with $\int_{\mathbb{R}^\nu} \rho(x)\, dx = \infty$. Let Λ be a large box and let $N = [\int_\Lambda \rho(x)\, d^\nu x]$. Put N particles in Λ, independently, each with identical distribution $\rho(x) / \int_\Lambda \rho(x)\, d^\nu x$. Let Ω be fixed. Prove in the limit $\Lambda \to \mathbb{R}^\nu$ the numbers of particles in Ω is a Poisson random variable with expectation $\int_\Omega \rho(x)\, d^\nu x$.

6. Prove the uniqueness assertion in Theorem 7.4.3.

7. Let $N(t)$ be the family of random variables constructed in Theorem 7.4.4. Prove that

$$\sum_{n=1}^\infty \sum_{j=1}^{2^n} \mathbb{P}\left(N\left(\frac{j+1}{2^n} \right) - N\left(\frac{j}{2^n} \right) \geq 2 \right) < \infty \tag{7.4.26}$$

Use this to prove that with probability one, the corresponding Stieltjes measure has weights one on all jumps.

8. Let $\lambda_1, \lambda_2, \ldots$ be the positions of pure points for the Poisson process on $[0, \infty)$ with density ρ. Prove that with $\lambda_0 \equiv 0$, $\{\lambda_{j+1} - \lambda_j\}_{j=1}^\infty$ are mutually independent, each with distribution $\mathbb{P}(\lambda_{j+1} - \lambda_j > t) = e^{-\rho t}$.

7.5. Markov Chains

> Any one who considers arithmetical methods of producing random digits
> is, of course, in a state of sin.
> —*J. von Neumann* [**971**][2]

We continue looking at sequences of random variables, $X_1, X_2, \ldots$, but want to go beyond the independence that has dominated so far. Of course, we've considered $S_n = X_1 + \cdots + X_n$ which are not independent, but we also want to go beyond independent increments. We'll use the language of

---

[2] *Note*: Often misquoted as "Anyone who attempts to generate random numbers by deterministic means is, of course, living in a state of sin." It is possible von Neumann later said it this way but I've been unable to find a reference

dynamics, thinking of j in X_j as time. We'll focus on a class called *Markov processes* where, in a sense we'll make precise, the future only depends on the past through the present. To further simplify, not only will "time" be discrete, but X_j will only take a finite set of values which we can think of as states, $s_1, \ldots, s_m$.

To make sense of "the future only depends on the past through the present," we introduce conditional probabilities.

Definition. Let A, B be events in a probability measure space with $\mathbb{P}(A) > 0$. Then the *conditional probability* of B, given A, is defined by

$$\mathbb{P}(B \mid A) = \frac{\mathbb{P}(A \cap B)}{\mathbb{P}(A)} \tag{7.5.1}$$

Intuitively, if we know event A happens, we expect to have to change probabilities but we want to use nothing more a priori than that we know A has happened. Notice that A and B are independent events if and only if

$$\mathbb{P}(B \mid A) = \mathbb{P}(B) \tag{7.5.2}$$

meeting a naive notion of conditional probabilities and of independence and that $B \mapsto \mathbb{P}(B \mid A)$ defines a probability measure.

Suppose now we imagine measuring finitely many random variables, $Y_1, Y_2, \ldots, Y_k$, taking values in a finite set, S. If $s_1, \ldots, s_k \in S$, we can look at the event

$$A(s_1, \ldots, s_k) = \{Y_1 = s_1, \ldots, Y_k = s_k\} \tag{7.5.3}$$

Then $\mathbb{P}(\cdot \mid A(s_1, \ldots, s_k))$ is a family of probabilities depending on $s_1, \ldots, s_k$ (if $\mathbb{P}(A(s_1^{(0)}, \ldots, s_k^{(0)})) = 0$ for some set of s's, we ignore that point). We write this as $\mathbb{P}(\cdot \mid Y_1 = s_1, \ldots, Y_k = s_k)$. We can now define a Markov chain by:

Definition. A *Markov chain* is a family of random variables, $X_1, X_2, \ldots$, taking values in a finite set, S, so that for each n and each B an event depending only on $X_{n+1}, X_{n+2}, \ldots$, we have

$$\mathbb{P}(B \mid X_1 = s_1, \ldots, X_n = s_n) \tag{7.5.4}$$

is only a function of s_n. We say the chain is *stationary* if the joint distribution of $(X_1, \ldots, X_k)$ and $(X_{n+1}, X_{n+2}, \ldots, X_{n+k})$ are the same for each $k, n = 1, 2, \ldots$. We say the chain is *nondegenerate* if each $s_1, s_2, \in S$,

$$\mathbb{P}(X_1 = s_1, X_2 = s_2) \neq 0 \tag{7.5.5}$$

Since S is finite, we can replace its values by the labels, that is, take $S = \{1, \ldots, k\}$. We now define matrices, $p^{(n)}$, by

$$p_{ij}^{(n)} = \mathbb{P}(X_n = i \mid X_1 = j) \tag{7.5.6}$$

For j fixed, $p_{ij}^{(n)}$ describes the probability distribution at time (n) assuming $X_1 = j$. Thus,

$$\sum_{i=1}^{k} p_{ij}^{(n)} = 1, \qquad j = 1, \ldots, k \tag{7.5.7}$$

We are going to prove the following result:

Theorem 7.5.1. *Let $\{X_n\}_{n=1}^{\infty}$ be a stationary, nondegenerate, Markov chain. Then there is a vector $q \in \mathbb{R}^k$ so that*

$$q_i > 0, \qquad \sum_{i=1}^{k} q_i = 1 \tag{7.5.8}$$

and so that for each j,

$$\lim_{n \to \infty} p_{ij}^{(n)} = q_i \tag{7.5.9}$$

with the rate of convergence being exponentially fast in n.

Thus, if we think of the chain as describing a dynamics, no matter what the value of X_1, as $n \to \infty$, the probability distribution of X_n approaches q. We'll begin by reducing this theorem to one in finite matrix theory and then prove that matrix theorem.

As a preliminary, we note

Lemma 7.5.2. *Let $\{C_j\}_{j=1}^{m}$ be a partition of a probability measure space into disjoint sets. Then*

$$\mathbb{P}(A \mid B) = \sum_{j=1}^{m} \mathbb{P}(A \mid B \cap C_j)\mathbb{P}(C_j \mid B) \tag{7.5.10}$$

In particular, if X, Y, Z are random variables taking values in a finite set, $S = \{s_j\}_{j=1}^{m}$, we have

$$\mathbb{P}(X = s_k \mid Y = s_\ell) = \sum_{j=1}^{m} \mathbb{P}(X = s_k \mid Y = s_\ell, Z = s_j)\mathbb{P}(Z = s_j \mid Y = s_\ell) \tag{7.5.11}$$

Proof. Since $\{C_j\}_{j=1}^{m}$ is a partition,

$$\mathbb{P}(A \cap B) = \sum_{j=1}^{m} \mathbb{P}(A \cap B \cap C_j) = \sum_{j=1}^{m} \frac{\mathbb{P}(A \cap B \cap C_j)}{\mathbb{P}(B \cap C_j)} P(B \cap C_j) \tag{7.5.12}$$

Dividing by $\mathbb{P}(B)$ yields (7.5.10). $\qquad \square$

Let T be the matrix, called the *transition matrix*,

$$T_{ij} = \mathbb{P}(X_2 = i \mid X_1 = j) \tag{7.5.13}$$

By stationarity,
$$T_{ij} = \mathbb{P}(X_n = i \mid X_{n-1} = j) \tag{7.5.14}$$
By the Markov property and the lemma,

$\mathbb{P}(X_n = i \mid X_1 = j)$

$$= \sum_{\ell=1}^{k} \mathbb{P}(X_n = i \mid X_{n-1} = \ell, X_1 = j)\mathbb{P}(X_{n-1} = \ell \mid X_1 = j)$$
$$\tag{7.5.15}$$

$$= \sum_{\ell=1}^{k} \mathbb{P}(X_n = i \mid X_{n-1} = \ell)\mathbb{P}(X_{n-1} = \ell \mid X_1 = j) \tag{7.5.16}$$

$$= \sum_{\ell=1}^{k} T_{i\ell}\mathbb{P}(X_{n-1} = \ell \mid X_1 = j) \tag{7.5.17}$$

In terms of matrices,
$$p^{(n)} = Tp^{(n-1)} \tag{7.5.18}$$
so since $p^{(1)} = T$, we have
$$p_{ij}^{(n)} = (T^n)_{ij} \tag{7.5.19}$$
Thus, we are reduced to understanding high powers of a special class of matrices:

Definition. A square matrix, T, is called *strictly stochastic* if its matrix elements are all strictly positive and its columns sum to 1.

Here is what we'll prove below:

Theorem 7.5.3. (Perron–Frobenius Theorem for Strictly Stochastic Matrices). *Let T be a finite strictly stochastic matrix. Then 1 is an algebraically simple eigenvalue with eigenvector*

$$\begin{pmatrix} q_1 \\ \vdots \\ q_n \end{pmatrix}$$

where each $q_j > 0$. Every other eigenvalue, λ, of T has $|\lambda| < 1$. For some $\alpha \in (0,1)$ and $C > 0$, we have that

$$\sup_{i,j}|(T^n)_{ij} - q_j| \leq C\alpha^n \tag{7.5.20}$$

Remark. This is a special case of a more general result discussed in the Notes and Problems 1 and 2. This more general result doesn't require that the columns sum to 1. Its proof requires an argument to show there is an eigenvector with strictly positive elements. In this case, for T^t, we have

$$\begin{pmatrix} 1 \\ \vdots \\ 1 \end{pmatrix}$$

is an eigenvector, and that's enough to avoid this extra argument.

Proof of Theorem 7.5.1 given Theorem 7.5.3. By (7.5.19), $p_{ij}^{(n)}$ are the matrix elements of T^n for a strictly stochastic matrix. (7.5.20) is the required result. □

To separate out existence of a positive eigenfunction from the rest of the argument, we start with the consequence of such existence.

Proposition 7.5.4. *Let A be an $n \times n$ matrix with strictly positive matrix elements. Suppose there is an eigenvector, x, with components $x_j > 0$ and*

$$Ax = \beta x \tag{7.5.21}$$

Then

(a) *For any $y \in \mathbb{C}^n$,*

$$|(Ay)_j| \leq \beta x_j \sup_k [|y_k| x_k^{-1}] \tag{7.5.22}$$

(b) *β has geometric multiplicity 1.*
(c) *β has algebraic multiplicity 1.*
(d) *All other eigenvalues, λ, have $|\lambda| < \beta$.*
(e) *For some $\alpha \in (0,1)$, $C > 0$, and P the projection associated to β in the Jordan normal form, we have that for all m,*

$$\|A^m - \beta^m P\| \leq C\beta^m \alpha^m \tag{7.5.23}$$

Remark. Problem 1 proves that A always has such a strictly positive eigenvector.

Proof. (a) Since $a_{ij} > 0$, we have that

$$|(Ay)_j| \leq \sum_{k=1}^{n} a_{jk} x_k (|y_k| x_k^{-1}) \tag{7.5.24}$$

$$\leq (\sup|y_k| x_k^{-1}) \beta x_j$$

proving (7.5.23).

(b) Let $\tilde{x}$ be another eigenvector for eigenvalue β. By replacing $\tilde{x}$ by $\mathrm{Re}\,\tilde{x}$ or $\mathrm{Im}\,\tilde{x}$, we can suppose $\tilde{x}$ is real. Let

$$\gamma = \min_j (\tilde{x}_j x_j^{-1}) \tag{7.5.25}$$

Then

$$(\tilde{x} - \gamma x)_j = x_j (\tilde{x}_j x_j^{-1} - \gamma) \geq 0 \tag{7.5.26}$$

with at least one component zero and one nonzero (since $\tilde{x}$ is not a multiple of x). But

$$A(\tilde{x} - \gamma x) = \beta(\tilde{x} - \gamma x) \tag{7.5.27}$$

Since $a_{ij} > 0$ and $(\tilde{x} - \gamma x)_j \geq 0$ and not all zero, this implies $(\tilde{x} - \gamma x)_j > 0$ for all j, which is a contradiction.

(c) We need only show that if $\beta P + N$ is the β component in the Jordan normal form for A, then $w \in \text{Ran}(P) \Rightarrow Nw = 0$. So suppose $Pw = w$ and $Nw \neq 0$. Let $N^\ell w = 0$, $N^{\ell-1}w \neq 0$. Then

$$A^m w = (\beta P + N)^m w = \sum_{j=0}^{\ell-1} \binom{m}{j} \beta^{m-j} N^j w \qquad (7.5.28)$$

Thus,

$$\beta^{-m}\|A^m w\| \to \infty \qquad (7.5.29)$$

since the norm is asymptotic to $\binom{m}{\ell-1}\beta^{-(\ell-1)}\|N^{\ell-1}w\|$.

This is inconsistent with (7.5.22) which implies

$$\|A^m y\| \leq \beta^m \left(\sup_j x_j\right) \sup_k(|y_k| x_k^{-1}) \qquad (7.5.30)$$

We conclude $N = 0$, so by (b), $\dim(P) = 1$.

(d) Since $a_{ij} > 0$, we have

$$|(Ay)_j| \leq (A|y|)_j \qquad (7.5.31)$$

with equality only if $y_j = |y_j|e^{i\theta}$ for a θ independent of j. This plus (7.5.22) implies any eigenvalue, λ, of A has $|\lambda| < \beta$ unless $y_j = |y_j|e^{i\theta}$, and then $\lambda = \beta$. Thus, any $\lambda \neq \beta$ has $|\lambda| < \beta$ as claimed.

(e) For any λ, since $N^n = 0$,

$$\|(\lambda P + N)^m\| \leq \sum_{j=0}^{n-1} \binom{m}{j} \|N^j\|\|\lambda\|^{m-j}\|P\|$$

If $\alpha = \beta^{-1}(\frac{1}{2}(\beta + \max_{\lambda \neq \beta}|\lambda|)) < 1$, this shows that

$$\|A^m - \beta^m P\| \leq C\beta^m \alpha^m \qquad (7.5.32)$$

since $m^{n-1}|\lambda|^{m-j}$ is dominated by $C(\alpha\beta)^m$. $\qquad \square$

Proof of Theorem 7.5.3. That the columns of T sum to 1 implies

$$\begin{pmatrix} 1 \\ \vdots \\ 1 \end{pmatrix}$$

is an eigenvector of T^t with eigenvalue 1. Thus, by the proposition, 1 is an algebraically simple eigenvalue of T^t and

$$\|(T^t)^n - P^t\| \to 0 \qquad (7.5.33)$$

as $n \to \infty$, where P^t is the associated Jordan normal form projection. By Proposition 1.7.7, $P_{ij}^t = q_i$, where $Tq = q$ and

$$\sum_{i=1}^k q_i = 1 \qquad (7.5.34)$$

(since the eigenvector of T^t has all 1's). By (7.5.33), $P_{ij}^t \geq 0$ so $q_i \geq 0$. Since

$$q_i = \sum_{j=1}^{k} t_{ij} q_j \tag{7.5.35}$$

we have $q_i > 0$ since $t_{ij} > 0$ and not all q_k are zero (by (7.5.34)). Thus, by the proposition, we have (7.5.20). □

While we have proven asymptotic results for Markov processes in terms of its transition matrix, we haven't actually proven the existence of any Markov processes. Here are two results that remedy that:

Theorem 7.5.5. *Let T be an arbitrary, strictly stochastic matrix. Then there is a unique stationary Markov chain with T as transition matrix.*

Proof. If we define joint distributions for $X_1, X_2, \ldots, X_n$ for each n that are consistent, then the Kolmogorov consistency theorem (Theorem 4.12.6) yields a single underlying probability space. Let $\{q_i\}_{i=1}^{k}$ be the unique positive vector obeying (7.5.34) and (7.5.35). Define a joint distribution

$$\mathbb{P}(X_1 = i_1, X_2 = i_2, \ldots, X_n = i_n) = q_{i_1} \prod_{j=1}^{n-2} t_{i_{j+1} i_j} \equiv P_{i_1, \ldots i_n}^{(n)} \tag{7.5.36}$$

By (7.5.35) and $\sum_{i=1}^{k} t_{ij} = 1$, we get

$$\sum_{i_1=1}^{k} p_{i_1 \ldots i_n}^{(n)} = p_{i_2 \ldots i_n}^{(n-1)}; \qquad \sum_{i_n=1}^{k} p_{i_1 \ldots i_n}^{(n)} = p_{i_1 \ldots i_{n-1}}^{(n-1)} \tag{7.5.37}$$

The second equation implies the consistency of the distributions and the normalization. The first implies the stationarity. Thus, we have the existence of a stationary chain. That it is Markov with transition matrix, T, is an easy calculation (Problem 5).

Thus, we have existence. To prove uniqueness, note that we know that limiting distributions of X_n as $n \to \infty$ is $\{q_i\}_{i=1}^{k}$ so stationarity implies this is the distribution of any X_n and, in particular, of X_1. If $p_{i_1 \ldots i_n}^{(n)}$ is the joint distribution of $X_1 = i_1, \ldots, X_n = i_n$, then the Markov property, stationarity, and that T is the transition matrix implies

$$p_{i_1 \ldots i_n}^{(n)} = t_{i_n i_{n-1}} p_{i_1 \ldots i_{n-1}}^{(n-1)} \tag{7.5.38}$$

This plus induction plus the above noted $p_i^{(1)} = q_i$ shows $p_n^{(n)}$ is given by (7.5.36), proving uniqueness. □

Theorem 7.5.6. *Let T be an arbitrary, strictly stochastic matrix. Let $\{r_i\}_{i=1}^{k}$ be an arbitrary set of probability weights (i.e., $r_i \geq 0$, $\sum_{i=1}^{k} r_i = 1$).*

Then there is a unique Markov process with (7.5.14) for each n and with $\mathbb{P}(X_1 = j) = n_j$. *Moreover, we have that* $\mathbb{P}(X_n = j) \to q_j$ *exponentially fast.*

Remark. Thus, the chain may not be stationary, but the transition matrix is assumed stationary.

Proof. Define $p^{(n)}_{i_1 \dots i_n}$ by (7.5.36) with q_i replaced by r_i. The second equation in (7.5.37) still holds, so these are consistent and define a Markov chain, and the proof of uniqueness is the same. $\mathbb{P}(X_n = j)$ is $(T^{n-1}r)_j$. Since $\sum_{j=1}^{n} r_j = 1$, $Pr \neq 0$, where P is the Jordan normal form projection onto eigenvector q so that same proof as Theorem 7.5.3 implies the convergence. $\qquad\square$

Notes and Historical Remarks. Markov processes are named after Andrei Markov (1856–1922), who we've already seen in connection with Markov's inequality, his work on the central limit theorem, and the continued fraction approach to the moment problem (the Markov in Riesz–Markov is his son, also named Andrei Markov (1903–79)).

Markov's 1906 paper [**631**] was motivated by a 1902 claim of the Moscow-based mathematician P. A. Nekrasov (1853–1924) [**678**]. The Moscow group had strong religious mystical underpinnings to their mathematics, and Nekrasov, who found that the law of large numbers held for pairwise independent random variables, claimed it only held under that hypothesis, justifying this on speculations concerning free will! Markov showed that Markov chains obeyed a strong law of large numbers and a central limit theorem (see Problems 3 and 4). Markov was an outspoken atheist.

Andrei Markov was a student of Chebyshev, noted not only as the inventor of Markov chains but for his work on the central limit theorem, on continued fractions (a precursor of Stieltjes' work on the moment problem), and for Markov's inequality. His best students all made reputations outside Russia: Tamarkin (Brown) and Uspensky (Stanford) in the United States, Besicovitch (Cambridge) in England, and Voronoy in Poland. His grandstudents included Dunford and Sierpinski.

Markov chains have a huge number of applications in a variety of sciences, and following a classic book of Kemeny–Snell [**485**], there is a vast textbook literature [**194, 269, 686, 769, 838, 894**]. A key extension to countable state spaces was initially done by Kolmogorov [**505**].

The Perron–Frobenius theorem has a more general form (Problems 1 and 2).

Theorem 7.5.7 (Perron–Frobenius Theorem). *Let T be a matrix with $t_{ij} > 0$. Then* $\mathrm{spr}(T) = \sup\{|\lambda| \mid \lambda \in \sigma(T)\}$ *is a simple eigenvalue of algebraic multiplicity* 1. *Every other eigenvalue,* λ, *has* $|\lambda| < \mathrm{spr}(T)$. *For some*

$\alpha \in (0,1)$ *and* C*, with* P *the spectral projection associated to* $\mathrm{spr}(T)$*, we have*

$$\|T - \mathrm{spr}(T)^n P\| \le C(\alpha\,\mathrm{spr}(T))^n \qquad (7.5.39)$$

Problem 1 proves T has a positive eigenvector. Problem 2 then uses Proposition 7.5.4 to prove this theorem.

Theorem 7.5.7 is named after 1907–12 work of Perron [**713**] and Frobenius [**330, 331**]. It was only in 1931 that von Mises [**959**] realized the applicability of this theorem to the study of Markov chains.

There are many extensions of the Perron–Frobenius theorem. It isn't necessary that each $t_{ij} > 0$. T is called *irreducible* if, for each i, j, there is n with $(T^n)_{ij} > 0$. It is also known (see, e.g., Gantmacher [**338**]; see Problem 6 also) that if T is irreducible and positive, $\sigma_r(T)$ is a simple eigenvalue, but there can be other eigenvalues, λ, with $|\lambda| = \sigma_r(T)$—they have to lie at $\sigma_r(T)\omega$, where ω is a root of unity (see Problem 7 for an example).

Infinite-dimensional analogs of the Perron–Frobenius theorem for self-adjoint semigroups have been used to prove nondegeneracy of the ground state in quantum mechanics; see Section XIII.12 of Reed–Simon [**765**] and its historical notes.

Problems

1. This problem will prove that an $n \times n$ matrix, T, with strictly positive matrix elements has a strictly positive eigenvector with eigenvalue

$$\lambda = \min\left\{ \max_{i=1,\ldots,n}\left[\sum_{j=1}^{n} \frac{t_{ij}x_j}{x_i} \right] \;\middle|\; x_i > 0, \sum_{j=1}^{n} x_i = 1 \right\} \qquad (7.5.40)$$

This is called the *Collatz–Wielandt formula* after [**203, 992**].

(a) Let $\Delta_{n-1} = \{(x_1,\ldots,x_n) \in \mathbb{R}^n \mid x_i \ge 0, \sum_{j=1}^{n} x_i = 1\}$. Define $f \colon \Delta_{n-1} \to (0, \infty]$ by

$$f(x) = \max_{i=1,\ldots,n}\left[\sum_{j=1}^{n} \frac{t_{ij}x_j}{x_i} \right] \qquad (7.5.41)$$

Prove that there is $x_j^{(0)} \in \Delta_{n-1}^{\mathrm{int}}$ so that

$$f(x^{(0)}) = \min_{x \in \Delta_{n-1}} f(x) \qquad (7.5.42)$$

(b) Prove that if (7.5.41) defines $f(x)$ for any $x \in \mathbb{R}_+^n = \{x \mid x_i > 0\}$, then (7.5.42) still holds.

(c) Suppose for some i_0,

$$\sum_{j=1}^{n} \frac{t_{i_0 j} x_j^{(0)}}{x_{i_0}^{(0)}} < f(x^{(0)}) \tag{7.5.43}$$

Prove that for ε small,

$$f(x_1^{(0)}, x_2^{(0)}, \ldots, x_{i_0}^{(0)} - \varepsilon, x \ldots x_n^{(0)}) < f(x^{(0)}) \tag{7.5.44}$$

and deduce that for all i, we have

$$\sum_{j=1}^{n} t_{ij} x_j^{(0)} = f(x^{(0)}) x_i^{(0)} \tag{7.5.45}$$

(d) Prove that T has an eigenvector with all positive components.

2. Combine Problem 1 and Proposition 7.5.4 to prove Theorem 7.5.7.

3. (Strong law of large numbers for Markov chains). Let $\{X_n\}_{n=1}^{\infty}$ be a stationary, nondegenerate Markov chain with the value v_j, in state j. Let $\{q_j\}_{j=1}^{k}$ be the invariant measure of Theorem 7.5.1. Prove that with probability 1, we have

$$\lim_{n\to\infty} \frac{1}{n} \sum_{j=1}^{n} X_n = \sum_{j=1}^{k} q_j v_j \tag{7.5.46}$$

4. Under the hypotheses of Problem 3, prove that

$$\sigma^2 = \lim_{n\to\infty} \frac{1}{n} \mathbb{E}\left(\left(\sum_{j=1}^{n} [X_j - \mathbb{E}(X_j)]\right)^2\right)$$

exists and that $\frac{1}{\sqrt{n}} \sum_{j=1}^{n} [X_j - \mathbb{E}(X_j)]$ converges in distribution to $N(0,\sigma)$.

5. Confirm that chain $\{X_j\}_{j=1}^{\infty}$ constructed in Theorem 7.5.5 has the Markov property.

6. Let T be an irreducible finite matrix with nonnegative matrix elements.

(a) Prove that for ε small, $(\mathbb{1} - \varepsilon T)^{-1}$ exists and has strictly positive matrix elements.

(b) Prove that T has a strictly positive eigenvector.

7. Let T be a permutation matrix, that is, for some $\pi \in \Sigma_n$, the symmetric groups,

$$T_{ij} = \begin{cases} 1 & \text{if } j = \pi(i) \\ 0, & \text{otherwise} \end{cases}$$

(a) Prove that T is unitary and conclude all its eigenvalues lie on $\partial\mathbb{D}$.

(b) Prove that if π has j cycles in its decomposition into disjoint cycles, then 1 is an eigenvalue of multiplicity j.

(c) If π is a single cycle, for example, $\pi(i) = i + 1$ (for $i < n$), 1 (for $i = n$), prove that the eigenvalues of π are the n-th roots of unity and each is simple.

(d) In general, prove that all the eigenvalues of T are roots of unity.

Chapter 8

Bonus Chapter: Hausdorff Measure and Dimension

Unfortunately, the world has not been designed for the convenience of mathematicians.

—*B. Mandelbrot* (1924–2010) [**626**]

Big Notions and Theorems: Outer Measure, Carthéodory's Theorem, Metric Outer Measure, Hausdorff Measure, Hausdorff Dimension, Rogers–Taylor Theorem, Box Counting Dimensions

In some ways, the two sections of this brief chapter should be bonus sections for Chapter 4. We've put them here to focus on Hausdorff dimensions as an important element of analysis independently of measure theory—it is also true that while we and many others discuss Hausdorff measure, there is essentially no discussion of integrals with respect to that measure.

That said, the ideas of Section 8.1, in particular, supplement Chapter 4. The central point of view of that chapter is Baire measure theory on compact Hausdorff spaces and its extensions to (σ-finite) Baire measures on σ-compact spaces. We did go beyond this somewhat by discussing (probability) measures on Polish spaces in Section 4.14 and, even more, some general measure theory in Section 4.13. But that section told only half the story. In the central section on Baire measure (Section 4.4), we constructed an integral on Baire functions and then used it to construct a measure on Baire sets.

In Section 4.13, we described how to go from a general (σ-finite) measure to an integral but were silent on how to actually construct measures. Section 8.1 will discuss the other half. We'll define an outer measure as a map, μ^*, from *all* subsets, 2^X, of a space X, to $[0, \infty]$ which is monotone, countably subadditive, and nontrivial ($\mu^*(\emptyset) = 0$). Associated to $[0, 1]$ is the outer measure

$$\mu^*(A) = \inf\{\sum_{j=1}^{N}(b_j - a_j) \mid A \subset \cup_{j=1}^{N}(a_j, b_j)\} \tag{8.0.1}$$

We'll then prove there is a natural subclass of 2^X which is a σ-algebra and so that μ^*, restricted to this set, is a measure. We'll also prove that this outer measure has a property shared by many other outer measures on metric spaces that make all Borel sets elements of the distinguished σ-algebra on which μ^* is a measure. This will provide a construction of Lebesgue measure that easily extends to Lebesgue–Stieltjes measures.

In Section 8.2, we'll fix $\mathbb{R}^\nu$ and $0 \le s \le \nu$ and define

$$h_s^*(A) = \lim_{\delta \downarrow 0} \inf\{\sum_{j=1}^{N}(\operatorname{diam} B_j)^s \mid B_j \text{ balls of } \operatorname{diam} \le \delta; A \subset \cup_{j=1}^{N} B_j\}$$
$$\tag{8.0.2}$$

This will be an outer measure and the corresponding Borel measure constructed via the method of Section 8.1 will be the s-dimensional Hausdorff measure. For $s < \nu$, it is not a σ-finite measure, but it is still useful. For any set $A \subset \mathbb{R}^\nu$, there is a unique s_0, called its Hausdorff dimension, so that $h_s(A) = \infty$ if $s < s_0$ and $h_s(A) = 0$ if $s > s_0$. We'll see how Hausdorff dimension can be used to classify singular continuous measures.

We remind the reader of an important convention we use: Baire measures, μ, are countably additive functions on the Baire sets with $\mu(K) < \infty$ for all compact G_δ. Borel measures are just countably additive functions on the Borel sets with no finiteness conditions. h_s for $s < \nu$ is a Borel measure but not a Baire measure.

8.1. The Carathéodory Construction

We discuss in this section a method of constructing countably additive set functions on certain σ-algebras including, in certain metric space situations, the Borel sets.

Definition. Let X be a set. An *outer measure* on X is a map, μ^*, from 2^X, the set of *all* subsets of X, to $[0, \infty]$ obeying

(i) $\mu^*(\emptyset) = 0$

(ii) μ^* is *monotone*, i.e., $A \subseteq B \Rightarrow \mu^*(A) \le \mu^*(B)$

(iii) μ^* is *countably subadditive*, i.e., for any countable collection of sets, $\{A_j\}_{j=1}^\infty$

$$\mu^*(\bigcup_{j=1}^\infty A_j) \le \sum_{j=1}^\infty \mu^*(A_j) \qquad (8.1.1)$$

Remark. For any $a \in [0,\infty]$, we interpret $a+\infty = \infty$. Any sum of elements of $[0,\infty]$ makes sense in $[0,\infty]$.

Proposition 8.1.1. (a) *Let $\mathcal{S}$ be a family of subsets of X so that $\emptyset \in \mathcal{S}$ and X is a countable union of sets in $\mathcal{S}$ and let $\mu_0 : \mathcal{S} \mapsto [0,\infty]$ obey $\mu_0(\emptyset) = 0$. Then*

$$\mu^*(A) = \inf\{\sum_{j=1}^\infty \mu_0(S_j) \mid A \subset \cup_{j=1}^\infty S_j; \text{ all } S_j \in \mathcal{S}\} \qquad (8.1.2)$$

is an outer measure.

(b) *If μ_δ^* is a family of outer measures, then*

$$\mu^*(A) = \sup_\delta \mu_\delta^*(A) \qquad (8.1.3)$$

is an outer measure

Proof. (a) Clearly $\mu^*(A) \ge 0$ and since $\emptyset \in \mathcal{S}$, $\mu^*(\emptyset) \le 0$ so $\mu^*(\emptyset) = 0$. If $A \subset B$, any cover of B is a cover of A, so μ^* is an inf over a larger set of values, i.e., $\mu^*(A) \le \mu^*(B)$.

Given $\{A_j\}_{j=1}^\infty$ and $\delta > 0$, pick $\{S_{j,k}\}_{j,k=1}^\infty$ so $S_{j,k} \in \mathcal{S}$, $A_j \subset \bigcup_{k=1}^\infty S_{j,k}$ and $\sum_{k=1}^\infty \mu_0(S_{j,k}) \le \mu^*(A_j) + \frac{\delta}{2^j}$. Then $\bigcup_{j=1}^\infty A_j \subset \bigcup_{j,k} S_{j,k}$ and

$$\sum_{j,k} \mu_0(S_{j,k}) \le \sum_{j=1}^\infty (\mu^*(A_j) + \frac{\delta}{2^j}) = \delta + \sum_{j=1}^\infty \mu^*(A_j)$$

Thus, $\mu^*(\bigcup_{j=1}^\infty A_j) \le \delta + \sum_{j=1}^\infty \mu^*(A_j)$. Since δ is arbitrary, we have (8.1.1).

(b) Clearly μ^* lies in $[0,\infty]$ and $\mu^*(\emptyset) = 0$. If $A \subset B$, for any δ, $\mu_\delta^*(A) \le \mu_\delta^*(B) \le \mu^*(B)$, i.e., $\mu^*(A) \le \mu^*(B)$. Similarly, for any δ,

$$\mu_\delta^*(\cup_{j=1}^\infty A_j) \le \sum_{j=1}^\infty \mu_\delta^*(A_j) \le \sum_{j=1}^\infty \mu^*(A_j)$$

so (8.1.1) holds. $\qquad \square$

Virtually all interesting uses of outer measure come from this proposition. (b) is used when we employ (a) and take $\mathcal{S}^{(\delta)}$ depending on δ with fewer sets as δ decreases. We use the same μ_0 but μ_δ^* is monotone increasing and $\mu^* = \sup_\delta \mu_\delta^* = \lim_{\delta \downarrow 0} \mu_\delta^*$. This is the procedure we'll use for Hausdorff measure in the next section (See (8.2.2)). As we are about to see, Lebesgue and Lebesgue–Stieltjes outer measures are of type (a).

Example 8.1.2 (Lebesgue outer measure). Let $X = [0,1]$ and $\mathcal{S} = \{[a,b] \mid 0 \leq a < b \leq 1\}$ and $\mu_0([a,b]) = b - a$. Then μ^* is called Lebesgue outer measure. We can do the same with $X = \mathbb{R}$. Notice that

$$\mu^*([a,b]) = \mu_0([a,b]) \tag{8.1.4}$$

□

Example 8.1.3 (Lebesgue–Stieltjes outer measure). Let α be a monotone function on $[0,1]$. If α is continuous, we can define μ_α^* as above with $\mu_0([a,b]) = \alpha(b) - \alpha(a)$. If α has discontinuities, we have to be more careful. In that case, we define $\alpha(a\pm) = \lim_{\varepsilon \downarrow 0} \alpha(a \pm \varepsilon)$ for $a \neq 0, 1$, with $\alpha(0_-) = \alpha(0)$, $\alpha(1_+) = \alpha(1)$. We can proceed in several ways. We can do as above but use for $b \neq 1$, (a,b) rather than $[a,b]$ with $\mu_0((a,b)) = \alpha(b_-) - \alpha(a_+)$. We can avoid problems by only letting $(a,b) \subset \mathcal{S}$ if a or b is not a point of discontinuity in $(0,1)$. Or we can demand $\alpha(a) = \alpha(a_-)$ (i.e., α continuous from below) except perhaps at $a = 1$ and take $\mathcal{S}$ to be half-open intervals $[a,b)$ or $\{1\}$ with $\mu_0([a,b)) = \alpha(b) - \alpha(a)$, $\mu_0(\{1\}) = \alpha(1) - \alpha(1_-)$. All these lead to the same μ_α^* with

$$\mu_\alpha^*((a,b)) = \alpha(b_-) - \alpha(a_+), \quad \mu_\alpha^*([a,b]) = \alpha(b_+) - \alpha(a_-)$$

With any of these constructions, $\mu^*([a,b)) = \mu_0([a,b))$.   □

Carathéodory's key realization is to look at a particular class of sets.

Definition. Given an outer measure, μ^*, we say $A \subset X$ is *μ^*-measurable* if and only if for all $Y \subset X$, we have

$$\mu^*(Y) = \mu^*(Y \cap A) + \mu^*(Y \setminus A) \tag{8.1.5}$$

By subadditivity, we always have that

$$\mu^*(Y) \leq \mu^*(Y \cap A) + \mu^*(Y \setminus A) \tag{8.1.6}$$

(since $Y = (Y \cap A) \cup (Y \setminus A)$) so (8.1.5) is equivalent to

$$\mu^*(Y) \geq \mu^*(Y \cap A) + \mu^*(Y \setminus A) \tag{8.1.7}$$

We let $\mathcal{M}$ be the set of μ^*-measurable sets. The main result of this section is

Theorem 8.1.4 (Carathéodory's Theorem). *Let μ^* be an outer measure on X. The set, $\mathcal{M}$, of μ^*-measurable sets is a σ-algebra and μ^* is a measure on those sets, i.e., μ^* is countably additive on the μ^*-measurable sets. Moreover, if $\mu^*(A) = 0$, A is μ^*-measurable, so $\mu^* \upharpoonright \mu^*$-measurable sets is a complete measure.*

Remark. Recall that a measure ν, is *complete* if $A \subset B$, B measurable, and $\nu(B) = 0$ implies A is measurable and $\nu(A) = 0$.

Proof. The proof is straightforward and has a number of distinct steps.

(1) $\mu^*(A) = 0 \Rightarrow A \in \mathcal{M}$; *in particular,* $\emptyset \in \mathcal{M}$. If $\mu^*(A) = 0$, then $Y \cap A \subset A$ so $\mu^*(Y \cap A) = 0$. Thus, (8.1.7) is equivalent to $\mu^*(Y) \geq \mu^*(Y \setminus A)$ which follows from monotonicity.

(2) $A \in \mathcal{M} \to X \setminus A \in \mathcal{M}$. Immediate if we note that $Y \cap A = Y \setminus (X \setminus A)$ and $Y \setminus A = Y \cap (X \setminus A)$.

(3) $A, B \in \mathcal{M} \Rightarrow A \cap B \in \mathcal{M}$; *thus (by (2)),* $\mathcal{M}$ *is closed under finite unions and intersections.* Let $Q^c = X \setminus Q$ and

$$C_1 = A \cap B, \quad C_2 = A^c \cap B, \quad C_3 = A \cap B^c, \quad C_4 = A^c \cap B^c \qquad (8.1.8)$$

Since $B \in \mathcal{M}$

$$\mu^*(Y \cap A) = \mu^*(Y \cap C_1) + \mu^*(Y \cap C_3); \quad \mu^*(Y \setminus A) = \mu^*(Y \cap C_2) + \mu^*(Y \cap C_4)$$

Thus, since $A \in \mathcal{M}$,

$$\begin{aligned}
\mu^*(Y) &= \mu^*(Y \cap C_1) + \mu^*(Y \cap C_2) + \mu^*(Y \cap C_3) + \mu^*(y \cap C_4) \\
&\geq \mu^*(Y \cap C_1) + \mu^*(Y \cap [C_2 \cup C_3 \cup C_4]) \qquad (8.1.9) \\
&= \mu^*(Y \cap (A \cap B)) + \mu^*(Y \setminus (A \cap B))
\end{aligned}$$

where (8.1.9) follows from subadditivity of μ^*. Thus (8.1.7) holds for $A \cap B$.

(4) *To prove* $\mathcal{M}$ *is a σ-algebra, it suffices to prove countable unions of disjoint sets in* $\mathcal{M}$ *lie in* $\mathcal{M}$. Let $\{A_j\}_{j=1}^{\infty}$ lie in $\mathcal{M}$. Let $B_k = A_k \setminus (\bigcup_{j=1}^{k-1} A_j)$. Then the $\{B_j\}_{j=1}^{\infty}$ are disjoint and lie in $\mathcal{M}$ by (2), (3). Moreover, $\bigcup_{j=1}^{\infty} A_j = \bigcup_{j=1}^{\infty} B_j$.

(5) *If* $\{A_j\}_{j=1}^{\infty}$ *are disjoint sets in* $\mathcal{M}$, *then for all* $Y \subset 2^X$,

$$\mu^*(Y \cap (\bigcup_{j=1}^{n} A_j)) = \sum_{j=1}^{n} \mu^*(Y \cap A_j) \qquad (8.1.10)$$

Let $B_m = \bigcup_{j=1}^{m} A_j$. We'll prove (8.1.10) by induction on n. For $n = 1$, the result is trivial. Suppose it holds for $n = m$. Then, since B_m is measurable

$$\begin{aligned}
\mu^*(Y \cap B_{m+1}) &= \mu^*(Y \cap B_m \cap B_{m+1}) + \mu^*((Y \cap B_{m+1}) \setminus B_m) \\
&= \mu^*(Y \cap B_m) + \mu^*(Y \cap A_{m+1}) \qquad (8.1.11) \\
&= \sum_{j=1}^{m+1} \mu^*(Y \cap A_j) \qquad (8.1.12)
\end{aligned}$$

(8.1.11) comes from $B_m \cap B_{m+1} = B_m$ (since $A_{m+1} \cap A_j = \emptyset$ if $j \leq m$) and $B_{m+1} \cap B_m^c = A_{m+1}$. (8.1.12) comes from the induction hypothesis. Thus, (8.1.10) is proven by induction.

(6) $\mathcal{M}$ *is a σ-algebra and μ^* is countable additive on $\mathcal{M}$.* By (4), we need only prove that for $\{A_j\}_{j=1}^{\infty}$ a disjoint sequence in $\mathcal{M}$ and any $Y \subset 2^X$, we have that

$$\mu^*(Y) \geq \mu^*(Y \cap \bigcup_{j=1}^{\infty} A_j) + \mu^*(Y \setminus \bigcup_{j=1}^{\infty} A_j) \qquad (8.1.13)$$

and that (since we have the opposite inequality by subadditivity)

$$\mu^*(\bigcup_{j=1}^{\infty} A_j) \geq \sum_{j=1}^{\infty} \mu^*(A_j) \qquad (8.1.14)$$

Suppose we prove that

$$\mu^*(Y) \geq \left[\sum_{j=1}^{\infty} (\mu^*(Y \cap A_j)) \right] + \mu^*(Y \setminus \bigcup_{j=1}^{\infty} A_j) \qquad (8.1.15)$$

Then, taking $Y = \bigcup_{j=1}^{\infty} A_j$, we get (8.1.14) and by subadditivity, $\sum_{j=1}^{\infty} \mu^*(Y \cap A_j) \geq \mu^*(Y \cap \bigcup_{j=1}^{\infty} A_j)$ so (8.1.15) implies (8.1.12). Thus, we need only prove (8.1.15).

Fix n. Since $\bigcup_{j=1}^{n} A_j$ is in $\mathcal{M}$:

$$\mu^*(Y) = \mu^*(Y \cap \bigcup_{j=1}^{n} A_j) + \mu^*(Y \setminus \bigcup_{j=1}^{n} A_j)$$

$$\geq \mu^*(Y \cap \bigcup_{j=1}^{n} A_j) + \mu^*(Y \setminus \bigcup_{j=1}^{\infty} A_j) \qquad (8.1.16)$$

$$\geq \mu^* \sum_{j=1}^{n} \mu^*(Y \cap A_j) + \mu^*(Y \setminus \bigcup_{j=1}^{\infty} A_j) \qquad (8.1.17)$$

where (8.1.16) uses monotonicity of μ^* and (8.1.17) uses (8.1.10). Taking $n \to \infty$, we see that (8.1.17) implies (8.1.15).

(7) *Putting it together.* In (2), (3), (6), we proved that $\mathcal{M}$ is a σ-algebra and μ^* is a measure on $\mathcal{M}$. By (1), $\mu^* \restriction \mathcal{M}$ is implied.

$\square$

While this theorem is simple and elegant, it could be that the only μ^*-measurable sets are those with $\mu^*(A) = 0$ and their complements. To see that, in many interesting examples, many other sets are measurable, we introduce a special class of outer measures.

Definition. Let (X, d) be a metric space. An outer measure, μ^*, on X is called a *metric outer measure* if for all $S_1, S_2 \in 2^X$

$$d(S_1, S_2) \equiv \inf\{d(x_1, x_2) \mid x_j \in S_j\} > 0 \Rightarrow \mu^*(S_1 \cup S_2) = \mu^*(S_1) + \mu^*(S_2) \qquad (8.1.18)$$

The reader can check (Problem 1) that the Lebesgue–Stieltjes outer measure of Example 8.1.3 is a metric outer measure (essentially because for any $\delta > 0$ in (8.1.2), one can restrict to $\{A_j\}_{j=1}^{\infty}$ with $A \subset \bigcup_{j=1}^{\infty} A_j \subset \{x \mid d(x, A) < \delta\}$).

Theorem 8.1.5. *Let μ^* be a metric outer measure. Then, any Borel set is μ^*-measurable.*

Proof. Since the μ^*-measurable sets are a σ-algebra and the Borel sets are the smallest σ-algebra containing the closed sets, we need only prove that for set, C, closed and $Y \subset X$, we have that

$$\mu^*(Y) \geq \mu^*(Y \cap C) + \mu^*(Y \setminus C) \tag{8.1.19}$$

Without loss, we can suppose that $\mu^*(Y) < \infty$ since (8.1.19) always holds if $\mu^*(Y) = \infty$. Define

$$B_n = \{x \in Y \setminus C \mid d(x, C) \geq \frac{1}{n}\} \tag{8.1.20}$$

Since $d(Y \cap C, B_n) \geq \frac{1}{n} > 0$, by (8.1.18)

$$\mu^*(Y \cap C) + \mu^*(B_n) = \mu^*((Y \cap C) \cup B_n) \leq \mu^*(Y) \tag{8.1.21}$$

by monotonicity. Thus, if we prove

$$\lim_{n \to \infty} \mu^*(B_n) = \mu^*(Y \setminus C) \tag{8.1.22}$$

we get (8.1.19) and the proof is done.

Let

$$F_n = B_{n+1} \setminus B_n = \{x \in Y \setminus C \mid \frac{1}{n+1} \leq d(x, C) < \frac{1}{n}\} \tag{8.1.23}$$

If $j \geq k+2$, $x \in F_j$ and $y \in F_k$, then $d(x, C) < \frac{1}{k+2}$. Thus, $\frac{1}{k+1} \leq d(y, C) < \frac{1}{k+2} + d(x, y)$, so $d(x, y) \geq \frac{1}{k+1} - \frac{1}{k+2}$, i.e., $d(F_j, F_k) > 0$. We have thus proven that

$$(j - k) \geq 2 \Rightarrow d(F_j, F_k) > 0 \tag{8.1.24}$$

By induction and (8.1.18)

$$\sum_{j=1}^{N} \mu^*(F_{2j}) = \mu^*(\bigcup_{j=1}^{N} F_{2j}) \leq \mu^*(Y \setminus C) \leq \mu^*(Y)$$

Similarly,

$$\sum_{j=1}^{N} \mu^*(F_{2j-1}) \leq \mu^*(Y) < \infty$$

Thus, by $\mu^*(Y) < \infty$, we have

$$\sum_{j=1}^{\infty} \mu^*(F_j) \le 2\mu^*(Y) < \infty \qquad (8.1.25)$$

Note next that

$$Y \setminus C = B_n \cup \bigcup_{j=n}^{\infty} F_j \qquad (8.1.26)$$

so, by countable subadditivity

$$Y \setminus C \le \mu^*(B_n) + \sum_{j=n}^{\infty} \mu^*(F_j) \qquad (8.1.27)$$

Since, by monotonicity, $\mu^*(B_n) \le \mu^*(Y \setminus C)$, we see that

$$|\mu^*(Y \setminus C) - \mu^*(B_n)| \le \sum_{j=n}^{\infty} \mu^*(F_j) \qquad (8.1.28)$$

goes to zero as $n \to \infty$ (by (8.1.25)). This proves (8.1.22), □

Corollary 8.1.6. *Let α be a monotone function on $[0,1]$. There is a unique Baire measure on $[0,1]$ with $\mu([a,b)) = \alpha(b_-) - \alpha(a_-)$ and $\mu(\{1\}) = \alpha(1) - \alpha(1_-)$.*

Proof. Uniqueness follows from the by now standard argument used often in Chapter 4: if μ_1, μ_2 are two such measures, the set on which they agree (given that $[0,1] = [0,1) \cup \{1\}$ so they agree on $[0,1]$) is a σ-algebra and since $(a,b) = \bigcup_{n=1}^{\infty} [a + \frac{1}{n}, b)$, they agree on all open sets, and the Borel sets are the smallest σ-algebra containing all open sets.

For existence, we note that, by Problem 1 and Example 8.1.3, there is a metric outer measure, μ^*, with $\mu^*([a,b)) = \alpha(b_-) - \alpha(a_-)$, $\mu^*(\{1\}) = \alpha(1) - \alpha(1_-)$, Thus by Theorem 8.1.4 and 8.1.5, such a μ exists. □

This is the "traditional" way to construct the Lebesgue–Stieltjes measure.

Notes and Historical Remarks. The Carathéodory construction is from Carathéodory [**158, 159**]. He also found the condition we call metric outer measure, sometimes called the Carathéodory condition. As usual, we believe when following Carathéodory's construction on metric outer measures, one wants to restrict not merely to the μ^*-measurable sets, but only to the Borel sets; see the Notes to Section 4.3.

Any of the measure theory monographs mentioned in the Notes to Section 4.4 will have a discussion of the Carathéodory construction. Bogachev's treatment [**104**] is encyclopedic.

Problems

1. (a) Let $S \subset [0,1)$ and $S_\delta = \{x \mid d(x,S) < \delta\}$. For any $[a,b) \subset [0,1]$, prove there are $a \leq a_1 < b_1 < a_2 < \ldots < b_\ell <$ so that each $[a_j, b_j) \subset S_\delta$ and

$$S \cap [a,b) = \bigcup_{j=1}^{\ell} [S \cap [a_j, b_j)]$$

(b) Prove that for any monotone function α on $[0,1]$ with $\alpha(a) = \alpha(a_-)$ for $a \in (0,1)$, prove that

$$\inf\{\sum_{j=1}^{\ell} [\alpha(b_j) - \alpha(a_j)] \mid S \subset \bigcup_{j=1}^{\ell} [a_j, b_j)\}$$

$$= \inf\{\sum_{j=1}^{\ell} [\alpha(b_j) - \alpha(a_j)] \mid S \subset \bigcup_{j=1}^{\ell} [a_j, b_j) \subset S_\delta\}$$

(c) Prove that the Lebesgue–Stieltjes outer measure is a metric outer measure. (*Hint*: Given S_1, S_2 with $d(S_1, S_2) = d > 0$, pick $\delta < \frac{d}{2}$ in (b).)

2. Let μ^* be an outer measure on a metric space for which every open set is measurable. Prove that μ^* is a metric outer measure. (*Hint*: If $d(S_1, S_2) = d > 0$, let $A = \{x \mid d(x, S_1) < \frac{d}{2}\}$.)

Remark. Thus, an outer measure is a metric outer measure if and only if all Borel sets are measurable!

8.2. Hausdorff Measure and Dimension

Let X be a separable metric space and $s \in [0, \infty)$ and $\delta > 0$. Define for $A \subset X$,

$$h^*_{\delta,s}(A) = \inf\{\sum_{j=1}^{N} (\text{diam } B_j)^s \mid N \in \{0, \ldots\} \cup \{\infty\},$$

$$\tag{8.2.1}$$

$$B_j \text{ open balls of diameter } < \delta; A \subset \bigcup_{j=1}^{N} B_j\}$$

It is traditional to use $\text{diam}(B_j) = 2r$ for $B_j = \{x \mid d(x, x_0) < r\}$. Define

$$h^*_s(A) = \lim_{\delta \downarrow 0} h^*_{s,\delta}(A) = \sup_{\delta > 0} h^*_{s,\delta}(A) \tag{8.2.2}$$

h_s is called the *s*-dimensional *Hausdorff outer measure*. In (8.2.2), the $\lim_{\delta \downarrow 0}$ is $\sup_{\delta > 0}$ since the family of allowed B_j's decreases as δ decreases, and thus the inf increases.

What we define above is sometimes called the *spherical Hausdorff outer measure* by those who take all covers by all sets in (8.2.1) (but still use $(\mathrm{diam}\,B_j)$ where $\mathrm{diam}(B_j) = \sup_{x,y \in B_j} d(x,y)$). If $\widetilde{h}^*_{\delta,s}$ is the inf over all such covers, clearly $\widetilde{h}^*_{\delta,s} \leq h^*_{\delta,s}$. But since, if $y_0 \in B$, $B \subset B_{\mathrm{diam}(B)}(y_0)$, the ball of radius $\mathrm{diam}(B)$ about y_0, and $\mathrm{diam}\big(B_{\mathrm{diam}(B)}(y)\big) \leq 2\,\mathrm{diam}(B)$. One sees that $h^*_{\delta,s} \leq 2^s \widetilde{h}^*_{\delta,s}$. It follows that the key notion of Hausdorff dimension is unaffected whether one takes all sets, or only takes balls as we do. In fact (see the Notes), on $\mathbb{R}^\nu$, the two h_ν's agree on Borel sets—this is obvious if $\nu = 1$ since any set B is contained in a closed interval of the same diameter.

By Proposition 8.1.1(a), $h^*_{\delta,s}$ is an outer measure and then by (b) of that proposition, h^*_s is an outer measure. Here is a summary of basic properties.

Theorem 8.2.1.

(a) *For each s, h^*_s is a metric outer measure.*

(b) *For $s < t$ and each $\delta > 0$ and each set A,*

$$h^*_{t,\delta}(A) \leq \delta^{t-s} h^*_{s,\delta}(A) \tag{8.2.3}$$

(c) *For $s < t$ and each set A,*

$$h^*_s(A) < \infty \Rightarrow h^*_t(A) = 0, \quad h^*_t(A) > 0 \Rightarrow h^*_s(A) = \infty \tag{8.2.4}$$

(d) *For each set A, there is a unique number $d \in [0, \infty]$ so that*

$$s > d \Rightarrow h^*_s(A) = 0, \quad s < d \Rightarrow h^*_s(A) = \infty \tag{8.2.5}$$

Remarks. 1. d is called the *Hausdorff dimension* of A written h-$\dim(A) = d$.

2. For each $0 \leq s \leq \nu$, there are Borel sets in $\mathbb{R}^\nu$ of Hausdorff dimension s (see Example 8.2.2).

3. If A has Hausdorff dimension d, it can happen that $h^*_d(A) = 0$, that $h^*_d(A) = \infty$, or that $0 < h^*_d(A) < \infty$ (see Problems 1 and 2).

4. If $X \subset \mathbb{R}^\nu$, $d \leq \nu$ for all $A \subset X$.

Proof. (a) Let $d(S_1, S_2) = d > 0$. If $\delta < d$, any ball B of diameter δ can intersect S_1 or S_2 but not both. This implies that for $\delta < d$,

$$h^*_{s,\delta}(S_1 \cup S_2) = h^*_{s,\delta}(S_1) + h^*_{s,\delta}(S_2) \tag{8.2.6}$$

Now take $\delta \downarrow 0$.

(b) If $A \subset \bigcup_{j=1}^N B_j$ and $\mathrm{diam}(B_j) < \delta$, then

$$\sum_{j=1}^N \mathrm{diam}(B_j)^t \leq \delta^{t-s} \sum_{j=1}^N \mathrm{diam}(B_j)^s \tag{8.2.7}$$

since $\mathrm{diam}(B)^{t-s} \leq \delta^{t-s}$. This implies (8.2.3).

(c) If $\alpha = h_s^*(A) < \infty$, then by (8.2.3)

$$h_{\delta,t}^*(t) \leq \delta^{t-s}\alpha \tag{8.2.8}$$

Taking $\delta \downarrow 0$ yields (8.2.4)

If $\alpha = h_t^*(A) > 0$, if $\alpha < \infty$, there is δ_0 so $\delta < \delta_0 \Rightarrow h_{t,\delta}^*(A) \geq \frac{\alpha}{2}$. If $\alpha = \infty$, $h_{t,\delta}^*(A) > 1$. By (8.2.3), for $\delta < \delta_0$

$$h_{\delta,s}^*(A) \geq \delta^{s-t}\alpha \quad (\text{or } \delta^{s-t} \text{ if } \alpha = \infty) \tag{8.2.9}$$

Taking $\delta \downarrow 0$, we see that $\lim h_{\delta,s}^*(A) = \infty$.

(d) Let

$$d = \inf\{s \mid h_s^*(A) = 0\} \tag{8.2.10}$$
$$= \infty \quad \text{if } h_s^*(A) = \infty \text{ for all } s.$$

If $s_0 > d$, there is $s_1 \leq s_0$ with $h_{s_1}^*(A) = 0$, so by (8.2.4), $h_{s_0}^*(A) = 0$. If $s_0 < d$, there is $s_1 \in (s_0, d)$ and then $h_{s_1}(A) > 0$. It follows by (8.2.4) that $h_{s_0}(A) = \infty$. $\qquad\square$

Since h_s^* is a metric outer measure, its restriction, h_s, to the Borel sets is a Borel measure called *Hausdorff s-dimensional measure* or sometimes just Hausdorff measure. If $X = \mathbb{R}^\nu$ and $s < \nu$, this measure is not σ-finite (Problem 3).

Recall (see Problem 5 of Section 4.11) that for integers, ν, the volume of the unit radius ball is $\tau_\nu = \frac{2\pi^{\nu/2}}{\nu\Gamma(\frac{\nu}{2})} = \pi^{\nu/2}/\Gamma(1 + \frac{\nu}{2})$. Thus, the volume of the ball of diameter 1 is $2^{-\nu}\tau_\nu$. We therefore define normalized Hausdorff measure to be

$$\mathcal{H}^s(A) = 2^{-s}\pi^{s/2}\left[\Gamma\left(1 + \frac{s}{2}\right)\right]^{-1} h_s^*(A) \tag{8.2.11}$$

on Borel sets.

It is a basic fact that we will not prove (but see the Notes) that on $\mathbb{R}^\nu$, $\mathcal{H}^\nu$ is the ordinary Lebesgue measure. (In Problem 4, the reader will at least prove the results for $\nu = 1$.) More generally, if $S \subset \mathbb{R}^\nu$ is a smooth bounded hypersurface of codimension r in $\mathbb{R}^\nu$, i.e., S is bounded and there is a C^∞ map $F : \mathbb{R}^\nu \to \mathbb{R}^r$ so that

$$\left\{\frac{\partial F_j}{\partial x_k}\right\}_{\substack{j=1,\ldots,r \\ k=1,\ldots,\nu}}$$

is rank r at each point in S and if $d\eta$ is the induced $(\nu - r)$-dimensional Riemann volume on S, then $d\eta = \mathcal{H}^{\nu-r}$.

One nice aspect is that every Borel set has a Hausdorff measure. Thus, a particular slick form of the isoperimetric inequality is one that says if $A \subset \mathbb{R}^\nu$ is open with Lebesgue volume, τ_ν, then the $\mathcal{H}^{\nu-1}$ area of ∂A is at least σ_ν. The point is that this makes sense for any open A, not merely those with a regular ∂A.

Example 8.2.2 (The classical Cantor set). Recall our construction of the Cantor set $C \subset [0,1]$—see Section 4.2. We defined C_1 to be the union of the two sets of those x whose base three decimal expansion have 0 or 2 for their first digit (where for those points with two expansions, e.g., $\frac{1}{3} = .1000\ldots0 = .022\ldots$, we require that one of the two expansions start with 0 or 2), i.e., $C_1 = [0, \frac{1}{3}] \cup [\frac{2}{3}, 1]$. C_2 is the first set of x that start with 0 or 2 in their first two digits. C_n has n 0's or 2's, so 2^n sets, each of size 3^{-n}. $C = \bigcap_{n=1}^\infty C_n$ is the closed, perfect Cantor set.

Since C is compact, covers by open balls can be replaced by finite covers. Then, by slightly deceasing the balls, we can consider closed intervals. $C_n \supset C$ so C_n is a cover by closed balls of diameter 3^{-n}, so

$$\sum_j \operatorname{diam}(B_j)^s = 2^n 3^{-ns} \tag{8.2.12}$$

Clearly, that s_0 where $2\,3^{-s_0} = 1$, i.e.,

$$s_0 = \log 2 / \log 3 \tag{8.2.13}$$

is special. If $s > s_0$, the right side of (8.2.12) goes to zero as $n \to \infty$ proving

$$s > s_0 \Rightarrow h_s(C) = 0 \tag{8.2.14}$$

Similarly, by (8.2.12), we see that

$$h_{s_0}(C) \le 1 \tag{8.2.15}$$

If $s < s_0$, the right side of (8.2.12) goes to infinity suggesting as $\delta \downarrow 0$, $h_{s,\delta}(C) \to \infty$, but since we must take an inf over all covers, it is more subtle to prove this. In fact, we claim

$$h_{s_0}(C) = 1 \Rightarrow h_s(C) = \infty \text{ if } s < s_0, \text{ so } h\text{-}\dim(C) = s_0 \tag{8.2.16}$$

We prove $h_{s_0,\delta}(C) = 1$ for all δ in a sequence of steps:

(1) *Without loss, in computing $h_{s_0,\delta}(C)$, we can consider covers by finitely many disjoint closed intervals* $[\alpha_j, \beta_j]$ *where* $\alpha_j \in \ell_-(C)$, $\beta_j \in \ell_+(C)$. Here $\ell_+(C)$ are upper boundary points of C. i.e., right-hand end points of the maximal intervals in $[0,1] \setminus C$ or $\{1\}$ and $\ell_-(C)$ are lower boundary points of C, i.e., left-hand points of maximal intervals in $[0,1] \setminus C$ or $\{0\}$; i.e., $\ell_- = \{\frac{1}{3}, \frac{1}{9}, \frac{7}{9}, \frac{1}{27}, \ldots\}$, $\ell_+ = \{\frac{2}{3}, \frac{2}{9}, \frac{8}{9}, \frac{2}{27}, \frac{8}{27}, \ldots\}$. Points in $\ell_+(C)$ have decimal expansions ending in $\ldots 22\ldots 2\ldots$ and in $\ell_-(C)$ ending in $\ldots .00\ldots 0\ldots$.

To see this, start with an arbitrary open cover of C by intervals of diameter $< \delta$. Since C is compact, we can arrange the cover to be $\{(\alpha_j^{(0)}, \beta_j^{(0)})\}_{j=1}^L$.

If some $\beta_j^{(0)}$ is in $\ell_-(C)$ decrease it slightly so it is $[0,1] \setminus C$. This decreases $\sum \mathrm{diam}(\alpha_j^{(0)}, \beta_j^{(0)})^s$ but still covers C. Do the same for $\alpha_j^{(0)}$.

Now replace each $(\alpha_j^{(0)}, \beta_j^{(0)})$ by $[\alpha_j^{(0)}, \beta_j^{(0)}]$. If $\beta_j^{(0)} \in [0,1] \setminus C$ decrease it to $\beta_j^{(1)}$, the lower end of the maximal interval it lies in. This $\beta_j^{(1)}$ lies in $\ell_+(C)$. If $\beta_j^{(0)} \in C$, use the fact (Problem 5) that any point in C is a limit for slightly larger points in $\ell_+(C)$. Thus, by increasing $\sum \mathrm{diam}(\alpha_j, \beta_j)^s$ by an arbitrarily small amount, we can arrange all $\beta_j^{(1)} \in \ell_+(C)$, $\alpha_j^{(1)} \in \ell_-(C)$.

If any two intervals lie one inside the other, throw out the smaller one. Then, we can suppose $\alpha_1^{(1)} < \alpha_2^{(1)} < \alpha_3^{(1)} < \dots$. If $\alpha_2^{(1)} < \beta_1^{(1)}$, increase $\alpha_2^{(1)}$ to the right endpoint of the maximal interval of $[0,1] \setminus C$ with $\beta_1^{(1)}$ on its left. Repeating this, we get disjoint intervals with $\alpha_j \in \ell_-(C), \beta_j \in \ell_+(C)$.

(2) *We claim* $\{[\alpha_j, \beta_j]\}_{j=1}^L$ *covers some* C_n. For since the intervals are disjoint, they are a minimal distance, η, apart. If $3^{-\ell} < \eta$ and $U = (b, a)$ is a maximal interval of $[0,1] \setminus C$ of size $3^{-\ell}$, then U must be inside some $[\alpha_j, \beta_j]$. If not, there is a j with $\beta_j = b$, $\alpha_{j+1} = a$ and so $\mathrm{dist}([\alpha_j, \beta_j], [\alpha_{j+1}, \beta_{j+1}]) = 3^{-\ell} < \eta$. Thus, C_ℓ is covered.

(3) *We claim each* $[\alpha_j, \beta_j]$ *is either a single closed component of* C_n *or else* $[\alpha_j, \beta_j] = J_j^- \cup I_j \cup J_j^+$ *where* $I_j = (b, a)$ *is a maximal open interval of* $[0,1] \setminus C$ *and* $J_j^- = [\alpha_j, b], J_j^+ = [a, \beta_j]$ *and*

$$|I_j| \geq \tfrac{1}{3}(\beta_j - \alpha_j) \tag{8.2.17}$$

For either $[\alpha_j, \beta_j]$ contains all of $(\tfrac{1}{3}, \tfrac{2}{3})$ or lies in a half set $[0, \tfrac{1}{3}], [\tfrac{2}{3}, 1]$. In the first case, take $I_j = (\tfrac{1}{3}, \tfrac{2}{3})$ which certainly obeys (8.2.16). In the second case, note that $|\beta_j - \alpha_j| \leq \tfrac{1}{3}$. $[\alpha_j, \beta_j]$ either contains the unique interval in $[0,1] \setminus C$ of size $\tfrac{1}{9}$ on the correct side or lies in a single half of size $\tfrac{1}{9}$. In the former, take I_j to be this interval of size $\tfrac{1}{9} \geq \tfrac{1}{3}|\beta_j - \alpha_j|$. Otherwise continue. After n steps, we must have a single component of C_n so either we stop with an I_j or at a single component of C_n.

(4) *If* $[\alpha_j, \beta_j] = J_j^- \cup I_j \cup J_j^+$, *then*

$$|\beta_j - \alpha_j|^{s_0} \geq |J_j^-|^{s_0} + |J_j^+|^{s_0} \tag{8.2.18}$$

To see this, note tht $|I_j| \geq \tfrac{1}{3}|\beta_j - \alpha_j|$ and $|J_j^-| + |I_j| + |J_j^+| = |\beta_j - \alpha_j|$ implies that

$$|\beta_j - \alpha_j| \geq \tfrac{3}{2}(|J_j^-| + |J_j^+|) \tag{8.2.19}$$

so, since $3^{s_0} = 2$,

$$|\beta_j - \alpha_j|^{s_0} \geq 2\left(\tfrac{1}{2}|J_j^-| + \tfrac{1}{2}|J_j^+|\right)^{s_0} \tag{8.2.20}$$

$$\geq |J_j^-|^{s_0} + |J_j^+|^{s_0} \tag{8.2.21}$$

since $f(t) = t^{s_0}$ has $f^n(t) = s_0(s_0 - 1)t^{s_0-2} < 0$ and so is concave.

(5) *We claim* $\sum_{j=1}^{L} |\beta_j - \alpha_j|^{s_0} \geq 1$ *proving* $h_{s_0,\delta}(C) \geq 1$ (*and since* (8.2.15) *holds,* $h_{s_0}(C) = 1$). By (8.2.21), if $[\alpha_j, \beta_j]$ is not a single interval of size 3^{-n}, we can only decrease $\sum \mathrm{diam}(\alpha_j, \beta_j)^{s_0}$ by removing the I_j's. Iterating this (noticing at each step, the maximal interval size must decrease by a factor of $\frac{1}{3}$), we get to a cover by the 2^n sets of size 3^{-n} for which the dim is 1. We have thus proven that

$$h\text{-dim}(C) = \log 2 / \log 3 \tag{8.2.22}$$

□

Example 8.2.3 (Generalized Cantor Sets). Fix $0 < \delta < \frac{1}{2}$. Consider the set, C_δ, you get by first removing the central set of size $(1 - 2\delta)$ leaving the intervals of size δ, then the middle pieces of size $(1 - 2\delta)\delta$ from these two pieces, leaving four intervals of size δ^2, ... After n steps one gets 2^n intervals of size δ^n. Their intersection is C_δ. The critical s_δ has $2^n \delta^{ns_\delta} = 1$, i.e.,

$$s_\delta = \log 2 / \log \delta^{-1} \tag{8.2.23}$$

As δ runs from $\frac{1}{2}$ down to 0, s_δ runs from 1 down to 0. As above, one can show (Problem 6), that s_δ is the h-dim of C_δ. In this way, we get sets of any Hausdorff dimension, $s \in (0, 1)$. If $A \subset \mathbb{R}$ has Hausdorff dimension s and $B = A \times \{0\}_{\nu_1} \times [0, 1]^{\nu_2} \subset \mathbb{R}^{\nu_1 + \nu_2 + 1}$, then it is not hard to see (Problem 10) that $h\text{-dim}(A) = s + \nu_2$. Thus, we see that $\mathbb{R}^\nu$ contains Borel sets A with $h\text{-dim}(A) = s$ for any $s \in [0, \nu]$.

□

Remarks. 1. We warn the reader that the "obvious fact" that $h\text{-dim}(A \times B) = h\text{-dim}(A) + h\text{-dim}(B)$ is false! In Problem 9, the reader will construct sets $A, B \subset [0, 1]$ each of Hausdorff dimension 0 so that $h\text{-dim}(A \times B) \geq 1$ (and, in fact, $h\text{-dim}(A \times B) = 1$ for this example).

2. That said, for the generalized Cantor set, C_j, of the above example, one can show (see the Notes) that

$$h\text{-dim}(C_1 \times \ldots \times C_\ell) = \sum_{j=1}^{\ell} h\text{-dim}(C_j) \tag{8.2.24}$$

Because Hausdorff measure is not σ-finite, a number of theorems familiar for Baire measures become false or harder to prove. If $s < t$, A is Borel and $h_s(A) = 0$, then by (8.2.4), $h_t(A) = 0$. But it is certainly not true that $dh_t = f dh_s$, indeed $h_t(A) \neq 0 \Rightarrow h_s(A) = \infty$. Thus, the Radon-Nikodym theorem fails for Hausdorff measures. This means that h_s-continuity of a measure μ (i.e., $h_s(A) = 0 \Rightarrow \mu(A)$) does not imply h_s-absolute continuity (i.e., $\forall \varepsilon > 0, \exists \delta > 0$ s.t. $h_s(A) < \delta \Rightarrow \mu(A) < \varepsilon$). That said, the notion of h_s-continuous and h_s singular will be useful and there will be a kind of Lebesgue decomposition.

Definition. Let μ be a Baire measure on $\mathbb{R}^\nu$. Let $0 \le s \le \nu$. We say that μ is h_s-*singular* if there exists a Borel set, A, so $\mu(\mathbb{R}^\nu \setminus A) = 0$, $h_s(A) = 0$. We say μ is h_s-*continuous* if $h_s(A) = 0 \Rightarrow \mu(A) = 0$.

Consider also regularity. If $0 \le s < \nu$, $h_s(A) = \infty$ for any open set, A, so outer regularity fails. That said, it can be proven (see the Notes) that for any Baire set, S, there is a G_δ set A with $S \subset A$ and $h_s(A) = h_s(S)$ and that h_s is inner regular. Since the proofs are more involved, we will not give these proofs nor use this result.

The last topic we'll explore in this section is using Hausdorff dimension to refine the class of singular continuous measures. For measures in $\mathbb{R}$, we've discussed a three-fold classification into the mutually disjoint classes of pure point, absolutely continuous, and singular continuous and proved that any measure has a unique decomposition into a sum of the three (see Section 4.7, especially Theorem 4.7.6).

In Problem 8 of Section 5.4, we saw a Baire generic measure was purely singular continuous suggesting that these measures are a rich and diverse class. Indeed, we can use $h_\alpha (0 < \alpha < 1)$ to distinguish between them. We'll see below that, given $\alpha \in (0,1)$, any Baire measure, μ, on $[0,1]$ can be written $\mu = \mu_{ac} + \mu_{as}$ where μ_{as} is h_α-singular and μ_{ac} is h_α-continuous.

Definition. A Baire measure, μ, on $[0,1]$ is called of *exact dimension* $\alpha \in [0,1]$ if and only if

(1) $0 \le \beta < \alpha$ and $h\text{-dim}(S) = \beta \Rightarrow \mu(S) = 0$.
(2) There is a set, S_0 of dimension α so that $\mu(\mathbb{R} \setminus S_0) = 0$.

Definition. Let μ be a Baire measure on $[0,1]$ and $x_0 \in [0,1]$. We say μ has *local dimension*, $\alpha(x_0)$, at x_0 in $\text{supp}(\mu)$ if for every ε, there is a δ so that $S \subset (x_0 - \delta,\ x_0 + \delta)$ and $\dim(S) < \alpha(x_0) - \varepsilon \Rightarrow \mu(S) = 0$ and there exists $S_0 \subset (x_0 - \delta,\ x_0 + \delta)$ so $h\text{-dim}(S_0) \le \alpha(x_0) + \varepsilon$ and $\mu\big((x_0 - \delta,\ x_0 + \delta) \setminus S_0\big) = 0$.

Example 8.2.4. We want to describe a family of natural measures, μ_p, on $[0,1]$ for $0 < p < 1$, all with support $[0,1]$. Let $F : \{0,1\}^{\mathbb{Z}_+} \to [0,1]$ by $F\big((x_n)_{n \ge 1}\big) = \sum_{n=1}^{\infty} \frac{x_n}{2^n}$. F is 2–1 on the countable family of dyadic rationals (except for 0 and 1) and otherwise 1–1. Let ν_p be the product measure on $\{0,1\}^{\mathbb{Z}_+}$ that makes x_n to a sequence of iidrv with $\text{Prob}(x_n = 0) = p$, $\text{Prob}(x_n = 1) = 1 - p$. Let $\mu_p(A) = \nu_p(F^{-1}[A])$. That is $x^{(0)}$ is the dyadic rational

$$x^{(0)} = \sum_{n=1}^{N_0} \frac{x_n^{(0)}}{2^n}, \quad x_{N_0}^{(0)} = 0 \qquad (8.2.25)$$

and if
$$N_m\big(F(x_n)\big) = \sharp(j < m \mid x_j = 0) \qquad (8.2.26)$$
then
$$\mu_p\big([x^{(0)}, x^{(0)} + \tfrac{1}{2^{N_0}})\big) = p^{N_{N_0}(x^{(0)})}(1-p)^{N_0 - N_{N_0}(x^{(0)})-1} \qquad (8.2.27)$$

It is easy to see that the support of each μ_p is all of $[0,1]$ (by (8.2.27)!). The strong law of large numbers (Theorem 7.2.5) says that if
$$A_p = \{x \mid \lim_{m\to\infty} N_m(x)/m = p\} \qquad (8.2.28)$$
then $\mu_p(\mathbb{R} \setminus A_p) = 0$. Thus, the μ_p are all mutually singular. We are heading towards proving more: we'll show that μ_p has exact dimension
$$d_p = -\frac{p \log p + (1-p)\log(1-p)}{\log(2)} \qquad (8.2.29)$$

$\square$

Given a Baire measure, μ, on $[0,1]$, the key object for us will be for each $\alpha \in [0,1]$:
$$D_\mu^\alpha(x) = \overline{\lim}_{\delta\downarrow 0} \frac{\mu(x-\delta, x+\delta)}{(2\delta)^\alpha} \qquad (8.2.30)$$
Henceforth, to avoid some extra words, we suppose μ has no pure points so $D_\mu^{\alpha=0}(x) = 0$. It is easy (Problem 11) to accommodate pure points. The following is elementary:

Proposition 8.2.5. (a) D_μ^α *is a measurable function of* x.

(b) *For each* x_0, *there is a unique* $\alpha(x_0)$ *so that* $\alpha > \alpha_0(x) \Rightarrow D_\mu^\alpha(x_0) = \infty$; $\alpha < \alpha_0(x) \Rightarrow D_\mu^\alpha(x_0) = 0$

(c) $\alpha(x_0) = \underline{\lim}_{\delta\downarrow 0} \dfrac{\log \mu(x_0-\delta, x_0+\delta)}{\log \delta}$ $\qquad (8.2.31)$

(d) *In* (8.2.31), *we can take* $\delta = 2^{-n}$, *i.e.,*
$$\alpha(x_0) = \underline{\lim}_{n\to\infty} -\frac{\log \mu(x_0 - 2^{-n}, x_0 + 2^{-n})}{n \log 2} \qquad (8.2.32)$$

In particular, $\alpha(x_0)$ *is measurable.*

Proof. (a) Let $f_{\delta,\alpha}(x)$ be the quantity in the limit (8.2.30). Each $f_{\delta,\alpha}(x)$ is continuous in x and it is easy to see the $\overline{\lim}$ is taken by going through rational δ, so D_μ^α is measurable by Theorem 4.3.6.

(b) Since $\frac{1}{(2\delta)^{\alpha-\alpha_0}}$ goes to ∞ (respectively, 0) as $\delta \downarrow 0$ if $\alpha > \alpha_0$ (respectively, $\alpha < \alpha_0$), we see $D_\mu^{\alpha_0}(x_0) < \infty \Rightarrow D_\mu^\alpha(x_0) = 0$ for $\alpha < \alpha_0$ and $D_\mu^{\alpha_0}(x_0) > 0 \Rightarrow D_\mu^\alpha(x_0) = \infty$ for $\alpha > \alpha_0$. If $\alpha_0(x_0) = \sup\{\alpha \mid D^\alpha(x_0) = 0\}$, then α_0 has the required property.

(c) Let $g_\delta(x_0)$ be the function inside the limit of (8.2.31) and $f_{\delta,\alpha}(x_0)$ as in the proof of (a). Then

$$2^\alpha f_{\delta,\alpha}(x_0) = \exp\big[(\log \delta)[g_\delta(x_0) - \alpha]\big] \qquad (8.2.33)$$

Thus $\alpha < \underline{\lim}\, g_\delta(x_0)$ implies $2^\alpha f_{\delta,\alpha}(x_0) \to 0$ and $\alpha > \underline{\lim}\, g_\delta(x_0)$ implies $\overline{\lim}\, 2^\alpha f_{\delta,\alpha}(x_0) = \infty$. (8.2.31) follows.

(d) It is immediate that $2^{-n-1} \leq \delta \leq 2^{-n}$ implies

$$g_{2^{-n-1}}(x_0)\left[\frac{\log(\delta)}{\log(\frac{\delta}{2})}\right] \leq g_\delta(x_0) \leq g_{2^{-n}}(x_0)\left[\frac{\log(2\delta)}{\log(\delta)}\right] \qquad (8.2.34)$$

The result is thus implied by

$$\lim_{\delta \downarrow 0} \frac{\log(2\delta)}{\log(\delta)} = 1 \qquad (8.2.35)$$

$\square$

Here is the main result that relates $D_\mu^\alpha(x_0)$ to Hausdorff measure:

Theorem 8.2.6 (Rogers–Taylor Theorem). *Let $d\mu$ be a Baire measure on* $[0,1]$. *Then*

(a) $h_\alpha(\{x \mid D_\mu^\alpha(x) = \infty\}) = 0$ $\qquad\qquad\qquad\qquad\qquad$ (8.2.36)

(b) $h_\alpha(S) = 0 \Rightarrow \mu(S \cap \{x \mid D_\mu^\alpha(x) < \infty\}) = 0$ $\qquad\quad$ (8.2.37)

Remark. The proof of (a) will require a Vitali covering theorem of the type only discussed in Section 2.3 of Part 3. Specifically, we'll need the following (see Problem 8 of that section): If $\{B_\gamma(x_\gamma)\}$ is a collection of balls in $\mathbb{R}$, there is a countable subcollection $\{B_{\delta_n}(x_n)\}_{n=1}^N$ so that these $B_{\delta_n}(x_n)$ are disjoint and

$$\bigcup_\gamma B_\gamma(x_\gamma) \subseteq \bigcup_{n=1}^N B_{4\delta_n}(x_n) \qquad (8.2.38)$$

(the 4 can be any number larger than 3). If there are finitely many balls to start with, one can replace 4 by 3 and the proof is a very simple argument. If we had proven inner regularity of h_α, we could get away with finite covers but we have not proven it although it is true.

Proof. (a) For $k = 1, 2, \ldots$, define

$$U_k = \{x \mid D_\mu^\alpha(x) > k\}, \quad U_\infty = \{x \mid D_\mu^\infty(x) = \infty\} \qquad (8.2.39)$$

We'll prove that

$$h_\alpha(U_k) \leq 4^\alpha k^{-1} \mu\big([0,1]\big) \qquad (8.2.40)$$

Since $U_\infty \subset U_k$, we obtain (8.2.36).

Given δ_0 and $x \in U_k$, we can find, by the definition of D_μ^α, $\delta_x < \frac{1}{8}\delta_0$ so that

$$\mu(x - \delta_x, x + \delta_x) > k(2\delta_x)^\alpha \tag{8.2.41}$$

By the Vitali covering theorem quoted above, we can find $\{x_j\}_{j=1}^N$ so if $S_j = (x_j - 4\delta_{x_j}, x + 4\delta_{x_j})$ then

$$U_k \subset \bigcup_x (x - \delta_x, x + \delta_x) \subset \bigcup_{j=1}^N S_j \tag{8.2.42}$$

and the $(x_j - \delta_{x_j}, x_j + \delta_{x_j})$ are disjoint. The latter implies that

$$\sum_{j=1}^N \mu(x_j - \delta_{x_j}, x_j + \delta_{x_j}) \leq \mu([0,1]) \tag{8.2.43}$$

By the fact that the S_j are a cover of U_k and $\operatorname{diam} S_j = 8\delta_{x_j} < \delta_0$, we have that

$$h_{\alpha,\delta_0}(U_k) \leq \sum_{j=1}^N \big[\operatorname{diam}(S_j)\big]^\alpha$$

$$\leq 4^\alpha \sum_{j=1}^N (2\delta_{x_j})^\alpha$$

$$\leq k^{-1}4^\alpha \sum_{j=1}^N \mu(x_j - \delta_j, x_j + \delta_j) \quad \text{(by (8.2.42))}$$

$$\leq k^{-1}4^\alpha \mu([0,1]) \quad \text{(by (8.2.43))}$$

as claimed.

(b) Let

$$\widetilde{D}_\mu^\alpha(x) = \sup_{0 < \delta_1, \delta_2 < 1} \frac{\mu(x - \delta_1, x + \delta_2)}{|\delta_1 + \delta_2|^\alpha} \tag{8.2.44}$$

We first claim that

$$\widetilde{D}_\mu^\alpha(x) < \infty \Leftrightarrow D_\mu^\alpha(x) < \infty \tag{8.2.45}$$

One half is immediate since $D_\mu^\alpha(x) \leq \widetilde{D}_\mu^\alpha(x)$. For the other half, notice that if $\delta = \max(\delta_1, \delta_2)$, then

$$\frac{\mu(x - \delta_1, x + \delta_2)}{|\delta_1 + \delta_2|} \leq 2^\alpha \frac{\mu(x - \delta_1, x + \delta_2)}{|2\delta|^\alpha} \tag{8.2.46}$$

and the only way the sup on the right can be infinite is if the $\overline{\lim}$ is infinite. This shows (8.2.45).

Define, for $k > 0$,

$$V_k = \{x \mid \widetilde{D}_\mu^\alpha(x) < k\} \tag{8.2.47}$$

We claim for any Borel set S and $\delta > 0$

$$\mu(S \cap V_k) \le k h^*_{\alpha,\delta}(S) \tag{8.2.48}$$

This implies if $h_\alpha(S) = 0$, then $\mu(S \cap V_k) = 0$ so

$$\mu\bigl(S \cap \{x \mid D^\alpha_\mu(x) < \infty\}\bigr) = \mu\bigl(S \cap (\bigcup_{k=1}^{\infty} V_k)\bigr) = 0 \tag{8.2.49}$$

proving (8.2.37)

Let $\{I_\beta\}$ be a cover of $S \cap V_k$ by open intervals. $\sum_\beta |I_\beta|^\alpha$ is only decreased if we throw away I_β's with $I_\beta \cap V_k = 0$ and shrink all I_β so $|I_\beta| \le 1$. Thus, we need only consider covers with those two properties. If $x_0 \in I_\beta \cap V_k$, then by the definition of $\widetilde{D}^\alpha_\mu(x_0)$,

$$\mu(I_\beta) \le \widetilde{D}^\alpha_\mu(x_0) \, |I_\beta|^\alpha \le k \, |I_\beta|^\alpha \tag{8.2.50}$$

Thus

$$\mu(S \cap V_k) \le \sum_\beta \mu(I_\beta) \le k \sum_\beta |I_\beta|^\alpha \tag{8.2.51}$$

Minimizing over all covers with $|I_\beta| < \delta$, we get

$$\mu(S \cap V_k) \le k h^*_{\alpha,\delta}(S \cap V_k) \le k h^*_{\alpha,\delta}(S) \tag{8.2.52}$$

proving (8.2.48) $\qquad\qquad\qquad\qquad\qquad\qquad\qquad\qquad\qquad\quad \square$

Corollary 8.2.7. *Let μ be a Baire measure on $[0,1]$. The for each $\alpha \in (0,1)$*

$$\mu = \mu_{\alpha s} + \mu_{\alpha c} \tag{8.2.53}$$

where $\mu_{\alpha s}$ is h_α-singular and $\mu_{\alpha c}$ is h_α-continuous.

Remarks. 1. We throw the pure point part in $\mu_{\alpha s}$ so it is easy to allow μ's with pure points.

2. We leave it to the reader (Problem 12) to show that the decomposition (8.2.53) is unique.

Proof. Define

$$\mu_{\alpha s}(A) = \mu\bigl(A \cap \{x \mid D^\alpha_\mu(x) = \infty\}\bigr) \tag{8.2.54}$$

$$\mu_{\alpha c}(A) = \mu\bigl(A \cap \{x \mid D^\alpha_\mu(x) < \infty\}\bigr) \tag{8.2.55}$$

With $S = \{x \mid D^\alpha_\mu(x) = \infty\}$, we have $\mu_{\alpha s}(\mathbb{R} \setminus S) = 0$ and, by (a) of the theorem, $h_\alpha(S) = 0$. By (b) of the theorem, $\mu_{\alpha c}$ is h_α-continuous $\quad \square$

Corollary 8.2.8. *Let μ be a measure on $[0,1]$. Then μ has exact dimension, α_0, if and only if $\alpha(x) = \alpha_0$ for μ-a.e. x.*

Proof. Suppose first that for μ-a.e. x, $\alpha(x) = \alpha_0$. If $\beta < \alpha_0$, then since $\frac{1}{2}(\beta + \alpha_0) < \alpha_0$, $D_\mu^{\frac{1}{2}(\beta+\alpha_0)}(x) = 0$ for all x, so if $h\text{-dim}(S) = \beta$, then $h_{\frac{\alpha_0+\beta}{2}}(S) = 0$ (since $\frac{1}{2}(\alpha_0 + \beta) > \beta$) and thus, by the theorem, $\mu(S) = 0$.

On the other hand, if

$$S_n = \{x \mid D_\mu^{\alpha_0+1/n}(x) = \infty\} \tag{8.2.56}$$

then $\mu(\mathbb{R} \setminus S_n) = 0$ and $h_{\alpha_0+1/n}(S_n) = 0$. It follows, if $S_0 = \bigcap_n S_n$, then $h\text{-dim}(S) \le \alpha_0$ and $\mu(\mathbb{R} \setminus S_0) = 0$. If $h\text{-dim}(S_0) < \alpha_0$, then $\mu(S_0) = 0$ by the first part of the proof, so $h\text{-dim}(S) = \alpha_0$. Thus μ has exact dimension α_0.

Conversely, suppose that μ has exact dimension, α_0. If $\alpha > \alpha_0$, since $\dim(S_0) = \alpha_0$, we have $h_\alpha(S_0) = 0$, so by the theorem $\mu(S_0 \cap \{x \mid D_\mu^\alpha(x) < \infty\}) = 0$. Since $\mu(\mathbb{R} \setminus S_0)$, we see that $\mu(\{x \mid D_\mu^\alpha(x) < \infty\}) = 0$, i.e., for a.e. x, $D_\mu^\alpha(x) = \infty$. Picking $\alpha = \alpha_0 + \frac{1}{n}$, we see that $\alpha(x) \le \alpha_0$ for a.e. x.

On the other hand, if $\alpha < \alpha_0$, then $h_\alpha(\{x \mid D_\mu^\alpha(x) = \infty\}) = 0$ by the theorem. Thus, $h\text{-dim}(\{x \mid D_\mu^\alpha(x) = \infty\}) \le \alpha$, so since μ has exact dimension α_0, we see that $\mu(\{x \mid D_\mu^\alpha(x) = \infty\}) = 0$. Picking $\alpha = \alpha_0 - \frac{1}{n}$, we see that for μ-a.e. x, $D_\mu^{\alpha_0-1/n}(x) < \infty$ and thus, for μ-a.e. x, $\alpha(x) \ge \alpha_0$. Therefore, as claimed $\alpha(x) > \alpha_0$ for a.e. x $\quad\square$

We want to prove that each μ_p given by Example 8.2.4 has exact dimension d_p given by (8.2.29). If $p = \frac{1}{2}$, μ_p is a Lebesgue measure which has exact dimension 1 as claimed. $d\mu_{1-p}(1 - x) = d\mu(x)$, and $d_{1-p} = d_p$, so we need only consider

$$0 < p < \tfrac{1}{2} \tag{8.2.57}$$

As a preliminary, we need to know that it is unlikely that there are really long strings of zeros in a base 2-expansion. Given $x \in [0,1]$ which is not a dyadic rational, we define $a_n(x)$ by

$$x = \sum_{n=1}^\infty \frac{a_n(x)}{2^n} \tag{8.2.58}$$

We define $C_n(x)$ by

$$C_n(x) = \begin{cases} 0 & \text{if } a_n(x) = 1 \\ \ell & \text{if } a_n(x) = \ldots = a_{n-\ell+1}(x) = 0, a_{n-\ell}(x) = 1 \end{cases} \tag{8.2.59}$$

Lemma 8.2.9. *For any $p \in (0,1)$, and $d\mu_p$-a.e. x, we have*

$$\lim_{n\to\infty} \frac{1}{n} C_n(x) = 0 \tag{8.2.60}$$

Remark. A more refined analysis (Problem 13) proves that for a.e. x

$$\overline{\lim}_{n\to\infty} \frac{C_n(x)}{\log n} = \frac{-1}{\log p} \tag{8.2.61}$$

Proof. Let $A_n = \{x \mid C_n(x) \geq [\sqrt{n}] + 1\}$. Then,

$$\mu_p(A_n) = p^{[\sqrt{n}]+1} \leq p^{\sqrt{n}} \qquad (8.2.62)$$

It follows that

$$\sum_{n=1}^{\infty} \mu_p(A_n) < \infty \qquad (8.2.63)$$

so by the first Borel–Cantelli lemma (Theorem 7.2.1), for μ_p-a.e. x, $x \notin A_n$ for all large n, i.e.

$$\overline{\lim} \, \frac{C_n(x)}{\sqrt{n}} \leq 1 \qquad (8.2.64)$$

which implies (8.2.60). □

Theorem 8.2.10. *Let μ_p be the measure on $[0,1]$ where each base 2 digit is independent and identically distributed and $\mu_p(\{a_n(x) = 0\}) = p$. Let d_p be given by (8.2.29). Then μ_p has exact dimension d_p.*

Proof. Without loss, we can take $0 < p < \frac{1}{2}$. By Corollary 8.2.8, we need to show that for μ_p-a.e. x, $\alpha(x) = d_p$. By Proposition 8.2.5, it suffices to prove

$$\lim_{n\to\infty} \frac{\log \mu(x - 2^{-n}, x + 2^n)}{n \log 2} = -d_p \qquad (8.2.65)$$

(we only need $\overline{\lim}$ but the limit is easy).

Since the dyadic rationals are countable, we can suppose x is not a dyadic rational. For such x, let

$$\Delta_n(x) = \text{dyadic interval of size } 2^{-n} \text{ containing } x \qquad (8.2.66)$$

$$\widetilde{\Delta}_n(x) = \begin{cases} \Delta^{(1)}(x + \frac{1}{2^n}) & \text{if } a_n(x) = 1 \\ \Delta^{(1)}(x - \frac{1}{2^n}) & \text{if } a_n(x) = 0 \end{cases} \qquad (8.2.67)$$

Then,

$$\Delta_n(x) \subset (x - 2^{-n}, x + 2^{-n}) \subset \Delta_n(x) \cup \widetilde{\Delta}_n(x) \qquad (8.2.68)$$

Thus, (8.2.65) follows if we prove that for a.e. x

$$\lim_{n\to\infty} \frac{\log \mu(\Delta_n(x))}{n \log 2} = -d_p \qquad (8.2.69)$$

$$\lim_{n\to\infty} \frac{\log \mu(\widetilde{\Delta}_n(x))}{n \log 2} \leq -d_p \qquad (8.2.70)$$

To prove (8.2.69), note that

$$\Delta_n(x) = \{j \mid a_j(x) = a_j(y), \, j = 1, \ldots, n\} \qquad (8.2.71)$$

With N_m given by (8.2.26). i.e.,

$$N_m(x) = \sharp(j < m \mid a_j(x) = 0) \qquad (8.2.72)$$

(8.2.71) implies that

$$\mu(\Delta_n(x)) = p^{N_{n+1}(x)}(1-p)^{n-N_{n+1}(x)} \tag{8.2.73}$$

Thus, for μ_p-a.e.x

$$\frac{\log \mu(\Delta_n(x))}{n} = \frac{N_{n+1}(x)}{n} \log p + \left(1 - \frac{N_{n+1}(x)}{n}\right) \log(1-p) \tag{8.2.74}$$

$$\to p \log p + (1-p) \log(1-p) = -(\log 2)d_p \tag{8.2.75}$$

since the strong law of large numbers says for μ_p-a.e. x

$$\frac{N_{n+1}(x)}{n} \to p \tag{8.2.76}$$

This proves (8.2.69).

If $a_n(x) = 0$, $a_j(x - \frac{1}{2^n})$ is 1 for $j = n, n-1, \ldots, n - C_n(x) + 1$ and 0 for $j = n - C_n(x)$ (with $a_n(x)$ the opposite) and for $j < n - C_n(x)$, $a_j(x) = a_j(x - \frac{1}{2^n})$. Thus, $C_n(x)$ of the p's in (8.2.73) are replaced by $(1-p)$ and one $(1-p)$ by p, i.e.,

$$a_n(x) = 0 \Rightarrow \mu(\widetilde{\Delta}_n(x)) = \left[\frac{(1-p)}{p}\right]^{C_n(x)-1} \mu(\Delta_n(x)) \tag{8.2.77}$$

Plugging this into (8.2.74) and using the lemma proves (8.2.70) with $\leq -d_p$ replaced by $-d_p$

If $a_n(x) = 1$ (8.2.77) holds with some number of $\left(\frac{p}{1-p}\right)$ factors, i.e.,

$$a_n(x) = 1 \Rightarrow \mu(\widetilde{\Delta}_n(x)) \leq \mu(\Delta_n(x)) \tag{8.2.78}$$

which implies (8.2.70)   □

Notes and Historical Remarks. The topics in this section are part of the subject called *geometric measure theory* which also includes the theory of minimal surfaces and parts of analysis that depend on the properties of very thin sets. Under the name geometric measure theory or the closely related rubric of fractals, an area of wide scientific importance, there is a huge literature of which we mention the following books [**270, 289, 293, 296, 521, 590, 625, 640, 666, 799, 857**].

The definition of Hausdorff measure and its use to define a dimension is from a 1919 paper of Hausdorff [**403**] with important developments by Besicovitch [**85**]. This last work is so important that some refer to *Hausdorff-Besicovitch dimension* for what we call h-dim.

This is not the only definition given for the dimension of a set. Two other popular notions are topological dimension and box-counting dimension. Topological dimension has to do with refinements of open covers. If

X is a topological space and $\mathfrak{A} = \{A_\alpha\}_{\alpha \in J}$ is an open cover, we call another open cover $\mathcal{B} = \{B_\beta\}_{\beta \in J}$ a *refinement* of $\mathfrak{A}$ if there is $f : J \to I$ so $B_\beta \subset A_{f(\beta)}$ (i.e., the elements of $\mathcal{B}$ are subsets of $\mathfrak{A}$). One says that X has *topological dimension* n if any cover has a refinement $\mathcal{B}$ so no point in X lies in more than $n + 1$ sets and no smaller number will do.

Notice that topological dimension is always an integer. A *fractal* is a set, S, in a metric space whose h-dim is different from its topological dimension. In particular, if h-$\dim(S)$ is not an integer, it is a fractal.

X has topological dimension 0 if and only if every cover has a refinement to disjoint open sets. For example, $\{1/n\}_{n=1}^{\infty} \cup \{0\}$ has dimension 0. $[0, 1]$ has topological dimension 1 since any cover has a refinement into intervals and then one can arrange to have only pairwise overlaps.

Topological dimension is sometimes called *covering dimension* or *Lebesgue covering dimension* since it appeared first in 1911 in Lebesgue [565]. It was Brouwer [133] who proved Lebesgue's conjecture that $\mathbb{R}^n$ has Lebesgue covering dimension n. Menger [650] wrote an important early book on the subject.

Another dimension that can be defined in any metric space is the *box-counting dimension*. Given a set, S, let $N(\varepsilon)$ be the minimum number of balls of diameter ε needed to cover X. Then

$$b\text{-}\dim(S) = \lim_{\varepsilon \downarrow 0} \frac{\log N(\varepsilon)}{\log(1/\varepsilon)} \tag{8.2.79}$$

assuming the limit exists. Otherwise, the lim sup is the *upper box dimension* and the lim inf the *lower box dimension*. As the name implies, on $\mathbb{R}^\nu$, one often uses boxes rather than balls, showing in many cases that the limit is the same. For example, $[0, 1]^d$ is covered by $2^n d$ boxes of side 2^{-n} and $\log(2^{nd})/\log(1/2^{-n}) = d$.

Returning to the diameter of balls, any cover by $N(\varepsilon)$ balls, each of diameter ε gives an upper bound to $h^*_{\alpha,\varepsilon}(S)$ by

$$N(\varepsilon)\varepsilon^\alpha = \exp\big(\log N(\varepsilon) - \alpha \log(1/\varepsilon)\big)$$
$$= \exp\left(\log\left(\frac{1}{\varepsilon}\right)\left[\frac{\log(N(\varepsilon))}{\log(1/\varepsilon)} - \alpha\right]\right) \tag{8.2.80}$$

It follows that if $\alpha > b\text{-}\dim(S)$, then $\lim_{\varepsilon \downarrow 0} h^*_{\alpha,\varepsilon}(S) = 0$, i.e., we have shown that

$$h\text{-}\dim(S) \leq b\text{-}\dim(S) \tag{8.2.81}$$

(and, in general, $h\text{-}\dim(S) \leq$ lower box $(S) \leq$ upper box (S)). We'll see soon it can happen that equality fails in (8.2.81).

Box dimensions are popular because they are often easier to compute than Hausdorff dimension (see Problem 14). But the lack of an underlying

countably additive measure means that countable sets, even countable closed
sets can have nonzero dimension. For example, for $\alpha > 0$, the set

$$S_\alpha = \{0\} \cup \{1/n^\alpha\}_{n=1}^\infty \tag{8.2.82}$$

has (!)

$$b\text{-dim}(S_\alpha) = 1/(1+\alpha) \tag{8.2.83}$$

(see Problem 15 or the paper of Mišik–Žáčik [**661**] which computes the b-dim(S) where $S = \{0\} \cup \{f(n)\}_{n=1}^\infty$ when f is a C^1 convex function of x going to zero as $x \to \infty$ as $\lim_{x\to\infty}\left\{\left[\log(x - \frac{f(x)}{f'(x)})\right]\left[-\log(-f'(x))\right]\right\}$ if the limit exists.)

This dimension goes back to Bouligand [**117**] in 1928 who called it *Cantor–Minkowski* dimension. It is often called *Minkowski dimension* or *Minkowski–Bouligand* or sometimes *metric dimension, Kolmogorov dimension*, or *entropy dimension*. Abry et al. [**1**] has a collection of articles on various notions of dimension.

Returning to the subject of Hausdorff measure, showing that the $h_{\alpha=1}$ measure of $[0,1]$ is 1 is an interesting exercise (Problem 4). The analog for the unit ball in $\mathbb{R}^\nu$ (i.e., $h_{\alpha=\nu}$ is 1) is the key to the proof that $\mathcal{H}^\nu$ Hausdorff (meaning both spherical Hausdorff and general cases) ν-dimensional measure, agrees with Lebesgue measure. For it is enough to check equality on a single set, since both Hausdorff and Lebesgue measure are translation invariant and so multiples of Haar measure (by Theorem 4.19.1). For a presentation of this calculation, see, for example, the book of Taylor [**911**].

As we noted, dimensions of Cartesian products can be tricky and surprising (see Problem 9). In general, one can prove that

$$h\text{-dim}(A) + h\text{-dim}(B) \le h\text{-dim}(A\times B) \le h\text{-dim}(A) + \text{lower-dim}(B) \tag{8.2.84}$$

(see the book of Falconer [**293**]). This completes the proof that the example of Problem 9 has h-dim$(A \times B) = 1$. It also shows that if h-dim$(B) = b$-dim(B) as is true for the generalized Cantor sets of Example 8.2.3, then h-dim$(A \times B) = h$-dim$(A) + h$-dim(B).

The inner regularity of Hausdorff measure is due to Besicovitch in 1952 [**86**]. The book of Rogers [**799**] has a clean exposition of both inner regularity and G_δ-outer regularity.

Theorem 8.2.6 is due to Rogers–Taylor [**800, 801**]. Our presentation follows the one in Rogers [**799**]. Rogers–Taylor develops more refined decompositions than the one into $d\mu_{\alpha c}$ plus $d\mu_{\alpha s}$—in general, for each $\alpha \in (0,1)$, there is a natural five-fold decomposition of any finite Baire measure on $[0,1]$.

The analysis of the measure μ_p (i.e., Theorem 8.2.10) follows del Rio et al. [**232**]. They also discuss the relation of $D_\mu^\alpha(x_0)$ to the divergence as $\varepsilon \downarrow 0$

of $\int \frac{d\mu(y)}{y-z}$ for $z = x_0 + i\varepsilon$ and an analysis of Hausdorff dimension properties of rank one perturbations of multiplication by x on $L^2([0,1], d\mu_p)$. Last [551] also discusses the connection between spectral theory and Hausdorff dimension.

A general measure, μ, may not have a local dimension. For example, if $p_1, p_2 \in (0,1)$ with $p_1 \neq p_2$ and $p_1 + p_2 \neq 1$, then $d\mu_{p_1} + d\mu_{p_2}$ does not have a local dimension at any point. That said, the notion of local dimension is useful. For example, Kiselev–Last–Simon [492] find interesting examples (discrete Schrödinger operators with random, decaying as $n^{-1/2}$, potentials) with local (but x_0-dependent) local dimensions.

Problems

1. If S_n is Borel and has h-dim $\alpha_0 - \frac{1}{n}$, prove that $S = \bigcup_{n=1}^{\infty} S_n$ has h-dim α_0 with $h_{\alpha_0}(S) = 0$.

2. Prove that if $0 < \alpha < 1$ and $h_\alpha(S) = 1$ for $S \subset [0,1]$, then $T = \bigcup_{n=1}^{\infty}(S \times \{q_n\}) \subset [0,1] \times [0,1]$ (where q_n is a countable subset of $[0,1]$) is an α-dimensional set with $h_\alpha(T) = \infty$.

3. Knowing that $h_\nu([0,1]^\nu) = 1$, prove that for any $\alpha < \nu$, h_α as a measure on $[0,1]^\nu$ is not σ-finite. (*Hint*: If $h_\alpha(S) < \infty$, then $h_\nu(S) = 0$.)

4. Prove that the $h^*_{1,\delta}$ outer measure of $[0,1] = 1$. (*Hint*: Use compactness and induction.)

5. Let C be the classical Cantor set and $\ell_\pm(C)$ the set of its upper/lower end points. Prove that for any $x \in C$, there are $\{x_n\}_{n=1}^\infty$, $\{y_n\}_{n=1}^\infty$, so $x_n < x \leq y_n$, $y_n - x_n \to 0$ and all $x_n \in \ell_-(C)$, all $y_n \in \ell_+(C)$. (*Hint*: Use the characterization of $\ell_\pm(C)$ in terms of base 3 decimal expansion. Alternatively, use the fact that C has empty interior.)

6. Repeat the analysis of h-$\dim(C)$ to prove that the set C_δ of Example 8.2.3 has h-dim, s_δ, given by (8.2.23).

7. Let (X, p), (Y, d) be two metric spaces. Let $F : X \to Y$ be globally Lipschitz, i.e., for some constant C and all $x, y \in X$,

$$d(F(x), F(y)) \leq Cp(x,y) \tag{8.2.85}$$

Prove that for $S \subset X$

$$h_\alpha(F[S]) \leq h_s(S) \tag{8.2.86}$$

and conclude that

$$h\text{-}\dim F[S] \leq h\text{-}\dim[S] \tag{8.2.87}$$

8. Let $1 \le m_1 < n_1 < m_2 \ldots$ be integers. For $x \in [0,1]$, let $a_n(x)$ be the digit of the base 2 decimal expansion, (8.2.58). Let

$$S = \{x \mid a_n(x) = 0, m_j \le n < n_j, j = 1, 2, \ldots\} \qquad (8.2.88)$$

(a) Prove that S can be covered by $2^{m_j - 1}$ intervals of size 2^{-n_j}.

(b) Prove that $h_\alpha(S) = 0$ if $\alpha > \underline{\lim}_{j \to \infty} \frac{n_j}{m_j}$

(c) Prove that $h\text{-dim}(S) \le \underline{\lim}_{j \to \infty} \frac{n_j}{m_j}$. In particular, if this $\underline{\lim}$ is 0, then S has $h\text{-dim}\,0$ (e.g., $n_j = (2j)!$, $m_j = (2j-1)!$, then $h\text{-dim}(S) = 0$.

9. Let S_1 be the set described in the last problem with $m_j = (2j-1)!$, $n_j = (2j)!$ and S_2 with $m_j = (2j)!$, $n_j = (2j+1)!$.

(a) Prove that $h\text{-dim}(S_1) = h\text{-dim}(S_2) = 0$.

(b) Prove that $S_1 + S_2 = [0,1]$.

(c) Prove that $h\text{-dim}(S_1 \times S_2) \ge 1$. (*Hint*: Let $f : [0,1] \times [0,1] \to [0,2]$ by $f(x+y) = x+y$. Prove f is Lipschitz and use Problem 7.)

Remark. For more on this subject, see Falconer's book.

10. Let $A \subset \mathbb{R}^\mu$, and let $\nu_1 \ge 0$, $\nu_2 \ge 0$ be given. Let $B \subset \mathbb{R}^{\mu+\nu_1+\nu_2}$ be given by $B = A \times \{0\}_{\nu_1} \times [0,1]^{\nu_2} \subset \mathbb{R}^{\mu+\nu_1+\nu_2}$, i.e.,

$$B = \{(x_1, x_2, x_3) \mid x_1 \in A \subset \mathbb{R}^\mu, x_2 = 0 \in \mathbb{R}^{\nu_1}, x_{3j} \in [0,1], x_3 \in \mathbb{R}^{\nu_2}\}$$

Prove that $h\text{-dim}(B) = h\text{-dim}(A) + \nu_2$.

11. Extend Proposition 8.2.5 to allow μ to have pure points.

12. Let μ be a finite Baire measure on $[0,1]$ and $\alpha \in [0,1]$. Suppose $\mu = \mu_{1\alpha s} + \mu_{1\alpha c} = \mu_{2\alpha s} + \mu_{2\alpha c}$ where $\mu_{j\alpha s}$ is h_α-singular and $\mu_{j\alpha c}$ is h_α-continuous. Prove that $\mu_{1\alpha s} = \mu_{2\alpha s}$, $\mu_{1\alpha c} = \mu_{2\alpha c}$.

13. Let $C_n(x)$ be given by (8.2.58) and $\mathbb{P}_p$ be the $d\mu_p$ probability.

(a) Prove that $\sum \mathbb{P}_p(\{x \mid C_n(x) \ge k \log n / (-\log p)\}) < \infty$ if and only if $k < 1$.

(b) Prove (8.2.61).

14. Prove that the box-counting dimension of the generalized Cantor set of Example 8.2.3 is $\log 2 / \log(\delta^{-1})$.

15. Let $S_1 = \{0, \frac{1}{2}, \frac{1}{3}, \frac{1}{4}, \ldots\}$. Prove that S_1 has box-counting dimension $\frac{1}{2}$!

Chapter 9

Bonus Chapter: Inductive Limits and Ordinary Distributions

> The advance of science is not comparable to the changes of a city, where old edifices are pitilessly torn down to give place to new, but to the continuous evolution of zoological types which develop ceaselessly and end by becoming unrecognizable to the common sight, but where an expert eye finds always traces of the prior work of the centuries past. One must not think then that the old-fashioned theories have been sterile or vain.
>
> —H. Poincaré [**735**]

Big Notions and Theorems: Strict Inductive Limit Topologies, LF Spaces, Montel Property, Ordinary Distributions

Consider $\mathcal{D}(\mathbb{R}^\nu) = C_0^\infty(\mathbb{R}^\nu)$, the C^∞ functions of compact support. We want to try to define distributions as linear functionals on $C_0^\infty(\mathbb{R}^\nu)$. A little thought shows the following is reasonable:

Definition. An *ordinary distribution* on $\mathbb{R}^\nu$ is a linear map, $\tau \colon \mathcal{D}(\mathbb{R}^\nu) \to \mathbb{R}$ so that for any $R > 0$, there is $N_R \in \mathbb{N}$ and $C_R \in (0, \infty)$ so that for all $f \in \mathcal{D}(\mathbb{R}^\nu)$ with $\operatorname{supp}(f) \subset \{x \mid |x| \le R\}$, we have

$$|\tau(f)| \le C_R \sum_{|\alpha| \le N_R} \|D^\alpha f\|_\infty \tag{9.0.1}$$

What makes this more general than tempered distributions is that as $R \to \infty$, C_R can go to infinity at an arbitrary rate and so can N_R. For example, when $\nu = 1$,

$$\tau = \sum_{n=0}^{\infty} e^n \delta^{(n)}(x - n) \tag{9.0.2}$$

has nontempered growth of constants and derivatives of arbitrary high order. The natural question we'll answer here is what is the topology on $\mathcal{D}$ so that linear functionals obeying (9.0.1) are precisely the continuous linear functionals in this topology.

Another closely related situation that we sidestepped earlier involves arbitrary Borel measures on $\mathbb{R}^\nu$: these we defined as consistent positive linear functionals on $C(\{x \mid |x| \leq n\})$. Again, one can ask what topology is put on $C_0(\mathbb{R}^\nu)$, the continuous functions of compact support, so that its continuous linear functionals are differences of positive Borel measures.

Section 9.1 will describe an abstract setting where X is a vector space and $X = \bigcup_{j=1}^{\infty} X_j$ is a union of increasing subspaces, $X_j \subset X_{j+1}$. We'll suppose each X_j has a locally convex topology so that X_j has the relative topology induced by the topology on X_{j+1}. The model for $\mathcal{D}(\mathbb{R}^\nu)$ is to take

$$X_n = \{f \in \mathcal{D}(\mathbb{R}^\nu) \mid \mathrm{supp}(f) \subset \{x \mid |x| \leq n\}\} \tag{9.0.3}$$

with the Fréchet topology defined by the norms

$$\|f\|_m = \sum_{|\alpha| \leq m} \|D^\alpha f\|_\infty \tag{9.0.4}$$

We'll prove there is a unique locally convex topology on X so that for any locally convex space, Y, and linear map, $T \colon X \to Y$, T is continuous in this topology if and only if $T \restriction X_j \to Y$ is continuous. We'll see that if each X_j is a closed proper subset of X_{j+1}, then this topology is not metrizable.

In Section 9.2, we'll discuss three examples: the two mentioned earlier and the simple one of polynomials.

Notes and Historical Remarks. For texts on the theory of topological vector spacing, including discussions of inductive limits, see [**121, 450, 518, 677, 794, 812, 931, 932**].

9.1. Strict Inductive Limits

The result that lets us define inductive topologies is:

Theorem 9.1.1. *Let X be a vector space over $\mathbb{K} = \mathbb{R}$ or $\mathbb{C}$ so that $X_1 \subset X_2 \subset \ldots$ are an increasing family of subspaces with*

$$X = \bigcup_{j=1}^{\infty} X_j \tag{9.1.1}$$

Suppose each X_j has a locally convex topology so that the relative topology on X_j generated by X_{j+1} is the given topology on X_j. Let

$$\mathcal{U} = \{U \subset X \mid U \text{ is a balanced, absorbing convex subset of } X$$
$$\text{so that each } U \cap X_j \text{ is open in } X_j\} \tag{9.1.2}$$

Then $\mathcal{U}$ is a neighborhood base of a locally convex topology on X. Moreover,

(a) *X is the strongest locally convex topology in which each embedding $T_j \colon X_j \to X$ is continuous.*

(b) *The relative topology X induces on X_j is the original topology.*

We'll need a preliminary lemma:

Lemma 9.1.2. *Let $Y_1 \subset Y$, a locally convex space with Y_1 a subspace. Let $V \subset Y_1$ be a balanced, convex set which is open in the relative topology induced by Y on Y_1. Then there is a balanced, convex, open set $U \subset Y$ so that*

$$U \cap Y_1 = V \tag{9.1.3}$$

Proof. Since V is relatively open, there is U_0 open in Y so $U_0 \cap Y_1 = V$. Since U_0 is a neighborhood of 0 in Y, there is a balanced, convex, open set of Y, U_1 with $0 \in U_1 \subset U_0$. Define

$$U = \{\alpha x + \beta y \mid x \in U_1, \, y \in V, \, |\alpha| + |\beta| = 1, \, \alpha \neq 0\} \tag{9.1.4}$$

$$= \bigcup_{y \in V, |\alpha| + |\beta| = 1, \alpha \neq 0} (\beta y + |\alpha| U_1) \tag{9.1.5}$$

is open as a union of open sets. Moreover, we claim

$$V \subset U \tag{9.1.6}$$

For V open implies that if $x \in V$, then $\gamma x \in V$ for some $\gamma \in [0, \Gamma)$ with $\Gamma > 1$. Thus, with $\beta = [\frac{1}{2}(1 + \Gamma)]^{-1}$, $\alpha = 1 - \beta$,

$$x = \alpha 0 + \beta[\tfrac{1}{2}(1 + \Gamma)x] \subset U$$

This shows that one can drop $\alpha \neq 0$ from (9.1.5) and that U is convex and balanced.

As we showed above, $V \subset U$ so $V \subset U \cap Y_1$. For the opposite inclusion, suppose $z \in U \cap Y_1$. Then

$$z = \alpha x + \beta y; \quad x \in U_1, \, y \in V, \, |\alpha| + |\beta| = 1, \, \alpha \neq 0 \tag{9.1.7}$$

Then $x = \alpha^{-1}(z - \beta y) \in Y_1$, since Y_1 is a subspace. Thus, $x \in U_1 \cap Y_1 \subset U_0 \cap Y_1 = V$. Thus, since V is balanced and convex, $z \in V$, that is, we have proven that $U \cap Y_1 \subset V$. $\qquad\square$

Proof of Theorem 9.1.1. Suppose first V_j is an open, balanced, convex subset of X_j. By the lemma, inductively pick balanced convex sets, $V_{j+1}, V_{j+2}, \ldots$, open in $X_{j+1}, X_{j+2}, \ldots$, so that $V_{\ell+1} \cap X_\ell = V_\ell$ and then, for $\ell > m \geq j$,

$$V_\ell \cap X_m = V_m \tag{9.1.8}$$

If $U = \bigcup_{\ell=j}^\infty V_\ell$, then U is balanced and convex and

$$U \cap X_k = \begin{cases} V_k, & k \geq j \\ V_j \cap X_k, & k < j \end{cases} \tag{9.1.9}$$

is open, balanced, and convex in X_k since for $k < j$, the topology is the relative topology. Thus, $U \subset \mathcal{U}$.

If $x \in X$, $x \neq 0$, then $x \in X_k$ for some k, so there is V_k with $x \notin V_k$ and V_k an open, balanced, convex subset of X_k. As above, we find $U \subset \mathcal{U}$ so $U \cap X_k = V_k$. In particular, $x \notin U$. Thus $\bigcap_{U \in \mathcal{U}} U = \{0\}$. Since $\lambda > 0$ and $U \in \mathcal{U}$ implies $\lambda U \in \mathcal{U}$, Corollary 5.7.6 implies $\mathcal{U}$ is the set of neighborhoods of a locally convex topology.

To prove (a), note if $T_j \colon X_j \to X$ is continuous in some topology, τ, on X and U is a τ-open, balanced, convex subset of X_j, then $T_j^{-1}[U] = U \cap X_j$ is an open, balanced, convex subset of X_j so $U \in \mathcal{U}$, that is, the topology generated by $\mathcal{U}$ is stronger than the given topology.

To prove (b), note that by the construction at the start, $\{U \cap X_j \mid U \in \mathcal{U}\}$ is precisely the open, balanced, convex sets in X_j, which says that the relative topology generated by the $\mathcal{U}$ topology is the original topology on X. $\qquad\square$

The topology just constructed is called the *strict inductive limit*. The word "strict" is here because there is also a construction where the condition that X_j has the X_{j+1} is replaced by the embedding of X_j in X_{j+1} is continuous; see the Notes. A strict inductive limit of Fréchet spaces is called an *LF space*.

Theorem 9.1.3. *Let X be a strict inductive limit of an increasing family of spaces, $\{X_j\}_{j=1}^\infty$, Y an arbitrary locally convex space, and $T \colon X \to Y$ a linear map. Then T is continuous if and only if each $T_j \equiv T \restriction X_j \colon X_j \to Y$ is continuous. This condition uniquely determines this strict inductive limit topology. In particular, $S \colon X \to \mathbb{K}$ is continuous if and only if for each j, there is a continuous seminorm ρ_α^j on X_j so that*

$$|S(x)| \leq \rho_\alpha^j(x) \qquad \text{for all } x \in X_j \tag{9.1.10}$$

Proof. Taking $T(x) = x$ which is continuous on each X_j shows that any two topologies obeying the $T \colon X \to Y$ property are homeomorphic under the identity map (i.e., the same). This proves uniqueness.

Since Y is locally convex, it suffices for continuity that $T^{-1}[W]$ be open for every open, balanced, convex set in Y. Such a $T^{-1}[W]$ is balanced and convex. It is open in the strict inductive limit topology if and only if each $T^{-1}[W] \cap X_j = T_j^{-1}[W]$ is open in X_j. □

We end with a property of convergence of sequences, which we use to prove certain strict inductive limits are not metrizable and to prove certain spaces have the Montel property.

Theorem 9.1.4. *Let X be a strict inductive limit of an increasing sequence of subspaces, $\{X_j\}_{j=1}^{\infty}$. Suppose each X_n is a closed proper subspace of X_{n+1}. Let $\{x_j\}_{j=1}^{\infty}$ be a sequence in x. Then $\{x_j\}_{j=1}^{\infty}$ converges in X if and only if for some X_m, all $x_j \in X_m$ and x_j converges in X_m.*

Proof. If all x_j lie in some X_m and $x_j \to x$ in X, since X_m is closed in each $X_{m+\ell}$, $\ell = 1, 2, \dots$, we see x must lie in X_m. Thus, the result follows if we prove any convergent sequence lies in a single X_m.

If $\{x_m\}$ is a sequence (converging to some x_∞) which doesn't lie in any X_m, we can find $Y_1, Y_2, \dots$ among the X_ℓ's, so $Y_1 \subsetneqq Y_2 \subsetneqq Y_3, \dots$, and $y_1, y_2, \dots$ a subsequence of the x's so $y_j \in Y_j \setminus Y_{j-1}$. As a subsequence, $y_j \to x_\infty$ also.

Given $L_1, \dots, L_{n-1}$, define L_n inductively as follows: $\ell_n \colon Y_n + [y_{n+1}] \to \mathbb{K}$ so $\ell_n \upharpoonright Y_n = 0$ and $\ell_n(y_{n+1}) = n + 1 - \sum_{j=1}^{n-1} L_j(y_{n+1})$. Since Y_n is closed, ℓ_n is continuous on $Y_n + [y_{n+1}]$ and thus, by the Hahn–Banach theorem, ℓ_n has an extension L_n to X. Let

$$L = \sum_{n=1}^{\infty} L_n \tag{9.1.11}$$

If $x \in Y_m$, then $L_n(x) = 0$ for $n \geq m$ so $L \upharpoonright Y_n = \sum_{n=1}^{m-1} L_n$ is continuous. Thus, L is well-defined on all of $X = \bigcup_{m=1}^{\infty} Y_m$ and L is continuous on X by Theorem 9.1.3 and the continuity of $L \upharpoonright Y_n$. Thus, $L(y_n) \to L(x_\infty)$. But $L(y_{n+1}) = n + 1$ (since $L_k(y_{n+1}) = 0$ if $k \geq n + 1$), so $L(y_{n+1})$ cannot converge to $L(x_\infty)$! This contradiction proves every convergent sequence must lie in a fixed X_m. □

Theorem 9.1.5. *Let X be a strict inductive limit of an increasing family of subspaces X_n so that each X_n is a proper closed subset of X_{n+1}. Then X is not metrizable.*

Proof. As a preliminary, we note each X_n is closed in X. We note first if $j \geq n + 1$, X_n is closed in X_j. For if $\{x_\alpha\}_{\alpha \in I}$ is a net in X_n, it lies in X_{j-1}, so any limit point is in X_{j-1}. Thus, if X_n is closed in X_{j-1}, it is closed in X_j. Repeating this argument finitely many times and using X_n closed in X_{n+1} proves that X_n is closed in X_j. Since

$$X \setminus X_n = \bigcup_{j=n+1}^{\infty} (X_j \setminus X_n) \tag{9.1.12}$$

we see $X \setminus X_n$ is open, that is, X_n is closed.

Suppose X is metrizable. Then we can find a countable family $\{U_n\}_{n=1}^{\infty}$ of balanced, open, convex subsets of X so $U_{n+1} \subset U_n$ and they are a neighborhood base in X for 0. It follows from the fact that X is Hausdorff that

$$\bigcap_{n=1}^{\infty} U_n = \{0\} \tag{9.1.13}$$

For each n, find $y_n \in X_{n+1} \setminus X_n$. Since U_n is open in X, it is absorbing, so for some $\lambda \neq 0$, $\lambda y_n \equiv x_n$ lies in U_n. Thus, we can find a sequence x_n with

$$x_n \in U_n \setminus X_n \tag{9.1.14}$$

Since $\{x_j\}_{j=n}^{\infty} \in U_n$, $x_n \to 0$ in X. Thus, by Theorem 9.1.4, there is N_0 so $x_n \in X_{N_0}$ for all n. But $x_{N_0} \notin X_{N_0}$ by (9.1.14). This contradiction shows that X does not have a countable neighborhood base, and so it is not metrizable. $\square$

Recall that a subset, S, of a locally convex space, Y, is called *bounded* if and only if for every continuous seminorm, ρ,

$$\sup_{y \in S} \rho(y) < \infty \tag{9.1.15}$$

We say Y has the *Montel property* if every closed bounded subset is compact (Montel spaces obey an additional technical property we'll not get into, but we note that Fréchet and LF spaces have this extra property). Note if S is bounded and $\ell \colon Y \to \mathbb{K}$ is a continuous linear functional, then

$$\sup_{y \in S} |\ell(y)| < \infty \tag{9.1.16}$$

since $|\ell(\cdot)|$ is a continuous seminorm.

The construction in the proof of Theorem 9.1.4 shows that if $S \cap X_j \neq \emptyset$, for each j, and each X_n is a closed proper subset of X_{n+1}, we can find $x_n \in S \cap (X_n \setminus X_{n-1})$ and a continuous $L \colon X \to \mathbb{K}$ so $L(x_n) \to \infty$. Thus,

Theorem 9.1.6. *Let X be a strict inductive limit of spaces X_n so X_n is a closed proper subspace of X_{n+1}. Then*

(a) *Any bounded set $S \subset X$ lies in some X_n.*
(b) *If each X_n has the Montel property, so does X.*

Proof. We proved (a) above. For (b), we note that if S is bounded in X, it lies in X_n, and by a simple argument (Problem 1), it is bounded in X_n. Since X_n has the Montel property, S is compact. $\qquad\square$

Notes and Historical Remarks. We put the word "strict" in inductive limit because there is a more general notion: We take $X = \bigcup_{n=1}^{\infty} X_n$ with $X_n \subset X_{n+1}$ with topologies τ_n on X_n. Instead of demanding τ_n to be the τ_{n+1}-relative topology, one only demands the natural embedding of X_n into X_{n+1} is continuous.

The notions of inductive limits and some of their properties were introduced around 1950 by Dieudonné–Schwartz [**244**] and Köthe [**517**]—the first paper defined LF spaces and the second, nonstrict inductive limits. For more on these subjects, see the list of book in the Notes to the introduction of this chapter.

Problems

1. Let $S \subset X \subset Y$, where Y is a locally convex space and X is a subspace with the relative topology. If S is bounded in Y, prove it is bounded in X. (*Hint*: Show the topology of X is generated by the restrictions of continuous seminorms on Y.)

9.2. Ordinary Distributions and Other Examples of Strict Inductive Limits

Example 9.2.1 (Polynomials). This is perhaps the simplest example of a strict inductive limit where each X_n is finite-dimensional. It also provides one of the simplest nonmetrizable locally convex spaces.

Let X_n be the complex polynomials of degree at most n, that is, $P(X) = \sum_{j=0}^{n} \alpha_j X^j$. Thus, $X_n \cong \mathbb{C}^{n+1}$. We can place the norm $\|P\|_n = \sum_{j=0}^{n} |\alpha_j|$. Thus, $\|P\|_n$ is independent of n so long as $n \geq \deg(P)$ (so $P \in X_n$).

The inductive limit topologies $\bigcup_n X_n$. This topology is distinct from the one induced by using $\| \cdot \|_n$ on $\bigcup X_n$, that is, taking ℓ^1 and letting X be the finite sequences in ℓ^1. It shows that while the inductive limit topology is the strongest locally convex topology in which $X_n \to X$ is continuous, it is not the only such topology and therefore illuminates Theorem 9.1.1. $\qquad\square$

Example 9.2.2 (Measures on a σ-compact space). Let Ω be a σ-compact space as discussed in Section 4.10, that is, $\Omega = \bigcup_{n=1}^{\infty} K_n$, where K_n is compact with $K_n \subset K_{n+1}^{\text{int}}$. Let

$$C_0(K) = \{f \in C(\Omega) \mid \text{supp}(f) \subset K\}$$

Then, if $X_n = C_0(K_n)$ with $\| \cdot \|_\infty$, the inductive limit space $X = C_0(\Omega)$ is the continuous functions of compact support.

The continuous linear functionals on X are exactly those maps $\ell\colon X \to \mathbb{C}$ so each $\ell\colon X_n \to \mathbb{C}$ is continuous. By the Hahn–Banach theorem, each $\ell \upharpoonright X_n$ extends to a measure on K_n. X^* is the set of consistent measures, μ_n, on K_n, so if $f \in C_0(K_n)$, then $\int f\,d\mu_n = \int f\,d\mu_m$ for all $m \geq n$. Theorem 4.10.3 describes the positive linear functionals in X^*. $\qquad\square$

Example 9.2.3 ($\mathcal{D}(\Omega)$, $\Omega \subset \mathbb{R}^\nu$). Let $\Omega \subset \mathbb{R}^\nu$ be open ($\Omega = \mathbb{R}^\nu$ is an interesting special case). We can write $\Omega = \bigcup_{n=1}^\infty K_n$ with K_n compact and $K_n \subset K_{n+1}^{\mathrm{int}}$. Let $X_n \equiv C_{00}^\infty(K_n) = \{f \mid f\colon \mathbb{R}^\nu \to \mathbb{R},\ f \text{ is } C^\infty,\ \mathrm{supp}(f) \subset K_n\}$ with the seminorms

$$\|f\|_{m,n} = \sup_{x \in K_n}\left[\sum_{|\alpha|\leq m}|D^\alpha f(x)|\right] \qquad (9.2.1)$$

It is easy to see for each n, X_n is a Fréchet space in the norms $\{\|\cdot\|_{m,n}\}_{m=1}^\infty$. X_n is a closed proper subspace of X_{n+1} in the relative topology. Thus, $\mathcal{D}(\Omega)$, the inductive limit, is an LF space to which Theorems 9.1.4, 9.1.5, and 9.1.6 apply. $\mathcal{D}(\mathbb{R}^\nu)^*$ is exactly the ordinary distributions as defined at the start of this chapter. The quoted theorems show that $\mathcal{D}(\Omega)$ is not metrizable and has the Montel property. We leave several properties of $\mathcal{D}(\Omega)$ or $\mathcal{D}(\mathbb{R}^\nu)$ to the Problems. $\qquad\square$

Notes and Historical Remarks. The set of continuous linear functionals in Examples 9.2.2 and 9.2.3 were introduced without the notion of inductive limit (much like our definition of distribution in the introduction). In particular, Schwartz defined $\mathcal{D}'(\Omega)$ in 1946 [**830**], while the proper topology for $\mathcal{D}$ was only discovered in 1950 [**244**]. It was all codified in his books [**832**].

Problems

1. (a) Prove a Schwartz kernel theorem for $C^\infty((\partial\mathbb{D})^\ell)$, the space discussed (when $\ell = 1$) in Section 6.3. (*Hint*: Use the realization of $C^\infty((\partial\mathbb{D})^\ell)$ as a sequence space.)

   (b) Consider the Fréchet space, $C_{00}^\infty([-L,L]^\nu)$, of C^∞ functions on $\mathbb{R}^\nu$ supported in $[-L,L]^\nu$. Prove that it is isomorphic to a closed subspace of the periodic functions of period L (under associated f to its periodic extension).

   (c) Deduce a Schwartz kernel theorem for $C_{00}^\infty([-L,L]^\nu)$.

   (d) Deduce a Schwartz kernel theorem for $\mathcal{D}(\mathbb{R}^\nu)$.

2. (a) Prove a local version of Theorem 6.2.9 for $\mathcal{D}'(\mathbb{R}^\nu)$. (*Hint*: Any continuous linear functional on $C_{00}^\infty(K)$ with K compact can be extended to $\mathcal{S}(\mathbb{R}^\nu)$.)

   (b) Find an example that shows there is no global version of Theorem 6.2.9 for $\mathcal{D}'(\mathbb{R}^\nu)$.

Bibliography

[1] P. Abry, P. Gonçalves, J. Lévy Véhel, eds., *Scaling, Fractals and Wavelets*, Digital Signal and Image Processing Series (ISTE, London), John Wiley & Sons, Inc., Hoboken, NJ, 2009. (Cited on 702.)

[2] W. J. Adams, *The Life and Times of the Central Limit Theorem*, 2nd edition, History of Mathematics, American Mathematical Society, Providence, RI; London Mathematical Society, London, 2009. (Cited on 654, 655, 743.)

[3] R. P. Agarwal, M. Meehan, and D. O'Regan, *Fixed Point Theory and Applications*, Cambridge Tracts in Mathematics, Cambridge University Press, Cambridge, 2001. (Cited on 485.)

[4] N. I. Akhiezer, *The Classical Moment Problem and Some Related Questions in Analysis*, Hafner Publishing, New York, 1965. (Cited on 434, 435.)

[5] N. I. Akhiezer and M. Krein, *Some Questions in the Theory of Moments*, translated by W. Fleming and D. Prill. Translations of Mathematical Monographs, American Mathematical Society, Providence, RI, 1962; The original Russian version was published in 1938 [Gosudarstv. Naučno-Tehn. Izdat. Ukrain., Kharkov, 1938]. (Cited on 444.)

[6] L. Alaoglu, *Weak convergence of linear functionals*, Bull. Amer. Math. Soc. **44** (1938), 196. (Cited on 447.)

[7] L. Alaoglu, *Weak topologies of normed linear spaces*, Ann. Math. (2) (1940) **41**, 252–267. (Cited on 447.)

[8] S. Albeverio, Yu. Kondratiev, Yu. Kozitsky, and M. Röckner, *The Statistical Mechanics of Quantum Lattice Systems. A Path Integral Approach*, EMS Tracts in Mathematics, European Mathematical Society (EMS), Zurich, 2009. (Cited on 313.)

[9] F. Albiac and J. L. Kalton, *Topics in Banach Space Theory*, Graduate Texts in Mathematics, Springer, New York, 2006. (Cited on 357, 444.)

[10] A. D. Alexandroff, *Additive set-functions in abstract spaces, I, II*, Rec. Math., Moscow (2) **8** (1940), 307–348; **9** (1941), 563–621. (Cited on 269.)

[11] P. Alexandroff, *Über die Metrisation der im Kleinen kompakten topologischen Räume*, Math. Ann. **92** (1924), 294–301. (Cited on 75.)

[12] P. Alexandroff, *Zur Begründung der n-dimensionalen mengentheoretischen Topologie*, Math. Ann. **94** (1925), 296–308. (Cited on 48, 60.)

[13] P. Alexandroff, *Über stetige Abbildungen kompakter Räume*, Math. Ann. **96** (1926), 555–571. (Cited on 106.)

[14] P. S. Alexandroff, *Über stetige Abbildungen kompakter Räume*, Math. Ann. **96** (1927), 555–571. (Cited on 203.)

[15] P. Alexandroff and H. Hopf, *Topologie. I*, Springer, Berlin, 1935. (Cited on 48, 106.)

[16] P. Alexandroff and P. Urysohn, *Zur Theorie der topologischen Räume*, Math. Ann. **92** (1924), 258–266. (Cited on 74.)

[17] E. M. Alfsen, *A simplified constructive proof of the existence and uniqueness of Haar measure*, Math. Scand. **12** (1963), 106–116. (Cited on 350.)

[18] E. M. Alfsen, *Compact Convex Sets and Boundary Integrals*, Springer, Berlin-Heidelberg-New York, 1971. (Cited on 465.)

[19] C. D. Aliprantis and K. Border, *Infinite Dimensional Analysis. A Hitchhiker's Guide*, Third edition. Springer, Berlin, 2006. (Cited on 443.)

[20] C. D. Aliprantis and O. Burkinshaw, *Locally Solid Riesz Spaces*, Pure and Applied Mathematics, Academic Press, New York-London, 1978. (Cited on 269.)

[21] C. D. Aliprantis and O. Burkinshaw, *Positive Operators*, Pure and Applied Mathematics, Academic Press, Orlando, FL, 1985. (Cited on 269.)

[22] N. Alon and J. H. Spencer, *The Probabilistic Method*, Third edition, With an appendix on the life and work of Paul Erdős, Wiley-Interscience Series in Discrete Mathematics and Optimization, John Wiley & Sons, Inc., Hoboken, NJ, 2008; First edition 1992. (Cited on 617.)

[23] D. Alpay, *The Schur Algorithm, Reproducing Kernel Spaces and System Theory*, SMF/AMS Texts and Monographs, American Mathematical Society, Providence, RI; Société Mathématique de France, Paris, 2001. (Cited on 126.)

[24] F. Altomare, *Korovkin-type theorems and approximation by positive linear operators*, Surv. Approx. Theory **5** (2010), 92–164. (Cited on 83.)

[25] F. Altomare and M. Campiti, *Korovkin-type Approximation Theory and Its Applications*, Appendix A by Michael Pannenberg and Appendix B by Ferdinand Beckhoff, de Gruyter Studies in Mathematics, Walter de Gruyter & Co., Berlin, 1994. (Cited on 83.)

[26] A. Ampère, *Recherche sur quelques points de la théorie des fonctions dérivées qui conduisent à une nouvelle démonstration du théorème de Taylor, et à l'expression finie des termes qu'on néglige lorsqu'on arrête cette série à un terme quelconque*, J. l'École Polytechnique **6** (1806), 148–181. (Cited on 155.)

[27] T. Ando, *Reproducing Kernel Spaces and Quadratic Inequalities*, Hokkaido University, Sapporo, 1987. (Cited on 126.)

[28] V. V. Andrievskii and H.-P. Blatt, *Discrepancy of Signed Measures and Polynomial Approximation*, Springer Monographs in Mathematics, Springer-Verlag, New York, 2002. (Cited on 453.)

[29] L. Antonne, *Sur l'Hermitien*, Rend. Circ. Mat. Palermo **16** (1902), 104–128. (Cited on 175.)

[30] D. Applebaum, *Lévy Processes and Stochastic Calculus*, Cambridge University Press, Camrbidge, 2004. (Cited on 659.)

[31] D. Applebaum, *Lévy processes—from probability to finance and quantum groups*, Notices Amer. Math. Soc. **51** (2004), 1336–1347. (Cited on 659.)

[32] R. F. Arens, *Duality in linear spaces*, Duke Math. J. **14** (1947), 787–794. (Cited on 443.)

[33] N. Aronszajn, *Über ein Urbildproblem*, Fund. Math. **17** (1931), 92–121. (Cited on 106.)

[34] N. Aronszajn, *Reproducing and Pseudo-Reproducing Kernels and Their Application to the Partial Differential Equations of Physics*, Studies in Partial Differential Equations, Technical Report 5, preliminary note, Harvard University, Graduate School of Engineering, Cambridge, MA, 1948. (Cited on 126.)

[35] N. Aronszajn, *Theory of reproducing kernels*, Trans. Amer. Math. Soc. **68** (1950), 337–404. (Cited on 126.)

[36] N. Aronszajn and K. T. Smith, *Invariant subspaces of completely continuous operators*, Ann. Math. (2) **60** (1954), 345–350. (Cited on 487.)

[37] C. Arzelà, *Sulla integrabilitá di una serie di funzioni*, Rom. Acc. L. Mem. (4) **1** (1885), 321–326. (Cited on 229.)

[38] C. Arzelà, *Sulle funzioni di linee*, [On functions of lines], Bologna Mem. **5** (1895), 225–244. (Cited on 75.)

[39] G. Ascoli, *Le curve limite di una varietà data di curve*, [The limit curve of a given family of curves], Rom. Acc. L. Mem. (3) **18** (1884), 521–586. (Cited on 14, 75.)

[40] G. Ascoli, *Sugli spazi lineari metrici e le loro varietà lineari*, Ann. Mat. Pura Appl. (4) **10** (1932), 33–81, 203–232. (Cited on 458.)

[41] R. B. Ash, *Probability and Measure Theory*, 2nd edition, Harcourt/Academic Press, Burlington, MA, 2000. (Cited on 230.)

[42] M. F Atiyah, R. Bott, and L. Gårding, *Lacunas for hyperbolic differential operators with constant coefficients. I., II.* Acta Math. **124** (1970), 109–189; Acta Math. **131** (1973), 145–206. (Cited on 607.)

[43] Y. Baba, *On maxima of Takagi–van der Waerden functions*, Proc. Amer. Math. Soc. **91** (1984), 373–376. (Cited on 164.)

[44] K. I. Babenko, *An inequality in the theory of Fourier integrals*, Izv. Akad. Nauk SSSR Ser. Mat. **25** (1961) 531–542. [Russian] (Cited on 563.)

[45] J. Baik, P. Deift, and K. Johansson, *On the distribution of the length of the longest increasing subsequence of random permutations*, J. Amer. Math. Soc. **12** (1999), 1119–1178. (Cited on 630.)

[46] J. Baik and T. M. Suidan, *A GUE central limit theorem and universality of directed first and last passage site percolation*, Int. Math. Res. Notices (2005), no. 6, 325–337. (Cited on 630.)

[47] R.-L. Baire, *Sur la théorie des fonctions discontinues*, C. R. Acad. Sci. Paris **129** (1899), 1010–1013. (Cited on 211.)

[48] R.-L. Baire, *Sur les fonctions de variables réelles*, Ann. di Mat. Pura Appl. **3** (1899), 1–123. (Cited on 407.)

[49] S. Banach, *Sur les opérations dans les ensembles abstraits et leur application aux équations intégrales*, Fund. Math. **3** (1922), 133–181. (Cited on 363, 485.)

[50] S. Banach, *Sur les lignes rectifiables et les surfaces dont l'aire est finie.* Fund. Math. **7** (1925), 225–236. (Cited on 318.)

[51] S. Banach, *Sur les fonctionelles linéaires, I*, Studia Math. **1** (1929), 211–216. (Cited on 424.)

[52] S. Banach, *Sur les fonctionelles linéaires, II*, Studia Math. **1** (1929), 223–239. (Cited on 408, 424, 425, 447.)

[53] S. Banach, *Théorème sur les ensembles de premiére catégorie*, Fund. Math. **16** (1930), 395–398. (Cited on 407.)

[54] S. Banach, *Über die Baire'sche Kategorie gewisser Funktionenmengen*, Studia Math. **3** (1931), 174–179. (Cited on 408.)

[55] S. Banach, *Théorie des opérations linéaires*, Monograf. Mat., Warsaw, 1932. English translation: *Theory of Linear Operations*, North-Holland Mathematical Library, North-Holland, Amsterdam, 1987. (Cited on 364, 408, 466, 486, 489, 501.)

[56] S. Banach and S. Mazur, *Zur Theorie der linearen Dimension*, Studia Math. **4** (1933), 100–112. (Cited on 357.)

[57] S. Banach and H. Steinhaus, *Sur le principe de la condensation de singularités*, Fund. Math. **9** (1927), 50–61. (Cited on 408.)

[58] S. Banach and A. Tarski, *Sur la décomposition des ensembles de points en parties respectivement congruentes*, Fund. Math. **6** (1924), 244–277. (Cited on 210.)

[59] V. Bargmann, *On a Hilbert space of analytic functions and associated integral transform I*, Comm. Pure Appl. Math. **14** (1961), 187–214. (Cited on 538.)

[60] V. Bargmann, *On a Hilbert space of analytic functions and an associated integral transform. II. A family of related function spaces. Application to distribution theory*, Comm. Pure Appl. Math. **20** (1967), 1–101. (Cited on 538.)

[61] O. E. Barndorff-Nielsen, T. Mikosch, and S. Resnick (editors), *Lévy Processes: Theory and Applications*, Birkhäuser, Basel, 2001. (Cited on 659.)

[62] H. Bauer, *Probability Theory and Elements of Measure Theory*, Probability and Mathematical Statistics, Academic Press, London-New York, 1981. (Cited on 230.)

[63] H. Bauer, *Measure and Integration Theory*, de Gruyter Studies in Mathematics, Walter de Gruyter & Co., Berlin, 2001. (Cited on 313.)

[64] H. S. Bear, *A Primer of Lebesgue Integration*, Academic Press, San Diego, CA, 1995. (Cited on 230.)

[65] B. Beauzamy, *Introduction to Banach Spaces and Their Geometry*, 2nd edition, North–Holland Mathematics Studies, Notas de Matemática [Mathematical Notes], North–Holland, Amsterdam, 1985. (Cited on 444.)

[66] W. Beckner, *Inequalities in Fourier analysis*, Ann. Math. (2) **102** (1975), 159–182. (Cited on 563.)

[67] R. Bellman, *The stability of solutions of linear differential equations*, Duke Math. J. **10** (1943), 643–647. (Cited on 486.)

[68] A. A. Bennett, *Newton's method in general analysis*, Proc. Nat. Acad. Sci. USA **2** (1916), 592–598. (Cited on 364.)

[69] G. Bennett and N. J. Kalton, *Consistency theorems for almost convergence*, Trans. Amer. Math. Soc. **198** (1974), 23–43. (Cited on 490.)

[70] Y. Benyamini, *Applications of the Universal Surjectivity of the Cantor Set*, Amer. Math. Monthly, **105** (1998), 832–839. (Cited on 203.)

[71] Y. Benyamini and J. Lindenstrauss, *Geometric Nonlinear Functional Analysis. Vol. 1*, AMS Colloquium Publications, American Mathematical Society, Providence, RI, 2000. (Cited on 357.)

[72] F. A. Berezin, *The Method of Second Quantization*, Academic Press, New York, 1966 (Translated from Russian). (Revised (augmented) second edition: Kluwer, Boston, 1989). (Cited on 538.)

[73] S. Bergman, *Über die Entwicklung der harmonischen Funktionen der Ebene und des Raumes nach Orthogonalfunktionen*, Math. Ann. **86** (1922), 238–271. (Cited on 126.)

[74] S. Bergman and M. Schiffer, *A representation of Green's and Neumann's functions in the theory of partial differential equations of second order*, Duke Math. J. **14** (1947), 609–638. (Cited on 126.)

[75] S. Bergman and M. Schiffer, *Kernel functions in the theory of partial differential equations of elliptic type*, Duke Math. J. **15**, (1948), 535–566. (Cited on 126.)

[76] S. Bergman and M. Schiffer, *Kernel Functions and Elliptic Differential Equations in Mathematical Physics*, Academic Press, New York, 1953. (Cited on 126.)

[77] A. Berlinet and C. Thomas-Agnan, *Reproducing Kernel Hilbert Spaces in Probability and Statistics*, Kluwer, Boston, 2004. (Cited on 126.)

[78] D. Bernoulli, *Reflexions et eclaricissement sur les nouvelles vibrations des corde*, Mémoires de l'Academie des Sciences de Berlin **9** (1753), 147–172. (Cited on 150.)

[79] Jakob Bernoulli, *Ars Conjectandi*, Thurneysen, Basel, 1713. (Cited on 628, 644.)

[80] A. R. Bernstein and A. Robinson, *Solution of an invariant subspace problem of K. T. Smith and P. R. Halmos*, Pacific J. Math. **16** (1966), 421–431. (Cited on 487.)

[81] I. N. Bernstein, *Modules over a ring of differential operators. Study of fundamental solutions of equations with constant coefficients*, Functional Anal. Appl. **5** (1971) 1–16. (Cited on 608.)

[82] S. N. Bernstein, *Démonstration du théorème de Weierstrass fondée sur le calcul des probabilités*, Comm. Soc. Math. Kharkow **13** (1912/1913), 1–2. (Cited on 82.)

[83] A. C. Berry, *The accuracy of the Gaussian approximation to the sum of independent variates*, Trans. Amer. Math. Soc. **49** (1941), 122–136. (Cited on 656.)

[84] J. Bertoin, *Lévy Processes*, Cambridge University Press, Cambridge, 1996. (Cited on 659.)

[85] A. S. Besicovitch, *On Linear Sets of Points of Fractional Dimensions*, Math. Ann. **101** (1929), 161–193. (Cited on 700.)

[86] A. S. Besicovitch, *On existence of subsets of finite measure of sets of infinite measure*, Indagationes Math. **14** (1952), 339–344. (Cited on 702.)

[87] C. Bessaga, *A note on universal Banach spaces of a finite dimension*, Bull. Acad. Polon. Sci. Sér. Sci. Math. Astr. Phys. **6** (1958), 97–101. (Cited on 357.)

[88] F. W. Bessel, *Über die Bestimmung des Gesetzes einer periodischen Erscheinung*, Astr. Nachr. **6** (1928), 333–348. (Cited on 117.)

[89] I. J. Bienaymé, *Considerations a l'appui de la decouverte de Laplace sur la loi de probabilite dans la methode des moindres carres*, C. R. Acad. Sci. Paris **37** (1853), 309-324. Reprinted in Liouville's J. Math. Pures Appl. (2) **12** (1867), 158–176. (Cited on 227.)

[90] P. Billingsley, *Convergence of Probability Measures*, 2nd edition, Wiley Series in Probability and Statistics: Probability and Statistics, John Wiley & Sons, Inc., New York, 1999. (Cited on 313, 327.)

[91] R. H. Bing, *Metrization of topological spaces*, Canadian J. Math. **3** (1951), 175–186. (Cited on 61.)

[92] N. H. Bingham, *Variants on the law of the iterated logarithm*, Bull. London Math. Soc. **18** (1986), 433–467. (Cited on 645.)

[93] G. Birkhoff, *Lattice Theory*, American Mathematical Society, New York, 1940. (Cited on 269.)

[94] Z. Birnbaum and W. Orlicz, *Über die Verallgemeinerung des Begriffes der zueinander konjugierten Potenzen*, Studia Math. **3** (1931), 1–67. (Cited on 388.)

[95] W. Blaschke, *Kreis und Kugel*, 2nd edition, Walter de Gruyter, Berlin, 1956; original 1916 edition, Veit, Leipzig. (Cited on 167.)

[96] R. P. Boas, *Some uniformly convex spaces*, Bull. Amer. Math. Soc. **46**, (1940), 304–311. (Cited on 392.)

[97] R. P. Boas, *Summation formulas and band-limited signals*, Tôhoku Math. J. **24** (1972), 121–125. (Cited on 569.)

[98] M. Bôcher, *Introduction to the theory of Fourier's series*, Ann. Math. (2) **7** (1906), 81–152. (Cited on 157.)

[99] M. Bôcher, *On Gibbs's phenomenon*, J. Reine Angew. Math. **144** (1914), 41–47. (Cited on 157.)

[100] S. Bochner, *Über orthogonale Systeme analytischer Funktionen*, Math. Z. **14** (1922), 180–207. (Cited on 126.)

[101] S. Bochner, *Vorlesungen über Fouriersche Integrale*, Akad. Verlag, Leipzig, 1932. English translation: *Lectures on Fourier Integrals*, Annals of Mathematics Studies, Princeton University Press, Princeton, NJ, 1959. (Cited on 512, 564.)

[102] S. Bochner, *Integration von Funktionen, deren Werte die Elemente eines Vektorraumes sind*, Fund. Math. **20** (1933), 262–276. (Cited on 341.)

[103] T. Bodineau and J. Martin, *A universality property for last-passage percolation paths close to the axis*, Electron. Comm. Probab. **10** (2005), 105–112 [electronic]. (Cited on 630.)

[104] V. I. Bogachev, *Measure Theory. Vol. I, II*, Springer-Verlag, Berlin, 2007. (Cited on 230, 686.)

[105] P. Bohl, *Über die Beweging eines mechanischen Systems in der Nähe einer Gleichgewichtslage*, J. Reine Angew. Math. **127** (1904), 179–276. (Cited on 487.)

[106] H. Bohman, *On approximation of continuous and analytic functions*, Ark. Math. **2** (1952-1954), 43–56. (Cited on 83.)

[107] H. F. Bohnenblust and A. Sobczyk, *Extensions of functionals on complex linear spaces*, Bull. Amer. Math. Soc. **44** (1938), 91–93. (Cited on 425.)

[108] B. Bolzano, *Rein analytischer Beweis des Lehrsatzes daß zwischen je zwei Werthen, die ein entgegengesetztes Resultat gewaehren, wenigstens eine reele Wurzel der Gleichung liege*, Prague, 1817. English version: S. B. Russ, *A translation of Bolzano's paper on the intermediate value theorem*, Hist. Math. **7** (1980), 156–185. (Cited on 73.)

[109] K. Border, *Fixed Point Theorems With Applications to Economics and Game Theory*, Cambridge University Press, Cambridge, 1989. (Cited on 485.)

[110] E. Borel, *Sur quelques points de la théorie des fonctions*, Ann. Sci. École Norm. Sup. (3) **12** (1895), 9–55. (Cited on 73.)

[111] E. Borel, *Sur l'interpolation*, C. R. Acad. Sci. Paris **124** (1897), 673–676. (Cited on 568.)

[112] E. Borel, *Leçons sur les fonctions discontinues*, Gauthier–Villars, Paris, 1898. (Cited on 211.)

[113] E. Borel, *Sur la recherche des singularités d'une fonction définie par un développement de Taylor*, C. R. Acad. Sci. Paris **127** (1898), 1001–1003. (Cited on 568.)

[114] E. Borel, *Les probabilités dénombrables et leurs applications arithmétiques*, Rend. Circ. Mat. Palermo **27** (1909), 247–271. (Cited on 644, 645.)

[115] A. N. Borodin and P. Salminen, *Handbook of Brownian Motion—Facts and Formulae*, 2nd edition, Probability and its Applications, Birkhäuser Verlag, Basel, 2002. (Cited on 327.)

[116] K. Borsuk, *Sur les rétractes*, Fund. Math. **17** (1931), 152–170. (Cited on 487.)

[117] G. Bouligand, *Ensembles impropres et nombre dimensionnel, I, II*, Bull. Sci. Math. (2) **52** (1928), 320–344; 361–376. (Cited on 702.)

[118] V. Bouniakowsky, *Sur quelques inegalités concernant les intégrales aux différences finies*, Mem. Acad. Sci. St. Petersbourg 7 **1** (1859), 1–18; available online at http://www-stat.wharton.upenn.edu/~steele/Publications/Books/CSMC/bunyakovsky.pdf. (Cited on 117.)

[119] N. Bourbaki, *Sur les espaces de Banach*, C. R. Acad. Sci. Paris **206** (1938), 1701–1704. (Cited on 125, 447.)

[120] N. Bourbaki, *Éléments de mathématique. Part I. Les structures fondamentales de l'analyse. Livre III. Topologie générale. Chapitres I et II*, Actual. Sci. Ind., Hermann & Cie., Paris, 1940; *Chapitres III et IV*, Actual. Sci. Ind., Hermann & Cie., Paris, 1942. (Cited on 48, 74, 99, 102, 106, 501.)

[121] N. Bourbaki, *Espaces vectoriels topologiques*, Chapitres 1 á 5, Éléments de mathématique, New edition, Masson, Paris, 1981. English translation, *Topological Vector Spaces. Chapters 1–5*, Elements of Mathematics, Springer-Verlag, Berlin, 1987. (Cited on 443, 501, 706.)

[122] N. Bourbaki, *Eléments de mathématique, Livre VI, Intégration*, Hermann & Cie, Paris, 1952. English translation, *Integration. I. Chapters 1–6*, translated from the 1959, 1965, and 1967 French originals, Elements of Mathematics, Springer-Verlag, Berlin, 2004; *Integration. II. Chapters 7–9*, translated from the 1963 and 1969 French originals, Elements of Mathematics, Springer-Verlag, Berlin, 2004. (Cited on 225, 230, 350.)

[123] J. Bourgain, *Real isomorphic complex Banach spaces need not be complex isomorphic*, Proc. Amer. Math. Soc. **96** (1986), 221–226. (Cited on 365.)

[124] S. C. Bradford, *Sources of information on specific subjects*, Engineering: An Illustrated Weekly Journal (London) **137** (1934), 85–86. (Cited on 658.)

[125] H. J. Brascamp and E. H. Lieb, *Best constants in Young's inequality, its converse, and its generalization to more than three functions*, Adv. in Math. **20** (1976), 151–173. (Cited on 563.)

[126] H. J. Brascamp, E .H. Lieb, and J. M. Luttinger, *A general rearrangement inequality for multiple integrals*, J. Funct. Anal. **17** (1974), 227–237. (Cited on 394.)

[127] L. Breiman, *Probability*, Society for Industrial and Applied Mathematics, Philadelphia, 1992. (Cited on 617.)

[128] D. M. Bressoud, *A Radical Approach to Real Analysis*, 2nd edition, Classroom Resource Materials Series, Mathematical Association of America, Washington, DC, 2007. (Cited on 225, 228.)

[129] D. M. Bressoud, *A Radical Approach to Lebesgue's Theory of Integration*, MAA Textbooks, Cambridge University Press, Cambridge, 2008. (Cited on 193, 203, 225, 228.)

[130] H. Brézis and E. Lieb, *A relation between pointwise convergence of functions and convergence of functionals*, Proc. Amer. Math. Soc. **88** (1983), 486–490. (Cited on 249.)

[131] J. Bros and D. Iagolnitzer, *Support essentiel et structure analytique des distributions*, Séminarie Goulaouic-Lions-Schwartz, No. 18, École Polytechnique, Paris, 1975–76. (Cited on 539.)

[132] L. E. J. Brouwer, *Über Abbildungen von Mannigfaltigkeiten*, Math. Ann. **71** (1912), 97–115. (Cited on 486.)

[133] L. E. J. Brouwer, *Über den natürlichen Dimensionsbegriff*, J. Reine Angew. Math. **142** (1913), 146–152. (Cited on 701.)

[134] G. Brown and W. Moran, *On orthogonality of Riesz products*, Proc. Cambridge Philos. Soc. **76** (1974), 173–181. (Cited on 582.)

[135] J. L. Brown, Jr., *On the error in reconstructing a non-bandlimited function by means of the bandpass sampling theorem*, J. Math. Anal. Appl. **18**, 75–84. (Cited on 575.)

[136] R. Brown, *A brief account of microscopical observations made in the months of June, July and August, 1827, on the particles contained in the pollen of plants; and on the general existence of active molecules in organic and inorganic bodies*, Phil. Mag. **4** (1828), 161–173. Available online at `http://sciweb.nybg.org/science2/pdfs/dws/Brownian.pdf`. (Cited on 326.)

[137] R. F. Brown, M. Furi, L. Górniewicz, and B. Jiang (editors), *Handbook of Topological Fixed Point Theory*, Springer, Dordrecht, 2005. (Cited on 485.)

[138] F. Bruhat, *Distributions sur un groupe localement compact et applications a l'etude des representations des groupes p-adiques*, Bull. Math. Soc. France **89** (1961), 43–75. (Cited on 513.)

[139] P. S. Bullen, D. S. Mitrinović, and P. M. Vasić, *Means and Their Inequalities*, Mathematics and its Applications (East European Series), D. Reidel Publishing, Dordrecht, 1988. (Cited on 388.)

[140] G. Buttazzo, *Semicontinuity, Relaxation and Integral Representation in the Calculus of Variations*, Pitman Research Notes in Mathematics Series, Longman Scientific & Technical, Harlow; John Wiley & Sons, New York, 1989. (Cited on 453.)

[141] P. L. Butzer, *A survey of the Whittaker–Shannon sampling theorem and some of its extensions*, J. Math. Res. Exposition **3** (1983), 185–212. (Cited on 569.)

[142] P. L. Butzer, P. J. S. G. Ferreira, J. R. Higgins, et al., *Interpolation and sampling: E.T. Whittaker, K. Ogura and their followers*, J. Fourier Anal. Appl. **17** (2011), 320-354. (Cited on 569.)

[143] P. L. Butzer, J. R. Higgins, and R. L. Stens, *Sampling theory of signal analysis*, in Development of Mathematics 1950–2000, pp. 193–234, Birkhäuser, Basel, 2000. (Cited on 569.)

[144] P. L. Butzer, G. Schmeisser, and R. L. Stens, *An introduction to sampling analysis*, in Information Technology: Transmission, Processing and Storage, pp. 17–121, Kluwer Academic/Plenum, New York, 2001. (Cited on 569.)

[145] P. L. Butzer and R. L. Stens, *The Euler–Maclaurin summation formula, the sampling theorem, and approximate integration over the real axis*, Linear Algebra Appl. **52/53** (1983), 141–155. (Cited on 569, 575.)

[146] P. L. Butzer and R. L. Stens, *Shannon's sampling theorem, Cauchy's integral formula, and related results*, in Anniversary Volume on Approximation Theory and Functional Analysis, pp. 363–377, Birkhäuser, Basel, 1984. (Cited on 569.)

[147] F. P. Cantelli, *Sulla legge dei grandi numeri*, Rend. R. Accad. Lincei **25** (1916), 39–45. (Cited on 644.)

[148] F. P. Cantelli, *Sulla probabilitá come limite della frequenza*, Rom. Acc. L. Rend. (5) **26** (1917), 39–45. (Cited on 630.)

[149] F. P. Cantelli, *Su due applicazioni di un teorema di G. Boole alle statistica matematica*, Rom. Acc. L. Rend. (5) **26** (1917), 295–302. (Cited on 644.)

[150] G. Cantor, *Über die Ausdehnung eines Satzes aus der Theorie der trigonometrischen Reihen*, Math. Ann. **5** (1872), 123–132. (Cited on 9.)

[151] G. Cantor, *Über eine Eigenschaft des Ingebriffes aller reelen algebraischen Zahlen*, J. Reine Angew. Math. **77** (1874), 258–262. (Cited on 16.)

[152] G. Cantor, *Ein Beitrag zur Mannigfaltigkeitslehre*, J. Reine Angew. Math. **84** (1878), 242–258. (Cited on 16.)

[153] G. Cantor, *Über unendliche lineare Punktmannigfaltigkeiten, 5. Fortsetzung*, Math. Ann. **21** (1883), 545–591. (Cited on 50, 201.)

[154] G. Cantor, *De la puissance des ensembles parfaits de points*, Acta Math. **4** (1884), 381–392. (Cited on 201.)

[155] G. Cantor, *Über eine elementare Frage der Mannigfaltigkeitslehre*, Jahresber. Deutsch. Math.-Verein. **1** (1891), 75–78. (Cited on 16.)

[156] C. Carathéodory, *Über den Variabilitätsbereich der Koeffizienten von Potenzreihen die gegebene Werte nicht annehmen*, Math. Ann. **64** (1907), 95–115. (Cited on 564.)

[157] C. Carathéodory, *Über den Variabilitätsbereich der Fourier'schen Konstanten von positiven harmonischen Funktionen*, Rend. Circ. Mat. Palermo **32** (1911), 193–217. (Cited on 464, 564.)

[158] C. Carathéodory, *Über das lineare Mass von Punktmengen, eine Verallgemeinerung des Längenbegriffs*, Nachr. Gesell. Wiss. Göttingen (1914), pp. 404–426; available online at https://eudml.org/doc/58921. (Cited on 686.)

[159] C. Carathéodory, *Vorlesungen über reelle Funktionen*, Teubner, Leipzig, 1918 (reprint: Chelsea Publishing Co., New York 1968). (Cited on 686.)

[160] S. Carl and S. Heikkilä, *Fixed Point Theory in Ordered Sets and Applications. From Differential and Integral Equations to Game Theory*, Springer, New York, 2011. (Cited on 485.)

[161] T. Carleman, *Sur le probleme des moments*, C. R. Acad. Sci. Paris **174** (1922), 1680–1682. (Cited on 433.)

[162] L. Carleson, *On convergence and growth of partial sums of Fourier series*, Acta Math. **116** (1966), 135–157. (Cited on 153.)

[163] R. Carmona, W. Masters, and B. Simon, *Relativistic Schrödinger operators: Asymptotic behavior of the eigenfunctions*, J. Funct. Anal. **91** (1990), 117–142. (Cited on 329.)

[164] L. Carroll, *Alice's Adventures in Wonderland*, MacMillan, London, 1865; available online at http://www.authorama.com/alice-in-wonderland-1.html. (Cited on 1.)

[165] H. Cartan, *Theorie des filtres*, C. R. Acad. Sci. Paris **205** (1937), 595–598. (Cited on 101.)

[166] H. Cartan, *Filtres et ultrafiltres*, C. R. Acad. Sci. Paris **205** (1937), 777–779. (Cited on 101.)

[167] H. Cartan, *Sur la mesure de Haar*, C. R. Acad. Sci. Paris **211** (1940), 759–762. (Cited on 350.)

[168] A. L. Cauchy, *Cours d'analyse de l'École Royale polytechnique. I. Analyse algébrique*, Debure, Paris, 1821. (Cited on 117, 388.)

[169] A. L. Cauchy, *Sur la developpement des fonctions en series, et sur l'integration des equations differentelles ou aux differences partielles*, Bull. Soc. Philomathique de Paris (1822),49–54. (Cited on 32.)

[170] A. L. Cauchy, *Resumé des leçons données a lÉcole Royale Polytechnique sur le calcul infinitéesimal*, Debure, Paris 1823; available online at `http://www.e-rara.ch/doi/10.3931/e-rara-25962`. (Cited on 193.)

[171] A. L. Cauchy, *Sur l'équation à l'aide de laquelle on détermine les inégalités séculaires des mouvements des planètes*, Exer. Math. **4** (1829). (Cited on 26.)

[172] A. L. Cauchy, *Résumé d'un mémoire sur la mécanique céleste et sur un nouveau calcul appelé calcul des limites*, presented to the Academie de Turin in a session on October 11, 1831 and published in Oeuvres complètes, Série 2 **12**, pp. 48–112, Gauthier–Villars, Paris, 1941. (Cited on 486.)

[173] A. L. Cauchy, *Sur les résultats moyens d'observations de méme nature, et sur les résultats les plus probables*, C. R. Acad. Sci. Paris **37** (1853), 198–206. (Cited on 630.)

[174] A. L. Cauchy, *sur les résultats moyens d'un très-grand nombre des observations*, C. R. Acad. Sci. Paris **37** (1853), 381–385. (Cited on 655.)

[175] B. Cavalieri, *Geometria indivisibilibus continuorum nova quadam ratione promota*, [Geometry, developed by a new method through the indivisibles of the continua], 1635. (Cited on 288.)

[176] A. Cayley, *A memoir on the theory of matrices*, Philos. Trans. Roy. Soc. London **148** (1858), 17–37. (Cited on 26.)

[177] E. Čech, *On bicompact spaces*, Ann. Math. **38** (1937), 823–844. (Cited on 101.)

[178] Ch. Cellérier, *Note sur les principes fondamentaux de l'analyse*, Bull. Sci. Math. (2) **14** (1890), 142–160. (Cited on 156.)

[179] S. B. Chae, *Lebesgue Integration*, 2nd edition, Universitext, Springer-Verlag, New York, 1995. (Cited on 225, 228.)

[180] K. Chandrasekharan, *Introduction to Analytic Number Theory*, Die Grundlehren der mathematischen Wissenschaften, Springer-Verlag, New York, 1968. (Cited on 574.)

[181] K. Chandrasekharan, *A course on Integration Theory*, Texts and Readings in Mathematics, Hindustan Book Agency, New Delhi, 1996. (Cited on 230.)

[182] P. L. Chebyshev, *Démonstration élémentaire d'une proposition générale de la théorie des probabilités*, J. Reine Angew. Math. **33** (1846), 259–267. (Cited on 644.)

[183] P. L. Chebyshev, *Des valeurs moyennes*, J. Math. Pures Appl. (2) **12** (1867), 177–884; published simultaneously in Russian in Mat. Sb. (2) **2** (1867), 1–9. (Cited on 227, 644.)

[184] P. L. Chebyshev, *Sur deux théorèmes relatifs aux probabilités*, originally published in Russian in Zapiski Akademii Nauk **55** (1887); French translation in Acta Math. **14** (1890/91), 305–315. (Cited on 655.)

[185] P. R. Chernoff, *A simple proof of Tychonoff's theorem via nets*, Amer. Math. Monthly **99** (1992), 932–934. (Cited on 102.)

[186] C. Chevalley and O. Frink, *Bicompactness of Cartesian products*, Bull. Amer. Math. Soc. **47** (1941), 612–614. (Cited on 102.)

[187] G. Choquet, *Unicité des représentations intégrales au moyen des points extrémeaux dans les cônes convexes reticulés*, C. R. Acad. Sci. Paris **243** (1956), 555–557. (Cited on 464, 465.)

[188] G. Choquet, *Exisence des représentations intégrales au moyen des points extrémeaux dans les cônes convexes*, C. R. Acad. Sci. Paris **243** (1956), 699–702. (Cited on 464.)

[189] G. Choquet, *Exisence des représentations intégrales dans les cônes convexes*, C. R. Acad. Sci. Paris **243** (1956), 736–737. (Cited on 464.)

[190] G. Choquet, *Le Théorème de représentation intégrales dans les ensemble convexes compacts*, Ann. Inst. Fourier Grenoble **10** (1960), 333–344. (Cited on 464.)

[191] G. Choquet, *Lectures on Analysis, Volume 1: Integration and Topological Vector Spaces; Volume II: Representation Theory; Volume III: Infinite Dimensional Measures and Problem Solutions*, W. A. Benjamin, New York-Amsterdam, 1969. (Cited on 465, 566.)

[192] G. Choquet and P. A. Meyer, *Existence et unicité des représentations intégrales dans les convexes compacts quelconque*, Ann. Inst. Fourier Grenoble **13** (1963), 139–154. (Cited on 465.)

[193] Y. S. Chow and H. Teicher, *Probability Theory: Independence, Interchangeability, Martingales*, Springer, New York, 1997. (Cited on 617.)

[194] K. L. Chung, *Markov Chains With Stationary Transition Probabilities*, 2nd edition, Die Grundlehren der mathematischen Wissenschaften, Springer-Verlag, New York, 1967. (Cited on 674.)

[195] K. L. Chung, *A Course in Probability Theory*, Academic Press, New York, 1974. (Cited on 617.)

[196] K. L. Chung and J. B. Walsh, *Markov Processes, Brownian Motion, and Time Symmetry*, 2nd edition, Grundlehren der Mathematischen Wissenschaften, Springer, New York, 2005. (Cited on 327.)

[197] K.-L. Chung and Z. X. Zhao, *From Brownian Motion to Schrödinger's Equation*, Grundlehren der Mathematischen Wissenschaften, Springer-Verlag, Berlin, 1995. (Cited on 327.)

[198] K. Ciesielski, *Set Theory for the Working Mathematician*, London Math. Soc. Stud. Texts, Cambridge University Press, Cambridge, UK, 1997. (Cited on 14.)

[199] Z. Ciesielski, *Hölder conditions for realizations of Gaussian processes*, Trans. Amer. Math. Soc. **99** (1961), 403–413. (Cited on 327.)

[200] J. A. Clarkson, *Uniformly convex spaces*, Trans. Amer. Math. Soc. **40** (1936), 396–414. (Cited on 388, 444.)

[201] P. J. Cohen, *The independence of the continuum hypothesis*, Proc. Nat. Acad. Sci. USA **50** (1983), 1143–1148. (Cited on 13.)

[202] D. L. Cohn, *Measure Theory*, reprint of the 1980 original, Birkhäuser Boston, Boston, MA, 1993. (Cited on 230.)

[203] L. Collatz, *Einschließungssatz für die charakteristischen Zahlen von Matrize*, Math. Z. **48** (1942), 221–226. (Cited on 675.)

[204] J. W. Cooley and J. W. Tukey *An algorithm for the machine calculation of complex Fourier series*, Math. Comp. **19** (1965) 297–301. (Cited on 155.)

[205] A. Córdoba and C. Fefferman, *Wave packets and Fourier integral operators*, Comm. Partial Differential Equations **3** (1978), 979–1005. (Cited on 539.)

[206] R. Courant and D. Hilbert, *Methods of Mathematical Physics. Vol II*, Wiley Interscience, New York, 1962. (Cited on 606.)

[207] M. Cowling, *The Kunze–Stein phenomenon*, Ann. Math. (2) **107** (1978), 209–234. (Cited on 563.)

[208] H. Cramér, *Über eine Eigenschaft der normalen Verteilungsfunktion*, Math. Z. **41** (1936),405–414. (Cited on 666.)

[209] H. Cramér, *Random Variables and Probability Distributions*, Cambridge University Press, Cambridge, 1937. (Cited on 656.)

[210] J. Cronin, *Fixed Points and Topological Degree in Nonlinear Analysis*, Mathematical Surveys, American Mathematical Society, Providence, RI, 1964. (Cited on 485, 487.)

[211] B. Dacorogna, *Direct Methods in the Calculus of Variations*, 2nd edition, Applied Mathematical Sciences, Springer, New York, 2008. (Cited on 453.)

[212] J. d'Alembert, *Recherches sur la courbe que forme une corde tendüe mise en vibration [Researches on the curve formed by a stretched string set into vibration]*, Histoire de l'Académie des sciences et belles-lettres (Berlin) vol. 3, pp. 214–249 (1747, published 1749). (Cited on 150, 606.)

[213] D. P. Dalzell, *On the completeness of a series of normal orthogonal functions*, J. London Math. Soc. **20** (1945), 87–93. (Cited on 136.)

[214] P. J. Daniell, *A general form of integral*, Ann. Math. **19** (1918), 279–294. (Cited on 229, 269.)

[215] L. Daston, *Classical Probability in the Enlightenment*, Princeton University Press, Princeton, NJ, 1988. (Cited on 628.)

[216] J. Dauben, *Georg Cantor and the battle for transfinite set theory*, in Proc. 9th ACMS Conference (Westmont College, Santa Barbara, CA, 2004), pp. 1–22; available online at http://www.acmsonline.org/journal/2004/Dauben-Cantor.pdf. (Cited on 16.)

[217] M. M. Day, *The spaces L^p with $0 < p < 1$*, Bull. Amer. Math. Soc. **46** (1940), 816–823. (Cited on 444.)

[218] M. M. Day, *Reflexive Banach spaces not isomorphic to uniformly convex spaces*, Bull. Amer. Math. Soc. **47** (1941), 313–317. (Cited on 444.)

[219] M. M. Day, *Means on semigroups and groups*, Bull. Amer. Math. Soc. **55** (1949), 1054–1055. (Cited on 486.)

[220] M. M. Day, *Means for the bounded functions and ergodicity of the bounded representations of semi-groups*, Trans. Amer. Math. Soc. **69** (1950), 276–291. (Cited on 486.)

[221] M. M. Day, *Normed Linear Spaces*, Third edition, Ergebnisse der Mathematik und ihrer Grenzgebiete, Springer-Verlag, New York-Heidelberg, 1973; (First edition: 1958). (Cited on 444.)

[222] S. R. Deans, *The Radon Transform and Some of Its Applications*, John Wiley & Sons, New York, 1983. (Cited on 548.)

[223] L. de Branges, *The Stone–Weierstrass theorem*, Proc. Amer. Math. Soc. **10** (1959), 822–824. (Cited on 466.)

[224] R. Dedekind, *Stetigkeit und irrationale Zahlen* (Continuity and Irrational Numbers), F. Vieweg, Braunschweig, 1872; English translation available online at http://www.archive.org/details/cu31924001586282. (Cited on 9.)

[225] R. Dedekind, *Was sind und was sollen die Zahlen?* (What are and what should the numbers be?), F. Vieweg, Braunschweig, 1888; English translation in Essays on the Theory of Numbers, Dover Publications, New York, 1963. (Cited on 9.)

[226] E. De Giorgi, *Semicontinuity Theorems in the Calculus of Variations*, Quaderni dell' Accademia Pontaniana **56**, Accademia Pontaniana, Naples, 2008. (Cited on 453.)

[227] P. Deift, T. Kriecherbauer, K. T-R. McLauglin, S. Venakides, and X. Zhou, *Uniform asymptotics for polynomials orthogonal with respect to varying exponential weight and applications to universality questions in random matrix theory*, Comm. Pure Appl. Math. **52** (1999), 1335–1425. (Cited on 630.)

[228] E. de Jonge and A. C. M. van Rooij, *Introduction to Riesz Spaces*, Mathematical Centre Tracts, Mathematisch Centrum, Amsterdam, 1977. (Cited on 269.)

[229] Ch. J. de la Vallée Poussin, *Sur l'approximation des fonctions d'une variable réelle et leurs dérivées par des polynomes et des suites limitées de Fourier*, Bull. Acad. Royale Belgique **3** (1908), 193–254. (Cited on 82, 161.)

[230] Ch. J. de la Vallée Poussin, *Sur la meilleure approximation des fonctions d'une variable réelle par des expressions d'ordre donné*, C. R. Acad. Sci. Paris Sér. I. Math. **166** (1918), 799–802. (Cited on 162.)

[231] J.-M. Delort, *F.B.I. Transformation. Second Microlocalization and Semilinear Caustics*, Lecture Notes in Math., Springer-Verlag, Berlin, 1992. (Cited on 539.)

[232] R. del Rio, S. Jitomirskaya, Y. Last, and B. Simon, *Operators with singular continuous spectrum. IV. Hausdorff dimensions, rank one perturbations, and localization*, J. Anal. Math. **69** (1996), 153–200. (Cited on 702.)

[233] A. de Moivre, *Approximatio ad summam terminorum binomii* $(a + b)^n$ *in seriem expansi*, 7 pages offprint. (Cited on 654.)

[234] A. de Moivre, *The Doctrine of Chances*, 2nd edition, Millar, London 1738. (Cited on 654.)

[235] A. Denjoy, *Une extension de l'intégrale de M. Lebesgue*, C. R. Acad. Sci. Paris **154** (1912), 859–862. (Cited on 230.)

[236] G. de Rham, *Variétés différentiables*, Hermann, Paris, 1955. (Cited on 513.)

[237] G. de Rham, *Sur un exemple de fonction continue sans dérivée*, Enseign. Math. (2) **3** (1957), 71–72. (Cited on 164.)

[238] R. Descartes, *La Geometrie*, Appendix I to Discours de la Méthode, Leiden, 1637. (Cited on 26.)

[239] R. A. DeVore and G. Lorentz, *Constructive Approximation*, Grundlehren der Mathematischen Wissenschaften, Springer-Verlag, Berlin, 1993. (Cited on 84.)

[240] J. Dieudonné, *Sur le théorème de Hahn–Banach*, Revue Sci. **79** (1941), 642–643. (Cited on 458.)

[241] J. Dieudonné, *La dualité dans les espaces vectoriels topologiques*, Ann. Sci. École Norm. Sup. (3) **59** (1942), 107–139. (Cited on 443.)

[242] J. Dieudonné, *Eléments d'Analyse. Vol. II*, Gauthier–Villars, Paris, 1968. (Cited on 350.)

[243] J. Dieudonné, *A History of Algebraic and Differential Topology, 1900–1960*, reprint of the 1989 edition, Modern Birkhäuser Classics, Birkhäuser Boston, Boston, MA, 2009. (Cited on 487.)

[244] J. Dieudonné and L. Schwartz, *La dualité dans les espaces $\mathcal{F}$ et $(\mathcal{LF})$*, Ann. Inst. Fourier Grenoble **1** (1949), 61–101 (1950). (Cited on 711, 712.)

[245] U. Dini, *Analisi infinitesimale*, Lezioni dettate nella R, Universitυa di Pisa, Anno accademico 1877–78. (Cited on 486.)

[246] U. Dini, *Fondamenti per la teoria delle funzioni di variabili reali*, Nistri, Pisa, 1878. Available online at http://ebooks.library.cornell.edu/cgi/t/text/pageviewer-idx?c=math;cc=math;idno=01580002;view=image;seq=1. (Cited on 202, 226, 231.)

[247] U. Dini, *Serie di Fourier e altre rappresentazioni analitiehe delle funzioni di una variabile reale*, Pisa, 1880. Available online at http://ebooks.library.cornell.edu/cgi/t/text/pageviewer-idx?c=math;cc=math;idno=02070001;view=image;seq=1. (Cited on 152.)

[248] P. A. M. Dirac, *The Principles of Quantum Mechanics*, 3rd edition, Clarendon Press, Oxford, 1947; first published in 1930. (Cited on 512, 538.)

[249] P. G. Lejeune-Dirichlet, *Sur la convergence des séries trigonométriques qui servent à représenter une fonction arbitraire entre des limites données*, J. Reine Angew. Math. **4** (1829), 157–169. (Cited on 151.)

[250] Z. Ditzian and V. Totik, *Moduli of Smoothness*, Springer Series in Computational Mathematics, Springer-Verlag, New York, 1987. (Cited on 84.)

[251] W. Doeblin, *Sur les sommes d'un grand nombre de variables aléatoires indépendantes*, Bull. Sci. Math. **63** (1939), 23–32, 35–64. (Cited on 658.)

[252] J. D. Dollard, *Quantum-mechanical scattering theory for short-range and Coulomb interactions*, Rocky Mountain J. Math. **1:1** (1971) 5–88. (Cited on 607.)

[253] M. D. Donsker, *An invariance principle for certain probability limit theorems*, Mem. Amer. Math. Soc. **1951**, (1951), 12 pp. (Cited on 328.)

[254] J. L. Doob, *Classical Potential Theory and Its Probabilistic Counterpart*, Grundlehren der Mathematischen Wissenschaften, Springer-Verlag, New York, 1984. (Cited on 327.)

[255] J. L. Doob, *Measure Theory*, Graduate Texts in Mathematics, Springer-Verlag, New York, 1994. (Cited on 230.)

[256] P. du Bois-Reymond, *Über die Fourierschen Reihen*, Nachr. Kön. Ges. Wiss. Göttingen **21** (1873), 571–582. (Cited on 152.)

[257] P. du Bois-Reymond, *Über asymptotische Werthe, infinitäre Approximationen und infinitäre Auflösung von Gleichungen. Nachträge*, Math. Ann. **8** (1875), 363–414. (Cited on 14.)

[258] P. du Bois-Reymond, *Der Beweis des Fundamentalsatzes der Integralrechnung*, Math. Ann. **16** (1880), 115–128. (Cited on 201.)

[259] R. M. Dudley, *Real Analysis and Probability*, revised reprint of the 1989 original, Cambridge Studies in Advanced Mathematics, Cambridge University Press, Cambridge, 2002. (Cited on 239, 313, 617.)

[260] P. Dugac, *Sur la correspondance de Borel et le théorème de Dirichlet–Heine–Weierstrass–Borel–Schoenflies–Lebesgue*, Arch. Internat. Hist. Sci. **39** (1989), 69–110. (Cited on 74.)

[261] N. Dunford and B. J. Pettis, *Linear operations among summable functions*, Proc. Nat. Acad. Sci. USA **25** (1939), 544–550. (Cited on 275.)

[262] N. Dunford and J. T. Schwartz, *Linear Operators. Part I. General Theory*, reprint of the 1958 original, Wiley Classics Library, John Wiley & Sons, New York, 1988. (Cited on 487.)

[263] J. Duoandikoetxea, *Fourier Analysis*, Graduate Studies in Mathematics, American Mathematical Society, Providence, RI, 2001. (Cited on 149.)

[264] R. Durrett, *Essentials of Stochastic Processes*, Springer Texts in Statistics, Springer-Verlag, New York, 1999. (Cited on 327.)

[265] R. Durrett, *Probability: Theory and Examples*, 4th edition, Cambridge Series in Statistical and Probabilistic Mathematics, Cambridge University Press, Cambridge, 2010. (Cited on 617.)

[266] A. Dvoretzky, P. Erdős, and S. Kakutani, *Double points of paths of Brownian motion in n-space*, Acta Sci. Math. Szeged **12**, (1950), 75–81. (Cited on 328.)

[267] H. Dym, *J Contractive Matrix Functions, Reproducing Kernel Hilbert Spaces and Interpolation*, CBMS Regional Conference Series in Mathematics, American Mathematical Society, Providence, RI, 1989. (Cited on 126.)

[268] H. Dym and H. P. McKean, *Fourier Series and Integrals*, Probability and Mathematical Statistics, Academic Press, New York-London, 1972. (Cited on 537, 574.)

[269] E. B. Dynkin, *Markov Processes, Vols. I, II*, Die Grundlehren der mathematischen Wissenschaften, Springer-Verlag, Heidelberg, 1965. (Cited on 674.)

[270] G. Edgar, *Measure, Topology, and Fractal Geometry*, Second edition, Undergraduate Texts in Mathematics, Springer, New York, 2008. (Cited on 700.)

[271] H. G. Eggleston, *Convexity*, Cambridge Tracts in Mathematics and Mathematical Physics, Cambridge University Press, New York, 1958. (Cited on 387.)

[272] D. Th. Egoroff, *Sur les suites de fonctions mesurables*, C. R. Acad. Sci. Paris **152** (1911), 244–246. (Cited on 249.)

[273] L. Ehrenpreis, *Solution of some problems of division. Part I. Division by a polynomial of derivation*, Amer. J. Math. **76** (1954), 883–903. (Cited on 607.)

[274] A. Einstein, *Über die von der molekularkinetischen Theorie der Wärme geforderte Bewegung von in ruhenden Flüssigkeiten suspendierten Teilchen*, Ann. Physik **17** (1905), 549–560; English translation online at `http://users.physik.fu-berlin.de/~kleinert/files/eins_brownian.pdf` (Cited on 326.)

[275] A. Einstein, *The World As I See It*, Philosophical Library, New York, 1949. (Cited on 606.)

[276] R. W. Emerson, "Self-Reliance" an essay included in *Essays: First Series*, Houghton, Mifflin and Company, Boston, MA, 1883; available online at `http://en.wikisource.org/wiki/Essays:_First_Series/Self-Reliance` (self-reliance only) and `https://archive.org/details/essaysfirstseconx00emer` (1883 collection of First and Second Series). (Cited on 1.)

[277] H. B. Enderton, *Elements of Set Theory*, Academic Press, New York-London, 1977. (Cited on 14.)

[278] P. Enflo, *On the invariant subspace problem in Banach spaces* in Séminaire Maurey-Schwartz (1975–1976) Espaces L^p, applications radonifiantes et géométrie des espaces de Banach, Exp. Nos. 14–15, 7 pp. Centre Math., École Polytech., Palaiseau, 1976. (Cited on 488.)

[279] P. Enflo, *On the invariant subspace problem for Banach spaces*, Acta Math. **158** (1987), 213–313. (Cited on 488.)

[280] M. Epple, *Felix Hausdorff's Considered Empiricism*, in The Architecture of Modern Mathematics, pp. 263–289, Oxford University Press, Oxford, 2006. (Cited on 49.)

[281] P. Erdős and A. Rényi, *On Cantor's series with convergent $\sum 1/q_n$*, Ann. Univ. Sci. Budapest Eötvös Sect. Math. **2** (1959), 93–109. (Cited on 646.)

[282] A. K. Erlang, *Sandsynlighetsregning og Telefonsamtaler*, Nytt tidsskrift for Matematik B, **20** (1909), 33–39. (English title: The theory of probabilities and telephone conversations.) (Cited on 666.)

[283] C. G. Esseen, *On the Liapunoff limit of error in the theory of probability*, Arkiv för matematik, astronomi och fysik **A28** (1942), 1–19. (Cited on 656.)

[284] L. Euler, *Intrzductio in Analysin Infinitorum*, apud Marcum-Michaelem Bousquet & socios, 1748. (Cited on 26.)

[285] L. Euler, *Sur la vibration des cordes*, Mémoires de l'Academie des Sciences de Berlin **4** (1750), 69–85, based on a talk at the Berlin Academy on May 16, 1748; available online at `http://eulerarchive.maa.org/pages/E140.html`. (Cited on 150.)

[286] L. Euler, *Methodus facilis inveniendi series per sinus cosinusve angulorum multiplorum procedentes, quarum usus in universa theoria astronomiae est amplissimus,*

Nova acta academiae scientiarum Petropolitanae **11** (1793), 1798, 94–113. Reprinted in Opera Omnia (Series I) **16** 311–332. Available online at `http://eulerarchive.maa.org/pages/E703.html`. (Cited on 150.)

[287] G. W. Evans, *Cavalieri's theorem in his own words*, Amer. Math. Monthly **24** (1917), 447–451. (Cited on 289.)

[288] L. C. Evans, *Partial Differential Equations*, American Mathematical Society, Providence, RI, 1998. (Cited on 606.)

[289] L. C. Evans and R. F. Gariepy, *Measure Theory and Fine Properties of Functions*, Studies in Advanced Mathematics, CRC Press, Boca Raton, FL, 1992. (Cited on 700.)

[290] P. Ewald, *Die Berechnung optischer und elektrostatischer Gitterpotentiale*, Ann. Phys. **369** (1921), 253–287. (Cited on 567.)

[291] G. M. Ewing, *Calculus of Variations with Applications*, corrected reprint of the 1969 original, Dover Publications, New York, 1985. (Cited on 453.)

[292] M. Fabian, P. Habala, P. Hájek, V. Montesinos, and V. Zizler, *Banach Space Theory. The basis for linear and nonlinear analysis*, CMS Books in Mathematics/Ouvrages de Mathématiques de la SMC, Springer, New York, 2011. (Cited on 357, 444.)

[293] K. Falconer, *Fractal Geometry. Mathematical Foundations and Applications*, 2nd edition. John Wiley & Sons, Hoboken, NJ, 2003. (Cited on 156, 700, 702.)

[294] K. Fan, *Entfernung zweier zufälligen Grössen und die Konvergenz nach Wahrscheinlichkeit*, Math. Z. **49** (1944), 681–683. (Cited on 630.)

[295] P. Fatou, *Séries trigonométriques et séries de Taylor*, Acta Math. **30** (1906), 335–340. (Cited on 161, 226, 249.)

[296] H. Federer, *Geometric Measure Theory*, Die Grundlehren der mathematischen Wissenschaften, Springer-Verlag New York Inc., New York, 1969. (Cited on 700.)

[297] L. Fejér, *Sur les singularités des séries de Fourier de fonctions continues*, Ann. Sci. École Norm. Sup. **28** (1911), 63–103. (Cited on 152, 158.)

[298] L. Fejér, *Über trigonometrische Polynome*, J. Reine Angew. Math. **146** (1916), 53–82. (Cited on 153.)

[299] L. Fejér, *Über Interpolation*, Nachr. Ges. Wiss. Göttingen, Mathematischphysikalische Klasse (1916), 66–91. (Cited on 82.)

[300] L. Fejér, *Über Weierstrasssche Approximation, besonders durch Hermitesche Interpolation*, Math. Ann. **102** (1930), 707–725. (Cited on 82.)

[301] W. Feller, *Über den zentralen Grenzwertsatz in der Wahrscheinlichkeitsrechnung I, II*, Math. Z. **40** (1935), 521–559; **42** (1937), 301–312. (Cited on 657.)

[302] W. Feller, *An Introduction to Probability Theory and Its Applications*, 3rd edition, Wiley, New York, 1968. (Cited on 617.)

[303] E. Fermi, *Un metodo statistico per la determinazione di alcune priorità dell'atome*, Rend. Accad. Naz. Lincei **6** (1927), 602–607. (Cited on 453.)

[304] R. P. Feynman, R. B. Leighton, and M. Sands, *The Feynman Lectures on Physics 2: Mainly Electromagnetism and Matter*, Addison-Wesley, Reading, MA, 1964. (Cited on 588.)

[305] E. Fischer, *Sur la convergence en moyenne*, C. R. Acad. Sci. Paris **144** (1907), 1022–1024. (Cited on 153, 226.)

[306] H. Fischer, *A History of the Central Limit Theorem. From Classical to Modern Probability Theory*, Sources and Studies in the History of Mathematics and Physical Sciences, Springer, New York, 2011. (Cited on 654.)

[307] V. Fock, *Konfigurationsraum und zweite Quantulung*, Z. Phys. **75** (1932), 622–647, 1932. (Cited on 538.)

[308] G. B. Folland, *Harmonic Analysis in Phase Space*, Annals of Mathematics Studies, Princeton University Press, Princeton, NJ, 1989. (Cited on 538.)

[309] G. B. Folland, *Fourier Analysis and Its Applications*, The Wadsworth & Brooks/Cole Mathematics Series, Wadsworth & Brooks/Cole, Pacific Grove, CA, 1992. (Cited on 149.)

[310] G. H. Folland, *Introduction to Partial Differential Equations*, Princeton University Press, Princeton, NJ, 1995. (Cited on 606.)

[311] J. Fourier, *Theorie Analytique de la Chaleur*, Firmin Didot, 1822. English translation: *The Analytical Theory of Heat*, Cambridge University Press, Cambridge, 1878; reissued by Cambridge University Press, 2009. (Cited on 151, 546, 607.)

[312] J. J. F. Fournier, *Sharpness in Young's inequality for convolution*, Pacific J. Math. **72** (1977), 383–397. (Cited on 563.)

[313] A. A. Fraenkel, *The notion "definite" and the independence of the axiom of choice*, originally published in 1922; reprinted in From Frege to Gödel: A Source Book in Mathematical Logic, 1879–1931 (J. van Heijenoort, ed.), pp. 284–289, Source Books in the History of the Sciences, Harvard University Press, 1967. (Cited on 13.)

[314] J. Franks, *A (Terse) Introduction to Lebesgue Integration*, Student Mathematical Library, American Mathematical Society, Providence, RI, 2009. (Cited on 230.)

[315] M. Fréchet, *Sur quelques points du calcul fonctionnel*, Palermo Rend. **22** (1906), 1–74; thesis, Gauthier–Villars, Paris. (Cited on 6, 47, 60, 74, 500.)

[316] M. Fréchet, *Sur les opérations Linéaire, (3e note)*, Trans. Amer. Math. Soc. **8** (1907), 433–446. (Cited on 125.)

[317] M. Fréchet, *Sur la notion de différentielle*, (French) C. R. Acad. Sci. Paris **152** (1911), 1050–1051. (Cited on 365.)

[318] M. Fréchet, *Sur l'intégrale d'une fonctionnelle étendue à un ensemble abstrait*, Bull. Sci. Math. **43** (1915), 248–265. (Cited on 229.)

[319] M. Fréchet, *Sur les ensembles abstraits*, Ann. Sci. École Norm. (3) **38** (1921), 341–388. (Cited on 60.)

[320] M. Fréchet, *Sur divers modes de convergence*, Enseign. Math. **22** (1922), 63. (Cited on 630.)

[321] M. Fréchet, *Les espaces abstraits topologiquement affines*, Acta Math. **47** (1926), 25–52. (Cited on 501.)

[322] M. Fréchet, *Les espaces abstraits*, Gauthier–Villars, Paris, 1928. (Cited on 363.)

[323] M. Fréchet, *Sur la definition axiomatique d'une classe d'espaces vectoriels distancies applicables vectoriellement sur l'espace de Hilbert*, Ann. Math. **36** (1935), 705–718. (Cited on 118.)

[324] I. Fredholm, *Sur une classe d'équations fonctionnelles*, Acta Math. **27** (1903), 365–390. (Cited on 47.)

[325] D. H. Fremlin, *Topological Riesz Spaces and Measure Theory*, Cambridge University Press, London-New York, 1974. (Cited on 269.)

[326] H. Freudenthal, *Teilweise geordnete Moduln*, Proc. Akad. Wet. Amsterdam **39** (1936), 641–651. (Cited on 269.)

[327] H. Freudenthal, *The cradle of modern topology, according to Brouwer's inedita*, Hist. Math. **2** (1975), 495–502. (Cited on 485, 487.)

[328] A. Friedman, *Partial Differential Equations of Parabolic Type*, Prentice Hall, Englewood Cliffs, NJ, 1964. (Cited on 606.)

[329] B. Fristedt and L. Gray, *A Modern Approach to Probability Theory*, Probability and its Applications, Birkhäuser, Boston, 1997. (Cited on 313, 617.)

[330] G. Frobenius, *Über Matrizen aus positiven Elementen*, S.-B. Preuss. Akad. Wiss. (Berlin), (1908), 471–476; (1909), 514–518. (Cited on 675.)

[331] G. Frobenius, *Über Matrizen aus nicht negativen Elementen*, S.-B. Preuss. Akad. Wiss. (Berlin), (1912), 456–477. (Cited on 675.)

[332] J. Fröhlich, and T. Spencer, *On the statistical mechanics of classical Coulomb and dipole gases*, J. Statist. Phys. **24** (1981), 617–701. (Cited on 608.)

[333] J. Fröhlich, and T. Spencer, *The Kosterlitz-Thouless transition in two-dimensional Abelian spin systems and the Coulomb gas*, Comm. Math. Phys. **81** (1981), 527–602. (Cited on 608.)

[334] G. Fubini, *Sugli integrali multipli*, Rom. Acc. L. Rend. (5) **16** (1907), 608–614. (Cited on 288.)

[335] G. Fubini, *Sulla derivazione per serie*, Rom. Acc. L. Rend. (5) **24** (1915), 204–206. (Cited on 319.)

[336] H. Furstenberg, *On the infinitude of primes*, Amer. Math. Monthly **62** (1955), 353. (Cited on 51.)

[337] F. Galton, *Natural Inheritance*, Macmillan, London, 1889; Available online at https://archive.org/details/naturalinherita03galtgoog (Cited on 648.)

[338] F. R. Gantmacher, *The Theory of Matrices. Vols. 1, 2*, Chelsea Publishing, New York, 1959. (Cited on 675.)

[339] D. J. H. Garling, *Inequalities: A Journey into Linear Analysis*, Cambridge University Press, Cambridge, 2007. (Cited on 387, 615.)

[340] R. Gateaux, *Sur les fonctionnelles continues et les fonctionnelles analytiques*, C. R. Acad. Sci. Paris **157** (1913), 325–327. (Cited on 365.)

[341] C. F. Gauss, *Disquisitiones arithmeticae*, Latin original, 1801. English translation, Yale University Press, New Haven, CT-London, 1966. (Cited on 26.)

[342] C. F. Gauss, *Carl Friedrich Gauss Werke*, Band **8**, Kön. Ges. Wiss. Göttingen, Teubner, Leipzig, 1900; note appears on page 88. (Cited on 567.)

[343] I. M. Gel'fand, *Sur un lemme de la théorie des espaces linéaires*, Zap. Nauk. Inst. Mat. Mekh. Kharkov. Mat. Tov. **13** (1936), 35–40. (Cited on 341.)

[344] I. M. Gel'fand, G. E. Shilov, N. Ya. Vilenkin, and M. I. Graev, *Generalized Functions. Vol. 1: Properties and Operations, Vol. 2: Spaces of Fundamental and Generalized Functions, Vol. 3: Theory of Differential Equations, Vol. 4: Applications of Harmonic Analysis, Vol. 5: Integral Geometry and Representation Theory*, Academic Press, New York-London, 1964–1968. (Cited on 513, 538, 548.)

[345] J. W. Gibbs, *Graphical methods in the thermodynamics of fluids*, Trans. Connecticut Acad. **2** (1873), 309–342. (Cited on 387.)

[346] J. W. Gibbs, *A method of geometrical representation of the thermodynamic properties of substances by means of surfaces*, Trans. Connecticut Acad. **2** (1873), 382–404. (Cited on 387.)

[347] J. W. Gibbs, *On the equilibrium of heterogeneous substances*, Trans. Connecticut Acad. **3** (1875–1876), 108–248; (1877–1878), 343–524. (Cited on 387.)

[348] J. W. Gibbs, *Fourier's series*, Nature **59** (1898), 200; **59** (1899), 606. (Cited on 157.)

[349] D. Gilbard and N. Trudinger, *Elliptic Partial Differential Equations of Second Order*, Springer, Berlin 1983. (Cited on 606.)

[350] J. Glimm and A. Jaffe, *Quantum Physics. A Functional Integral Point of View*, Springer-Verlag, New York-Berlin, 1981. (Cited on 329.)

[351] B. V. Gnedenko, *K teorii oblastei prityazheniya ustoichivykh zakonov*, Uchenye zapiski Moskovskogo universiteta **30** (1939), 61–82. [Russian] (Cited on 658.)

[352] B. V. Gnedenko and A. N. Kolmogorov, *Limit Distributions for Sums of Independent Random Variables*, Addison–Wesley, Cambridge, MA, 1954; (Russian original 1949). (Cited on 658, 659.)

[353] K. Goebel and W. A. Kirk, *Topics in Metric Fixed Point Theory*, Cambridge Studies in Advanced Mathematics, Cambridge University Press, Cambridge, 1990. (Cited on 485.)

[354] H. H. Goldstine, *Weakly complete Banach spaces*, Duke Math. J. **4** (1938), 125–131. (Cited on 444.)

[355] E. Goursat, *Sur la théorie des fonctions implicites*, Bull. Soc. Math. France **31** (1903), 184–192. (Cited on 485, 486.)

[356] L. Grafakos, *Classical Fourier Analysis*, 2nd edition, Graduate Texts in Mathematics, Springer, New York, 2008. (Cited on 149.)

[357] L. Grafakos, *Modern Fourier Analysis*, 2nd edition, Graduate Texts in Mathematics, Springer, New York, 2009. (Cited on 149.)

[358] L. Graham and J-M. Kantor, *Naming Infinity. A true story of religious mysticism and mathematical creativity*, The Belknap Press of Harvard University Press, Cambridge, MA, 2009. (Cited on 249.)

[359] J. P. Gram, *Über die Entwickelung reeller Functionen in Reihen mittelst der Methode der kleinsten Quadrate*, J. Reine. Angew. Math. **94** (1883), 41–73. (Cited on 134.)

[360] A. Granas and J. Dugundji, *Fixed Point Theory*, Springer Monographs in Mathematics, Springer-Verlag, New York, 2003. (Cited on 485.)

[361] H. Grassmann, *Lehrbuch der Arithmetik*, Berlin, 1861. (Cited on 9.)

[362] I. Grattan-Guinness, *The Development of the Foundations of Mathematical Analysis from Euler to Riemann*, The MIT Press, Cambridge, MA–London, 1970. (Cited on 150.)

[363] I. Grattan-Guinness, *A mathematical union: William Henry and Grace Chisholm Young*, Ann. of Sci. **29** (1972), 105–186. (Cited on 372.)

[364] G. Grätzer, *Lattice Theory. First Concepts and Distributive Lattices*, W. H. Freeman and Co., San Francisco, CA, 1971. (Cited on 11.)

[365] J. Gray, *Did Poincaré say "set theory is a disease"?* Math. Intelligencer **13** (1991), 19–22. (Cited on 37.)

[366] G. Green, *An Essay on the Application of Mathematical Analysis to the Theories of Electricity and Magnetism*, Nottingham, 1828; available online at http://arxiv.org/abs/0807.0088. (Cited on 606.)

[367] F. P. Greenleaf, *Invariant Means on Topological Groups and Their Applications*, Van Nostrand Reinhold, New York-Toronto-London, 1969. (Cited on 486.)

[368] G. Grimmett and D. R. Stirzaker, *Probability and Random Processes*, 2nd edition, The Clarendon Press, Oxford University Press, New York, 1992. (Cited on 617.)

[369] H. Groemer, *Geometric Applications of Fourier Series and Spherical Harmonics*, Encyclopedia of Mathematics and Its Applications, Cambridge University Press, Cambridge, 1996. (Cited on 167.)

[370] H. Groemer and R. Schneider, *Stability estimates for some geometric inequalities*, Bull. London Math. Soc. **23** (1991), 67–74. (Cited on 167.)

[371] J. Grolous, *Un théorème sur les fonctions*, Bull. Soc. Philomathique de Paris **3** (1875), 401. (Cited on 387.)

[372] T. H. Gronwall, *Note on the derivative with respect to a parameter of the solutions of a system of differential equations*, Ann. Math. **20** (1919), 292–296. (Cited on 486.)

[373] A. Grothendieck, *Résumé de la théorie métrique des produits tensoriels topologiques*, Bol. Soc. Mat. São Paulo **8** (1953), 1–79. (Cited on 182.)

[374] A. Grothendieck, *Sur certains sous-espaces vectoriels de L^p*, Canadian J. Math. **6** (1954), 158–160. (Cited on 413.)

[375] A. Haar, *Der Massbegriff in der Theorie der kontinuierlichen Gruppen*, Ann. Math. **34** (1933), 147–169. (Cited on 350.)

[376] I. Hacking, *The Emergence of Probability. A philosophical study of early ideas about probability, induction and statistical inference*, Second edition, Cambridge University Press, Cambridge, 2006. (Cited on 628.)

[377] J. Hadamard, *Leçons sur la propagation des ondes et les équations de l'hydrodynamique*, Hermann, Paris, 1903. (Cited on 512.)

[378] J. Hadamard, *Sur les opérations fonctionelles*, C. R. Acad. Sci. Paris **136** (1903), 351–354. (Cited on 75, 238.)

[379] J. Hadamard, *Sur quelques applications de l'indice de Kronecker*, J. Tannery (ed.), *Introduction à la théorie des fonctions d'une variable*, Hermann **2** (1910), 875–891. (Cited on 487.)

[380] J. Hadamard, *Lectures on Cauchy's Problem in Linear Partial Differential Equations*, Dover Publications, New York, 1953; photo-offset reprint of a book originally published by the Yale University Press, New Haven, 1923. (Cited on 512, 607.)

[381] H. Hahn, *Mengentheoretische Charakterisierung der stetigen Kurven*, Sitzungsber. Akad. Wiss. Wien **123** (1914), 2433–2487. (Cited on 205.)

[382] H. Hahn, *Theorie der reellen funktionen*, Springer, Berlin, 1921; Available online at http://quod.lib.umich.edu/cgi/t/text/text-idx?c=umhistmath; idno=ACM1546. (Cited on 269.)

[383] H. Hahn, *Über Folgen linearer Operationen*, Monatsh. Math. **32** (1922), 3–88. (Cited on 364.)

[384] H. Hahn, *Über lineare Gleichungssysteme in linearen Räumen*, J. Reine Angew. Math. **157** (1927), 214–229. (Cited on 424.)

[385] H. Hahn, *Über stetige Streckenbilder*, Atti del Congresso Internazionale dei Mathematici, Bologna, t. II (1928), 217–220. (Cited on 205.)

[386] P. R. Halmos, *Measure Theory*, Graduate Texts in Mathematics, Springer-Verlag, New York, 1974; First edition, Van Nostrand, New York, 1950. (Cited on 211, 230.)

[387] P. R. Halmos, *Von Neumann on measure and ergodic theory*, Bull. Amer. Math. Soc. **64** (1958), 86–94. (Cited on 257.)

[388] P. R. Halmos, *Naive Set Theory*, Undergraduate Texts in Mathematics, Springer-Verlag, New York-Heidelberg, 1974; reprint of the 1960 edition. (Cited on 13.)

[389] H. Hamburger, *Über eine Erweiterung des Stieltjesschen Momentenproblems*, Math. Ann. **81** (1920), 235–319; **82** (1921), 120–164, 168–187. (Cited on 433.)

[390] H. Hankel, *Vorlesungen über die complexen Zahlen und ihre Functionen*, Voss, 1867. (Cited on 9.)

[391] H. Hankel, *Untersuchungen über die unendlich oft oscillirenden und unstetigen Funktionen. Ein Beitrag zur Feststellung des Begriffes der Funktion überhaupt*, Universitätspr. Tübingen, 1870. (Cited on 202.)

[392] O. Hanner, *On the uniform convexity of L^p and l^p*, Ark. Mat. **3** (1956), 239–244. (Cited on 388.)

[393] G. H. Hardy, *Weierstrass's non-differentiable function*, Tran. Amer. Math. Soc. **17** (1916), 301–325. (Cited on 156.)

[394] G. H. Hardy, *Notes on special systems of orthogonal functions, IV: The orthogonal functions of Whittaker's cardinal series*, Proc. Cambridge Philos. Soc. **37** (1941), 331–348. (Cited on 569.)

[395] G. H. Hardy and J. E. Littlewood, *Some problems of diophantine approximation*, Acta Math. **37** (1914), 155–239. (Cited on 645.)

[396] G. H. Hardy and J. E. Littlewood, *Some problems of diophantine approximation: A remarkable trigonometrical series*, Proc. Nat. Acad. Sci. USA **2** (1916), 583–586. (Cited on 582.)

[397] G. H. Hardy, J. E. Littlewood, G. Pólya, *Inequalities* (original version 1934), Reprint of the 1952 edition, Cambridge Mathematical Library, Cambridge University Press, Cambridge, 1988. (Cited on 394.)

[398] Harish-Chandra, *Discrete series for semisimple Lie groups. I. Construction of invariant eigendistributions, II. Explicit determination of the characters*, Acta Math. **113** (1965), 241–318; **116** (1966), 1–111. (Cited on 513.)

[399] P. Hartman and A. Wintner, *On the law of the iterated logarithm*, Amer. J. Math. **63** (1941), 169–176 (Cited on 645.)

[400] A. Hatcher, *Algebraic Topology*, Cambridge University Press, Cambridge, 2002. Available online at http://www.math.cornell.edu/~hatcher/AT/AT.pdf. (Cited on 487.)

[401] F. Hausdorff, *Bemerkung über den Inhalt von Punktmengen*, Math. Ann. **75** (1914), 428–434. (Cited on 210.)

[402] F. Hausdorff, *Grundzüge der Mengenlehre*, Veit and Co., Leipzig, 1914; reprinted by Chelsea, New York, 1949. (Cited on 35, 48, 50, 60, 210, 645, 733.)

[403] F. Hausdorff, *Dimension und äußeres Maß*, Math. Ann. **79** (1919), 157–179. (Cited on 700.)

[404] F. Hausdorff, *Eine Ausdehnung des Parsevalschen Satzes über Fourierreihen*, Math. Z. **16** (1923), 163–169. (Cited on 336, 563.)

[405] F. Hausdorff, *Mengenlehre*, zweite, neubearbeitete Auflage, Verlag Walter de Gruyter & Co., Berlin, 1927; second edition of [**402**]. (Cited on 203.)

[406] T. Hawkins, *Lebesgue's Theory of Integration. Its Origins and Development*, reprint of the 1979 corrected 2nd edition, AMS Chelsea Publishing, Providence, RI, 2001. (Cited on 225, 228.)

[407] O. Heaviside, *On operators in physical mathematics*, London R. S. Proc. **52** (1893), 504–529; **54** (1894), 105–143. (Cited on 512.)

[408] E. Heine, *Die Elemente der Functionenlehre*, J. Reine Angew. Math. **74** (1872), 172–188. (Cited on 9, 73.)

[409] S. Helgason, *The Radon Transform*, Progress in Mathematics, Birkhäuser, Boston, 1980. (Cited on 548.)

[410] E. Hellinger, *Zur Stieitjesschen Kettenbruchtheorie*, Math. Ann. **86** (1922), 18–29. (Cited on 433.)

[411] E. Hellinger and O. Toeplitz, *Grundlagen für eine Theorie der unendlichen Matrizen*, Math. Ann. **69** (1910), 289–330. (Cited on 413.)

[412] E. Helly, *Über lineare Funktionaloperationen*, Wien. Ber. **121** (1912), 265–297. (Cited on 238, 424, 447.)

[413] E. Helly, *Über Systeme linearer Gleichungen mit unendlich vielen Unbekannten*, Monatsh. Math. **31** (1921), 60–91. (Cited on 364, 425, 426.)

[414] L. L. Helms, *Introduction to Potential Theory*, Pure and Applied Mathematics, Wiley–Interscience, New York, 1969. (Cited on 453.)

[415] G. Hellwig, *Partial Differential Equations*, Blaisdell, New York, 1964. (Cited on 606.)

[416] R. Henderson, *Moral values*, Bull. Amer. Math. Soc. **1** (1894), 46–51. (Cited on 387.)

[417] R. Henstock, *Theory of Integration*, Butterworths, London, 1963. (Cited on 230.)

[418] G. Herglotz, *Über Potenzreihen mit positivem, reellem Teil im Einheitskreis*, Ber. Ver. Ges. wiss. Leipzig **63** (1911), 501–511. (Cited on 565.)

[419] J. Herival, *Joseph Fourier. The Man and the Physicist*, Clarendon Press, Oxford, 1975. (Cited on 151.)

[420] C. Hermite, *Sur la théorie des formes quadratiques ternaires indéfinies*, J. Reine Angew. Math. **47** (1854), 307–312. (Cited on 26.)

[421] C. Hermite, *Remarque sur un theoreme de M. Cauchy*, C. R. Acad. Sci. Paris **41** (1855), 181–183. (Cited on 175.)

[422] E. Hernández, H. Šikić, G. L. Weiss, aand E. N. Wilson, *The Zak transform(s)*, in Wavelets and Multiscale Analysis: Theory and Analysis (Applied and Numerical Harmonic Analysis), 151–157, Birkhäuser/Springer, 2011. (Cited on 519.)

[423] E. Hewitt and R. E. Hewitt, *The Gibbs–Wilbraham phenomenon: An episode in Fourier analysis*, Arch. Hist. Exact Sci. **21** (1979), 129–160. (Cited on 157.)

[424] J. R. Higgins, *Five short stories about the cardinal series*, Bull. Amer. Math. Soc. (N.S) **12** (1985), 45–89. (Cited on 568.)

[425] D. Hilbert, *Mathematical Problems*, Bull. Amer. Math. Soc. **8** (1902), 437–479. (Cited on 17.)

[426] D. Hilbert, *Grundzüge einer allgemeinen Theorie der linearen Integralgleichungen. Vierte Mitteilung*, Nachr. Kön. Ges. Wiss. Göttingen (1906), 157–227. (Cited on 117, 125, 447.)

[427] D. Hilbert, *Hermann Minkowski*, Nachr. Kön. Ges. Wiss. Göttingen (1909), 72–101; Math. Ann. **68** (1910), 445–471. (Cited on 387.)

[428] D. Hilbert, *Über das Unendliche*, Math. Ann. **95** (1926), 161–190. (Cited on 15.)

[429] R. Høegh-Krohn and B. Simon, *Hypercontractive semigroups and two-dimensional self-coupled Bose fields*, J. Funct. Anal. **9** (1972), 121–180. (Cited on 290.)

[430] E. Hölder, *Über einen Mittelwertsatz*, Nachr. Akad. Wiss. Göttingen. Math.-Phys. Kl. (1889), 38–47. (Cited on 372, 387.)

[431] L. Hörmander, *On the theory of general partial differential operators*, Acta Math. **94** (1955) 161–248. (Cited on 608.)

[432] L. Hörmander, *On the division of distributions by polynomials*, Ark. Mat. **3** (1958) 555–568. (Cited on 608.)

[433] L. Hörmander, *Linear Partial Differential Operators*, Die Grundlehren der mathematischen Wissenschaften, Academic Press, New York; Springer-Verlag, Berlin-Göttingen-Heidelberg, 1963. (Cited on 513.)

[434] L. Hörmander, *The Analysis of Linear Partial Differential Operators. I. Distribution Theory and Fourier Analysis, II. Differential Operators with Constant Coefficients*, Grundlehren der Mathematischen Wissenschaften, Springer-Verlag, Berlin, 1983; *III. Pseudodifferential Operators, IV. Fourier Integral Operators*, Grundlehren der Mathematischen Wissenschaften, Springer-Verlag, Berlin, 1985. (Cited on 513, 606.)

[435] A. Horn, *On the singular values of a product of completely continuous operators*, Proc. Nat. Acad. Sci. USA **36** (1950), 374–375. (Cited on 394.)

[436] J. Horváth, *Topological Vector Spaces and Distributions, Vol. I*, Addison-Wesley Publishing Co., Reading, MA–London–Don Mills, Ont., 1966. (Cited on 443.)

[437] P. Howard and J. E. Rubin, *Consequences of the Axiom of Choice*, Mathematical Surveys and Monographs, American Mathematical Society, Providence, RI, 1998. (Cited on 13.)

[438] R. A. Hunt, *On the convergence of Fourier series*, in Proc. Orthogonal Expansions and their Continuous Analogues, (Edwardsville, Ill., 1967), pp. 235–255, Southern Illinois University Press, Carbondale, IL, 1968. (Cited on 153.)

[439] A. Hurwitz, *Über die Erzeugung der Invarianten durch Integration*, Nachr. Kön. Ges. Wiss. Göttingen (1897), 71–90. (Cited on 350.)

[440] A. Hurwitz, *Sur le problème des isopérimètres*, C. R. Acad. Sci. Paris **132** (1901), 401–403. (Cited on 167.)

[441] A. Hurwitz, *Sur quelques applications géométriques des séries de Fourier*, Ann. Sci. École Norm. (3) **19** (1902), 357–408. (Cited on 167.)

[442] C. Huygens, *De Ratiociniis in Ludo Aleae*, Elsevirii, Leiden, 1657. A copy of the 1714 English translation is available at `http://www.stat.ucla.edu/history/huygens.pdf`. (Cited on 628.)

[443] C. Huygens, *Traité de la lumière*, Leyden, 1690, translated by Silvanus P. Thompson, Chicago University Press, 2005; original available online at `http://gallica.bnf.fr/ark:/12148/bpt6k5659616j`; English translation at `http://www.gutenberg.org/catalog/world/readfile?fk_files=1496936`. (Cited on 607.)

[444] M. E. H. Ismail, *Classical and Quantum Orthogonal Polynomials in One Variable*, Encyclopedia of Mathematics and its Application, Cambridge University Press, Cambridge, 2009. (Cited on 135.)

[445] V. I. Istrăţescu, *Fixed Point Theory. An Introduction*, Mathematics and its Applications, D. Reidel Publishing, Dordrecht-Boston, MA, 1981. (Cited on 485.)

[446] D. Jackson, *The general theory of approximation by polynomials and trigonometric sums*, Bull. Amer. Math. Soc. **27**, 415–431. (Cited on 81.)

[447] M. C. G. J. Jacobi, *Suite des Notices sur Les Fonctions Elliptiques*, Crelle's Journal **3** (1828), 303–310. (Cited on 567.)

[448] C. G. Jacobi, *Demonstratio formulae $\int_0^1 w^{a-1}(1 - w)^{b-1}\, \partial w = \frac{\int^\infty e^{-x} x^{a-1}\, \partial x \cdot \int_0^\infty e^{-x} x^{b-1}\, \partial w}{\int_0^\infty e^{-x} x^{a+b-1}\, \partial w} = \frac{\Gamma a \Gamma b}{\Gamma(a+b)}$*, J. Reine Angew. Math. **11** (1834), 307. (Cited on 289.)

[449] I. M. James, *Topological and Uniform Spaces*, Undergraduate Texts in Mathematics, Springer-Verlag, New York, 1987. (Cited on 367.)

[450] H. Jarchow, *Locally Convex Spaces*, Mathematische Leitfäden, B. G. Teubner, Stuttgart, 1981. (Cited on 706.)

[451] J. L. Jensen, *Sur les fonctions convexes et les inégalités entre les valeurs moyennes*, Acta Math. **30** (1906), 175–193. (Cited on 387.)

[452] F. John, *Partial Differential Equations*, Springer, New York, 1982. (Cited on 606, 608.)

[453] W. B. Johnson and J. Lindenstrauss, ed., *Handbook of the Geometry of Banach Spaces*, 2 Vols., North-Holland Publishing Co., Amsterdam, 2001. (Cited on 357.)

[454] C. Jordan, *Traité des substitutions et des équations algébriques*, Gauthier–Villars, Paris, 1870. Available at http://archive.org/details/traitdessubsti00jorduoft. (Cited on 26.)

[455] C. Jordan, *Sur la série de Fourier*, C. R. Acad. Sci. Paris **92** (1881), 228–230. (Cited on 152, 193, 269, 318.)

[456] C. Jordan, *Cours d'analyse de l'École Polytechnique, Tome I. Calcul différentiel*, 2nd edition, Gauthier–Villars, Paris, 1893. (Cited on 50.)

[457] P. Jordan and J. von Neumann, *On inner products in linear metric spaces*, Ann. Math. **36** (1935), 719–723. (Cited on 117.)

[458] J. Jost and X. Li-Jost, *Calculus of variations*, Cambridge Studies in Advanced Mathematics, Cambridge University Press, Cambridge, 1998. (Cited on 453.)

[459] J. Jost, *Partial Differential Equations*, Springer, New York, 2002. (Cited on 606.)

[460] R. Jost, *The General Theory of Quantized Fields*, Lectures in Applied Mathematics, American Mathematical Society, Providence, RI, 1965. (Cited on 513.)

[461] H. Junek, *Locally Convex Spaces and Operator Ideals*, Teubner–Texte zur Mathematik, B. G. Teubner Verlagsgesellschaft, Leipzig, 1983. (Cited on 443.)

[462] M. Kac, *On some connections between probability theory and differential and integral equations*, in Proc. Second Berkeley Sympos. on Mathematical Statistics and Probability, 1950, pp. 189–215, University of California Press, Berkeley and Los Angeles, 1951. (Cited on 328.)

[463] R. V. Kadison, *A representation theory for commutative topological algebra*, Mem. Amer. Math. Soc., 1951, (1951), 39 pp. (Cited on 92.)

[464] J.-P. Kahane, *Lacunary Taylor and Fourier series*, Bull. Amer. Math. Soc. **70** (1964), 199–213. (Cited on 156.)

[465] J.-P. Kahane, *Commutative harmonic analysis*, in A Panorama of Hungarian Mathematics in the Twentieth Century, I (J. Horváth, ed.), pp. 159–192, Bolyai Soc. Math. Studies, Springer, Berlin, 2006. (Cited on 153.)

[466] S. Kakutani, *Two fixed-point theorems concerning bicompact convex sets*, Proc. Imp. Acad. Tokyo **14** (1939), 242–245. (Cited on 486.)

[467] S. Kakutani, *Weak topologies and regularity of Banach spaces*, Proc. Imp. Acad. Tokyo **15** (1939), 169–173. (Cited on 444.)

[468] S. Kakutani, *Weak topology, bicompact sets and the principle of duality*, Proc. Imp. Acad. Tokyo **16** (1940), 63–67. (Cited on 447.)

[469] S. Kakutani, *Concrete representation of abstract (M)-spaces. (A characterization of the space of continuous functions)*, Ann. Math. (2) **42** (1941), 994–1024. (Cited on 92, 238.)

[470] S. Kakutani, *Topological properties of the unit sphere of a Hilbert space*, Proc. Imp. Acad. Tokyo **19** (1943), 269–271. (Cited on 486.)

[471] S. Kakutani, *Two-dimensional Brownian motion and harmonic functions*, Proc. Imp. Acad. Tokyo **20** (1944), 706–714. (Cited on 608.)

[472] S. Kakutani, *On equivalence of infinite product measures*, Ann. Math. (2) **49** (1948), 214–224. (Cited on 298.)

[473] S. Kakutani and K. Kodaira, *Über das Haarsche Mass in der lokal bikompakten Gruppe*, Proc. Imp. Acad. Tokyo **20** (1944), 444–450. (Cited on 211.)

[474] O. Kallenberg, *Foundations of Modern Probability*, Springer, New York, 1997. (Cited on 617.)

[475] N. J. Kalton, *An elementary example of a Banach space not isomorphic to its complex conjugate*, Canad. Math. Bull. **38** (1995), 218–222. (Cited on 365.)

[476] Y. Kannai, *An elementary proof of the no-retraction theorem*, Amer. Math. Monthly **88** (1981), 264–268. (Cited on 487.)

[477] Pl. Kannappan, *Functional Equations and Inequalities With Applications*, Springer, New York-London, 2009. (Cited on 118.)

[478] I. Karatzas and S. E. Shreve, *Brownian Motion and Stochastic Calculus*, 2nd edition, Graduate Texts in Mathematics, Springer-Verlag, New York, 1991. (Cited on 327.)

[479] Y. Katznelson, *An Introduction to Harmonic Analysis*, 3rd edition, Cambridge Mathematical Library, Cambridge University Press, Cambridge, 2004. (Cited on 149, 153.)

[480] A. S. Kechris, *Classical Descriptive Set Theory*, Graduate Texts in Mathematics, Springer-Verlag, New York, 1995. (Cited on 313.)

[481] J. L. Kelley, *Convergence in topology*, Duke Math. J. **17** (1950), 277–283. (Cited on 98, 102.)

[482] J. L. Kelley, *The Tychonoff product theorem implies the axiom of choice*, Fund. Math. **37** (1950), 75-76. (Cited on 102.)

[483] J. L. Kelley, *Note on a theorem of Krein and Milman*, J. Osaka Inst. Sci. Tech. Part I, **3** (1951), 1–2. (Cited on 464.)

[484] J. L. Kelley, *General Topology*, reprint of the 1955 edition, Graduate Texts in Mathematics, Springer-Verlag, New York-Berlin, 1975. (Cited on 48, 106, 367.)

[485] J. G. Kemeny and J. L. Snell, *Finite Markov Chains*, Van Nostrand, Princeton, NJ, 1960. (Cited on 674.)

[486] A. Khinchin, *Über einen Satz der Wahrscheinlichkeitsrechnung*, Fund. Math. **6** (1924), 9–20. (Cited on 645.)

[487] A. Khinchin, *Sur la loi forte des grands nombres*, C. R. Acad. Sci. Paris **186** (1928), 285–287. (Cited on 645.)

[488] A. Khinchin, *Zur Theorie der unbegrenzt teilbaren Verteilungen*, Mat. Sb. (Moskva) (2) **44** (1937), 79–120. (Cited on 658.)

[489] D. Khoshnevisan, *Probability*, Graduate Studies in Mathematics, American Mathematical Society, Providence, RI, 2007. (Cited on 617.)

[490] G. R. Kirchhoff, *Vorlesungen über mathematischen Physik*, Ann. Physik **18** (1883). (Cited on 607.)

[491] W. A. Kirk and B. Sims, *Handbook of Metric Fixed Point Theory*, Kluwer Academic Publishers, Dordrecht, 2001. (Cited on 485.)

[492] A. Kiselev, Y. Last and B. Simon, *Modified Prüfer and EFGP transforms and the spectral analysis of one-dimensional Schrödinger operators*, Commun. Math. Phys. **194** (1998), 1–45. (Cited on 703.)

[493] V. L. Klee, *Some characterizations of reflexivity*, Revista Ci., Lima **52** (1950), 15–23. (Cited on 458.)

[494] V. L. Klee, *Convex sets in linear spaces*, Duke Math. J. **18** (1951), 443–466. (Cited on 458.)

[495] V. L. Klee, *Convex sets in linear spaces, II*, Duke Math. J. **18** (1951), 875–883. (Cited on 458.)

[496] V. L. Klee, *Convex sets in linear spaces, III*, Duke Math. J. **20** (1953), 105–111. (Cited on 458.)

[497] V. L. Klee, *Separation properties of convex cones*, Proc. Amer. Math. Soc. **6** (1955), 313–318. (Cited on 458.)

[498] V. L. Klee, *Strict separation of convex sets*, Proc. Amer. Math. Soc. **7** (1956), 735–737. (Cited on 458.)

[499] V. L. Klee, *Maximal separation theorems for convex sets*, Trans. Amer. Math. Soc. **134** (1968), 133–147. (Cited on 458.)

[500] B. Knaster and C. Kuratowski, *Sur les ensembles connexes*, Fund. Math. **2** (1921), 206–255. (Cited on 50, 408.)

[501] A. N. Kolmogorov, *Une série de Fourier–Lebesgue divergente partout*, C. R. Acad. Sci. Paris **183** (1926), 1327–1328. (Cited on 153.)

[502] A. N. Kolmogorov, *Über die Summen durch den Zufall bestimmter unabhängiger Grössen*, Math. Ann. **99** (1928), 309–319; Math. Ann. **102** (1929), 484–488. (Cited on 629.)

[503] A. N. Kolmogorov, *Ober das Gesetz des Iterierten Logarithmus*, Math. Ann. **101** (1929), 126–135. (Cited on 645.)

[504] A. N. Kolmogorov, *Sur la loi forte des grands nombres*, C. R. Acad. Sci. Paris **191** (1930), 910–912. (Cited on 629.)

[505] A. N. Kolmogorov, *Über die analytischen Methoden in der Wahrscheinlichkeitsrechnung*, Math. Ann. **104** (1931), 415–458. (Cited on 674.)

[506] A. N. Kolmogorov, *Sulla forma generale di un processo stocastico omogeneo*, Rend. Reale Acad. Lincei **15** (1932), 805–808, 866–869. (Cited on 658.)

[507] A. N. Kolmogorov, *Grundbegriffe der Wahrscheinlichkeitsrechnung*, Springer, Berlin, 1933; English translation, *Foundations of the Theory of Probability*, Chelsea Publishing Company, New York, 1950. (Cited on 298, 328, 627, 629, 645.)

[508] A. N. Kolmogorov, *Zur Normierbarkeit eines allgemeinen topologischen linearen Raumes*, Studia Math. **5** (1934), 29–33. (Cited on 364.)

[509] A. N. Kolmogorov, *Stationary sequences in Hilbert space*, Bull. Univ. Moscow **2** (1941), 40 pp. [Russian]. (Cited on 126.)

[510] H. König, *An explicit formula for fundamental solutions of linear partial differential equations with constant coefficients*, Proc. Amer. Math. Soc. **120** (1994) 1315–1318. (Cited on 608.)

[511] L. B. Koralov and Ya. G. Sinai *Theory of Probability and Random Processes*, 2nd edition, Universitext, Springer, Berlin, 2007. (Cited on 617.)

[512] T. W. Körner, *Fourier Analysis*, 2nd edition, Cambridge University Press, Cambridge, 1989. (Cited on 107, 149, 151, 355.)

[513] T. W. Körner, *Besicovitch via Baire*, Studia Math. **158** (2003), 65–78. (Cited on 409.)

[514] P. P. Korovkin, *On convergence of linear positive operators in the space of continuous functions*, Dokl. Akad. Nauk. SSSR (N.S.) **90** (1953), 961–964. (Cited on 83.)

[515] P. P. Korovkin, *Linear Operators and Approximation Theory*, Translated from the 1959 Russian edition, Russian Monographs and Texts on Advanced Mathematics and Physics, Vol. III, Gordon and Breach Publishers, Inc., New York; Hindustan Publishing Corp., Delhi. India, 1960. (Cited on 83.)

[516] V. A. Kotelnikov, *On the carrying capacity of the ether and wire in telecommunications*, Material for the First All-Union Conference on Questions of Communication, Izd. Red. Upr. Svyazi RKKA, Moscow, 1933. [Russian] (Cited on 567.)

[517] G. Köthe, *Über die Vollständigkeit einer Klasse lokalkonvexer Räume*, Math. Z. **52** (1950), 627–630. (Cited on 711.)

[518] G. Köthe, *Topological Vector Spaces, I*, Die Grundlehren der mathematischen Wissenschaften, Springer-Verlag, New York, 1969. (Cited on 443, 706.)

[519] G. Köthe, *Topological Vector Spaces, II*, Die Grundlehren der Mathematischen Wissenschaften, Springer-Verlag, New York–Berlin, 1979. (Cited on 443.)

[520] S. G. Krantz and H. R. Parks, *The Implicit Function Theorem. History, Theory, and Applications*, Birkhäuser Boston, Boston, MA, 2002. (Cited on 486.)

[521] S. G. Krantz and H. Parks, *Geometric Integration Theory*, Birkhäuser Boston, Boston, MA, 2008. (Cited on 700.)

[522] M. Krasnosel'skiĭ and Ya. Rutickiĭ, *Convex Functions and Orlicz Spaces*, P. Noordhoff, Groningen, 1961. (Cited on 388.)

[523] M. G. Krein, *On a problem of extrapolation of A. N. Kolmogorov*, Dokl. Akad. Nauk SSSR **46** (1945), 306–309. (Cited on 435.)

[524] M. G. Krein, *Hermitian positive kernels on homogeneous spaces, I, II*, Ukr. Mat. Zh. **1** (1949) 64–98; **2** (1950), 10–59 [Russian]; English translation in Eleven Papers on Analysis, pp. 69–108 and 109–164, American Mathematical Society Translations, Series 2, American Mathematical Society, Providence, RI, 1963. (Cited on 126.)

[525] M. G. Krein, *The ideas of P. L. Čebyšev and A. A. Markov in the theory of limiting values of integrals and their further development*, Uspehi Matem. Nauk (N.S.) **6** (1951), 3–120; English translation, American Mathematical Society Translations, Series 2, American Mathematical Society, Providence, RI, 1959. (Cited on 433.)

[526] M. Krein and S. Krein, *On an inner characteristic of the set of all continuous functions defined on a bicompact Hausdorff space*, C. R. (Doklady) Acad. Sci. URSS (N.S.) **27** (1940), 427–430. (Cited on 92.)

[527] M. Krein and V. Šmulian, *On regulary convex sets in the space conjugate to a Banach space*, Ann. Math. (2) **41** (1940), 556–583. (Cited on 465.)

[528] M. Krein and D. Milman, *On extreme points of regularly convex sets*, Studia Math. **9** (1940), 133–138. (Cited on 464.)

[529] L. Kronecker, *Über Systeme von Funktionen mehrerer Variabeln*, Monatsber. Berlin Akad. (1869), 159–193; 688–698. (Cited on 487.)

[530] C. S. Kubrusly, *Measure Theory. A First Course*, Elsevier/Academic Press, Amsterdam, 2007. (Cited on 230.)

[531] K. Kunen, *Set Theory*, Studies in Logic (London), College Publications, London, 2011. (Cited on 14.)

[532] R. A. Kunze, L^p *Fourier transforms on locally compact unimodular groups*, Trans. Amer. Math. Soc. **89** (1958), 519–540. (Cited on 563.)

[533] R. A. Kunze and E. M. Stein, *Uniformly bounded representations and harmonic analysis of the 2×2 real unimodular group*, Amer. J. Math. **82** (1960), 1–62. (Cited on 563.)

[534] K. Kuratowski, *Une méthode d'élimination des nombres transfinis des raisonnements mathématiques*, Fund. Math. **3** (1922), 76–108. (Cited on 13.)

[535] K. Kuratowski, *La propriété de Baire dans les espaces métriques*, Fund. Math. **16** (1930), 390–394. (Cited on 407.)

[536] K. Kuratowski, *Wstęp do teorii mnogości i topologii*, [Introduction to the theory of sets and topology], second improved edition, Państwowe Wydawnictwo Naukowe (PWN), Warsaw, 1962. (Cited on 48.)

[537] K. Kuratowski and W. Sierpinski, *Le théorème de Borel–Lebesgue dans la théorie des ensembles abstraits*, Fund. Math. **2** (1921), 172–178. (Cited on 60.)

[538] J. Kurzweil, *Generalized ordinary differential equations and continuous dependence on a parameter*, Czech. Math. J. **7 (82)** (1957) 418–449. [Russian] (Cited on 230.)

[539] J. L. Lagrange, *Recherches sur la méthode de maximis et minimis*, Miscellanea Taurinensia **1** (1759), 18–42. (Cited on 26.)

[540] J. L. Lagrange, *Nouvelle méthode pour résoudre les équations littérales par le moyen des séries*, Mémoires de l'Académie Royale des Sciences et Belles-Lettres de Berlin **24** (1770), 251–326. (Cited on 486.)

[541] K. W. Lamson, *A general implicit function theorem with an application to problems of relative minima*, Amer. J. Math. **42** (1920), 243–256. (Cited on 364.)

[542] E. Landau, *Über die Approximation einer stetigen Funktion durch eine ganze rationale Funktion*, Rend. Circ. Mat. Palermo **25** (1908), 337–346. (Cited on 82, 162.)

[543] E. Landau, *Foundations of Analysis. The Arithmetic of Whole, Rational, Irrational and Complex Numbers*, Chelsea Publishing Company, New York, 1951; originally published by Akademische Verlag, Leipzig, 1930. (Cited on 9.)

[544] N. S. Landkof, *Foundations of Modern Potential Theory*, Springer-Verlag, Berlin-New York, 1972. (Cited on 453.)

[545] S. Lang, *Real and Functional Analysis*, 3rd edition, Graduate Texts in Mathematics, Springer-Verlag, New York, 1993. (Cited on 350, 351.)

[546] P.-S. Laplace, *Mémoire sur l'inclinaison moyenne des orbites des cométes, sur la figure de la terre et sur les fonctions*, Mémoires de l'Académie Royale des Sciences de Paris, 1773. (Cited on 654.)

[547] P.-S. Laplace, *Mémoire sur la probabilités*, Mémoires de l'Académie Royale des Sciences de Paris, 1781, 227–332. (Cited on 289, 292, 654.)

[548] P.-S. Laplace, *Mémoire sur la théorie de l'anneau de Saturne*, Mémoires de l'Académie Royale des Sciences de Paris, 1787/1789, 201–234. (Cited on 606.)

[549] P.-S. Laplace, *Mémoire sur les approximations des formules qui sont fonctions de très grands nombres et sur leur application aux probabilités*, Mémoires de l'Académie Royale des Sciences de Paris, 1809, 353–415. (Cited on 654.)

[550] P.-S. Laplace, *Théorie analytique des probabilités*, Courcier, Paris, 1st edition 1812, 2nd edition 1814, 3rd enlarged edition 1820. (Cited on 654.)

[551] Y. Last, *Quantum dynamics and decompositions of singular continuous spectra*, J. Funct. Anal. **142** (1996), 406–445. (Cited on 703.)

[552] G. F. Lawler, *Introduction to Stochastic Processes*, Chapman & Hall Probability Series, Chapman & Hall, New York, 1995. (Cited on 327.)

[553] P. D. Lax, *Functional Analysis*, Pure and Applied Mathematics (New York), Wiley-Interscience, New York, 2002. (Cited on 185, 186, 225.)

[554] S. R. Lay, *Convex Sets and Their Applications*, revised reprint of the 1982 original, Robert E. Krieger Publishing, Malabar, FL, 1992. (Cited on 387.)

[555] H. Lebesgue, *Sur l'approximation des fonctions*, Bull. Sci. Math. **22** (1898), 278–287. (Cited on 82.)

[556] H. Lebesgue, *Sur quelques surfaces non réglées applicables sur le plan*, C. R. Acad. Sci. Paris **128** (1899), 1502–1505. (Cited on 229.)

[557] H. Lebesgue, *Sur la définition de l'aire d'une surface*, C. R. Acad. Sci. Paris **129** (1899), 870–873. (Cited on 229.)

[558] H. Lebesgue, *Sur la définition de Certaines Integral de surface*, C. R. Acad. Sci. Paris **131** (1901), 867–870. (Cited on 229.)

[559] H. Lebesgue, *Sur le minimum de Certaines integral*, C. R. Acad. Sci. Paris **131** (1901), 935–937. (Cited on 229.)

[560] H. Lebesgue, *Sur une généralisation de l'intégrale définie*, C. R. Acad. Sci. Paris **132** (1901), 1025–1028. (Cited on 229, 249.)

[561] H. Lebesgue, *Intégrale, longueur, aire*, Ann. di Mat. Pura Appl. (3) **7** (1902), 231–359; sep. Thése, Milan: Rebeschini. 129 S. 4°. (Cited on 229.)

[562] H. Lebesgue, *Leçons sur l'Intégration et la Recherche des Fonctions Primitives*, Gauthier–Villars, Paris, 1904. Aavailable online at `http://www.archive.org/details/LeconsSurLintegration`. (Cited on 204, 229, 249, 257, 318.)

[563] H. Lebesgue, *Sur la méthode de M. Goursat pour la résolution de l'équation de Fredholm*, Bull. Soc. Math. France **36** (1908), 3–19. (Cited on 249.)

[564] H. Lebesgue, *Sur l'intégration des fonctions discontinues*, Ann. Sci. École Norm. Sup. (3) **27** (1910), 361–450. (Cited on 249.)

[565] H. Lebesgue, *Sur la non-applicabilité de deux domaines appartenant à des espaces à et dimensions*, Math. Ann. **70** (1911), 166–168. (Cited on 701.)

[566] L. Le Cam, *The central limit theorem around 1935*, Statist. Sci. **1** (1986), 78–96. (Cited on 654, 657.)

[567] N. J. Lennes, *Curves in non-metrical analysis situs*, Bull. Amer. Math. Soc. **12** (1905–06), 284. (Cited on 50.)

[568] N. J. Lennes, *Curves in non-metrical analysis situs with applications in the calculus of variations*, Amer. J. Math. **33** (1911), 287–326. (Cited on 50.)

[569] D. Lenz and P. Stollmann, *Generic sets in spaces of measures and generic singular continuous spectrum for Delone Hamiltonians*, Duke Math. J. **131** (2006), 203–217. (Cited on 411.)

[570] J. Leray, *Topologie des espaces abstraits de M. Banach*, C. R. Acad. Sci. Paris **200** (1935), 1082–1084. (Cited on 487.)

[571] J. Leray, *Les problemes non lineaires*, Enseign. Math. **35** (1936), 139–151. (Cited on 487.)

[572] J. Leray and J. Schauder, *Topologie et équations fonctionnelles*, Ann. Sci. École Norm. Sup. (3) **51** (1934), 45–78. (Cited on 487.)

[573] M. Lerch, *About the main theorem of the theory of generating functions*, Rozpravy Ceske Akademie **I** (1892), 681–685. [Czech] (Cited on 82.)

[574] B. Levi, *Sopra l'integrazione delle serie*, Ist. Lombardo Accad. Sci. Lett. Rend. (2) **39** (1906), 775–780. (Cited on 249.)

[575] P. Lévy, *Sur la rôle de la loi de Gauss dans la théorie des erreurs*, C. R. Acad. Sci. Paris **174** (1922), 855-857. (Cited on 657.)

[576] P. Lévy, *Sur la détermination des lois de probabilité par leurs fonctions charactéristiques*, C. R. Acad. Sci. Paris **175** (1922), 854–856. (Cited on 655.)

[577] P. Lévy, *Théorie des erreurs. La loi de Gauss et les lois exceptionelles*, Bull. Soc. Math. France **52** (1924), 49–85. (Cited on 656.)

[578] P. Lévy, *Calcul des probabilités*, Gauthier–Villars, Paris, 1925. (Cited on 655, 657.)

[579] P. Lévy, *Propriétés asymptotiques des sommes de variables aléatoires indépendantes ou enchaînées*, J. Math. Pures Appl. (9) **14** (1935), 347–402. (Cited on 657.)

[580] P. Lévy, *Détermination générale des lois limites*, C. R. Acad. Sci. Paris **202** (1936), 2027–2029. (Cited on 658.)

[581] P. Lévy, *Théorie de l'addition des variables aléatoires*, Gauthier–Villars, Paris, 1937. (Cited on 657, 659.)

[582] P. Lévy, *Processus Stochastiques et Mouvement Brownien. Suivi d'une note de M. Loève*, Gauthier–Villars, Paris, 1948. (Cited on 327.)

[583] H. Lewy, *An example of a smooth linear partial differential equation without solution*, Ann. Math. **66** (1957), 155–158. (Cited on 608.)

[584] M. Liao, *Lévy Processes in Lie Groups*, Cambridge University Press, Cambridge, 2004. (Cited on 659.)

[585] E. H. Lieb, *Thomas–Fermi and related theories of atoms and molecules*, Rev. Modern Phys. **53** (1981), 603–641. (Cited on 454.)

[586] E. H. Lieb, *Gaussian kernels have only Gaussian maximizers*, Invent. Math. **102** (1990), 179–208. (Cited on 563.)

[587] E. H. Lieb and M. Loss, *Analysis*, Graduate Studies in Mathematics, American Mathematical Society, Providence, RI, 1997. (Cited on 275, 451.)

[588] E. H. Lieb and B. Simon, *The Thomas–Fermi theory of atoms, molecules and solids*, Adv. in Math. **23** (1977), 22–116. (Cited on 454.)

[589] T. M. Liggett, *Continuous Time Markov Processes. An Introduction*, Graduate Studies in Mathematics, American Mathematical Society, Providence, RI, 2010. (Cited on 327.)

[590] F. Lin and X. Yang, *Geometric Measure Theory—An Introduction*, Advanced Mathematics (Beijing/Boston), Science Press Beijing, Beijing; International Press, Boston, MA, 2002. (Cited on 700.)

[591] J. W. Lindeberg, *Eine neue Herleitung des Exponentialgesetzes in der Wahrscheinlichkeitsrechnung*, Math. Z. **15** (1922), 211–225. (Cited on 656.)

[592] E. Lindelöf, *Sur l'application de la méthode des approximations successives aux équations différentielles ordinaires du premier ordre*, C. R. Acad. Sci. Paris **114** (1894), 454–457. (Cited on 485.)

[593] E. Lindelöf, *Sur quelques points de la théorie des ensembles*, C. R. Acad. Sci. Paris **137** (1904), 697–700. (Cited on 60.)

[594] J. Lindenstrauss and L. Tzafriri, *Classical Banach spaces, I. Sequence spaces*, Ergebnisse der Mathematik und ihrer Grenzgebiete, Springer-Verlag, Berlin-New York, 1977. (Cited on 444.)

[595] J. Lindenstrauss and L. Tzafriri, *Classical Banach spaces, II. Function spaces*, Ergebnisse der Mathematik und ihrer Grenzgebiete, Springer-Verlag, Berlin-New York, 1979. (Cited on 444.)

[596] J. E. Littlewood, *The converse of Abel's theorem on power series*, Proc. London Math. Soc. (2) **9** (1911), 434–448. (Cited on 154.)

[597] J. E. Littlewood, *Lectures on the Theory of Functions*, Oxford University Press, Oxford, 1944. (Cited on 249.)

[598] M. Loève, *Probability Theory*, 3rd edition, Van Nostrand, Princeton, NJ-Toronto-London, 1963. (Cited on 617.)

[599] M. Loève, *Paul Lévy, 1886–1971*, Ann. Probab. **1** (1971), 1–18. (Cited on 655, 659.)

[600] S. Łojasiewicz, *Sur le problème de la division*, Studia Math. **18** (1959) 87–136. (Cited on 608.)

[601] V. I. Lomonosov, *Invariant subspaces of the family of operators that commute with a completely continuous operator*, [Russian], Funkcional. Anal. i Priložen. **7** (1973), 55–56. (Cited on 488.)

[602] L. H. Loomis, *An Introduction to Abstract Harmonic Analysis*, Van Nostrand, Toronto-New York-London, 1953. (Cited on 350, 565.)

[603] E. R. Lorch, *On a calculus of operators in reflexive vector spaces*, Trans. Amer. Math. Soc. **45** (1939), 217–234. (Cited on 425.)

[604] G. G. Lorentz, *A contribution to the theory of divergent sequences*, Acta Math. **80** (1948), 167–190. (Cited on 490.)

[605] G. G. Lorentz, *Approximation of Functions*, Second edition, Chelsea Publishing Co., New York, 1986; First edition Holt, Rinehart and Winston, New York 1966. (Cited on 83.)

[606] G. G. Lorentz, *Mathematics and politics in the Soviet Union from 1928 to 1953*, J. Approx. Theory **116** (2002), 169–223. (Cited on 227.)

[607] H. Löwig, *Komplexe Euklidische Räume von beliebiger endlicher oder transfiniter Dimensionszahl*, Acta Litterarum ac Scientiarum **7** (1934–1935), 1–33. (Cited on 117, 425.)

[608] Lucretius, *De Rerum Natura* [On the Nature of Things], English translation at `http://classics.mit.edu/Carus/nature_things.html`. (Cited on 326.)

[609] J. Lützen, *The Prehistory of the Theory of Distributions*, Studies in the History of Mathematics and Physical Sciences, Springer-Verlag, New York-Berlin, 1982. (Cited on 513.)

[610] N. Lusin, *Sur les propriétés des fonctions mesurables*, C. R. Acad. Sci. Paris **154** (1912), 1688–1690. (Cited on 226.)

[611] W. A. J. Luxemburg, *Banach Function Spaces*, Thesis, Technische Hogeschool te Delft, 1955. (Cited on 388.)

[612] W. A. J. Luxemburg, *Arzelà's dominated convergence theorem for the Riemann integral*, Amer. Math. Monthly **78** (1971), 970–979. (Cited on 229.)

[613] W. A. J. Luxemburg, *Some Aspects of the Theory of Riesz Spaces*, University of Arkansas Lecture Notes in Mathematics, University of Arkansas, Fayetteville, AR, 1979. (Cited on 269.)

[614] W. A. J. Luxemburg and A. C. Zaanen, *Riesz Spaces. Vol. I*, North–Holland, Amsterdam-London; American Elsevier, New York, 1971. (Cited on 269.)

[615] A. M. Lyapunov, *Sur une proposition de la théorie des probabilités*, Bull. Acad. Impériale des Sciences de St.-Pétersbourg (5) **13** (1900), 359–386; English translation in [**2**, pp. 151–171]. (Cited on 655.)

[616] A. M. Lyapunov, *Nouvelle forme du théorème sur la limite de probabilité*, Mémoires Acad. Impériale des Sciences de St.-Pétersbourg (8) **12**, 1–24; English translation in [**2**, pp. 175-191]. (Cited on 655.)

[617] R. Lyons, *Fourier–Stieltjes coefficients and asymptotic distribution modulo 1*, Ann. Math. **122** (1985), 155–170. (Cited on 582.)

[618] R. Lyons, *Seventy years of Rajchman measures*, J. Fourier Anal. Appl. (1995), Special Issue, 363–377. (Cited on 582.)

[619] G. W. Mackey, *On infinite-dimensional linear spaces*, Trans. Amer. Math. Soc. **57** (1945), 155–207. (Cited on 443.)

[620] G. W. Mackey, *On convex topological linear spaces*, Trans. Amer. Math. Soc. **60** (1946), 519–537. (Cited on 443.)

[621] S. Mac Lane, *Jobs in the 1930s and the views of George D. Birkhoff*, Math. Intelligencer **16** (1994), 9–10. (Cited on 562.)

[622] B. Malgrange, *Existence et approximation des solutions des équations aux dérivées partielles et des ééquations de convolution*, Ann. Inst. Fourier **6** (1955/56), 271–355. (Cited on 607.)

[623] L. Maligranda, *Why Hölder's inequality should be called Rogers' inequality*, Math. Inequal. Appl. **1** (1998), 69–83. (Cited on 372, 388.)

[624] P. Malliavin, *Integration and Probability*, Graduate Texts in Mathematics, Springer-Verlag, New York, 1995. (Cited on 230.)

[625] B. B. Mandelbrot, *The Fractal Geometry of Nature*, W. H. Freeman and Co., San Francisco, Calif., 1982. (Cited on 700.)

[626] B. B. Mandelbrot and R. L. Hudson, *The (Mis)behavior of Markets. A fractal view of risk, ruin, and reward*, Basic Books, New York, 2004. (Cited on 679.)

[627] M. Mandelkern, *A short proof of the Tietze–Urysohn extension theorem*, Arch. Math. (Basel) **60** (1993), 364–366. (Cited on 62.)

[628] J. H. Manheim, *The Genesis of Point Set Topology*, Pergamon Press, Oxford-Paris-Frankfurt; The Macmillan Co., New York, 1964. (Cited on 35.)

[629] R. Mansuy and M. Yor, *Aspects of Brownian Motion*, Universitext, Springer-Verlag, Berlin, 2008. (Cited on 327.)

[630] A. Markov, *Sur les racines de l'équation $e^{x^2} \frac{d^m e^{-x^2}}{dx^m} = 0$*, Bull. Acad. Impériale des Sciences de St.-Pétersbourg (5) **9** (1898), 435–446. (Cited on 655.)

[631] A. Markov, *Extension of the law of large numbers to dependent quantities*, Izvestiia Fiz.-Matem. Obsch. Kazan Univ., (2nd Ser.) **15** (1906), 135–156 [Russian]. English translation: *The extension of the law of large numbers onto quantities depending on each other*, in Probability and Statistics. Russian Papers (O. B. Sheynin, ed.), pp. 143–158, NG Verlag, Berlin, 2004. (Cited on 674.)

[632] A. Markov, *Ischislenie Veroiatnostei (Calculus of Probability)*, St. Petersburg. Subsequent editions: 1908, 1913; posthumous: Gosizdat, Moscow, 1924. (Cited on 227.)

[633] A. Markov, *Wahrscheinlichkeitsrechnung*, translation of the 2nd Russian edition, Teubner, Leipzig, 1912. (Cited on 655.)

[634] A. Markov, *Quelques théorèmes sur les ensembles abéliens*, C. R. Acad. Sci. URSS **1** (1936), 311–313. (Cited on 486.)

[635] A. Markov, *On mean values and exterior densities*, Mat. Sbornik **4 (46)** (1938), 165–191. (Cited on 238.)

[636] A. S. Markus, *Characteristic numbers and singular numbers of the sum and product of linear operators*, Soviet Math. Dokl. **3** (1962), 104–108; Russian original in Dokl. Akad. Nauk SSSR **146** (1962), 34–36. (Cited on 394.)

[637] R. J. Marks II, *Introduction to Shannon Sampling and Interpolation Theory*, Springer Texts in Electrical Engineering, Springer-Verlag, New York, 1991. (Cited on 568.)

[638] A. W. Marshall and I. Olkin, *Inequalities: Theory of Majorization and Its Applications*, Mathematics in Science and Engineering, Academic Press, New York-London, 1979. (Cited on 394.)

[639] A. Martínez-Finkelshtein, *Equilibrium problems of potential theory in the complex plane*, in Orthogonal Polynomials and Special Functions, pp. 79–117, Lecture Notes in Mathematics, Springer, Berlin, 2006. (Cited on 453.)

[640] P. Mattila, *Geometry of Sets and Measures in Euclidean Spaces, Fractals and Rectifiability*, Cambridge Studies in Advanced Mathematics, Cambridge University Press, Cambridge, 1995. (Cited on 700.)

[641] R. M. Mazo, *Brownian Motion. Fluctuations, Dynamics, and Applications*, International Series of Monographs on Physics, Oxford University Press, New York, 2002. (Cited on 327.)

[642] S. Mazur, *Über konvexe Mengen in linearen normierten Räumen*, Studia Math. **4** (1933), 70–84. (Cited on 388, 458.)

[643] S. Mazur and W. Orlicz, *Sur les espaces métriques linéaires, I*, Studia Math. **10** (1948), 184–208. (Cited on 501.)

[644] S. Mazurkiewicz, *Sur les lignes de Jordan*, Fund. Math. **1** (1920), 166–209. (Note: this paper references earlier Polish language papers on the subject) (Cited on 205.)

[645] J. McCarthy, *An everywhere continuous nowhere differentiable function*, Amer. Math. Monthly **60**, (1953), 709. (Cited on 165.)

[646] H. P. McKean, Jr., *Stochastic Integrals*, Probability and Mathematical Statistics, Academic Press, New York-London, 1969. (Cited on 327.)

[647] F. A. Medvedev, *Scenes from the History of Real Functions*, Science Networks, Historical Studies, Birkhäuser Verlag, Basel, 1991. (Cited on 155.)

[648] R. E. Megginson, *An Introduction to Banach Space Theory*, Graduate Texts in Mathematics, Springer-Verlag, New York, 1998. (Cited on 408, 444.)

[649] H. Mehrtens, *Die Entstehung der Verbandstheorie*, Arbor Scientiarum: Contributions to the History of Science, Series A: Proceedings, VI. Gerstenberg Verlag, Hildesheim, 1979. (Cited on 269.)

[650] K. Menger, *Dimensionstheorie*, B. G Teubner Publishers, Leipzig, 1928. (Cited on 701.)

[651] C. Meray, *Nouveau précis d'analyse infinitésimale*, F. Savy, Paris, 1872; available online at `http://gallica.bnf.fr/ark:/12148/bpt6k995638`. (Cited on 9.)

[652] P. Meyer-Nieberg, *Banach Lattices*, Universitext, Springer-Verlag, Berlin, 1991. (Cited on 269.)

[653] H. N. Mhaskar and D. V. Pai, *Fundamentals of Approximation Theory*, CRC Press, Boca Raton, FL; Narosa Publishing House, New Delhi, India, 2000. (Cited on 83, 84.)

[654] A. D. Michal and M. Wyman, *Characterization of complex couple spaces*, Ann. Math. (2) **42** (1941), 247–250. (Cited on 365.)

[655] V. P. Mikhailov, *Partial Differential Equations*, Mir Publishers, Moscow, 1978. (Cited on 606.)

[656] D. P. Milman, *On some criteria for the regularity of spaces of type (B)*, C. R. (Doklady) Acad. Sci. URSS **20** (1938), 243–246. (Cited on 444.)

[657] J. Milnor, *Analytic proofs of the "hairy ball theorem" and the Brouwer fixed-point theorem*, Amer. Math. Monthly **85** (1978), 521–524. (Cited on 487.)

[658] H. Minkowski, *Geometrie der Zahlen*, Teubner, Leipzig, 1896. 1910 version available online at `http://www.archive.org/details/geometriederzahl00minkrich` or `http://gallica.bnf.fr/ark:/12148/bpt6k99643x`. (Cited on 371, 574.)

[659] H. Minkowski, *Theorie der Konvexen Körper, Insbesondere Begründung ihres Oberflächenbegriffs*, Gessamelte Abhandlungen II, Leipzig, 1911. (Cited on 371, 387, 464.)

[660] R. A. Minlos, *Generalized random processes and their extension to measures*, Trudy. Moskov. Mat. Obsc. **8** (1959), 497–518. (Cited on 565.)

[661] L. Mišik, Jr.and T. Žáčik, *A formula for calculation of metric dimension of converging sequences*, Comment. Math. Univ. Carolin. **40** (1999), 393–401. (Cited on 702.)

[662] S. Mizohata, *Solutions nulles et solutions non analytiques*, J. Math. Kyoto Univ. **2** (1962) 271–302. (Cited on 608.)

[663] E. H. Moore and H. L. Smith, *A general theory of limits*, Amer. J. Math. **44** (1922), 102–121. (Cited on 98.)

[664] G. H. Moore, *The emergence of open sets, closed sets, and limit points in analysis and topology*, Hist. Math. **35** (2008), 220–241. (Cited on 48.)

[665] R. L. Moore, *Concerning upper semi-continuous collections of continua which do not separate a given continuum*, Proc. Nat. Acad. USA **10** (1924), 356–360. (Cited on 106.)

[666] F. Morgan, *Geometric Measure Theory, A Beginner's Guide*, Fourth edition, Elsevier/Academic Press, Amsterdam, 2009. (Cited on 700.)

[667] P. Mörters and Y. Peres, *Brownian Motion*, Cambridge Series in Statistical and Probabilistic Mathematics, Cambridge University Press, Cambridge, 2010. (Cited on 327, 328.)

[668] Y. N. Moschovakis, *Descriptive Set Theory*, Second edition, Mathematical Surveys and Monographs, American Mathematical Society, Providence, RI, 2009. (Cited on 14.)

[669] R. F. Muirhead, *Some methods applicable to identities and inequalities of symmetric algebraic functions of n letters*, Proc. Edinburgh Math. Soc. **21** (1902), 144–162. (Cited on 394.)

[670] J. R. Munkres, *Topology: A First Course*, Prentice-Hall, Inc., Englewood Cliffs, N.J., 1975. (Cited on 61.)

[671] F. J. Murray, *Linear transformations in $\mathfrak{L}_p$, $p > 1$*, Trans. Amer. Math. Soc. **39** (1936), 83–100. (Cited on 425.)

[672] F. J. Murray and J. von Neumann *On rings of operators*, Ann. Math. (2) **37** (1936), 116–229. (Cited on 182.)

[673] D. H. Mushtari, *Probabilities and Topologies on Linear Spaces*, Kazan Tracts in Mathematics, Kazan Mathematics Foundation, Kazan, 1996. (Cited on 313.)

[674] J. Mycielski, *A system of axioms of set theory for the rationalists*, Notices Amer. Math. Soc. **53** (2006), 206–213. (Cited on 12.)

[675] L. Nachbin, *The Haar integral*, Van Nostrand, Princeton, NJ-Toronto-London, 1965. (Cited on 350.)

[676] J. Nagata, *On a necessary and sufficient condition of metrizability*, J. Inst. Polytech. Osaka City Univ. Ser. A. Math. **1**, (1950), 93–100. (Cited on 61.)

[677] L. Narici and E. Beckenstein, *Topological Vector Spaces*, 2nd edition, Pure and Applied Mathematics, CRC Press, Boca Raton, FL, 2011. (Cited on 443, 706.)

[678] P. A. Nekrasov, *The Philosophy and Logic of the Science of Mass Phenomena in Human Activity*, Moscow, 1902 [Russian]. (Cited on 674.)

[679] E. Nelson, *Regular probability measures on function space*, Ann. Math. (2) **69** (1959), 630–643. (Cited on 327.)

[680] E. Nelson, *Construction of quantum fields from Markoff fields*, J. Funct. Anal. **12** (1973), 97–112. (Cited on 329.)

[681] E. Nelson, *The free Markoff field*, J. Funct. Anal. **12** (1973), 211–227. (Cited on 329.)

[682] Y. A. Neretin, *Lectures on Gaussian Integral Operators and Classical Groups*, EMS Series of Lectures in Mathematics, European Mathematical Society, Zürich, 2011. (Cited on 538.)

[683] I. Newton, *De Analysi per Æquations Numero Terminorum Infinitas*, written in 1669, published in 1711 by William Jones. (Cited on 486.)

[684] R. Nevanlinna, *Asymptotische Entwickelungen beschrankter Funktionen und das Stiettjessche Momentenproblem*, Ann. Acad. Sci. Fenn. A **18**, (1922), 52 pp. (Cited on 433.)

[685] O. Nikodym, *Sur une généralisation des intégrales de M. J. Radon*, Fund. Math. **15** (1930), 131–179. (Cited on 257.)

[686] J. R. Norris, *Markov chains*, reprint of 1997 original, Cambridge Series in Statistical and Probabilistic Mathematics, Cambridge University Press, Cambridge, 1998. (Cited on 674.)

[687] H. Nyquist, *Certain topics in telegraph transmission theory*, Trans. AIEE **47** (1928), 617–644. (Cited on 567.)

[688] F. Oberhettinger, *Tables of Fourier Transforms and Fourier Transforms of Distributions*, Springer-Verlag, Berlin, 1990. (Cited on 630.)

[689] K. Ogura, *On a certain transcendental integral function in the theory of interpolation*, Tôhoku Math. J. **17** (1920), 64–72. (Cited on 569.)

[690] W. Orlicz, *Über Räume L^M*, Bull. intern. de l'Acad. Pol., série A, Cracow (1936). (Cited on 388.)

[691] N. Ortner and P. Wagner, *A short proof of the Malgrange-Ehrenpreis theorem*, in Functional analysis, Proc. 1st International Workshop (Trier, 1994), pp. 343–352, de Gruyter, Berlin, 1996. (Cited on 608.)

[692] N. Ortner and P. Wagner, *A survey on explicit representation formulae for fundamental solutions of linear partial differential operators*, Acta Appl. Math. **47** (1997) 101–124. (Cited on 608.)

[693] M. S. Osborne, *Locally Convex Spaces*, Graduate Texts in Mathematics, Springer, Berlin, 2014. (Cited on 443.)

[694] W. F. Osgood, *Non-uniform convergence and the integration of series term by term*, Amer. J. Math. **19** (1897), 155–190. (Cited on 229, 407.)

[695] E. Outerelo and J. M. Ruiz, *Mapping Degree Theory*, Graduate Studies in Mathematics, American Mathematical Society, Providence, RI; Real Sociedad Matemática Española, Madrid, 2009. (Cited on 487.)

[696] J. C. Oxtoby, *Measure and Category. A Survey of the Analogies Between Topological and Measure Spaces*, 2nd edition, Graduate Texts in Mathematics, Springer-Verlag, New York-Berlin, 1980. (Cited on 408.)

[697] J. Pál, *Zwei kleine Bemerkungen*, Tohoku Math. J. **6** (1914), 42–43. (Cited on 84.)

[698] R. E. A. C. Paley, N. Wiener, and A. Zygmund, *Notes on random functions*, Math. Z. **37** (1933), 647–668. (Cited on 328.)

[699] V. Pareto, *Cours d'Economie Politique*, Rouge, Lausanne, 1897. (Cited on 658.)

[700] M.-A. Parseval des Chênes, *Mémoire sur les séries et sur l'intégration complète d'une équation aux différences partielles linéaire du second ordre, à coefficients constants*, presented before the Académie des Sciences (Paris) on 5 April 1799. This article was published in Mémoires présentés à l'Institut des Sciences, Lettres et Arts, par divers savants, et lus dans ses assemblées. Sciences, mathématiques et physiques. (Savants étrangers.) **1** (1806), 638–648. (Cited on 150.)

[701] M.-A. Parseval, a chapter in *Traité des Différences et des Séries: Faisant Suite Au Traité du Calcul Différentiel et du Calcul Intégral* by Silvestre Francois Lacroix, 1800. (Cited on 607.)

[702] E. Parzen, *Time Series Analysis Papers*, Holden–Day, San Francisco, CA-London-Amsterdam, 1967. (Cited on 126.)

[703] E. Parzen, *Statistical inference on time series by RKHS methods*, in 1970 Proc. 12th Biennial Sem. Canad. Math. Congr. on Time Series and Stochastic Processes: Convexity and Combinatorics (Vancouver, BC, 1969), pp. 1–37, Canad. Math. Congr., Montreal. (Cited on 126.)

[704] G. Peano, *Sull'integrabilità delle equazioni differenziali del primo ordine*, Atti Accad. Sci. Torino **21** (1886), 437–445. (Cited on 485.)

[705] G. Peano, *Calcolo geometrico secondo l'Ausdehnungslehre di H. Grassmann preceduto dalle operazioni della logica deduttiva*, 1888 [English translation: *Geometric Calculus: According to the Ausdehnungslehre of H. Grassmann*, Birkhäuser, Boston, 1999]. (Cited on 26.)

[706] G. Peano, *Arithmetices principia, nova methodo exposita*, (The principles of arithmetic, presented by a new method), Bocca, Torino, 1889. (Cited on 9.)

[707] G. Peano, *Demonstration de l'intégrabilité des équations différentielles ordinaires*, Math. Ann. **37** (1890), 182–228. (Cited on 485.)

[708] C. Pearcy and A. L. Shields, *A survey of the Lomonosov technique in the theory of invariant subspaces*, in Topics in Operator Theory, Math. Surveys, No. 13, pp. 219–229, American Mathematical Society, Providence, RI, 1974 (Cited on 488.)

[709] J. E. Pečarić, F. Proschan, and Y. L. Tong, *Convex Functions, Partial Orderings, and Statistical Applications*, Mathematics in Science and Engineering, Academic Press, Boston, 1992. (Cited on 387.)

[710] G. K. Pedersen, *The existence and uniqueness of the Haar integral on a locally compact topological group*, unpublished note, Nov. 2000. Available online at `www.math.ku.dk/kurser/2004-2/mat3re/haarintegral.ps`. (Cited on 350.)

[711] C. S. Peirce, *On the logic of number*, Amer. J. Math. **4** (1881), 85–95. (Cited on 9.)

[712] P. Pérez Carreras and J. Bonet, *Barrelled Locally Convex Spaces*, North-Holland Mathematics Studies, Notas de Matemática, North-Holland Publishing Co., Amsterdam, 1987. (Cited on 443.)

[713] O. Perron, *Zur Theorie der Matrices*, Math. Ann. **64** (1907), 248–263. (Cited on 675.)

[714] O. Perron, *Über den Integralbegriff*, Sitzungsber. der Heidelberger Akademie der Wissenschaften, Abtielung A. Abhandlung **16**, 1914. (Cited on 230.)

[715] B. J. Pettis, *On integration in vector spaces*, Trans. Amer. Math. Soc. **44** (1938), 277–304. (Cited on 341.)

[716] B. J. Pettis, *A proof that every uniformly convex space is reflexive*, Duke Math. J. **5** (1939), 249–253. (Cited on 444.)

[717] J. Peyrière, *Sur les produits de Riesz*, C. R. Acad. Sci. Paris Sér. A-B **276** (1973), A1417–A1419. (Cited on 582.)

[718] R. R. Phelps, *Extreme points in function algebras*, Duke Math. J. **32** (1965), 267–277. (Cited on 468.)

[719] R. R. Phelps, *Integral representations for elements of convex sets*, in Studies in Functional Analysis, pp. 115–157, MAA Stud. Math. **21**, Mathematical Association of America, Washington, DC, 1980. (Cited on 465.)

[720] R. R. Phelps, *Lectures on Choquet's Theorem*, 2nd edition, Lecture Notes in Mathathematics, Springer-Verlag, Berlin, 2001. (Cited on 387.)

[721] R. S. Phillips, *Integration in a convex linear topological space*, Trans. Amer. Math. Soc. **47** (1940), 114–145. (Cited on 443.)

[722] E. Picard, *Mémoire sure théorie des equations aux derives partielles et la méthode des approximations successives*, J. Math. Pures Appl. **5** (1890), 4232-441. (Cited on 485.)

[723] E. Picard, *Sur la représentation approchée des fonctions*, C. R. Heb. Séances Acad. Sci. Paris **112** (1891), 183–186. (Cited on 82, 161.)

[724] E. Picard, *Sur l'application des méthodes d'approximations successives à l'étude de certaines équations différentielles ordinaires*, J. Math. Anal. Appl. (4) **9** (1893), 217–271. (Cited on 485.)

[725] J.-P. Pier, *Amenable Locally Compact Groups*, Pure and Applied Mathematics (New York), John Wiley & Sons, New York, 1984. (Cited on 486.)

[726] A. Pietsch, *Nuclear Locally Convex Spaces*, Translated from the second German edition by William H. Ruckle, Ergebnisse der Mathematik und ihrer Grenzgebiete, Springer-Verlag, New York-Heidelberg, 1972. (Cited on 443.)

[727] A. Pietsch, *History of Banach Spaces and Linear Operators*, Birkhäuser Boston, Boston, MA, 2007. (Cited on 363, 447.)

[728] A. Pinkus, *Weierstrass and approximation theory*, J. Approx. Theory **107** (2000), 1–66. (Cited on 81, 83, 156.)

[729] A. Pinkus, *Density in approximation theory*, Surv. Approx. Theory **1** (2005), 1–45. (Cited on 83.)

[730] M. Plancherel, *Contribution à l'étude de la représentation d'une fonction arbitraire par des intégrales définies*, Rend. Circ. Mat. Palermo **30** (1910), 289–335. (Cited on 150, 546.)

[731] J. Plemelj, *Ein Ergänzungssatz zur Cauchyschen Integraldarstellung analytischer Funktionen, Randwerte betreffend*, Monatsch. für Math. u. Phys. **19** (1908), 205–210. (Cited on 512.)

[732] H. Poincaré, *Sur les courbes definies par les équations différentielles*, J. Math. Anal. Appl. **2** (1886), 151–217. (Cited on 486.)

[733] H. Poincaré, *La logique et l'intuition dans la science mathématique et dans l'enseignement*, 1889. (Cited on 355.)

[734] H. Poincaré, *Analysis Situs*, J. l'École Polytechnique ser. 2 **1** (1895), 1–123. (Cited on 486.)

[735] H. Poincaré, *The Value of Science*, Dover Publications, New York, 1958; French original *La valeur de la science*, Flammarion, Paris, 1905. (Cited on 705.)

[736] S. D. Poisson, *Remarques sur une équation qui se présente dans la théorie de l'attraction des sphéroïdes*, Bull. Soc. Philomathique de Paris **3** (1813) 388–392. (Cited on 606, 607.)

[737] S. D. Poisson, *Sur l'intégrale de l'équation relative aux vibrations des surfaces élastiques et au mouvement des ondes*, Bull. Soc. Philomathique de Paris (1818) 125–128. (Cited on 606, 607.)

[738] S. D. Poisson, *Memoire sur l' integration de quelques equations linéaires aux differ-ences partielles, et particulierement de l'équation generale du mouvement des fluides élastique*, Mémoires Acad. Sci. Inst. France Sci. **3** (1819) 121–176. (Cited on 606.)

[739] S. D. Poisson, *Suite du Memoire sur les integrals definies et sur la sommation des series*, J. l'Ecole Polytechnique **19** (1823), 404–509. (Cited on 289.)

[740] S. D. Poisson, *Sur la probabilité des résultats moyens des observations*, Connaissance des Tems pour l'an 1827 (1824), 273–302. (Cited on 630.)

[741] S. D. Poisson, *Mémoire sur le calcul numérique des intégrales définies*, Mémoires Acad. Sci. Inst. France **6** (1827), 571–602. (Cited on 567.)

[742] S. D. Poisson, *Mémoire sur la proportion des naissances des filles et des garcons*, Mémoires Acad. Sci. Inst. France **9** (1830), 239–308. (Cited on 666.)

[743] S. D. Poisson, *Recherches sur la Probabilité des Jugements, Principalement en Matiére Criminelle*, C. R. Acad. Sci. **1**, (1835) 473–494. (Cited on 644.)

[744] S. D. Poisson, *La loi de grands nombres*, C. R. Acad. Sci. **2**, (1836) 377–382. (Cited on 644.)

[745] S. D. Poisson, *Probabilité des jugements en matière criminelle et en matière civile, précédées des règles générales du calcul des probabilitiés*, Bachelier, Paris, 1837. (Cited on 666.)

[746] G. Pólya, *Über den zentralen Grenzwertsatz der Wahrscheinlichkeitsrechnung und das Momentenproblem*, Math. Z. **8** (1920), 171–181. (Cited on 654.)

[747] G. Pólya, *Herleitung des Gaußschen Fehlergesetzes aus einer Funktionalgleichung*, Math. Z. **18** (1923), 96–108. (Cited on 657.)

[748] S. C. Port and C. J. Stone, *Brownian Motion and Classical Potential Theory*, Probability and Mathematical Statistics, Academic Press, New York–London, 1978. (Cited on 608.)

[749] A. Povzner, *Über positive Funktionen auf einer Abelschen Gruppe*, Dokl. Akad. Nauk SSSR (N.S.) **28** (1940), 294–295. (Cited on 565.)

[750] H. A. Priestley, *Introduction to Integration*, Oxford Science Publications, The Clarendon Press, Oxford University Press, New York, 1997. (Cited on 230.)

[751] Yu. V. Prokhorov, *Convergence of random processes and limit theorems in probability theory*, Theory Probab. Appl. **1** (1956), 157–214; Russian original in Teor. Veroyatnost. i Primenen. **1** (1956), 177–238. (Cited on 313.)

[752] H. Rademacher, *Fourier analysis in Number Theory (lecture notes)*, Cornell Univ., Ithaca, New York, 1956. (Cited on 574.)

[753] J. Radon, *Theorie und Anwendungen der absolut additiven Mengenfunktionen*, Wien. Ber. **122** (1913), 1295–1438. (Cited on 229, 257.)

[754] J. Radon, *Über die Bestimmung von Funktionen durch ihre Integralwerte längs gewisser Mannigfaltigkeiten*, Reports on the Proceedings of the Royal Saxonian Academy of Sciences at Leipzig, mathematical and physical section **69**, pp. 262–277, Teubner, Leipzig, 1917. English translation: *On the determination of functions by their integral values along certain manifolds*, Conf. Proc. Lecture Notes Math. Phys., pp. 324–339, International Press, Cambridge, MA, 1994. (Cited on 548.)

[755] D. Raikov, *On the decomposition of Poisson laws*, C. R. (Doklady) Acad. Sci. URSS **14**, 9–11. (Cited on 666.)

[756] D. Raikov, *Positive definite functions on commutative groups with an invariant measure*, C. R. (Doklady) Acad. Sci. URSS (N.S.) **28** (1940), 296–300. (Cited on 565.)

[757] A. Rajchman, *Sur l'unicité du développement trigonométrique*, Fund. Math. **3** (1922), 287–302. (Cited on 582.)

[758] T. Ransford, *Potential Theory in the Complex Plane*, Cambridge University Press, New York, 1995. (Cited on 453.)

[759] M. M. Rao, *Measure Theory and Integration*, 2nd edition, Monographs and Textbooks in Pure and Applied Mathematics, Marcel Dekker, New York, 2004. (Cited on 230.)

[760] J. R. Ravetz, *Vibrating Strings and Arbitrary Functions*, in The Logic of Personal Knowledge, pp. 71–88, The Free Press, Glencoe, IL, 1961. (Cited on 150.)

[761] C. J. Read, *A solution to the invariant subspace problem on the space ℓ^1*, Bull. London Math. Soc. **17** (1985), 305–317. (Cited on 488.)

[762] C. J. Read, *A short proof concerning the invariant subspace problem*, J. London Math. Soc. (2) **34** (1986), 335–348. (Cited on 488.)

[763] M. Reed and B. Simon, *Methods of Modern Mathematical Physics, I: Functional Analysis*, Academic Press, New York, 1972. (Cited on 538.)

[764] M. Reed and B. Simon, *Methods of Modern Mathematical Physics, II. Fourier Analysis, Self-Adjointness*, Academic Press, New York, 1975. (Cited on 538, 566.)

[765] M. Reed and B. Simon, *Methods of Modern Mathematical Physics, IV: Analysis of Operators*, Academic Press, New York, 1977. (Cited on 675.)

[766] S. Reich and D. Shoikhet, *Nonlinear Semigroups, Fixed Points, and Geometry of Domains in Banach Spaces*, Imperial College Press, London, 2005. (Cited on 485.)

[767] F. Rellich, *Spektraltheorie in nichtseparabeln Räumen*, Math. Ann. **110** (1934), 342–356. (Cited on 122.)

[768] M. Renardy and R. C. Rogers, *An Introdiction to Partial Differential Equations*, Springer, New York, 2004. (Cited on 606.)

[769] D. Revuz, *Markov Chains*, Mathematical Library, North-Holland, Amsterdam-New York, 1984. (Cited on 674.)

[770] D. Revuz and M. Yor, *Continuous Martingales and Brownian Motion*, 3rd edition, Grundlehren der Mathematischen Wissenschaften, Springer-Verlag, Berlin, 1999. (Cited on 327.)

[771] I. Richards, *On the Fourier inversion theorem for R^1*, Proc. Amer. Math. Soc. **19** (1968), 145. (Cited on 518.)

[772] G. F. B. Riemann, *Über die Darstellbarkeit einer Function durch eine trigonometrische Reihe*, Habilitationsschrift, Universität Göttingen, 1854. Published posthumously in Abhandlungen der Königl. Gesellschaft der Wissenschaften zu Göttingen, **13**, 1867. Available online in German at http://www.maths.tcd.ie/pub/HistMath/People/Riemann/Trig/. (Cited on 193, 228.)

[773] G. F. B. Riemann, *Über die Fortpflanzung ebener Luftwellen von endlicher Schwingungsweite*, Abhandlungen der Königlichen Gesellschaft der Wissenschaften zu Göttingen **8** (1860) 43–65. (Cited on 607.)

[774] G. F. B. Riemann, *Über die Hypothesen, welche der Geometrie zu Grunde liegen*, written in 1854. Published posthumously in Abhandlungen der Königlichen Gesellschaft der Wissenschaften zu Göttingen **13** (1867). Available online in German and in translation at http://www.maths.tcd.ie/pub/HistMath/People/Riemann/Geom/. (Cited on 546.)

[775] F. Riesz, *Sur les systèmes orthogonaux de fonctions*, C. R. Acad. Sci. Paris **144** (1907), 615–619. (Cited on 153, 226.)

[776] F. Riesz, *Sur une espèce de géométrie analytique systèmes de fonctions of sommables*, C. R. Acad. Sci. Paris **144** (1907), 1409–1411. (Cited on 125.)

[777] F. Riesz, *Die Genesis des Raumbegriffes*, Math. naturw. Ber. Ung. **24** (1909), 309–353. (Cited on 6, 47, 50, 51.)

[778] F. Riesz, *Stetigkeit und abstrakte Mengenlehre*, Rom. 4. Math. Kongr. **2** (1909), 18–24. (Cited on 6, 47, 74.)

[779] F. Riesz, *Sur les opérations fonctionnelles linéaires*, C. R. Acad. Sci. Paris **149** (1910), 974–977. (Cited on 193, 229.)

[780] F. Riesz, *Untersuchungen über Systeme integrierbarer Funktionen*, Math. Ann. **69** (1910), 449–497. (Cited on 250, 275, 372, 447.)

[781] F. Riesz, *Sur certains systèmes singuliers d'équations intégrales*, Ann. Sci. Ecole Norm. Sup. (3) **28** (1911), 33–62. (Cited on 229, 238, 565.)

[782] F. Riesz, *Les systèmes d'équations à une infinité d'inconnues*, Gauthier–Villars, Paris, 1913. (Cited on 117, 371.)

[783] F. Riesz, *Über lineare Funktionalgleichungen*, Acta Math. **41** (1916), 71–98. (Cited on 364.)

[784] F. Riesz *Sur le théorème de M. Egoroff et sur les opérations fonctionnelles linéaires*, Acta Litt. ac Scient. Univ. Hung. **1** (1922), 18–26. (Cited on 249, 433.)

[785] F. Riesz, *Über die Randwerte einer analytischen Funktion*, Math. Z. **18** (1923), 87–95. (Cited on 581.)

[786] F. Riesz, *Sur la décomposition des opérations fonctionnelles linéaires*, Atti Congresso Bologna **3** (1930), 143–148. (Cited on 269.)

[787] F. Riesz, *Zur Theorie des Hilbertschen Raumes*, Acta Szeged **7** (1934), 34–38. (Cited on 122, 125.)

[788] F. Riesz, *Sur quelques notions fondamentales dans la théorie générale des opérations linéaires*, Ann. Math. (2) **41** (1940), 174–206. (Cited on 269.)

[789] M. Riesz, *Sur le problème des moments. I, II, III*, Ark. Mat. Astr. Fys. **16** (1922) no. 12, no. 19; **17** (1923), no. 16. (Cited on 424.)

[790] M. Riesz, *Sur les fonctions conjuguées*, Math. Z. **27** (1928), 218–244. (Cited on 153, 563.)

[791] M. Riesz, *Sur les maxima des formes bilinéaires et sur les fonctionelles linéaires*, Acta Math. **49** (1927), 465–497. (Cited on 563.)

[792] J. R. Ringrose, *A note on uniformly convex spaces*, J. London Math. Soc. **34** (1959), 92. (Cited on 444.)

[793] A. W. Roberts and D. E. Varberg, *Convex Functions*, Pure and Applied Mathematics, Academic Press, New York-London, 1973. (Cited on 387.)

[794] A. P. Robertson and W. Robertson, *Topological Vector Spaces*, reprint of the 2nd edition, Cambridge Tracts in Mathematics, Cambridge University Press, Cambridge-New York, 1980. (Cited on 706.)

[795] G. Robin, *Sur la distribution de l'électricité à la surface des conducteurs fermés des conducteurs ouverts*, Ann. Sci. Ecole Norm. Sup. (3) III. Supplément, (1886), 3–58. (Cited on 453.)

[796] R. T. Rockafellar, *Convex Analysis*, Princeton Mathematical Series, Princeton University Press, Princeton, NJ 1970; reprinted 1997. (Cited on 387.)

[797] G. Roepstorff, *Path Integral Approach to Quantum Physics. An Introduction*, Texts and Monographs in Physics, Springer-Verlag, Berlin, 1994. (Cited on 327.)

[798] C. A. Rogers, *A less strange version of Milnor's proof of Brouwer's fixed-point theorem*, Amer. Math. Monthly **87** (1980), 525–527. (Cited on 487.)

[799] C. A. Rogers, *Hausdorff Measures*, Reprint of the 1970 original, with a foreword by K. J. Falconer, Cambridge Mathematical Library, Cambridge University Press, Cambridge, 1998. (Cited on 700, 702.)

[800] C. A Rogers and S. J. Taylor, *The analysis of additive set functions in Euclidean space*, Acta Math. **101** (1959), 273–302. (Cited on 702.)

[801] C. A Rogers and S. J. Taylor, *Additive set functions in Euclidean space. II.*, Acta Math. **109** (1963), 207–240. (Cited on 702.)

[802] L. J. Rogers, *An extension of a certain theorem in inequalities*, Mess. (2) **17** (1887), 145–150. (Cited on 372.)

[803] J.-P. Rosay, *A very elementary proof of the Malgrange-Ehrenpreis theorem*, Amer. Math. Monthly **98** (1991), 518–523. (Cited on 607.)

[804] P. C. Rosenbloom, and D. V. Widder, *A temperature function which vanishes initially*, Amer. Math. Monthly **65** (1958), 607–609. (Cited on 608.)

[805] W. Rudin, *Fourier Analysis on Groups*, Interscience Tracts in Pure and Applied Mathematics, Interscience Publishers, New York-London, 1962. (Cited on 565.)

[806] V. Runde, *Lectures on Amenability*, Lecture Notes in Mathematics, Springer-Verlag, Berlin, 2002. (Cited on 486.)

[807] E. B. Saff and V. Totik, *Logarithmic Potentials With External Fields*, Grundlehren der Mathematischen Wissenschaften, Springer-Verlag, Berlin, 1997. (Cited on 453.)

[808] H. Sagan, *Space-filling Curves*, Universitext, Springer-Verlag, New York, 1994. (Cited on 204.)

[809] S. Saitoh, *Theory of Reproducing Kernels and Its Applications*, Pitman Research Notes in Mathematics Series, John Wiley & Sons, New York, 1988. (Cited on 126.)

[810] S. Saks, *Theory of the Integral*, 2nd revised edition, Dover Publications, New York, 1964. An unabridged and corrected republication of the 2nd revised edition, published by Stechert, New York, in 1937 as Volume VII in the Monografie Matematyczne series. (Cited on 238.)

[811] H. H. Schaefer, *Banach Lattices and Positive Operators*, Die Grundlehren der mathematischen Wissenschaften, Springer-Verlag, New York-Heidelberg, 1974. (Cited on 269.)

[812] H. H. Schaefer and M. P. Wolff, *Topological Vector Spaces*, 2nd edition, Graduate Texts in Mathematics, Springer-Verlag, New York, 1999. (Cited on 706.)

[813] R. Schatten, *On the direct product of Banach spaces*, Trans. Amer. Math. Soc. **53** (1943), 195–217. (Cited on 182.)

[814] J. Schauder, *Über die Umkehrung linearer, stetiger Funktionaloperationen*, Studia Math. **2** (1930), 1–6. (Cited on 408.)

[815] J. Schauder, *Der Fixpunktsatz in Funktionalräumen*, Studia Math. **2** (1930), 171–180. (Cited on 487.)

[816] E. Schechter, *Handbook of Analysis and Its Foundations*, Academic Press, San Diego, CA, 1997. (Cited on 12.)

[817] H. Scheffé, *A useful convergence theorem for probability distributions*, Ann. Math. Stat. **18** (1947), 434–438. (Cited on 249.)

[818] E. Schmidt, *Über die Auflösung linearer Gleichungen mit unendlich vielen Unbekannten*, Palermo Rend. **25** (1908), 53–77. (Cited on 117, 122, 134.)

[819] A. Schoenflies, *Die Entwickelung der Lehre von den Punktmannigfaltigkeiten*, Jahresber. Deutsch. Math. Ver. **8** (1900), 1–251. (Cited on 50.)

[820] A. Schoenflies, *Beiträge zur Theorie der Punktmengen. I*, Math. Ann. **58** (1904), 195–234. (Cited on 74.)

[821] A. Schoenflies, *Die Entwickelung der Lehre von den Punktmannigfaltigkeiten*, Teubner, Leipzig, 1908. (Cited on 117.)

[822] A. Schoenflies, *Die Krisis in Cantor's mathematischem Schaffen*, Acta Math. **50** (1927), 1–23. (Cited on 15.)

[823] W. Schoutens, *Lévy Processes in Finance: Pricing Financial Derivatives*, Wiley Series in Probability and Statistics, Wiley, West Sussex, England, 2003. (Cited on 659.)

[824] E. Schrödinger, *Quantizierung als Eigenwertproblem (Erste Mitteilung)*, Ann. Physik **79** (1926), 361–376. (Cited on 607.)

[825] I. Schur, *Über eine Klasse von Matrizen, die sich einer gegebenen Matrix zuordnen lassen*, Diss. Berlin. 76 S., 1901. (Cited on 350.)

[826] I. Schur, *Über die charakteristischen Wurzeln einer linearen Substitution mit einer Anwendung auf die Theorie der Integralgleichungen*, Math. Ann. **66** (1909), 488–510. (Cited on 175.)

[827] I. Schur, *Über lineare Transformationen in der Theorie der unendlichen Reihen*, J. Reine Angew. Math. **151** (1921), 79–111. (Cited on 444.)

[828] I. Schur, *Über eine Klasse von Mittelbildungen mit Anwendungen auf die Determinantentheorie*, Sitzungsber. Berlin Math. Gesellschaft **22** (1923), 9–20. (Cited on 394.)

[829] H. A. Schwarz, *Über ein Flächen kleinsten Flächeninhalts betreffendes Problem der Variationsrechnung*, Acta Societatis scientiarum Fennicae **XV** (1888), 318–361; available online at `http://www-stat.wharton.upenn.edu/~steele/Publications/Books/CSMC/Schwarz.pdf`. (Cited on 117.)

[830] L. Schwartz, *Généralisation de la notion de fonction, de dérivation, de transformation de Fourier et applications mathématiques et physiques*, Ann. Univ. Grenoble Sect. Sci. Math. Phys. (N.S.) **21** (1946), 57–74. (Cited on 513, 712.)

[831] L. Schwartz, *Théorie des distributions et transformation de Fourier*, Ann. Univ. Grenoble Sect. Sci. Math. Phys. (N.S.) **23** (1948), 7–24. (Cited on 513.)

[832] L. Schwartz, *Théorie des distributions. I, II*, Publ. Inst. Math. Univ. Strasbourg **9**, **10**, Hermann, Paris, 1950, 1951. (Cited on 513, 712.)

[833] L. Schwartz, *Sous-espaces hilbertiens d'espaces vectoriels topologiques et noyaux associés (noyaux reproduisants)*, J. Anal. Math. **13** (1964) 115–256. (Cited on 126, 565.)

[834] L. Schwartz, *Théorie des distributions*, Hermann, Paris, 1966. (Cited on 513.)

[835] I. E. Segal, *Mathematical characterization of the physical vacuum for a linear Bose-Einstein field. (Foundations of the dynamics of infinite systems. III)*, Illinois J. Math. **6** (1962), 500–523. (Cited on 538.)

[836] I. E. Segal, *Mathematical Problems of Relativistic Physics*, American Mathematical Society, Providence, RI, 1963. (Cited on 538.)

[837] H. Seifert and W. Threlfall, *Seifert and Threlfall: A Textbook of Topology*, translated from the German edition of 1934 by Michael A. Goldman with a preface by Joan S. Birman with "Topology of 3-dimensional fibered spaces" by Seifert, translated from the German by Wolfgang Heil, Pure and Applied Mathematics, Academic Press, New York-London, 1980. (Cited on 106.)

[838] E. Seneta, *Nonnegative Matrices and Markov Chains*, 2nd edition, Springer Series in Statistics, Springer-Verlag, New York, 1981. (Cited on 674.)

[839] C. Severini, *Sulle successioni di funzioni ortogonali*, Atti Acc. Gioenia. (5) 3, 10 S (1910). (Cited on 249.)

[840] C. E. Shannon, *Communication in the presence of noise*, Proc. Institute of Radio Engineers **37** (1949), 10–21. (Cited on 567.)

[841] A. Shen and N. K. Vereshchagin, *Basic Set Theory*, Translated from the 1999 Russian edition by A. Shen, Student Mathematical Library, American Mathematical Society, Providence, RI, 2002. (Cited on 14.)

[842] A. N. Shiryayv, *Probability*, Springer-Verlag, New York, 1984. (Cited on 617.)

[843] V. Shmulyan, *Über lineare topologische Räume*, Mat. Sb. **7 (49)** (1940), 425–448. (Cited on 447.)

[844] J. A. Shohat and J. D. Tamarkin, *The Problem of Moments*, Mathematical Surveys, American Mathematical Society, New York, 1943. (Cited on 434.)

[845] C. L. Siegel, *Neuer Beweis des Satzes von Minkowski über lineare Formen*, Math. Ann. **87** (1922), 36–38. (Cited on 574.)

[846] R. Siegmund-Schultze, *Mathematicians Fleeing from Nazi Germany. Individual fates and global impact*, Princeton University Press, Princeton, NJ, 2009. (Cited on 562.)

[847] B. Simon, *Distributions and their Hermite expansions*, J. Math. Phys. **12** (1970), 140–148. (Cited on 537.)

[848] B. Simon, *The P(φ)₂ Euclidean (Quantum) Field Theory*, Princeton Series in Physics, Princeton University Press, Princeton, NJ 1974. (Cited on 329, 617.)

[849] B. Simon, *Functional Integration and Quantum Physics*, Pure and Applied Mathematics, Academic Press, New York-London, 1979; 2nd edition, AMS Chelsea Publishing, Providence, RI, 2005. (Cited on 327, 328, 329, 566.)

[850] B. Simon, *Operators with singular continuous spectrum: I. General operators*. Ann. Math. **141** (1995), 131–145. (Cited on 411.)

[851] B. Simon, *The classical moment problem as a self-adjoint finite difference operator*, Adv. in Math. **137** (1998), 82–203. (Cited on 434, 435, 436.)

[852] B. Simon, *Orthogonal Polynomials on the Unit Circle, Part 1: Classical Theory*, AMS Colloquium Publications, American Mathematical Society, Providence, RI, 2005. (Cited on 135, 564, 582.)

[853] B. Simon, *Orthogonal Polynomials on the Unit Circle, Part 2: Spectral Theory*, AMS Colloquium Publications, American Mathematical Society, Providence, RI, 2005. (Cited on 135.)

[854] B. Simon, *Equilibrium measures and capacities in spectral theory*, Inverse Problems and Imaging **1** (2007), 713–772. (Cited on 453.)

[855] B. Simon, *Szegő's Theorem and Its Descendants: Spectral Theory for L^2 Perturbations of Orthogonal Polynomials*, Princeton University Press, Princeton, NJ, 2010. (Cited on 135, 434, 435.)

[856] B. Simon, *Convexity: An Analytic Viewpoint*, Cambridge Tracts in Mathematics, Cambridge University Press, Cambridge, 2011. (Cited on 387, 388, 394, 443, 464, 465, 565, 566.)

[857] L. Simon, *Lectures on Geometric Measure Theory*, in Proceedings of the Centre for Mathematical Analysis, Australian National University, 3. Australian National University, Centre for Mathematical Analysis, Canberra, 1983. (Cited on 700.)

[858] J. Sjöstrand, *Singularités analytiques microlocales. [Microlocal analytic singularities]*, Astérisque **95** (1982) 1–166. (Cited on 539.)

[859] T. Skolem, *Some remarks on axiomatized set theory*, originally published in 1922; reprinted in From Frege to Gödel: A Source Book in Mathematical Logic, 1879–1931 (J. van Heijenoort, ed.), pp. 290–301, Source Books in the History of the Sciences, Harvard University Press, 1967. (Cited on 13.)

[860] I. V. Sleshinskii, *K teorii sposoba naimenshikh kvadratov*, Zapiski mat. otdeleniya novorossiskogo obshchestva estestvoispitatelei **14** (1892), 201–264. (Cited on 655.)

[861] D. R. Smart, *Fixed Point Theorems*, Cambridge Tracts in Mathematics, Cambridge University Press, London-New York, 1974. (Cited on 485.)

[862] Yu. Smirnov, *A necessary and sufficient condition for metrizability of topological space*, Dokl. Akad. Nauk. SSSR (N.S.) **77** (1951), 197-200. (Cited on 61.)

[863] H. J. S. Smith, *On the integration of discontinuous functions*, Proc. London Math. Soc. (1), **6** (1875), 140–153. (Cited on 201.)

[864] S. L. Sobolev, *Sur une généralisation de la formule de Kirchhoff*, Dokl. Akad. Nauk. SSSR **1** (1933), 256–262. (Cited on 607.)

[865] S. L. Sobolev, *Méthode nouvelle à résoudre le problème de Cauchy pour les équations linéaires hyperboliques normales*, Mat. Sb. **1 (43)** (1936), 39–72. (Cited on 512.)

[866] S. L. Sobolev, *On a theorem of functional analysis*, Mat. Sb. **4 (46)** (1938), 471–497. [Russian] (Cited on 512.)

[867] V. Sokhotskii, *About definite integrals and functions used in developments of series (English transltion)*, Ph.D. thesis, University of St. Petersburg, 1873. (Cited on 512.)

[868] R. M. Solovay, *A model of set-theory in which every set of reals is Lebesgue measurable*, Ann. Math. (2) **92** (1970), 1–56. (Cited on 211.)

[869] H. E. Soper, *Tables of Poisson's Exponential Binomial Limit*, Biometrika, **10** (1914), 25–35. (Cited on 666.)

[870] G. Soukhomlinoff, *Über Fortsetzung von linearen Funktionalen in linearen komplexen Räumen und linearen Quaternionräumen*, (Russian; with German summary), Rec. Math., Moscow, (2) **3** (1938), 353–358. (Cited on 425.)

[871] E. Stade, *Fourier Analysis*, Pure and Applied Mathematics (New York), Wiley-Interscience, Hoboken, NJ, 2005. (Cited on 149.)

[872] H. Stahl and V. Totik, *General Orthogonal Polynomials*, in Encyclopedia of Mathematics and its Applications, Cambridge University Press, Cambridge, 1992. (Cited on 453.)

[873] J. M. Steele, *The Cauchy–Schwarz Master Class. An Introduction to the Art of Mathematical Inequalities*, MAA Problem Books Series, Mathematical Association of America, Washington, DC; Cambridge University Press, Cambridge, 2004. (Cited on 373.)

[874] L. A. Steen and J. A. Seebach, Jr., *Counterexamples in Topology*, reprint of the 2nd (1978) edition, Dover, Mineola, NY, 1995. (Cited on 408.)

[875] E. M. Stein and R. Shakarchi, *Fourier Analysis. An Introduction*, Princeton Lectures in Analysis, Princeton University Press, Princeton, NJ, 2003. (Cited on 149.)

[876] E. M. Stein and R. Shakarchi, *Functional Analysis. Introduction to further topics in analysis*, Princeton Lectures in Analysis, Princeton University Press, Princeton, NJ, 2011. (Cited on 409.)

[877] H. Steinhaus, *Sur les distances des points des ensembles de mesure positive*, Fund. Math. **1** (1920), 93–104. (Cited on 570.)

[878] H. Steinhaus, *Les probabilités dénombrables et leur rapport à la théorie de la mesure*, Fund. Math. **4** (1923), 286–310. (Cited on 629.)

[879] H. Steinhaus, *Über die Wahrscheinlichkeit dafür, dass der Konvergenzkreis einer Potenzreihe ihre natürliche Grenze ist*, Math. Z. **31** (1929), 408–416. (Cited on 629.)

[880] K. Stellmacher, *Ein Beispiel einer Huygensschen Differentialgleichung*, Nachr. Akad. Wiss. Göttingen, Math.-Phys. Kl, IIa, **10** (1953) 133-138. (Cited on 607.)

[881] T. Stieltjes, *Recherches sur les fractions continues*, Ann. Fac. Sci. Univ. Toulouse **8** (1894–1895), J76–J122; ibid. **9**, A5–A47. (Cited on 193, 194, 433.)

[882] S. M. Stigler, *Studies in the history of probability and statistics. XXXIII. Cauchy and the witch of Agnesi: An historical note on the Cauchy distribution*, Biometrika **61** (1974), 375–380. (Cited on 630.)

[883] D. Stirzaker, *Elementary Probability*, Second edition, Cambridge University Press, Cambridge, UK, 2003. (Cited on 617.)

[884] M. H. Stone, *Linear Transformations in Hilbert Space. III. Operational Methods and Group Theory*, Proc. Nat. Acad. Sci. USA **16** (1930) 172–175. (Cited on 117, 435.)

[885] M. H. Stone, *Applications of the theory of Boolean rings to general topology*, Trans. Amer. Math. Soc. **41** (1937), 375–481. (Cited on 92, 466.)

[886] M. H. Stone, *The generalized Weierstrass approximation theorem*, Math. Magazine **21** (1948), 167–184, 237–254. (Cited on 92.)

[887] W. F. Stout, *Almost Sure Convergence*, Academic Press, New York, 1974. (Cited on 645.)

[888] R. F. Streater and A. S. Wightman, *PCT, Spin and Statistics, and All That*, W. A. Benjamin, New York-Amsterdam, 1964. (Cited on 513.)

[889] R. S. Strichartz, *A Guide to Distribution Theory and Fourier Transforms*, CRC Press, Boca Raton, FL, 1994. (Cited on 493.)

[890] K. R. Stromberg, *The Banach-Tarski paradox*, Amer. Math. Monthly **86** (1979), 151–161 (Cited on 211.)

[891] K. R. Stromberg, *Probability for Analysts*, Chapman & Hall Probability Series, Chapman & Hall, New York, 1994. (Cited on 327.)

[892] D. W. Stroock, *A Concise Introduction to the Theory of Integration*, 3rd edition, Birkhäuser Boston, Boston, MA, 1999. (Cited on 230.)

[893] D. W. Stroock, *An Introduction to the Analysis of Paths on a Riemannian Manifold*, Mathematical Surveys and Monographs, American Mathematical Society, Providence, RI, 2000. (Cited on 327.)

[894] D. W. Stroock, *An Introduction to Markov Processes*, Graduate Texts in Mathematics, Springer-Verlag, Berlin, 2005. (Cited on 674.)

[895] D. W. Stroock, *Probability Theory. An analytic view*, Second edition, Cambridge University Press, Cambridge, UK, 2011. (Cited on 617.)

[896] D. W. Stroock, *Mathematics of Probability*, Graduate Studies in Mathematics, American Mathematical Society, Providence, RI, 2013. (Cited on 617.)

[897] Student, *On the Error of Counting with a Haemacytometer*, Biometrika, **5** (1907), 351–360. (Cited on 666.)

[898] J. J. Sylvester, *Additions to the articles, "On a New Class of Theorems" and "On Pascal's Theorem"*, Philos. Magazine **37** (1850), 363–370. (Cited on 26.)

[899] J. J. Sylvester, *A demonstration of the theorem that every homogeneous quadratic polynomial is reducible by real orthogonal substitution to the form of a sum of positive and negative squares*, Philos. Magazine **4** (1852), 138–142. (Cited on 26.)

[900] K. Symanzik, *Euclidean quantum field theory*, in Local Quantum Theory, Proc. Internat. School of Physics Enrico Fermi, Course 45, Academic Press, New York, 1969. (Cited on 329.)

[901] G. Szegő, *Über orthogonale Polynome, die zu einer gegebenen Kurve der komplexen Ebene gehören*, Math. Z. **9** (1921), 218–270. (Cited on 126.)

[902] G. Szegő, *Orthogonal Polynomials*, AMS Colloquium Publications, American Mathematical Society, Providence, RI, 1939; 3rd edition, 1967. (Cited on 135.)

[903] T. Takagi, *A simple example of the continuous function without derivative*, Tokio Math. Ges. **1** (1903), 176–177. (Cited on 164.)

[904] T. Tao, *Analysis I*, Texts and Readings in Mathematics, Hindustan Book Agency, New Delhi, 2006. (Cited on 9.)

[905] T. Tao, *Analysis II*, Texts and Readings in Mathematics, Hindustan Book Agency, New Delhi, 2006. (Cited on 6.)

[906] A. Tarski, *Sur les ensembles finis*, Fund. Math. **6** (1924), 45–95; available online at `http://matwbn.icm.edu.pl/ksiazki/fm/fm6/fm619.pdf`. (Cited on 13.)

[907] A. E. Taylor, *General Theory of Functions and Integration*, Blaisdell Publishing, New York-Toronto-London, 1965. (Cited on 230.)

[908] A. E. Taylor, *A study of Maurice Fréchet. I. His early work on point set theory and the theory of functionals*, Arch. Hist. Exact Sci. **27** (1982), 233–295. (Cited on 500, 501, 502.)

[909] A. E. Taylor, *A study of Maurice Fréchet. II. Mainly about his work on general topology, 1909–1928*, Arch. Hist. Exact Sci. **34** (1985), 279–380. (Cited on 501.)

[910] A. E. Taylor, *A study of Maurice Fréchet. III. Fréchet as analyst, 1909–1930*, Arch. Hist. Exact Sci. **37** (1987), 25–76. (Cited on 501.)

[911] M. E. Taylor, *Measure Theory and Integration*, Graduate Studies in Mathematics, American Mathematical Society, Providence, RI, 2006. (Cited on 230, 327, 702.)

[912] M. E. Taylor, *Partial Differential Equations. I. Basic theory*, Applied Mathematical Sciences. Springer-Verlag, New York, 1996; *Partial Differential Equations II: Qualitative Studies of Linear Equations*, Applied Mathematical Sciences, Springer-Verlag, New York, 2010. Partial Differential Equations III: Nonlinear Equations, Applied Mathematical Sciences, Springer-Verlag, New York, 2010. (Cited on 606.)

[913] B. Taylor, *Methodus incrementorum directa et inversa*, 1715. (Cited on 32, 150.)

[914] O. T'edone. *Sull'integratione dell'equazione $\frac{\partial^2 \varphi}{\partial t^2} - \sum_{i=1}^{m} \frac{\partial^2 \varphi}{\partial x_i^2} = 0$*, Ann. di Mat. Pura Appl. (IIIa) **i** (1898) 1–23. (Cited on 607.)

[915] L. H. Thomas, *The calculation of atomic fields*, Proc. Cambridge Philos. Soc. **23** (1927), 542–548. (Cited on 453.)

[916] O. Thorin, *An extension of a convexity theorem due to M. Riesz*, Fys. Sallsk. Forh. **8** (1938), no. 14. (Cited on 563.)

[917] O. Thorin, *Convexity theorems generalizing those of M. Riesz and Hadamard*, Thesis; Ak. Avh. Lund, 1948. (Cited on 563.)

[918] H. Tietze, *Über Funktionen, die auf einer abgeschlossenen Menge stetig sind*, J. Reine Angew. Math. **145** (1915), 9–14. (Cited on 61.)

[919] H. Tietze, *Beiträge zur allgemeinen Topologie. I. Axiome für verschiedene Fassungen des Umgebungsbegriffs*, Math. Ann. **88** (1923), 290–312. (Cited on 60, 75.)

[920] E. C. Titchmarsh, *A contribution to the theory of Fourier transforms*, Proc. London Math. Soc. (2) **23** (1924), 279–289. (Cited on 563.)

[921] E. C. Titchmarsh, *Obituary: Godfrey Harold Hardy*, J. London Math. Soc. **25** (1950), 82–101. (Cited on 583.)

[922] M. J. Todd, *The Computation of Fixed Points and Applications*, Lecture Notes in Economics and Mathematical Systems, Springer-Verlag, Berlin-New York, 1976. (Cited on 485.)

[923] O. Toeplitz, *Über die Fouriersche Entwickelung positiver Funktionen*, Rend. Circ. Mat. Palermo **32** (1911), 191–192. (Cited on 564.)

[924] O. Toeplitz, *Das algebraische Analogen zu einem Satze von Fejér*, Math. Z. **2** (1918), 187–197. (Cited on 175.)

[925] L. Tonelli, *Sull' integrazione per parti*, Rom. Acc. L. Rend. (5) **18** (1909), 246–253. (Cited on 288.)

[926] L. Tonelli, *La semicontinuita nel calcolo delle variazioni*, Rend. Circ. Mat. Palermo **44** (1920), 167–249. (Cited on 453.)

[927] L. Tonelli, *Fondamenti di Calcolo delle Variazioni*, Zanicelli, Bolonia, 1921. (Cited on 453.)

[928] A. Torchinsky *The Fourier Transform and the Wave Equation*, Amer. Math. Monthly **118** (2011) 599–609. (Cited on 607.)

[929] C. A. Tracy and H. Widom, *Level-spacing distributions and the Airy kernel*, Comm. Math. Phys. **159** (1994), 151–174. (Cited on 630.)

[930] C. A. Tracy and H. Widom, *Distribution functions for largest eigenvalues and their applications*, in Proc. Internat. Cong. Math., Vol. I (Beijing, 2002), pp. 587–596, Higher Ed. Press, Beijing, 2002. (Cited on 630.)

[931] F. Trèves, *Locally Convex Spaces and Linear Partial Differential Equations*, Die Grundlehren der mathematischen Wissenschaften, Springer-Verlag, New York, 1967. (Cited on 706.)

[932] F. Trèves, *Topological Vector Spaces, Distributions and Kernels*, unabridged republication of the 1967 original, Dover Publications, Mineola, NY, 2006. (Cited on 182, 706.)

[933] F. Trèves, *Basic Linear Partial Differential Equations*, Academic Press, New York, 1975. (Cited on 606.)

[934] F. Trèves, G. Pisier, and M. Yor, *Laurent Schwartz (1915–2002)*, Notices Amer. Math. Soc. **50** (2003), 1072–1084. (Cited on 511, 513.)

[935] H. Triebel, *Fourier Analysis and Function Spaces (Selected Topics)*, Teubner Verlag., Leipzig, 1977. (Cited on 149.)

[936] H. F. Trotter, *An elementary proof of the central limit theorem*, Arch. Math. **10** (1959) 226–234. (Cited on 656.)

[937] M. Tsuji, *Potential Theory in Modern Function Theory*, reprint of the 1959 original, Chelsea, New York, 1975. (Cited on 453.)

[938] J. W. Tukey, *Convergence and Uniformity in Topology*, Annals of Mathematics Studies, Princeton University Press, Princeton, NJ, 1940. (Cited on 13.)

[939] J. W. Tukey, *Some notes on the separation of convex sets*, Portugaliae Math. **3** (1942), 95–102. (Cited on 458.)

[940] A. Tychonoff, *Über die topologische Erweiterung von Räumen*, Math. Ann. **102** (1929), 544–561. (Cited on 60, 101.)

[941] A. Tychonoff, *Ein Fixpunktsatz*, Math. Ann. **111** (1935), 767–776. (Cited on 443, 487.)

[942] A. Tychonoff, *Theoremes d'unicity pour l'Equation du chaleur*, Mat. Sb. **42** (1935), 199–216. (Cited on 608.)

[943] P. Urysohn, *Über die Mächtigkeit der zusammenhängenden Mengen*, Math. Ann. **94** (1925), 262–295. (Cited on 61.)

[944] P. Urysohn, *Zum Metrisationsproblem*, Math. Ann. **94** (1925), 309–315. (Cited on 61.)

[945] B. van Brunt, *The Calculus of Variations*, Universitext, Springer-Verlag, New York, 2004. (Cited on 453.)

[946] S. R. S. Varadhan, *Stochastic Processes*, Courant Lecture Notes in Mathematics, Courant Institute of Mathematical Sciences, New York; American Mathematical Society, Providence, RI, 2007. (Cited on 313.)

[947] A. P. Veselov, *Huygens' Principle and Integrability*, in Progress in Math. 169, pp. 259–275, Birkhäuser, Basel 1997. (Cited on 607.)

[948] G. Vitali, *Sul problema della misura dei gruppi di punti di una retta*, Tip. Gamberini e Parmeggiani, Bologna, 1905. (Cited on 210.)

[949] G. Vitali, *Sull' integrazione per serie*, Rend. Circ. Mat. Palermo **23** (1907), 137–155. (Cited on 249.)

[950] G. Vitali, *Sulla condizione di chiusura di un sistema di funzioni ortogonali*, Rom. Acc. L. Rend. (5) **30** (1921), No. 2, 498–501. (Cited on 136.)

[951] J. Voit, *The Statistical Mechanics of Financial Markets*, 3rd edition, Texts and Monographs in Physics, Springer-Verlag, Berlin, 2005. (Cited on 658.)

[952] V. Volterra, *Alcune osservazioni sulle funzioni punteggiate discontinue*, [Some observations on point-wise discontinuous functions], Giornale di Matematiche **19** (1881), 76–86. (Cited on 201, 202.)

[953] V. Volterra, *Sulle vibrazioni luminose nei mezzi isotropi* Rend. Accad. Nazl. Lincel **1** (1892) 161–170. (Cited on 607.)

[954] V. Volterra, *Sur les vibrations des corps élastiques isotropes*, Acta Math. **18** (1894) 161–232. (Cited on 607.)

[955] V. Volterra, *Sul principio di Dirichlet*, Rend. Circ. Mat. Palermo **11** (1897), 83–86. (Cited on 82.)

[956] H. von Helmholtz, *On the Sensations of Tone as a Physiological Basis for the Theory of Music*, Vieweg and Sons, Braunscweig, 1863; English translation available online at https://archive.org/details/onsensationsofto00helmrich. (Cited on 607.)

[957] R. von Mises, *Grundlagender Wahrscheinlichkeitsrechnung*, Math. Z. 5 **191** (1919), 52–99. (Cited on 629.)

[958] R. von Mises, *Wahrscheinlichkeit, Statistik und Wahrheit*, Springer-Verlag, Vienna, 1928. (Cited on 629.)

[959] R. von Mises, *Wahscheinlichkeitsrechnung*, Fr. Deuticke, Leipzig-Vienna, 1931. (Cited on 675.)

[960] J. von Neumann, *Mathematische Begründung der Quantenmechanik*, Nachr. Göttingen **1927** (1927), 1–57. (Cited on 117.)

[961] J. von Neumann, *Zur Theorie der Gesellschaftsspiele*, Math. Ann. **100** (1928), 295–320. (Cited on 485.)

[962] J. von Neumann, *Allgemeine Eigenwerttheorie Hermitescher Funktionaloperatoren*, Math. Ann. **102** (1929), 49–131. (Cited on 117.)

[963] J. von Neumann, *Zur allgemeinen Theorie des Masses*, Fund. Math. **13** (1929), 73–116. Available online at `http://matwbn.icm.edu.pl/ksiazki/fm/fm13/fm1316.pdf`. (Cited on 210, 486.)

[964] J. von Neumann, *Zur Algebra der Funktionaloperationen und Theorie der Normalen Operatoren*, Math. Ann. **102** (1930), 370–427. (Cited on 174.)

[965] J. von Neumann, *Zum Haarschen Maß in Topologischen Gruppen*, Compositio Math. **1** (1934), 106–114. (Cited on 350.)

[966] J. von Neumann, *On complete topological spaces*, Trans. Amer. Math. Soc. **37** (1935), 1–20. (Cited on 364, 443.)

[967] J. von Neumann, *On a certain topology for rings of operators*, Ann. Math. **37** (1936), 111–115. (Cited on 174, 350.)

[968] J. von Neumann, *The uniqueness of Haar's measure*, Mat. Sb. **1** (1936), 721–734. (Cited on 257.)

[969] J. von Neumann, *Über ein ökonomisches Gleichungssystem und eine Verallgemeinerung des Brouwerschen Fixpunktsatzes*, Ergebn. Math. Kolloqu. Wien **8** (1937), 73–83. (Cited on 485.)

[970] J. von Neumann, *On rings of operators. III*, Ann. Math. **41** (1940), 94–161. (Cited on 257.)

[971] J. von Neumann, *Various techniques used in connection with random digits*, Journal of Research of the National Bureau of Standards, Appl. Math. Series **3** (1951), 36–38, available online at `www-apr.lip6.fr/~lumbroso/References/VonNeumann51.pdf`. (Cited on 667.)

[972] P. Wagner, A new constructive proof of the Malgrange-Ehrenpreis theorem. Amer. Math. Monthly **116** (2009), 457–462. (Cited on 608.)

[973] S. Wagon, *The Banach–Tarski Paradox*, Encyclopedia of Mathematics and its Applications , Cambridge University Press, Cambridge, 1985. (Cited on 210.)

[974] J. S. Walker, *Fourier Analysis*, Oxford University Press, New York, 1988. (Cited on 149.)

[975] H. S. Wall, *Analytic Theory of Continued Fractions*, Van Nostrand, New York, 1948. (Cited on 434.)

[976] J. Wallis, *A Treatise of Algebra, Both Historical and Practical*, John Playford, London, 1685. (Cited on 32.)

[977] G. N. Watson, *The Constants of Landau and Lebesgue*, Quart. J. Math. Oxford **1** (1930), 310–318. (Cited on 412.)

[978] K. Weierstrass, *Über continuierliche Functionen eines reellen Arguments, die für keinen Werth des letzteren einen bestimmten Differentialquotienten besitzen*, Königliche Akademie der Wissenschaften, 18 Juli 1872. (Cited on 156.)

[979] K. Weierstrass, *Über die analytische Darstellbarkeit sogenannter willkürlicher Functionen einer reellen Veränderlichen*, Sitzungsber. der Akademie zu Berlin (1885), 633–639 and 789–805. (Cited on 81.)

[980] A. Weil, *L'intégration dans les groupes topologiques et ses applications*, Actual. Sci. Ind., Hermann et Cie., Paris, 1940. [This book has been republished by the author at Princeton, N. J., 1941.] (Cited on 350, 367, 565.)

[981] P. Weiss, *An estimate of the error arising from misapplication of the sampling theorem*, Notices Amer. Math. Soc. **10** (1963), 351. (Cited on 575.)

[982] H. Weyl, *The Concept of a Riemann Surface*, Dover Publications, 2009; reprint of the 1955 edition published by Addison-Wesley, Reading, Mass. Original: *Die Idee der Riemannschen Fläche*, B. G. Teubner, Leipzig, 1913. (Cited on 47.)

[983] H. Weyl, *Das gruppentheoretische Fundament der Tensorrechnung*, Nachr. Kön. Ges. Wiss. Göttingen **1924** (1924), 218–224. (Cited on 350.)

[984] H. Weyl, *Über die Symmetrie der Tensoren und die Tragweite der symbolischen Methode in der Invariantentheorie*, Palermo Rend. **48** (1924), 29–36. (Cited on 350.)

[985] H. Weyl, *Inequalities between the two kinds of eigenvalues of a linear transformation*, Proc. Nat. Acad. Sci. USA. **35** (1949), 408–411. (Cited on 394.)

[986] G. F. Wheeler and W. P. Crummett, *The vibrating string controversy*, Amer. J. Phys. **55** (1987), 33–37. (Cited on 150.)

[987] L. Whitaker, *On the Poisson Law of Small Numbers*, Biometrika, **10** (1914), 36–71. (Cited on 666.)

[988] R. Whitley, The Kreĕn-Šmulian theorem. Proc. Amer. Math. Soc. **97** (1986), 376–377. (Cited on 465.)

[989] H. Whitney, *Tensor products of Abelian groups*, Duke Math. J. **4** (1938), 495–528. (Cited on 182.)

[990] E. T. Whittaker, *On the functions which are represented by the expansions of the interpolation theory*, Proc. Royal Soc. Edinburgh, Sec. A **35** (1915), 181–194. (Cited on 567, 568.)

[991] D. V. Widder, *Positive temperatures on an infinite rod*, Trans. Amer. Math. Soc. **55** (1944), 85–95. (Cited on 608.)

[992] H. Wielandt, *Unzerlegbare, nicht negative Matrizen*, Math. Z. **52** (1950), 642–648. (Cited on 675.)

[993] N. Wiener, *On the theory of sets of points in terms of coninuous transformations*, Comptes rendus du congrés internat. des math. (1920), 312–315. (Cited on 364.)

[994] N. Wiener, *Differential space*, J. Math. Phys. **2** (1923), 132–174. (Cited on 327.)

[995] N. Wiener, *The operational calculus*, Math. Ann. **95** (1926), 557–584. (Cited on 513.)

[996] N. Wiener, *Generalized harmonic analysis*, Acta Math. **55** (1930), 117–258. (Cited on 537.)

[997] N. Wiener, *Ex-prodigy: My Childhood and Youth*, Simon and Schuster, New York, 1953. (Cited on 326.)

[998] N. Wiener, *The Fourier Integral and Certain of Its Applications*, Dover Publications, New York, 1959; an unaltered republication of the 1933 edition, University Press, Cambridge. (Cited on 537, 567.)

[999] A. S. Wightman, *Quantum field theory in terms of vacuum expectation values*, Phys. Rev. (2) **101** (1956), 860–866. (Cited on 513.)

[1000] A. S. Wightman and L. Gårding, *Fields as operators-valued distributions in relativistic quantum theory*, Ark. Fysik **28** (1964), 129–184. (Cited on 513.)

[1001] H. Wilbraham, *On a certain periodic function*, Cambridge and Dublin Math. J. **3** (1848), 198–201. (Cited on 157.)

[1002] H. Wilcox and D. L. Myers, *An Introduction to Lebesgue Integration and Fourier Series*, Applied Mathematics Series—Mathematics for Engineering and Science, Krieger Publishing, Huntington, NY, 1978. (Cited on 230.)

[1003] R. L. Wilder, *Evolution of the topological concept of "connected"*, Amer. Math. Monthly **85** (1978), 720–726. (Cited on 50.)

[1004] S. Willard, *General Topology*, reprint of the 1970 original, Dover Publications, Mineola, NY, 2004. (Cited on 48, 61, 106, 205, 367.)

[1005] D. Williams, *Probability with Martingales*, Cambridge Mathematical Textbooks, Cambridge University Press, Cambridge, 1991. (Cited on 617.)

[1006] A. Wintner, *On the differentiation of infinite convolutions*, Amer. J. Math. **57** (1935), 363–366. (Cited on 514.)

[1007] K. Yoshida, *On a vector lattice with unit*, Proc. Japan Acad. Tokyo **17** (1941), 121–124. (Cited on 92.)

[1008] W. H. Young, *The Fundamental Theorems of the Differential Calculus*, Cambridge Tracts in Mathematics and Mathematical Physics, Cambridge University Press, Cambridge, 1910. (Cited on 365.)

[1009] W. H. Young, *On classes of summable functions and their Fourier series*, Proc. R. Soc. A **87** (1912), 225–229. (Cited on 372.)

[1010] W. H. Young, *On the determination of the summability of a function by means of its Fourier constants*, Proc. London Math. Soc. (2) **12** (1913), 71–88. (Cited on 563.)

[1011] W. H. Young, *On the multiplication of successions of Fourier constants*, Proc. London Royal Soc. **87** (1913), 331–339. (Cited on 563.)

[1012] A. C. Zaanen, *On a certain class of Banach spaces*, Ann. of Math. (2) **47** (1946), 654–666. (Cited on 388.)

[1013] A. C. Zaanen, *Riesz Spaces. II*, North–Holland Mathematical Library, North–Holland Publishing, Amsterdam, 1983. (Cited on 269.)

[1014] A. C. Zaanen, *Introduction to Operator Theory in Riesz Spaces*, Springer-Verlag, Berlin, 1997. (Cited on 269.)

[1015] P. P. Zabreĭko, *A theorem for semiadditive functionals*, (Russian), Funkcional. Anal. i Priložen. **3** (1969), 86–88; English translation: Functional Analysis and Applications, **3** (1969), 70–72. (Cited on 408.)

[1016] T. Zamfirescu, *Most monotone functions are singular*, Amer. Math. Monthly **88** (1981), 456–458. (Cited on 411.)

[1017] S. Zaremba, *L'équation biharmonique et une classe remarquable de fonctions fondamentales harmoniques*, Krak. Anz. (1907), 147–196 [Polish]. (Cited on 126.)

[1018] E. Zermelo, *Beweis, dass jede Menge wohlgeordnet werden kann*, Math. Ann. **59** (1904), 514–516. (Cited on 13.)

[1019] E. Zermelo, *Untersuchungen ̈ber die Grundlagen der Mengenlehre I*, Math. Ann. **65** (1908), 261–281; English translation in J. van Heijenoort, *Investigations in the foundations of set theory*, in From Frege to Gödel: A Source Book in Mathematical Logic, 1879–1931, pp. 199–215, Source Books in the History of the Sciences, Harvard University Press, 1967. (Cited on 13.)

[1020] K. Zhu, *Analysis on Fock Spaces*, Graduate Texts in Mathematics, Springer, New York, 2012. (Cited on 538.)

[1021] D. E. Zitarelli, *Connected sets and the AMS, 1901–1921*, Notices Amer. Math. Soc. **56** (2009), 450–458. (Cited on 50.)

[1022] M. Zorn, *A remark on method in transfinite algebra*, Bull. Amer. Math. Soc. **41** (1935), 667–670. (Cited on 13.)

[1023] A. Zygmund, *On lacunary trigonometric series*, Trans. Amer. Math. Soc. **34** (1932), 435–446. (Cited on 581.)

[1024] A. Zygmund, *Trigonometric Series. Vol. I, II*, 3rd edition, Cambridge Mathematical Library, Cambridge University Press, Cambridge, 2002. (Cited on 149, 582.)

Symbol Index

765

Subject Index

Author Index

Index of Capsule Biographies